1997

UNIFORM FIRE CODE™

VOLUME 2

Second Printing

Publication date: April 1997

ISSN 0896-9736
ISBN 1-884590-85-3 (soft cover edition)
ISBN 1-884590-86-1 (loose leaf edition)
ISBN 1-884590-95-0 (2-vol. set—soft cover)
ISBN 1-884590-96-9 (2-vol. set—loose leaf)

publication by

International Fire Code Institute
5360 Workman Mill Road
Whittier, California 90601-2298
(562) 699-0124

Cover photos courtesy of Factory Mutual Engineering Corporation
and Los Angeles County Department of Public Works.

PRINTED IN THE U.S.A.

Preface

Introduction: The *Uniform Fire Code* (UFC) is the United States' premier model fire code. Since its initiation in 1971, the code has become internationally recognized for its role in setting the pace of fire prevention, fire protection and public safety.

Fire codes represent one of today's most rapidly changing regulatory arenas. New challenges presented by hazardous materials, flammable and combustible liquids, explosives, high-piled combustible storage, aerosol product storage, and building operations are among the many issues shaping the future of fire prevention, fire protection and public safety. Additionally, fire codes have evolved far beyond their traditional roles as maintenance codes and now address many issues related to new construction and special hazards in buildings. As a model code developed through a consensus code development process, the *Uniform Fire Code* provides jurisdictions with an opportunity to adopt a fire code that is comprehensive, up-to-date and consistent with codes of other jurisdictions. Adoption of the *Uniform Fire Code* also relieves jurisdictions from the burdensome process of independently developing regulations.

History: The 1997 edition is the 10th edition of the *Uniform Fire Code.* Now published by the International Fire Code Institute, the code was initially published as a model code document in 1971 through a cooperative effort of the Western Fire Chiefs Association and the International Conference of Building Officials. The code was updated in 1973 and has since been published on a three-year schedule. Editions include 1971, 1973, 1976, 1979, 1982, 1985, 1988, 1991, 1994 and 1997.

Two-Volume Set: Provisions of the *Uniform Fire Code* and the *Uniform Fire Code Standards* have been redesignated as a two-volume set of the *Uniform Fire Code.* Volume 1 contains the provisions previously contained in the *Uniform Fire Code* and Volume 2 contains provisions previously in the *Uniform Fire Code Standards.* This redesignation emphasized that both books are truly part of the *Uniform Fire Code* when the code is adopted.

Overview of Volume Two: An objective of the International Fire Code Institute is to provide cities, counties, states and governmental agencies with a set of codes and standards that is correlated and that meets statutory requirements for adoption by reference. *Uniform Fire Code* Volume 2 is a part of this set of publications and provides for adoption of standards that are specifically referred to within various sections of *Uniform Fire Code* Volume 1. In developing the standards, consideration was given to the responsibilities of the jurisdiction that adopts and applies them.

Standards 10-1, 10-2, 24-1, 52-1, 62-1, 74-1, 79-1, 79-2, 79-3, 79-4, 79-5, 80-2, 80-3, 81-1, 81-2, 81-4, 82-1 and Appendix A-III-C-1 are based on National Fire Protection Association (NFPA) standards. These standards contain amendments designed to meet statutory requirements for adoption and correlate with the *Uniform Fire Code.* Some of these standards are adopted by transcription and others are adopted by reference. Adoption methodologies are in accordance with the IFCI Adoption of Standards Policy.

For standards adopted by reference, the user must refer to the NFPA standard, which is not included as a part of this document, in addition to the amendments contained herein. For standards adopted by transcription, Part II of the standard contains the unabridged NFPA standard.

Standard 80-4 is based on CGA Standard CGA P-18. This standard contains amendments designed to meet statutory requirements for adoption and correlate with the *Uniform Fire Code.* This particular standard is adopted by transcription. Again, adoption methodologies are in accordance with the IFCI Adoption of Standards Policy.

Metrication: The *Uniform Fire Code* was metricated for the 1994 edition. Metric equivalents are provided in parentheses following English units. Formulas are also provided with metric equivalents. Metric equivalent formulas immediately follow English formulas and are denoted by "For **SI:**" preceding the metric equivalent. Some formulas do not use dimensions and, thus, are not provided with metric equivalents. Tables are provided with multiplying conversion factors in subheadings for each tabulated unit of measurement.

Metric equivalents included in the code represent approximate conversions from English units. Where metric units are shown in parentheses adjacent to English units, the English units shall be the exact code requirement, and the metric equivalent shall be considered as an approximation.

It is recognized that some of the selected units for metric conversions, such as the use of millimeters for most dimensions of length, may be nonstandard; however, unit selections were based on those used by the *Uniform Building Code* at the request of the General Services Administration, an agency of the United States Government.

How the Code is Revised: The *Uniform Fire Code* is updated on an annual basis. At the conclusion of each update cycle, an annual supplement to the current edition is published, except for every third year when all approved code changes are consolidated into a new edition of the code. Updating is accomplished through a consensus code development process administered by the International Fire Code Institute that allows anyone to submit proposals to revise the code and comment on the proposals of others through regular public hearings. Participants in the code development process represent a wide cross-section of fire officials, building officials, design professionals, manufacturers, developers, insurance organizations, researchers, industry associations and other interested parties.

Marking of Revisions as Compared to the 1994 Edition: Care should be exercised that the provisions of the NFPA standards are applied only in accordance with the amendments set forth herein. To facilitate use, a vertical marking ▭ appears in the margin of NFPA standards that have been transcribed in Part II to identify those sections amended by Part I. The vertical marking ——— in the margin of Part II indicates a revision to the marked section as compared to the previous edition of the NFPA standard. Because some of the updated NFPA standards have skipped editions from those previously published as *Uniform Fire Code* standards, changes other than those marked with bars may have occurred as compared to the 1994 edition of Volume 2.

Solid vertical lines in the margins within the body of the code indicate a change from the requirements of the 1994 UFC except where an entire standard was revised, a new standard was added or a change was minor. Where an entire standard was revised or a new standard was added, a notation appears at the beginning of that standard. The revision may be a new code provision, a revised provision or a provision that has been relocated from elsewhere in the code.

Deletion indicators (➧) are provided in the margin where a paragraph or item listing has been deleted or relocated to another portion of the code.

About the International Fire Code Institute

The International Fire Code Institute (IFCI) is a not-for-profit public service benefit corporation dedicated to public safety. The Institute is a membership association representing fire officials, building officials, design professionals, manufacturers, developers, insurance organizations, researchers, industry associations and other interested parties. Cosponsored by the International Association of Fire Chiefs (IAFC), the International Conference of Building Officials (ICBO) and the Western Fire Chiefs Association (WFCA), the institute was formed to act as an advocate for fire officials and as publishers of the *Uniform Fire Code*™ (UFC) to promote the continued success of the UFC. The Institute began operations in October 1991, and together with IFCI's sister organizations, ICBO and WFCA, IFCI has nearly 70 years experience developing and promulgating model codes, including more than 20 years developing and promulgating the *Uniform Fire Code.*

The Institute occupies a unique niche among fire-safety organizations as the first organization in the United States to focus on model fire codes, and it has quickly become a leading fire-safety organization. The most well-known function of IFCI is the organization's role in administration of the *Uniform Fire Code* and ancillary programs.

The Institute has four major organizational objectives:

1. To promote international uniformity of fire prevention, hazardous material and building construction regulations;
2. To provide a forum in which persons interested in the prevention, control and suppression of fires, explosions and hazardous materials incidents can exchange methods of improved safety and ideas;
3. To continue publishing, developing and promoting the *Uniform Fire Code*; and
4. To provide education and support services for the *Uniform Fire Code.*

The Institute has already had a dramatic impact on the fire prevention profession. New programs and projects offered by IFCI include publication of the *IFCI Fire Code Journal,* the nation's first magazine to focus on fire code related issues. The *IFCI Fire Code Journal* is also unique in that it covers activities of interest in all of the model code organizations, not just those in the Uniform Codes, so that IFCI's members can keep abreast of major fire- and life-safety issues affecting codes throughout the United States. The Institute also offers numerous professional development seminars for fire code enforcers and users, nationally recognized certification programs for fire inspectors and underground storage tank installers and inspectors, and computer-assisted tools for using the UFC. Several additional projects to support fire code users are also under development.

Membership is currently available to individuals and organizations with an interest in fire codes, and membership benefits include receiving copies of each new edition of the *Uniform Fire Code* and annual supplements; the *IFCI Fire Code Journal* magazine; all proposed revisions to the *Uniform Fire Code,* code application and enforcement assistance by a staff of engineers, and discounts on publications, educational offerings and video training programs.

For further information on the International Fire Code Institute, please contact IFCI's office at (562) 699-0124, fax (562) 699-4522.

1997 UFC/IFCI STANDARDS[1]

UFC Standard	Source Standard	Edition (* = New for 97 Code)	Adoption Method
10–1	NFPA 10	1990	Transcription
10–2	NFPA 72	1993*	Transcription
24–1	NFPA 407	1990	Reference
52–1	NFPA 52	1992	Transcription
62–1	NFPA 86	1990	Reference
74–1	NFPA 99[2]	1993	Reference
79–1	NFPA 11	1988	Reference
79–2	NFPA 15	1990	Reference
79–3	NFPA 704	1990	Transcription
79–4	NFPA 385	1990	Reference
79–5	NFPA 386	1990	Reference
79–6	IFCI	1994	Transcription
79–7	IFCI	1994*	Transcription
80–1	IFCI	1994*	Transcription
80–2	NFPA 50	1990	Reference
80–3	NFPA 50B	1994*	Reference
80–4	CGA P-18	1992*	Transcription
81–1	NFPA 231	1990	Transcription
81–2	NFPA 231C	1991	Transcription
81–3	IFCI	1994	Transcription
81–4	NFPA 231C	1995*	Reference
82–1	NFPA 58	1989	Transcription
88–1	IFCI	1994*	Transcription
Appendix: A–III–C–1	NFPA 25	1992*	Reference

[1]Due to the new policy on Method 2, "adoption by reference" for standards, many of the amendments that changed secondary standards references to "nationally recognized standards" have been deleted. The new general paragraph in front of each standard advises that secondary standards are only for reference as approved.

[2]Chapters 2 and 4 only.

CODES AND RELATED PUBLICATIONS

The International Conference of Building Officials (ICBO) publishes a family of codes, each correlated with the *Uniform Building Code*™ to provide jurisdictions with a complete set of building-related regulations for adoption. Some of these codes are published in affiliation with other organizations such as the International Fire Code Institute (IFCI) and the International Code Council (ICC). Reference materials and related codes also are available to improve knowledge of code enforcement and administration of building inspection programs. Publications and products are continually being added, so inquiries should be directed to Conference headquarters for a listing of available products. Many codes and references are also available on CD-ROM or floppy disk. These are denoted by (*). The following publications and products are available from ICBO:

CODES

***Uniform Building Code**, Volumes 1, 2 and 3. The most widely adopted model building code in the United States, the performance-based *Uniform Building Code* is a proven document, meeting the needs of government units charged with the enforcement of building regulations. Volume 1 contains administrative, fire- and life-safety and field inspection provisions; Volume 2 contains structural engineering design provisions; and Volume 3 contains material, testing and installation standards.

***Uniform Mechanical Code™.** Provides a complete set of requirements for the design, construction, installation and maintenance of heating, ventilating, cooling and refrigeration systems; incinerators and other heat-producing appliances.

International Plumbing Code™. Provides consistent and technically advanced requirements that can be used across the country to provide comprehensive regulations of modern plumbing systems. Setting minimum regulations for plumbing facilities in terms of performance objectives, the IPC provides for the acceptance of new and innovative products, materials and systems.

International Private Sewage Disposal Code™. Provides flexibility in the development of safety and sanitary individual sewage disposal systems and includes detailed provisions for all aspects of design, installation and inspection of private sewage disposal systems.

International Mechanical Code™. Establishes minimum regulations for mechanical systems using prescriptive and performance-related provisions. It is founded on broad-based principles that make possible the use of new materials and new mechanical designs.

Uniform Zoning Code™. This code is dedicated to intelligent community development and to the benefit of the public welfare by providing a means of promoting uniformity in zoning laws and enforcement.

***Uniform Fire Code™**, Volumes 1 and 2. The premier model fire code in the United States, the *Uniform Fire Code* sets forth provisions necessary for fire prevention and fire protection. Published by the International Fire Code Institute, the *Uniform Fire Code* is endorsed by the Western Fire Chiefs Association, the International Association of Fire Chiefs and ICBO. Volume 1 contains code provisions compatible with the *Uniform Building Code,* and Volume 2 contains standards referenced from the code provisions.

***Urban-Wildland Interface Code™.** Promulgated by IFCI, this code regulates both land use and the built environment in designated urban-wildland interface areas. This newly developed code is the only model code that bases construction requirements on the fire-hazard severity exposed to the structure. Developed under a grant from the Federal Emergency Management Agency, this code is the direct result of hazard mitigation meetings held after devastating wildfires.

Uniform Housing Code™. Provides complete requirements affecting conservation and rehabilitation of housing. Its regulations are compatible with the *Uniform Building Code.*

Uniform Code for the Abatement of Dangerous Buildings™. A code compatible with the *Uniform Building Code* and the *Uniform Housing Code* which provides equitable remedies consistent with other laws for the repair, vacation or demolition of dangerous buildings.

Uniform Sign Code™. Dedicated to the development of better sign regulation, its requirements pertain to all signs and sign construction attached to buildings.

Uniform Administrative Code™. This code covers administrative areas in connection with adoption of the *Uniform Building Code, Uniform Mechanical Code* and related codes. It contains provisions which relate to site preparation, construction, alteration, moving, repair and use and occupancies of buildings or structures and building service equipment, including plumbing, electrical and mechanical regulations. The code is compatible with the administrative provisions of all codes published by the Conference.

Uniform Building Security Code™. This code establishes minimum standards to make dwelling units resistant to unlawful entry. It regulates swinging doors, sliding doors, windows and hardware in connection with dwelling units of apartment houses or one- and two-family dwellings. The code gives consideration to the concerns of police, fire and building officials in establishing requirements for resistance to burglary which are compatible with fire and life safety.

Uniform Code for Building Conservation™. A building conservation guideline presented in code format which will provide a community with the means to preserve its existing buildings while achieving appropriate levels of safety. It is formatted in the same manner as the *Uniform Building Code,* is compatible with other Uniform Codes, and may be adopted as a code or used as a guideline.

Dwelling Construction under the Uniform Building Code™. Designed primarily for use in home building and apprentice training, this book contains requirements applicable to the construction of one- and two-story dwellings based on the requirements of the *Uniform Building Code.* Available in English or Spanish.

Dwelling Construction under the Uniform Mechanical Code™. This publication is for the convenience of the homeowner or contractor interested in installing mechanical equipment in a one- or two-family dwelling in conformance with the *Uniform Mechanical Code.*

Supplements to UBC and related codes. Published in the years between editions, the Supplements contain all approved changes, plus an analysis of those changes.

Uniform Building Code—1927 Edition. A special 60th anniversary printing of the first published *Uniform Building Code.*

One and Two Family Dwelling Code. Promulgated by ICC, this code eliminates conflicts and duplications among the model codes to achieve national uniformity. Covers mechanical and plumbing requirements as well as construction and occupancy.

Application and Commentary on the One and Two Family Dwelling Code. An interpretative commentary on the *One and Two Family Dwelling Code* intended to enhance uniformity of interpretation and application of the code nationwide. Developed by the three model code organizations, this document includes numerous illustrations of code requirements and the rationale for individual provisions.

Model Energy Code. This code includes minimum requirements for effective use of energy in the design of new buildings and structures and additions to existing buildings. It is based on American Society of Heating, Refrigeration and Air-conditioning Engineers Standard 90A-1980 and was originally developed jointly by ICBO, BOCA, SBCCI and the National Conference of States on Building Codes and Standards under a contract funded by the United States Department of Energy. The code is now maintained by ICC and is adopted by reference in the *Uniform Building Code.*

National Electrical Code®. The electrical code used throughout the United States. Published by the National Fire Protection Association, it is an indispensable aid to every electrician, contractor, architect, builder, inspector and anyone who must specify or certify electrical installations.

TECHNICAL REFERENCES AND EDUCATIONAL MATERIALS

Analysis of Revisions to the Uniform Codes™. An analysis of changes between the previous and new editions of the Uniform Codes is provided. Changes between code editions are noted either at the beginning of chapters or in the margins of the code text.

***Handbook to the Uniform Building Code.** The handbook is a completely detailed and illustrated commentary on the *Uniform Building Code,* tracing historical background and rationale of the codes through the current edition. Also included are numerous drawings and figures clarifying the application and intent of the code provisions. Also available in electronic format.

***Handbook to the Uniform Mechanical Code.** An indispensable tool for understanding the provisions of the current UMC, the handbook traces the historical background and rationale behind the UMC provisions, includes 160 figures which clarify the intent and application of the code, and provides a chapter-by-chapter analysis of the UMC.

***Uniform Building Code Application Manual.** This manual discusses sections of the *Uniform Building Code* with a question-and-answer format, providing a comprehensive analysis of the intent of the code sections. Most sections include illustrative examples. The manual is in loose-leaf format so that code applications published in *Building Standards* magazine may be inserted. Also available in electronic format.

***Uniform Mechanical Code Application Manual.** As a companion document to the *Uniform Mechanical Code,* this manual provides a comprehensive analysis of the intent of a number of code sections in an easy-to-use question-and-answer format. The manual is available in a loose-leaf format and includes illustrative examples for many code sections.

***Uniform Fire Code Applications Manual.** This newly developed manual provides questions and answers regarding UFC provisions. A comprehensive analysis of the intent of numerous code sections, the manual is in a loose-leaf format for easy insertion of code applications published in IFCI's *Fire Code Journal.*

Quick-Reference Guide to the Occupancy Requirements of the 1997 UBC. Code requirements are compiled in this publication by occupancy groups for quick access. These tabulations assemble requirements for each occupancy classification in the code. Provisions, such as fire-resistive ratings for occupancy separations in Table 3-B, exterior wall and opening protection requirements in Table 5-A-1, and fire-resistive ratings for types of construction in Table 6-A, are tabulated for quick reference and comparison.

Plan Review Manual. A practical text that will assist and guide both the field inspector and plan reviewer in applying the code requirements. This manual covers the nonstructural and basic structural aspects of plan review.

Field Inspection Manual. An important fundamental text for courses of study at the community college and trade or technical school level. It is an effective text for those studying building construction or architecture and includes sample forms and checklists for use in the field.

Building Department Administration. An excellent guide for improvement of skills in departmental management and in the enforcement and application of the Building Code and other regulations administered by a building inspection department. This textbook will also be a valuable aid to instructors, students and those in related professional fields.

Building Department Guide to Disaster Mitigation. This new, expanded guide is designed to assist building departments in developing or updating disaster mitigation plans. Subjects covered include guidelines for damage mitigation, disaster-response management, immediate response, mutual aid and inspections, working with the media, repair and recovery policies, and public information bulletins. This publication is a must for those involved in preparing for and responding to disaster.

Building Official Management Manual. This manual addresses the unique nature of code administration and the managerial duties of the building official. A supplementary insert addresses the budgetary and financial aspects of a building department. It is also an ideal resource for those preparing for the management module of the CABO Building Official Certification Examination.

Legal Aspects of Code Administration. A manual developed by the three model code organizations to inform the building official on the legal aspects of the profession. The text is written in a logical sequence with explanation of legal terminology. It is designed to serve as a refresher for those preparing to take the legal module of the CABO Building Official Certification Examination.

Illustrated Guide to Conventional Construction Provisions of the UBC. This comprehensive guide and commentary provides detailed explanations of the conventional construction provisions in the UBC, including descriptive discussions and illustrated drawings to convey the prescriptive provisions related to wood-frame construction.

Introduction to the Uniform Building Code. A workbook that provides an overview of the basics of the UBC.

Uniform Building Code Update Workbook. This manual addresses many of the changes to the administrative, fire- and life-safety, and inspection provisions appearing in the UBC.

UMC Workbook. Designed for independent study or use with instructor-led programs based on the *Uniform Mechanical Code,* this comprehensive study guide consists of 16 learning sessions, with the first two sessions reviewing the purpose, scope, definitions and administrative provisions and the remaining 14 sessions progressively exploring the requirements for installing, inspecting and maintaining heating, ventilating, cooling and refrigeration systems.

UBC Field Inspection Workbook. A comprehensive workbook for studying the provisions of the UBC. Divided into 12 sessions, this workbook focuses on the UBC combustible construction requirements for the inspection of wood-framed construction.

Concrete Manual. A publication for individuals seeking an understanding of the fundamentals of concrete field technology and inspection practices. Of particular interest to concrete construction inspectors, it will also benefit employees of concrete producers, contractors, testing and inspection laboratories and material suppliers.

Reinforced Concrete Masonry Construction Inspector's Handbook. A comprehensive information source written especially for masonry inspection covering terminology, technology, materials, quality control, inspection and standards. Published jointly by ICBO and the Masonry Institute of America.

You Can Build It! Sponsored by ICBO in cooperation with CABO, this booklet contains information and advice to aid "do-it-yourselfers" with building projects. Provides guidance in necessary procedures such as permit requirements, codes, plans, cost estimation, etc.

Guidelines for Manufactured Housing Installations. A guideline in code form implementing the *Uniform Building Code* and its companion code documents to regulate the permanent installation of a manufactured home on a privately owned, nonrental site. A commentary is included to explain specific provisions, and codes applying to each component part are defined.

Accessibility Reference Guide. This guide is a valuable resource for architects, interior designers, plan reviewers and others who design and enforce accessibility provisions. Features include accessibility requirements, along with detailed commentary and graphics to clarify the provisions; cross-references to other applicable sections of the UBC and the Americans with Disabilities Act Accessibility Guidelines; a checklist of UBC provisions on access and usability requirements; and many other useful references.

Educational and Technical Reference Materials. The Conference has been a leader in the development of texts and course material to assist in the educational process. These materials include vital information necessary for the building official and subordinates in carrying out their responsibilities and have proven to be excellent references in connection with community college curricula and higher-level courses in the field of building construction technology and inspection and in the administration of building departments. Included are plan review checklists for structural, nonstructural, mechanical and fire-safety provisions and a full line of videotapes and automated products.

TABLE OF CONTENTS

UNIFORM FIRE CODE STANDARD 10-1

SELECTION, INSTALLATION, INSPECTION, MAINTENANCE AND TESTING OF PORTABLE FIRE EXTINGUISHERS

See Sections 1002.1, 1006.2.7, 1102.5.2.3, 2401.13, 3209, 3208, 4502.8.2, 4503.7.1, 5201.9, 7901.5.3, 7902.5.1.2.1 and 7904.5.1.2, *Uniform Fire Code*

This standard, with certain exceptions, is based on the National Fire Protection Association Standard for Portable Fire Extinguishers, NFPA 10—1990.[1]

Part I of this standard contains exceptions to NFPA 10—1990.[1]

Part II of this standard contains NFPA 10—1990[1] reproduced in its entirety with permission of the publisher.

▨▨▨▨ vertically in the margin of Part II indicates there is a revision to the provisions within Part I.

Supplemental standards referenced by NFPA 10—1990[1] shall only be considered as guidelines subject to approval by the chief.

[1]The current edition is NFPA 10—1994.

Part I

SECTION 10.101 — AMENDMENTS

The Standard for Portable Fire Extinguishers, NFPA 10—1990, applies to the selection, installation, inspection, maintenance and testing of portable fire extinguishers except as follows:

1. Sec. 1-1 is revised as follows:

1-1 Scope.

The provisions of this standard apply to the selection, installation, inspection, maintenance and testing of portable extinguishing systems except when a provision in *Uniform Fire Code,* Volume 1 is applicable, in which case *Uniform Fire Code,* Volume 1 provisions take precedence.

2. Sec. 1-2 is deleted.

3. Sec. 1-3 is revised by amending the definition of "authority having jurisdiction" as follows:

AUTHORITY HAVING JURISDICTION is the official responsible for the administration and enforcement of this standard.

The definitions of "approved," "labeled" and "listed" shall be as set forth in *Uniform Fire Code,* Volume 1.

The definition of "should" is deleted.

4. Sec. 1-5.2 is revised by substituting the phrase "UFC Standard 81-1" for the phrase "NFPA 231, *Standard for Indoor General Storage.*"

5. Sec. 1-7 (b) is revised as follows:

(b) Hazardous materials shall be identified in accordance with UFC Standard 79-3. Hazardous materials shall be classified in accordance with Article 80, *Uniform Fire Code.*

6. Sec. 2-1 is revised as follows:

2-1 General Requirements.

Extinguishers shall be suitable for the anticipated growth and character of the fire, the construction and occupancy of the individual property or premises, the vehicle or hazard to be protected, and ambient-temperature conditions. Selection of the class, size, number and location of extinguishers shall be as specified in the *Uniform Fire Code,* Volume 1 when applicable; when not, the selection shall be required by this standard. Where extinguishers are required but a specific class, size, number or location is not given, the selection shall be subject to the approval of the chief and the following:

1. The gross weight of the extinguisher and the physical ability of the anticipated user.

2. Exposure of the extinguisher to corrosive atmospheres.

3. Adverse reaction between the agent in the extinguisher and the material or equipment being protected.

4. Mobility of wheeled units over terrain of the premises and the configuration of routes which may limit access.

5. The effective range of the extinguishers which could be subject to wind or draft conditions.

6. The ability and number of available personnel to operate the extinguisher.

7. The health and safety of the user.

To protect the health and safety of the user, the chief is authorized to require installation of extended-throw nozzles, special ventilation and other protective measures, including the training of personnel.

7. Sec. 2-3.2 is revised as follows:

2-3.2 Fire Extinguisher and Size and Placement for Cooking Grease Fires. A sodium bicarbonate or potassium bicarbonate dry-chemical-type portable fire extinguisher having a minimum rating of 40-B shall be installed within 30 feet (9144 mm) of commercial food heat-processing equipment, as measured along an unobstructed path of travel.

8. Sec. 3-1.5 is revised as follows:

3-1.5 The type, size, number and placement of fire extinguishers for special storage occupancies is addressed in UFC Standard 81-1, High-piled General Storage of Combustibles in Buildings; UFC Standard 81-2, High-piled Rack Storage of Combustibles in Buildings; and NFPA 231-D, Storage of Rubber Tires.

9. Sec. 3-2.2 is revised as follows:

3-2.2 One half of the fire extinguishers required by Table 3-2.1 are allowed to be omitted when the building is equipped with a Class II or III standpipe system that complies with *Uniform Fire Code,* Article 10 and the Building Code. See UBC Standard 9-2.

10. Sec. 4-1.1 is revised as follows:

4-1.1 Approved existing extinguisher installations maintained in accordance with the conditions under which they were approved are allowed to continue in use. Such extinguishers shall be maintained in a safe and operative condition and shall be inspected and recharged as required by this standard.

EXCEPTIONS: 1. Soda acid, foam, loaded stream, antifreeze and water fire extinguishers of the inverting type shall not be recharged or placed in service for fire-protection use.

2. Vaporizing liquid extinguishers containing carbon tetrachloride or chlorobromomethane shall not be installed or used in any location for fire-protection use.

11. Sec. 4-5.3.8 is revised by deleting the first sentence and substituting as follows:

The removal of Halon 1211 from extinguishers shall be accomplished using only a listed halon closed-recovery system.

12. Sec. 5-5.1.2 is revised as follows:

5-5.1.2 The equipment for testing compressed gas cylinders and cartridges shall be an approved water-jacket type.

13. Sec. 5-5.2 is revised as follows:

5-5.2 Testing Procedures for Low Pressure Gas Types. The testing procedures for the internal examination and hydraulic testing of noncompressed gas cylinders and shells shall be in accordance with approved standards.

14. Sec. 5-5.3 is revised as follows:

5-5.3 Testing Procedures for Hose Assemblies. The hydrostatic testing procedures for hose assemblies shall be in accordance with nationally recognized standards.

15. Chapter 6 is deleted.

Part II

Contents

NFPA 10

Standard for

Portable Fire Extinguishers

1990 Edition

NOTICE: An asterisk (*) following the number or letter designating a paragraph indicates explanatory material on that paragraph in Appendix A.

Information on referenced publications can be found in Chapter 6 and Appendix G.

Chapter 1 Introduction

1-1* Scope. The provisions of this standard apply to the selection, installation, inspection, maintenance, and testing of portable extinguishing equipment. The requirements given herein are **MINIMUM**. Portable extinguishers are intended as a first line of defense to cope with fires of limited size. They are needed even if the property is equipped with automatic sprinklers, standpipe and hose, or other fixed protection equipment (*see 3-1.1, 3-1.5, 3-2.1, and 3-2.3*). They do not apply to permanently installed systems for fire extinguishment, even though portions of such systems may be portable (such as hose and nozzles attached to a fixed supply of extinguishing agent).[1]

1-2* Purpose. This standard is prepared for the use and guidance of persons charged with selecting, purchasing, installing, approving, listing, designing, and maintaining portable fire extinguishing equipment. The fire protection requirements of this standard are general in nature and are not intended to abrogate the specific requirements of other NFPA standards for specific occupancies.

Nothing in this standard shall be construed as a restriction on new technologies or alternative arrangements, provided that the level of protection as herein described is not lowered and is acceptable to the authority having jurisdiction.

1-3 Definitions.

Approved. Acceptable to the "authority having jurisdiction."

NOTE: The National Fire Protection Association does not approve, inspect or certify any installations, procedures, equipment, or materials nor does it approve or evaluate testing laboratories. In determining the acceptability of installations or procedures, equipment or materials, the authority having jurisdiction may base acceptance on compliance with NFPA or other appropriate standards. In the absence of such standards, said authority may require evidence of proper installation, procedure or use. The authority having jurisdiction may also refer to the listings or labeling practices of an organization concerned with product evaluations which is in a position to determine compliance with appropriate standards for the current production of listed items.

Authority Having Jurisdiction. The "authority having jurisdiction" is the organization, office or individual responsible for "approving" equipment, an installation or a procedure.

NOTE: The phrase "authority having jurisdiction" is used in NFPA documents in a broad manner since jurisdictions and "approval" agencies vary as do their responsibilities. Where public safety is primary, the "authority having jurisdiction" may be a federal, state, local or other regional department or individual such as a fire chief, fire marshal, chief of a fire prevention bureau, labor department, health department, building official, electrical inspector, or others having statutory authority. For insurance purposes, an insurance inspection department, rating bureau, or other insurance company representative may be the "authority having jurisdiction." In many circumstances the property owner or his designated agent assumes the role of the "authority having jurisdiction"; at government installations, the commanding officer or departmental official may be the "authority having jurisdiction."

BTC. The Board of Transport Commissioners of Canada, which formerly had jurisdiction over high pressure cylinders and cartridges.

Class A Fires. Fires in ordinary combustible materials, such as wood, cloth, paper, rubber, and many plastics.

Class B Fires. Fires in flammable liquids, oils, greases, tars, oil-base paints, lacquers, and flammable gases.

Class C Fires. Fires that involve energized electrical equipment where the electrical nonconductivity of the extinguishing media is of importance. (When electrical equipment is de-energized, extinguishers for Class A or B fires may be used safely.)

Class D Fires. Fires in combustible metals, such as magnesium, titanium, zirconium, sodium, lithium, and potassium.

CTC. The Canadian Transport Commission, which has jurisdiction over high pressure cylinders and cartridges.

DOT. The U.S. Department of Transportation, which has jurisdiction over high pressure cylinders and cartridges.

Dry Chemical Closed Recovery System. A system that provides for the transfer of dry chemical agent between extinguishers and recovery containers that is closed to prevent the loss of agent to the atmosphere.

Factory Test Pressure. The pressure at which the shell was tested at time of manufacture. This pressure is shown on the nameplate.

[1] Fixed systems are covered by the following NFPA standards: NFPA 11, *Standard for Low Expansion Foam and Combined Agent Systems*; NFPA 11A, *Standard for Medium- and High-Expansion Foam Systems*; NFPA 12, *Standard on Carbon Dioxide Extinguishing Systems*; NFPA 12A, *Standard on Halon 1301 Fire Extinguishing Systems*; NFPA 12B, *Standard on Halon 1211 Fire Extinguishing Systems*; NFPA 13, *Standard for the Installation of Sprinkler Systems*; NFPA 14, *Standard for the Installation of Standpipe and Hose Systems*; NFPA 15, *Standard for Water Spray Fixed Systems for Fire Protection*; NFPA 16, *Standard on Deluge Foam-Water Sprinkler and Foam-Water Spray Systems*; NFPA 17, *Standard for Dry Chemical Extinguishing Systems*; and NFPA 96, *Standard for the Installation of Equipment for the Removal of Smoke and Grease-Laden Vapors from Commercial Cooking Equipment.*

Film Forming Agents. The film forming agents referenced in this standard are AFFF (aqueous film forming foam) and FFFP (film forming fluoroprotein foam) types including both grades: not approved for polar solvents (water-soluble flammable liquids), and approved for polar solvents.

Halogenated Agents. Halogenated agents referenced in this standard are bromochlorodifluoromethane (Halon 1211), bromotrifluoromethane (Halon 1301), and mixtures of Halon 1211 and Halon 1301 (Halon 1211/1301).

Note: Halon 1211 and Halon 1301 are included in the "Montreal Protocol on Substances that Deplete the Ozone Layer," signed September 16, 1987. The protocol limits production of Halons 1211 and 1301 to 1986 production levels and places restrictions on imports and exports. It also contains provisions to facilitate the imposition of further restrictions.

Halon Closed Recovery System. A system that provides for the transfer of halon between extinguishers, supply containers, and recharge and recovery containers so that none of the halon escapes to the atmosphere.

The system's supply or recharge and recovery container shall be capable of maintaining the halon in a sealed environment until it is reused or returned to the agent manufacturer.

High Pressure Cylinder. For the purposes of this standard, high pressure cylinders and cartridges are those containing nitrogen or compressed air at a service pressure higher than 500 psig at 70°F (21.1°C), or carbon dioxide.

ICC. The Interstate Commerce Commission, which had jurisdiction over high pressure cylinders and cartridges prior to 1967.

Inspection. A "quick check" that an extinguisher is available and will operate. It is intended to give reasonable assurance that the extinguisher is fully charged and operable. This is done by seeing that it is in its designated place, that it has not been actuated or tampered with, and that there is no obvious or physical damage or condition to prevent its operation.

Labeled. Equipment or materials to which has been attached a label, symbol or other identifying mark of an organization acceptable to the "authority having jurisdiction" and concerned with product evaluation, that maintains periodic inspection of production of labeled equipment or materials and by whose labeling the manufacturer indicates compliance with appropriate standards or performance in a specified manner.

Listed. Equipment or materials included in a list published by an organization acceptable to the "authority having jurisdiction" and concerned with product evaluation, that maintains periodic inspection of production of listed equipment or materials and whose listing states either that the equipment or material meets appropriate standards or has been tested and found suitable for use in a specified manner.

NOTE: The means for identifying listed equipment may vary for each organization concerned with product evaluation, some of which do not recognize equipment as listed unless it is also labeled. The "authority having jurisdiction" should utilize the system employed by the listing organization to identify a listed product.

Low Pressure Gas Cylinder. For the purpose of this standard, low pressure gas cylinders are those containing nitrogen, compressed air, and/or halon at a service pressure of 500 psig or lower at 70°F (21.1°C). The cylinders may also contain noncorrosive, non-pressure generating dry materials such as dry chemical or dry powder agents or water based agents in cylinders protected against internal corrosion.

Maintenance. A thorough examination of the extinguisher. It is intended to give maximum assurance that an extinguisher will operate effectively and safely. It includes a thorough examination and any necessary repair or replacement. It will normally reveal if hydrostatic testing is required.

Mild Steel Shell. All other steel shells, except for stainless steel and steel used for high pressure cylinders.

Nonrechargeable Fire Extinguisher. A nonrechargeable (nonrefillable) fire extinguisher is not capable (nor intended) of undergoing complete maintenance, hydrostatic testing, and being restored to its full operating capability by the standard practices used by fire equipment dealers and distributors.

Nonrechargeable (nonrefillable) fire extinguishers are marked "Discharge and Dispose of After Any Use" or "Discharge and Return to the Manufacturer After Any Use" or with a similar equivalent marking. Some extinguishers that are physically rechargeable are marked nonrechargeable and are therefore considered by this standard to be nonrechargeable (nonrefillable) fire extinguishers.

Portable Fire Extinguisher. A portable device containing an extinguishing agent that can be expelled under pressure for the purpose of suppressing or extinguishing a fire.

Rechargeable (Refillable) Fire Extinguisher. A rechargeable (refillable) extinguisher is capable of undergoing complete maintenance, including internal inspection of the pressure vessel, replacement of all substandard parts and seals, and hydrostatic testing. The extinguisher is capable of being recharged with agent, pressurized, and restored to its full operating capability by the standard practices used by fire equipment dealers and distributors. Rechargeable (refillable) extinguishers are marked "Recharge Immediately After Any Use" or with a similar equivalent marking.

Recharging. The replacement of the extinguishing agent (also includes the expellant for certain types of extinguishers).

Self-Expelling Extinguisher. An extinguisher in which the agents have sufficient vapor pressure at normal operating temperatures to expel themselves.

Service Pressure. The normal operating pressure as indicated on the gage and nameplate of an extinguisher.

Servicing. Includes one or more of the following: (1) maintenance, (2) recharging, and (3) hydrostatic testing.

Shall. Indicates a mandatory requirement.

Should. Indicates a recommendation or that which is advised but not required.

Stored Pressure Extinguisher. An extinguisher in which both the extinguishing material and expellant gas are kept in a single container and which includes a pressure indicator or gage.

Water-Type Fire Extinguisher. A water type extinguisher contains water based agents, such as water, foam, AFFF, FFFP, antifreeze, and loaded stream.

1-4 Classification, Ratings, and Performance of Fire Extinguishers.

1-4.1 Portable fire extinguishers are classified for use on certain classes of fires and rated for relative extinguishing effectiveness at a temperature of 70°F (21.1°C) by testing laboratories. This is based on the preceding classification of fires and the fire-extinguishment potentials as determined by fire tests.

1-4.2* The classification and rating system described in this standard is that of Underwriters Laboratories Inc. and Underwriters Laboratories of Canada, and is based on extinguishing preplanned fires of determined size and description as follows:

CLASS A RATING — Wood and excelsior.

CLASS B RATING — Two-in. (5.1-cm) depth n-heptane fires in square pans.

CLASS C RATING — No fire test. Agent must be a nonconductor of electricity.

CLASS D RATING — Special tests on specific combustible metal fires.

1-4.3 Portable fire extinguishers used to comply with this standard shall be listed and labeled and meet or exceed all the requirements of one of the fire test standards and one of the appropriate performance standards shown below:

(a) Fire Test Standards: ANSI/UL 711, CAN4-S508-M83

(b) Performance Standards:

1. Carbon Dioxide Types: ANSI/UL 154, CAN 4-S503-M83
2. Dry Chemical Types: ANSI/UL 299, ULC-S504
3. Water Types: ANSI/UL 626, CAN4-S507-M83
4. Halon Types: ANSI/UL 1093, ULC-S512
5. Foam Types: ANSI/UL 8

1-4.4* The identification of the listing and labeling organization, the fire test, and performance standard that the extinguisher meets or exceeds shall be clearly marked on each extinguisher.

Exception: Extinguishers manufactured prior to January 1, 1986.

1-4.5* An organization listing, labeling, and marking extinguishers used to comply with the requirements of this standard shall utilize a third party certification program for portable fire extinguishers that meets or exceeds ANSI/UL 1803, *Standard for Factory Follow-Up on Third Party Certified Portable Fire Extinguishers.*

Exception No. 1: Extinguishers manufactured prior to January 1, 1989.

Exception No. 2: Certification organizations accredited by the Standards Council of Canada.

1-5 Classification of Hazards.

1-5.1 Light (Low) Hazard. Light hazard occupancies are locations where the total amount of Class A combustible materials, including furnishings, decorations, and contents, is of minor quantity. This may include some buildings or rooms occupied as offices, classrooms, churches, assembly halls, guest room areas of hotels/motels, etc. This classification anticipates that the majority of content items are either noncombustible or so arranged that a fire is not likely to spread rapidly. Small amounts of Class B flammables used for duplicating machines, art departments, etc., are included provided that they are kept in closed containers and safely stored.

1-5.2 Ordinary (Moderate) Hazard. Ordinary hazard occupancies are locations where the total amount of Class A combustibles and Class B flammables are present in greater amounts than expected under light (low) hazard occupancies. These occupancies could consist of dining areas, mercantile shops and allied storage, light manufacturing, research operations, auto showrooms, parking garages, workshop or support service areas of light (low) hazard occupancies, and warehouses containing Class I or Class II commodities as defined by NFPA 231, *Standard for General Storage.*

1-5.3 Extra (High) Hazard. Extra hazard occupancies are locations where the total amount of Class A combustibles and Class B flammables present, in storage, production use, and/or finished product is over and above those expected and classed as ordinary (moderate) hazards. These occupancies could consist of woodworking, vehicle repair, aircraft and boat servicing, cooking areas, individual product display showrooms, product convention center displays, and storage and manufacturing processes such as painting, dipping, coating, including flammable liquid handling. Also included is warehousing of or in-process storage of other than Class I and Class II commodities.

1-6 General Requirements.

1-6.1 The classification of extinguishers shall consist of a LETTER that indicates the class of fire on which an extinguisher has been found to be effective, preceded by a rating NUMERAL (Class A and B only) that indicates the relative extinguishing effectiveness.

Exception: Extinguishers classified for use on Class C or D hazards shall not be required to have a numeral preceding the classification letter.

1-6.2 Portable extinguishers shall be maintained in a fully charged and operable condition, and kept in their designated places at all times when they are not being used.

1-6.3 Extinguishers shall be conspicuously located where they will be readily accessible and immediately available in the event of fire. Preferably they shall be located along normal paths of travel, including exits from areas.

1-6.4 Cabinets housing extinguishers shall not be locked.

Exception: Where extinguishers are subject to malicious use, locked cabinets may be used provided they include means of emergency access.

1-6.5* Extinguishers shall not be obstructed or obscured from view.

Exception: In large rooms, and in certain locations where visual obstruction cannot be completely avoided, means shall be provided to indicate the location.

1-6.6* Extinguishers shall be installed on the hangers or in the brackets supplied, mounted in cabinets, or set on shelves unless the extinguishers are of the wheeled type.

1-6.7 Extinguishers installed under conditions where they are subject to dislodgement shall be installed in brackets specifically designed to cope with this problem.

1-6.8 Extinguishers installed under conditions where they are subject to physical damage shall be protected from impact.

1-6.9 Extinguishers having a gross weight not exceeding 40 lb (18.14 kg) shall be installed so that the top of the extinguisher is not more than 5 ft (1.53 m) above the floor. Extinguishers having a gross weight greater than 40 lb (18.14 kg) (except wheeled types) shall be so installed that the top of the extinguisher is *not more* than $3^1/_2$ ft (1.07 m) above the floor. In no case shall the clearance between the bottom of the extinguisher and the floor be less than 4 in. (10.2 cm).

1-6.10 Operating instructions shall be located on the front of the extinguisher. Other labels and markings shall not be placed on the front.

Exception: In addition to manufacturers' labels, other labels that specifically relate to operation, classification, or warning information shall be permitted on the front.

1-6.11 Extinguishers mounted in cabinets or wall recesses or set on shelves shall be placed in a manner such that the extinguisher operating instructions face outward. The location of such extinguishers shall be marked conspicuously (*see 1-6.5*).

1-6.12* Where extinguishers are installed in closed cabinets that are exposed to elevated temperatures, cabinets shall be provided with screened openings and drains.

1-6.13* Water-type (water, foam, AFFF, wetting agent, and soda-acid) extinguishers shall not be installed in areas where temperatures are outside the range of 40°F to 120°F (4°C to 49°C). All other types shall not be installed in areas where temperatures are outside the range of –40°F to 120°F (–40°C to 49°C).

Exception No. 1: When extinguishers are installed in locations subject to temperatures outside these ranges, they shall be of a type approved and listed for the temperature to which they are exposed, or they must be placed in an enclosure capable of maintaining the stipulated range of temperatures.

Exception No. 2: Extinguishers containing plain water only can be protected to temperatures as low as –40°F (–40°C) by the addition of an antifreeze stipulated on the extinguisher nameplate. Calcium chloride solutions shall not be used in stainless steel extinguishers.

Exception No. 3: Some extinguishers that use nitrogen rather than carbon dioxide as an expellant gas are approved or listed for temperatures as low as –65°F (–54°C).

1-6.14* An extinguisher instruction manual shall be provided to the owner or his agent giving condensed instructions and cautions necessary to the installation, operation, inspection, and maintenance of the extinguisher(s). The manual shall refer to this standard as a source of detailed instruction.

1-7* Identification of Contents. An extinguisher shall have attached to it in the form of a label, tag, stencil, or similar manner the following information:

(a) Contents product name as it appears on the manufacturer's Material Safety Data Sheet (MSDS).

(b) A listing of the hazardous material identification in accordance with the National Paint and Coatings Association, *Hazardous Materials Identification Systems (HMIS)*. [In Canada, see *Workplace Hazardous Materials Identification Systems (WHMIS)*].

(c) A list of any hazardous materials which are in excess of 1.0 percent of the contents.

(d) A list of each chemical in excess of 5.0 percent of the contents.

(e) Information as to what is hazardous about the agent in accordance with the *Material Safety Data Sheet (MSDS)*.

(f) The manufacturer's name, mailing address, and phone number as shown on the *Material Safety Data Sheet (MSDS)*.

Exception: Extinguishers manufactured before July 1, 1991.

1-8 Units. Metric units of measurement in this standard are in accordance with the modernized metric system known as the International System of Units (SI). One unit (liter), outside of but recognized by SI, is commonly used in international fire protection. The units are listed in Table 1-8 with conversion factors.

Table 1-8

Name of Unit	Unit Symbol	Conversion Factor
Liter	L	1 gal = 3.785 L
cu decimeter	dm^3	1 gal = 3.785 dm^3

For additional conversion and information see ASTM E 380, *Standard for Metric Practice.*

1-8.1 If a value for measurement as given in this standard is followed by an equivalent value in other units, the first stated is to be regarded as the requirement. A given equivalent value may be approximate.

1-8.2 The conversion procedure for the SI units has been to multiply the quantity by the conversion factor and then round the result to the appropriate number of significant digits.

Chapter 2 Selection of Extinguishers

2-1* General Requirements. The selection of extinguishers for a given situation shall be determined by the character of the fires anticipated, the construction and occupancy of the individual property, the vehicle or hazard to be protected, ambient-temperature conditions, and other factors. (*See Table A-2-1, Appendix A.*) The number, size, placement, and limitations of use of extinguishers required shall meet the requirements of Chapter 3.

2-1.1* Use of halogenated agent fire extinguishers shall be limited to applications where a clean agent is necessary to extinguish fire efficiently without damaging the equipment or area being protected, or where the use of alternate agents can cause a hazard to personnel in the area.

Exception: Halogenated agent types of extinguishers installed before January 1, 1991.

2-2 Selection by Hazard.

2-2.1 Extinguishers shall be selected for the specific class(es) of hazards to be protected in accordance with the following subdivisions.

2-2.1.1* Extinguishers for protecting Class A hazards shall be selected from the following: water-type and multipurpose dry chemical.

Exception: For halogenated agent type extinguishers, see 2-1.1.

2-2.1.2 Extinguishers for protection of Class B hazards shall be selected from the following: aqueous film forming foam (AFFF), film forming fluoroprotein foam (FFFP), carbon dioxide, dry chemical types, and halogenated agent types.

2-2.1.3* Extinguishers for protection of Class C hazards shall be selected from the following: carbon dioxide[1] and dry chemical types.

Exception: For halogenated agent type extinguishers, see 2-1.1.

2-2.1.4* Extinguishers and extinguishing agents for the protection of Class D hazards shall be of types approved for use on the specific combustible-metal hazard.

2-3 Application for Specific Hazards.

2-3.1 Class B Fire Extinguishers for Pressurized Flammable Liquids and Pressurized Gas Fires. Fires of this nature are considered to be a special hazard. Class B fire extinguishers containing agents other than dry chemical are relatively ineffective on this type of hazard due to stream and agent characteristics. Selection of extinguishers for this type of hazard shall be made on the basis of recommendations by manufacturers of this specialized equipment. The system used to rate the effectiveness of extinguishers on Class B fires (flammable liquids in depth) is not applicable to these types of hazards. It has been determined that special nozzle design and rates of agent application are required to cope with such hazards. Caution: It is undesirable to attempt to extinguish this type of fire unless there is reasonable assurance that the source of fuel can be promptly shut off.

2-3.2 Fire Extinguisher Size and Placement for Cooking Grease Fires. Extinguishers provided for the protection of cooking grease fires shall be only of the sodium bicarbonate or potassium bicarbonate dry chemical type. Installation shall be in accordance with Table 3-3.1 for Extra (High) Hazard. (*See NFPA 96, Standard for the Installation of Equipment for the Removal of Smoke and Grease-Laden Vapors from Commercial Cooking Equipment.*)

2-3.3 Three-Dimensional Class B Fires. A three-dimensional Class B fire involves Class B materials in motion such as pouring, running, or dripping flammable liquids and generally includes vertical as well as one or more horizontal surfaces. Fires of this nature are considered to be a special hazard. Selection of extinguishers for this type of hazard shall be made on the basis of recommendations by manufacturers of this specialized equipment. The system used to rate extinguishers on Class B fires (flammable liquids in depth) is not directly applicable to this type of hazard.

NOTE: The installation of fixed systems should be considered when applicable.

[1] Carbon dioxide extinguishers equipped with metal horns are not considered safe for use on fires in energized electrical equipment and, therefore, are not classified for use on Class C hazards.

2-3.4 Water-Soluble Flammable Liquid Fires (Polar Solvents). AFFF and FFFP type fire extinguishers shall not be used for the protection of water-soluble flammable liquids, such as alcohols, acetone, esters, ketones, etc., unless specifically referenced on the extinguisher nameplate.

2-3.5* Electronic Equipment Fires. Extinguishers for the protection of delicate electronic equipment shall be selected from the following: carbon dioxide and halogenated agent types.

2-3.6* Wheeled Extinguishers. Wheeled extinguishers shall be considered for hazard protection when fulfillment of the following requirements is necessary:

(a) High agent flow rates.

(b) Increased agent stream range.

(c) Increased agent capacity.

(d) High hazard areas.

2-4 Application for Specific Locations.

2-4.1 Aircraft Protection. Extinguishers used onboard aircraft for fire protection shall be selected and installed in accordance with NFPA 408, *Standard for Aircraft Hand Fire Extinguishers*.

2-4.2 Pleasure and Commercial Motor Craft. Extinguishers used onboard watercraft for fire protection shall be selected and installed in accordance with NFPA 302, *Fire Protection Standard for Pleasure and Commercial Motor Craft*.

Chapter 3 Distribution of Extinguishers

3-1 General Requirements.

3-1.1* The minimum number of fire extinguishers needed to protect a property shall be determined as outlined in Chapter 3 of this standard. Frequently, additional extinguishers may be installed to provide more suitable protection. Extinguishers having ratings less than specified in Tables 3-2.1 and 3-3.1 may be installed provided they are not used in fulfilling the minimum protective requirements of this chapter.

3-1.2* Fire extinguishers shall be provided for the protection of both the building structure, if combustible, and the occupancy hazards contained therein.

3-1.2.1 Required building protection shall be provided by fire extinguishers suitable for Class A fires.

3-1.2.2* Occupancy hazard protection shall be provided by fire extinguishers suitable for such Class A, B, C, or D fire potentials as may be present.

3-1.2.3 Extinguishers provided for building protection may be considered also for the protection of occupancies having a Class A fire potential.

3-1.2.4 Combustible buildings having an occupancy hazard subject to Class B and/or Class C fires shall have a standard complement of Class A fire extinguishers for building protection, plus additional Class B and/or Class C extinguishers. Where fire extinguishers have more than one letter classification (such as 2-A:20-B:C), they may be considered to satisfy the requirements of each letter class.

3-1.3 Rooms or areas shall be classified generally as light (low) hazard, ordinary (moderate) hazard, or extra (high) hazard. Limited areas of greater or lesser hazard shall be protected as required.

3-1.4 On each floor level, the area protected and the travel distances are based on extinguishers installed in accordance with Tables 3-2.1 and 3-3.1.

3-1.5 The type, size, number, and placement for special storage occupancies is covered by NFPA 231, *Standard for General Storage*; NFPA 231C, *Standard for Rack Storage of Materials*; and NFPA 231D, *Standard for Storage of Rubber Tires*.

3-2 Fire Extinguisher Size and Placement for Class A Hazards.

3-2.1 Minimal sizes of fire extinguishers for the listed grades of hazards shall be provided on the basis of Table 3-2.1 except as modified by 3-2.2. Extinguishers shall be located so that the maximum travel distances shall not exceed those specified in Table 3-2.1, except as modified by 3-2.2. (*See Appendix E.*)

Table 3-2.1

	Light (Low) Hazard Occupancy	Ordinary (Moderate) Hazard Occupancy	Extra (High) Hazard Occupancy
Minimum rated single extinguisher	2-A	2-A	4-A*
Maximum floor area per unit of A	3,000 sq ft	1,500 sq ft	1,000 sq ft
Maximum floor area for extinguisher	11,250 sq ft **	11,250 sq ft**	11,250 sq ft**
Maximum travel distance to extinguisher	75 ft	75 ft	75 ft

*Two $2^1/_2$-gal (9.46-L) water-type extinguishers can be used to fulfill the requirements of one 4-A rated extinguisher.

**See Appendix E-3-3.

For SI Units: 1 ft = 0.305 m; 1 sq ft = 0.929 m^2

3-2.1.1 Certain smaller extinguishers that are charged with multipurpose dry chemical, Halon 1211, or Halon 1211/1301 are rated on Class B and Class C fires, but have insufficient effectiveness to earn the minimum 1-A rating even though they have value in extinguishing smaller Class A fires. They shall not be used to meet the requirements of 3-2.1.

3-2.2 Up to one-half of the complement of extinguishers as specified in Table 3-2.1 may be replaced by uniformly spaced 1½-in. (3.81-cm) hose stations for use by the occupants of the building. When hose stations are so provided, they shall conform to NFPA 14, *Standard for the Installation of Standpipe and Hose Systems*. The location of hose stations and the placement of fire extinguishers shall be such that the hose stations do not replace more than every other extinguisher.

3-2.3 Where the area of the floor of a building is less than that specified in Table 3-2.1, at least one extinguisher of the minimum size recommended shall be provided.

3-2.4 The protection requirements may be fulfilled with extinguishers of higher rating provided the travel distance to such larger extinguishers shall not excceed 75 ft (22.7 m).

3-2.5 For Class A extinguishers rated under the rating classification system used prior to 1955, their equivalency shall be in accordance with Table 3-2.5.

Table 3-2.5

All Water & Loaded Stream Types	Pre-1955 Rating	Equivalency
1¼ to 1¾ gal	A-2	1-A
2½ gal	A-1	2-A
4 gal	A-1	3-A
5 gal	A-1	4-A
17 gal	A	10-A
33 gal	A	20-A

For SI Units: 1 gal = 3.785 L.

3-3 Fire Extinguisher Size and Placement for Class B Fires Other than for Fires in Flammable Liquids of Appreciable Depth.

3-3.1 Minimal sizes of fire extinguishers for the listed grades of hazard shall be provided on the basis of Table 3-3.1. Extinguishers shall be located so that the maximum travel distances shall not exceed those specified in the table used. (*See Appendix E.*)

Exception: Extinguishers of lesser rating, desired for small specific hazards within the general hazard area, may be used, but shall not be considered as fulfilling any part of the requirements of Table 3-3.1.

3-3.2 Two or more extinguishers of lower rating shall not be used to fulfill the protection requirements of Table 3-3.1.

Exception: Up to three AFFF or FFFP extinguishers of at least 2½-gal (9.46-L) capacity may be used to fulfill extra (high) hazard requirements.

3-3.3 The protection requirements may be fulfilled with extinguishers of higher ratings provided the travel distance to such larger extinguishers shall not exceed 50 ft (15.25 m).

Table 3-3.1

Type of Hazard	Basic Minimum Extinguisher Rating	Maximum Travel Distance to Extinguishers (ft)	(m)
Light (low)	5-B	30	9.15
	10-B	50	15.25
Ordinary (moderate)	10-B	30	9.15
	20-B	50	19.25
Extra (high)	40-B	30	9.15
	80-B	50	15.25

NOTE 1: The specified ratings do not imply that fires of the magnitudes indicated by these ratings will occur, but rather to give the operators more time and agent to handle difficult spill fires that may occur.

NOTE 2: For fires involving water-soluble flammable liquids, *see 2-3.4.*

NOTE 3: For specific hazard applications, *see Section 2-3.*

3-3.4 For Class B extinguishers rated under the rating classification system used prior to 1955, their equivalency shall be in accordance with Table 3-4.5.

3-4 Fire Extinguisher Size and Placement for Class B Fires in Flammable Liquids of Appreciable Depth.[1]

3-4.1* Portable fire extinguishers shall not be installed as the sole protection for flammable liquid hazards of appreciable depth [greater than ¼ in. (0.64 cm)] where the surface area exceeds 10 sq ft (0.93 m^2).

Exception: Where personnel who are trained in extinguishing fires in the protected hazards, or a counterpart, are available on the premises, the maximum surface area shall not exceed 20 sq ft (1.86 m^2).

3-4.2 For flammable liquid hazards of appreciable depth, such as in dip or quench tanks, a Class B fire extinguisher shall be provided on the basis of at least two numerical units of Class B extinguishing potential per sq ft (0.0929 m^2) of flammable liquid surface of the largest tank hazard within the area.

Exception No. 1: Where approved automatic fire protection devices or systems have been installed for a flammable liquid hazard, additional portable Class B fire extinguishers may be waived. Where so waived, Class B extinguishers shall be provided as covered in 3-3.1 to protect areas in the vicinity of such protected hazards.

Exception No. 2: AFFF or FFFP type extinguishers may be provided on the basis of 1-B of protection per sq ft of hazard.

[1] For dip tanks containing flammable or combustible liquids exceeding 150-gal (568-L) liquid capacity or having a liquid surface exceeding 4 sq ft (0.38 m^2), see NFPA 34, *Standard for Dipping and Coating Processes Using Flammable or Combustible Liquids*, for requirements of automatic extinguishing facilities.

3-4.3 Two or more extinguishers of lower ratings shall not be used in lieu of the extinguisher required for the largest tank.

Exception: Up to three AFFF or FFFP extinguishers of $2^1/_2$-gal (9.46-L) capacity may be used to fulfill these requirements.

3-4.4 Travel distances for portable extinguishers shall not exceed 50 ft (15.25 m). (*See Appendix E.*)

3-4.4.1 Scattered or widely separated hazards shall be individually protected. An extinguisher in the proximity of a hazard shall be carefully located to be accessible in the presence of a fire without undue danger to the operator.

3-4.5 For Class B extinguishers rated under the rating classification system used prior to 1955, their equivalency shall be in accordance with Table 3-4.5.

3-5 Fire Extinguisher Size and Placement for Class C Hazards. Extinguishers with Class C ratings shall be required where energized electrical equipment may be encountered that would require a nonconducting extinguishing medium. This will include fire either directly involving or surrounding electrical equipment. Since the fire itself is a Class A or Class B hazard, the extinguishers are sized and located on the basis of the anticipated Class A or B hazard.

NOTE: Electrical equipment should be de-energized as soon as possible to prevent reignition.

Table 3-4.5

Type and Capacity	Pre-1955	Equivalency
Foam		
$2^1/_2$ gal	B-1	2-B
5 gal	B-1	5-B
17 gal	B	10-B
33 gal	B	20-B
Carbon Dioxide		
Under 7 lb	B-2	1-B
7 lb	B-2	2-B
10 to 12 lb	B-2	2-B
15 to 20 lb	B-1	2-B
25 to 26 lb	B-1	5-B
50 lb	B-1	10-B
75 lb	B-1	10-B
100 lb	B	10-B
Dry Chemical		
4 to $6^1/_4$ lb	B-2	2-B
$7^1/_2$ lb	B-2	5-B
10 to 15 lb	B-1	5-B
20 lb	B-1	10-B
30 lb	B-1	20-B
75 lb and up	B	40-B

For SI Units: 1 gal = 3.785 L; 1 lb = 0.454 kg.

3-5.1 For extinguishers classified under the system used prior to 1955, the pre-1955 classifications of "C-2," "C-1," and "C" shall be equivalent to the current "C" designation.

Exception: Carbon dioxide extinguishers with metal horns shall not carry any "C" classification.

3-6 Fire Extinguisher Size and Placement for Class D Hazards.

3-6.1 Extinguishers or extinguishing agents with Class D ratings shall be provided for fires involving combustible metals.

3-6.2 Extinguishing equipment shall be located not more than 75 ft (22.7 m) from the Class D hazard. (*See Appendix E.*)

3-6.3 Size determination shall be on the basis of the specific combustible metal, its physical particle size, area to be covered, and recommendations by the extinguisher manufacturer on data from control tests conducted.

Chapter 4 Inspection, Maintenance, and Recharging

4-1 General.

4-1.1 This chapter is concerned with the rules governing inspection, maintenance, and recharging of extinguishers. These factors are of prime importance in ensuring operation at the time of a fire.

4-1.2 The procedure for inspection and maintenance of fire extinguishers varies considerably. Minimal knowledge is necessary to perform a monthly "quick check" or inspection in order to follow the inspection procedure as outlined in Section 4-3. A trained person who has undergone the instructions necessary to reliably perform maintenance and has the manufacturer's service manual shall service the fire extinguishers not more than one year apart, as outlined in Section 4-4.

4-1.3 The owner or designated agent or occupant of a property in which extinguishers are located shall be responsible for such inspection, maintenance, and recharging.

4-1.4* Maintenance, servicing, and recharging shall be performed by trained persons having available the appropriate servicing manual(s), the proper types of tools, recharge materials, lubricants, and manufacturer's recommended replacement parts or parts specifically listed for use in the extinguisher.

4-1.5 Tags or labels shall not be placed on the front of the extinguisher.

Exception: Labels indicating extinguisher use.

4-2 Definitions.

4-2.1 Inspection. Inspection is a "quick check" that an extinguisher is available and will operate. It is intended to give reasonable assurance that the extinguisher is fully charged and operable. This is done by seeing that it is in its designated place, that it has not been actuated or tampered with, and that there is no obvious physical damage or condition to prevent operation.

4-2.2 Maintenance. Maintenance is a thorough examination of the extinguisher. It is intended to give maximum assurance that an extinguisher will operate effectively and safely. It includes a thorough examination and any necessary repair or replacement. It will normally reveal if hydrostatic testing is required.

4-2.3 Recharging. Recharging is the replacement of the extinguishing agent and also includes the expellant for certain types of extinguishers.

4-3 Inspection.

4-3.1* Frequency. Extinguishers shall be inspected when initially placed in service and thereafter at approximately 30-day intervals. Extinguishers shall be inspected at more frequent intervals when circumstances require.

4-3.2 Procedures. Periodic inspection of extinguishers shall include a check of at least the following items:

(a) Located in designated place.

(b) No obstruction to access or visibility.

(c) Operating instructions on nameplate legible and facing outward.

(d) Seals and tamper indicators not broken or missing.

(e) Determine fullness by weighing or "hefting."

(f) Examine for obvious physical damage, corrosion, leakage, or clogged nozzle.

(g) Pressure gage reading or indicator in the operable range or position.

4-3.3 Corrective Action. When an inspection of any extinguisher reveals a deficiency in any of the conditions listed in (a) and (b) of 4-3.2, immediate corrective action shall be taken.

4-3.3.1 Rechargeable Extinguishers. When an inspection of any rechargeable extinguisher reveals a deficiency in any of the conditions listed in (c), (d), (e), (f), and (g) of 4-3.2, it shall be subjected to applicable maintenance procedures.

4-3.3.2 Nonrechargeable Dry Chemical Extinguisher. When an inspection of any nonrechargeable dry chemical extinguisher reveals a deficiency in any of the conditions listed in (c), (e), (f), and (g) of 4-3.2, it shall be discharged and removed from service.

4-3.3.3 Nonrechargeable Halogenated Agent Extinguisher. When an inspection of any nonrechargeable extinguisher containing a halon agent reveals a deficiency in any of the conditions listed in (c), (e), (f), and (g) of 4-3.2, it shall be removed from service, not discharged, and returned to the manufacturer.

If the extinguisher is not returned to the manufacturer, it shall be returned to a fire equipment dealer or distributor to permit recovery of the halon.

4-3.4 Recordkeeping.

4-3.4.1 Personnel making inspections shall keep records of those extinguishers that were found to require corrective actions.

4-3.4.2 At least monthly, the date the inspection was performed and the initials of the person performing the inspection shall be recorded.

4-4* Maintenance.

4-4.1 Frequency. Extinguishers shall be subjected to maintenance not more than one year apart or when specifically indicated by an inspection. Maintenance procedures shall be performed in accordance with 4-4.2.

4-4.1.1 Stored pressure types containing a loaded stream agent shall be disassembled on an annual basis and subjected to complete maintenance. Prior to disassembly, the extinguisher shall be fully discharged to check the operation of the discharge valve and pressure gage.

4-4.1.2* A conductivity test shall be conducted annually on all carbon dioxide hose assemblies. Hose assemblies found to be nonconductive shall be replaced.

4-4.1.3* Every six years, stored pressure extinguishers that require a 12-year hydrostatic test shall be emptied and subjected to the applicable maintenance procedures. The removal of agent from halogenated agent extinguishers shall only be done using a halon closed recovery system. When the applicable maintenance procedures are performed during periodic recharging or hydrostatic testing, the six-year requirement shall begin from that date.

Exception: Nonrechargeable extinguishers shall not be hydrostatically tested but shall be removed from service at a maximum interval of 12 years from the date of manufacture. Nonrechargeable halogenated agent extinguishers shall be disposed of in accordance with 4-3.3.3.

4-4.1.4 Extinguishers out of service for maintenance or recharge shall be replaced by spare extinguishers of the same type and at least equal rating.

4-4.2* Procedures. Maintenance procedures shall include a thorough examination of the three basic elements of an extinguisher:

(a) mechanical parts,

(b) extinguishing agent, and

(c) expelling means.

Exception: During annual maintenance, it is not necessary to internally examine nonrechargeable extinguishers, carbon dioxide extinguishers, or stored pressure extinguishers except for those types specified in 4-4.1.1. However, such extinguishers shall be thoroughly examined externally in accordance with the applicable items of 4-4.2(a).

4-4.3* Recordkeeping. Each extinguisher shall have a tag or label securely attached that indicates the month and year the inspections, maintenance, and recharging were performed and shall identify the person performing the service.[1]

4-4.3.1 For the six-year requirement of 4-4.1.3, this information shall be included on a separate label. Expired labels shall be removed.[1]

4-4.3.2 Labels indicating inspection, maintenance, hydrostatic retests, and six-year maintenance shall not be placed on the front of the extinguisher.

4-5 Recharging.

4-5.1* General.

4-5.1.1 All rechargeable-type extinguishers shall be recharged after any use or as indicated by an inspection or when performing maintenance.

4-5.1.2 When performing the recharging, the recommendations of the manufacturer shall be followed. For recharge chemicals, see 4-5.3.1.

NOTE: Some manufacturers require that their extinguishers be returned to the factory for recharging.

4-5.1.3* The amount of recharge agent shall be verified by weighing. The recharged gross weight shall be the same as the gross weight that is marked on the label.

NOTE: For those extinguishers that do not have the gross weight marked on the label, a permanent label that indicates the gross weight shall be affixed to the cylinder. The label containing the gross weight shall be a durable material of a pressure-sensitive, self-destruct type.

4-5.1.4 Conversion of Extinguisher Types. No extinguisher shall be converted from one type to another, nor shall any extinguisher be converted to use a different type of extinguishing agent.

4-5.1.5* Leak Test. After recharging, a leak test shall be performed on stored pressure and self-expelling types.

4-5.2 Frequency.

4-5.2.1 Soda-Acid, Foam, Cartridge-Operated Water, and Pump Tank. Every 12 months, soda-acid, foam, inverting types, pump tank water, and pump tank calcium chloride base antifreeze types of extinguishers shall be recharged with new chemicals or water, as applicable.

NOTE: Soda-acid, cartridge-operated water, and foam extinguishers of the inverting type must be removed from service no later than when the next hydrostatic test is due.

4-5.2.2 Wetting Agent. The agent in stored pressure wetting agent (wet chemical) extinguishers shall be replaced annually.

[1] Under special circumstances or when local requirements are in effect, additional information may be desirable or required.

NOTE: Only the agent specified on the nameplate shall be used for recharging. The use of water or other agents is prohibited.

4-5.2.3 AFFF and FFFP. The premixed agent in liquid charge type AFFF (aqueous film forming foam) and FFFP (film forming fluoroprotein foam) extinguishers shall be replaced at least once every three years. The agent in solid charge type AFFF extinguishers shall be replaced once every five years.

Exception: The agent in nonpressurized AFFF and FFFP extinguishers that is subjected to agent analysis in accordance with manufacturer's instructions need not be replaced.

4-5.3 Procedures.

4-5.3.1* Recharge Agents. Only those agents specified on the nameplate, or agents proven to have equal chemical composition and physical characteristics, shall be used. Tests shall be conducted to assure equal performance. Agents listed specifically for use with that extinguisher shall be considered to meet these requirements.

4-5.3.2* Mixing of Dry Chemicals. Multipurpose dry chemicals shall not be mixed with alkaline-based dry chemicals.

4-5.3.3 Topping Off. The remaining dry chemical in a discharged extinguisher may be reused provided that it is thoroughly checked for the proper type, contamination, and condition. Dry chemical found to be of the wrong type, or contaminated, shall not be reused.

4-5.3.4 Dry Chemical Agent Reuse. Extinguishers removed for six-year maintenance or hydrostatic testing shall be emptied. The dry chemical agent may be reused provided a closed recovery system is used and the agent is stored in a sealed container to prevent contamination.

Prior to reuse, the dry chemical shall be thoroughly checked for the proper type, contamination, and condition. Where doubt exists with respect to the type, contamination, or condition of the dry chemical, the dry chemical shall be discarded.

4-5.3.5 Dry Powder. Pails or drums containing dry powder agents for scoop or shovel application for use on metal fires shall be kept full and covered at all times. The dry powder shall be replaced if found damp. (*See A-4-5.3.1.*)

4-5.3.6 Removal of Moisture. For all nonwater types of extinguishers, any moisture shall be removed before recharging.

4-5.3.7 Halogenated Agent. Halon-type extinguishers shall only be charged with the proper type and weight of halon agent as specified on the nameplate.

Halon purchased for recharging shall meet the appropriate military specification which details the agent's quantitative values of the physical properties including boiling point, nonvolatile residue, moisture contents, color, acidity, and purity percentage of the agent.

The following military specifications are applicable:

For Halon 1211, bromochlorodifluoromethane, MIL-B-38741 dated July 30, 1965 and amendment No. 2 dated April 9, 1984.

For Halon 1301, bromotrifluoromethane, MIL-M-12218C dated October 26, 1977 and amendment No. 1 dated December 24, 1981.

For mixtures of Halon 1211 and Halon 1301, the quantitative values in the military specifications of Halon 1211 and Halon 1301 will be additive in proportion to the weight percentages of the agents in the mixture.

4-5.3.8 Halogenated Agent Reuse. The removal of agent from halogenated agent extinguishers shall only be done using a halon closed recovery system. The extinguisher cylinder shall be examined internally for contamination and/or corrosion. The halon agent, retained in the system recovery cylinder, shall be reused only if no evidence of internal contamination is observed in the extinguisher cylinder. Halon removed from extinguishers that exhibit evidence of internal contamination or corrosion shall be processed in accordance with the extinguisher manufacturer's instructions.

4-5.3.9 Carbon Dioxide. The vapor phase of carbon dioxide shall not be less than 99.5 percent carbon dioxide. The water content of the liquid phase shall not be more than 0.01 percent by weight [-30°F (-34.4°C) dew point]. Oil content of the carbon dioxide shall not exceed 10 ppm by weight.

4-5.3.10 Water Types. When recharging stored pressure extinguishers, overfilling will result in improper discharge. The proper amount of liquid agent shall be determined by using one of the following:

(a) exact measurement by weight,

(b) exact measurement in volume,

(c) use of an anti-overfill tube when provided, or

(d) use of a fill mark on extinguisher shell, if provided.

4-5.4 Precautionary Pressurization Measures.

4-5.4.1* Pressure Gages. Replacement pressure gages shall have the proper indicated charging (service) pressure, be marked for use with the agent in the extinguisher, and be compatible with the extinguisher valve body material. The gage used to set the regulated source of pressure shall be calibrated at least annually.

4-5.4.2 Stored Pressure Extinguishers. A rechargeable stored pressure-type extinguisher shall be pressurized only to the charging pressure specified on the extinguisher nameplate. The manufacturer's pressurizing adaptor shall be connected to the valve assembly before pressurizing the extinguisher. A regulated source of pressure, set no higher than 25 psi (172 kPa) above the operating (service) pressure, shall be used to pressurize fire extinguishers.

WARNING 1: An unregulated source of pressure, such as a nitrogen cylinder without a pressure regulator, should never be used because the extinguisher could be overpressurized and possibly rupture.

WARNING 2: Never leave an extinguisher connected to the regulator of a high-pressure source for an extended period of time. A defective regulator could cause the container to rupture due to excess pressure.

4-5.4.3* Pressurizing Gas. Only standard industrial-grade nitrogen with a dew point of -60°F (-51.1°C) or lower CGA nitrogen (specification G10.1, grades D through P) shall be used to pressurize stored pressure dry chemical and halon-type fire extinguishers. Compressed air through moisture traps shall not be used for pressurizing even though so stated in the instructions on older extinguishers.

Exception: Compressed air may be used from special compressor systems capable of delivering air with a dew point of -60°F (-51.1°C) or lower. The special compressor system shall be equipped with an automatic monitoring and alarm system to assure that the dew point remains at or below -60°F (-51.1°C) at all times.

Chapter 5 Hydrostatic Testing

5-1 General.

5-1.1 Hydrostatic testing shall be performed by persons trained in pressure testing procedures and safeguards, and having available suitable testing equipment, facilities, and appropriate servicing manual(s).

5-1.2 If, at any time, an extinguisher shows evidence of corrosion or mechanical injury, it shall be hydrostatically tested, subject to the provisions of 5-1.3 and 5-1.4.

Exception No. 1: Pump tanks.

Exception No. 2: Nonrechargeable fire extinguishers other than halogenated agent types shall be discharged and discarded.

Exception No. 3: Nonrechargeable halogenated agent type extinguishers (see 4-3.3.3).

5-1.3 Examination of Cylinder Condition. When an extinguisher cylinder or shell has one or more conditions listed in this subdivision, it shall not be hydrostatically tested, but shall be destroyed by the owner or at his or her direction:

(a) When there exist repairs by soldering, welding, brazing, or use of patching compounds.

NOTE: For welding or brazing on mild steel shells, consult the manufacturer of the extinguisher.

(b) When the cylinder or shell threads are damaged.

(c) When there exists corrosion that has caused pitting, including under removable nameplate band assemblies.

(d) When the extinguisher has been burned in a fire.

(e) When a calcium chloride type of extinguishing agent was used in a stainless steel extinguisher.

(f) When the shell is of copper or brass construction joined by soft solder or rivets.

(g) All inverting-type extinguishers.

5-1.4* Aluminum Shell/Cylinder. Extinguishers having aluminum cylinders or shells suspected of being exposed to temperatures in excess of 350°F (177°C) shall be removed from service and subjected to a hydrostatic test.

5-2 Frequency. At intervals not exceeding those specified in Table 5-2, extinguishers shall be hydrostatically tested.

NOTE: For nonrechargeable extinguishers, see 4-4.1.3.

Exception No. 1: Extinguishers utilizing a cylinder that has DOT or CTC markings shall be hydrostatically tested, or replaced, according to the requirements of DOT or CTC.

Exception No. 2: For extinguishers not covered in Exception No. 1, the first retest may be conducted within 12 months of the specified test intervals.

Table 5-2

Hydrostatic Test Interval for Extinguishers

Extinguisher Type	Test Interval (Years)
Soda-Acid	Note 1
Cartridge-Operated Water and/or Antifreeze	Note 1
Stored Pressure Water, Loaded Stream, and/or Antifreeze	5
Wetting Agent	5
Foam	Note 1
AFFF (Aqueous Film Forming Foam)	5
FFFP (Film Forming Fluoroprotein Foam)	5
Dry Chemical with Stainless Steel Shells	5
Carbon Dioxide	5
Dry Chemical, Stored Pressure, with Mild Steel Shells, Brazed Brass Shells, or Aluminum Shells	12
Halogenated Agents	12
Dry Powder, Stored Pressure, Cartridge- or Cylinder-Operated, with Mild Steel Shells	12

NOTE 1: Extinguishers with copper or brass shells joined by soft solder were prohibited from further hydrostatic testing effective May 18, 1978. [*See 5-1.3(f).*] Extinguishers with stainless steel or brazed brass shells that were permitted to remain in service had had a five-year hydrostatic test interval. Effective December 22, 1987, when the hydrostatic test date arrives, all types of inverting extinguishers shall not be tested but removed from service. [*See 5-1.3(g).*]

NOTE 2: Stored pressure water extinguishers with fiberglass shells (pre-1976) are prohibited from hydrostatic testing due to manufacturer's recall.

5-2.1 High Pressure Cylinders and Cartridges. Nitrogen cylinders or cartridges used for inert gas storage used as an expellant for wheeled extinguishers shall be hydrostatically tested every five years.

Exception: Cylinders (except those charged with carbon dioxide) complying with Part 173.34 (e) 15, Title 49, Code of Federal Regulations, may be hydrostatically tested every 10 years.

5-2.2 Nitrogen cartridges and carbon dioxide cartridges used as an expellant for hand portable extinguishers that have DOT or CTC markings shall be hydrostatically tested or replaced according to the requirements of DOT or CTC.

Exception No. 1: Cartridges not exceeding 2 in. (5.1 cm) outside diameter and having a length less than 2 ft (.61 m) are exempt from periodic hydrostatic retest.

Exception No. 2: Cartridges with DOT stamp 3E are exempt from periodic hydrostatic retest.

5-2.3 Hose Assemblies. A hydrostatic test shall be performed on extinguisher hose assemblies equipped with a shutoff nozzle at the end of the hose. The test interval shall be the same as specified for the extinguisher on which the hose is installed.

5-3 Test Pressures.

5-3.1 High Pressure Cylinders.

5-3.1.1 Carbon dioxide extinguishers shall be tested at $\frac{5}{3}$ the service pressure as stamped into the cylinder.

Exception: Carbon dioxide extinguishers having cylinder specification ICC3 shall be tested at 3,000 psi (20 685 kPa).

5-3.1.2 Nitrogen cylinders and carbon dioxide cylinders used with wheeled extinguishers shall be tested at $\frac{5}{3}$ the service pressure as stamped into the cylinder.

5-3.2 Stored Pressure Types. All stored pressure extinguishers shall be hydrostatically tested at the factory test pressure not to exceed three times the normal operating pressure.

NOTE: Extinguishers that are required to be returned to the manufacturer for recharging shall be hydrostatically tested only by the manufacturer.

5-3.3 Cartridge-Operated Types. Cartridge- or cylinder-operated dry chemical and dry powder types of extinguishers shall be hydrostatically tested at their original factory test pressure as shown on the nameplate or shell.

5-3.4 Test Pressures for Hose Assemblies.

5-3.4.1 Carbon dioxide hose assemblies requiring a hydrostatic pressure test shall be tested at 1,250 psi (8619 kPa).

5-3.4.2 Dry chemical and dry powder hose assemblies requiring a hydrostatic pressure test shall be tested at 300 psi (2068 kPa) or at service pressure, whichever is higher.

5-4 Test Equipment.

5-4.1 General.

5-4.1.1 This standard only permits the hydrostatic testing of pressure vessels used as fire extinguishers.

WARNING: If air or gas is used as a sole medium for pressure testing, or if all air is not vented from the vessel prior to hydrostatic testing, the failure of the extinguisher vessel will be violent and dangerous.

5-4.1.2 When extinguisher shells, cylinders, or cartridges fail a hydrostatic pressure test, they shall be destroyed by the owner at his or her direction.

5-4.2 Test Equipment for High Pressure Types.

5-4.2.1 The equipment for testing cylinders and cartridges shall be of the water jacket type that meets the specifications of the pamphlet *Methods for Hydrostatic Testing of Compressed Gas Cylinders* (CGA C-1), published by the Compressed Gas Association.

5-4.2.2 Hose assemblies of carbon dioxide extinguishers that require a hydrostatic test shall be tested within a protective cage device.

5-4.3* Test Equipment for Low Pressure Gas Types.

5-4.3.1 The equipment for testing low pressure gas types consists of the following:

(a) A hydrostatic test pump, hand or power operated, to be capable of producing not less than 150 percent of the test pressure. It is to include appropriate check valves and fittings.

(b) A flexible connection for attachment to the test pump. It shall be provided with necessary fittings to test through the extinguisher nozzle, test bonnet, or hose outlet, as is applicable.

(c) A protective cage or barrier for personnel protection, designed to provide visual observation of the extinguisher under test.

5-4.3.2 Drying equipment is required to dry all nonwater types of extinguishers that have passed the hydrostatic test.

5-5 Testing Procedures.

5-5.1 High Pressure Types.

5-5.1.1 In addition to the visual examinations required prior to test as stated in 5-1.3, an internal examination shall be made prior to the hydrostatic test. The procedures for this internal examination shall be in accordance with the requirements of the *Standard for Visual Inspection of Compressed Gas Cylinders* (CGA C-6) and *Standard for Visual Inspection of High-Pressure Aluminum Compressed Gas Cylinders* (CGA C-6.1), published by the Compressed Gas Association.

5-5.1.2 The hydrostatic testing of high pressure cylinders and cartridges shall be in accordance with the procedures specified in the pamphlet *Methods for Hydrostatic Testing of Compressed Gas Cylinders* (CGA C-1), published by the Compressed Gas Association.

5-5.2* Testing Procedures for Low Pressure Gas Types. The testing procedures for low pressure gas cylinders and shells and hose assemblies are detailed in Appendix A of this standard.

5-5.3* Testing Procedures for Hose Assemblies. The testing procedures for hose assemblies requiring a hydrostatic test are detailed in Appendix A.

5-5.4 Recording of Tests.

5-5.4.1 High Pressure Types. For high pressure gas cylinders and cartridges passing a hydrostatic test, the month, year, and the DOT identification number shall be stamped into the cylinder in accordance with the requirements set forth by DOT or the Canadian Transport Commission.

NOTE: It is important that the recording (stamping) be placed only on the shoulder, top head, neck, or footring (when so provided) of the cylinder.

5-5.4.2* Noncompressed Low Pressure Gas Types. Extinguisher shells of the low pressure gas type that pass a hydrostatic test shall have the test information recorded on a suitable metallic label or equally durable material. The label shall be affixed to the shell by means of a heatless process. These labels shall be self-destructive when removal from an extinguisher shell is attempted. The label shall include the following information:

(a) Month and year the test was performed, indicated by a perforation, such as by a hand punch.

(b) Test pressure used.

(c) Name or initials of person performing the test, or name of agency performing the test.

5-5.4.3 Hose assemblies passing a hydrostatic test do not require recording.

Chapter 6 Referenced Publications

6-1 The following documents or portions thereof are referenced within this standard and shall be considered part of the requirements of this document. The edition indicated for each reference is the current edition as of the date of the NFPA issuance of this document.

6-1.1 NFPA Publications. National Fire Protection Association, 1 Batterymarch Park, P.O. Box 9101, Quincy, MA 02269-9101.

NFPA 11-1988, *Standard for Low Expansion Foam and Combined Agent Systems*

NFPA 11A-1988, *Standard for Medium- and High-Expansion Foam Systems*

NFPA 12-1989, *Standard on Carbon Dioxide Extinguishing Systems*

NFPA 12A-1989, *Standard on Halon 1301 Fire Extinguishing Systems*

NFPA 12B-1990, *Standard on Halon 1211 Fire Extinguishing Systems*

NFPA 13-1989, *Standard for the Installation of Sprinkler Systems*

NFPA 14-1990, *Standard for the Installation of Standpipe and Hose Systems*

NFPA 15-1990, *Standard for Water Spray Fixed Systems for Fire Protection*

NFPA 16-1986, *Standard on Deluge Foam-Water Sprinkler and Foam-Water Spray Systems*

NFPA 17-1990, *Standard for Dry Chemical Extinguishing Systems*

NFPA 34-1989, *Standard for Dipping and Coating Processes Using Flammable or Combustible Liquids*

NFPA 96-1987, *Standard for the Installation of Equipment for the Removal of Smoke and Grease-Laden Vapors from Commercial Cooking Equipment*

NFPA 231-1990, *Standard for General Storage*

NFPA 231C-1986, *Standard for Rack Storage of Materials*

NFPA 231D-1989, *Standard for Storage of Rubber Tires*

NFPA 302-1989, *Fire Protection Standard for Pleasure and Commercial Motor Craft*

NFPA 408-1989, *Standard for Aircraft Hand Fire Extinguishers.*

6-1.2 Other Publications.

6-1.2.1 ASTM Publication. American Society for Testing and Materials, 1916 Race Street, Philadelphia, PA 19103.

ASTM E 380-1989, *Standard for Metric Practice.*

6-1.2.2 CGA Publications. Compressed Gas Association, 1235 Jefferson Davis Highway, Arlington, VA 22202.

CGA C-1-1975, *Methods for Hydrostatic Testing of Compressed Gas Cylinders*

CGA C-6-1984, *Standard for Visual Inspection of Compressed Gas Cylinders (Steel)*

CGA C-6.1-1984, *Standard for Visual Inspection of High-Pressure Aluminum Compressed Gas Cylinders.*

6-1.2.3 CAN Publications. Standards Council of Canada, 350 Sparks Street, Ottawa, ONT K1R 7S8.

CAN4-S503-M83, *Standard for Carbon Dioxide Hand and Wheeled Fire Extinguishers*

CAN4-S504-77, *Standard for Dry Chemical and Dry Powder Hand and Wheeled Fire Extinguishers*

CAN4-S507-M83, *Standard for 9 Litre Stored Pressure Water Type Fire Extinguishers*

CAN4-S508-M83, *Standard for Rating and Fire Testing of Fire Extinguishers.*

6-1.2.4 ULC Publication. Underwriters Laboratories of Canada, 7 Crouse Road, Scarborough, ONT M1R 3A9.

ULC-S504-77, *Standard for Dry Chemical and Dry Powder Hand and Wheeled Fire Extinguishers*

ULC-S512-77, *Standard for Halogenated Agent Fire Extinguishers.*

6-1.2.5 UL Publications. Underwriters Laboratories Inc., 333 Pfingsten Road, Northbrook, IL 60062.

ANSI/UL 8-1983, *Foam Fire Extinguishers*

ANSI/UL 154-1984, *Standard for Carbon Dioxide Fire Extinguishers*

ANSI/UL 299-1982, *Standard for Dry Chemical Fire Extinguishers*

ANSI/UL 626-1982, *Standard for 2$^1/_2$ Gallon Stored Pressure Water Type Fire Extinguishers*

ANSI/UL 711-1979, *Standard for Rating and Fire Testing Extinguishers*

ANSI/UL 1093-1984, *Standard for Halogenated Agent Fire Extinguishers*

ANSI/UL 1803-1986, *Standard for Factory Follow-up on Third Party Certified Portable Fire Extinguishers.*

6-1.2.6 US Government Publication. Superintendent of Documents, U.S. Government Printing Office, Washington, DC 20402.

Code of Federal Regulations, Title 49-1979.

Appendix A

This Appendix is not a part of the requirements of this NFPA document, but is included for information purposes only.

A-1-1 Principles of Fire Extinguishment. Many fires are small at origin and may be extinguished by the use of proper portable fire extinguishers. It is strongly recommended that the fire department be notified as soon as a fire is discovered. This alarm should not be delayed awaiting results of application of portable fire extinguishers.

Fire extinguishers can represent an important segment of any overall fire protection program. However, their successful functioning depends upon the following conditions having been met:

1. The extinguisher is properly located and in working order.
2. The extinguisher is of proper type for a fire that may occur.
3. The fire is discovered while still small enough for the extinguisher to be effective.
4. The fire is discovered by a person ready, willing, and able to use the extinguisher.

A-1-2 Responsibility. The owner or occupant of a property in which fire extinguishers are located has an obligation for the care and use of these extinguishers at all times. The nameplate(s) and instruction manual should be read and thoroughly understood by all persons who may be expected to use extinguishers.

To discharge this obligation, the owner or occupant should give proper attention to the inspection, maintenance, and recharging of this fire protective equipment and should also train personnel in the correct use of fire extinguishers on the different types of fires that may occur on the property.

An owner or occupant should recognize fire hazards on his property and plan in advance exactly how and with what a fire will be fought. The owner/occupant must see that everyone knows how to call the fire department and stress that they should do so for every fire, no matter how small it may be.

On larger properties, a private fire brigade should be established and trained. Personnel must be assigned to inspect each fire extinguisher periodically. Other personnel may have the duty of maintaining and recharging such equipment at proper intervals.

Portable fire extinguishers are appliances to be used by the occupants of a fire-endangered building or area. They are primarily of value for immediate use on small fires. They have a limited quantity of extinguishing material, and therefore must be used properly so this material is not wasted.

Extinguishers are mechanical devices. They need care and maintenance at periodic intervals to be sure they are ready to operate properly and safely. Parts or internal chemicals may deteriorate in time and need replacement. They are pressure vessels, in most cases, and so must be treated with respect and handled with care.

A-1-4.2 The classification and rating is found on the label affixed to the extinguisher.

EXAMPLE: An extinguisher is rated and classified 4-A:20-B:C. This indicates the following:

1. It should extinguish approximately twice as much Class A fire as a 2-A [2$^1/_2$-gal (9.46-L) water] rated extinguisher.

2. It should extinguish approximately twenty times as much Class B fire as a 1-B rated extinguisher.

3. It is suitable for use on energized electrical equipment.

Currently, laboratories classify extinguishers for use on Class A fires with the following ratings: 1-A, 2-A, 3-A, 4-A, 6-A, 10-A, 20-A, 30-A, and 40-A. Effective June 1, 1969, extinguishers classified for use on Class B fires have the following ratings: 1-B, 2-B, 5-B, 10-B, 20-B, 30-B, 40-B, 60-B, 80-B, 120-B, 160-B, 240-B, 320-B, 480-B, and 640-B. Ratings from 1-A to 20-A and 1-B to 20-B, inclusive, are based on indoor fire tests; ratings at or above 30-A and 30-B are based on outdoor fire tests.

Ratings of 4-B, 6-B, 8-B, 12-B, and 16-B, previously used to classify individual extinguishers for use on Class B fires, were not used for new extinguishers after June 1, 1969. Existing extinguishers having these ratings are acceptable if they have been properly inspected and maintained in accordance with this standard.

For Class B fires, it must be recognized that the amount of fire that can be extinguished by a particular extinguisher is related to the degree of training and experience of the operator.

For fire extinguishers classified for use on Class C fires, no NUMERAL is used since Class C fires are essentially either Class A or Class B fires involving energized electrical wiring and equipment. The size of the different suitable extinguishers installed should be commensurate with the size and extent of the Class A or Class B components, or both, of the electrical hazard or containing equipment being protected.

For extinguishers classified for use on Class D fires, no NUMERAL is used. The relative effectiveness of these extinguishers for use on specific combustible metal fires is detailed on the extinguisher nameplate.

Extinguishers that are effective on more than one Class of fire have multiple LETTER and NUMERAL-LETTER classifications and ratings.

A-1-4.4 Authorities having jurisdiction should determine the acceptability and credibility of the organization listing or labeling extinguishers. Authorities should determine if the organization tests to all the requirements of the standard. Factors such as the structure of the organization, its principle fields of endeavor, its reputation and established expertise, its involvement in the standards-writing process, and the extent of its follow-up service programs should all be assessed before recognition is given.

A-1-4.5 Authorities having jurisdiction should determine the thoroughness of the factory follow-up quality assurance program exercised by third party certification organizations listing and labeling portable fire extinguishers. The specified factory follow-up standard provides a minimum basis for that determination. Application of the factory follow-up standard provides a reasonable assurance that portable extinguishers sold to the public continue to have the same structural reliability and performance as the extinguishers the manufacturer originally submitted to the listing and labeling organization for evaluation.

A-1-6.5 Acceptable means of identifying the extinguisher locations may include arrows, lights, signs, or coding of the wall or column.

A-1-6.6 In situations where extinguishers must be temporarily provided, a good practice is to provide portable stands, consisting of a horizontal bar on uprights with feet, on which the extinguishers may be hung.

A-1-6.12 Vented extinguisher cabinets should utilize tinted glass and be constructed to prevent the entrance of insects and the accumulation of water. Vented extinguisher cabinets constructed in this manner will lower the maximum internal temperature 10–15°F (5.6–8.3°C).

A-1-6.13 The following precautions should be noted where extinguishers are located in areas that have temperatures outside the range of 40°F to 120°F (4°C to 49°C).

(a) AFFF and FFFP extinguishers cannot be protected against temperatures below 40°F (4°C) by adding an antifreeze charge because it will tend to destroy the effectiveness of the extinguishing agent.

(b) Plain water extinguishers should not be protected against temperatures below 40°F (4°C) with ethylene glycol antifreeze. Do not use calcium chloride solutions in stainless steel extinguishers.

(c) Extinguishers installed in machinery compartments, diesel locomotives, automotive equipment, marine engine compartments, and hot processing facilities can easily be subjected to temperatures above 120°F (49°C). Selection of extinguishers for hazard areas with temperatures above the listed limits should be made on the basis of recommendations by manufacturers of this equipment.

A-1-6.14 The manual may be specific to the extinguisher involved or it may cover many types.

A-1-7 OSHA federal regulations require that manufacturers communicate information as to the type of chemicals in a product that may be hazardous and the level of hazard. This information is contained in the Material Safety

Data Sheets (MSDS) created for each chemical or mixture of chemicals and is summarized on labels or tags attached to the product. Additionally, state and local authorities have enacted similar acts and regulations requiring identification of chemicals and hazardous ingredients in products. MSDS's for fire extinguisher agents are available on request from a fire equipment dealer or distributor, or the fire equipment manufacturer.

The identification of contents information will enable determination of the type of chemicals contained in the extinguisher and help to resolve complications arising from an unusual use of the agent. The Hazardous Materials Identification System (HMIS) [In Canada, see Workplace Hazardous Materials Identification Systems (WHMIS)] used has a three-place format with numerical indexes from 0 to 4. The first place is for Toxic Properties, the second place is for Flammability, and the third place is for Reactivity with other chemicals. Most fire extinguishers have a 0 numerical index in the second and third places because they are nonflammable and relatively inert.

Information on the HMIS may be obtained from Label Master, Inc., Chicago, IL or National Paint and Coatings Association, Washington, DC. Figure A-1-7 is a typical chemical contents identification marking. The information may be integrated into the standard extinguisher label in some form or may be contained on a separate label or tag.

CONTENTS: ABC DRY CHEMICAL/HMIS 1-0-0 MUSCOVITE MICA, MONOAMMONIUM PHOSPHATE AMMONIUM SULFATE/NUISANCE DUST IRRITANT/CONTENTS UNDER PRESSURE (Manufacturer's Name, Mailing Address, Phone Number)

Figure A-1-7 Extinguisher, Contents Information.

A-2-1 Conditions of Selection.

A. Physical Conditions that Affect Selection.

(1) *Gross Weight.* In the selection of an extinguisher, the physical ability of the user should be contemplated. When the hazard exceeds the capability of a hand portable extinguisher, wheeled extinguishers or fixed systems (*see Section 1-1*) should be considered.

(2) *Corrosion.* In some extinguisher installations, there exists a possibility of exposing the extinguisher to a corrosive atmosphere. When this is the case, consideration should be given to providing the extinguishers so exposed with proper protection or providing extinguishers that have been found suitable for use in these conditions.

(3) *Agent Reaction.* The possibility of adverse reactions, contamination, or other effects of an extinguishing agent on either manufacturing processes or on equipment, or both, should be considered in the selection of an extinguisher.

(4) *Wheeled Units.* When wheeled extinguishers are used, consideration should be given to the mobility of the extinguisher within the area in which it will be used. For outdoor locations, the use of proper rubber-tired or wide-rimmed wheel designs should be considered according to terrain. For indoor locations, the size of doorways and passages should be large enough to permit ready passage of the extinguisher.

(5) *Wind and Draft.* If the hazard is subject to winds or draft, the use of extinguishers and agents having sufficient range to overcome these conditions should be considered.

(6) *Availability of Personnel.* Consideration should be given to the number of persons available to operate the extinguishers, the degree of training provided, and the physical capability of the operator.

B. Health and Safety Conditions that Affect Selection.

(1) When selecting an extinguisher, consideration should be given to health and safety hazards involved in its maintenance and use, as described in the following paragraphs.

(2) Prominent caution labels on the extinguisher, warning signs at entry points to confined spaces, provision for remote application, extra-long-range extinguisher nozzles, special ventilation, provision of breathing apparatus and other personal protective equipment, and adequate training of personnel are among measures that should be considered to minimize the effects of these hazards.

(3) Halogenated agent-type extinguishers contain agents whose vapor has a low toxicity. However, their decomposition products can be hazardous. When using these extinguishers in unventilated places, such as small rooms, closets, motor vehicles, or other confined spaces, operators and others should avoid breathing the gases produced by thermal decomposition of the agent.

(4) Carbon dioxide extinguishers contain an extinguishing agent that will not support life when used in sufficient concentration to extinguish a fire. The use of this type of extinguisher in an unventilated space can dilute the oxygen supply. Prolonged occupancy of such spaces can result in loss of consciousness due to oxygen deficiency.

(5) Extinguishers not rated for Class C hazards (water, antifreeze, soda-acid, loaded stream, AFFF, FFFP, wetting agent, foam, and carbon dioxide with metal horns) present a shock hazard if used on fires involving energized electrical equipment.

(6) Dry chemical extinguishers, when used in a small unventilated area, may reduce visibility for a period of up to several minutes. Dry chemical, discharged in an area, may also clog filters in air-cleaning systems.

(7) Most fires produce toxic decomposition products of combustion and some materials may produce highly toxic gases. Fires may also consume available oxygen or produce dangerously high exposure to convected or radiated heat. All of these may affect the degree to which a fire can be safely approached with extinguishers. (*See Underwriters Laboratories Inc., Bulletin of Research No. 53 — July, 1963.*[1])

Table A-2-1 summarizes the characteristics of extinguishers and may be used as an aid in selecting extinguishers in accordance with Chapter 2. The ratings given are those that were in effect at the time this standard was prepared. Current listings should be consulted for up-to-date ratings.

[1] Survey of Available Information on the Toxicity of the Combustion and Thermal Decomposition Products of Certain Building Materials under Fire Conditions.

Table A-2-1 Characteristics of Extinguishers

Extinguishing Agent	Method of Operation	Capacity	Horizontal Range of Stream	Approximate Time of Discharge	Protection Required Below 40°F (4°C)	UL or ULC Classifications*
Water	Stored Pressure, Cartridge, or Pump	2½ gal	30-40 ft	1 min	Yes	2-A
	Pump	4 gal	30-40 ft	2 min	Yes	3-A
	Pump	5 gal	30-40 ft	2-3 min	Yes	4-A
Water (Wetting Agent)	Stored Pressure	1½ gal	20 ft	30 sec	Yes	2-A
	Carbon Dioxide Cylinder	25 gal (wheeled)	35 ft	1½ min	Yes	10-A
	Carbon Dioxide Cylinder	45 gal (wheeled)	35 ft	2 min	Yes	30-A
	Carbon Dioxide Cylinder	60 gal (wheeled)	35 ft	2½ min	Yes	40-A
Water (Soda-Acid)	Chemically generated expellant	2½ gal	30-40 ft	1 min	Yes	2-A
	Chemically generated expellant	17 gal (wheeled)	50 ft	3 min	Yes	10-A
	Chemically generated expellant	33 gal (wheeled)	50 ft	3 min	Yes	20-A
Loaded Stream	Stored Pressure or Cartridge	2½ gal	30-40 ft	1 min	No	2 to 3-A:1-B
	Carbon Dioxide Cylinder	33 gal (wheeled)	50 ft	3 min	No	20-A
Foam	Chemically generated expellant	2½ gal	30-40 ft	1½ min	Yes	2-A:4 to 6-B
	Chemically generated expellant	17 gal (wheeled)	50 ft	3 min	Yes	10-A:10 to 12-B
	Chemically generated expellant	33 gal (wheeled)	50 ft	3 min	Yes	20-A:20 to 40-B
AFFF, FFFP	Stored Pressure	2½ gal	20-25 ft	50 sec	Yes	3-A:20 to 40-B
	Nitrogen Cylinder	33 gal	30 ft	1 min	Yes	20-A:160-B
Carbon Dioxide**	Self-Expelling	2½ to 5 lb	3-8 ft	8 to 30 sec	No	1 to 5-B:C
	Self-Expelling	10 to 15 lb	3-8 ft	8 to 30 sec	No	2 to 10-B:C
	Self-Expelling	20 lb	3-8 ft	10 to 30 sec	No	10-B:C
	Self-Expelling	50 to 100 lb (wheeled)	3-10 ft	10 to 30 sec	No	10 to 20-B:C
Dry Chemical (Sodium Bicarbonate)	Stored Pressure	1 to 2½ lb	5-8 ft	8 to 12 sec	No	2 to 10-B:C
	Cartridge or Stored Pressure	2¾ to 5 lb	5-20 ft	8 to 25 sec	No	5 to 20-B:C
	Cartridge or Stored Pressure	6 to 30 lb	5-20 ft	10 to 25 sec	No	10 to 160-B:C
	Stored Pressure	50 lb (wheeled)	20 ft	35 sec	No	160-B:C
	Nitrogen Cylinder or Stored Pressure	75 to 350 lb (wheeled)	15-45 ft	20 to 105 sec	No	40 to 320-B:C
Dry Chemical (Potassium Bicarbonate)	Cartridge or Stored Pressure	2 to 5 lb	5-12 ft	8 to 10 sec	No	5 to 30-B:C
	Cartridge or Stored Pressure	5½ to 10 lb	5-20 ft	8 to 20 sec	No	10 to 80-B:C
	Cartridge or Stored Pressure	16 to 30 lb	10-20 ft	8 to 25 sec	No	40 to 120-B:C
	Cartridge or Stored Pressure	48 to 50 lb (wheeled)	20 ft	30 to 35 sec	No	120 to 160-B:C
	Nitrogen Cylinder or Stored Pressure	125 to 315 lb (wheeled)	15-45 ft	30 to 80 sec	No	80 to 640-B:C
Dry Chemical (Potassium Chloride)	Cartridge or Stored Pressure	2 to 5 lb	5-8 ft	8 to 10 sec	No	5 to 10-B:C

	Cartridge or Stored Pressure	5 to 9 lb	8-12 ft	10 to 15 sec	No	20 to 40-B:C
	Cartridge or Stored Pressure	9½ to 20 lb	10-15 ft	15 to 20 sec	No	40 to 60-B:C
	Cartridge or Stored Pressure	19½ to 30 lb	5-20 ft	10 to 25 sec	No	60 to 80-B:C
	Cartridge or Stored Pressure	125 to 200 lb (wheeled)	15-45 ft	30 to 40 sec	No	160-B:C
Dry Chemical (Ammonium Phosphate)	Stored Pressure	1 to 5 lb	5-12 ft	8 to 10 sec	No	1 to 5-A† and 2 to 10-B:C
	Stored Pressure or Cartridge	2½ to 9 lb	5-12 ft	8 to 15 sec	No	1 to 4-A and 10 to 40-B:C
	Stored Pressure or Cartridge	9 to 17 lb	5-20 ft	10 to 25 sec	No	2 to 20-A and 10 to 80-B:C
	Stored Pressure or Cartridge	17 to 30 lb	5-20 ft	10 to 25 sec	No	3 to 20-A and 30 to 120-B:C
	Stored Pressure or Cartridge	45 to 50 lb (wheeled)	20 ft	25 to 35 sec	No	20 to 301-A 80 to 160-B:C
	Nitrogen Cylinder or Stored Pressure	110 to 315 lb (wheeled)	15-45 ft	30 to 60 sec	No	20 to 40-A and 60 to 320-B:C
Dry Chemical (Foam Compatible)	Cartridge or Stored Pressure	4¾ to 9 lb	5-20 ft	8 to 10 sec	No	10 to 20-B:C
	Cartridge or Stored Pressure	9 to 27 lb	5-20 ft	10 to 25 sec	No	20 to 30-B:C
	Cartridge or Stored Pressure	18 to 30 lb	5-20 ft	10 to 25 sec	No	40 to 60-B:C
	Nitrogen Cylinder or Stored Pressure	150 to 350 lb (wheeled)	15-45 ft	20 to 150 sec	No	80 to 240-B:C
Dry Chemical (Potassium Bicarbonate Urea based)	Stored Pressure	5 to 11 lb	11-22 ft	18 sec	No	40 to 80-B:C
	Stored Pressure	9 to 23 lb	15-30 ft	17 to 33 sec	No	60 to 160-B:C
		175 lb (wheeled)	70 ft	62 sec	No	480-B:C
Halon 1301 (Bromotrifluoromethane)	Stored Pressure	2½ lb	4-6 ft	8 to 10 sec	No	2-B:C
Halon 1211 (Bromochlorodifluoromethane)	Stored Pressure	.09 to 2 lb	6-10 ft	8 to 10 sec	No	1 to 2-B:C
		2 to 3 lb	6-10 ft	8 to 10 sec	No	5-B:C
		5½ to 9 lb	9-15 ft	8 to 15 sec	No	1-A:10-B:C
		13 to 22 lb	14-16 ft	10 to 18 sec	No	2 to 4-A and 20 to 80-B:C
		50 lb	35 ft	30 sec	No	10-A:120-B:C
		150 lb (wheeled)	20-35 ft	30 to 44 sec	No	30-A:160 to 240-B:C
Halon 1211/1301 (Bromochlorodifluoromethane Bromotrifluoromethane) mixtures	Stored Pressure or Self-Expelling	0.9 to 5 lb	3-12 ft	8 to 10 sec	No	1 to 10-B:C
	Stored Pressure	9 to 20 lb	10-18 ft	10 to 22 sec	No	1-A:10-B:C to 4-A:80-B:C

Notes to Table A-2-1

*UL and ULC ratings checked as of July 24, 1987. Readers concerned with subsequent ratings should review the pertinent "lists" and "supplements" issued by these laboratories: Underwriters Laboratories Inc., 333 Pfingsten Road, Northbrook, IL 60062, or Underwriters Laboratories of Canada, 7 Crouse Road, Scarborough, Ont., Canada M1R 3A9.

**Carbon dioxide extinguishers with metal horns do not carry a "C" classification.

†Some small extinguishers containing ammonium phosphate-base dry chemical do not carry an "A" classification.

NOTE: Halon should be used only where its unique properties are deemed necessary.

A-2-1.1 Halogenated agent is highly effective for extinguishing fire and evaporates after use, leaving no residue. Halon agent is, however, included in the Montreal Protocol list of controlled substances developed under the United Nations, Environment Program. Where agents other than halon can satisfactorily protect the hazard, use them instead of halon. Halon use should be limited to extinguishment of unwanted fire and should not be used for routine training of personnel.

A-2-2.1.1 It is recommended that inverting types of extinguishers be replaced with currently available models. Manufacture of inverting types of extinguishers and their listing by Underwriters Laboratories Inc. was discontinued in 1969. As the availability of suitable replacement parts and recharge materials diminishes, it has become increasingly difficult to maintain these types of extinguishers in a safe and reliable operating condition. Inverting type extinguishers (soda-acid, foam, and cartridge-operated water) are now considered obsolete and are required to be removed from service no later than the next required date for hydrostatic testing.

A-2-2.1.3 The use of dry chemical extinguishers on wet energized electrical equipment (such as rain-soaked utility poles, high-voltage switch gear, and transformers) may aggravate electrical leakage problems. The dry chemical in combination with moisture provides an electrical path that can reduce the effectiveness of insulation protection. The removal of all traces of dry chemical from such equipment after extinguishment is recommended.

A-2-2.1.4 Extinguishers and Extinguishing Agents for Class D Hazards.

(1) Chemical reaction between burning metals and many extinguishing agents (including water) may range from explosive to inconsequential depending in part on the type, form, and quantity of metal involved. In general, the hazards from a metal fire are significantly increased when such extinguishing agents are applied.

NOTE: The advantages and limitations of a wide variety of commercially available metal fire extinguishing agents are discussed in Chapter 5 of Section 19 of the NFPA *Fire Protection Handbook* (16th Edition).

(2) The agents and extinguishers discussed in this section are of specialized types and their use often involves special techniques peculiar to a particular combustible metal. A given agent will not necessarily control or extinguish all metal fires. Some agents are valuable in working with several metals; others are useful in combating only one type of metal fire. The authorities having jurisdiction should be consulted in each case to determine the desired protection for the particular hazard involved.

(3) Certain combustible metals and reactive chemicals require special extinguishing agents or techniques. If there is doubt, applicable NFPA standards should be consulted or reference made to NFPA 49, *Hazardous Chemicals Data*, or NFPA 325M, *Fire Hazard Properties of Flammable Liquids, Gases, and Volatile Solids*.

(4) Reference should be made to the manufacturer's recommendations for use and special technique for extinguishing fires in various combustible metals.

(5) Fire of high intensity may occur in certain metals. Ignition is generally the result of frictional heating, exposure to moisture, or exposure from a fire in other combustible materials. The greatest hazard exists when these metals are in the molten state, in finely divided forms of dust, turnings, or shavings.

NOTE: The properties of a wide variety of combustible metals and the agents available for extinguishing fires in these metals are discussed in Chapter 10 of Section 5 and Chapter 5 of Section 19 of the NFPA *Fire Protection Handbook* (16th Edition).

A-2-3.5 Delicate electronic equipment includes but is not limited to data processing, computers, CAD, CAM, robotics, and reproduction equipment. Use of other extinguishers and extinguishing agents may damage beyond repair both the equipment at the source of the fire and related equipment in the immediate vicinity of the fire. Dry chemical residue will probably not be able to be completely and immediately removed and, in addition, multipurpose dry chemical, when exposed to temperatures in excess of 250°F (121°C) or relative humidity in excess of 50 percent, may cause corrosion.

A-2-3.6 Wheeled extinguishers are available in capacities ranging from 50 to 350 lb (23 to 159kg). These extinguishers are capable of delivering higher agent flow rates and greater agent stream range than the normal portable-type extinguishers. Wheeled extinguishers are capable of furnishing increased fire extinguishing effectiveness for high hazard areas and have added importance when a limited number of people are available.

A-3-1.1 Distribution Considerations. Items that affect distribution of portable fire extinguishers are: the area and arrangement of the building occupancy conditions, the severity of the hazard, the anticipated classes of fire, other protective systems or devices, and the distances to be traveled to reach extinguishers. In addition, anticipated rate of fire spread, the intensity and rate of heat development, the smoke contributed by the burning materials, and the accessibility of a fire to close approach with portable extinguishers should be considered. Wheeled extinguishers have additional agent and range and should be considered for areas where the additional protection is needed. Portable extinguishers offer the occupant a means to assist in evacuation of a building or occupancy. They are useful to knock down the fire if it occurs along the evacuation route. Whenever possible, the individual property should be surveyed for actual protection requirements.

A-3-1.2 Most buildings have Class A fire hazards. In any occupancy, there may be a predominant hazard with "special hazard" areas requiring supplemental protection. For example, a hospital will generally have need for Class A extinguishers covering patients' rooms, corridors, offices, etc., but will need Class B extinguishers in laboratories, kitchens, and where flammable anesthetics are stored or handled, and Class C extinguishers in electrical switch gear or generator rooms.

A-3-1.2.2 If extinguishers intended for different classes of fires are grouped, their intended use should be marked conspicuously to aid in the choice of the proper extinguisher at the time of a fire. In an emergency, the tendency is to reach for the closest extinguisher. If this extinguisher is of the wrong type, the user may well endanger himself or herself and the property he or she is endeavoring to protect. Wherever possible, it is preferable to have only those extinguishers available that can be safely used on any type of fire in the immediate vicinity.

A-3-4.1 Where such personnel are not available, the hazard should be protected by fixed systems.

A-4-1.4 A fire equipment servicing agency is usually the most reliable means available to the public for having maintenance and recharging performed. Large industries may find it desirable to establish their own maintenance and recharge facilities training personnel to perform these functions. Service manuals and parts lists should be obtained from the extinguisher manufacturer.

A-4-3.1 Frequency of extinguisher inspections should be based on the need of the area in which extinguishers are located. The required monthly inspection is a minimum. An inspection should be more frequent if any of the following exist:

(a) High frequency of fires in the past.

(b) Severe hazards.

(c) Susceptibility to tampering, vandalism, or malicious mischief.

(d) Possibility of, or experience with, theft of extinguishers.

(e) Locations that make extinguishers susceptible to mechanical injury.

(f) Possibility of visible or physical obstructions.

(g) Exposure to abnormal temperatures or corrosive atmospheres.

(h) Characteristics of extinguishers, such as susceptibility to leakage.

A-4-4 Maintenance. Persons usually performing maintenance operations come from two major groups:

(a) Extinguisher service agencies.

(b) Trained industrial safety or maintenance personnel.

Extinguishers owned by individuals are often neglected because there is no planned periodic follow-up program. It is recommended that such owners become familiar with their extinguishers so they can detect telltale warnings from inspection that may suggest the need for maintenance. When maintenance is indicated, it should be performed by trained persons having proper equipment. (*See 4-1.4.*)

The purpose of a well-planned and well-executed maintenance program is to afford maximum probability that an extinguisher:

(a) Will operate properly between the time intervals established for maintenance examinations in the environment to which it is exposed, and

(b) Will not constitute a potential hazard to persons in its vicinity or to operators or rechargers of extinguishers.

Any replacement parts needed should be obtained from the manufacturer or his representative.

A-4-4.1.2 Carbon dioxide hose assemblies have a continuous metal braid that connects to both couplings to minimize the static shock hazard. The reason for the conductivity test is to determine that the hose is conductive from the inlet coupling to the outlet orifice. A basic conductivity tester consists of a flashlight having an open circuit and a set of two wires with a conductor (clamps or probe) at each end.

A-4-4.1.3 Halon removed from an extinguisher is kept in a closed recovery charging system until disposition can be made of whether to recharge the halon back into an extinguisher or return unsatisfactory halon to a manufacturer for proper disposal. An efficient Halon 1211 closed recovery/charging system will have a clear sight glass for monitoring the cleanliness of the Halon 1211 and a means for determining if the acceptable water moisture content of the halon has been exceeded. Some closed recovery systems have a means of mechanically filtering the Halon 1211 and removing excess water. They also have a motor driven pump system which permits transferring halon into an extinguisher or supply container without the need to vent the receiving container to reduce its pressure before halon transfer. Closed recovery/charging systems also include the plumbing, valves, regulators, and safety relief devices to permit convenient, quick transfer of the Halon 1211.

A-4-4.2 Maintenance Procedures. For convenience, the following check lists are organized into two parts. The first Table A-4-4.2(a) is arranged by mechanical parts (components and containers) common to most extinguishers. The second, Table A-4-4.2(b), is arranged by extinguishing material and expelling means and involves a description of the problems peculiar to each agent.

A-4-4.3 Recordkeeping. In addition to the required tag or label (*see 4-4.3*), a permanent file record should be kept for each extinguisher. This file record should include the following information as applicable:

(a) The maintenance date and the name of person or agency performing the maintenance.

(b) The date when last recharged and the name of person or agency performing the recharge.

(c) The hydrostatic retest date and the name of person or agency performing the hydrostatic test.

(d) Description of dents remaining after passing a hydrostatic test.

(e) The date of the six-year maintenance for stored pressure dry chemical and halogenated agent types (*see 4-4.1.3*).

A-4-5.1 General Safety Guidelines for Recharging.

(a) Make sure all pressure is vented from extinguisher before attempting to remove valve body or fill closure. Warning: Do not depend on pressure indicating devices to tell if container is under pressure as they could malfunction.

Table A-4-4.2(a) Mechanical Parts
Extinguisher Part, Check Points and Corrective Action

Shell	Corrective Action
1. Hydrostatic test date or date of manufacture†	1. Retest if needed
2. Corrosion†	2. Conduct hydrostatic test and refinish; or discard
3. Mechanical damage (denting or abrasion)†	3. Conduct hydrostatic test and refinish; or discard
4. Paint condition	4. Refinish
5. Presence of repairs (welding, soldering, brazing, etc.)	5. Discard or consult manufacturer
6. Damaged threads (corroded, crossthreaded, or worn)	6. Discard or consult manufacturer
7. Broken hanger attachment, carrying handle lug	7. Discard or consult manufacturer
8. Sealing surface damage (nicks or corrosion)†	8. Clean, repair, and leak test; or discard
Nameplate	**Corrective Action**
1. Illegible wording	1. Clean or replace
2. Corrosion or loose plate	2. Inspect shell under plate (see Shell Check Points) and reattach plate
Nozzle or Horn	**Corrective Action**
1. Deformed, damaged, or cracked	1. Replace
2. Blocked openings	2. Clean
3. Damaged threads (corroded, crossthreaded, or worn)	3. Replace
4. Aged (brittle)	4. Replace
Hose Assembly	**Corrective Action**
1. Damaged (cut, cracked, or worn)	1. Replace
2. Damaged couplings or swivel joint (cracked or corroded)	2. Replace
3. Damaged threads (corroded, crossthreaded, or worn)	3. Replace
4. Inner tube cut at couplings	4. Repair or replace
5. Electrically nonconductive between couplings (CO_2 hose only)	5. Replace
6. Hose obstruction	6. Remove obstruction or replace
Valve Locking Device	**Corrective Action**
1. Damaged (bent, corroded, or binding)	1. Repair and lubricate; or replace
2. Missing	2. Replace
Gage or Pressure-Indicating Device	**Corrective Action**
1. Immovable, jammed, or missing pointer (pressure test)†	1. Depressurize and replace gage
2. Missing, deformed, or broken crystal†	2. Depressurize and replace gage
3. Illegible or faded dial†	3. Depressurize and replace gage
4. Corrosion†	4. Depressurize and check calibration, clean and refinish; or replace gage
5. Dented case or crystal retainer†	5. Depressurize and check calibration; or replace gage
6. Immovable or corroded pressure-indicating stem (nongage type)†	6. Replace head assembly, depressurize, and replace shell or complete extinguisher
Shell or Cylinder Valve	**Corrective Action**
1. Corroded, damaged or jammed level, handle, spring, stem, or fastener joint†	1. Depressurize, check freedom of movement, and repair; or replace
2. Damaged outlet threads (corroded, crossthreaded, or worn)†	2. Depressurize and replace
Nozzle Shutoff Valve	**Corrective Action**
1. Corroded, damaged, jammed or binding lever, spring, stem, or fastener joint	1. Repair and lubricate; or replace
2. Plugged, deformed, or corroded nozzle tip or discharge passage	2. Clean or replace
Puncture Mechanism	**Corrective Action**
1. Damaged, jammed, or binding puncture lever, stem, or fastener joint	1. Replace
2. Dull or damaged cutting or puncture pin	2. Replace
3. Damaged threads (corroded, crossthreaded, or worn)	3. Replace
Gas Cartridge	**Corrective Action**
1. Corrosion	1. Replace cartridge
2. Damaged seal disc (injured, cut, or corroded)	2. Replace cartridge
3. Damaged threads (corroded, crossthreaded, or worn)	3. Replace cartridge
4. Illegible weight markings	4. Replace cartridge
Gas Cylinders	**Corrective Action**
1. Hydrostatic test date or date of manufacture	1. Retest if needed
2. Corrosion	2. Conduct hydrostatic test and refinish or discard
3. Paint condition	3. Refinish
4. Presence of repairs (welding, soldering, brazing, etc.)	4. Discard or consult manufacturer
5. Damaged threads (corroded, crossthreaded, or worn)	5. Discard or consult manufacturer

Wheel Cap or Fill Cap	Corrective Action
1. Corroded, cracked, or broken	1. Replace
2. Damaged threads (corroded, crossthreaded, or worn)	2. Replace
3. Sealing surface damage (nicked, deformed, or corroded)	3. Clean, repair, and leak test; or replace
4. Blocked vent hole or slot	4. Clean

Non-Rechargeable Shell	Corrective Action
1. Corrosion†	1. Depressurize and replace shell
2. Damaged seal disc (injured, cut, or corroded)†	2. Depressurize and replace shell
3. Damaged threads (corroded, crossthreaded, or worn)†	3. Replace shell
4. Illegible weight markings†	4. Depressurize and replace shell

Carriage and Wheels	Corrective Action
1. Corroded, bent, or broken carriage	1. Repair or replace
2. Damaged wheel (buckled or broken spoke, bent rim or axle, loose tire, low pressure, jammed bearing)	2. Clean, repair, and lubricate; or replace

Carrying Handle	Corrective Action
1. Broken handle lug	1. Discard shell or valve; or consult manufacturer
2. Broken handle	2. Replace
3. Corroded, jammed, or worn fastener joint	3. Clean or replace

Seals or Tamper Indicator	Corrective Action
1. Broken or missing	1. Check under Agent and Expelling Means for specific action

Hand Pump	Corrective Action
1. Corroded, jammed, or damaged pump	1. Repair and lubricate; or replace
2. Improper adjustment of packing nut	2. Adjust

Inner Cage, Chamber Stopple, Acid Container, or Tube	Corrective Action
1. Corroded, damaged, bent, cracked, or distorted	1. Replace

Pressurizing Valve	Corrective Action
1. Leaking seals	1. Depressurize and replace valve or core

Gasket "O" Ring and Seals	Corrective Action
1. Damaged (cut, cracked, or worn)†	1. Replace and lubricate
2. Missing†	2. Replace and lubricate
3. Aged or weathered (compression set, brittle, cracked)†	3. Replace and lubricate

Brackets	Corrective Action
1. Corroded, worn, or bent	1. Repair and refinish; or replace
2. Loose or binding fit	2. Adjust fit or replace
3. Worn, loose, corroded, or missing screw or bolt	3. Tighten or replace
4. Worn bumper, webbing, or grommet	4. Replace

Gas Tube and Siphon or Pickup Tube	Corrective Action
1. Corroded, dented, cracked, or broken	1. Replace
2. Blocked tube or openings in tube	2. Clean or replace

Safety Relief Device	Corrective Action
1. Corroded or damaged†	1. Depressurize and replace or consult manufacturer
2. Broken, operated, or plugged†	2. Depressurize and replace or repair

Pressure Regulators	Corrective Action
1. External condition	1.
(a) Damage	(a) Replace regulator
(b) Corrosion	(b) Clean regulator or replace
2. Pressure relief — corroded, plugged, dented, leaking, broken, or missing	2. Disconnect regulator from pressure source; replace pressure relief
3. Protective bonnet relief hole — tape missing or seal wire broken or missing	3. Check regulator in accordance with manufacturer's regulator test procedures
4. Adjusting screw — lock pin missing	4. Check regulator in accordance with manufacturer's regulator test procedures
5. Gages	5.
(a) Immovable, jammed, or missing pointer	(a) Disconnect regulator from pressure source; replace gage
(b) Missing or broken crystal	(b) Replace crystal
(c) Illegible or faded dial	(c) Replace gage
(d) Corrosion	(d) Check calibration, clean and refinish, or replace gage
(e) Dented case or crystal retainer	(e) Check calibration or replace gage

6. Regulator Hose (a) Cut, cracked, abraded, or deformed exterior (b) Corroded or cracked coupling (c) Corroded, crossthreaded, or worn coupling threads	6. (a) Conduct hydrostatic test or replace hose (b) Replace hose (c) Replace hose

NOTE: For disposable type extinguishers those items indicated with a dagger (†) cannot be inspected and serviced. If the corrective action requires the depressurization of the extinguisher, disposable halogenated agent fire extinguishers shall not be depressurized but returned to the manufacturer or service agency for proper disposal and reclaiming of the extinguishing agent.

Table A-4-4.2(b) Agent and Expelling Means
Extinguisher Type and Part, Check Points and Corrective Action

Self-Generating	
Soda-Acid Water	**Corrective Action**
1. Recharging date due	1. Empty, clean, and recharge
2. Improper fill levels in acid bottle and shell	2. Empty, clean, and recharge
3. Agent condition (check for sediment)	3. Empty, clean, and recharge
Foam	**Corrective Action**
1. Recharging date due	1. Empty, clean, and recharge
2. Improper fill levels in inner container and shell	2. Empty, clean, and recharge
3. Agent condition (check for sediment)	3. Empty, clean, and recharge
Self-Expelling	
Carbon Dioxide	**Corrective Action**
1. Improper weight	1. Recharge to proper weight
2. Broken or missing tamper indicator	2. Leak test and weigh, recharge or replace indicator
Halon 1301 Bromotrifluoromethane	**Corrective Action**
1. Punctured cylinder seal disc	1. Replace shell
2. Improper weight	2. Replace shell or return to manufacturer for refilling
3. Broken or missing tamper indicator	3. Examine cylinder seal disc, replace indicator
Combination Halon 1211/1301	**Corrective Action**
1. Improper weight	1. Return to manufacturer (see 4-3.3)
2. Broken or missing tamper indicator	2. Return to manufacturer (see 4-3.3)
Mechanical Pump	
Water and Antifreeze	**Corrective Action**
1. Improper fill level	1. Refill
2. Defective pump	2. Clean, repair, and lubricate, or replace
Hand Propelled — Bucket or Scoop	
Water and Antifreeze	**Corrective Action**
1. Improper fill level	1. Refill
2. Antifreeze — improper charge (check specific gravity or recharge record)	2. Recharge
3. Missing bucket	3. Replace
Dry Powder	**Corrective Action**
1. Improper fill level	1. Refill
2. Agent condition (contamination or caking)	2. Discard and replace
3. Missing scoop	3. Replace
Gas Cartridge or Cylinder	
Dry Chemical and Dry Powder Types	**Corrective Action**
1. Improper weight or charge level	1. Refill to correct weight
2. Agent condition (contamination, caking, or wrong agent)	2. Empty and refill
3. (a) For cartridge (1) Punctured seal disc (2) Improper weight (3) Broken or missing tamper indicator	3. (a) (1) Replace cartridge (2) Replace cartridge (3) Examine seal disc, replace indicator
(b) For gas cylinder with gage (1) Low pressure (2) Broken or missing tamper indicator	(b) (1) Replace cylinder (2) Leak test — replace indicator
(c) For gas cylinder without gage (1) Low pressure (attach gage and measure pressure) (2) Broken or missing tamper indicator	(c) (1) Leak test. If normal, leak test and repair indictor. If low — replace cylinder. (2) Measure pressure — leak test — replace indicator

Water, Antifreeze, and Loaded Stream	Corrective Action
1. Improper fill level	1. Refill to correct level
2. (a) Agent condition (1) Dirty, cloudy, or sediment (2) If antifreeze or loaded stream — improper charge (check specific gravity, recharge record, or weigh)	2. (a) (1) Empty and refill (2) Recharge
3. Punctured cartridge seal disc	3. Replace cartridge
4. Improper cartridge weight	4. Replace
5. Broken or missing indicator	5. Examine seal disc — replace indicator

Wetting Agent	Corrective Action
1. Improper fill level	1. Refill
2. Agent condition (sediment and incorrect surface tension) *(See NFPA 18 — Standard on Wetting Agents.)*	2. Empty and refill
3. Improper cartridge weight	3. Replace
4. Broken or missing tamper indicator	4. Leak test cartridge — weigh — replace indicator

Stored Pressure

Combination Halon 1211/1301	Corrective Action
1. Refillable (a) Improper extinguisher agent (b) Improper gage pressure (c) Broken or missing tamper indicator	1. (a) Return to manufacturer (see 4-4.3) (b) Return to manufacturer (see 4-4.3) (c) Examine extinguisher, leak test, replace tamper indicator
2. Nonrechargeable extinguisher with pressure indicator (a) Low pressure (b) Broken or missing tamper indicator	2. (a) Return to manufacturer (see 4-4.3) (b) Leak test, check pressure, replace tamper indicator

Dry Chemical and Dry Powder Types	Corrective Action
1. Refillable (a) Improper extinguisher weight (b) Improper gage pressure (c) Broken or missing tamper indicator	1. (a) Refill to correct weight (b) Repressurize and leak test (c) Leak test and replace indicator
2. Disposable shell with pressure indicator (a) Punctured seal disc (b) Low pressure (c) Broken or missing tamper indicator	2. (a) Replace shell (b) Depressurize; replace shell (c) Check pressure — check seal disc — replace indicator
3. Disposable shell without pressure indicator (a) Punctured seal disc (b) Low weight (c) Broken or missing tamper indicator	3. (a) Replace shell (b) Depressurize; replace shell (c) Check seal disc — replace indicator
4. Nonrechargeable extinguisher with pressure indicator (a) Low pressure (b) Broken or missing tamper indicator	4. (a) Depressurize and discard extinguisher (b) Leak test — check pressure — replace indicator

Halon 1211 Bromochlorodifluoromethane	Corrective Action
1. Broken or missing tamper indicator	1. Weigh, leak test, and replace indicator
2. Improper gage pressure	2. Weigh, repressurize, and leak test
3. Improper weight	3. Leak test and refill to correct weight

Water, Antifreeze, and Loaded Stream	Corrective Action
1. Improper fill level (by weight or observation)	1. Refill to correct level
2. Agent condition if antifreeze or loaded stream. Improper charge (check recharge record or weigh)	2. Empty and refill
3. Improper gage pressure	3. Repressurize and leak test
4. Broken or missing tamper indicator	4. Leak test — replace indicator

AFFF and FFFP Liquid Charge	Corrective Action
1. Improper fill level (by weight or observation)	1. Empty and recharge with new solution
2. Agent condition (presence of precipitate or other foreign matter)	2. Empty and recharge with new solution
3. Improper gage pressure	3. Repressurize and leak test
4. Broken or missing tamper indicator	4. Leak test — replace indicator

AFFF Solid Charge	Corrective Action
1. Improper fill level (by weight or observation)	1. Refill to correct level
2. Improper gage pressure	2. Repressurize and leak test
3. Broken or missing valve tamper indicator	3. Leak test — replace indicator
4. Presence of liquid moisture in solid charge or burning	4. Replace solid charge and change tamper indicator tape
5. Missing charge housing seal plug	5. Inspect for all the above — replace plug

(b) Use proper recharge materials when refilling a fire extinguisher. Mixing of some extinguishing agents could cause a chemical reaction resulting in a dangerous pressure buildup in the container.

(c) The weight of agent as specified on the nameplate is critical. Overfilling may render the extinguisher dangerous or ineffective.

(d) All sealing components should be cleaned and properly lubricated to prevent leakage after recharge.

(e) Check pressure indicating device to ascertain that it is reading properly.

(f) Most manufacturers recommend the use of dry nitrogen as an expellant gas for stored pressure extinguishers. Limiting charging pressure regulator setting to 25 psi (172 kPa) above service pressure as per 4-5.4.1 prevents gage damage and loss of calibration. *Warning:* Never connect the extinguisher to be charged directly to the high-pressure source. Connecting directly to the high-pressure source could cause the container to rupture, resulting in injury. Never leave an extinguisher connected to the regulator of a high-pressure source for an extended period of time. A defective regulator could cause the container to rupture due to excess pressure.

(g) Use the manufacturer's recommended charging adaptor to prevent damage to valve and its components.

(h) When recharging separate expellant source extinguishers, make sure filled enclosure is in place and tightened down. Replace all safety devices prior to installing replacement cartridges.

(i) Only those gas cartridges recommended by the manufacturer should be used. Cartridge features such as pressure relief, puncturing capabilities, fill density, and thread compatibility are designed and approved to specific functional requirements.

(j) Use proper safety seals as other types, i.e., meter seals, may not break at the prescribed requirements.

(k) Regulators utilized on wheeled extinguishers are factory pinned at the operating pressure and should not be field adjusted.

A-4-5.1.3 To determine the gross weight, the entire extinguisher should be weighed empty. The weight of the specified recharge agent should be added to this amount.

A-4-5.1.5 Leak Test. The leak test required for stored pressure and self-expelling types must be sufficiently sensitive to ensure that the extinguisher will remain operable for at least one year. Any tamper indicators or seals must be replaced after recharging.

A-4-5.3.1 Recharge Agents. On properties where extinguishers are maintained by the occupant, a supply of recharging agents should be kept on hand. These agents should meet the requirements of 4-5.3.1.

The intent of this provision is to maintain the efficiency of each extinguisher as produced by the manufacturer and as labeled by one or more of the fire testing laboratories. For example, the extinguishing agent and the additives used in the various types of dry chemical extinguishers vary in chemical composition and in particle size and, thus, in flow characteristics. Each extinguisher is designed to secure maximum efficiency with the particular formulation used. Changing the agent from that specified on the extinguisher nameplate may affect flow rates, nozzle discharge characteristics, the quantity of available agent (as influenced by density), and would void the label of the testing laboratory.

Certain recharging materials deteriorate with age, exposure to excessive temperature, and exposure to moisture. Storage of recharge agents for long periods of time should be avoided.

Dry powder used for combustible metal fires (Class D) must not become damp as the powder will not be free flowing. In addition, when dry powder contains sufficient moisture, a hazardous reaction may result when applied to a metal fire.

A-4-5.3.2 Mixing multipurpose dry chemicals with alkaline-based dry chemicals may result in a chemical reaction capable of developing sufficient pressures to rupture an extinguisher. Substituting a different formulation for the one originally employed could cause malfunctioning of the extinguisher or result in substandard performance.

A-4-5.3.6 Removal of Moisture. Moisture within a nonwater-type extinguisher creates both a serious corrosion hazard to the extinguisher shell and indicates what is probably an inoperative extinguisher. Moisture may enter at the following times:

(1) After a hydrostatic test.

(2) When recharging is being performed.

(3) When the valve has been removed from the cylinder.

(4) By use of compressed air and a moisture trap for pressurizing nonwater types.

A-4-5.3.7 Halon Extinguisher Recharging. If the extinguisher valve is removed for servicing, it is recommended that the extinguisher be purged with nitrogen or a vacuum be drawn on the extinguisher cylinder prior to recharging.

A-4-5.3.9 Dry Ice Converters. In general, carbon dioxide obtained by converting dry ice to liquid will not be satisfactory unless it is properly processed to remove excess water and oil. If dry ice converters are used, the following required steps must be taken:

(a) Employ moisture-absorbent cartridges containing silica gel or activated alumina of adequate capacity. These cartridges need to be periodically reactivated by heating at 300°F (149°C) for two hours in an open vented condition in order to keep them in an absorbent condition. At temperatures below 32°F (0°C), the cartridges act as a filter, and above 32°F (0°C), they absorb moisture directly. Various telltale compositions are available that, by means of color, indicate the degree of absorptivity still available in the gel.

(b) An extra operation is required to minimize the water within the converter. This operation consists of blowing off a short burst of liquid carbon dioxide from the bottom of the converter in order to blow off free water. This operation can only be performed above 32°F (0°C). With the converter contents colder than 32°F (0°C), blowing off is ineffectual.

The preferred source of carbon dioxide for recharging extinguishers is from a low-pressure [300 psi at 0°F (2068 kPa at −17.8°C)] supply, either directly or via dry cylinders used as an intermediary means.

A-4-5.4.1 Pressure Gages. If it becomes necessary to replace a pressure gage on a fire extinguisher, in addition to knowing the charging pressure, it is important to know the type of extinguishing agent for which the gage is suitable as well as the valve body with which the gage is compatible. This information may be available in the form of markings on the dial face. Where the marking is provided, the extinguishing agent is indicated by references such as "Use Dry Chemicals Only," while the valve body compatibility is indicated as follows:

(a) Gages intended for use with aluminum or plastic valve bodies are marked with a line above the gage manufacturer's code letter.

(b) Gages intended for use with brass or plastic valve bodies are marked with a line below the manufacturer's code letter.

(c) Universal gages that can be used with aluminum, brass, or plastic valve bodies are marked with lines above and below the manufacturer's code letter or by the absence of any line above or below the manufacturer's code letter.

Using the proper replacement gage as to pressure range, extinguishing agent, and valve body compatibility is recommended to avoid or to reduce gage-related problems.

A-4-5.4.3 Typical Specification of Equipment Capable of Producing Dry Air. The compressor/dryer module shall be a fully enclosed, factory-assembled, and factory-tested package of a vertical design (compressor above motor). It shall incorporate the compressor driver, purification system, controls, interconnecting piping, and wiring. Scope of supply shall include:

Compressor. The compressor block shall be multistage, air cooled, oil lubricated, and rated for continuous duty at 5000 psig with a charging rate of ________CFM. The crankcase shall be fully enclosed with oversized ball bearings on each end. The connecting rods shall utilize needle bearings on both ends. Pistons shall be aluminum or cast iron and shall incorporate piston rings on all stages. Cylinders shall be of cast iron. Relief valves and individually mounted intercoolers shall be utilized after each stage of compression. The aftercooler shall be designed to deliver final air at a temperature not to exceed 20°F above ambient. The compressor flywheel shall incorporate a high velocity cooling fan for maximum heat dissipation. An automatic condensate drain system shall be supplied as standard equipment on all systems.

Dryer System. The system shall be of a multichamber arrangement, each constructed of aluminum alloy with a tensile strength of 83,000 psi and designed for 5000 psi working pressure with a 4 to 1 safety factor. The first chamber shall be a mechanical separator to eliminate oil and water. Subsequent chambers shall utilize replacement cartridges to further remove moisture and oil vapor. The dryer system shall process ________CF before cartridge replacement. The air delivered shall have a −60°F (−51.1°C) dew point or lower.

Controls/Instrumentation. The compressor module shall incorporate a gage panel to include the following: interstage and final discharge pressure gages, lube oil pressure gage (where applicable), hour meter, and power-on light. All pressure gages shall be liquid-filled. The control system shall consist of all devices to monitor the operation of the compressor including motor starter with overload detectors and switches to shut the compressor down in the event that high temperature or low oil pressure (on pressure lubricated compressors) occurs. An air pressure switch shall be supplied to automatically start and stop the compressor to maintain adequate system pressure. [The unit shall come complete with a cartridge monitoring system that combines both moisture monitoring and timed shutdown. The moisture monitor checks air quality continuously and is calibrated to indicate when a dew point of −60°F (−51.1°C) has been reached. When moisture is detected, a yellow light comes on and the digital timer comes into operation. At the conclusion of a 1- to 2-hour timing period, shutdown occurs and a red light comes on.]

A-5-1.4 Structural integrity of aluminum shells or cylinders is reduced when exposed to temperatures in excess of 350°F (177°C). These temperatures may occur under fire exposure without any visual evidence or during repainting operations where oven drying is utilized.

A-5-4.3 Test Equipment for Low Pressure Gas Types.

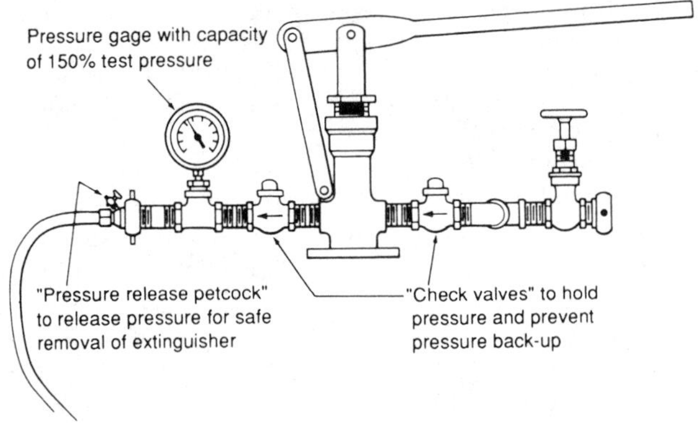

Figure A-5-4.3(a) Hydrostatic Hand Pump.

A-5-5.2 Testing Procedures for Low Pressure Gas Types.

(a) All valves, internal parts, and hose assemblies must be removed and the extinguisher emptied.

Exception: On some dry chemical and dry powder extinguishers (cartridge-operated), the manufacturer recommends that certain internal parts not be removed.

(b) All dry chemical and dry powder types of extinguishers must have all traces of extinguishing materials removed from inside the shell before filling with water.

(c) On all dry chemical and dry powder extinguishers having an externally mounted gas cartridge for creating discharge pressure, the cartridge (and some cartridge receivers) must be removed and a suitable plug inserted into the shell opening at the point of removal.

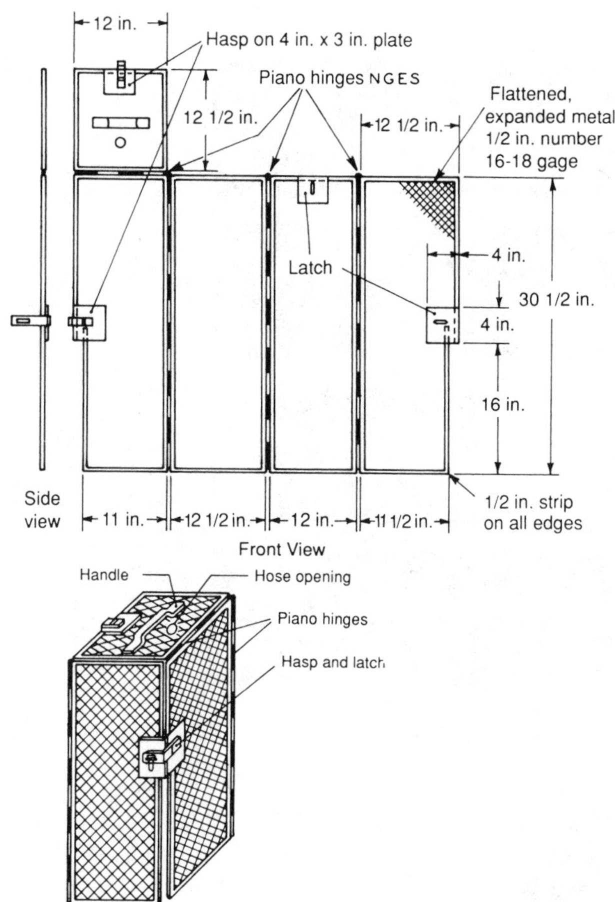

For SI Units: 1 in. = 25.4 mm.

Figure A-5-4.3(b) This illustrates a low-pressure, portable hydrostatic test cage useful to protect service personnel during such operations. It is used for hydrostatic tests of extinguishers of the type described in Section 5-5. It is not used for hydrostatic testing of high pressure cylinders. The cage should not be anchored to the floor during test operations. Such cages can be made by any metal fabricator.

(d) All wheeled extinguishers equipped with a shutoff nozzle at the outlet end of the hose must have the hose (complete with couplings but without the discharge nozzle) removed and tested separately.

NOTE: To conduct maintenance or a hydrostatic test on wheeled extinguishers equipped with a regulator(s), disconnect the regulator or low-pressure hose from the agent container. Test the regulator in accordance with procedures stated in A-4-4.2 of the Maintenance Check List.

(e) On all wheeled stored pressure dry chemical extinguishers, the head assembly is to be removed and replaced with a suitable test bonnet.

(f) The hose of the hydrostatic test pump is then attached by the flexible connection to the discharge nozzle, hose assembly, test bonnet, or test fitting, as is applicable. In the case of wheeled dry chemical and dry powder extinguishers, procedures and fittings should be those recommended by the manufacturer.

(g) The extinguisher is then placed in the protective test cage or barrier or, in the case of wheeled units, placed behind the protective shield before applying the test pressure.

(h) The water supply to the test pump is to be turned on and the extinguisher then filled to the top of its collar.

(i) For extinguishers tested with their cap in place, the cap must be tightened SLOWLY while the water supply remains open. When all of the entrapped air within the shell has been bled off and after water emerges, the cap must be tightened fully.

(j) For extinguishers tested with a test bonnet or fitting, the bonnet or fitting must be tightened FULLY while the water supply remains open. When all of the entrapped air within the shell has been bled off and after water emerges, the vent must be closed tightly.

(k) Pressure is then applied at a rate-of-pressure rise so the test pressure is reached in not less than 30 seconds. This test pressure is maintained for at least 30 seconds. Observations are made at this time to note any distortion or leakage of the extinguisher shell.

(l) If no distortion or leakage is noted and if the test pressure has not dropped, the pressure on the extinguisher shell may be released. The extinguisher is then considered to have passed the hydrostatic test.

(m) All traces of water and moisture must be removed from all dry chemical, dry powder, and halogenated agent extinguishers by use of a cylinder dryer. If a heated air stream is used, the temperature within the shell must not exceed 150°F (66°C).

(n) Any extinguisher shell that fails this hydrostatic test must be destroyed by the owner at his or her discretion.

A-5-5.3 Testing Procedures for Hose Assemblies.

(a) The discharge nozzle must be removed from the hose assembly without removal of any hose couplings.

(b) For dry chemical and dry powder types, all traces of dry chemical or dry powder must be removed.

(c) The hose assembly is then placed into a protective device, if available, whose design will permit visual observation of the test. Personnel testing the hose assembly should remain a safe distance away from the hose being tested.

(d) The hose must be completely filled with water before testing.

(e) Pressure then is applied at a rate-of-pressure rise to reach the test pressure within one minute. The test pressure is to be maintained for one full minute. Observations are then made to note any distortion or leakage.

(f) If no distortion or leakage is noted, or the test pressure has not dropped, or the couplings have not moved, the pressure is then to be released. The hose assembly is then considered to have passed the hydrostatic test.

(g) Hose assemblies passing the test must then be completely dried internally. If heat is used for drying, the temperature must not exceed 150°F (66°C).

(h) Hose assemblies failing a hydrostatic test must be destroyed.

A-5-5.4.2 Hydrostatic Test Label. Figure A-5-5.4.2 is a guide to the design of a hydrostatic test label.

		JAN.	FEB.	MAR.	APR.	MAY	JUNE					H.T. by ____ 1977-1978-1979-1980
				HYDRO TESTED BY								
TESTED TO (PSI)	hundreds	1	2	3	4	5	6	7	8	9	0	
	tens	1	2	3	4	5	6	7	8	9	0	
	units	1	2	3	4	5	6	7	8	9	0	
		JULY	AUG.	SEPT.	OCT.	NOV.	DEC.					

Figure A-5-5.4.2

Appendix B Recommended Markings to Indicate Extinguisher Suitability According to Class of Fire

This Appendix is not a part of the requirements of this NFPA document, but is included for information purposes only.

B-1 General.

B-1-1 Markings should be applied by decals that are durable and color fade resistant.

Color Separation Identification (picture symbol objects are white; backgroud borders are white)
Blue* — background for "YES" symbols
Black — background for symbols with slash mark ("NO")
— class of fire symbols and wording
Red* — slash mark for black background symbols

B-1-2 Markings should be located on the front of the extinguisher shell. Size and form should permit easy legibility at a distance of 3 ft (1 m). The labels shown in Table B-2-1 are consistent with extinguishers that have been tested and listed in accordance with fire test standards (*see 1-4.3*).

B-1-3 Where markings are applied to wall panels, etc., in the vicinity of extinguishers, they should permit easy legibility at a distance of 15 ft (4.6 m).

B-2 Recommended Marking System.

B-2-1 The recommended marking system is a pictorial concept that combines the uses and nonuses of extinguishers on a single label (*see Table B-2-1*).

Table B-2-1
Typical Pictorial Extinguisher Marking Labels

*NOTE: Recommended colors, per PMS (Pantone Matching System):

(BLUE-299)

(RED-Warm Red)

B-2-2 Letter-shaped symbol markings, as previously recommended, are shown in Table B-2-2.

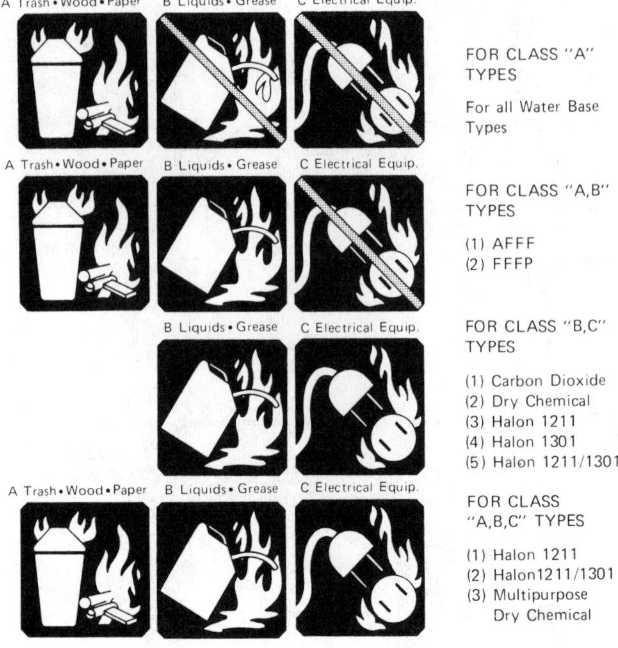

Table B-2-1

Table B-2-2

Ordinary

Combustibles

1. Extinguishers suitable for "Class A" fires should be identified by a triangle containing the letter "A." If colored, the triangle is colored green.*

Flammable

B

Liquids

2. Extinguishers suitable for "Class B" fires should be identified by a square containing the letter "B." If colored, the square is colored red.*

Electrical

Equipment

3. Extinguishers suitable for "Class C" fires should be identified by a circle containing the letter "C." If colored, the circle is colored blue*

Combustible

Metals

4. Extinguishers suitable for fires involving metals should be identified by a five-pointed star containing the letter "D." If colored, the star is colored yellow.*

Extinguishers suitable for more than one class of fire should be identified by multiple symbols placed in a horizontal sequence.

NOTE: Recommended colors from the PMS (Pantone Matching System) are:

Green — Basic Green
Red — 192 Red
Blue — Process Blue
Yellow — Basic Yellow

Appendix C Extinguisher Selection

This Appendix is not a part of the requirements of this NFPA document, but is included for information purposes only.

C-1 Principles of Selecting Extinguishers.

C-1-1 Selection of the best portable fire extinguisher for a given situation depends on:

(a) the nature of the combustibles or flammables that might be ignited,

(b) the potential severity (size, intensity, and speed of travel) of any resulting fire,

(c) effectiveness of the extinguisher on that hazard,

(d) the ease of use of the extinguisher,

(e) the personnel available to operate the extinguisher and their physical abilities and emotional reactions as influenced by their training,

(f) the ambient temperature conditions and other special atmospheric considerations (wind, draft, presence of fumes),

(g) suitability of the extinguisher for its environment,

(h) any anticipated adverse chemical reactions between the extinguishing agent and the burning materials,

(i) any health and operational safety concerns (exposure of operators during the fire control efforts), and

(j) the upkeep and maintenance requirements for the extinguisher.

C-1-2 Portable fire extinguishers are designed to cope with fires of limited size, and are necessary and desirable even though the property may be equipped with automatic sprinkler protection, standpipe and hose systems, or other fixed fire protective equipment.

C-1-3 A fire incident creates conditions of stress and intense excitement. Under these conditions the choice of a correct extinguisher must be made quickly. The protection planner can help to secure selection of the correct extinguisher by (1) locating the extinguisher near fire hazards for which they are suitable, (2) by use of extinguishers suitable for more than one class of fire, (3) by clearly marking the intended use (*see Appendix B*), and (4) by training of employees in the use of proper extinguishers. The use of conspicuous markings to readily identify an extinguisher's suitability is particularly important where extinguishers are grouped or where multiple fire hazards are present in an area.

C-2 Matching Extinguishers to the Hazard.

C-2-1 The first step in evaluating the selection of an extinguisher for the protection of a property is to determine the nature of the materials that might be ignited. Some extinguishers are suitable for only one class of fire, others for two, and still others for three. For example, a plain water extinguisher is suitable for Class A fires only.

C-2-2 The successful use of a Class A extinguisher on an incipient fire is directly related to the quantity of combustible material (contents and interior finish or both) involved. The amount of combustibles is sometimes referred to as the "fire loading" of a building, figured as the average pounds of combustibles per square foot of area. The larger the amount of combustibles, the greater the fire loading and the greater the potential fire hazard that the extinguisher may be called upon to combat. Based on this concept, Class A fire extinguishers are allocated according to the average fire loading that may be encountered in the occupancy to be protected.

C-2-3 Virtually every structure, even if of fire-resistive or noncombustible construction, has some combustible building components in the form of interior finish, partitions, etc. Thus, for building protection, extinguishers suitable for Class A fires are standard. Likewise, in virtually every situation, whether it be a building, a vehicle, or an outdoor exposure, ordinary combustible materials are found.

C-2-4 It is also true that where ordinary combustibles are present, there may be the need for extinguishers suitable for use on Class B and C fires (i.e., in the dining areas of a restaurant the principal combustibles present are wood, paper, and fabrics, which are Class A materials; however, in the kitchen area the essential hazard involves cooking greases, and a Class B extinguisher should be installed).

C-2-5 As another example, although in hospitals there is a general need for Class A extinguishers to cover spaces such as the patients' rooms, corridors, offices, etc., Class B:C extinguishers should be available in the laboratories, kitchens, areas where flammable anesthetics are stored or handled, or in electrical switchgear or generator rooms. Each area should be surveyed for its actual fire extinguisher requirements, keeping in mind the variety of conditions that exist in that particular area.

C-2-6 In connection with Class B (flammable liquid) fires, four basic conditions may exist: (1) flammable liquid fires of appreciable depth [$^1/_4$ in. (.63 cm) or more] such as those occurring in dip tanks and quench tanks in industrial plants, (2) spill fires or running fires where the depth of the liquid does not accumulate appreciably, (3) pressurized flammable liquid or gas fires from damaged vessels or product lines, and (4) cooking grease fires of appreciable depth such as those occurring in deep fat fryers.

Each of these four conditions presents significantly different problems in extinguishment which can also be further complicated by variations between indoor and outdoor conditions.

C-2-7 The selection of Class B extinguishers to be used on pressurized flammable liquids and pressurized gas fires requires special consideration. Fires of this nature are considered to be a special hazard and only dry chemical types of extinguishers should be employed. Other types of Class B rated fire extinguishers are relatively ineffective on these hazards. It has been determined that special dry chemical nozzle designs and rates of application are required to cope with such hazards.

CAUTION: It is undesirable to attempt to extinguish this type of fire unless there is reasonable assurance that the source of fuel can be promptly shut off.

C-2-8 The Class B ratings given by testing laboratories are based on flammable liquid fires of appreciable depth. The numeral thus derived is an approximate indication of the relative fire extinguishing potential of the extinguisher.

C-2-9 The size and type of the Class C extinguisher selected should be based on the construction features of the electrical equipment, the degree of agent contamination that can be tolerated, the size and extent of Class A and Class B components, or both, that are a part of the equipment, and the nature and amount of combustible materials in the immediate vicinity. For example, large motors and power panels will contain a considerable amount of Class A insulating materials as compared to the Class B material in an oil-filled transformer.

C-2-10 Once an analysis is made of the nature of the combustibles present and their potential fire severity, a study is made of the various candidate extinguishers that might be provided to meet fire protection needs.

C-3 Selecting the Right Extinguisher.

C-3-1 Selecting the right extinguisher for the class of hazard depends on a careful analysis of the advantages and disadvantages (under various conditions) of the various types available. The following paragraphs review some of the points that should be considered.

C-3-2 Water-type Extinguishers.

C-3-2.1 The most popular type is the 2$^1/_2$ gal (9.46 L) stored pressure water extinguisher. These extinguishers are being used to replace inverting types of water extinguishers (soda-acid and cartridge-operated water) that are no longer manufactured. An important advantage of the stored pressure water type, as opposed to inverting types, is its ability to be discharged intermittently. Some models are suitable for use at freezing conditions when charged as specified on the nameplate.

C-3-2.2 Since the pump tank extinguisher (hand-carry type) cannot be operated while being carried, it is considered somewhat more difficult to use. However, it does possess some advantages over stored pressure under certain applications. It is an excellent choice for use as a standby extinguisher on welding or cutting operations, protecting buildings in remote locations, and for use by the construction industry. It can easily be filled from any convenient, relatively clean water supply, can be used without the need for pressurization, and can be easily maintained. For freezing conditions, chemical additives containing corrosion inhibitors can be used; however, copper and nonmetallic tank models are recommended because they will not corrode as easily. The back pack style of pump tank, which can be carried and operated at the same time, is ideally suited for use in combating brush fires.

C-3-3 AFFF and FFFP Extinguishers. AFFF (aqueous film forming foam) and FFFP (film forming fluoroprotein) type extinguishers are rated for use on both Class A and Class B fires. They are not suitable for use in freezing temperatures. An advantage of this type on Class B flammable liquid fires of appreciable depth is the ability of the agent to float on and secure the liquid surface, which helps to prevent reignition.

C-3-4 Carbon Dioxide Extinguishers. The principal advantage of CO_2 (carbon dioxide) extinguishers is that the agent does not leave a residue after use. This may be a significant factor where protection is needed for delicate and costly electronic equipment. Other typical applications are food preparation areas, laboratories, and printing or duplicating areas. Since the agent is discharged in the form of a gas/snow cloud, it has a relatively short range of 3 to 8 ft (1 to 2.4 m). This type of extinguisher is not recommended for outdoor use where windy conditions prevail, or for indoor use in locations that are subject to strong air currents because the agent may rapidly dissipate and prevent extinguishment. The concentration needed for fire extinguishment reduces the amount of oxygen (air) needed for life safety when the discharge is in a confined area (space).

C-3-5 Halogenated Agent Extinguishers.

C-3-5.1 The bromochlorodifluoromethane (Halon 1211) extinguisher has an agent that is similar to carbon dioxide in that it is suitable for cold weather installation and leaves no residue. Some larger models of Halon 1211 extinguishers are listed for use on Class A as well as Class B and C fires. Compared to carbon dioxide on a weight-of-agent basis, bromochlorodifluoromethane (Halon 1211) is at least twice as effective. When discharged, the agent is in the combined form of a gas/mist with about twice the range of carbon dioxide. To some extent, windy conditions or strong air currents may make extinguishment difficult by causing the rapid dispersal of the agent.

C-3.5.2 In general, bromotrifluoromethane (Halon 1301) extinguishers have features and characteristics similar to carbon dioxide extinguishers in that they are suitable for cold weather installation and leave no residue. Halon 1301 extinguishers are listed for Class B and C fires. Compared to carbon dioxide on a weight-of-agent basis, bromotrifluoromethane (Halon 1301) is at least as effective. When discharged, the agent is in the combined form of a gas/mist. To some extent, windy conditions or strong air currents may make extinguishment difficult by causing the rapid dispersal of the agent.

C-3-5.3 Extinguishers containing a mixture of Halon 1211 and Halon 1301 share properties of the other halogenated agent-type extinguishers such as leaving no residue after use and minimizing thermal shock. The mixture of halogenated agents will discharge in the form of a gas/mist with the ratio of gas to mist increasing with higher ratios of Halon 1301 to Halon 1211. The discharge range will likewise be affected by the ratio of Halon 1301 to Halon 1211 with the range decreasing as the proportion of Halon 1301 increases. To some extent, windy conditions or strong air currents may make extinguishments difficult by causing the rapid dispersal of the agent.

C-3-6 Dry Chemical Extinguishers.

C-3-6.1 Due to the different designs and the various types of dry chemical agents, choosing the most suitable dry chemical extinguisher requires careful evaluation. Hand portable models have a discharge stream that ranges from 10 to 30 ft (3 to 9 m) depending on extinguisher size. Compared with carbon dioxide or halogenated agent extinguishers, they will also perform better under windy conditions.

C-3-6.2 Dry chemical extinguishers are available in two basic styles: stored pressure and cartridge-operated. The stored pressure (rechargeable) type is the most widely used and is best suited where infrequent use is anticipated and where skilled personnel with professional recharge equipment are available. The cartridge-operated type has the advantage of being quickly refilled in remote locations without the need for special equipment. Some dry chemical models can be equipped with long-range (high velocity) nozzles or applicators that are beneficial in applying the agent under certain special fire fighting conditions.

C-3-6.3 There are five available types of dry chemical agent, and each has certain advantages and disadvantages. These advantages and disadvantages should be reviewed by potential users.

C-3-6.4 The potassium and urea-potassium base bicarbonate agents are selected in preference to sodium bicarbonate, principally because of their greater fire extinguishing capabilities. If corrosion is not a factor, potassium chloride can also be included in this group. However, the potassium chloride base agent is corrosive and does not have any specific extinguishing characteristics that are superior to the potassium bicarbonate base agents.

C-3-6.5 The ammonium phosphate base agent (multipurpose) is the only dry chemical agent that is suitable for Class A protection. In addition to Class B and Class C protection, the residues of multipurpose dry chemical when left in contact with metal surfaces can cause corrosion.

C-3-6.6 Where dry chemical extinguishers are utilized for Class C protection, it is important to consider that the residue of potassium chloride is more corrosive than other dry chemicals and that a multipurpose base agent will be more difficult to remove because it first softens when in contact with hot surfaces and then hardens when it cools. Any of the other dry chemical agents, depending on protection requirements, may prove to be a more practical choice for Class C protection.

C-3-7 Wheeled Extinguishers.

C-3-7.1 The selection of any type of wheeled extinguisher is generally associated with a recognized need to provide additional protection for special hazards or large, extra-hazard areas. Where wheeled extinguishers are to be installed, consideration should be given to mobility within the area in which it will be used.

C-3-7.2 For outdoor locations, models with rubber tires or wide-rim wheels will be easier to transport. For indoor locations, doorways, aisles, and corridors need to be wide enough to permit the ready passage of the extinguisher. Because of the magnitude of the fire it will generally be used on, this type of extinguisher should be reserved for use by operators who have actually used the equipment, who have received special instructions on the use of the equipment, or who have used the equipment in live fire training.

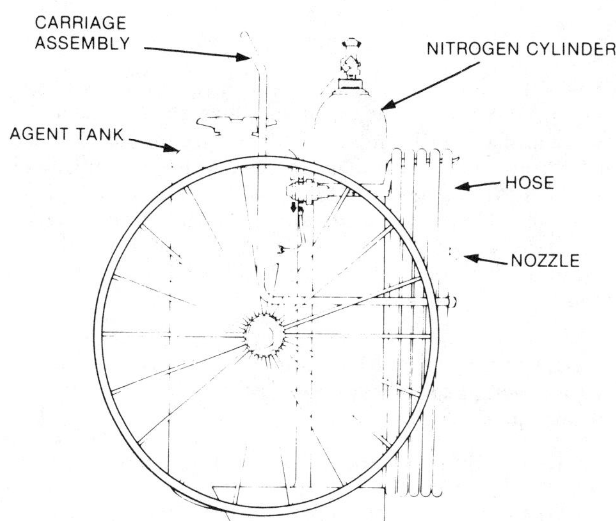

Figure C-3-7(a) Cylinder-Operated Dry Chemical Type.

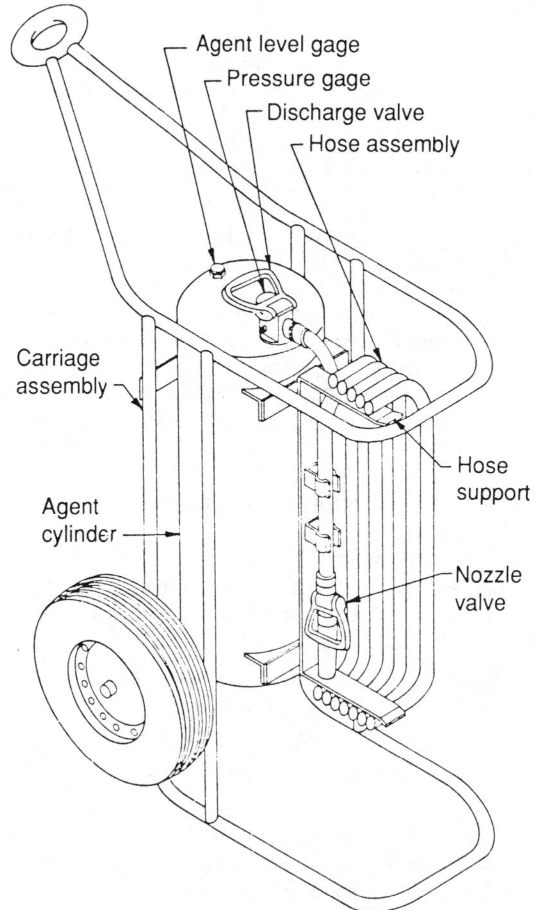

Figure C-3-7(b) Stored Pressure Halon 1211 Type.

Appendix D Operation and Use

This Appendix is not a part of the requirements of this NFPA document, but is included for information purposes only.

D-1 General.

D-1-1 Persons who are expected to use an extinguisher should be made familiar with all information contained in the manufacturer's nameplate(s) and the instruction manual. Proper operation of a fire extinguisher requires the operator to execute several basic steps in a certain sequence. The extinguisher designer, the approval agencies, the installer, and the protection planner can influence significantly the ease and likelihood of these steps being accomplished properly.

D-1-1.1 Fire extinguishers will be used by one or more of the following groups of people, listed in descending order of their probable skill:

Fire departments (municipal or industrial) (trained).

Employees (business or industrial) (trained or untrained).

Private owners (home, car, boat, etc.) (untrained).

The general public (untrained).

D-1-1.2 Where employees have not been trained, operation of extinguishers may be seriously delayed, the extinguishing material may be wasted due to poor application techniques, and more extinguishers may have to be used, or the fire may not be extinguished.

D-1-1.3 It is not enough for the protection planner to determine the hazard of a location or area within a building and then select a proper type and size of fire extinguisher to fit the hazard. He must take into account any problems of getting the extinguisher into action, and the difficulty of properly applying the extinguishing agent. He should also consider who is the most likely to use the extinguisher, and estimate the degree of skill or training that person may have.

D-1-2 Methods of Extinguisher Operation.

D-1-2.1 The methods of operation of extinguishers are most conveniently arranged by grouping extinguishers according to their expelling means. Six methods are in common use.

(a) *Self-generating.* Actuation causes gases that provide expellant energy to be generated.

(b) *Self-expelling.* The agents have sufficient vapor pressure at normal operating temperatures to expel themselves.

(c) *Gas Cartridge or Cylinder.* Expellant gas is confined in a separate pressure vessel until an operator releases it to pressurize the extinguisher shell.

(d) *Stored Pressure.* The extinguishing material and expellant gas are kept in a single container.

(e) *Mechanically Pumped.* The operator provides expelling energy by means of a pump, and the vessel containing the agent is not pressurized.

(f) *Hand Propelled.* The material is applied with scoop, pail, or bucket.

D-1-2.2 Several different extinguishing materials are handled by each of these expelling means. Table D-1-2 lists the agent and expelling means combinations that are or have been in use.

Table D-1-2
Extinguisher Operation and Methods of Expelling

	Expelling Methods					
Extinguishing Materials	**Self-Generating**	**Self-Expelling**	**Cartridge or N_2 Cylinder**	**Stored Pressure**	**Pump**	**Hand**
Water and Antifreeze			x	x	x	x
Soda-Acid (Water)	x					
Wetting Agent			x	x		
Foam	x					
AFFF and FFFP			x	x		
Loaded Stream			x	x		
Multipurpose Dry Chemical			x	x		
Carbon dioxide		x				
Dry Chemical			x	x		
Halogenated Agents		x		x		
Dry Powder (Metal Fires)			x	x		x

D-2 Basic Steps to Operate Extinguishers.

D-2.1 The basic steps necessary to put an extinguisher into operation are:

Recognition as an extinguisher.

Selection and suitability of an extinguisher.

Transport of an extinguisher to the fire.

Actuation of the extinguisher.

Application of the extinguishing agent to the fire.

D-2-2 Recognition as an Extinguisher. The following will help a person to recognize an extinguisher.

D-2-2.1 Approval agencies require permanent marking on the front of fire extinguishers indicating their purpose, content, and usage.

D-2-2.2 Additional markings, not a part of the device, may be needed to indicate the location of an extinguisher. These should preferably be standardized throughout the property so all extinguishers are easily "spotted." These markings may be in the form of electric lights, placards, mounting boards, overhead signs, color panels or stripes, or cabinets. They may be distinctively colored by painting or reflective taping.

D-2-2.3 If extinguishers are located along the normal exit paths from an area, personnel are more inclined to take them and return to the site of a fire.

D-2-3 Transport of an Extinguisher to the Fire.

D-2-3.1 An extinguisher should be mounted and located so it can be easily removed in a fire emergency and brought to the site of the fire as quickly as possible. It should be readily accessible without need for moving or climbing over stock, materials, or equipment.

D-2-3.2 Portability is affected by the weight of the extinguisher, travel distance to a possible fire, the need for carrying the unit up or down stairs or ladders, the need for using gloves, the overall congestion of the premises, and the physical ability of the operators.

D-2-3.3 In the case of wheeled extinguishers, the width of aisles and doorways and the nature of the flooring and outside grounds over which the extinguisher must be moved should be taken into account.

D-2-4 Actuation of the Extinguisher.

D-2-4.1 Once the extinguisher has been transported to the fire site, it must be placed into operation without delay. Employees should be familiar with any steps needed to actuate any extinguisher. Here is where previous training is most valuable, since there is little time to stop and read operating instructions on the nameplate.

D-2-4.2 To actuate an extinguisher, one or more of the following steps are required:

POSITION FOR OPERATION — The intended position for operation is usually marked on the extinguisher. When the position of operation is obvious (such as when one hand holds the extinguisher and the other hand holds the nozzle), this information may be omitted.

REMOVAL OF RESTRAINING OR LOCKING DEVICES — Many extinguishers have an operation safeguard or locking device that prevents accidental actuation. The most common device is a lock pin or ring pin which must be withdrawn before operation.

Other forms of such devices are clips, cams, levers, or hose or nozzle restrainers. Most tamper indicators (such as wire and lead seals) will break with removal of the restraining device.

On some extinguishers the restraining device is arranged to disengage when the unit is normally handled. No separate motion is required. This type of restraining device is especially suited for use by private owners and the general public since prior instruction is seldom possible.

START OF DISCHARGE — This requires one or more of several actions such as inverting, bumping, turning or squeezing a valve handle or lever, pushing a lever, or pumping. These may cause a gas to be generated, release a gas from a separate container, open a normally closed valve, or create a pressure within the container.

AGENT APPLICATION — This act involves direction of the stream of extinguishing agent onto the fire. Nameplate information has advisory notes regarding the application of the agent to different types of fires. Specific application techniques are described in Section D-3.

D-2-5 Expellant Gas/Pressure.

D-2-5.1 Many of the extinguishers described in this appendix are of the stored pressure or cartridge-operated type. Since the operating characteristics of these two types are similar, regardless of agent used, they are described generally in the following paragraphs.

D-2-5.2 In stored pressure models, the expellant gas and extinguishing agent are stored in a single chamber, and the discharge is controlled by a shutoff valve or nozzle.

D-2-5.3 In cartridge-operated models, the expellant gas is stored in a separate cartridge or may be stored in an expellant-gas cylinder (wheeled models), located within or adjacent to the shell containing the extinguishing agent. These extinguishers are actuated by releasing the expellant gas that expels the agent. In most models, the discharge may subsequently be controlled by a shutoff valve or nozzle.

D-3 Application Techniques.

D-3-1 General.

D-3-1.1 Many fire extinguishers deliver their entire quantity of extinguishing material in 8 to 10 seconds (although some take 30 seconds or longer to discharge). The agent must be applied correctly at the outset since there is seldom time for experimentation. In many extinguishers the discharge may be started or stopped by a valve. When using some extinguishers on flammable liquid fires, the fire may flare up momentarily when the agent is initially applied.

D-3-1.2 The best technique of applying the extinguisher discharge on a fire varies with the type of extinguishing material.

D-4 Extinguisher Characteristics.

D-4-1 Water Types. This includes water, antifreeze, soda-acid, wetting agent, and loaded stream extinguishers. These extinguishers are intended primarily for use on Class A fires. The stream should be directed at the base of the flames, and after extinguishment of flames, directed generally at smoldering or glowing surfaces. Application should begin as close as possible to the fire. Deep-seated fires should be thoroughly soaked and may need to be "broken apart" to effect complete extinguishment.

D-4-1.1 Stored Pressure Water. Hand extinguishers of this type are usually available in $2^1/_2$-gal (9.46-L) capacity with a fire extinguishment rating of 2-A. Since the agent used is fresh water, this extinguisher cannot be installed in areas subjected to temperatures below 40°F (4°C). This same type of extinguisher is also manufactured in an antifreeze model charged with an approved solution that will afford protection to temperatures as low as −40°F (−40°C). The extinguisher weighs about 30 lb (14 kg) and has a solid stream range of approximately 35 to 40 ft (10.7 to 12.2 m) horizontally. This extinguisher can be operated intermittently, but under continuous use, it has a discharge time of about 55 seconds. The operating lever is held in a locked position to prevent accidental discharge while being carried. Most manufacturers use a ring pin that must be pulled out before the operating lever can be depressed. To do this, it is best to set the extinguisher on the ground and, while loosely holding the combination handle in one hand, pull out the ring pin (or release a small latch) with the other hand. Then, grasp the hose and nozzle in one hand and squeeze the discharge lever with the other.

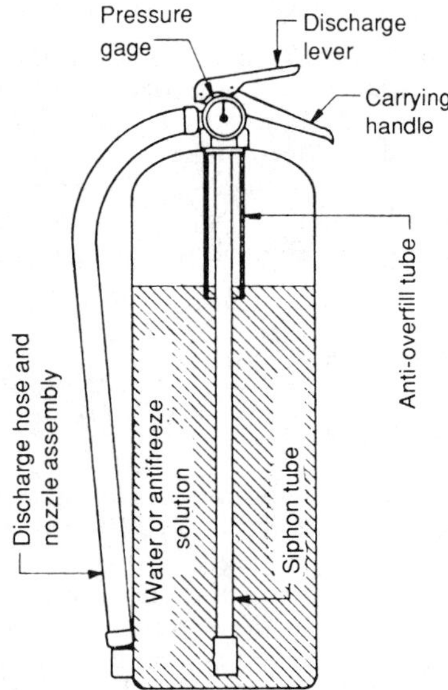

Figure D-4-1.1 Stored Pressure Water Extinguisher.

D-4-1.2 Loaded Stream. Hand extinguishers of this type have been made with liquid capacities from 1 to 2½ gal (3.8 to 9.46 L) having fire extinguishing ratings of 1-A:1-B to 3-A:1-B. Due to limited effectiveness, these extinguishers are no longer recognized (listed) for use on Class B fires. Wheeled extinguishers have been made having liquid capacities of 17 and 33 gal (64 and 125 L) [trade designations 20 and 40 gal (76 and 151 L)] having fire extinguishment ratings of 10-A to 20-A. The chemical used is a solution of an alkali-metal-salt that will not freeze at temperatures as low as −40°F (−40°C).

D-4-1.3 Pump Tank. Extinguishers of this type have been made in 1½- to 5-gal (5.7- to 19-L) capacities with fire extinguishment ratings of 1-A to 4-A. The most common type is 2½ gal (9.46 L), rated at 2-A. These extinguishers have cylindrical metal containers and carrying handles. In some models, the carrying handle is combined with the pump handle, and in others it is attached to the container. A built-in, hand-operated vertical piston pump, to which a short rubber hose and nozzle are attached, provides the means for discharging the water onto the fire. The pump is of the double-acting type, which discharges a stream of water on both the up and down strokes. When brought to a fire, the pump tank is placed on the ground and, to steady the unit, the operator puts one foot on a small extension bracket attached to the base. To force the water through the hose, the operator then pumps the handle up and down. To work around the fire, or to move closer to the fire as the flames subside, the operator must stop pumping and carry the extinguisher to a new location. The force, range, and duration of the stream are dependent, to a degree, on the operator.

They can be filled with either plain water or antifreeze charges recommended by the extinguisher manufacturer. Common salt or other freezing depressants may corrode the extinguisher, damage the pump assembly, or affect the fire extinguishing capability. Copper shell and nonmetallic models do not corrode as easily as steel and are recommended for use in conjunction with antifreeze agents.

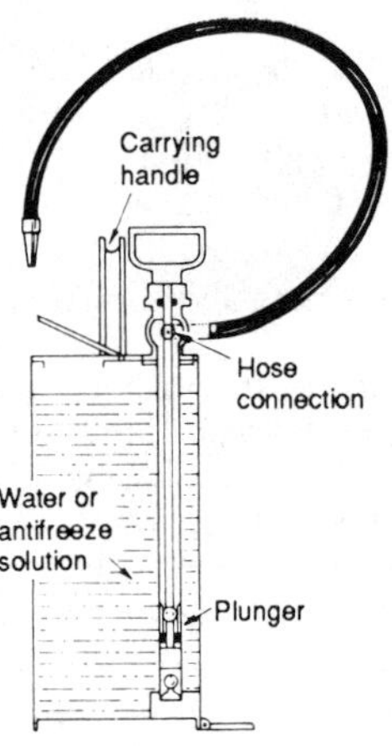

Figure D-4-1.3 Pump Tank Fire Extinguisher.

D-4-1.4 Back Pack. This type of pump extinguisher is primarily used for fighting outdoor fires in brush and wildlands. The tank has a capacity of 5 gal (19 L) and weighs approximately 50 lb (23 kg) when full. Although it is listed by UL, it does not have a designated rating. Generally, plain water is used as the extinguishant. However, antifreeze agents, wetting agents, or other special water-base agents may be used. The tank may be constructed of fiberglass, stainless steel, galvanized steel, or brass. As its name implies, it is designed to be carried on the operator's back. The back pack extinguisher has a large opening for fast refilling as well as a tight fitting filter to prevent foreign material from entering and clogging the pump. This design permits convenient refilling from nearby water sources such as ponds, lakes, or streams. The most commonly used model has a trombone-type, double-acting piston pump connected to the tank by a short length of rubber hose. Discharge occurs when the operator, holding the pump in both hands, moves the piston section back and forth. Models have also been manufactured with compression pumps mounted on the right side of the tank. Expellant pressure is built up with about 10 strokes of the handle, and then maintained by continual slow, easy pumping strokes. Discharge is controlled with the left hand by means of a lever-operated shutoff nozzle attached to the end of the hose.

D-4-1.5 Soda-Acid. This extinguisher was most commonly manufactured in the 2½-gal (9.46-L) size, weighing approximately 30 lb (14 kg) fully charged, with a listed rating of 2-A. Some models were manufactured in the hand

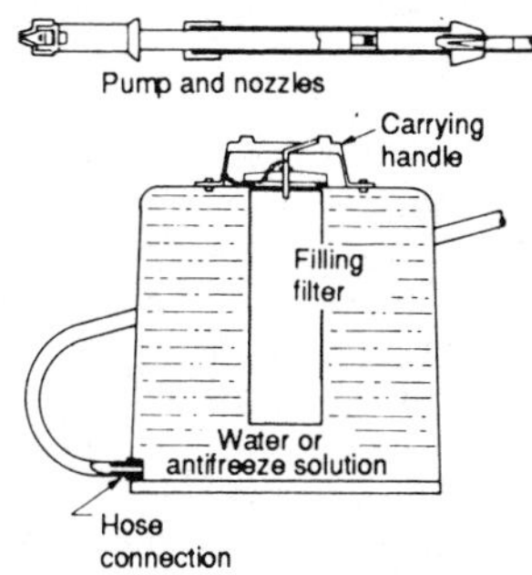

Figure D-4-1.4 Pump Tank Back Pack Fire Extinguisher.

portable sizes of $1^1/_4$ and $1^1/_2$ gal (4.7 and 5.7 L) and in wheeled models with liquid capacities of 17 and 33 gal (64 and 125 L) [trade designations, 20 and 40 gal (76 and 151 L)] having fire extinguishment ratings of 10-A and 20-A. These extinguishers are now considered obsolete since their manufacture in the United States was discontinued in 1969; they should be replaced with currently available models. As its name implies, this extinguisher contains two chemicals: sodium bicarbonate and sulfuric acid. To operate, the extinguisher must be inverted, which causes intermixing of these products and produces a chemical reaction that forms carbon dioxide gas to expell the extinguishing agent, consisting principally of water in a neutral state. Once the extinguisher is inverted, it is carried by a handle recessed in the bottom of the shell. The discharge time for this extinguisher is approximately 55 seconds. This extinguisher cannot be installed in locations that are subjected to temperatures below 40°F (4°C). Antifreeze additives cannot be added for protection.

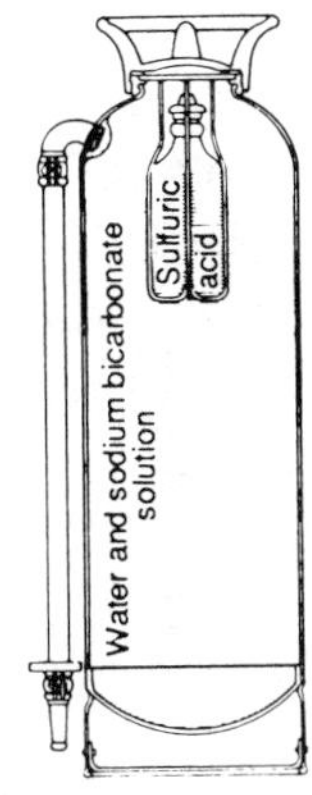

Figure D-4-1.5 Soda-Acid Fire Extinguisher.

D-4-1.6 Cartridge-Operated Water. This type of extinguisher closely resembles the soda-acid extinguisher. In general, their operational and fire fighting characteristics are very similar. The most common model manufactured was the $2^1/_2$-gal (9.46-L) size, which had a listed rating of 2-A. Some $1^1/_4$-gal (4.7-L) models rated at A-1 were also manufactured. This extinguisher is now considered obsolete since its manufacture in the United States was discontinued in 1969; they should be replaced with currently available models. The extinguisher shell contains water, with a small cylinder of carbon dioxide gas that provides the expellant force to discharge the water. Models were also manufactured that employed an approved antifreeze agent in place of water. For locations subjected to temperatures below 40°F (4°C), the antifreeze model should be used. To operate, invert the extinguisher and bump it gently on the ground (hard surface) while holding the recessed bottom handle. In some models, bumping may not be necessary because the weight of the gas cartridge causes it to fall against a puncturing device. Sometimes this model must be lightly bumped on the ground in order to break the seal.

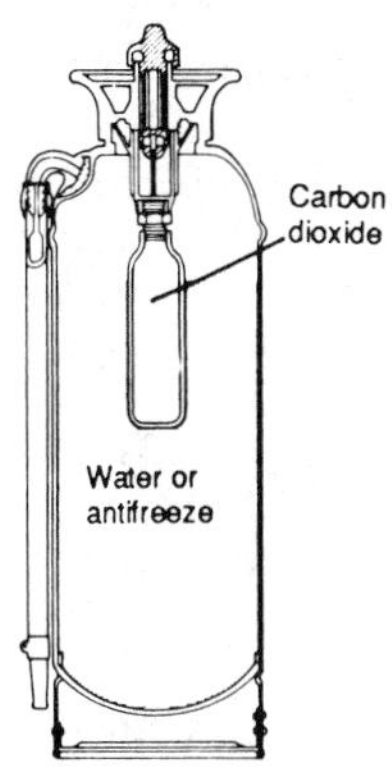

Figure D-4-1.6 Cartridge-Operated Water Fire Extinguisher.

D-4-1.7 Wetting Agent. Extinguishers of this type are usually available in hand portable models of $1^1/_2$ gal (5.7 L) and in wheeled models having liquid capacities of 45 and 60 gal (170 and 228 L). These extinguishers have ratings of 2-A, 30-A, and 40-A, respectively. The extinguishing agent used is a surface-active material added to water in proper quantities to materially reduce the surface tension of the water and thus increase penetrating and spreading characteristics (*see NFPA 18, Standard on Wetting Agents*). Hand portable models are of the stored pressure design and are operated essentially the same as other stored pressure types. Wheeled extinguishers are operated by a separate carbon dioxide cartridge containing the expellant gas which, when released, expels the agent through the hose nozzle. These extinguishers must be protected from exposure to temperatures below 40°F (4°C).

D-4-1.8 Fire Pails, Drums with Pails, and Bucket Tanks.

D-4-1.8.1 Small water supplies applied with fire pails are of limited fire-extinguishing value. The following combinations are considered as possessing two units of extinguishing potential (2-A) for Class A fires.

(a) Five 12-qt (11-L) water-filled standard fire pails.

(b) Six 10-qt (9-L) water-filled standard fire pails.

(c) Drum, cask, or barrel of approximately 55-gal (208-L) capacity, with at least three standard fire pails attached.

(d) Bucket tanks of 25- to 55-gal (95- to 208-L) capacity, with standard fire pails [either (a) or (b) above] immersed therein.

D-4-1.8.2 Standard fire pails are made of galvanized steel of at least No. 24 USS gage, with rounded bottoms welded in place or otherwise suitably reinforced, furnished with stamped ears welded in place, and with strong wire bail and loose-fitting metal covers to exclude debris and retard evaporation.

D-4-1.8.3 Casks, drums, or barrels should preferably be of metal of No. 24 USS gage thickness or better, and should have covers. Fire pails may be hung on sides of the containers or immersed therein. Pails, casks, drums, or bucket tanks should be painted bright red with the word "FIRE" stenciled in large letters on their outside with black or other contrasting colored paint. If antifreezing solution is used, the surfaces of pails, drums, or bucket tanks should be coated with red lead or oil, followed by a coat of asphalt-base paint. Casks should be heavily coated with pitch.

D-4-1.8.4 When located where continued temperatures below 40°F (4°C) may be encountered, containers should be filled with an antifreeze solution consisting of 75 to 80 percent calcium chloride (free from magnesium chloride) dissolved in water. Table D-4-1.8.4 shows approximately the temperature at which the solutions will freeze.

Table D-4-1.8.4

To Make 10 Gallons Antifreeze Solutions*

Approx. Freezing Temp. °F	°C	Water gal	L	Calcium Chloride lb	kg	Specific Gravity	Degrees Baume
10	−12	9	34	20	9.1	1.139	17.7
0	−18	8 1/2	32	25	11	1.175	21.6
−10	−23	8	30	29 1/2	13	1.205	24.7
−20	−29	8	30	33 1/2	15	1.228	26.9
−30	−34	8	30	36 1/2	17	1.246	28.6
−40	−40	8	30	40	18	1.263	30.2

*This solution should not be used in extinguishers. Only solutions supplied by the manufacturers should be used in stored pressure and cartridge-operated water extinguishers and in pump tank extinguishers where an antifreeze solution is desired.

D-4-2 Foam Types. These extinguishers are intended for use on Class A and Class B fires. On flammable liquid fires of appreciable depth, best results are obtained when the discharge from the extinguisher is played against the inside of the back wall of the vat or tank just above the burning surface to permit the natural spread of the foam back over the burning liquid. If this cannot be done, the operator should stand far enough away from the fire to allow the foam to fall lightly upon the burning surface — the stream should not be directed into the burning liquid. Where possible, the operator should walk around the fire while directing the stream to get maximum coverage during the discharge period. For fires in ordinary combustible materials, the foam may be used to coat the burning surface directly. For flammable-liquid spill fires, the foam may be flowed over a burning surface by bouncing it off the floor just in front of the burning area. Foam is not effective on flammable liquids and gases escaping under pressure. The type of foam produced is not suitable for fires involving ethers, alcohols, esters, acetone, lacquer thinners, carbon disulfide, and other flammable liquids that either break down or penetrate the foam blanket.

D-4-2.1 AFFF and FFFP. Extinguishers of this type are usually available in hand portable models of 2 1/2-gal (9.46-L) liquid solution or solid charge types and in wheeled models having a liquid capacity of 33 gal (125 L). These extinguishers have ratings of 3-A:20-B, 3-A:40-B, and 20-A:160-B, respectively. The extinguishing agent is a solution of film forming surfactant in water that forms mechanical foam when discharged through an aspirating nozzle. On Class A fires, the agent acts as both a coolant and penetrant to reduce temperatures to below the ignition level. On Class B fires, the agent acts as a barrier to exclude air or oxygen from the fuel surface.

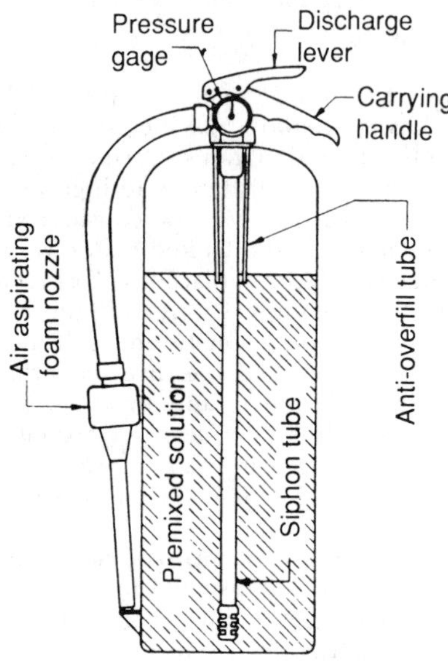

Figure D-4-2.1(a) Stored Pressure AFFF or FFFP Liquid Extinguisher.

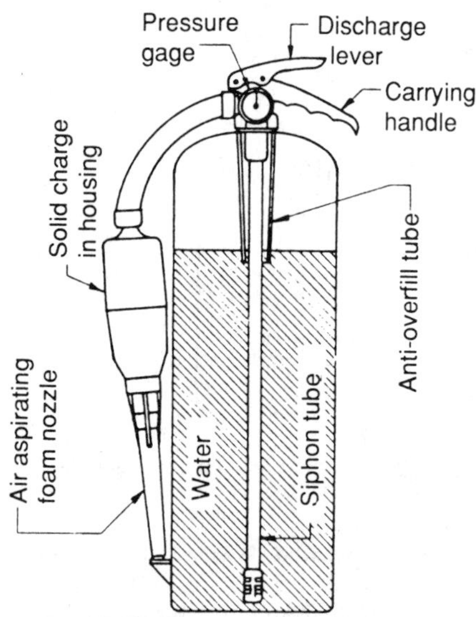

Figure D-4-2.1(b) Stored Pressure AFFF Solid Charge Extinguisher.

Grades of these agents are also suitable for the protection of water-soluble flammable liquids (polar solvents) such as alcohols, acetone, esters, ketones, etc. The suitability of these extinguishers for polar solvent fires must be specifically referenced on the nameplate.

Specific information of the properties and limitations of AFFF and FFFP are contained in NFPA 11, *Standard for Low Expansion Foam and Combined Agent Systems*.

The hand portable models closely resemble stored pressure water extinguishers except for the special types of nozzles. They are available in two basic types. One type contains a liquid solution of AFFF or FFFP in the tank [*see Figure D-4-2.1(a)*]. The other type contains plain water in the tank and a replaceable charge of solid AFFF in a compartment of the nozzle [*see Figure D-4-2.1(b)*]. Both types are placed into operation by the same procedure used for water extinguishers. Wheeled types are operated by a separate nitrogen cylinder containing the expellant gas which, when released, pressurizes the agent container. The discharge is controlled by a special aspirating shut-off type of nozzle at the end of the hose assembly. These types of extinguishers can be used only in locations not subject to freezing conditions unless special measures are provided to prevent agent from freezing as recommended by the manufacturer.

D-4-2.2 Foam (Chemical). Foam extinguishers are similar in external appearance to soda-acid extinguishers. They were most commonly manufactured in the $2^1/_2$-gal (9.46-L) size, weighing about 30 lb (14 kg) fully charged. A typical listed rating for the $2^1/_2$-gal (9.46-L) size was 2-A:4-B. Other sizes manufactured included $1^1/_4$-gal (4.7-L) and $1^1/_2$-gal (5.7-L) hand portables and wheeled models with liquid capacities of 17 and 33 gal (64 and 125 L) [trade designations, 20 and 40 gal (76 and 151 L)] having fire extinguishment ratings from 10-A:12-B to 20-A:40-B. These extinguishers are now considered obsolete since their manufacture in the United States was discontinued in 1969; they should be replaced with currently available models. The extinguisher has an inner chamber or cylinder, fitted with a loose stopple, which contains an aluminum sulfate solution. The main extinguisher shell is filled with a solution of sodium bicarbonate and a foam-stabilizing agent. To operate, the extinguisher must be inverted, which allows the intermixing of these agents. Carbon dioxide gas is formed to expell the liquid foam extinguishant, which expands at the ratio of about one to eight. These extinguishers cannot be installed in locations that are subjected to temperatures below 40°F (4°C).

Antifreeze additives cannot be used to provide protection against freezing temperatures. The general method of placing this extinguisher into operation is the same as for the soda-acid extinguisher.

D-4-3 Carbon Dioxide Type. This type of extinguisher is primarily intended for use on Class B and Class C fires. They have a limited range and are affected by draft and wind; thus, initial application must start reasonably close to the fire. On all fires, the discharge should be directed at the base of the flames. The discharge should be applied to the burning surface even after the flames are extinguished, to allow added time for cooling and to prevent possible reflash. The most commonly used method of agent application on contained flammable liquid fires is to start at the near edge and direct the discharge in a slow, side-to-side sweeping motion, gradually progressing toward the back of the fire. The other method is called overhead application. The discharge horn is directed in a dagger or downward position (at an angle of about 45 degrees) toward the center of the burning area. Generally, the horn is not moved, as in the other method, because the discharge stream enters the fire from above and spreads out in all directions over burning surface. For spill fires, the side-to-side sweeping motion may give better results.

On fires involving electrical equipment, discharge should be directed at the source of the flames. It is important to de-energize the equipment as soon as possible, to eliminate the potential of reignition.

The carbon dioxide agent extinguishes by diluting the surrounding atmosphere with an inert gas, so that oxygen levels are kept below the percentage required for combustion. When this type of extinguisher is used in an unventilated space, such as a small room, closet, or other confined area, prolonged occupancy of that space can result in the loss of consciousness due to oxygen deficiency.

Hand extinguishers of this type are usually available at capacities from $2^1/_2$ to 20 lb (1.1 to 9.1 kg) having fire extinguishment ratings from 1- to 10-B:C. Wheeled carbon dioxide extinguishers are usually available in capacities from 50 to 100 lb (23 to 45 kg) having fire extinguishment ratings from 10- to 20-B:C. The carbon dioxide is retained under its own pressure in a fluid condition at room temperature. The agent is self-expelling and is discharged by operation of a valve that causes the carbon dioxide to be expelled through a horn in its vapor and solid phase. To operate, the extinguisher is held in an upright position, the locking ring pin is pulled, and the operating lever is squeezed. On the smaller 2- to 5-lb (0.91- to 2.3-kg) models, the discharge horn is attached to the valve assembly by a metal tube/swing joint connector. The smaller models are designed to be operated with one hand. On the larger hand portables, the discharge horn is attached to several feet of flexible hose. These extinguishers require a "two hand" operation. The minimum discharge time for hand portables varies from 8 to 30 seconds, depending upon size. The maximum range of the discharge stream is from 3 to 8 ft (1 to 2.4 m).

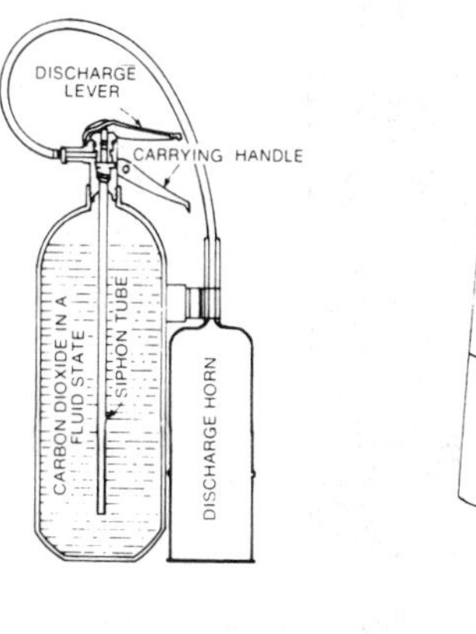

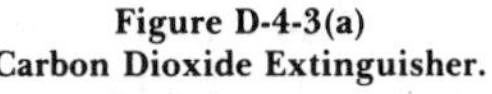

Figure D-4-3(a)
Carbon Dioxide Extinguisher.

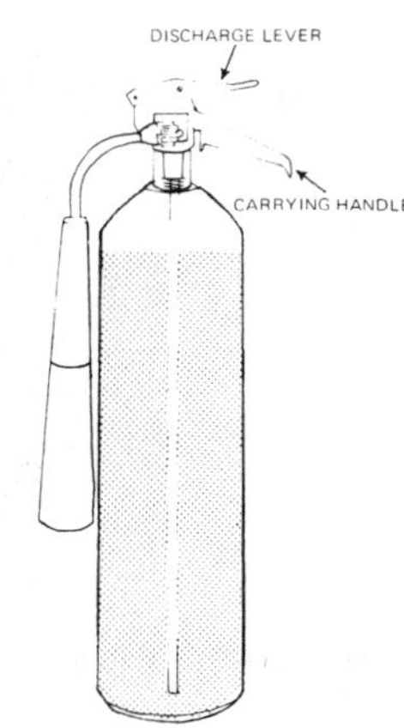

Figure D-4-3(b)
Carbon Dioxide Extinguisher.

D-4-4 Halogenated Agent Types. Halon 1211- or Halon 1211/1301-type extinguishers are rated for use on Class B and Class C fires. Larger models also are rated for Class A fires. Halon 1301 extinguishers are intended primarily for use on Class B and Class C fires. On flammable liquid fires, best results are obtained when the discharge from the extinguisher is employed to sweep the flame off the burning surface, applying the discharge first at the near edge of the fire and gradually progressing toward the back of the fire by moving the discharge nozzle slowly from side to side. In using extinguishers of this type in unventilated places, such as small rooms, closets, or confined spaces, operators and other persons should avoid breathing the extinguishing agent or the gases produced by thermal decomposition.

D-4-4.1 Bromochlorodifluoromethane — Halon 1211. Stored pressure extinguishers of this type are available in capacities from 2 to 22 lb (0.91 to 10 kg) having fire extinguishment ratings from 2-B:C to 4-A:80-B:C and wheeled models with a capacity of 150 lb (68 kg) and a fire extinguishment rating of 30-A:160-B:C. Although the agent is retained under pressure in a liquid state and is self-expelling, a booster charge of nitrogen is added to ensure proper operation. Upon actuation, the vapor pressure causes the agent to expand so that the discharge stream consists of a mixture of liquid droplets and vapor. The smaller sizes have a horizontal stream range of 9 to 15 ft (2.7 to 4.6 m) that is not affected by wind as much as carbon dioxide or Halon 1301. Deep-seated Class A fires may need to be broken apart to effect complete extinguishment. On Class B fires, the discharge is applied in a side-to-side motion gradually progressing toward the back of the fire. The extinguisher should be discharged initially from not closer than 8 ft (2.4 m) to prevent splashing when applied to depths of flammable liquid.

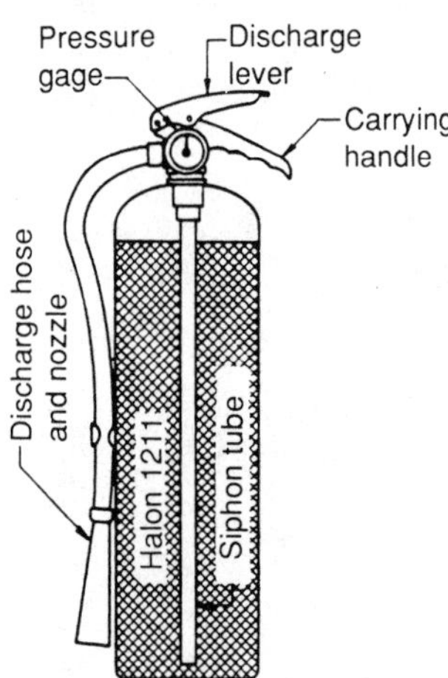

Figure D-4-4.1 Halon 1211 Stored Pressure Fire Extinguisher.

D-4-4.2 Bromotrifluoromethane — Halon 1301. Stored pressure extinguishers of this type may be available in capacities of 3 and 4 lb (1.36 and 1.81 kg) having fire extinguishment ratings from 2-B:C to 5-B:C. The design, operation characteristics, and fire fighting techniques are similar to that of carbon dioxide extinguishers. The discharge varies from 13 to 15 seconds depending on size, with a stream range of 4 to 6 ft (1.2 to 1.8 m). Upon activation, the vapor pressure causes the agent to expand so that the discharge stream consists of a mixture of liquid droplets and vapor. Although the agent has a high vapor pressure and is self-expelling, a booster charge of nitrogen is added to improve operation.

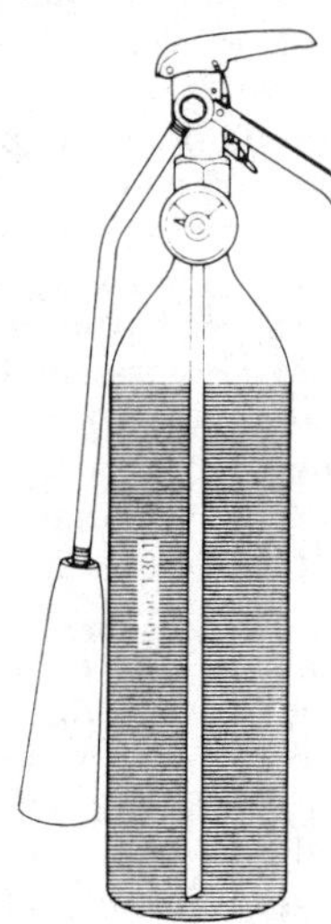

Figure D-4-4.2 Halon 1301 Stored Pressure Fire Extinguisher.

D-4-4.3 Bromochlorodifluoromethane / Bromotrifluoromethane Mixtures — Halon 1211 and Halon 1301. Extinguishers of this type are available in capacities from 1.0 to 20 lb (0.45 to 9 kg) having fire extinguishment ratings from 1-B:C to 4-A:80-B:C. The halogenated agent mixture is retained under pressure in a liquid state and is self-expelling. Some of these extinguishers are superpressurized with nitrogen. Upon actuation, the vapor pressure causes the agent to expand so that the discharge stream is in the form of a gas/mist. These extinguishers have a horizontal stream range of 3 to 18 ft (0.9 to 5.5 m) that is not affected by wind as much as carbon dioxide or Halon 1301. Deep-seated Class A fires may need to be broken apart to effect complete extinguishment. On Class B fires, the discharge is applied in a side-to-side motion progressing toward the back of the fire.

D-4-5 Dry Chemical Types. Dry chemical extinguishers (sodium bicarbonate, potassium bicarbonate, potassium bicarbonate urea base, bicarbonate urea base, or potassium chloride base) are intended primarily for use on Class B and Class C fires. Dry chemical extinguishers (multipurpose ammonium phosphate base) are intended for use on Class A, Class B, and Class C fires. There are two methods whereby a dry chemical agent can be discharged from an extinguisher shell depending on the basic design of the extinguisher. They are the cartridge/cylinder-operated method and the stored pressure method. Regardless of extinguisher design, the method of agent application is basically the same. Stored pressure extinguishers are available in capacities from 1 to 30 lb (0.5 to 14 kg) for hand extinguishers and 125 to 250 lb (57 to 113.5 kg) for wheeled extinguishers. Cartridge/cylinder-operated extinguishers are available in capacities from 4 to 30 lb (1.8 to

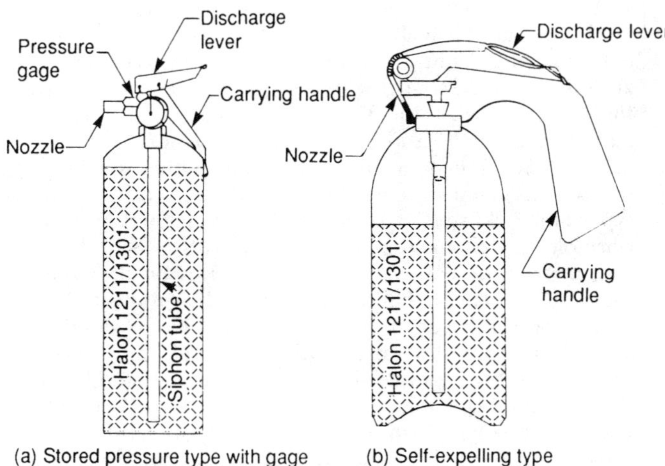

Figure D-4-4.3.

14 kg) for hand extinguishers and 45 to 350 lb (20 to 159 kg) for wheeled extinguishers.

Dry chemical extinguishers are also available in nonrechargeable, nonrefillable types that contain the agent and expellant gas in a single, nonreuseable, factory-filled container. Most dry chemical extinguishers having ratings of 20-B and less will discharge their contents in 8 to 20 seconds. Extinguishers with higher ratings may take as long as 30 seconds. Therefore, since there is little time for experimentation, it is important that the operator be prepared to correctly apply the agent at the outset. All dry chemical extinguishers can be carried and operated simultaneously, and can be discharged intermittently. The discharge stream has a horizontal range of 5 to 30 ft (1.5 to 9.2 m), depending on extinguisher size. When used on outdoor fires, maximum effectiveness can be achieved when the direction of the wind is on the back of the operator.

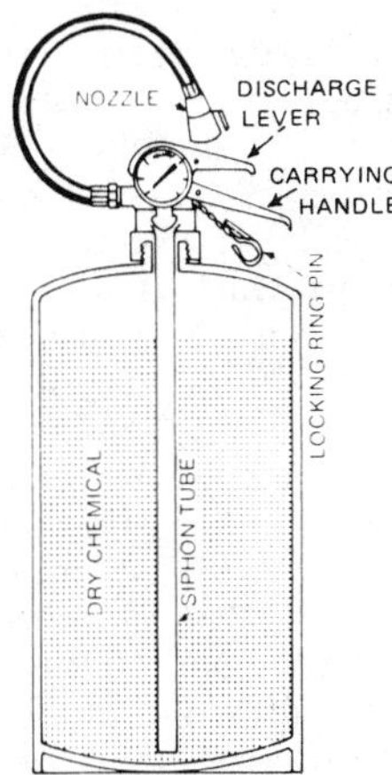

Figure D-4-5(a) Stored Pressure Dry Chemical Extinguisher.

Special long-range nozzles are available where potential fire fighting conditions may require greater distance. These nozzles are also useful on pressurized gas or liquid fires, or where strong winds prevail. All dry chemical

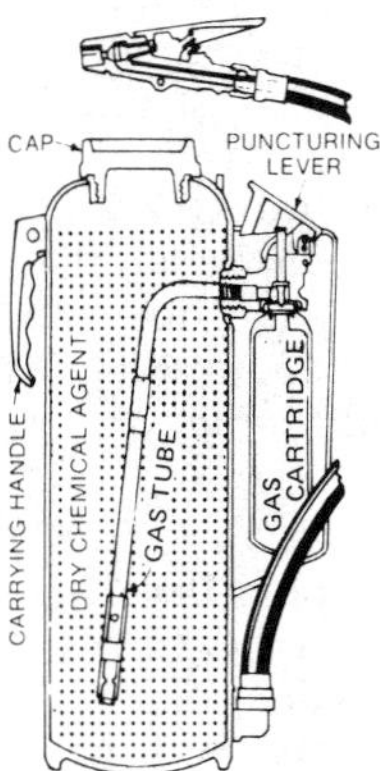

Figure D-4-5(b) Cartridge-Operated Dry Chemical Extinguisher.

agents can be used at the same time that water (straight stream or fog) is being applied. The use of dry chemical extinguishers on wet energized electrical equipment (such as rain-soaked utility poles, high-voltage switch gear, and transformers) may aggravate electrical leakage problems. The dry chemical, in combination with moisture, provides an electrical path that can reduce the effectiveness of insulation protection. The removal of all traces of dry chemical from such equipment after extinguishment is recommended.

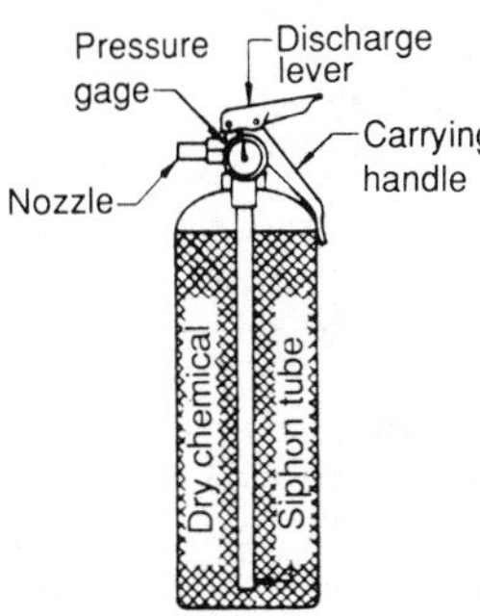

Figure D-4-5(c) Stored Pressure Dry Chemical with Fixed Nozzle.

D-4-5.1 Ordinary Dry Chemical Extinguishers (Class B and Class C Fires). Hand extinguishers of this type are available with fire extinguishing ratings of 1-B:C to 160-B:C and wheeled models having fire extinguishment ratings from 80-B:C to 640-B:C. The fire extinguishing agent used is a specially treated material in a finely divided form. Types of agents available are: sodium bicarbonate base, potassium bicarbonate base, potassium chloride base, or potassium bicarbonate urea base. Some formulations of these agents are specially treated to be relatively compatible for use with air foam (mechanical foam). For use on flammable liquid fires, the stream should be directed at the base of the flame. Best results are generally obtained by attacking the near edge of the fire and progressing toward the back of the fire by moving the nozzle rapidly with a side-to-side sweeping motion. Care must also be taken not to direct the initial discharge directly at the burning surface at close range [less than 5 to 8 ft (1.5 to 2.4 m)] because the high velocity of the stream may cause splashing and/or scattering of the burning material. Although not listed for use on Class A fires, ordinary dry chemical may be used to rapidly knock down the flames. Once the flames are extinguished, the operator can kick or poke apart the fire debris. This will assist and hasten the natural cooling of the burning embers. Hot spots or small areas that reignite can be controlled with short intermittent bursts of agent. Water should then be applied to extinguish burning embers or deep-seated hot spots. It is recommended that this method of extinguishment be attempted only if the operator has had training and previous experience in this technique.

D-4-5.2 Multipurpose Dry Chemical Extinguishers (Class A, Class B, and Class C Fires). Extinguishers of this type contain an ammonium phosphate base agent. Hand extinguishers are available with fire extinguishment ratings of 1-to 20-A and 10- to 120-B:C and wheeled models with fire extinguishment ratings of 20- to 40-A and 60- to 320-B:C. Multipurpose agents are used in exactly the same manner as ordinary dry chemical agents on Class B fires. For use on Class A fires, the multipurpose agent has the additional characteristic of softening and sticking when in contact with hot surfaces. In this way, it can adhere to burning materials and form a coating that will smother and isolate the fuel from air. When applying the agent, it is important to try to coat all burning areas in order to eliminate or minimize the number of small embers that may be a potential source of reignition. The agent itself has little cooling effect and because of its surface coating characteristic it cannot penetrate below the burning surface. For this reason, extinguishment of deep-seated fires may not be accomplished unless the agent is discharged below the surface or the material is broken apart and spread out.

D-4-6 Dry Powder Types. These extinguishers and agents are intended for use on Class D fires and specific metals, following special techniques and manufacturer's recommendations for use. The extinguishing agent may be applied from an extinguisher or by scoop and shovel. The technique of applying the agent to the fire may vary with the type and form of the agent and combustible metal. The application of the agent should be of sufficient depth to adequately cover the fire area and provide a smothering blanket. Additional applications may be necessary to cover any hot spots that may develop. The material should be left undisturbed until the mass has cooled before disposal is attempted. Care should be taken to avoid scattering the burning metal. Fires in finely divided combustible metal or combustible metal alloy scrap that is moist, wet with water or water-soluble machine lubricants, or on water-wetted surfaces, is likely to burn rapidly and violently. They may even be of an explosive nature. They can develop so much heat that they cannot be approached closely enough to permit proper application of the extinguishing medium. Where the burning metal is on a combustible surface, the fire should be covered with dry powder, then a 1- or 2-in. (2.5- or 5.1-cm) layer of powder spread out nearby and the burning metal shoveled into this layer with more dry powder added as needed.

D-4-6.1 Dry Powder Extinguisher. Dry powder extinguishers are available in a hand portable, 30-lb (14-kg) cartridge-operated model and 150-lb (68-kg) and 350-lb (159-kg) cylinder-operated wheeled models. Stored pressure dry powder extinguishers with an extension wand applicator are available in a 30-lb (14-kg) model. The extinguishing agent is composed of sodium chloride, with additives to render it free flowing in order to cause it to form a crust over the fire. A thermoplastic material is added to bind the sodium chloride particles into a solid mass when applied on burning metals. Other specialized dry powder agents are available for use in fighting specific types of metal fires. With the nozzle fully opened, the hand portable models have a range of 6 to 8 ft (1.8 to 2.4 m). The method of agent application depends on the type of metal, the quantity that is burning, and its physical form. In the case of a very hot fire, initial discharge should be started at maximum range with the nozzle fully opened. Once control is established, the nozzle valve should be partially closed to produce a soft heavy flow so that complete coverage can be accomplished safely at close range. The nozzle is designed so that the operator can throttle or reduce the rate and force of the agent discharge. Since combustible metal fires can produce complex and difficult fire fighting conditions, it is advisable to get specific details on equipment use from the manufacturer.

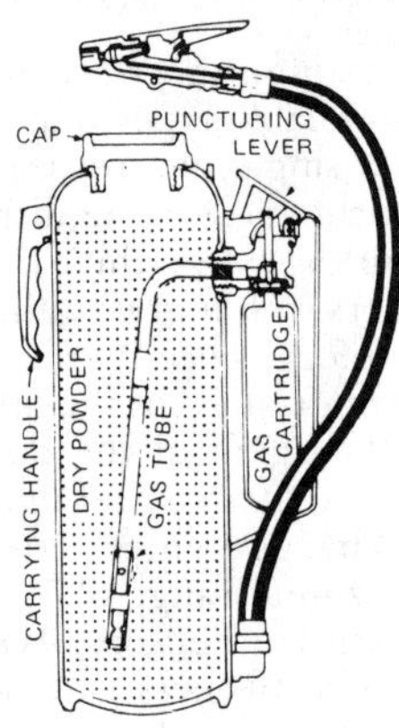

Figure D-4-6.1(a) Cartridge-Operated Dry Powder Extinguisher.

D-4-6.2 Bulk Dry Powder Agent. In bulk form, dry powder extinguishing agents are available in 40- and 50-lb (18- and 23-kg) pails and 350-lb (159-kg) drums. In addition to the sodium chloride base agent, a dry powder material called G-1 is also available. This material consists of graded, granular graphite to which is added compounds containing phosphorus to improve its fire extinguishing effectiveness. Whereas the sodium chloride can be used in a dry powder extinguisher or applied by shovel or hand scoop, the G-1 agent must be applied to the fire by hand. When G-1 is applied to a metal fire, the heat of the fire causes the phosphorus compounds to generate vapors that blanket the fire and prevent air from reaching the burning metal. The graphite, being a good conductor of heat, cools the metal to below the ignition point. Each extinguishing agent is listed for use on the specific combustible metal fires for which it has been found acceptable, as determined by individual investigations. Such information, together with the recommended method of application limitations, is given on the agent container. It is important to note that dry powder extinguishing agents should not be confused with dry chemical extinguishing agents. (*See D-4-5.*)

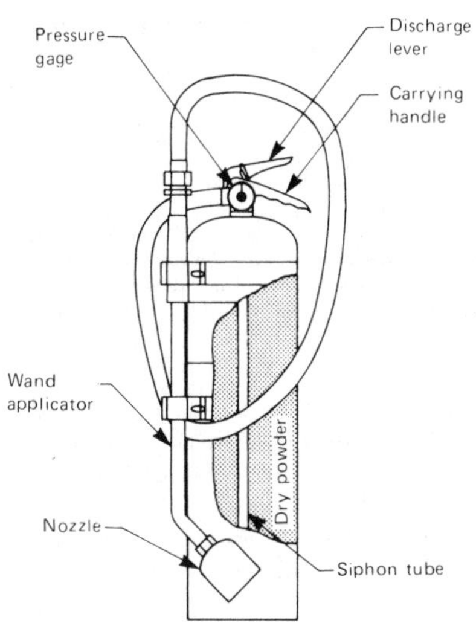

Figure D-4-6.1(b) Stored Pressure Dry Powder Extinguisher with Wand Applicator.

Appendix E Distribution

This Appendix is not a part of the requirements of this NFPA document, but is included for information purposes only.

E-1 Distribution of Fire Extinguishers.

E-1-1 Portable fire extinguishers are most effectively utilized when they are readily available in sufficient number and with adequate extinguishing capacity for use by persons familiar with their operation.

E-1-2 In fire emergencies where extinguishers are relied upon, someone usually has to "travel" from the fire in order to obtain the device, and then return to the fire before beginning extinguishing operations. This connotes "time," with the number of seconds or minutes governed mainly by the "travel distance" involved in securing the extinguisher and placing it in operation.

E-1-3 Sometimes extinguishers are purposely kept nearby (as in welding operations); however, recognizing that a fire outbreak usually cannot be prejudged as to location, extinguishers are more often strategically positioned throughout areas.

E-1-4 Travel distance is not merely a simple circle radius matter, but is the actual distance the user of the extinguisher will need to walk. Consequently, travel distance will be affected by partitions, location of doorways, aisles, piles of stored materials, machinery, etc.

E-2 Arrangement in a Building. The actual placement of fire extinguishers can best be accomplished through a physical survey of the area to be protected. In general, locations should be selected that will:

(a) provide uniform distribution

(b) provide easy accessibility

(c) be relatively free from blocking by storage and equipment, or both

(d) be near normal paths of travel

(e) be near entrance and exit doors

(f) be free from the potential of physical damage

(g) be readily visible, and

(h) be installed on a floor-by-floor basis.

E-3 Class A Extinguisher Distribution.

E-3-1 Table 3-2.1 is a guideline for determining the minimum number and rating of extinguishers for Class A fire protection needs in accordance with the occupancy hazard. In certain instances, through a fire protection analysis of specific areas, process hazards, or building configurations, extinguishers with higher ratings may be required. This does not mean, however, that the recommended maximum travel distances can be exceeded.

E-3-2 Where the floor area of a building is less than 3,000 sq ft (279 m^2), at least one extinguisher of the minimum size recommended should be provided.

The first step in calculating Class A fire extinguisher needs is to determine the proper class of occupancy (light, ordinary, or extra hazard). Depending on the rating of the extinguisher (1-A to 40-A), the maximum area that it will protect can be determined. For example, each 2$^1/_2$-gal (9.46-L) stored pressure water extinguisher (rated 2-A) will protect an area of 3,000 sq ft (279 m^2) in an ordinary hazard occupancy. The requirements in Table 3-2.1 also specify that the travel distance (actual walking distance) from any point to the nearest extinguisher shall not exceed 75 ft (22.7 m). It is necessary to select extinguishers that fulfill both the distribution and travel distance requirements for a particular occupancy classification.

E-3-3 If a building floor area was unobstructed and circular in shape with a radius of 75 ft (22.7 m), it would be possible to place one extinguisher at the center without exceeding the 75 ft (22.7 m) travel distance. In that case an area of 17,700 sq ft (1644 m^2) could be assigned to one extinguisher of adequate A rating, e.g., Light Hazard 6-A, Ordinary Hazard 20-A (no 12-A extinguisher ratings), Extra Hazard 20-A (no 18-A extinguisher ratings). However, as buildings are usually rectangular in shape, the largest square area that can be formed with no point more than 75 ft (22.7 m) from the center is 11,250 sq ft (1045 m^2), which is the area of a square [106 × 106 ft (32 × 32 m)] inscribed within a 75-ft (22.7-m) radius circle. (*See Figure E-3-3.*)

E-3-4 The following examples of distribution illustrate the number and placement of extinguishers according to occupancy type and rating. The sample building is 150 × 450 ft (46 × 137 m), giving a floor area of 67,500 sq ft (6271 m^2). Although several different ways of placing extinguishers are given, a number of other locations could have been used with comparable results.

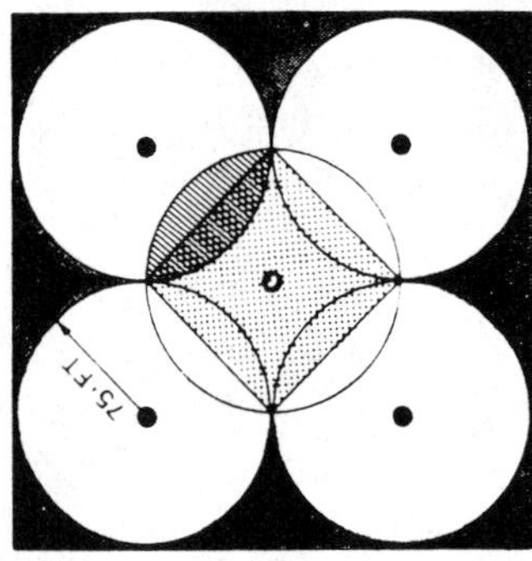

Figure E-3-3 The Dotted Squares Show the Maximum Area [11,250 sq ft (1045 m²)] that an Extinguisher Can Protect within the Limits of the 75-ft (22.7-m) Radius.

The area that can be protected by one extinguisher with a given A rating is shown in Table E-3-4. These values are determined by multiplying the maximum floor area per unit of A shown in Table 3-2.1 by the various A ratings, until a value of 11,250 sq ft (1045 m²) is exceeded.

Table E-3-4

Maximum Area To Be Protected per Extinguisher, Sq Ft

Class A Rating Shown on Extinguisher	Light (Low) Hazard Occupancy	Ordinary (Moderate) Hazard Occupancy	Extra (High) Hazard Occupancy
1A	—	—	—
2A	6,000	3,000	—
3A	9,000	4,500	—
4A	11,250	6,000	4,000
6A	11,250	9,000	6,000
10A	11,250	11,250	10,000
20A	11,250	11,250	11,250
30A	11,250	11,250	11,250
40A	11,250	11,250	11,250

For SI Units: 1 sq ft = 0.0929 m².
Note: 11,250 is considered a practical limit.

E-3-5 The first example demonstrates placement at the maximum protection area limits [11,250 sq ft (1045 m²)] allowed in Table 3-2.1 for each class of occupancy. Installing extinguishers with higher ratings will not affect distribution or placement.

Example 1:

$$\frac{67{,}500}{11{,}250} = 6$$
- 4-A Extinguishers for Light Hazard Occupancy
- 10-A Extinguishers for Ordinary Hazard Occupancy
- 20-A Extinguishers for Extra Hazard Occupancy

E-3-6 This placement, along outside walls, would not be acceptable because the travel distance rule is clearly violated (*see Figure E-3-6*). Relocation and/or additional extinguishers are needed.

E-3-7 Examples 2 and 3 are for extinguishers having ratings which correspond to protection areas of 6,000 and 3,000 sq ft (557 and 279 m²), respectively. The examples

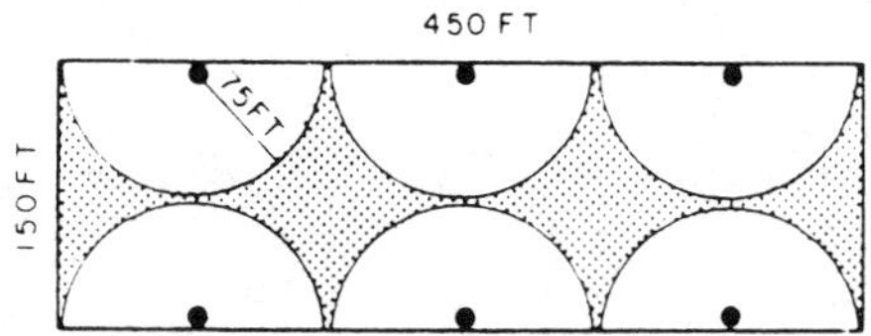

Figure E-3-6 A Diagrammatic Representation of Extinguishers Located along the Outside Walls of a 450- by 150-ft (137- by 46-m) Building. (The dots represent extinguishers.) The shaded areas indicate "voids" which are farther than 75 ft (227 m) to the nearest extinguisher.

show only one of many ways these extinguishers could be placed. As the number of lower rated extinguishers increases, meeting the travel distance requirement generally becomes less of a problem. Similar examples could be worked out for protection areas of 4,000 and 4,500 sq ft (372 and 418 m²), as required by Table 3-2.1.

Example 2:

$$\frac{67{,}500}{6{,}000} = 12$$
- 2-A Extinguishers for Light Hazard Occupancy
- 4-A Extinguishers for Ordinary Hazard Occupancy
- 6-A Extinguishers for Extra Hazard Occupancy

E-3-8 Extinguishers could be mounted on exterior walls or, as shown in Figure E-3-8(a), on building columns or interior walls, and conform to both distribution and travel distance rules.

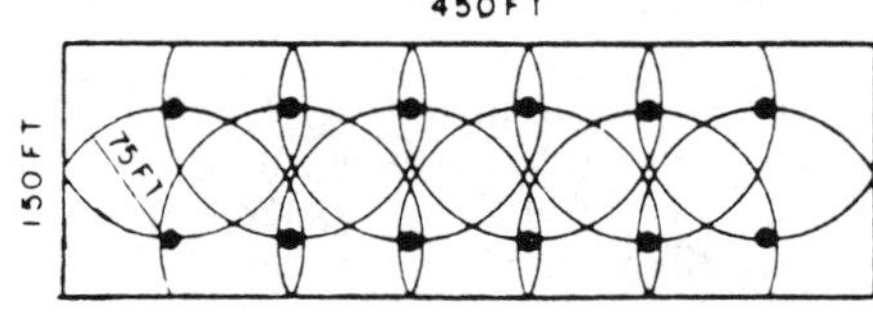

Figure E-3-8(a) Requirements for Both Travel Distance and Extinguisher Distribution Are Met in This Configuration Representing 12 Extinguishers Mounted on Building Columns or Interior Walls.

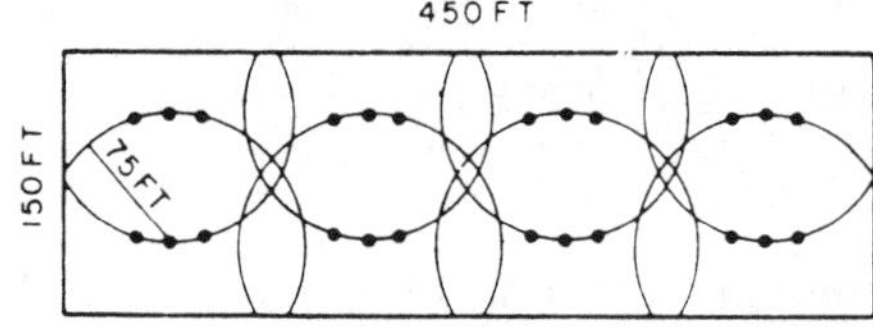

Figure E-3-8(b) Extinguishers Grouped Together.

Example 3:

$$\frac{67{,}500}{3{,}000} = 24$$
- 1-A Extinguishers for Light Hazard Occupancy
- 2-A Extinguishers for Ordinary Hazard Occupancy
- 3-A Extinguishers for Extra Hazard Occupancy

E-3-9 This arrangement, illustrated in Figure E-3-8(b), shows extinguishers grouped together on building columns or interior walls in a manner that still conforms to distribution and travel distance rules.

E-4 Class B Extinguisher Distribution.

E-4-1 Normal Class B fire hazards fall into two quite different general categories regarding requirements for extinguishers. One condition is where the fire does not involve flammable liquids in appreciable depth, such as spilled fuel on an open surface, a fire involving vapors issuing from a container or piping system, or a running fire from a broken container.

E-4-2 The other condition is where the fire involves flammable liquids in appreciable depth [defined as a depth of liquid greater than $^1/_4$ in. (.63 cm)], such as fires involving open tanks of flammable liquids commonly found in industrial plants (dip tanks used for coating, finishing, treating, or similar processes).

E-4-3 In situations where flammable liquids are not in appreciable depth, extinguishers should be provided according to Table 3-3.1. Once the type of hazard is determined, the selected Class B extinguisher must have a rating equal to or greater than that specified, and be so located that the maximum travel distance is not exceeded.

E-4-4 The reason the basic maximum travel distance to Class B extinguishers is 50 ft (15.25 m) as opposed to 75 ft (22.7 m) for Class A extinguishers is that flammable liquid fires reach their maximum intensity almost immediately. It is imperative that the extinguisher be brought to the fire in a much shorter period of time than allowed for a slower developing Class A fire.

E-4-5 Even though Table 3-3.1 specifies maximum travel distances for Class B extinguisher placement, judgment should be exercised in actually establishing them. The extinguisher may be placed closer to the hazard it is protecting, up to a point where the extinguisher itself might be involved in the fire or access to it made difficult because of flame, heat, or smoke.

E-4-6 Where an entire room or area is judged to be a Class B hazard (such as an automobile repair garage), extinguishers should be placed at regular intervals so that the maximum walking distance from any point to the nearest extinguisher does not exceed the travel distances specified in Table 3-3.1.

For fires in flammable liquids of appreciable depth, a Class B fire extinguisher is provided on the basis of two numerical units of Class B extinguishing potential per sq ft (0.0929 m^2) of flammable liquid surface for the largest tank within the area. The travel distance requirements in Table 3-3.1 should also be used to locate extinguishers for spot hazard protection; however, the type of hazard and the availability of the extinguisher must be carefully evaluated.

E-4-7 One extinguisher can be installed to provide protection against several hazards, provided travel distances are not exceeded. Where hazards are scattered or widely separated and travel distances are exceeded, then individual protection should be installed according to the square foot rule.

E-4-8 When fixed Class B extinguishing systems are installed, the provision of portable fire extinguishers may be waived for that one hazard, but not for the structure, other special hazards, or the rest of the contents. Sometimes a burning tank can result in burning liquid spills outside the range of the fixed equipment, or the fire may originate adjacent to the tank rather than in its liquid content. Therefore, having portable extinguishers available is desirable, even though hazards of this type are protected with fixed extinguishing systems.

E-4-9 The selection of the proper type and size of Class B extinguishers for fires in pressurized fuels is made on the basis of the recommendations of the manufacturers of this specialized equipment available for that type of hazard. Special nozzle design and rates of agent application are necessary in order to be able to cope with hazards of this magnitude. Also, it is generally undesirable to attempt to extinguish pressurized fuel fires unless there is reasonable assurance that the source of fuel can be promptly shut off, thus avoiding a possible explosion. The travel distances for hand portable extinguishers should not exceed those specified in Table 3-3.1.

E-5 Class C Extinguisher Distribution.

E-5-1 To protect extinguisher operators in situations where live electrical equipment may be encountered, extinguishers with Class C ratings are required. Extinguishers so rated utilize a nonconducting extinguishant. Types of extinguishers possessing Class C ratings employ carbon dioxide, dry chemical, or halogenated agents.

E-5-2 When the power to a piece of electrical equipment is cut off, the fire changes character to that of a Class A, Class B, or a combined Class A and B fire depending on the nature of the burning electrical components and any material burning in the immediate vicinity.

E-5-3 De-energizing electrical equipment eliminates the possibility of shock hazards to the extinguisher operator should the operator accidentally come into physical contact with the equipment, or should the operator bring any conductive part of an extinguisher within arcing distance. De-energizing also eliminates fault currents from prolonging the fire or from being a source of reignition. Switches or circuit breakers that cut electric power to specific equipment can prevent hazardous side effects (e.g., plunging an entire multistory building into darkness or shutting down the essential electric power that supplies life support equipment, etc.). Often, fires involving an electrical component are relatively minor and, by a short application of a Class C extinguishant, can be effectively extinguished without disturbing electrical continuity.

E-5-4 The capacity of the extinguishers supplied for each major Class C hazard situation must be individually judged according to:

(a) the size of the electrical equipment,

(b) the configuration of the electrical equipment (particularly the enclosures of units) that influences agent distribution,

(c) the effective range of the extinguisher stream,

(d) the amount of Class A and B material involved.

Each of these factors influences the amount and type of agent needed, the desired rate of agent discharge, the associated duration of application, and the potential wastage factors.

E-5-5 For large installations of electrical apparatus where the power continuity is critical, fixed fire protection is desirable. At locations where such fixed systems are installed, it is practical to also provide Class C portable fire extinguisher units to handle quickly discovered fires: obviously, the number and size of these units can be reduced under such conditions.

E-6 Class D Extinguisher Distribution.

E-6-1 For Class D hazards, the availability of special portable extinguishers (or equivalent equipment to contain or extinguish any fire developing in a combustible metal) is particularly important. Extinguishing equipment for such fires should be located no more than 75 ft (22.7 m) from the hazard.

E-6-2 Use of the wrong extinguisher can instantly increase or spread the fire. Quantitatively, the amount of agent needed is normally measured by the surface area of combustible metals that might become involved, plus the potential severity of the fire as influenced by the shape and form of the metal. Because fires in magnesium fines are more difficult to extinguish than fires involving magnesium scrap, the amount of agent needed to handle fires in magnesium fines is correspondingly greater. Extinguishers labeled for Class D fires are not necessarily equally effective on all combustible metal fires. Often, extinguishers so labeled might be hazardous when used on some metal fires. Unless the effect of the extinguishing agent is known for the metal being considered, tests should be made with representative material.

E-7 Sample Problem. A light-occupancy office building needs to be protected by portable fire extinguishers. The floor area is 11,100 sq ft (1031 m^2) and of unusual design (*see floor plan that follows*).

The most common extinguisher selections would be $2^1/_2$-gal (9.46-L) stored water pressure models rated 2-A. According to Tables 3-2.1 and E-3-4, two extinguishers are needed (11,100 divided by 6,000 = 2). Travel distance requirements are 75-ft (22.7-m) maximum.

The two units are placed at Points 1 and 2, and a check is made on the travel distance requirement. Because of the area's unusual shape, it is found that the shaded areas exceed the 75-ft (22.7-m) distance. Two additional extinguishers (at Points 3 and 4) are needed. The additional extinguishers afford more flexibility in placement, and alternate locations are indicated. It is important to consider any partitions, walls, or other obstructions in determining the travel distance.

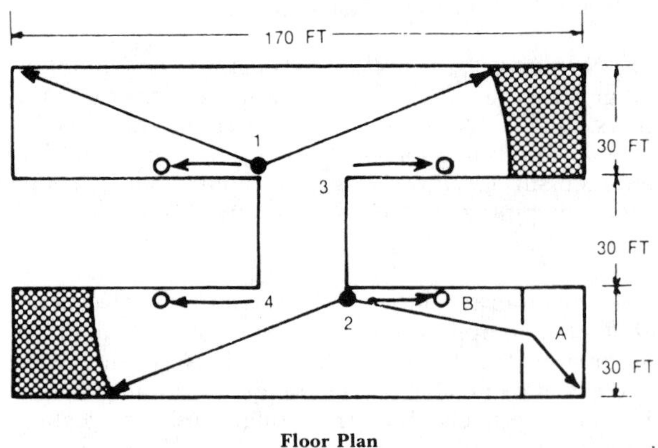

Floor Plan

As an additional item, consider that Area A contains a small printing and duplicating department that uses flammable liquids. This area is judged to be an ordinary Class B hazard. A 10-B:C or 20-B:C extinguisher should be specified to protect this area.

There are now two alternatives to be considered. First, a fifth extinguisher, either carbon dioxide or ordinary dry chemical, with a rating of 10-B:C or 20-B:C could be specified. Second, the water extinguisher at Point 2 could be replaced with a multipurpose dry chemical extinguisher that has a rating of at least 2-A:10-B:C. It should be located near Point B, keeping in mind the 75-ft (22.7-m) travel distance for the 2-A protection and the 30- or 50-ft (9.25- or 15.25-m) travel distance required for the Class B protection that this extinguisher provides.

Appendix F Selection of Extinguishers for Home Hazards

This Appendix is not a part of the requirements of this NFPA document, but is included for information purposes only.

F-1 General Information.

F-1-1 The information in this appendix is intended to be used as a guide for the selection and placement of fire extinguishers to be used in residences.

F-1-1.1 Fire hazards found in a home are Class A (ordinary combustible materials such as wood, drapes, upholstery, paper); Class B (flammable liquids such as grease in a frying pan, gasoline, paint, solvents, fuel oil); and Class C (live electrical equipment such as caused by faulty wiring, overheated fuse boxes, frayed electrical cords). Portable extinguishers offer the occupant a means for extinguishing small fires. They are also useful to knock down a fire should it occur in the evacuation route.

F-1-1.2 Before you select a fire extinguisher, identify and know the hazard on which it may be used and be certain the extinguisher is listed as approved by a recognized testing laboratory.

F-1-1.3 A fire extinguisher is basically a storage container for a specific chemical agent. It is a device intended to extinguish small fires in their early stages. The contents will be discharged under pressure, making it possible for the agent to reach the fire while the occupant remains at a relatively safe distance.

F-1-1.4 These extinguishers are manufactured either as refillable or disposable types.

F-1-1.5 An instruction manual is provided with each extinguisher, giving condensed instructions and cautions necessary to the installation, operation, inspection, and maintenance. The manual may be specific to the extinguisher involved, or it may cover many types. The manual refers to this standard as a source of detailed instructions.

F-1-2 Types of Extinguishers. The following table summarizes the characteristics of extinguishers and may be used as an aid in selecting extinguishers in accordance with this appendix.

F-1-3 Selection of Extinguishers for Home Hazards.

F-1-3.1 There are three ways to select a fire extinguisher:

(a) Select an extinguisher rated for Class A, B, and C fires.

(b) Select an extinguisher especially designed for a specific fire likely to occur in particular areas.

(c) Select a combination of the two.

F-1-3.2 The size and weight of the extinguishers are important, as in some instances an extinguisher may be used by people of limited physical ability. However, make sure the extinguishers selected are of sufficient size to cope with the anticipated hazard.

NOTE: Specific information on individual extinguisher characteristics that will aid in selection is contained in Appendix C. Details on operation and use are covered in Appendix D.

F-1-3.3 Halon 1211 extinguisher labels contain information as to the size of room or area that can be properly and safely protected. When using these extinguishers in unventilated places, such as small rooms, closets, motor vehicles, or other confined spaces, operators and others should avoid breathing the gases produced by the thermal decomposition of the agent.

F-1-4 Extinguisher Location and Mounting.

F-1-4.1 Fire extinguishers should be installed in plain view, in an accessible spot, near room exits that provide an escape route. Locate your extinguishers away from fire hazards (the stove, the paint shelf), because if a fire starts there your extinguisher would be out of reach.

F-1-4.2 Install extinguishers so that the top is not more than five feet above the floor. They must be easy to reach and remove, and placed where they will not be damaged.

F-1-5 Precautions. Get people out of the house and call the fire department, THEN use the extinguisher. In fighting a home fire:

(a) Keep near a door that can be used as an escape route.

(b) Stay low. Avoid breathing the heated smoke, vapors, or fumes as much as possible, as well as the extinguishing agents.

(c) If the fire gets too big, get out, closing the door behind you.

F-1-6 Owner's Inspection. Refer to extinguisher nameplate and owner's instruction manual.

Table F-1-2 Fire Extinguisher/Agent Characteristics

Suitable for Use on Type of Fire[1]	Agent Characteristics	Recommended Sizes	Horizontal Range	Discharge Time
DRY CHEMICAL	Sodium Bicarbonate or Potassium Bicarbonate or Potassium Chloride. Discharges a white or bluish cloud. Leaves residue that must be thoroughly cleaned up after extinguishment.	2 to 10 lb	6 to 10 ft	8 to 25 sec
MULTIPURPOSE DRY CHEMICAL	Basically Ammonium Phosphate. Discharges a yellow cloud. Leaves residue that must be thoroughly and quickly cleaned up after extinguishment.	$2^1/_2$ to 10 lb	5 to 10 ft	8 to 25 sec
FOAM AFFF	Basically water amd detergent. A chemical agent when discharged forms a foamy solution. Protect from freezing.	$2^1/_2$ gal	20 to 25 ft	50 sec
CARBON DIOXIDE	Basically an inert gas that discharges a cold white cloud. Leaves no residue.	5 to 10 lb	3 to 8 ft	8 to 12 sec
HALOGENATED AGENTS	Basically halogenated hydrocarbons. Discharges a white vapor. Leaves no residue. Non-freezing.	1 to 7 lb	4 to 15 ft	8 to 15 sec
HALOGENATED AGENTS	Basically halogenated hydrocarbons. Discharges a white vapor. Leaves no residue. Non-freezing.	9 to 14 lb	10 to 20 ft	10 to 15 sec
WATER[2]	Basically tap water. Discharges in a solid stream. Protect from freezing.	$2^1/_2$ gal	30 to 40 ft	1 minute

[1]For further explanation of symbols, see Section 1-3 and Table B-2-1.

[2]A garden hose connected to a suitable weather-protected hose connection is advisable for use in fighting Class A fires. This should not be considered as a replacement for extinguishers.

For SI Units: 1 ft = 0.305 m; 1 lb = 0.454 kg; 1 gal = 3.785 L.

Appendix G Referenced Publications

G-1 The following documents or portions thereof are referenced within this standard for informational purposes only and thus are not considered part of the requirements of this document. The edition indicated for each reference is the current edition as of the date of the NFPA issuance of this document.

G-1-1 NFPA Publications. National Fire Protection Association, 1 Batterymarch Park, P.O. Box 9101, Quincy, MA 02269-9101.

NFPA 11-1988, *Standard for Low Expansion Foam and Combined Agent Systems*

NFPA 18-1990, *Standard on Wetting Agents*

NFPA 49-1975, *Hazardous Chemicals Data*

NFPA 325M-1984, *Fire Hazard Properties of Flammable Liquids, Gases, and Volatile Solids*

NFPA *Fire Protection Handbook*, 1986 (16th Edition).

G-1-2 Other Publications.

G-1-2.1 UL Publication. Underwriters Laboratories Inc., 333 Pfingsten Rd., Northbrook, IL 60062.

Bulletin of Research No. 53, July 1963.

Index

-F-

-G-

-H-

-I-

-L-

UNIFORM FIRE CODE STANDARD 10-2
INSTALLATION, MAINTENANCE AND USE OF FIRE-PROTECTION SIGNALING SYSTEMS

See Sections 1007.2.12.2.3, 1007.3.1, 1007.3.3.5, 6313.3 and 6320.1, *Uniform Fire Code*

NOTE: This standard has been revised in its entirety.

This standard, with certain exceptions, is based on the National Fire Protection Association's National Fire Alarm Code, NFPA 72—1993.[1]

Part I of this standard contains exceptions to NFPA 72—1993.[1]

Part II of this standard contains NFPA 72—1993[1] reproduced in its entirety with permission of the publisher.

▭ vertically in the margin of Part II indicates there is a revision to the provisions within Part I.

Supplemental standards referenced by NFPA 72—1993[1] shall only be considered as guidelines subject to approval by the chief.

[1]The current edition is NFPA 72—1996.

Part I

SECTION 10.201 — AMENDMENTS

The National Fire Alarm Code, NFPA 72—1993, applies except as follows:

1. Sec. 1-3.2 is deleted.

2. Sec. 1-3.3 is revised by substituting the phrase "the Electrical Code" for the phrase "NFPA 70, *National Electrical Code®*."

3. Sec. 1-4 is revised by amending the definitions of "authority having jurisdiction," "combination system," "local supervisory system," "supervisory service" and "supervisory signal" as follows:

AUTHORITY HAVING JURISDICTION is the official responsible for the administration and enforcement of this standard.

COMBINATION SYSTEM is a local fire alarm system for fire alarm or supervisory service, or a household fire warning system whose components are allowed to be used in whole or in part in common with a nonfire signaling system, such as an emergency alarm system, a paging system, a burglar alarm system, or a process monitoring supervisory system, without degradation of or hazard to the fire alarm system.

LOCAL SUPERVISORY SYSTEM is a local system arranged to supervise the operative condition of automatic sprinkler systems or other systems for the protection of life and property against a fire hazard.

SUPERVISORY SERVICE is the service required to monitor the operative condition of fixed suppression systems or other systems for the protection of life and property.

SUPERVISORY SIGNAL is a signal indicating the need of action in connection with the supervision of fire suppression systems or equipment, or with the maintenance features of related systems.

The term "certificate of completion" is replaced with "fire alarm certificate of compliance" and defined as follows:

FIRE ALARM CERTIFICATE OF COMPLIANCE is the fire alarm certificate of compliance required by UFC Standard 10-2 that shall be permanently mounted in or adjacent to the protective signaling system control unit.

The definitions of "alarm signal," "annunciator," "approved," "labeled," and "listed" shall be as set forth in *Uniform Fire Code,* Volume 1.

The definitions of "combination fire alarm and guard's tour box," "delinquency signal," "guard signal," "guard's tour supervision," and "should" are deleted.

4. Sec. 1-5.2.2 is revised by substituting the phrase "the Electrical Code" for the phrase "NFPA 70, *National Electrical Code.*"

5. Sec. 1-5.2.3 is revised by deleting Exception Nos. 1 and 2 and adding a new exception as follows:

> **EXCEPTION:** When the primary power is supplied by a dedicated branch circuit of an emergency or standby power system in accordance with the Electric Code, a secondary power supply is not required.

Also:

The note to the exception is revised as follows:

NOTE to Exception: A trouble signal is not required where operating power is being supplied by a dedicated branch circuit of an emergency or standby power system, if it is capable of providing the hours of operation required by Section 1-5.2.5 and loss of primary power is otherwise indicated (e.g., by loss of building lighting).

6. Sec. 1-5.2.9.1 is revised by substituting the phrase "the Electrical Code" for the phrase "NFPA 70, *National Electrical Code,* Article 480."

7. Sec. 1-5.2.9.2 (a) is revised as follows:

(a) Adequate facilities shall be provided to automatically maintain the battery fully charged under all conditions of normal operation and, in addition, to recharge batteries within 48 hours after fully charged batteries have been subject to a single discharge cycle as specified in Section 1-5.2.5. Upon attaining a fully charged condition, the charge rate shall not be so excessive as to result in battery damage.

8. Sec. 1-5.2.10.1 is revised by amending the exception as follows:

1-5.2.10.1 An engine-driven generator shall be used only where a person specifically trained in its operation is on duty at all times.

> **EXCEPTION:** Where acceptable to the authority having jurisdiction and where the requirements of Section 1-5.2.5 (b) or (c) are met, a person specifically trained in the operation of a generator dedicated to the fire alarm system shall not be required to be on duty at all times.

9. Sec. 1-5.2.10.2 is revised by substituting the phrase "nationally recognized standards" for the phrase "NFPA 110, *Standard for Emergency and Standby Power Systems.*"

10. Sec. 1-5.2.10.4 is deleted.

11. Sec. 1-5.2.10.5 is revised as follows:

1-5.2.10.5 Sufficient fuel shall be available in storage for 6 months of testing plus the capacity specified in Section 1-5.2.5.

EXCEPTIONS: 1. If a reliable source of supply is available at any time on two-hour notice, sufficient fuel shall be in storage for 12 hours of operation at full load.

2. Fuel systems using natural or manufactured gas supplied through reliable utility mains shall not be required to have fuel storage tanks unless located in Seismic Zone 3 or 4 as defined in the Building Code.

12. Sec. 1-5.5.3 is revised by substituting the phrase "the Electrical Code" for the phrase "NFPA 70, *National Electrical Code,* Article 800."

13. Sec. 1-5.5.4 is revised as follows:

1-5.5.4 Wiring. The installation of wiring, cable and equipment shall be in accordance with the Electric Code.

14. Sec. 1-7.1.2 is revised as follows:

1-7.1.2 Before requesting final approval of the installation, where required by the authority having jurisdiction, the installing contractor shall furnish a written statement to the effect that the system has been installed in accordance with approved plans and tested in accordance with the manufacturer's specifications and the requirements of this standard.

15. Sec. 1-7.2 is revised by changing the title as follows:

1-7.2 Certificate of Compliance

16. Sec. 1-7.2.1 is revised by adding a sentence to the end of the paragraph as follows:

The fire alarm certificate of compliance required by UFC Standard 10-2 shall be permanently mounted in or adjacent to the protective signaling system control unit.

17. Figure 1-7.2.1 is revised by substituting the phrase "Certificate of Compliance" for the phrase "Certificate of Completion" in the title.

18. Figure 1-7.2.1, Item 5, is revised by deleting the following:

GUARD'S TOUR, Items (a), (b), (c) and the Note.

19. Sec. 2-2.1.1.3 is revised by substituting the phrase "nationally recognized standards" for the phrase "NFPA 13D, *Standard for the Installation of Sprinkler Systems in One- and Two-Family Dwellings and Mobile Homes,* or NFPA 13R, *Standard for the Installation of Sprinkler Systems in Residential Occupancies Up to and Including Four Stories in Height.*"

20. Sec. 2-2.2.2 is revised as follows:

2-2.2.2* Standard Signal. Alarm notification appliances used with a household fire warning system and single- and multiple-station smoke detectors shall produce the audible emergency evacuation signal described in ANSI Section 3.41, *Audible Emergency Evacuation Signals.*

21. Sec. 2-3.2.2 is revised by substituting the phrase "the Electrical Code" for the phrase "NFPA 70, *National Electrical Code,* Article 760."

22. Sec. 2-3.3.1 is revised by amending the first paragraph as follows:

2-3.3.1 Household fire warning equipment in existing structures shall be permitted to be powered by a battery, provided that the battery is monitored to ensure that the following conditions are met:

23. Sec. 2-4.2.1 is revised by substituting the phrase "nationally recognized standards" for the phrases "ANSI/UL 268, *Smoke Detectors for Fire Protective Signaling Systems,*" and "ANSI/UL 217, *Single and Multiple Station Smoke Detectors.*"

24. Sec. 2-5.3 is revised by substituting the phrase "the Electrical Code" for the phrase "NFPA 70, *National Electrical Code,* Article 760."

25. Sec. 3-2.4, Exception No. 5 to (b), is revised by substituting the phrase "the Building Code and UBC Standard 9-1" for the phrase "NFPA 13, *Standard for the Installation of Sprinkler Systems.*"

26. Sec. 3-3 is revised by deleting Item (h).

27. Sec. 3-4.2, Exception No. 3, is revised by substituting the phrase "the Building Code and UBC Standard 9-1" for the phrase "NFPA 13, *Standard for the Installation of Sprinkler Systems.*"

28. Table 3-5.1 is revised by deleting Item E, Number 3, "Guard's Tour."

Also:

Item E, Number 4, is revised as follows:

4. Process, Security, and Other Devices in Combination with 1 and 2 Above.

Also:

Item E, Number 5, is revised as follows:

5. Process, Security, and Other Devices Not Combined with 1 and 2 Above.

29. Sec. 3-7.2 (a) is revised as follows:

3-7.2 Distinctive Evacuation Signal.

(a)* Section 1-5.4.7 requires that fire alarm signals be distinctive in sound from other signals and that this sound not be used for any other purpose. To meet this requirement, the fire alarm signal used to notify building occupants of the need to evacuate (leave the building) shall be ANSI Section 3.41, *Audible Emergency Evacuation Signal.*

30. Sec. 3-8.9.3 is revised by substituting the phrase "nationally recognized standards" for the phrase "NFPA standards."

31. Sec. 3-8.10 is revised by substituting the phrase "nationally recognized standards" for the phrase "NFPA 20, *Standard for the Installation of Centrifugal Fire Pumps.*"

32. Sec. 3-8.12 is deleted.

33. Sec. 3-8.13 is deleted.

34. Sec. 3-8.15.4 is amended by revising the first paragraph as follows:

3-8.15.4* For each group of elevators within a building, two elevator control circuits shall be terminated at the designated elevator controller within the group's elevator machine rooms. The operation of the elevators shall be in accordance with nationally recognized standards. The smoke detectors shall be connected to the two elevator control circuits as follows:

35. Sec. 3-9.3.3 is revised by substituting the phrase "nationally recognized standards" for the phrase "NFPA standards."

36. Sec. 3-10.2 is revised by substituting the phrase "nationally recognized standards" for the phrase "NFPA standards."

37. Sec. 3-11.1 is revised by substituting the phrase "the Electrical Code" for the phrase "NFPA 70, *National Electrical Code,* Article 760."

38. Sec. 3-12.3.2 is revised by substituting the phrase "the Mechanical Code" for the phrase "NFPA 90A, *Standard for the Installation of Air Conditioning and Ventilating Systems.*"

39. Sec. 3-12.3.3 is revised by substituting the phrase "the Mechanical Code" for the phrase "NFPA 90A, *Standard for the Installation of Air Conditioning and Ventilating Systems.*"

40. Sec. 3-12.4.6.2 is revised as follows:

3-12.4.6.2 Loudspeakers shall be located in accordance with UFC Section 1007.2.12.2.3.

41. Sec. 4-2.2.2.4 is revised by substituting the phrase "the Electrical Code" for the phrase "NFPA 70, *National Electrical Code,* Article 810."

42. Sec. 4-2.3.3.3.8 is deleted.

43. Sec. 4-3.2.2 is revised by deleting the word "guard" in the first sentence.

44. Sec. 4-3.6.1.2 is deleted.

45. Sec. 4-3.6.1.2.1 is deleted.

46. Sec. 4-4.3.3 is revised by substituting the phrase "nationally recognized standards" for the phrase "UFC Standard 10-1, Standard for Portable Fire Extinguishers."

47. Sec. 4-4.6.7.2 is deleted.

48. Sec. 4-6 is deleted.

49. Sec. 4-7.4.1 (b) 2 is revised as follows:

2. All conductors shall be installed in rigid conduit or electrical metallic tubing in accordance with the Electric Code.

50. Sec. 4-7.4.1 (b) 6 is revised by substituting the phrase "the Electrical Code" for the phrase "NFPA 70, *National Electrical Code,* Article 310."

51. Sec. 4-7.5 is revised as follows:

4-7.5 Personnel. Personnel necessary to receive and act on signals from auxiliary fire alarm systems shall be in accordance with nationally recognized standards.

52. Sec. 4-7.6 is revised as follows:

4-7.6 Operations. Operations for auxiliary fire alarm systems shall be in accordance with nationally recognized standards.

53. Sec. 5-1.3.4 is revised by substituting the phrase "nationally recognized standards" for the phrase "NFPA standard" in the first sentence, and by substituting the phrase "the Mechanical Code" for the phrase "NFPA 90A, *Standard for the Installation of Air Conditioning and Ventilating Systems*" in Exception No. 3.

54. Sec. 5-2.2 is revised by substituting the phrase "nationally recognized standard" for the phrase "NFPA standard."

55. Sec. 5-2.7.1.2 is revised by deleting the note at the end of the exception.

56. Sec. 5-3.1.4 is deleted.

57. Sec. 5-3.2 is revised by substituting the phrase "nationally recognized" for the phrase "NFPA."

58. Sec. 5-3.5.5.1 is revised by deleting the last sentence.

59. Sec. 5-3.7.5 is revised by substituting the phrase "UFC Standard 81-2" for the phrase "NFPA 231C, *Standard for Rack Storage of Materials.*"

60. Sec. 5-5.2 is revised by substituting the phrase "nationally recognized" for the phrase "NFPA."

61. Sec. 5-6.1 is revised by substituting the phrase "nationally recognized" for the phrase "NFPA."

62. Sec. 5-9.1 is revised as follows:

5-9.1 Manual fire alarm boxes shall be used only for fire alarm-initiating purposes.

63. Sec. 5-9.1.2 (a) is revised as follows:

(a) Manual fire alarm boxes shall be provided at every exit from each floor level.

64. Sec. 5-9.2 is deleted.

65. Sec. 5-11 is revised by deleting the note.

66. Sec. 5-11.4.2 is revised by substituting the phrase "the Mechanical Code" for the phrase "NFPA 90A, *Standard for the Installation of Air Conditioning and Ventilating Systems.*"

67. Sec. 5-11.5.2.1 is revised by substituting the phrase "nationally recognized" for the phrase "NFPA."

68. Sec. 5-11.5.2.2 is revised by substituting the phrase "nationally recognized" for the phrase "NFPA."

69. Sec. 6-1.2 is revised by substituting the phrase "nationally recognized" for the phrase "NFPA."

70. Sec. 6-2.1 is revised by deleting the definitions of "general audible" and "general visible."

71. Sec. 6-4.2 is revised as follows:

6-4.2 Light Pulse Characteristics. The flash rate shall not exceed three flashes per second or be less than one flash per second.

72. Sec. 7-1.1.1 is revised by adding an exception as follows:

> **EXCEPTION:** Single-station smoke detectors installed in dwelling units of Group R Occupancies.

73. Table 7-2.2, Item 2, is revised by substituting the phrase "nationally recognized standards" for the phrase "NFPA 110, *Standard for Emergency and Standby Power Systems.*"

Also:

Item 4 is revised by substituting the phrase "nationally recognized standards" for the phrase "NFPA 111, *Standard on Stored Electrical Energy Emergency and Standby Power Systems.*"

Also:

Item 7 is deleted.

Also:

Item 13 (i) is revised by substituting the phrase "nationally recognized standards" for the phrase "NFPA 25, *Standard for the Inspection, Testing, and Maintenance of Water-Based Fire Protection Systems.*"

Also:

Item 18 is revised by substituting the phrase "nationally recognized standards" for the phrase "NFPA standards."

Also:

Item 19 is deleted.

74. Table 7-3.1 is revised by deleting Item 8.

75. Sec. 7-3.2.2 is revised by substituting the phrase "nationally recognized" for the phrase "NFPA."

76. Table 7-3.2 is revised by deleting Item 13 and revising the note following the table as follows:

NOTE: For testing addressable and analog described devices, which are normally affixed to either a single molded assembly or twist lock type affixed to a base, TESTING SHALL BE DONE UTILIZING THE SIGNALING STYLE CIRCUITS (Styles 0.5 through 7). Analog type detectors shall be tested with the same criteria.

77. Figure 7-5.1, Inspection and Testing Form, is revised by changing the categories as follows:

SIGNALING LINE CIRCUITS is revised by substituting the phrase "Chapter 3" for the phrase "NFPA 72."

TYPE BATTERY, Item (c), is revised by substituting the phrase "the Electric Code" for the phrases "NFPA 70, Article 700," "NFPA 70, Article 701," and "NFPA 70, Article 702" and

by revising the last line to read "Optional standby system described in the Electrical Code."

Also:

Revise the final section as follows:

THIS TEST WAS PERFORMED IN ACCORDANCE WITH APPLICABLE NATIONALLY RECOGNIZED STANDARDS.

78. Chapter 8 is deleted.

Part II

Reproduced with permission from the National Fire Alarm Code, NFPA 72, copyright 1993, National Fire Protection Association, 1 Batterymarch Park, Box 9101, Quincy, Massachusetts 02269–9101. Persons desiring to reprint in whole or in part any portion of the National Fire Alarm Code, NFPA 72—1993, must secure permission from the National Fire Protection Association. The following standard is not necessarily the latest revision used by NFPA. If the reader desires to compare with that version, the same is available from NFPA.

Contents

NFPA 72

National Fire Alarm Code

1993 Edition

NOTICE: An asterisk (*) following the number or letter designating a paragraph indicates explanatory material on that paragraph in Appendix A.

Information on referenced publications can be found in Chapter 8 and Appendix C.

Chapter 1 Fundamentals of Fire Alarm Systems

1-1 Scope. This code deals with the application, installation, performance, and maintenance of fire alarm systems and their components.

[From NFPA 72 - 1990, 1-1 modified]

1-2 Purpose.

1-2.1* The purpose of this code is to define the means of signal initiation, transmission, notification, and annunciation; the levels of performance; and the reliability of the various types of fire alarm systems. This code defines the features associated with these systems, and also provides the information necessary to modify or upgrade an existing system to meet the requirements of a particular system classification. It is the intent of this code to establish the required levels of performance, extent of redundancy, and quality of installation, but not the methods by which these requirements are to be achieved.

[From NFPA 72, 1-2.1 modified]

1-2.2 Any reference or implied reference to a particular type of hardware is for the purpose of clarity and shall not be interpreted as an endorsement.

[From NFPA 72, 1-2.2]

1-3 General.

1-3.1 This code classifies fire alarm systems as follows:

(a) Household fire warning systems

(b) Protected premises fire alarm systems

1. Local fire alarm systems

(c) Off-premises fire alarm systems

1. Auxiliary fire alarm systems
   (i) Local energy type
   (ii) Parallel telephone type
   (iii) Shunt type
2. Remote station fire alarm systems
3. Proprietary fire alarm systems
4. Central station fire alarm systems
5. Municipal fire alarm systems.

1-3.2 A device or system having materials or forms different from those detailed in this code shall be permitted to be examined and tested according to the intent of the code and, if found equivalent, shall be approved.

[From NFPA 72 - 1990, 1-3.2, and NFPA 71, 1-1.3 modified]

1-3.3 The intent and meaning of the terms used in this code are, unless otherwise defined herein, the same as those of NFPA 70, *National Electrical Code.®*

[From NFPA 72 - 1990, 1-3.3]

1-4 Definitions. For the purposes of this code, the following terms have the meanings shown below:

[From NFPA 72 - 1990]

Active Multiplex System. A multiplexing system in which transponders are employed to transmit status signals of each initiating device or initiating device circuit within a prescribed time interval.

[From NFPA 71 modified]

Active Signaling Element. A component within a circuit interface such as a transistor, silicon controlled rectifier, or relay whose function is to impress a signal on the multiplexed signaling line circuit.

[From NFPA 71 modified]

Addressable Device. A fire alarm system component with discreet identification that can have its status individually identified or that is used to individually control other functions.

[New paragraph]

Adverse Condition. Any occurrence to a communications or transmission channel that interferes with the proper transmission and/or interpretation of status change signals at the supervising station. (*See also Trouble Signal.*)

[From NFPA 71 modified]

Air Sampling-Type Detector. A detector that consists of a piping or tubing distribution network from the detector to the area(s) to be protected. An aspiration fan in the detector housing draws air from the protected area back to the detector through air sampling ports, piping, or tubing. At the detector, the air is analyzed for fire products.

[From NFPA 72E - 1990, 2-2.2.3]

Alarm. A warning of fire danger.

[New paragraph]

Alarm Service. The service required following the receipt of an alarm signal.

[From NFPA 71]

Alarm Signal. A signal indicating an emergency requiring immediate action, such as a signal indicative of fire.

[From NFPA 72 - 1990 and NFPA 71 modified]

Alarm Verification Feature. A feature of automatic fire detection and alarm systems to reduce unwanted alarms wherein smoke detectors must report alarm conditions for a minimum period of time, or confirm alarm conditions within a given time period, after being reset to be accepted as a valid alarm initiation signal.

[From NFPA 72 - 1990 modified]

Alert Tone. An attention-getting signal to alert occupants of the pending transmission of a voice message.

[From NFPA 72 - 1990]

Analog Initiating Device (Sensor). An initiating device that transmits a signal indicating varying degrees of condition as contrasted with a conventional initiating device, which can only indicate an on/off condition.

[New paragraph]

Annunciator. A unit containing two or more indicator lamps, alpha-numeric displays, or other equivalent means in which each indication provides status information about a circuit, condition, or location.

[From NFPA 72 - 1990 modified]

Approved. Acceptable to the "authority having jurisdiction."

NOTE: The National Fire Protection Association does not approve, inspect or certify any installations, procedures, equipment, or materials nor does it approve or evaluate testing laboratories. In determining the acceptability of installations or procedures, equipment or materials, the authority having jurisdiction may base acceptance on compliance with NFPA or other appropriate standards. In the absence of such standards, said authority may require evidence of proper installation, procedure or use. The authority having jurisdiction may also refer to the listings or labeling practices of an organization concerned with product evaluations which is in a position to determine compliance with appropriate standards for the current production of listed items.

[From NFPA 72 - 1990, NFPA 71, NFPA 72E, NFPA 72G, NFPA 72H, and NFPA 74]

Authority Having Jurisdiction. The "authority having jurisdiction" is the organization, office or individual responsible for "approving" equipment, an installation or a procedure.

NOTE: The phrase "authority having jurisdiction" is used in NFPA documents in a broad manner since jurisdictions and "approval" agencies vary as do their responsibilities. Where public safety is primary, the "authority having jurisdiction" may be a federal, state, local or other regional department or individual such as a fire chief, fire marshal, chief of a fire prevention bureau, labor department, health department, building official, electrical inspector, or others having statutory authority. For insurance purposes, an insurance inspection department, rating bureau, or other insurance company representative may be the "authority having jurisdiction." In many circumstances the property owner or his designated agent assumes the role of the "authority having jurisdiction"; at government installations, the commanding officer or departmental official may be the "authority having jurisdiction."

[From NFPA 72 - 1990, NFPA 71, NFPA 72E, NFPA 72G, NFPA 72H, and NFPA 74]

Automatic Extinguishing System Operation Detector. A device that detects the operation of an extinguishing system by means appropriate to the system employed.

Automatic Extinguishing System Supervision. Devices that respond to abnormal conditions that could affect the proper operation of an automatic sprinkler system or other fire extinguishing system, including but not limited to control valves; pressure levels; liquid agent levels and temperatures; pump power and running, engine temperature and overspeed; and room temperature.

[New paragraphs]

Automatic Fire Detectors. Fire is a phenomenon that occurs when a substance reaches a critical temperature and reacts chemically with oxygen (for example) to produce heat, flame, light, smoke, water vapor, carbon monoxide, carbon dioxide, or other products and effects.

An automatic fire detector is a device designed to detect the presence of fire and initiate action. For the purpose of this code, automatic fire detectors are classified as listed below.

[NFPA 72E - 1990, 2-1, 2-2.1 modified]

Fire-Gas Detector. A device that detects gases produced by a fire.

[From NFPA 72E - 1990, 2-2.1.4]

Heat Detector. A device that detects abnormally high temperature or rate-of-temperature rise.

[From NFPA 74 and NFPA 72E]

Other Fire Detectors. Devices that detect a phenomenon other than heat, smoke, flame, or gases produced by a fire.

[From NFPA 72E - 1990, 2-2.1.5]

Radiant Energy Sensing Fire Detector. A device that detects radiant energy (such as ultraviolet, visible, or infrared) that is emitted as a product of combustion reaction and obeys the laws of optics.

[From NFPA 72E - 1990, 2-2.1.3]

Smoke Detector. A device that detects visible or invisible particles of combustion.

[From NFPA 74]

Auxiliary Box. A fire alarm box that can be operated from one or more remote actuating devices.

[From NFPA 1221 modified]

Auxiliary Fire Alarm System. A system connected to a municipal fire alarm system for transmitting an alarm of fire to the public fire service communication center. Fire alarms from an auxiliary fire alarm system are received at the public fire service communication center on the same equipment and by the same methods as alarms transmitted manually from municipal fire alarm boxes located on streets.

(a) *Local Energy Type.* An auxiliary system that employs a locally complete arrangement of parts, initiating devices, relays, power supply, and associated components to automatically trip a municipal transmitter or master box over electric circuits that are electrically isolated from the municipal system circuits.

(b) *Parallel Telephone Type.* An auxiliary system connected by a municipally controlled individual circuit to the protected property to interconnect the initiating devices at the protected premises and the municipal fire alarm switchboard.

(c) *Shunt Auxiliary Type.* An auxiliary system electrically connected to an integral part of the municipal alarm system extending the municipal circuit into the protected premises to interconnect the initiating devices, which, when operated, open the municipal circuit shunted around the trip coil of the municipal transmitter or master box, which is thereupon energized to start transmission without any assistance whatsoever from a local source of power.

[From NFPA 72 - 1990 modified]

Box Battery. The battery supplying power for an individual fire alarm box where radio signals are used for the transmission of box alarms.

[From NFPA 1221 modified]

Bridging Point. The location where the distribution of signaling line circuits to trunk facilities or leg facilities, or both, occurs.

[From NFPA 71 modified]

Carrier. High frequency energy that can be modulated by voice or signaling impulses.

[From NFPA 72 - 1990]

Carrier System. A means of conveying a number of channels over a single path by modulating each channel on a different carrier frequency and demodulating at the receiving point to restore the signals to their original form.

[From NFPA 71]

Ceiling. The upper surface of a space, regardless of height. Areas with a suspended ceiling would have two ceilings, one visible from the floor and one above the suspended ceiling.

Ceiling Height. The height from the continuous floor of a room to the continuous ceiling of a room or space.

[From NFPA 72E]

Ceiling Surfaces. Ceiling surfaces referred to in conjunction with the locations of initiating devices are as follows:

[From NFPA 72E - 1990, 2-4 and 2-4.1]

(a) *Beam Construction.* Ceilings having solid structural or solid nonstructural members projecting down from the ceiling surface more than 4 in. (100 mm) and spaced more than 3 ft (0.9 m), center to center.

[From NFPA 72E - 1990, 2-4.1.1]

(b) *Girders.* Girders support beams or joists and run at right angles to the beams or joists. When the top of girders are within 4 in. (100 mm) of the ceiling, they are a factor in determining the number of detectors and are to be considered as beams. When the top of the girder is more than 4 in. (100 mm) from the ceiling, it is not a factor in detector location.

[From NFPA 72E - 1990, 2-4.1.2]

Central Station. A supervising station that is listed for central station service.

[From NFPA 71, 1-3 modified]

Central Station Fire Alarm System. A system or group of systems in which the operations of circuits and devices are transmitted automatically to, recorded in, maintained by, and supervised from a listed central station having competent and experienced servers and operators who, upon receipt of a signal, take such action as required by this code. Such service is to be controlled and operated by a person, firm, or corporation whose business is the furnishing, maintaining, or monitoring of supervised fire alarm systems.

[From NFPA 71 modified and TIA 304 revised, SC 90-44]

Central Station Service. The use of a system or a group of systems in which the operations of circuits and devices at a protected property are signaled to, recorded in, and supervised from a listed central station having competent and experienced operators who, upon receipt of a signal, take such action as required by this code. Related activities at the protected property such as equipment installation, inspection, testing, maintenance, and runner service are the responsibility of the central station or a listed fire alarm service - local company. Central station service is controlled and operated by a person, firm, or corporation whose business is the furnishing of such contracted services or whose properties are the protected premises.

Certificate of Completion. A document that acknowledges the features of installation, operation (performance), service, and equipment with representation by the property owner, system installer, system supplier, service organization, and the authority having jurisdiction.

[From NFPA 72 modified]

Certification. A systematic program using randomly selected follow-up inspections of the certified systems installed under the program, which allows the listing organization to verify that a fire alarm system complies with all the requirements of this code. A system installed under such a program is identified by the issuance of a certificate and is designated as a certificated system.

[From NFPA 71 modified]

Certification of Personnel. A formal program of related instruction and testing as provided by a recognized organization or the authority having jurisdiction.

NOTE: This definition applies only to municipal fire alarm systems.

[From NFPA 1221 modified]

Channel. A path for voice or signal transmission utilizing modulation of light or alternating current within a frequency band.

[From NFPA 71, NFPA 72 - 1990, and NFPA 1221 modified]

Circuit Interface. A circuit component that interfaces initiating devices and/or control circuits, indicating appliances and/or circuits, system control outputs, and other signaling line circuits to a signaling line circuit.

[New paragraph]

Combination Detector. A device that either responds to more than one of the fire phenomenon or employs more than one operating principle to sense one of these phenomenon. Typical examples are a combination of a heat detector with a smoke detector or a combination rate-of-rise and fixed-temperature heat detector.

[From NFPA 72E]

Combination Fire Alarm and Guard's Tour Box. Manually operated box for separately transmitting a fire alarm signal and a distinctive guard patrol tour supervisory signal.

[From NFPA 72 - 1990]

Combination System. A local fire alarm system for fire alarm, supervisory, or guard's tour supervisory service, or a household fire warning system whose components may be used in whole or in part in common with a nonfire signaling system, such as a paging system, a burglar alarm system, or a process monitoring supervisory system, without degradation of or hazard to the fire alarm system.

[From NFPA 72 - 1990 and NFPA 74 modified]

Communication Channel. A circuit or path connecting subsidiary station(s) to supervising station(s) over which signals are carried.

[From NFPA 71 modified]

Compatibility Listed. A specific listing process that applies only to two-wire devices (such as smoke detectors) designed to operate with certain control equipment.

Compatible (Equipment). Equipment that interfaces mechanically or electrically together as manufactured without field modification.

Control Unit. A system component that monitors inputs and controls outputs through various types of circuits.

[New paragraphs]

Delinquency Signal. A signal indicating the need of action in connection with the supervision of guards or system attendants.

[From NFPA 71 and NFPA 72 - 1990 modified]

Derived Channel. A signaling line circuit that uses the local leg of the public switched network as an active multiplex channel, while simultaneously allowing that leg's use for normal telephone communications.

[From NFPA 71]

Digital Alarm Communicator Receiver (DACR). A system component that will accept and display signals from digital alarm communicator transmitters (DACTs) sent over the public switched telephone network.

[From NFPA 72 - 1990 and NFPA 71 modified]

Digital Alarm Communicator System (DACS). A system in which signals are transmitted from a digital alarm communicator transmitter (DACT) located at the protected premises through the public switched telephone network to a digital alarm communicator receiver (DACR).

[From NFPA 72 - 1990 and NFPA 71 modified]

Digital Alarm Communicator Transmitter (DACT). A system component at the protected premises to which initiating devices or groups of devices are connected. The DACT will seize the connected telephone line, dial a preselected number to connect to a DACR, and transmit signals indicating a status change of the initiating device.

[From NFPA 72 - 1990 and NFPA 71 modified]

Digital Alarm Radio Receiver (DARR). A system component composed of two subcomponents: one that receives and decodes radio signals, the other that annunciates the decoded data. These two subcomponents can be coresident at the central station or separated by means of a data transmission channel.

[From NFPA 71]

Digital Alarm Radio System (DARS). A system in which signals are transmitted from a digital alarm radio transmitter (DART) located at a protected premises through a radio channel to a digital alarm radio receiver (DARR).

[From NFPA 71 modified]

Digital Alarm Radio Transmitter (DART). A system component connected to or an integral part of a DACT that is used to provide an alternate radio transmission channel.

[From NFPA 71]

Display. The visual representation of output data other than printed copy.

[From NFPA 72 - 1990]

Dual Control. The use of two primary trunk facilities over separate routes or different methods to control one communication channel.

[From NFPA 71]

Evacuation. The withdrawal of occupants from a building.

NOTE: Evacuation does not include relocation of occupants within a building.

[From NFPA 72 - 1990]

Evacuation Signal. Distinctive signal intended to be recognized by the occupants as requiring evacuation of the building.

[From NFPA 72 - 1990]

Exit Plan. Plan for the emergency evacuation of the premises.

Family Living Unit. That structure, area, room, or combination of rooms in which a family (or individual) lives. This is meant to cover living area only and not common usage areas in multifamily buildings such as corridors, lobbies, basements, etc.

[From NFPA 74]

Fire Alarm Control Unit (Panel). A system component that receives inputs from automatic and manual fire alarm devices and may supply power to detection devices and transponder(s) or off-premises transmitter(s). The control unit may also provide transfer of power to the notification appliances and transfer of condition to relays or devices connected to the control unit. The fire alarm control unit can be a local fire alarm control unit or master control unit.

[New paragraph]

Fire Alarm/Evacuation Signal Tone Generator. A device that, upon command, produces a fire alarm/ evacuation tone.

[From NFPA 72 - 1990 modified]

Fire Alarm Signal. A signal initiated by a fire alarm initiating device such as a manual fire alarm box, automatic fire detector, waterflow switch, or other device whose activation is indicative of the presence of a fire or fire signature.

Fire Alarm System. A system or portion of a combination system consisting of components and circuits arranged to monitor and annunciate the status of fire alarm or supervisory signal initiating devices and to initiate appropriate response to those signals.

[New paragraphs]

Fire Command Center. The principal manned or unmanned location where the status of the detection, alarm communications, and control systems is displayed and from which the system(s) can be manually controlled.

[From NFPA 72 - 1990 modified]

Fire Rating. The classification indicating in time (hours) the ability of a structure or component to withstand fire conditions.

Fire Safety Function Control Device. The fire alarm system component that directly interfaces with the control system that controls the fire safety function.

Fire Safety Functions. Building and fire control functions that are intended to increase the level of life safety for occupants or to control the spread of harmful effects of fire.

[New paragraphs]

Fire Warden. Building staff or tenant trained to perform assigned duties in the event of a fire emergency.

[From NFPA 72 - 1990]

Guard Signal. A supervisory signal monitoring the performance of guard patrols.

Guard's Tour Supervision. Devices that are manually or automatically initiated to indicate the route being followed and the timing of a guard's tour.

[New paragraphs]

Household. The family living unit in single-family detached dwellings, single-family attached dwellings, multifamily buildings, and mobile homes.

[From NFPA 74]

Household Fire Alarm System. A system of devices that produces an alarm signal in the household for the purpose of notifying the occupants of the presence of a fire so they may evacuate the premises.

[From NFPA 74 modified]

Hunt Group. A group of associated telephone lines within which an incoming call is automatically routed to an idle (not busy) telephone line for completion.

[From NFPA 72 - 1990 and NFPA 71]

Initiating Device. A system component that originates transmission of a change of state condition, such as a smoke detector, manual fire alarm box, supervisory switch, etc.

Initiating Device Circuit. A circuit to which automatic or manual initiating devices are connected where the signal received does not identify the individual device operated.

[From NFPA 72 - 1990]

Integrated System. A computer-based control system, listed for use as a fire alarm system, in which certain components are common to nonfire monitoring and control functions.

[New paragraph]

Intermediate Fire Alarm or Fire Supervisory Control Unit. A control unit used to provide area fire alarm or area fire supervisory service that, when connected to the proprietary fire alarm system, becomes a part of that system.

[From NFPA 72 - 1990 modified]

Labeled. Equipment or materials to which has been attached a label, symbol or other identifying mark of an organization acceptable to the "authority having jurisdiction" and concerned with product evaluation, that maintains periodic inspection of production of labeled equipment or materials and by whose labeling the manufacturer indicates compliance with appropriate standards or performance in a specified manner.

[From NFPA 71, NFPA 72 - 1990, NFPA 72G, NFPA 74, and NFPA 1221]

Leg Facility. That portion of a communication channel that connects not more than one protected premises to a primary or secondary trunk facility. The leg facility includes the portion of the signal transmission circuit from its point of connection with a trunk facility to the point where it is terminated within the protected premises at one or more transponders.

[From NFPA 71 and NFPA 72 - 1990 modified]

Level Ceilings. Those ceilings that are actually level or have a slope of $1^1/_2$ in. or less per ft (41.7 mm per m).

[From NFPA 72E - 1990, 2-3.1.1]

Line-Type Detector. A device in which detection is continuous along a path. Typical examples are rate-of-rise pneumatic tubing detectors, projected beam smoke detectors, and heat-sensitive cable.

[From NFPA 72E - 1990, 2-2.2.1]

Listed. Equipment or materials included in a list published by an organization acceptable to the "authority having jurisdiction" and concerned with product evaluation, that maintains periodic inspection of production of listed equipment or materials and whose listing states either that the equipment or material meets appropriate standards or has been tested and found suitable for use in a specified manner.

NOTE: The means for identifying listed equipment may vary for each organization concerned with product evaluation, some of which do not recognize equipment as listed unless it is also labeled. The "authority having jurisdiction" should utilize the system employed by the listing organization to identify a listed product.

[From NFPA 71, NFPA 72 - 1990, NFPA 72G, NFPA 74, and NFPA 1221]

Loading Capacity. The maximum number of discrete elements of fire alarm systems permitted to be used in a particular configuration.

Local Control Unit (Panel). A control unit that serves the protected premises or a portion of the protected premises and indicates the alarm via notification appliances inside the protected premises.

[New paragraphs]

Local Fire Alarm System. A local system sounding an alarm at the protected premises as the result of the manual operation of a fire alarm box or the operation of protection equipment or systems, such as water flowing in a sprinkler system, the discharge of carbon dioxide, the detection of smoke, or the detection of heat.

[From NFPA 72 - 1990 modified]

Local Supervisory System. A local system arranged to supervise the performance of guard's tours, or the operative condition of automatic sprinkler systems or other systems for the protection of life and property against a fire hazard.

[From NFPA 72 - 1990]

Local System. A system that produces a signal at the premises protected.

Loss of Power. The reduction of available voltage at the load below the point at which equipment will function as designed.

[From NFPA 71]

Low Power Radio Transmitter. Any device that communicates with associated control/receiving equipment by some kind of low power radio signals.

[From NFPA 72 - 1990 modified]

Maintenance. Repair service, including periodically recurrent inspections and tests, required to keep the fire alarm system and its component parts in an operative condition at all times, together with replacement of the system or of its components, when for any reason they become undependable or inoperable.

[From NFPA 71 and NFPA 72 - 1990]

Manual Fire Alarm Box. A manually operated device used to initiate an alarm signal.

[New paragraph]

Master Box. A municipal fire alarm box that may also be operated by remote means.

[From NFPA 72 - 1990]

Master Control Unit (Panel). A control unit that serves the protected premises or portion of the protected premises as a local control unit and accepts inputs from other fire alarm control units.

[New paragraph]

Multiple Station Alarm Device. Two or more single-station alarm devices that may be interconnected so that actuation of one causes all integral or separate audible alarms to operate. It may also consist of one single-station alarm device having connections for other detectors or manual fire alarm box.

[From NFPA 74 modified]

Multiplexing. A signaling method characterized by simultaneous or sequential transmission, or both, and reception of multiple signals on a signaling line circuit or a communication channel including means for positively identifying each signal.

[From NFPA 71 modified]

Municipal Fire Alarm Box (Street Box). An enclosure housing a manually operated transmitter used to send an alarm to the public fire service communication center.

[From NFPA 72 - 1990 modified]

Municipal Fire Alarm System. A system of alarm initiating devices, receiving equipment, and connecting circuits (other than a public telephone network) used to transmit alarms from street locations to the public fire service communication center.

[From NFPA 1221 modified]

Municipal Transmitter. A transmitter that can only be tripped remotely, used to send an alarm to the public fire service communication center.

[From NFPA 72 - 1990 modified]

Nonrestorable Initiating Device. A device whose sensing element is designed to be destroyed in the process of operation.

[From NFPA 72E - 1990, 2-2.3.1]

Notification Appliance. A fire alarm system component such as a bell, horn, speaker, strobe, printer, etc., that provides an audible or visible output, or both.

[New paragraph]

Notification Appliance Circuit. A circuit or path directly connected to a notification appliance(s).

[From NFPA 71, NFPA 72 - 1990, and NFPA 72H modified]

Off-Hook. To make connection with the public switched telephone network in preparation to dial a telephone number.

On-Hook. To disconnect from the public switched telephone network.

[From NFPA 72 - 1990 and NFPA 71]

Ownership. Any property, building, contents, etc., under legal control by occupant, by contract, or by holding of title or deed.

[New paragraph]

Paging System. A system intended to page one or more persons such as by means of voice over loudspeaker, by means of coded audible signals or visible signals, or by means of lamp annunciators.

[From NFPA 72 - 1990 modified]

Parallel Telephone System. A telephone system in which an individually wired circuit is used for each fire alarm box.

[From NFPA 72 - 1990 and NFPA 1221 modified]

Permanent Visual Record (Recording). Immediately readable, not easily alterable, print, slash, punch, etc., listing all occurrences of status change.

[From NFPA 72 - 1990]

Plant. One or more buildings under the same ownership or control on a single property.

[From NFPA 71]

Positive Alarm Sequence. An automatic sequence that results in an alarm signal, even if manually delayed for investigation, unless the system is reset.

Power Supply. A source of electrical operating power including the circuits and terminations connecting it to the dependent system components.

Primary Battery (Dry Cell). A nonrechargeable battery requiring periodic replacement.

[New paragraphs]

Primary Trunk Facility. That part of a transmission channel connecting all leg facilities to a supervising or subsidiary station.

[From NFPA 71, 1-3 modified]

Prime Contractor. The one company contractually responsible for providing central station services to a subscriber as required by this code. This may be either a listed central station or a listed fire alarm service - local company.

[New paragraph - TIA 304 revised, SC 90-44]

Private Radio Signaling. A radio system under control of the proprietary supervising station.

Proprietary Fire Alarm System. An installation of fire alarm systems that serve contiguous and noncontiguous properties under one ownership from a proprietary supervising station located at the protected property, where trained, competent personnel are in constant attendance. This includes the proprietary supervising station; power supplies; signal initiating devices; initiating device circuits; signal notification appliances; equipment for the automatic, permanent visual recording of signals; and equipment for initiating the operation of emergency building control services.

[From NFPA 72 - 1990 modified]

Proprietary Supervising Station. A location to which alarm or supervisory signaling devices on proprietary fire alarm systems are connected and where personnel are in attendance at all times to supervise operation and investigate signals.

Protected Premises. The physical location protected by a fire alarm system.

[New paragraphs]

Public Fire Service Communication Center. The building or portion of the building used to house the central operating part of the fire alarm system; usually the place where the necessary testing, switching, receiving, transmitting, and power supply devices are located.

[From NFPA 72 - 1990]

Public Switched Telephone Network. An assembly of communications facilities and central office equipment operated jointly by authorized common carriers that provides the general public with the ability to establish communications channels via discrete dialing codes.

[From NFPA 71]

Radio Alarm Central Station Receiver (RACSR). A system component that receives data and annunciates that data at the central station.

[From NFPA 71 modified]

Radio Alarm Satellite Station Receiver (RASSR). A system component that receives radio signals. This component is resident at a satellite station, located at a remote receiving location.

Radio Alarm System (RAS). A system in which signals are transmitted from a radio alarm transmitter (RAT) located at a protected premises through a radio channel to two or more radio alarm satellite station receivers (RASSR), and that are annunciated by a radio alarm central station receiver (RACSR) located at the central station.

Radio Alarm Transmitter (RAT). A system component at the protected premises to which initiating devices or groups of devices are connected. The RAT transmits signals indicating a status change of the initiating devices.

[From NFPA 71]

Radio Channel. A band of frequencies of a width sufficient to permit its use for radio communications.

NOTE: The width of the channel depends on the type of transmissions and the tolerance for the frequency of emission. Normally allocated for radio transmission in a specified type for service by a specified transmitter.

[From NFPA 1221, 1-3]

Record Drawings. Drawings (as-built) that document the location of all devices, appliances, wiring sequences, wiring methods, and connections of the components of the fire alarm system as installed.

[From NFPA 72H modified]

Relocation. The movement of occupants from a fire zone to a safe area within the same building.

Remote Station Fire Alarm System. A system installed in accordance with this code to transmit alarm, supervisory, and trouble signals from one or more protected premises to a remote location at which appropriate action is taken.

[From NFPA 72 - 1990]

Repeater Facility. Equipment needed to relay signals between supervisory stations, subsidiary stations, and protected premises.

[From NFPA 72 - 1990 modified]

Repeater Station. The location of the equipment needed for a repeater facility.

[From NFPA 71 modified]

Restorable Initiating Device. A device whose sensing element is not ordinarily destroyed in the process of operation. Restoration may be manual or automatic.

[From NFPA 72E - 1990, 2-2.3.2]

Runner. A person other than the required number of operators on duty at central, supervising, or runner stations (or otherwise in contact with these stations) available for prompt dispatching, when necessary, to the protected premises.

Runner Service. The service provided by a runner at the protected premises, including resetting and silencing of all equipment transmitting fire alarm or supervisory signals to the off-premise location.

[New paragraphs]

Satellite Trunk. A circuit or path connecting a satellite to its central or proprietary supervising station.

[From NFPA 72 - 1990 modified]

Scanner. Equipment located at the telephone company wire center that monitors each local leg and relays status changes to the alarm center. Processors and associated equipment may also be included.

[From NFPA 71]

Secondary Trunk Facility. That part of a transmission channel connecting two or more, but less than all, leg facilities to a primary trunk facility.

[From NFPA 71, 1-3]

Separate Sleeping Area. The area or areas of the family living unit in which the bedrooms (or sleeping rooms) are located. For the purpose of this code, bedrooms (or sleeping rooms) separated by other use areas, such as kitchens or living rooms (but not bathrooms), shall be considered as separate sleeping areas.

[From NFPA 74 modified]

Shall. Indicates a mandatory requirement.

[From NFPA 72 - 1990, NFPA 71, NFPA 74, and NFPA 1221]

Shapes of Ceilings. The shapes of ceilings are classified as follows:

[From NFPA 72E - 1990, 2-3 and 2-3.1]

Sloping Ceilings. Those having a slope of more than 1½ in. per ft (41.7 mm per m). Sloping ceilings are further classified as follows:

(a) *Sloping-Peaked Type.* Those in which the ceiling slopes in two directions from the highest point. Curved or domed ceilings may be considered peaked with the slope figured as the slope of the chord from highest to lowest point. (*See Figure A-5-2.7.4.1.*)

(b) *Sloping-Shed Type.* Those in which the high point is at one side with the slope extending toward the opposite side. (*See Figure A-5-2.7.4.2.*)

[From NFPA 72E - 1990, 2-3.1.2]

Smooth Ceiling. A surface uninterrupted by continuous projections, such as solid joists, beams, or ducts, extending more than 4 in. (100 mm) below the ceiling surface.

NOTE: Open truss constructions are not considered to impede the flow of fire products unless the upper member in continuous contact with the ceiling projects below the ceiling more than 4 in. (100 mm).

[From NFPA 72E - 1990, 2-4.1.4]

Should. Indicates a recommendation or that which is advised but not required.

[From NFPA 72 - 1990, NFPA 72G, NFPA 72H, NFPA 71, NFPA 74, and NFPA 1221]

Signal. A status indication communicated by electrical or other means.

[New paragraph]

Signal Transmission Sequence. A DACT that obtains dial tone, dials the number(s) of the DACR, obtains verification that the DACR is ready to receive signals, transmits the signals, and receives acknowledgment that the DACR has accepted that signal before disconnecting (going on-hook).

[From NFPA 71]

Signaling Line Circuit. A circuit or path between any combination of circuit interfaces, control units, or transmitters over which multiple system input signals or output signals, or both, are carried.

[From NFPA 72 - 1990, NFPA 71, and NFPA 72H modified]

Signaling Line Circuit Interface. A system component that connects a signaling line circuit to any combination of initiating devices, initiating device circuits, notification appliances, notification appliance circuits, system control outputs, and other signaling line circuits.

[From NFPA 72 - 1990 and NFPA 72H modified]

Single Station Alarm Device. An assembly incorporating the detector, control equipment, and the alarm-sounding device in one unit operated from a power supply either in the unit or obtained at the point of installation.

[From NFPA 74]

Solid Joist Construction. Ceilings having solid structural or solid nonstructural members projecting down from the ceiling surface a distance of more than 4 in. (100 mm) and spaced at intervals 3 ft (0.9 m) or less, center to center.

[From NFPA 72E - 1990, 2-4.1.3]

Spacing. A horizontally measured dimension relating to the allowable coverage of fire detectors.

[From NFPA 72E]

Spot-Type Detector. A device whose detecting element is concentrated at a particular location. Typical examples are bimetallic detectors, fusible alloy detectors, certain pneumatic rate-of-rise detectors, certain smoke detectors, and thermoelectric detectors.

[From NFPA 72E - 1990, 2-2.2.2]

Story. The portion of a building included between the upper surface of a floor and upper surface of the floor or roof next above.

[From NFPA 74]

Subscriber. The recipient of contractual supervising station signal service(s). In case of multiple, noncontiguous properties having single ownership, the term "subscriber" refers to each protected premises or its local management.

[From NFPA 71, 1-3 modified]

Subsidiary Station. A subsidiary station is a normally unattended location, remote from the supervising station and linked by communication channel(s) to the supervising station. Interconnection of signal-receiving equipment or communication channel(s) from protected buildings with channel(s)to the supervising station is accomplished at this location.

[From NFPA 71 and NFPA 72 - 1990 modified]

Supervising Station. A facility that receives signals and where personnel are in attendance at all times to respond to these signals.

[New paragraph]

Supervisory Service. The service required to monitor performance of guard tours and the operative condition of fixed suppression systems or other systems for the protection of life and property.

Supervisory Signal. A signal indicating the need of action in connection with the supervision of guard tours, fire suppression systems or equipment, or with the maintenance features of related systems.

[From NFPA 71 and NFPA 72 - 1990 modified]

Supplementary. As used in this code, supplementary refers to equipment or operations not required by this code and designated as such by the authority having jurisdiction.

[From NFPA 71 and NFPA 72 - 1990]

Switched Telephone Network. An assembly of communications facilities and central office equipment operated jointly by authorized service providers, which provide the general public with the ability to establish transmission channels via discrete dialing.

[From NFPA 71, 1-3 modified]

System Unit. The active subassemblies at the central station utilized for signal receiving, processing, display, or recording of status change signals; a failure of one of these subassemblies would cause the loss of a number of alarm signals by that unit.

[From NFPA 71]

Transmission Channel. A circuit or path connecting transmitters to supervising stations or subsidiary stations on which signals are carried.

[New paragraph]

Transmitter. A system component that provides an interface between signaling line circuits, initiating device circuits, or control units and the transmission channel.

[From NFPA 71 modified]

Transponder. A multiplex alarm transmission system functional assembly located at the protected premises.

[From NFPA 71]

Trouble Signal. A signal initiated by the fire alarm sys tem, indicative of a fault in a monitored circuit or component.

[From NFPA 71, NFPA 72 - 1990, NFPA 74, and NFPA 1221 modified]

Trunk Facility. That part of a transmission channel connecting two or more leg facilities to the central supervising station or subsidiary station.

[From NFPA 72 - 1990 modified]

Trunk Primary Facility. That part of a transmission channel connecting all leg facilities to a central or proprietary supervising station or subsidiary station.

Trunk Secondary Facility. That part of a transmission channel connecting two or more, but less than all, leg facilities to a primary trunk facility.

[From NFPA 71 modified]

WATS (Wide Area Telephone Service). Telephone company service allowing reduced costs for certain telephone call arrangements; may be in-WATS or 800-number service where calls can be placed from anywhere in the continental U.S. to the called party at no cost to the calling party, or out-WATS, a service whereby, for a flat-rate charge, dependent on the total duration of all such calls, a subscriber may make an unlimited number of calls within a prescribed area from a particular telephone terminal without the registration of individual call charges.

[From NFPA 71]

Zone. A defined area within the protected premises. A zone may define an area from which a signal can be received, an area to which a signal can be sent, or an area in which a form of control can be executed.

[From NFPA 72 - 1990]

1-5 Fundamentals.

1-5.1 Common System Fundamentals. The provisions of this chapter shall apply to Chapters 3 through 7.

1-5.1.1 The provisions of this chapter cover the basic functions of a complete fire alarm system. These systems are primarily intended to provide notification of fire alarm, supervisory, and trouble conditions, alert the occupants, summon appropriate aid, and control fire safety functions.

1-5.1.2 Equipment. Equipment constructed and installed in conformity with this code shall be listed for the purpose for which it is used.

[New paragraphs]

1-5.2 Power Supplies.

1-5.2.1 Scope. The provisions of this section apply to power supplies used for fire alarm systems.

[From NFPA 72 - 1990, 5-1, and NFPA 71, 2-2.1.1 modified]

1-5.2.2 Code Conformance. All power supplies shall be installed in conformity with the requirements of NFPA 70, *National Electrical Code*, for such equipment, and with the requirements indicated in this section.

[From NFPA 72 - 1990, 5-2; NFPA 71, 2-2.1.3 modified; and NFPA 1221, 4-1.5.1.1 modified]

1-5.2.3 Power Sources. Fire alarm systems shall be provided with at least two independent and reliable power supplies, one primary and one secondary (standby), each of which shall be of adequate capacity for the application.

[New paragraph]

Exception No. 1: Where the primary power is supplied by a dedicated branch circuit of an emergency system in accordance with NFPA 70, National Electrical Code, Article 700, or a legally required standby system in accordance with NFPA 70, National Electrical Code, Article 701, a secondary supply is not required.

Exception No. 2: Where the primary power is supplied by a dedicated branch circuit of an optional standby system in accordance with NFPA 70, National Electrical Code, Article 702, which also meets the performance requirements of Article 700 or Article 701, a secondary supply is not required.

NOTE to Exceptions No. 1 and No. 2: A trouble signal is not required where operating power is being supplied by either of the two sources of power indicated in Exceptions No. 1 and No. 2 above, if they are capable of providing the hours of operation required by 1-5.2.5 and loss of primary power is otherwise indicated (e.g., by loss of building lighting).

[From NFPA 72 - 1990, 5-3, 5-3.1; NFPA 71, 2-2.1.1, par. 2 modified; and NFPA 1221, 4-1.5.2 modified]

Where dc voltages are employed they shall be limited to no more than 350 volts above earth ground.

[From NFPA 71, 2-2.1.1 par. 3]

1-5.2.4 Primary Supply. The primary supply shall have a high degree of reliability, shall have adequate capacity for the intended service, and shall consist of one of the following:

(a) Light and power service arranged in accordance with 1-5.2.8,

(b) Engine-driven generator or equivalent arranged in accordance with 1-5.2.10.

[From NFPA 72 - 1990, 5-3.2; NFPA 71, 2-2.1.4 modified; and NFPA 1221, 4-1.5.2(a) modified]

1-5.2.5 Secondary Supply Capacity and Sources. The secondary supply shall automatically supply the energy to the system within 30 seconds and without loss of signals, wherever the primary supply is incapable of providing the minimum voltage required for proper operation. The secondary (standby) power supply shall supply energy to the system in the event of total failure of the primary (main) power supply or when the primary voltage drops to a level insufficient to maintain functionality of the control equipment and system components. Under maximum normal load, the secondary supply shall have sufficient capacity to operate a local, central station or proprietary system for 24 hours, or an auxiliary or remote station system for 60 hours; and then, at the end of that period, operate all alarm notification appliances used for evacuation or to direct aid to the location of an emergency for 5 minutes. The secondary power supply for emergency voice/alarm communications service shall be capable of operating the system under maximum normal load for 24 hours and then be capable of operating the system during a fire or other emergency condition for a period of 2 hours. Fifteen minutes of evacuation alarm operation at maximum connected load shall be considered the equivalent of 2 hours of emergency operation.

The secondary supply shall consist of one of the following:

(a) A storage battery arranged in accordance with 1-5.2.9.

(b) An automatic starting engine-driven generator arranged in accordance with 1-5.2.10 and storage batteries with 4 hours capacity arranged in accordance with 1-5.2.9.

(c) Multiple engine-driven generators, one of which is arranged for automatic starting, arranged in accordance with 1-5.2.10, capable of supplying the energy required herein with the largest generator out of service. It shall be permitted for the second generator to be pushbutton start.

Operation on secondary power shall not affect the required performance of a fire alarm system. The system shall produce the same alarm, supervisory, and trouble signals and indications (excluding the ac power indicator) when operating from the standby power source as produced when the unit is operating from the primary power source.

[From NFPA 72 - 1990, 5-3.3; NFPA 71, 2-2.1.5 modified, 2-2.2 modified; and NFPA 1221, 4-1.5.2(c) modified]

1-5.2.6 Continuity of Power Supplies.

(a) Where signals could be lost on transfer of power between the primary and secondary sources, rechargeable batteries of sufficient capacity to operate the system under maximum normal load for 15 minutes shall assume the load in such a manner that no signals are lost if either of the following conditions exists:

1. Secondary power is supplied in accordance with 1-5.2.5(a) or 1-5.2.5(b), and the transfer is made manually; or

2. Secondary power is supplied in accordance with 1-5.2.5(c).

(b) Where signals will not be lost due to transfer of power between the primary and secondary sources, one of the following arrangements shall be made:

1. The transfer shall be automatic.

2. Special provisions shall be made to allow manual transfer within 30 seconds of loss of power.

3. The transfer shall be arranged in accordance with 1-5.2.5(a).

(c)* Where a computer system of any kind or size is used to receive or process signals, an uninterruptible power supply (UPS) with sufficient capacity to operate the system for at least 15 minutes, or until the secondary supply is capable of supplying the UPS input power requirements, shall be required if either of the following conditions apply:

1. Status of signals previously received will be lost upon loss of power.

2. The computer system cannot be restored to full operation within 30 seconds of loss of power.

[From NFPA 71, 2-2.1.6]

1-5.2.6.1* Uninterruptible Power System Bypass. A positive means for disconnecting the input and output of the UPS system while maintaining continuity of power supply to the load shall be provided.

[From NFPA 71, 2-2.1.8]

1-5.2.7 Power Supply for Remotely Located Control Equipment. Additional power supplies, where provided for control units, circuit interfaces, or other equipment essential to system operation, located remote from the main control unit, shall be comprised of a primary and secondary power supply that shall meet the same requirements as for 1-5.2.1 through 1-5.2.8

[From NFPA 72 - 1990, 5-3.5]

1-5.2.7.1 Power supervisory devices shall be arranged so as not to impair the receipt of fire alarm or supervisory signals.

[New paragraph]

1-5.2.8 Light and Power Service.

[From NFPA 72 - 1990, 5-4, and NFPA 71, 2-2.4 modified]

1-5.2.8.1 A light and power service employed to operate the system under normal conditions shall have a high degree of reliability and capacity for the intended service. This service shall consist of one of the following:

(a) *Two-Wire Supplies.* A two-wire supply circuit may be used for either the primary operating power supply or the trouble signal power supply of the signaling system.

(b) *Three-Wire Supplies.* A three-wire ac or dc supply circuit having a continuous unfused neutral conductor, or a polyphase ac supply circuit having a continuous unfused neutral conductor where interruption of one phase does not prevent operation of the other phase, may be used with one side or phase for the primary operating power supply and the other side or phase for the trouble signal power supply of the fire alarm system.

[From NFPA 72 - 1990, 5-4.1]

1-5.2.8.2 Connections to the light and power service shall be on a dedicated branch circuit. The circuit and connections shall be mechanically protected. The circuit disconnecting means shall have a red marking, be accessible only to authorized personnel, and be identified as "FIRE ALARM CIRCUIT CONTROL." The location of the circuit disconnecting means shall be permanently identified at the fire alarm control unit.

[From NFPA 71, 2-2.4.1 modified; NFPA 72 - 1990, 5-4.2 modified; and NFPA 1221, 4-1.5.1.2, 4-1.5.1.4 modified]

1-5.2.8.3 Overcurrent Protection. An overcurrent protective device of suitable current-carrying capacity and capable of interrupting the maximum short-circuit current to which it may be subject shall be provided in each ungrounded conductor. The overcurrent protective device shall be enclosed in a locked or sealed cabinet located immediately adjacent to the point of connection to the light and power conductors.

[From NFPA 71, 2-2.4.2]

1-5.2.8.4 Circuit breakers or engine stops shall not be installed in such a manner as to cut off the power for lighting or for operating elevators.

[From NFPA 72 - 1990, 5-4.3]

1-5.2.9* Storage Batteries.

[From NFPA 72 - 1990, 5-5]

1-5.2.9.1 Location. Storage batteries shall be so located that the fire alarm equipment, including overcurrent devices, are not adversely affected by battery gases and shall conform to the requirements of NFPA 70, *National Electrical Code*, Article 480. Cells shall be suitably insulated against grounds and crosses and shall be substantially mounted in such a manner as not to be subject to mechanical injury. Racks shall be suitably protected against deterioration.

[From NFPA 71, 2-2.3.1, 2-2.3.2 modified, 2-2.3.3; NFPA 72 - 1990, 5-5.2; and NFPA 1221, 4-1.5.6.1 modified, 4-1.5.6.3, 4-1.5.6.2]

1-5.2.9.2 Battery Charging.

(a) Adequate facilities shall be provided to automatically maintain the battery fully charged under all conditions of normal operation and, in addition, to recharge batteries within 48 hours after fully charged batteries have been subject to a single discharge cycle as specified in 1-5.2.5. Upon attaining a fully charged condition, the charge rate shall not be so excessive as to result in battery damage.

(b) A reliable source of power shall be provided for charging the batteries.

(c) Central stations shall maintain spare parts or units available and employed to restore failed charging capacity prior to the consumption of one-half of the capacity of the batteries for the central station equipment.

(d)* Batteries shall be either trickle or float charged.

(e) A rectifier employed as a battery charging source of supply shall be of adequate capacity. A rectifier employed as a charging means shall be energized by an isolating transformer.

[From NFPA 71, 2-2.3.4, and NFPA 72 - 1990, 5-5.1]

1-5.2.9.3 Overcurrent Protection. The batteries shall be protected against excessive load current by overcurrent devices having a rating not less than 150 percent and not more than 250 percent of the maximum operating load in the alarm condition. The batteries shall be protected from excessive charging current by overcurrent devices or by automatic current-limiting design of the charging source.

[From NFPA 71, 2-2.3.5, and NFPA 72 - 1990, 5-5.4 modified]

1-5.2.9.4 Metering. The charging equipment shall provide either integral meters or readily accessible terminal facilities for the connection of portable meters by which the battery voltage and charging current can be determined.

1-5.2.9.5 Under-Voltage Detection. An under-voltage detection device shall be provided to detect a failure of the charging source and initiate a trouble signal.

[From NFPA 71, 2-2.3.6, and NFPA 72 - 1990, 5-5.3 modified]

1-5.2.10 Engine-Driven Generator.

[From NFPA 71, 2-2.6 modified; NFPA 72 - 1990, 5-6; and NFPA 1221, 4-1.5.5 modified]

1-5.2.10.1 An engine-driven generator shall be used only where a person specifically trained in its operation is on duty at all times.

Exception: Where acceptable to the authority having jurisdiction and where the requirements of 1-5.2.5(b) and (c) are met, a person specifically trained in the operation of a generator dedicated to the fire alarm system shall not be required to be on duty at all times.

[From NFPA 71, 2-2.6.1 without Exception, and NFPA 72 - 1990, 5-6.1]

1-5.2.10.2 The installation of such units shall conform to the provisions of NFPA 110, *Standard for Emergency and Standby Power Systems*, except as restricted by the provisions of this section.

[From NFPA 71, 2-2.6.2; NFPA 72 - 1990, 5-6.2 modified; and NFPA 1221, 4-1.5.5.2 modified]

1-5.2.10.3 Capacity. The unit shall be of a capacity sufficient to operate the system under the maximum normal load conditions in addition to all other demands placed upon the unit, such as those of emergency lighting.

[From NFPA 71, 2-2.6.4, and NFPA 1221, 4-1.5.5.6 modified]

1-5.2.10.4 Fuel. Fuel shall be stored in outside underground tanks whenever possible, and gravity feed shall not be used. Gasoline deteriorates with age. Where gasoline-driven generators are used, fuel shall be supplied from a frequently replenished "working" tank, or other means provided, to ensure that gasoline will always be fresh.

[From NFPA 71, 2-2.6.3; NFPA 72 - 1990, 5-6.3; and NFPA 1221, 4-1.5.5.4 modified]

1-5.2.10.5 Sufficient fuel shall be available in storage for 6 months of testing plus the capacity specified in 1-5.2.5. For public fire alarm reporting systems, refer to 4-6.7.3.4.

Exception No. 1: If a reliable source of supply is available at any time on 2-hour notice, sufficient fuel shall be in storage for 12 hours of operation at full load.

Exception No. 2: Fuel systems using natural or manufactured gas supplied through reliable utility mains shall not be required to have fuel storage tanks unless located in seismic risk zone 3 or greater as defined in ANSI A-58.1, Building Code Requirements for Minimum Design Loads in Buildings and Other Structures.

[From NFPA 72 - 1990, 5-6.4, and NFPA 1221, 4-1.5.5.4, 4-1.5.5.5 modified]

1-5.2.10.6 A separate storage battery and separate automatic charger shall be provided for starting the engine-driven generator and shall not be used for any other purpose.

[From NFPA 71, 2-2.6.5; NFPA 72 - 1990, 5-6.5; and NFPA 1221, 4-1.5.5.7 modified]

1-5.2.11* Primary Batteries.

1-5.2.11.1 Location. Primary batteries shall be located in a clean, dry place accessible for servicing and where the ambient air temperature will not be less than 40°F (4.4°C) and not more than 100°F (37.8°C).

[From NFPA 71, 2-2.5.1]

1-5.2.11.2 Separation of Cells. Primary batteries shall be housed in a locked, substantial enclosure or otherwise suitably protected against movement, injury, and moisture. Reliable separation between cells shall be provided to prevent contact between terminals of adjacent cells and between battery terminals and other metal parts, which may result in depletion of the battery or other deterioration. Battery cells having containers constructed of other than suitable electrical insulating material shall be located on insulating supports.

[From NFPA 71, 2-2.5.2]

1-5.2.11.3 Capacity. A primary battery shall have sufficient capacity to supply 125 percent of the maximum normal load for not less than one year.

[From NFPA 71, 2-2.5.4]

1-5.3 Compatibility.

1-5.3.1 All initiating devices, notification appliances, and control equipment constructed and installed in conformity with this code shall be listed for the purpose for which they are intended.

[From NFPA 71, 1-4.2 modified; NFPA 72, 2-1.2 modified; NFPA 72E, 2-5.1 modified; and NFPA 1221, 4-1.1.2, 4-1.3.1]

1-5.3.2 All fire detection devices that receive their power from the initiating device circuit or signaling line circuit of a fire alarm control unit shall be listed for use with the control unit.

[From NFPA 72E, 2-5.1.1 modified]

1-5.4 System Functions.

[New title]

1-5.4.1 Local Fire Safety Functions. Fire safety functions shall be permitted to be performed automatically. The performance of automatic fire safety functions shall not interfere with power for lighting or for operating elevators. This does not preclude the combination of fire alarm services with other services requiring monitoring of operations.

[From NFPA 72, 3-7.1 modified]

1-5.4.2 Alarm Signals.

[From NFPA 71, 6-2.1.2 modified, and NFPA 72, 2-4.3]

1-5.4.2.1* Coded Alarm Signal. A coded alarm signal shall consist of not less than three complete rounds of the number transmitted, and each round shall consist of not less than three impulses.

[From NFPA 71, 6-2.1.1 modified, and NFPA 72, 2-4.3]

1-5.4.3 Supervisory Signals.

1-5.4.3.1 Coded Supervisory Signal. A coded supervisory signal shall be permitted to consist of two rounds of the number transmitted to indicate a supervisory off-normal condition, and one round of the number transmitted to indicate the restoration of the supervisory condition to normal.

[From NFPA 72 - 1990, 2-4.4]

1-5.4.3.2 Combined Coded Alarm and Supervisory Signal Circuits. Where both coded sprinkler supervisory signals and coded fire or waterflow alarm signals are transmitted over the same signaling line circuit, provision shall be made either to obtain alarm signal precedence or sufficient repetition of the alarm signal to prevent the loss of an alarm signal.

[From NFPA 72 - 1990, 2-4.5]

1-5.4.4 Fire alarms, supervisory signals, and trouble signals shall be distinctively and descriptively annunciated.

[From NFPA 72 - 1990, 2-4.6.2]

1-5.4.5 Where status indicators are required to be provided for emergency equipment or fire safety functions, they shall be arranged to reflect accurately the actual status of the associated equipment or function.

[From NFPA 72 - 1990, 2-4.6.3]

1-5.4.6 Trouble Signal.

[From NFPA 71, 2-4.2, and NFPA 72 - 1990, 2-4.7]

1-5.4.6.1 General. Trouble signals and their restoration to normal shall be indicated within 200 seconds at the locations identified in 1-5.4.6.2 or 1-5.4.6.3. Trouble signals required to indicate at the protected premises shall be indicated by distinctive audible signals. These audible trouble signals shall be distinctive from alarm signals. If an intermittent signal is used, it shall sound at least once every 10 seconds with a minimum time duration of one-half second. An audible trouble signal may be common to several supervised circuits. The trouble signal(s) shall be located in an area where it is likely to be heard.

1-5.4.6.2 Visible and audible trouble signals and visible indication of their restoration to normal shall be indicated at the following locations:

(a) Control unit (central equipment) for local fire alarm systems

(b) Building fire command center for emergency voice/alarm communication systems

(c) Central station or remote station location for systems installed in compliance with Chapter 4.

[From NFPA 71, 2-4.2.1 modified, and NFPA 72, 2-4.7.1 modified]

1-5.4.6.3 Trouble signals and their restoration to normal shall be visibly and audibly indicated at the proprietary supervising station for systems installed in compliance with Chapter 4.

[From NFPA 72 - 1990, 9-8.3.3]

1-5.4.6.4 Audible Trouble Signal Silencing Switch.

[From NFPA 72 - 1990, 2-4.7.2]

1-5.4.6.4.1 A switch for silencing the trouble notification appliance(s) shall be permitted only if it transfers the trouble indication to a lamp or other acceptable visible indicator adjacent to the switch. The visible indication shall persist until the trouble has been corrected. The audible trouble signal shall sound if the switch is in its silence position and no trouble exists.

[From NFPA 72 - 1990, 2-4.7.2.1]

1-5.4.6.4.2 Where an audible trouble notification appliance is also used to indicate a supervisory condition, as permitted in 1-5.4.7(b), a trouble signal silencing switch shall not prevent subsequent sounding of supervisory signals.

[From NFPA 72 - 1990, 2-4.7.2.2]

1-5.4.7 Distinctive Signals. Audible alarm notification appliances for a fire alarm system shall produce signals that are distinctive from other similar appliances used for other purposes in the same area. The distinction among signals shall be as follows:

(a) Fire alarm signals shall be distinctive in sound from other signals and this sound shall not be used for any other purpose. (*See 3-7.2.*)

(b)* Supervisory signals shall be distinctive in sound from other signals. This sound shall not be used for any other purpose except that it may be employed to indicate a trouble condition. Where the same sound is used for both supervisory signals and trouble signals, distinction between signals shall be by other appropriate means such as visible annunciation.

(c) Fire alarm, supervisory, and trouble signals shall take precedence over all other signals.

[From NFPA 72 - 1990, 2-4.10 modified]

Exception: Signals from hold-up alarms or other life threatening signals shall be permitted to take precedence over supervisory and trouble signals if acceptable to the authority having jurisdiction.

[New paragraph]

1-5.4.8 Alarm Signal Deactivation. A means for turning off the alarm notification appliances shall be permitted only if it is key-operated, located within a locked cabinet, or arranged to provide equivalent protection against unauthorized use. Such a means shall be permitted only if a visible zone alarm indication or equivalent has been provided as specified in 1-5.7.1 and subsequent alarms on other initiating device circuits will cause the notification appliances to reactivate. A means that is left in the "off" position when there is no alarm shall operate an audible trouble signal until the means is restored to normal. Where automatically turning off the alarm notification appliances is permitted by the authority having jurisdiction, the alarm shall not be turned off in less than 5 minutes unless otherwise permitted by the authority having jurisdiction.

[From NFPA 72A - 1990, 2-4.11 modified]

1-5.4.9 Supervisory Signal Silencing. A switch for silencing the supervisory signal sounding appliance(s) shall be permitted only if it is key-operated, located within a locked cabinet, or arranged to provide equivalent protection against unauthorized use. Such a switch shall be permitted only if it transfers the supervisory indication to a lamp or other visible indicator and subsequent supervisory signals from other zones will cause the supervisory signal indicating appliances to resound. A switch left in the "silence" position where there is no supervisory off-normal signal shall operate a visible signal silence indicator and cause the trouble signal to sound until the switch is restored to normal.

[From NFPA 72 - 1990, 2-4.12 modified]

1-5.4.10 Presignal Feature. Where permitted by the authority having jurisdiction, systems shall be permitted to have a feature where initial fire alarm signals will sound only in department offices, control rooms, fire brigade stations, or other constantly attended central locations and where human action is subsequently required to activate a general alarm, or a feature where the control equipment delays general alarm by more than one minute after the start of the alarm processing. Where there is a connection to a remote location, it shall activate upon initial alarm signal.

NOTE: A system provided with an alarm verification feature as permitted by 3-8.2.3 is not considered a presignal system since the delay in signal produced is 60 seconds or less and requires no human intervention.

[From NFPA 72 - 1990, 2-4.1]

1-5.5 Performance and Limitations.

[From NFPA 72 - 1990, 2-3]

1-5.5.1 Voltage, Temperature, and Humidity Variation. Unless otherwise listed, equipment shall be installed in locations where conditions do not exceed the following:

(a)* Eighty-five percent and at 110 percent of the nameplate primary (main) and secondary (standby) input voltage(s)

(b) Ambient temperatures of 32°F (0°C) and 120°F (49°C) for a minimum duration at each extreme of 3 hours

(c) Relative humidity of 85 percent ± 5 percent and an ambient temperature of 86°F ± 3°F (30°C ± 2°C) for a duration of at least 24 hours.

[From NFPA 72 - 1990, 2-3.1 modified, and NFPA 1221, 4-1.3.3 modified, 4-1.3.9]

1-5.5.2 Installation and Design.

[From NFPA 71, 1-5, and NFPA 72 - 1990, 2-1 modified]

1-5.5.2.1 All systems shall be installed in accordance with the specifications and standards approved by the authority having jurisdiction.

[From NFPA 71, 1-5.1, and NFPA 72 - 1990, 2-1.1 modified]

1-5.5.2.2 Devices and appliances shall be so located and mounted that accidental operation or failure will not be caused by vibration or jarring.

[From NFPA 71, 1-5.2, and NFPA 72, 2-1.3 modified]

1-5.5.2.3 All apparatus requiring rewinding or resetting to maintain normal operation shall be restored to normal as promptly as possible after each alarm and kept in normal condition for operation.

[From NFPA 71, 1-5.4 modified; NFPA 72, 2-5.6 modified; and NFPA 1221, 4-1.3.6 modified]

1-5.5.3 To reduce the possibility of damage by induced transients, circuits and equipment shall be properly protected in accordance with requirements as set forth in NFPA 70, *National Electrical Code*, Article 800.

[From NFPA 71, 1-5.5]

1-5.5.4* Wiring. The installation of all wiring, cable, and equipment shall be in accordance with NFPA 70, *National Electrical Code*, and specifically with Article 760, *Fire Protective Signaling Systems*; Article 770, *Optical Fiber Cables*; and Article 800, *Communication Circuits, National Electrical Code*, where applicable. Optical fiber cables shall be protected against mechanical injury in accordance with Article 760.

[From NFPA 71, 2-1; NFPA 72 - 1990, 2-1.4 modified; and NFPA 1221, 4-1.3.11, 4-1.4.1.7]

1-5.5.5 Grounding. All systems shall test free of grounds.

Exception: Parts of circuits or equipment that are intentionally and permanently grounded to provide ground-fault detection, noise suppression, emergency ground signaling, and circuit protection grounding.

[From NFPA 71, 1-5.3; NFPA 72 - 1990, 2-1.5; and NFPA 1221, 4-1.3.10]

1-5.5.6 Initiating Devices.

[From NFPA 72 - 1990, 2-3.2]

1-5.5.6.1 Initiating devices of both the manual or automatic type shall be selected and installed as to minimize false alarms.

[From NFPA 72 - 1990, 2-3.2.1 modified]

1-5.5.6.2 Fire alarm boxes of the manually operated type shall comply with 3-8.1.

[From NFPA 72 - 1990, 2-3.2.2]

1-5.6 Protection of Control Equipment. In areas that are not continuously occupied, automatic smoke detection shall be provided at each control unit(s) location to provide notification of fire at that location.

Exception: Should ambient conditions prohibit installation of automatic smoke detection, automatic heat detection shall be permitted.

[From NFPA 72 - 1990, 2-1.6 modified]

1-5.7 Visible Indication (Annunciation).

[New title]

1-5.7.1 Visible Zone Alarm Indication. Where required, the location of an operated initiating device shall be visibly indicated by building, floor, fire zone, or other approved subdivision by annunciation, printout, or other approved means. The visible indication shall not be canceled by the operation of an audible alarm silencing means.

[From NFPA 72 - 1990, 2-4.6 modified]

1-5.7.1.1 The primary purpose of fire alarm system annunciation is to enable responding personnel to quickly and accurately identify the location of a fire, and to indicate the status of emergency equipment or fire safety functions that might affect the safety of occupants in a fire situation. All required annunciation means shall be readily accessible to responding personnel and shall be located as required by the authority having jurisdiction to facilitate an efficient response to the fire situation.

[From NFPA 72 - 1990, 2-4.6.1 modified]

1-5.7.1.2 Zone of Origin. Fire alarm systems serving two or more zones shall identify the zone of origin of the alarm initiation by annunciation or coded signal.

[From NFPA 72, 2-4.2]

1-5.7.2 Alarm annunciation at the fire command center shall be by means of audible and visible indicators.

[From NFPA *101*, 7-6.7.2 modified]

1-5.7.3 For the purpose of alarm annunciation, each floor of the building shall be considered as a separate zone.

[From NFPA *101*, 7-6.7.3]

1-5.7.4 A system supervisory signal shall be annunciated at the fire command center by means of an audible and visible indicator.

[From NFPA *101*, 7-6.7.6 modified]

1-5.7.5 A system trouble signal shall be annunciated at the fire command center by means of an audible and visible indicator.

[From NFPA *101*, 7-6.7.5 modified]

1-5.7.6 Where the system serves more than one building, each building shall be indicated separately.

[From NFPA *101*, 7-6.7.7 modified]

1-5.8 Monitoring Integrity of Installation Conductors and Other Signaling Channels.

[From NFPA 72 - 1990, 4-2, and NFPA 71, 2-4 modified]

1-5.8.1 All means of interconnecting equipment, devices, and appliances and wiring connections shall be monitored for the integrity of the interconnecting conductors or equivalent path so that the occurrence of a single open or a single ground fault condition in the installation conductors or other signaling channels and their restoration to normal shall be automatically indicated within 200 seconds.

NOTE: The provisions of a double loop or other multiple path conductor or circuit to avoid electrical monitoring is not acceptable.

[From NFPA 72 - 1990, 6-3, 4-2.1 modified, 4-3 modified; and NFPA 71, 2-4.1 modified]

Exception No. 1: Styles of initiating device circuits, signaling line circuits, and notification appliance circuits tabulated in Tables 3-5.1, 3-6.1, and 3-7.1 that do not have an "X" under "Trouble" for the abnormal condition indicated.

[From NFPA 72 - 1990, 4-2.1 Exception No. 1]

Exception No. 2: Shorts between conductors, except as required by 1-5.8.3, 1-5.8.4, 1-5.8.5.2, Tables 3-5.1, 3-6.1, and 3-7.1, are not covered by this code.

[From NFPA 72 - 1990, 4-2.1 Exception No. 2]

Exception No. 3: A noninterfering shunt circuit, provided that a fault circuit condition on the shunt circuit wiring results only in the loss of the noninterfering feature of operation.

[From NFPA 72 - 1990, 4-2.1 Exception No. 7]

Exception No. 4: Connections to and between supplementary system components, provided that single open, ground, or short circuit conditions of the supplementary equipment and/or interconnecting means does not affect the required operation of the fire alarm system.

[From NFPA 72 - 1990, 4-2.1 Exception No. 5]

Exception No. 5: The circuit of an alarm notification appliance installed in the same room with the central control equipment, provided that the notification appliance circuit conductors are installed in conduit or equivalently protected against mechanical injury.

[From NFPA 72 - 1990, 4-2.1 Exception No. 8]

Exception No. 6: A trouble signal circuit.

[From NFPA 72 - 1990, 4-2.1 Exception No. 9]

Exception No. 7: Interconnection between equipment within a common enclosure.

NOTE: This code does not have jurisdiction over monitoring integrity of conductors within equipment, devices, or appliances.

[From NFPA 71, 2-4.1 Exception No. 13, and NFPA 72-1990, 4-2.1 Exception No. 10]

Exception No. 8: Interconnection between enclosures containing control equipment located within 20 ft (6 m) when the conductors are installed in conduit or equivalently protected against mechanical injury.

[From NFPA 72 - 1990, 4-2.1 Exception No. 11]

Exception No. 9: Conductors for ground detection, where a single ground does not prevent the required normal operation of the system.

[From NFPA 72 - 1990, 4-2.1 Exception No. 12]

Exception No. 10: Central station circuits serving notification appliances within a central station.

[New paragraph)

Exception No. 11: Pneumatic rate-of-rise systems of the continuous line type in which the wiring terminals of such devices are connected in multiple across electrically supervised circuits.

[From NFPA 71, 2-4.1 Exception No. 12]

1-5.8.2 Interconnection means shall be arranged so that a single break or single ground fault will not cause an alarm signal.

[From NFPA 72 - 1990, 4-2.2]

1-5.8.3 An open, ground, or short circuit fault on the installation conductors of one alarm notification appliance circuit shall not affect the operation of any other alarm notification circuit.

[From NFPA 72 - 1990, 4-2.3]

1-5.8.4 The occurrence of a wire-to-wire short circuit fault on any alarm notification appliance circuit shall result in a trouble signal at the protected premises.

[New paragraph]

Exception No. 1: A circuit employed to produce a supplementary local alarm signal, provided that the occurrence of a short circuit on the circuit in no way affects the required operation of the fire alarm system.

[From NFPA 71, 2-4.1 Exception No. 11]

Exception No. 2: The circuit of an alarm notification appliance installed in the same room with the central control equipment, provided that the notification appliance circuit conductors are installed in conduit or equivalently protected against mechanical injury.

[From NFPA 72, 4-2.1 Exception No. 8]

Exception No. 3: Central station circuits serving notification appliances within a central station.

[From NFPA 71, 2-4.1 Exception No. 8 modified]

1-5.8.5 Monitoring Integrity of Emergency Voice/Alarm Communication Systems.

[New title]

1-5.8.5.1* Monitoring Integrity of Speaker Amplifier and Tone-Generating Equipment. Where speakers are used to produce audible fire alarm signals, the following shall apply:

(a) Failure of any audio amplifier shall result in an audible trouble signal.

(b) Failure of any tone-generating equipment shall result in an audible trouble signal.

Exception: Tone-generating and amplifying equipment enclosed as integral parts and serving only a single listed loudspeaker need not be monitored.

[From NFPA 72 - 1990, 4-4]

1-5.8.5.2 Where a two-way telephone communication circuit is provided, its installation wires shall be monitored for a short circuit fault that would make the telephone communication circuit inoperative.

[From NFPA 72 - 1990, 10-2.2]

1-5.8.6 Monitoring Integrity of Power Supplies.

[From NFPA 72 - 1990, 4-5]

1-5.8.6.1 All primary and secondary power supplies shall be monitored for the presence of voltage at the point of connection to the system.

[NFPA 72 - 1990, 4-5.1 modified, 4-5.2 modified]

Exception No. 1: A power supply for supplementary equipment.

[From NFPA 72 - 1990, 4-5.1 modified]

Exception No. 2: The neutral of a three-, four-, or five-wire ac or dc supply source.

[From NFPA 71, 2-4.1 Exception No. 5, and NFPA 72 - 1990, 4-2.1 Exception No. 6 modified]

Exception No. 3: In a central station, the main power supply, if the fault condition is otherwise so indicated as to be obvious to the operator on duty.

[From NFPA 71, 2-4.1 Exception No. 9]

Exception No. 4: The output of an engine-driven generator that is part of the secondary power supply, if the generator is tested weekly per Chapter 7.

[New paragraph]

1-5.8.6.2 Power supply sources and electrical supervision for digital alarm communications systems shall be in accordance with 1-5.2 and 1-5.8.1.

NOTE: Since digital alarm communicator systems establish communications channels between the protected premises and the central station via the public switched telephone network, the requirement to supervise circuits between the protected premises and the central station (*see 1-5.8.1*) is considered met when the communications channel is periodically tested in accordance with 4-2.3.2.1.10.

[From NFPA 71, 5-4.1]

1-5.8.6.3 The primary power failure trouble signal for the DACT shall not be transmitted until the actual battery capacity is depleted at least 25 percent, but not more than 50 percent.

[From NFPA 71, 5-4.2]

1-6 System Interfaces. The requirements by which fire alarm systems interface with other fire protective systems and fire safety functions can be found in Chapter 3.

[New paragraph]

1-7 Documentation.

[From NFPA 72 - 1990, 2-2]

1-7.1 Approval and Acceptance.

[New title]

1-7.1.1 The authority having jurisdiction shall be notified prior to installation or alteration of equipment or wiring. At its request, complete information regarding the system or system alterations, including specifications, wiring diagrams, battery calculation, and floor plans shall be submitted for approval.

[From NFPA 71, 1-4.1; NFPA 72, 2-2.1; and NFPA 72E, 2-5.1.2 modified]

1-7.1.2 Before requesting final approval of the installation, where required by the authority having jurisdiction the installing contractor shall furnish a written statement to the effect that the system has been installed in accordance with approved plans and tested in accordance with the manufacturer's specifications and the appropriate NFPA requirements.

[From NFPA 72E, 2-5.1.3 modified]

1-7.2 Certificate of Completion.

[New title]

1-7.2.1* A certificate (*see Figure 1-7.2.1*) shall be prepared for each system. Parts 1, 2, and 4 through 10 shall be completed after the system is installed and the installation wiring has been checked. Part 3 shall be completed after the operational acceptance tests have been completed. A preliminary copy of the certificate shall be given to the system owner and, when requested, to other authorities having jurisdiction after completion of the installation wiring tests, and a final copy after completion of the operational acceptance tests.

[From NFPA 72, 2-2.2 modified, and NFPA 71, 1-4.3 modified]

1-7.2.2* Every system shall include the following documentation, which shall be delivered to the owner or the owner's representative upon final acceptance of the system.

(a)* An owner's manual and installation instructions covering all system equipment, and

(b) Record drawings.

[From NFPA 72 - 1990, 2-2.3 modified and A-2-2.2.3(a)]

1-7.2.3 Central Station Fire Alarm Systems. It shall be conspicuously indicated by the prime contractor (*see Chapter 4*) that the fire alarm system providing service at a protected premises complies with all applicable requirements of this code by providing a means of verification as specified in either 1-7.2.3.1 or 1-7.2.3.2.

[From NFPA 71, 1-2.3 modified]

1-7.2.3.1 The installation shall be certificated.

[From NFPA 71, 1-2.3.1]

1-7.2.3.1.1 Central station fire alarm systems providing service that complies with all requirements of this code shall be certificated by the organization that has listed the prime contractor, and a document attesting to this certification shall be located on or near the fire alarm system control unit or, if no control unit exists, on or near a fire alarm system component.

[From NFPA 71, 1-2.3.1.1 modified]

1-7.2.3.1.2 A central repository of issued certification documents, accessible to the authority having jurisdiction, shall be maintained by the organization that has listed the central station.

[From NFPA 71, 1-2.3.1 modified]

1-7.2.3.2 The installation shall be placarded.

[From NFPA 71, 1-2.3.2]

1-7.2.3.2.1 Central station fire alarm systems providing service that complies with all requirements of this code shall be conspicuously marked by the prime contractor to indicate compliance. The marking shall be by one or more securely affixed placards.

[From NFPA 71, 1-2.3.2.1 modified]

1-7.2.3.2.2 The placard(s) shall be 20 sq in. (130 cm^2) or larger, shall be located on or near the fire alarm system control unit or, if no control unit exists, on or near a fire alarm system component, and shall identify the central station and, if applicable, the prime contractor by name and telephone number.

[From NFPA 71, 1-2.3.2.2 modified]

1-7.3 Records. A complete unalterable record of the tests and operations of each system shall be kept for at least 2 years. The record shall be available for examination and, where required, reported to the authority having jurisdiction. Archiving of records by any means shall be permitted if hard copies of the records can be provided promptly when requested.

[From NFPA 71, 1-4.5 modified, and NFPA 72 - 1990, 2-5.7 modified]

Exception: Where off-premises monitoring is provided, records of all signals, tests, and operations recorded at the supervising station shall be maintained for not less than one year.

[New paragraph]

Certificate of Completion

Name of Protected Property: ______________________________

Address: ______________________________

Rep. of Protected Prop. (name/phone): ______________________________

Authority Having Jurisdiction: ______________________________

Address/Phone Number: ______________________________

1. Type(s) of System or Service:

_____ NFPA 72, Chapter 3 — Local
If alarm is transmitted to location(s) off premise, list where received:
____

_____ NFPA 72, Chapter 3 — Emergency Voice/Alarm Service
Quantity of voice/alarm channels: _________ Single: _________ Multiple: _________
Quantity of speakers installed: _________ Quantity of speaker zones: _________
Quantity of telephones or telephone jacks included insystem: _________

_____ NFPA 72, Chapter 4 — Auxiliary
Indicate type of connection:
Local energy, _________ Shunt, _________ Parallel telephone
Location and telephone number for receipt of signals:
____

_____ NFPA 72, Chapter 4 — Remote Station
Alarm: ______________________________

Supervisory: ______________________________

_____ NFPA 72, Chapter 4 — Proprietary
If alarms are retransmitted to public fire service communications center or others, indicate location and telephone number of the organization receiving alarm:
____

Indicate how alarm is retransmitted:
____

_____ NFPA 72, Chapter 4 — Central Station
The Prime Contractor:
____

Central Station Location:
____

Means of transmission of signals from the protected premise to the central station:

_____ McCulloh　　_____ Multiplex　　_____ One-Way Radio
_____ Digital Alarm Communicator　　_____ Two-Way Radio　　_____ Others

Means of transmission of alarms to the public fire service communications center:

1. ______________________________

2. ______________________________

System Location: ______________________________

	Organization Name/Phone	Representative Name/Phone
Installer	________________	________________
Supplier	________________	________________
Service Organization	________________	________________

Figure 1-7.2.1 Certificate of Completion.

[From NFPA 72 - 1990, 2-2.2 modified, and NFPA 71, 1-4.3 modified]

Location of Record (As-Built) Drawings:

____

Location of Owners Manuals:

____

Location of Test Reports:

____

A contract, dated ______________, for test and inspection in accordance with NFPA standard(s) No.(s) __________, dated ______________, is in effect.

2. Certification of System Installation
(Fill out after installation is complete and wiring checked for opens, shorts, ground faults, and improper branching, but prior to conducting operational acceptance tests.)

This system has been installed in accordance with the NFPA standards as listed below, was inspected by __________ on ______________, includes the devices listed below and has been in service since ______________

_____ NFPA 72, Chapters 1 3 4 5 6 7 (circle all that apply)
_____ NFPA 70, *National Electrical Code*, Article 760
_____ Manufacturer's Instructions
_____ Other (specify): ______________________________

Signed: ______________________________ Date: __________

Organization: ______________________________

3. Certification of System Operation
All operational features and functions of this system were tested by ______________ on ____________ and found to be operating properly in accordance with the requirements of:

_____ NFPA 72, Chapters 1 3 4 5 6 7 (circle all that apply)
_____ NFPA 70, *National Electrical Code*, Article 760
_____ Manufacturer's Instructions
_____ Other (specify): ______________________________

Signed: ______________________________ Date: __________

Organization: ______________________________

4. Alarm Initiating Devices and Circuits (Use blanks to indicate quantity of devices.)

MANUAL

a) _______ Manual Stations _______ Noncoded, Activating _______ Transmitters _______ Coded
b) _______ Combination Manual Fire Alarm and Guard's Tour Coded Stations

AUTOMATIC
Coverage: Complete: __________ Partial: __________

a) _____ Smoke Detectors _____ Ion _____ Photo
b) _____ Duct Detectors _____ Ion _____ Photo
c) _____ Heat Detectors _____ FT _____ RR _____ FT/RR _____ RC
d) _____ Sprinkler Water Flow Switches: _____ Noncoded, activating _____ Transmitters _____ Coded
e) _____ Other (list): ______________________________

5. Supervisory Signal Initiating Devices and Circuits (Use blanks to indicate quantity of devices.)

GUARD'S TOUR

a) _____ Coded Stations
b) _____ Noncoded Stations Activating __________ Transmitters
c) _____ Compulsory Guard Tour System Comprised of _____ Transmitter Stations and _____ Intermediate Stations

Note: Combination devices recorded under 4(b) and 5(a).

SPRINKLER SYSTEM

a) _____ Coded Valve Supervisory Signaling Attachments
Valve Supervisory Switches Activating _____ Transmitters
b) _____ Building Temperature Points
c) _____ Site Water Temperature Points
d) _____ Site Water Supply Level Points

Figure 1-7.2.1 Certificate of Completion. (cont.)

[From NFPA 72 - 1990, 2-2.2 modified, and NFPA 71, 1-4.3 modified]

Electric Fire Pump:

e) _____ Fire Pump Power
f) _____ Fire Pump Running
g) _____ Phase Reversal

Engine-Driven Fire Pump:

h) _____ Selector in Auto Position
i) _____ Engine or Control Panel Trouble
j) _____ Fire Pump Running

Engine-Driven Generator:

k) _____ Selector in Auto Position
l) _____ Control Panel Trouble
m) _____ Transfer Switches
n) _____ Engine Running

Other Supervisory Function(s) (specify): ____________________

____
____
____
____

6. Alarm Notification Appliances and Circuits
Quantity of indicating appliance circuits connected to the system: ____________
Types and quantities of alarm indicating appliances installed:

a) _____ Bells _____ Inch
_____ Speakers
b) _____ Horns
c) _____ Chimes
d) _____ Other: ____________
e) _____ Visual Signals Type: ____________
_____ with audible _____ w/o audible
f) _____ Local Annunciator

7. Signaling Line Circuits:
Quantity and Style (See NFPA 72, Table 3-6.1) of signaling line circuits connected to system:
Quantity: ____________ Style: ____________

8. System Power Supplies

a) Primary (Main): Nominal Voltage: ____________ Current Rating: ____________
Overcurrent Protection: Type: ____________ Current Rating: ____________
Location: ____________________

b) Secondary (Standby):
_____ Storage Battery: Amp-Hour Rating ____________
Calculated capacity to drive system, in hours: _____ 24 _____ 60
_____ Engine-driven generator dedicated to fire alarm system:
Location of fuel storage: ____________

c) Emergency or Standby System used as backup to Primary Power Supply, instead of using a Secondary Power Supply:
_____ Emergency System described in NFPA 70, Article 700
_____ Legally Required Standby System described in NFPA 70, Article 701
_____ Optional Standby System described in NFPA 70, Article 702, which also meets the performance requirements of Article 700 or 701

9. System Software

a) Operating System Software Revision Level(s): ____________
b) Application Software Revision Level(s): ____________
c) Revision Completed by: ____________________
(name) (firm)

10. Comments:

____
(signed) for Central Station or Alarm Service Company (title) (date)

Figure 1-7.2.1 Certificate of Completion. (cont.)

[From NFPA 72 - 1990, 2-2.2 modified, and NFPA 71, 1-4.3 modified]

Frequency of routine tests and inspections, if other than in accordance with the referenced NFPA standards(s):

___

___

___

System deviations from the referenced NFPA standard(s) are: ___

___

___

___

(signed) for Central Station or Alarm Service Company (title) (date)

Upon completion of the system(s) satisfactory test(s) witnessed (if required by the authority having jurisdiction):

___

(signed) representative of the authority having jurisdiction (title) (date)

Figure 1-7.2.1 Certificate of Completion. (cont.)

[From NFPA 72 - 1990, 2-2.2 modified, and NFPA 71, 1-4.3 modified]

Chapter 2* Household Fire Warning Equipment

2-1 General.

[New title]

2-1.1* Scope. This chapter contains minimum requirements for the selection, installation, operation, and maintenance of fire warning equipment for use within family living units. The requirements of the other chapters do not apply except as specifically indicated.

[From NFPA 74 - 1989, 1-1 modified]

2-1.2 General Provisions.

[From NFPA 74 - 1989, 1-2]

2-1.2.1 This code is primarily concerned with life safety, not with protection of property. It presumes that the family has an exit plan.

[From NFPA 74 - 1989, 1-2.1]

2-1.2.2 A control and associated equipment, multiple or single station alarm device(s), or any combination thereof shall be permitted to be used as a household fire warning system, provided the requirements of 2-1.3.1 are met.

[From NFPA 74 - 1989, 1-2.2 modified]

2-1.2.3 Detection and alarm systems for use within the protected household are covered by this chapter.

[From NFPA 74 - 1989, 1-2.3 modified]

2-1.2.4 Supplementary functions, including the extension of an alarm beyond the household, shall be permitted and shall not interfere with the performance requirements of this chapter.

[From NFPA 74 - 1989, 1-2.4 modified]

2-1.2.5 Where the authority having jurisdiction requires a household fire warning system to comply with the requirements of Chapter 4 or any other chapters of this code, the requirements of Section 2.2 shall still apply.

[From NFPA 74 - 1989, 1-2.5 modified]

2-1.2.6 Definitions of Chapter 1 shall apply.

2-1.2.7 This chapter does not exclude the use of fire alarm systems complying with other chapters of this code in household applications, provided all of the requirements of this chapter are met or exceeded.

[New paragraphs]

2-1.3 Approval.

[From NFPA 74 - 1989, 1-3]

2-1.3.1 All devices, combination of devices, and equipment to be installed in conformity with this chapter shall be approved or listed for the purposes for which they are intended.

[From NFPA 74 - 1989, 1-3.1.1 modified]

2-1.3.2 A device or system of devices having materials or forms different from those detailed in the chapter may be examined and tested according to the intent of the chapter and, if found equivalent, may be approved.

[From NFPA 74 - 1989, 1-3.1.2 modified]

2-1.3.3 Equivalency. Nothing in this code is intended to prevent the use of systems, methods, or devices of equivalent or superior quality, strength, fire resistance, effectiveness, durability, and safety over those prescribed by this code, provided technical documentation is submitted to the authority having jurisdiction to demonstrate equivalency and the system, method, or device is approved for the intended purpose.

[New paragraph]

2-2 Basic Requirements.

[From NFPA 74 - 1989, Chap. 2]

2-2.1 Required Protection.

[From NFPA 74 - 1989, 2-1]

2-2.1.1* This code requires the following detectors within the family living unit.

[From NFPA 74 - 1989, 2-1.1]

2-2.1.1.1 Smoke detectors shall be installed outside of each separate sleeping area in the immediate vicinity of the bedrooms and on each additional story of the family living unit, including basements and excluding crawl spaces and unfinished attics. In new construction a smoke detector also shall be installed in each sleeping room.

[From NFPA 74 - 1989, 2-1.1.1 modified]

2-2.1.1.2* For family living units with one or more split levels (i.e., adjacent levels with less than one full story separation between levels), a smoke detector required by 2-2.1.1.1 shall suffice for an adjacent lower level, including basements. (*See Figure A-2-2.1.1.2.*)

Exception: Where there is an intervening door between one level and the adjacent lower level, a smoke detector shall be installed on the lower level.

[From NFPA 74 - 1989, 2-1.1.2]

2-2.1.1.3 Automatic sprinkler systems provided in accordance with NFPA 13D, *Standard for the Installation of Sprinkler Systems in One- and Two-Family Dwellings and Mobile Homes*, or NFPA 13R, *Standard for the Installation of Sprinkler Systems in Residential Occupancies Up to and Including Four Stories in Height*, shall be interconnected to sound alarm notification appliances throughout the dwelling when a fire warning system is provided.

2-2.2* Alarm Notification Appliances. Each detection device shall cause the operation of an alarm that shall be clearly audible in all bedrooms over background noise levels with all intervening doors closed. The tests of audibility level shall be conducted with all household equipment that may be in operation at night in full operation.

Examples of such equipment are window air conditioners and room humidifiers. (*See A-2-2.2 for additional information.*)

[From NFPA 74 - 1989, 2-2]

2-2.2.1 In new construction, where more than one smoke detector is required by 2-2.1, they shall be so arranged that operation of any smoke detector shall cause the alarm in all smoke detectors within the dwelling to sound.

Exception: Configurations that provide equivalent distribution of the alarm signal.

[From NFPA 74 - 1989, 2-2.1]

2-2.2.2* Standard Signal. Alarm notification appliances used with a household fire warning system and single and multiple station smoke detectors shall produce the audible emergency evacuation signal described in ANSI S3.41, *Audible Emergency Evacuation Signals*. This requirement shall become effective on July 1, 1996.

2-2.3 Alarm Notification Appliances for the Hearing Impaired. In a household occupied by one or more hearing impaired persons, each initiating device shall cause the operation of visible alarm signal(s) in accordance with 2-4.4.2. Since hearing deficits are often not apparent, the responsibility to advise appropriate persons shall rest with the hearing impaired party. The responsibility for compliance shall rest with the occupants of the family living unit.

Exception: A listed tactile signal shall be permitted to be employed.

[New paragraphs]

2-3 Power Supplies.

2-3.1 General.

[From NFPA 74 - 1989, Chap. 3]

2-3.1.1 All power supplies shall have sufficient capacity to operate the alarm signal(s) for at least 4 continuous minutes.

[From NFPA 74 - 1989, 3-1.1]

2-3.1.2 For electrically powered detectors, an ac primary power source shall be utilized in all new construction. In existing households, ac primary power is preferred; however, where such is not practical, a monitorized battery primary power source is permitted.

[From NFPA 74 - 1989, 3-1.1.1]

2-3.2 Primary Power Supply — AC.

[From NFPA 74 - 1989, 3-2]

2-3.2.1 An ac primary (main) power source shall be a dependable commercial light and power supply source. A visible "power on" indicator shall be provided.

[From NFPA 74 - 1989, 3-2.1]

2-3.2.2 All electrical systems designed to be installed by other than a qualified electrician shall be powered from a source not in excess of 30 volts that meets the requirements for power limited fire alarm circuits as defined in NFPA 70, *National Electrical Code*, Article 760.

[From NFPA 74 - 1989, 3-2.2]

2-3.2.3 A restraining means shall be used at the plug-in of any cord connected installation.

[From NFPA 74 - 1989, 3-2.3]

2-3.2.4 AC primary (main) power shall be supplied either from a dedicated branch circuit or the unswitched portion of a branch circuit also used for power and lighting. Operation of a switch (other than a circuit breaker) or a ground fault circuit interrupter shall not cause loss of primary (main) power.

[From NFPA 74 - 1989, 3-2.4 modified]

Exception No. 1: Detectors with a supervised rechargeable standby battery that provides at least 4 months' operation with a fully charged battery.

[From NFPA 74 - 1989, TIA 89-1]

Exception No. 2: Where a ground-fault circuit interrupter serves all electrical circuits within the household.

[New paragraph]

2-3.2.5 Neither loss nor restoration of primary (main) power shall cause an alarm signal in excess of 2 seconds within nor any alarm signal outside the living unit.

[From NFPA 74 - 1989, 3-2.5 modified]

2-3.2.6 Where a secondary (standby) battery is provided, the primary (main) power supply shall be of sufficient capacity to operate the system under all conditions of loading with any secondary (standby) battery disconnected or fully discharged.

[From NFPA 74 - 1989, 3-2.7]

2-3.3 Primary Power Supply — Monitored Battery.
[From NFPA 74 - 1989, 3-3]

2-3.3.1 Household fire warning equipment shall be permitted to be powered by a battery, provided that the battery is monitored to ensure that the following conditions are met:
[From NFPA 74 - 1989, 3-3.1]

(a) All power requirements are met for at least 1 year's life, including monthly testing.
[From NFPA 74 - 1989, 3-3.1(a) modified]

(b) A distinctive audible trouble signal is given before the battery is incapable of operating (from aging, terminal corrosion, etc.) the device(s) for alarm purposes.
[From NFPA 74 - 1989, 3-3.1(b)]

(c) For a unit employing a lock-in alarm feature, automatic transfer is provided from alarm to a trouble condition.
[From NFPA 74 - 1989, 3-3.1(c)]

(d) The unit is capable of producing an alarm signal for at least 4 minutes at the battery voltage at which a trouble signal is normally obtained, followed by not less than 7 days of trouble signal operation.
[From NFPA 74 - 1989, 3-3.1(d)]

(e) The audible trouble signal is produced at least once every minute for 7 consecutive days.
[From NFPA 74 - 1989, 3-3.1(e)]

(f) Acceptable replacement batteries are clearly identified by manufacturer's(s') name and model number(s) on the unit near the battery compartment.
[From NFPA 74 - 1989, 3-3.1(f)]

(g) A readily noticeable visible indication shall be displayed when a primary battery is removed from the unit.
[From NFPA 74 - 1989, 3-3.1(g)]

(h) Any unit that uses a nonrechargeable battery as a primary power supply that is capable of a 10-year or greater service life, including testing, and meets the requirements of (b) thru (e) above, shall not be required to have a replaceable battery.

2-3.4 Secondary (Standby) Power Supply.

2-3.4.1 Removal or disconnection of a battery used as a secondary (standby) power source shall cause a distinctive audible or visible trouble signal.

2-3.4.2 Acceptable replacement batteries shall be clearly identified by manufacturer's(s') name and model number(s) on the unit near the battery compartment.

2-3.4.3 If required by law for disposal reasons, rechargeable batteries shall be removable.

2-3.4.4 Automatic recharging shall be provided where a rechargeable battery is used as the secondary (standby) supply. The supply shall be capable of operating the system for at least 24 hours in the normal condition, followed by not less than 4 minutes of alarm. Loss of the secondary (standby) source shall sound an audible trouble signal at least once every minute.

2-3.4.4.1 The battery shall be recharged within 4 hours if power is provided from a circuit that can be switched on or off other than by a circuit breaker, or within 48 hours when power is provided from a circuit that cannot be switched on or off other than by a circuit breaker.

2-3.4.5 Where automatic recharging is not provided, the battery shall be monitored to ensure that the following conditions are met:

(a) All power requirements are met for at least 1 year's life.

(b) A distinctive audible trouble signal is given before the battery capacity has been depleted below the level required to produce an alarm signal for 4 minutes.
[New paragraphs and title]

2-3.5 Primary Power — Nonelectrical. A suitable spring-wound mechanism shall provide power for the nonelectrical portion of a listed single station detector. A visible indication shall be provided to show that sufficient operating power is not available.
[From NFPA 74 - 1989, 3-4 modified]

2-4 Equipment Performance.
[From NFPA 74 - 1989, Chap. 4]

2-4.1 General. The failure of any nonreliable or short-life component that renders the detector inoperable shall be readily apparent to the occupant of the living unit without the need for test.
[From NFPA 74 - 1989, 4-1]

2-4.2 Smoke Detectors.
[From NFPA 74 - 1989, 4-2]

2-4.2.1 Each smoke detector shall detect abnormal quantities of smoke that may occur in a dwelling, shall properly operate in the normal environmental conditions of a household, and shall be in compliance with ANSI/UL 268, *Smoke Detectors for Fire Protective Signaling Systems*, or ANSI/UL 217, *Single and Multiple Station Smoke Detectors*.
[From NFPA 74 - 1989, 4-2.1]

2-4.3* Heat Detectors. Each heat detector, including a heat detector integrally mounted on a smoke detector, shall detect abnormally high temperature or rate-of-temperature rise, and all such detectors shall be listed or approved for not less than 50-ft (15-m) spacing.
[From NFPA 74 - 1989, 4-3 modified]

2-4.3.1* Fixed-temperature detectors shall have a temperature rating at least 25°F (14°C) above the normal ambient temperature and shall not exceed 50°F (28°C) higher than the maximum anticipated ambient temperature in the room or space where installed.
[From NFPA 74 - 1989, 4-3.1]

2-4.4 Alarm Signaling Intensity.
[From NFPA 74 - 1989, 4-4 modified]

2-4.4.1 All alarm-sounding appliances shall have a minimum rating of 85 dBA at 10 ft (3 m).

Exception: An additional sounding appliance intended for use in the same room as the user, such as a bedroom, may have a sound pressure level as low as 75 dBA at 10 ft (3 m).

[From NFPA 74 - 1989, 4-4.1]

2-4.4.2 Visible notification appliances used in rooms where hearing impaired person(s) sleep shall have a minimum rating of 177 candela for a maximum room size of 14 ft by 16 ft (4.27 m by 4.88 m). For larger rooms, the visible notification appliance shall be located within 16 ft (4.88 m) of the pillow. Visible notification appliances in other areas shall have a minimum rating of 15 candela.

Exception: Where a visible notification appliance in a sleeping room is mounted more than 24 in. below the ceiling, a minimum rating of 110 candela shall be permitted.

[New paragraphs]

2-4.5 Control Equipment.

[From NFPA 74 - 1989, 4-5]

2-4.5.1 The control equipment shall be automatically restoring on restoration of electrical power.

[From NFPA 74 - 1989, 4-5.1]

2-4.5.2 The control equipment shall be of a type that "locks in" on an alarm condition. Smoke detection circuits need not lock in.

[From NFPA 74 - 1989, 4-5.2]

2-4.5.3 If a reset switch is provided, it shall be a self-restoring type.

[From NFPA 74 - 1989, 4-5.3]

2-4.5.4 An alarm-silencing switch or an audible trouble-silencing switch shall not be provided unless its silenced position is indicated by a readily apparent signal.

[From NFPA 74 - 1989, 4-5.4]

2-4.5.5 Each electrical fire warning system and each single station smoke detector shall have an integral test means to permit the householder to check the system and sensitivity of the detector(s).

[From NFPA 74 - 1989, 4-5.5]

2-4.6 Monitoring Integrity of Installation Conductors.

2-4.6.1 All means of interconnecting initiating devices or notification appliances shall be monitored for the integrity of the interconnecting pathways up to the connections to the device or appliance so that the occurrence of a single open or single ground fault, which prevents normal operation of the system, will be indicated by a distinctive trouble signal.

Exception No. 1: Conductors connecting multiple-station detectors, provided a single fault on the wiring will not prevent single-station operation of any of the interconnected detectors.

Exception No. 2: Circuits extending from single- or multiple-station detectors to required remote notification appliances provided operation of the test feature on any detector will cause all connected appliances to activate.

[New paragraphs]

2-4.7 Combination System.

[From NFPA 74 - 1989, 4-7]

2-4.7.1 Where common wiring is employed for a combination system, the equipment for other than the fire warning signaling system shall be connected to the common wiring of the system so that short circuits, open circuits, grounds, or any fault in this equipment or interconnection between this equipment and the fire warning system wiring shall not interfere with the supervision of the fire warning system, or prevent alarm or trouble signal operation.

[From NFPA 74 - 1989, 4-7.1]

2-4.7.2 In a fire/burglar system, the operation shall be as follows:

(a) A fire alarm signal shall take precedence or be clearly recognizable over any other signal even when the nonfire alarm signal is initiated first.

(b) Distinctive alarm signals shall be obtained between fire alarms and other functions such as burglar alarms. The use of a common sounding appliance for fire and burglar alarms is acceptable if distinctive signals are obtained. (*See 2-2.2.2.*)

[From NFPA 74 - 1989, 4-7.2]

2-4.8 Low Power Wireless Systems. Household fire warning systems utilizing low power wireless transmission of signals within the protected household shall comply with the requirements of Section 3-13, except for 3-13.4.5.

2-4.9 Digital Alarm Communicators.

2-4.9.1 Household fire warning systems that employ off-premises transmission of signals via digital alarm communicators shall comply with the provisions of section 4-2.3.2 with the following exceptions:

(a) For 4-2.3.2.1.6 only one telephone line shall be required for one- and two-family residences.

(b) For 4-2.3.2.1.8 each DACT need only be programmed to call a single DACR number.

(c) For 4-2.3.2.1.10 each DACT serving a one- or two-family residence shall transmit a test signal to its associated receiver at least once a month.

[New paragraphs and title]

2-5 Installation.

[From NFPA 74 - 1989, Chap. 5]

2-5.1 General.

[From NFPA 74 - 1989, 5-1]

2-5.1.1 General Provisions.

[From NFPA 74 - 1989, 5-1.1]

2-5.1.1.1 All equipment shall be installed in a workman-like manner.

[From NFPA 74 - 1989, 5-1.1.1]

2-5.1.1.2 All devices shall be so located and mounted that accidental operation will not be caused by jarring or vibration.

[From NFPA 74 - 1989, 5-1.1.2]

2-5.1.1.3 All installed household fire warning equipment shall be mounted so as to be supported independently of its attachment to wires.

[From NFPA 74 - 1989, 5-1.1.3]

2-5.1.1.4 All equipment shall be restored to normal as promptly as possible after each alarm or test.

[From NFPA 74 - 1989, 5-1.1.4]

2-5.1.1.5 The supplier or installing contractor shall provide the owner with:

(a) An instruction booklet illustrating typical installation layouts

(b) Instruction charts describing the operation, method and frequency of testing, and proper maintenance of household fire warning equipment

(c) Printed information for establishing a household emergency evacuation plan

(d) Printed information to inform owners where they may obtain repair or replacement service, and where and how parts requiring regular replacement (such as batteries or bulbs) may be obtained within two weeks.

[From NFPA 74 - 1989, 5-1.1.5]

2-5.1.2 Multiple-Station Detector Interconnection.

[From NFPA 74 - 1989, 5-1.2]

(a) Where the interconnected wiring is unsupervised, no more than 18 detectors shall be interconnected in a multiple station configuration.

(b) Where the interconnecting wiring is supervised, the number of interconnected detectors shall be limited to 64.

[New paragraphs]

2-5.1.2.1* Interconnection that causes other detectors to sound shall be limited to an individual family living unit. Remote annunciation from single- or multiple-station detectors shall be permitted.

[From NFPA 74 - 1989, 5-1.2.1 modified]

2-5.1.2.2 No more than 12 smoke detectors may be interconnected in a multiple-station connection.

[New paragraph]

2-5.2* Detector Location and Spacing.

[From NFPA 74 - 1989, 5-2]

2-5.2.1* Smoke Detectors.

[From NFPA 74 - 1989, 5-2.1]

2-5.2.1.1 Smoke detectors in rooms with ceiling slopes greater than 1 ft rise per 8 ft (1 m rise per 8 m) horizontally shall be located at the high side of the room.

[From NFPA 74 - 1989, 5-2.1.1]

2-5.2.1.2 A smoke detector installed in a stairwell shall be so located as to ensure that smoke rising in the stairwell cannot be prevented from reaching the detector by an intervening door or obstruction.

[From NFPA 74 - 1989, 5-2.1.2]

2-5.2.1.3 A smoke detector installed to detect a fire in the basement shall be located in close proximity to the stairway leading to the floor above.

[From NFPA 74 - 1989, 5-2.1.3]

2-5.2.1.4 A smoke detector installed to protect a sleeping area in accordance with 2-2.1.1.1 shall be located outside of the bedrooms but in the immediate vicinity of the sleeping area.

[From NFPA 74 - 1989, 5-2.1.4]

2-5.2.1.5 The smoke detector installed to comply with 2-2.1.1.1 on a story without a separate sleeping area shall be located in close proximity to the stairway leading to the floor above.

[From NFPA 74 - 1989, 5-2.1.5]

2-5.2.1.6* Smoke detectors shall be mounted on the ceiling at least 4 in. (102 mm) from a wall or on a wall with the top of the detector not less than 4 in. (102 mm) nor more than 12 in. (305 mm) below the ceiling.

Exception: Where the mounting surface might become considerably warmer or cooler than the room, such as a poorly insulated ceiling below an unfinished attic or an exterior wall, the detectors shall be mounted on an inside wall.

2-5.2.1.7 Smoke detectors shall not be located within kitchens or garages, or in other spaces where temperatures can fall below 32°F (0°C) or exceed 100°F (38°C). Smoke detectors shall not be located closer than 3 ft (0.9 m) from:

(a) The door to a kitchen or a bathroom containing a tub or shower

(b) Supply registers of a forced air heating or cooling system.

Exception: Detectors specifically listed for the application.

[New paragraphs]

2-5.2.2* Heat Detectors.

[From NFPA 74 - 1989, 5-2.2]

2-5.2.2.1 On smooth ceilings, heat detectors shall be installed within the strict limitations of their listed spacing.

[From NFPA 74 - 1989, 5-2.2.1]

2-5.2.2.2 For sloped ceilings having a rise greater than 1 ft in 8 ft (1 m in 8 m) horizontally, the detector shall be located on or near the ceiling at or within 3 ft (0.9 m) of the peak. The spacing of additional detectors, if any, shall be based on a horizontal distance measurement, not on a measurement along the slope of the ceiling.

[From NFPA 74 - 1989, 5-2.2.2]

2-5.2.2.3* Heat detectors shall be mounted on the ceiling at least 4 in. (102 mm) from a wall or on a wall with the top of the detector not less than 4 in. (102 mm) nor more than 12 in. (305 mm) below the ceiling.

Exception: Where the mounting surface might become considerably warmer or cooler than the room, such as a poorly insulated ceiling below an unfinished attic or an exterior wall, the detectors shall be mounted on an inside wall.

[New paragraphs]

2-5.2.2.4 In rooms with open joists or beams, all ceiling-mounted detectors shall be located on the bottom of such joists or beams.

[From NFPA 74 - 1989, 5-2.2.4]

2-5.2.2.5* Detectors installed on an open-joisted ceiling shall have their smooth ceiling spacing reduced where this spacing is measured at right angles to solid joists; in the case of heat detectors, this spacing shall not exceed one-half of the listed spacing.

[From NFPA 74 - 1989, 5-2.2.5]

2-5.3 Wiring and Equipment. The installation of wiring and equipment shall be in accordance with the requirements of NFPA 70, *National Electrical Code*, Article 760.

[From NFPA 74 - 1989, 5-3]

2-6 Maintenance and Tests.

[From NFPA 74 - 1989, Chap. 6]

2-6.1* Maintenance. If batteries are used as a source of energy, they shall be replaced in accordance with the recommendations of the alarm equipment manufacturer.

[From NFPA 74 - 1989, 6-1]

2-6.2* Tests.

2-6.2.1 Single- and Multiple-Station Smoke Detectors. Homeowners shall inspect and test smoke detectors and all connected appliances in accordance with the manufacturer's instructions at least once a month.

[From NFPA 74 - 1989, 6-2 modified]

2-6.2.2 Fire Alarm Systems. Homeowners shall test systems in accordance with the manufacturer's instructions and shall have every residential fire alarm system tested by a qualified service technician at least every 3 years. This test shall be conducted according to the methods of Chapter 7.

[New paragraph]

2-7 Markings and Instructions. All household fire warning equipment or systems shall be plainly marked with the following information on the unit:

[From NFPA 74 - 1989, 7-1.1.1]

(a) Manufacturer's or listee's name, address, and model number

[From NFPA 74 - 1989, 7-1.2.1]

(b) A mark or certification that the unit has been approved or listed by a testing laboratory

[From NFPA 74 - 1989, 7-1.2.2]

(c) Electrical rating (if applicable)

[From NFPA 74 - 1989, 7-1.2.3]

(d) Temperature rating (if applicable)

[From NFPA 74 - 1989, 7-1.2.4]

(e) Spacing rating (if applicable)

[From NFPA 74 - 1989, 7-1.2.5]

(f) Operating instructions

[From NFPA 74 - 1989, 7-1.2.6]

(g) Test instructions

[From NFPA 74 - 1989, 7-1.2.7]

(h) Maintenance instructions

[From NFPA 74 - 1989, 7-1.2.8]

(i) Replacement and service instructions.

Exception: When space limitations prohibit inclusion of 2-7.1(g), 2-7.1(h), and 2-7.1(i), a permanent label or plaque suitable for permanent attachment within the living unit shall be provided with the equipment and referenced on the equipment. In the case of a household fire warning system, the required information shall be prominently displayed at the control panel.

[From NFPA 74 - 1989, 7-1.2.9)

Chapter 3 Protected Premises Fire Alarm Systems

3-1 Scope. This chapter provides requirements for the application, installation, and performance of fire alarm systems, including fire alarm and supervisory signals, within protected premises.

3-2 General. The systems covered in this chapter are intended to be used for the protection of life by automatically indicating the necessity for evacuation of the building or fire area, and for the protection of property through the automatic notification of responsible persons and for the automatic activation of fire safety functions. The requirements of the other chapters shall also apply except where they conflict with the requirements of this chapter.

[New paragraphs]

Exception: For household fire warning equipment protecting a single living unit, see Chapter 2.

[From NFPA 72 - 1990, 6-1 modified]

3-2.1 Systems requiring transmission of signals to continually manned locations providing supervising station service (e.g., central station, proprietary, remote station) shall also comply with the applicable requirements of Chapter 4.

3-2.2 All protected premises fire alarm systems shall be maintained and tested in accordance with Chapter 7.

3-2.3 Fire alarm systems provided for evacuation of occupants shall have one or more notification appliances listed for the purpose on each floor of the building, so located that they shall have the characteristics for public mode described in Chapter 6.

[New paragraphs]

3-2.4* The system shall be so designed and installed that attack by fire:

(a) in an evacuation zone, causing loss of communications to this evacuation zone, shall not result in loss of communications to any other evacuation zone.

(b) causing failure of equipment or a fault on one or more installation wiring conductors of one communications path shall not result in total loss of communications to any evacuation zone.

[From NFPA 72 - 1990, 10-3.1 modified]

Exception No. 1 to (a) and (b): Systems that, on alarm, automatically sound evacuation signals throughout the protected premises.

Exception No. 2 to (a) and (b): Where there is a separate means acceptable to the authority having jurisdiction for voice communications to each floor or evacuation zone.

Exception No. 3 to (b): The fire command station and the central control equipment.

Exception No. 4 to (b): Where the installation wiring is enclosed in a 2-hour rated enclosure, other than a stairwell.

[From NFPA 72 - 1990, 10-3.1)

Exception No. 5 to (b): Where the installation wiring is enclosed within a 2-hour rated stairwell in a fully sprinklered building in accordance with NFPA 13, Standard for the Installation of Sprinkler Systems.

[From NFPA 72 - 1990, 10-3.1 modified]

Exception No. 6 to (b): When the evacuation zone is directly attacked by fire within the zone.

[From NFPA 72 - 1990, 10-3.1]

3-3 Applications. Protected premises fire alarm systems include one or more of the following features:

(a) Manual alarm signal initiation

(b) Automatic alarm signal initiation

(c) Monitoring of abnormal conditions in fire suppression systems

(d) Activation of fire suppression systems

(e) Activation of fire safety functions

(f) Activation of alarm notification appliances

(g) Emergency voice/alarm communications

(h) Guard's tour supervisory service

(i) Process monitoring supervisory systems

(j) Activation of off-premises signals

(k) Combination systems

(l) Integrated systems.

[From NFPA 72 - 1990, 3-1 modified]

3-4 Performance of Initiating Device, Notification Appliance, and Signaling Line Circuits.

3-4.1* Circuit Designations. Initiating device, notification appliance, and signaling line circuits shall be designated by class or style, or both, depending on the circuits' capability of being able to continue to operate during specified fault conditions.

3-4.1.1 Class. Initiating device, notification appliance, and signaling line circuits shall be permitted to be designated as either Class A or Class B, depending on the capability of the circuit to transmit alarm and trouble signals during nonsimultaneous single circuit fault conditions as specified by the following:

(a) Circuits capable of transmitting an alarm signal during a single open or a nonsimultaneous single ground fault on a circuit conductor shall be designated as Class A.

(b) Circuits not capable of transmitting an alarm beyond the location of the fault conditions specified in (a) above shall be designated as Class B.

Faults on both Class A and Class B circuits shall result in a trouble condition on the system in accordance with the requirements of 1-5.8.

3-4.1.2 Style. Initiating device, notification appliance, and signaling line circuits shall be permitted to also be designated by style depending on the capability of the circuit to transmit alarm and trouble signals during specified simultaneous multiple circuit fault conditions in addition to the single circuit fault conditions considered in the designation of the circuits by class.

(a) An initiating device circuit shall be permitted to be designated as either Style A, B, C, D, or E, depending on its ability to meet the alarm and trouble performance requirements shown in Table 3-5.1, during a single open, single ground, wire-to-wire short, or loss of carrier fault condition.

(b) A notification appliance circuit shall be permitted to be designated as either Style W, X, Y, or Z, depending on its ability to meet the alarm and trouble performance requirements shown in Table 3-7.1, during a single open, single ground, or wire-to-wire short fault condition.

(c) A signaling line circuit shall be permitted to be designated as either Style 0.5, 1, 2, 3, 3.5, 4, 4.5, 5, 6, or 7, depending on its ability to meet the alarm and trouble performance requirements shown in Table 3-6.1, during a single open, single ground, wire-to-wire short, simultaneous wire-to-wire short and open, simultaneous wire-to-wire short and ground, simultaneous open and ground, and loss of carrier fault conditions.

3-4.2* All styles of Class A circuits using physical conductors (metallic, optical fiber) shall be installed such that the outgoing and return conductors, exiting from and returning to the control unit respectively, are routed separately. The outgoing and return (redundant) circuit conductors shall not be run in the same cable assembly (multiconductor cable), enclosure, or raceway.

Exception No. 1: For a distance not to exceed 10 ft (3 m) where the outgoing and return conductors enter or exit initiating device, notification appliance, or control unit enclosures; or

[New paragraphs]

Exception No. 2: Where the vertically run conductors are enclosed (installed) in a 2-hour rated enclosure other than a stairwell; or

Exception No. 3: Where the vertically run conductors are enclosed (installed) in a 2-hour rated stairwell in a building fully sprinklered in accordance with NFPA 13, Standard for the Installation of Sprinkler Systems.

[From NFPA 72 - 1990, 2-6 modified]

Exception No. 4: Where looped conduit/raceway systems are provided, single conduit/raceway drops to individual devices or appliances shall be permitted.

Exception No. 5: Where looped conduit/raceway systems are provided, single conduit/raceway drops to multiple devices or appliances installed within a single room not exceeding 1000 sq ft (92.9 m^2) in area shall be permitted.

[New paragraphs]

3-5 Performance and Capacities of Initiating Device Circuits (IDC).

[From NFPA 72 - 1990, 2-6 modified]

3-5.1* The assignment of class designations, style designations, or both to initiating device circuits shall be based on their performance capabilities under abnormal (fault) conditions in accordance with the requirements of Table 3-5.1.

Table 3-5.1 Performance and Capacities of Initiating Device Circuits (IDC)

G = Systems with ground detection shall indicate systems trouble with a single ground.
R = Required capability.
X = Indication required at protected premises and as required by Chapter 4.
α = Style exceeds minimum requirements for Class A.
* = See A-3-5.1.

Class	B			B			B			A			A		
Style	A			B			C			D			Eα		
	Alarm	Trouble	Alarm Receipt Capability During Abnormal Condition	Alarm	Trouble	Alarm Receipt Capability During Abnormal Condition	Alarm	Trouble	Alarm Receipt Capability During Abnormal Condition	Alarm	Trouble	Alarm Receipt Capability During Abnormal Condition	Alarm	Trouble	Alarm Receipt Capability During Abnormal Condition
Abnormal Condition	1	2	3	4	5	6	7	8	9	10	11	12	13	14	15
A. Single Open		X			X			X			X	X		X	X
B. Single Ground		R			G	R		G	R		G	R		G	R
C. Wire-to-Wire Short	X			X				X		X				X	
D. Loss of Carrier (If Used)/Channel Interface								X						X	
Note: The following sections apply only where signals are transmitted to a proprietary supervising station in accordance with Section 4-4.															
E. Maximum Quantity per Initiating Device Circuit															
1. Fire Alarm															
(a) Manual Fire Alarm Boxes		2			5			5			25			25	
(b) Water Flow Alarm Devices		1			2			2			5			5	
(c) Discharge Alarm from Other Fire Suppression Systems		1			2			2			5			5	
(d) Automatic Fire Detectors		*			*			*			*			*	
2. Fire Supervisory															
(a) Sprinkler Supervisory Devices		2			4			4			20			20	
(b) Other Fire Suppression Supervisory Devices		2			4			4			20			20	
3. Guard's Tour		1			1			1			1			1	
4. Process, Security, and Other Devices in Combination with 1, 2, and 3 Above		0			0			0			0			0	
5. Process, Security, and Other Devices Not Combined with 1, 2, and 3 Above		5			10			10			20			20	
6. Buildings		1			1			1			1			1	
7. Intermediate Fire Alarm or Fire Supervisory Control Unit		1			1			1			1			1	
F. Maximum Quantity of Initiating Device Circuits per Circuit Interface Between IDC & SLC															
1. Per Limits of E above		10			10			10			10			10	
2. With Following Limitations Fulfilled		10			20			20			50			50	
(a) One Water Flow per IDC															
(b) Maximum of Four Sprinkler Supervisory Devices															
(c) Maximum of Five Process, Security, and Other Devices on a Separate IDC															
(d) Maximum of One Intermediate Fire Alarm or Fire Supervisory Control Unit per IDC															

[From NFPA 72 - 1990, 2-6.2 modified]

3-5.2 The loading of initiating device circuits on systems connected to a proprietary supervising station shall not exceed the capacities listed in Table 3-5.1 for their assigned style designations. The loading of initiating device circuits designated only as Class A or Class B (without a style designation) shall not exceed the capacities for the style with the lowest capacities in their class (Style A for Class B circuits, and Styles D or E for Class A circuits).

NOTE: Though Styles D and E have been assigned the same capacities, the choice between the two styles depends on the desired system performance. Style D circuits transmit an alarm signal, while Style E circuits only transmit a trouble signal on the occurrence of a wire-to-wire short on the circuit. A similar distinction exists between Class B, Styles B and C, which have also been assigned the same capacities.

[New paragraphs]

3-5.3 Numbered initiating device groups listed in Table 3-5.1, Section E, shall not be combined on the same initiating device circuit.

Exception No. 1: When implementing 3-8.1.2, manual means and automatic means shall be permitted to be combined on the same initiating device circuit.

Exception No. 2: Where only one fire alarm box is required, it shall be permitted to be connected to the waterflow initiating device circuit.

[From NFPA 72 - 1990, 2-6.3]

3-6 Performance and Capacities of Signaling Line Circuits (SLC).

[From NFPA 72 - 1990, 2-7 modified]

3-6.1* The assignment of class designations or style designations, or both, to signaling line circuits shall be based on their performance capabilities under abnormal (fault) conditions in accordance with the requirements of Table 3-6.1.

[New paragraph]

3-6.2 The loading of signaling line circuits shall not exceed the capacities listed in Table 3-6.1 for their assigned style designation. The loading of signaling line circuits designated only as Class A or Class B (without a style designation) shall not exceed the capacities for the style with the lowest capacities in their class (Styles 0.5 or 1 for Class B circuits, and Style 2 for Class A circuits).

NOTE: Sections H and I of Table 3-6.1 provide information regarding capacities where protected premises fire alarm equipment, as covered in this chapter, is used in a proprietary fire alarm system. For information regarding proprietary supervisory stations, see Section 4-4.

Exception: Where a Class A signaling line circuit is so arranged that a single open or ground fault, or short circuit between wires of the same signaling line circuit does not cause the loss of fire alarm signals from more than a single zone as defined in 1-5.7.3 and 1-5.7.6, the maximum number of initiating devices per signaling line circuit shall be unlimited.

3-7 Notification Appliance Circuits (NAC).

3-7.1 Performance. The assignment of class designations or style designations, or both, to notification appliance circuits shall be based on their performance capabilities under abnormal (fault) conditions in accordance with the requirements of Table 3-7.1.

[New paragraphs and title]

3-7.2 Distinctive Evacuation Signal.

(a)* Section 1-5.4.7 requires that fire alarm signals be distinctive in sound from other signals and that this sound not be used for any other purpose. To meet this requirement, the fire alarm signal used to notify building occupants of the need to evacuate (leave the building) shall be ANSI S3.41, *American National Standard Audible Emergency Evacuation Signal*. This requirement shall become effective July 1, 1996.

(b) The use of the American National Standard Audible Emergency Evacuation Signal shall be restricted to situations where it is desired to have all occupants hearing the signal evacuate the building immediately. It shall not be used where, with the approval of the authority having jurisdiction, the planned action during a fire emergency is not evacuation, but relocation of the occupants from the affected area to a safe area within the building, or their protection in place (e.g., high rise buildings, health care facilities, penal institutions, etc.).

3-8 System Requirements. (*See also Section 5-9.*)

3-8.1 Manual Fire Alarm Signal Initiation.

[New paragraphs and titles]

3-8.1.1 Fire alarm boxes shall be listed for the intended application, installed in accordance with Chapter 5, and tested in accordance with Chapter 7.

[From NFPA 71 and 72, 3-2.2 modified]

3-8.1.2 For fire alarm systems employing automatic fire detectors or waterflow detection devices, at least one fire alarm box shall be provided to initiate a fire alarm signal. This fire alarm box shall be located where required by the authority having jurisdiction.

[From NFPA 72 - 1990, 3-2.4 modified]

Exception: Fire alarm systems dedicated to elevator recall control and supervisory as permitted in 3-8.15.1.

[From NFPA 71 - 1989, 3-3.2.1 modified]

3-8.1.3 Where signals from fire alarm boxes and other fire alarm initiating devices within a building are transmitted over the same signaling line circuit, there shall be no interference with fire alarm box signals when both types of initiating devices are operated at or near the same time. Provision of the shunt noninterfering method of operation shall be acceptable for this performance.

[From NFPA 72 - 1990, 3-2.5]

3-8.2 Automatic Fire Alarm Signal Initiation.

[From NFPA 72 - 1990, 3-3 modified]

3-8.2.1 Automatic alarm initiating devices shall be listed for the intended application and installed in accordance with Chapter 5.

[From NFPA 72 - 1990, 3-3.1 modified]

Table 3-6.1 Performance and Capacities of Signaling Line Circuits (SLC)

G = Systems with ground detection shall indicate system trouble with a single ground.
M = May be capable of alarm with wire-to-wire short.
R = Required capability.
X = Indication required at protected premises and as required by Chapter 4.
α = Style exceeds minimum requirements for Class A.

Class	B			B			A			B			B			B			B			A			A			A		
Style	0.5			1			2α			3			3.5			4			4.5			5α			6α			7α		
	Alarm	Trouble	Alarm Receipt Capability During Abnormal Condition	Alarm	Trouble	Alarm Receipt Capability During Abnormal Condition	Alarm	Trouble	Alarm Receipt Capability During Abnormal Condition	Alarm	Trouble	Alarm Receipt Capability During Abnormal Condition	Alarm	Trouble	Alarm Receipt Capability During Abnormal Condition	Alarm	Trouble	Alarm Receipt Capability During Abnormal Condition	Alarm	Trouble	Alarm Receipt Capability During Abnormal Condition	Alarm	Trouble	Alarm Receipt Capability During Abnormal Condition	Alarm	Trouble	Alarm Receipt Capability During Abnormal Condition	Alarm	Trouble	Alarm Receipt Capability During Abnormal Condition
Abnormal Condition	1	2	3	4	5	6	7	8	9	10	11	12	13	14	15	16	17	18	19	20	21	22	23	24	25	26	27	28	29	30
A. Single Open		X			X			X	R		X			X			X			X	R		X	R		X	R		X	R
B. Single Ground		X			G	R		G	R		G	R		X			G	R		X			G	R		G	R		G	R
C. Wire-to-Wire Short									M		X			X			X			X			X			X			X	R
D. Wire-to-Wire Short & Open									M		X			X			X			X			X			X			X	
E. Wire-to-Wire Short & Ground								G	M		X			X			X			X			X			X			X	
F. Open and Ground								X	R		X			X			X			X			X			X	X		X	R
G. Loss of Carrier (If Used)/ Channel Interface														X			X			X			X			X			X	

Note: The following sections apply only where signals are transmitted to a proprietary supervising station in accordance with Section 4-4.

	0.5	1	2α	3	3.5	4	4.5	5α	6α	7α
H. Maximum quanitity per Signaling Line Circuit β										
1. Initiating Devices (All Types)	250	250	250	300	300	500	500	750	1000	unlimited
2. Buildings	25	25	25	50	50	75	75	75	100	100
I. Maximum Quantity per Proprietary Supervising Station (PSS)										
1. Initiating Device Circuits	500	500	500	1000	1000	1000	1000	1500	2000	2000
2. IDCs with Redundant PSS Control Equipment[1]	1000	1000	1000	2000	2000	2000	2000	3000	unlimited	unlimited
3. Buildings	25	25	25	25	25	50	50	75	400	400
4. Buildings with Redundant PSS Control Equipment[1]	25	25	25	50	50	100	100	150	unlimited	unlimited

Note 1: When the supervisory station multiplex control unit is duplicated and a switchover can be accomplished in not more than 90 seconds with no loss of signals during this period, the capacity of the system is unlimited.
β = See the exception to 3-6.2.

[From NFPA 72 - 1990, 2-7.2 modified]

Table 3-7.1 Notification Appliance Circuits (NAC)

Class	B		B		B		A	
Style	W		X		Y		Z	
G = Systems with ground detection shall indicate system trouble with a single ground. X = Indication required at protected premises.	Trouble Indication at Protected Premises	Alarm Capability During Abnormal Conditions	Trouble Indication at Protected Premises	Alarm Capability During Abnormal Conditions	Trouble Indication at Protected Premises	Alarm Capability During Abnormal Conditions	Trouble Indication at Protected Premises	Alarm Capability During Abnormal Condition
Abnormal Condition	1	2	3	4	5	6	7	8
Single Open	X		X	X	X		X	X
Single Ground	X		X		G	X	G	X
Wire-to-Wire Short	X		X		X		X	

[From NFPA 72 - 1990, 6-4 modified]

3-8.2.2 Automatic alarm initiating devices having integral trouble contacts shall be wired on the initiating device circuit so that a trouble condition within a device does not impair the alarm transmission from any other initiating device.

NOTE: Though a trouble signal is required when a plug-in initiating device is removed from its base, it is not considered as a trouble condition within the device and the requirement of 3-8.2.2 does not apply.

[From NFPA 72 - 1990, 3-3.2]

3-8.2.3* Systems equipped with alarm verification features shall be permitted, provided:

(a) A smoke detector continuously subjected to a smoke concentration above alarm threshold magnitude initiates a system alarm within 1 minute.

(b) Actuation of an alarm initiating device other than a smoke detector shall cause a system alarm signal within 15 seconds.

[From NFPA 72 - 1990, 3-3.3 modified]

3-8.2.4 Where individual alarm initiating devices are used to control the operation of equipment as permitted by 1-5.4.1, this control capability shall remain operable even if all of the initiating devices connected to the same circuit are in an alarm state.

[From NFPA 72 - 1990, 3-3.4 modified]

3-8.2.5 Systems that require the operation of two automatic detection devices to initiate the alarm response shall be permitted, provided:

(a) They are not prohibited by the authority having jurisdiction.

(b) There are at least two automatic detection devices in each protected space.

(c) Automatic detection device area spacing is no more than one-half that determined by the application of Chapter 5.

(d) The alarm verification feature is not used.

[From NFPA 72 - 1990, 3-3.5 modified]

3-8.3 Positive Alarm Sequence.

3-8.3.1 Systems having positive alarm features complying with the following shall be permitted where approved by the authority having jurisdiction.

[From NFPA 72 - 1990, 3-3.6 modified]

3-8.3.1.1 The signal from an automatic fire detection device selected for positive alarm sequence operation shall be acknowledged at the control unit by trained personnel within 15 seconds of annunciation in order to initiate the alarm investigation phase. If the signal is not acknowledged within 15 seconds, all building and remote signals shall be activated immediately and automatically.

[From NFPA 72 - 1990, 3-3.6.1 modified]

3-8.3.1.2 Trained personnel shall have up to 180 seconds during the alarm investigation phase to evaluate the fire condition and reset the system. If the system is not reset during this investigation phase, all building and remote signals shall be activated immediately and automatically.

[From NFPA 72 - 1990, 3-3.6.2 modified]

3-8.3.2 If a second automatic fire detector selected for positive alarm sequence is actuated during the alarm investigation phase, all normal building and remote signals shall be activated immediately and automatically.

[From NFPA 72 - 1990, 3-3.6.3 modified]

3-8.3.3 If any other initiating device is actuated, all building and remote signals shall be activated immediately and automatically.

[From NFPA 72 - 1990, 3-3.6.4 modified]

3-8.3.4* The system shall provide means to bypass the positive alarm sequence.

[From NFPA 72 - 1990, 3-3.6.5]

3-8.4* Concealed Detectors. Where a remote alarm indicator is provided for an automatic fire detector in a concealed location, the location of the detector and the area protected by the detector shall be prominently indicated either at the remote alarm indicator by a permanently attached placard or by other approved means.

[From NFPA 72 - 1990, 3-3.7]

3-8.5 Automatic Drift Compensation. Where automatic drift compensation of sensitivity for a fire detector is provided, the control unit shall give an indication identifying the affected detector when the limit of compensation is reached.

[New paragraph]

3-8.6 Waterflow Alarm Signal Initiation.
[From NFPA 72 - 1990, 3-4.1 modified]

3-8.6.1 The provisions of 3-8.6 apply to sprinkler system signaling attachments that initiate an alarm indicating a flow of water in the system. Waterflow initiating devices shall be listed for the intended application and installed in accordance with Chapter 5.
[From NFPA 72 - 1990, 3-4.1.1 modified]

3-8.6.2 A dry-pipe or preaction sprinkler system that is supplied with water by a connection beyond the alarm initiating device of a wet-pipe system shall be equipped with a separate waterflow alarm initiating pressure switch or other approved means to initiate a waterflow alarm.
[From NFPA 72 - 1990, 3-4.1.4 modified]

3-8.6.3 The number of waterflow switches permitted to be connected to a single initiating device circuit shall not exceed five.
[From NFPA 72 - 1990, 6-2.2 modified, and NFPA 71, 6-4.1.2]

3-8.7 Supervisory Signal Initiation.
[From NFPA 72 - 1990, 3-4.2 modified]

3-8.7.1 General. The provisions of this section apply to the monitoring of sprinkler and other fire protection systems for the initiation of a supervisory signal indicating an off-normal condition that may adversely affect the performance of the system.
[From NFPA 72 - 1990, 3-4.2.1 modified]

3-8.7.1.1 Supervisory devices shall be listed for the intended application and installed in accordance with Chapter 5.
[New paragraph]

3-8.7.1.2 The number of supervisory devices permitted to be connected to a single initiating device circuit shall not exceed 20.
[From NFPA 71, 6-4.2 modified, and NFPA 72 - 1990, 6-2.3 modified]

3-8.7.2* Provisions shall be made for supervising the conditions that are essential for the proper operation of sprinkler and other fire suppression systems.
[From NFPA 72 - 1990, 3-4.2.2 modified]

Exception: Those conditions related to water mains, tanks, cisterns, reservoirs, and other water supplies controlled by a municipality or a public utility.
[From NFPA 72 - 1990, 3-4.2.2 Exception]

3-8.7.3 Signals shall distinctively indicate the particular function (such as valve position, temperature, pressure, etc.) of the system that is off-normal and also indicate its restoration to normal.
[From NFPA 72 - 1990, 3-4.2.3 modified]

NOTE: Cancellation of the off-normal signal is acceptable as a restoration signal except where separate recording of all changes of state is a specific requirement. (*See Chapter 4.*)
[From NFPA 72 - 1990, 3-4.2.5 modified]

3-8.7.4 A dry-pipe sprinkler system equipped for waterflow alarm signaling shall be supervised for off-normal system air pressure.
[From NFPA 72 - 1990, 3-4.2.4 modified]

3-8.7.5 A control valve shall be supervised to initiate a distinctive signal indicating movement of the valve from its normal position. The off-normal signal shall remain until the valve is restored to its normal position. The off-normal signal shall be obtained during the first two revolutions of the hand wheel or during one-fifth of the travel distance of the valve control apparatus from its normal position.
[From NFPA 72 - 1990, 3-4.2.5 modified]

3-8.7.6 An initiating device for supervising the position of a control valve shall not interfere with the operation of the valve, obstruct the view of its indicator, or prevent access for valve maintenance.
[New paragraph]

3-8.7.7 Pressure Supervision. Pressure sources shall be supervised to obtain two separate and distinct signals, one indicating that the required pressure has been increased or decreased, and the other indicating restoration of the pressure to its required value.

(a) A pressure supervisory signal initiating device for a pressure tank shall indicate both high and low pressure conditions. A signal shall be obtained where the required pressure is increased or decreased 10 psi (70 kPa) from the required pressure value.

(b) A pressure supervisory signal initiating device for a dry-pipe sprinkler system shall indicate both high and low pressure conditions. A signal shall be obtained when the required pressure is increased or decreased 10 psi (70 kPa) from the required pressure value.

(c) A steam pressure supervisory initiating device shall indicate a low pressure condition. A signal shall be obtained where the pressure is reduced to a value that is 110 percent of the minimum operating pressure of the steam operated equipment supplied.

(d) An initiating device for supervising the pressure of sources other than those specified above shall be provided as required by the authority having jurisdiction.

3-8.7.8 Water Temperature Supervision. Exposed water storage containers shall be supervised to obtain two separate and distinct signals, one indicating that the temperature of the water has been lowered to 40°F (4.4°C), and the other indicating restoration to a temperature above 40°F (4.4°C).
[From NFPA 71 - 1989]

3-8.8 Signal Annunciation. Protected premises fire alarm systems shall be arranged to annunciate alarm, supervisory, and trouble signals in accordance with 1-5.7.
[New paragraph]

3-8.9 Signal Initiation from Automatic Fire Suppression System Other Than Waterflow.
[From NFPA 71, 3-4.3]

3-8.9.1 The operation of an automatic fire suppression system installed within the protected premises shall be indicated on the protected premises fire alarm system.
[From NFPA 71, 3-4.3.1]

3-8.9.2 A supervisory signal shall indicate the off-normal condition and its restoration to normal appropriate to the system employed.

[From NFPA 71, 3-4.4.1 modified]

3-8.9.3 The integrity of each fire suppression system actuating device and its circuit shall be supervised in accordance with 1-5.8.1 and with other applicable NFPA standards.

[From NFPA 72 - 1990, 3-7.2.1 modified]

3-8.10 Pump Supervision. Automatic fire pumps and special service pumps shall be supervised in accordance with NFPA 20, *Standard for the Installation of Centrifugal Fire Pumps*, and the authority having jurisdiction.

[From NFPA 72 - 1990, 3-4.2.9 modified]

3-8.10.1 Supervision of electric power supplying the pump shall be made on the line side of the motor starter. All phases and phase reversal shall be supervised.

[From NFPA 71, 3-4.4.6 modified]

3-8.10.2 Where both sprinkler supervisory signals and pump running signals are transmitted over the same signaling circuits, provisions shall be made to obtain pump running signal preference unless the circuit is so arranged that no signals will be lost.

[From NFPA 72 - 1990, 3-4.2.9]

3-8.11 Tampering.

[From NFPA 72, 3-4.3]

3-8.11.1 Automatic fire suppression system alarm and supervisory signal initiating devices and their circuits shall be so designed and installed that they cannot be readily tampered with, opened, or removed without initiating a signal. This provision specifically includes junction boxes installed outside of buildings to facilitate access to the initiating device circuit.

[From NFPA 72 - 1990, 3-4.3.1 modified]

3-8.11.2* If a valve is installed in the connection between a signal attachment and the fire suppression system to which it is attached, such a valve shall be supervised in accordance with the requirements of Chapter 5.

[From NFPA 72 - 1990, 3-4.3.2]

3-8.12 Guard's Tour Supervisory Service.

[From NFPA 72 - 1990, 3-5 modified]

3-8.12.1 Guard's tour reporting stations shall be listed for the application.

[New paragraph]

3-8.12.2 The number of guard's tour reporting stations, their locations, and the route to be followed by the guard for operating the stations shall be approved for the particular installation in accordance with NFPA 601, *Standard on Guard Service in Fire Loss Prevention*.

[From NFPA 72 - 1990, 3-5.1.1 modified]

3-8.12.3 A permanent record indicating every time each signal-transmitting station is operated shall be made at the main control unit. Where intermediate stations that do not transmit a signal are employed in conjunction with signal-transmitting stations, distinctive signals shall be transmitted at the beginning and end of each tour of a guard, and a signal-transmitting station shall be provided at intervals not exceeding ten stations. Intermediate stations that do not transmit a signal shall be capable of operation only in a fixed sequence.

[From NFPA 72 - 1990, 3-5.1.3 and 3-5.2.7]

3-8.13 Suppressed (Exception Reporting) Signal System.

[From NFPA 72 - 1990, 3-5.2]

3-8.13.1 The system shall comply with the provisions of 3-8.12.2.

[From NFPA 72 - 1990, 3-5.2.1, and NFPA 71, 3-2.2.1]

3-8.13.2 The system shall transmit a start signal to the signal-receiving location and shall be initiated by the guard at the start of continuous tour rounds.

[From NFPA 72 - 1990, 3-5.2.2 modified, and NFPA 71, 3-2.2.2]

3-8.13.3 The system shall automatically transmit a delinquency signal within 15 minutes after the predetermined actuation time if the guard fails to actuate a tour station as scheduled.

[From NFPA 72 - 1990, 3-5.2.3, and NFPA 71, 3-2.2.3]

3-8.13.4 A finish signal shall be transmitted within a predetermined interval after the guard completes each tour of the premises.

[From NFPA 72 - 1990, 3-5.2.4, and NFPA 71, 3-2.2.4]

3-8.13.5 For periods of over 24 hours, during which tours are continuously conducted, a start signal shall be transmitted at least every 24 hours.

[From NFPA 72 - 1990, 3-5.2.5, and NFPA 71, 3-2.2.6]

3-8.13.6 The start, delinquency, and finish signals shall be recorded at the signal-receiving location.

[From NFPA 72 - 1990, 3-5.2.6 modified, and NFPA 71, 3-2.2.7]

3-8.14 Combination Systems.

[From NFPA 72 - 1990, 3-6]

3-8.14.1* Fire alarm systems shall be permitted to share components, equipment, circuitry, and installation wiring with nonfire alarm systems.

[From NFPA 72 - 1990, 3-6.1 modified]

3-8.14.2 Where common wiring is employed for combination systems, the equipment for other than fire alarm systems shall be permitted to be connected to the common wiring of the system. Short circuits, open circuits, or grounds in this equipment or between this equipment and the fire alarm system wiring shall not interfere with the supervision of the fire alarm system or prevent alarm or supervisory signal transmissions.

[From NFPA 72 - 1990, 3-6.2 modified]

3-8.14.3 To maintain the integrity of fire alarm system functions, the removal, replacement, failure, or maintenance procedure on any hardware, software, or circuit not required to perform any of the fire alarm system functions shall not cause loss of any of these functions.

[From NFPA 72 - 1990, 3-6.3]

Exception: Where the hardware, software, and circuits are listed for fire alarm use.

3-8.14.4 Speakers used as alarm notification appliances on fire alarm systems shall not be used for nonemergency purposes.

[New paragraphs]

Exception: Where the fire command station is constantly attended by a trained operator, selective paging shall be permitted.

[From NFPA 72 - 1990, 3-6.4]

3-8.14.5 In combination systems, fire alarm signals shall be distinctive, clearly recognizable, and take precedence over any other signal even when a nonfire alarm signal is initiated first.

[From NFPA 72 - 1990, 3-6.5 modified]

3-8.15 Elevator Recall for Fire Fighters' Service.

[From NFPA 72 - 1990, 3-7.3]

3-8.15.1* System type smoke detectors located in elevator lobbies, elevator hoistways, and elevator machine rooms, which are used to initiate fire fighters' service recall, shall be connected to the building fire alarm system. In facilities without a building fire alarm system, these smoke detectors shall be connected to a dedicated fire alarm system control unit that shall be designated "Elevator Recall Control and Supervisory Panel" on the record drawings. Unless otherwise required by the authority having jurisdiction, only the elevator lobby, elevator hoistway, and the elevator machine room smoke detectors shall be used to recall elevators for fire fighters' service.

[From NFPA 72 - 1990, 3-7.3.1 modified]

3-8.15.2 Each elevator lobby, elevator hoistway, and elevator machine room smoke detector shall be capable of initiating elevator recall when all other devices on the same initiating device circuit have been manually or automatically placed in the alarm condition.

[From NFPA 72 - 1990, 3-7.3.2]

3-8.15.3 When actuated, each elevator lobby, elevator hoistway, and elevator machine room smoke detector shall initiate an alarm condition on the building fire alarm system and shall visibly indicate, at the control unit and required remote annunciators, the alarm initiation circuit or zone from which the alarm originated.

[From NFPA 72 - 1990, 3-7.3.3]

Exception: Where approved by the authority having jurisdiction, the elevator hoistway and machine room detectors shall be permitted to initiate a supervisory signal.

[New paragraph]

3-8.15.4* For each group of elevators within a building, two elevator control circuits shall be terminated at the designated elevator controller within the group's elevator machine room(s). The operation of the elevators shall be in accordance with ANSI/ASME A17.1, *Safety Code for Elevators and Escalators*, Rules 211.3 through 211.8. The smoke detectors shall be connected to the two elevator control circuits as follows:

(a) The smoke detector located in the designated elevator recall lobby shall be connected to the first elevator control circuit.

[From NFPA 72 - 1990, 3-7.3.5]

(b) The smoke detectors in the remaining elevator lobbies, elevator hoistways, and the elevator machine room shall be connected to the second elevator control circuit except that when the elevator machine room is located at the designated landing, then that elevator machine room smoke detector shall be connected to the first elevator control circuit. In addition, where the elevator is equipped with front and rear doors, then the smoke detectors in both lobbies at the designated level shall be connected to the first elevator control circuit.

3-8.16 Elevator Shutdown.

3-8.16.1* Where heat detectors are used to shut down elevator power prior to sprinkler operation, the detector shall have both a lower temperature rating and a higher sensitivity [often characterized by a lower Response Time Index (RTI)] when compared to the sprinkler.

3-8.16.2 Where heat detectors are used for elevator power shutdown prior to sprinkler operation, they shall be placed within 2 feet of each sprinkler head and be installed in accordance with the requirements of Chapter 5. Alternatively, engineering methods (such as in Appendix B) shall be permitted to be used to select and place heat detectors to ensure response prior to any sprinkler head under a variety of fire growth rate scenarios.

3-8.16.3* Where pressure or waterflow switches are used to shut down elevator power immediately upon or prior to the discharge of water from sprinklers, the use of devices with time delays shall not be permitted.

3-9 Fire Safety Control Functions.

3-9.1 Scope. The provisions of this section apply to the minimum requirements for the interconnection of fire safety control functions (e.g., fan control, door control, etc.) to the fire alarm system. These fire safety functions are not intended to provide notification of alarm, supervisory, or trouble conditions; alert or control occupants; or summon aid.

3-9.2 General.

3-9.2.1 An auxiliary relay connected to the fire alarm system used to initiate control of fire safety functions shall be located within 3 ft (1 m) of the controlled circuit or device. The auxiliary relay shall function within the voltage and current limitations of the control unit. The installation wiring between the fire alarm system control unit and the auxiliary relay shall be monitored for integrity.

Exception: Control devices that operate on loss of power or on loss of power to the auxiliary relay shall be considered self-monitoring for integrity.

3-9.2.2 Fire safety functions shall not interfere with other operations of the fire alarm control system.

3-9.2.3 Transfer of data over listed serial communication ports shall be an acceptable means of interfacing between the fire alarm control unit and fire safety function control devices.

3-9.2.4 The fire safety function control devices shall be listed as compatible with the fire alarm control unit, so as not to interfere with the control unit's operation.

3-9.2.5 The interfaced systems shall be acceptance tested together in the presence of the authority having jurisdiction to ensure proper operation of the fire alarm system and the interfaced system(s).

3-9.2.6 Where manual controls for emergency control functions are required to be provided, they shall provide visible indication of the status of the associated control circuits.

3-9.3 Heating, Ventilation, and Air Conditioning (HVAC) Systems.

3-9.3.1 The provisions of 3-9.3 apply to the basic method by which a fire alarm system interfaces with the HVAC systems.

3-9.3.2 All detection devices used to cause the operation of smoke dampers, fire dampers, fan control, smoke doors, and fire doors shall be monitored for integrity in accordance with 1-5.8 where connected to the fire alarm system serving the protected premises.

3-9.3.3 Connections between fire alarm systems and the HVAC system for the purpose of monitoring and control shall operate and be monitored in accordance with applicable NFPA standards.

3-9.4 Door Release Service.

3-9.4.1 This section applies to the methods of connection of door hold release devices and to integral door hold release, closer, and smoke detection devices.

3-9.4.2 All detection devices used for door hold release service, whether integral or stand alone, shall be monitored for integrity in accordance with 1-5.8 where connected to the fire alarm system serving the protected premises.

3-9.4.3 All door hold release and integral door release and closure devices used for release service shall be monitored for integrity in accordance with 3-9.2.

3-9.5 Door Unlocking Devices.

3-9.5.1 Any device or system intended to effect the locking/unlocking of emergency exits shall be connected to the fire alarm system serving the protected premises.

3-9.5.2 All emergency exits connected in accordance with 3-9.5.1 shall unlock upon receipt of any fire alarm signal by the fire alarm system serving the protected premises.

3-9.5.3 All emergency exits connected in accordance with 3-9.5.1 shall unlock upon loss of the primary power to the fire alarm system serving the protected premises. The secondary power supply shall not be utilized to maintain these doors in the locked condition.

3-10 Suppression System Actuation.

3-10.1 Fire alarm systems listed for releasing service shall be permitted to provide automatic or manual actuation of fire suppression systems.

3-10.2 The integrity of each releasing device (e.g., solenoid, relay, etc.) shall be supervised in accordance with applicable NFPA standards.

3-10.3 The integrity of the installation wiring shall be monitored in accordance with the requirements of Chapter 1.

3-10.4 Fire alarm systems used for fire suppression releasing service shall be provided with a disconnect switch to permit system testing without activating the fire suppression systems. Operation of the disconnect switch shall cause a trouble signal at the fire alarm control unit.

3-10.5 Sequence of operation shall be consistent with the applicable suppression system standards.

3-10.6* Each space protected by an automatic fire suppression system actuated by the fire alarm system shall contain one or more automatic fire detectors installed in accordance with Chapter 5.

3-11* Interconnected Fire Alarm Control Units. Fire alarm systems shall be permitted to be either integrated systems combining all detection, notification, and auxiliary functions in a single system, or a combination of component subsystems. Fire alarm system components shall be permitted to share control equipment or be able to operate as stand alone subsystems, but shall in any case be arranged to function as a single system. All component subsystems shall be capable of simultaneous, full load operation without degradation of the required, overall system performance.

3-11.1 The method of interconnection of control units shall be by the following recognized means:

(a) Properly rated electrical contacts

(b) Compatible digital data interfaces

(c) Other listed methods

and shall meet the monitoring requirements of 1-5.8 and the requirements of NFPA 70, *National Electrical Code*, Article 760.

3-11.2 Where approved by the authority having jurisdiction, interconnected control units providing localized detection, evacuation signaling, and auxiliary functions shall be permitted to be monitored by a fire alarm system as initiating devices.

3-11.2.1 Each interconnected control unit shall be separately monitored for alarm, trouble, and supervisory conditions.

3-11.2.2 Interconnected control unit alarm signals shall be permitted to be monitored by zone or combined as common signals as appropriate.

[New paragraphs and titles]

3-12 Emergency Voice/Alarm Communications.
[From NFPA 72 - 1990, Chap. 10]

3-12.1 Application. This section describes the requirements for emergency voice/alarm communications. The primary purpose is to provide dedicated manual and automatic facilities for the origination, control, and transmission of information and instructions pertaining to a fire alarm emergency to the occupants (including fire department personnel) of the building. It is the intent of this section to establish the minimum requirements for emergency voice/alarm communications.

3-12.2 Monitoring the integrity of speaker amplifiers, tone-generating equipment, and two-way telephone communications circuits shall be in accordance with 1-5.8.5.

3-12.3 Survivability.

3-12.3.1 The fire command station and the central control unit shall be located within a minimum 1-hour rated fire-resistive area and shall have a minimum 3-ft (1-m) clearance about the face of the fire command station control equipment.

Exception: Where approved by the authority having jurisdiction, the fire command station control equipment shall be permitted to be located in a lobby or other approved space.
[From NFPA 72 - 1990, 10-3.2 modified]

3-12.3.2 Where the fire command station control equipment is remote from the central control equipment, the wiring between the two shall be installed in conduit or other metal raceway that is routed through areas whose characteristics are at least equal to the limited combustible characteristics as defined in NFPA 90A, *Standard for the Installation of Air Conditioning and Ventilating Systems*. The maximum run of conduit or raceway shall not exceed 100 ft (30 m) or shall be enclosed in a 2-hour fire rated enclosure.
[From NFPA 72 - 1990, 10-3.3]

3-12.3.3 The primary power supply installation wiring between the central control equipment and the main service entrance shall also be routed through areas whose characteristics are at least equal to the limited combustible characteristics as defined in NFPA 90A, *Standard for the Installation of Air Conditioning and Ventilating Systems*.
[From NFPA 72 - 1990, 10-3.4]

3-12.3.4 The secondary (standby) power supply shall be provided in accordance with 1-5.2.5.
[From NFPA 72 - 1990, 10-3.5 modified]

3-12.4 Voice/Alarm Signaling Service.
[From NFPA 72 - 1990, 10-4]

3-12.4.1* General. The purpose of the voice/alarm signaling service is to provide an automatic response to the receipt of a signal indicative of a fire emergency. Subsequent manual control capability of the transmission and audible reproduction of evacuation tone signals, alert tone signals, and voice directions on a selective and all-call basis, as determined by the authority having jurisdiction, is also required from the fire command station.

Exception: Where the fire command station or remote monitoring location is constantly attended by trained operators, and operator acknowledgment of receipt of a fire alarm signal is received within 30 seconds, automatic response is not required.
[From NFPA 72 - 1990, 10-4.1]

3-12.4.2 Multichannel Capability. When required by the authority having jurisdiction, the system shall allow the application of an evacuation signal to one or more zones and, at the same time, shall permit voice paging to the other zones selectively or in any combination.
[From NFPA 72 - 1990, 10-4.2]

3-12.4.3 Functional Sequence.
[From NFPA 72 - 1990, 10-4.3]

3-12.4.3.1 In response to an initiating signal indicative of a fire emergency, the system shall automatically transmit, either immediately or after a delay acceptable to the authority having jurisdiction, the following:
[From NFPA 72 - 1990, 10-4.3.1]

(a) An alert tone of 3 to 10 seconds' duration followed by a message (or messages when multichannel capability is provided) shall be repeated at least three times to direct the occupants of the alarm signal initiation zone and other zones in accordance with the building's fire evacuation plan; or

(b) An evacuation signal to the alarm signal initiation zone and other zones in accordance with the building's fire evacuation plan.
[From NFPA 72 - 1990, 10-4.3.1 modified]

3-12.4.3.2 Failure of the message described by 3-12.4.3.1(a), where used, shall sound the evacuation signal automatically. Provisions for manual initiation of voice instructions or evacuation signal generation shall be provided.

Exception: Different functional sequences shall be permitted where approved by the authority having jurisdiction.
[From NFPA 72 - 1990, 10-4.3.2 modified]

3-12.4.3.3 Live voice instructions shall override all previously initiated signals on that channel.
[From NFPA 72 - 1990, 10-4.3.3]

3-12.4.3.4 Where provided, manual controls for emergency voice/alarm communications shall be arranged to provide visible indication of the on/off status for their associated evacuation zones.
[New paragraph]

3-12.4.4 Voice and Tone Devices. The alert tone preceding any message shall be permitted to be a part of the voice message or to be transmitted automatically from a separate tone generator.
[From NFPA 72 - 1990, 10-4.4.1]

3-12.4.5 Fire Command Station.
[From NFPA 72 - 1990, 10-4.5]

3-12.4.5.1 A fire command station shall be provided near a building entrance or other location approved by the authority having jurisdiction. The fire command station shall provide a communications center for the arriving fire department and shall provide for control and display of the status of detection, alarm, and communications systems. The fire command station shall be permitted to be physically combined with other building operations and security centers as permitted by the authority having jurisdiction. Operating controls for use by the fire department shall be clearly marked.

[From NFPA 72 - 1990, 10-4.5.1]

3-12.4.5.2 The fire command station shall control the emergency voice/alarm communications signaling service and, where provided, the two-way telephone communications service.

[From NFPA 72 - 1990, 10-4.5.2]

3-12.4.6 Loudspeakers.

[From NFPA 72 - 1990, 10-4.6]

3-12.4.6.1 Loudspeakers and their enclosures shall be listed for voice/alarm signaling service and installed in accordance with Chapter 6.

[From NFPA 72 - 1990, 10-4.6.1 modified]

3-12.4.6.2* There shall be at least two loudspeakers in each paging zone of the building, so located that signals can be clearly heard regardless of the maximum noise level produced by machinery or other equipment under normal conditions of occupancy. (*See Section 6-3.*)

[From NFPA 72 - 1990, 10-4.6.2 modified]

3-12.4.6.3 Each elevator car shall be equipped with a single loudspeaker connected to the paging zone serving the elevator group in which the elevator car is located.

[From NFPA 72 - 1990, 10-4.6.3]

3-12.5 Evacuation Signal Zoning.

3-12.5.1 Where two or more evacuation signaling zones are provided, such zones shall be arranged consistent with the fire or smoke barriers within the protected premises. Undivided fire areas shall not be divided into multiple evacuation signaling zones.

NOTE: This section does not prohibit provision of multiple notification appliance circuits within a single evacuation signaling zone (i.e., separate circuits for audible and visible signals, redundant circuits provided to enhance survivability, or multiple circuits necessary to provide sufficient power/capacity).

Exception: Stairwells not exceeding two stories in height.

3-12.5.2 Where multiple notification appliance circuits are provided within an single evacuation signaling zone, all of the notification appliances within the zone shall be arranged to activate simultaneously, either automatically or by actuation of a common, manual control.

Exception: Where the different notification appliance circuits within an evacuation signaling zone perform separate functions (i.e., presignal and general alarm signals, predischarge and discharge signals, etc.).

[New paragraphs and title]

3-12.6 Two-Way Telephone Communications Service.

[From NFPA 72 - 1990, 10-5]

3-12.6.1 Two-way telephone communications equipment shall be listed for two-way telephone communications service and installed in accordance with 3-12.6.

[From NFPA 72 - 1990, 10-5.1 modified]

3-12.6.2 Two-way telephone communications service, where provided, shall be available for use by the fire service. Additional uses, where specifically permitted by the authority having jurisdiction, shall be permitted to include signaling and communication for a building fire warden organization, signaling and communication for reporting a fire and other emergencies, (i.e., voice call box service, signaling, and communication for guard's tour service) and other uses. Variation of equipment and system operation provided to facilitate additional use of the two-way telephone communications service shall not adversely affect performance when used by the fire service.

[From NFPA 72 - 1990, 10-5.2]

3-12.6.3* Two-way telephone communications service shall be capable of permitting the simultaneous operation of any five telephone stations in a common talk mode.

[From NFPA 72 - 1990, 10-5.3]

3-12.6.4 A notification signal at the fire command station, distinctive from any other alarm or trouble signal, shall indicate the off-hook condition of a calling telephone circuit. Where a selective talk telephone communications service is supplied, a distinctive visible indicator shall be furnished for each selectable circuit so that all circuits with telephones off-hook are continuously and visibly indicated.

[From NFPA 72 - 1990, 10-5.5]

3-12.6.5 A switch for silencing the audible call-in signal sounding appliance shall be permitted only if it is key operated, in a locked cabinet, or given equivalent protection from use by unauthorized persons. Such a switch shall be permitted only if it operates a visible indicator and sounds a trouble signal whenever the switch is in the silence position where there are no telephone circuits in an off-hook condition. Where a selective talk telephone system is used, such a switch shall be permitted only if subsequent telephone circuits going off-hook will operate the distinctive off-hook audible signal sounding appliance.

[From NFPA 72 - 1990, 10-5.6]

3-12.6.6 The minimum requirement for fire service use shall be common talk, i.e., a conference or party line circuit. The minimum requirement for fire warden use, where provided, shall be a selective talking system controlled at the fire command station. Either system shall be capable of operation with five telephone stations connected together. There shall be at least one fire service telephone station or jack per floor and at least one per exit stairway. Where provided, there shall be at least one fire warden station or jack to serve each fire paging zone.

[From NFPA 72 - 1990, 10-5.7]

3-12.6.7 Where the control equipment provided does not indicate the location of the caller (common talk systems), each telephone station or phone jack shall be clearly and permanently labeled to allow the caller to readily identify his location to the fire command station by voice.

3-12.6.8 Where telephone jacks are provided, a sufficient quantity of portable handsets, as determined by the authority having jurisdiction, shall be stored at the fire command station for distribution during an incident to responding personnel.

[New paragraphs]

3-13* Special Requirements for Low Power Radio (Wireless) Systems.

[From NFPA 72 - 1990, 6-5 modified]

3-13.1 Compliance with this section shall require the use of low power radio equipment specifically listed for the purpose.

NOTE: Equipment solely listed for household use does not comply with this requirement.

[From NFPA 72 - 1990, 6-5.1 modified]

3-13.2 Power Supplies. A primary battery (dry cell) shall be permitted to be used as the sole power source of a low power radio transmitter when all of the following conditions are met:

(a) Each transmitter shall serve only one device and shall be individually identified at the receiver/control unit.

(b) The battery shall be capable of operating the low power radio transmitter for not less than one year before the battery depletion threshold is reached.

(c) A battery depletion signal shall be transmitted before the battery has depleted to a level insufficient to support alarm transmission after 7 additional days of normal operation. This signal shall be distinctive from alarm, supervisory, tamper, and trouble signals; shall visibly identify the affected low power radio transmitter; and, if silenced, shall automatically resound at least once every 4 hours.

(d) Catastrophic (open or short) battery failure shall cause a trouble signal identifying the affected low power radio transmitter at its receiver/control unit. If silenced, the trouble signal shall automatically resound at least once every 4 hours.

(e) Any mode of failure of a primary battery in a low power radio transmitter shall not affect any other low power radio transmitter.

[From NFPA 72 - 1990, 6-5.2 modified]

3-13.3 Alarm Signals.

[From NFPA 72 - 1990, 6-5.3]

3-13.3.1 When actuated, each low power radio transmitter shall automatically transmit an alarm signal.

NOTE: This requirement is not intended to preclude verification and local test intervals prior to alarm transmission.

[From NFPA 72 - 1990, 6-5.3.1 modified]

3-13.3.2 Each low power radio transmitter shall automatically repeat alarm transmission at intervals not exceeding 60 seconds until the initiating device is returned to its normal condition.

[From NFPA 72 - 1990, 6-5.3.2 modified]

3-13.3.3 Fire alarm signals shall have priority over all other signals.

[From NFPA 72 - 1990, 6-5.3.3 modified]

3-13.3.4 The maximum allowable response delay from activation of an initiating device to receipt and display by the receiver/control unit shall be 90 seconds.

[From NFPA 72 - 1990, 6-5.3.4 modified]

3-13.3.5 An alarm signal from a low power radio transmitter shall latch at its receiver/control unit until manually reset and shall identify the particular initiating device in alarm.

[From NFPA 72 - 1990, 6-5.3.5 modified]

3-13.4 Supervision.

[From NFPA 72 - 1990, 6-5.4]

3-13.4.1 The low power radio transmitter shall be specifically listed as using a transmission method that shall be highly resistant to misinterpretation of simultaneous transmissions and to interference (e.g., impulse noise and adjacent channel interference).

[From NFPA 72 - 1990, 6-5.4.1 modified]

3-13.4.2 The occurrence of any single fault that disables transmission between any low power radio transmitter and the receiver/control unit shall cause a latching trouble signal within 200 seconds.

Exception: Where Federal Communications Commission (FCC) regulations prevent meeting the 200-second requirement, the time period for a low power radio transmitter with only a single alarm initiating device connected shall be permitted to be increased to four times the minimum time interval permitted for a one-second transmission up to:

(a) Four hours maximum for a transmitter serving a single initiating device

(b) Four hours maximum for a re-transmission device (repeater) if disabling of the repeater or its transmission does not prevent the receipt of signals at the receiver/control unit from any initiating device transmitter.

[From NFPA 72 - 1990, 6-5.4.2 modified]

3-13.4.3 A single fault on the signaling channel shall not cause an alarm signal.

[From NFPA 72 - 1990, 6-5.4.3]

3-13.4.4 The normal periodic transmission from a low power radio transmitter shall provide assurance of successful alarm transmission capability.

[From NFPA 72 - 1990, 6-5.4.4 modified]

3-13.4.5 Removal of a low power radio transmitter from its installed location shall cause immediate transmission of a distinctive supervisory signal that indicates its removal and individually identifies the affected device. Household fire warning systems do not need to comply with this requirement.

[From NFPA 72 - 1990, 6-5.4.5 modified]

3-13.4.6 Reception of any unwanted (interfering) transmission by a retransmission device (repeater) or by the main receiver/control unit, for a continuous period of 20 seconds or more, shall cause an audible and visible trouble indication at the main receiver/control unit. This indication shall identify the specific trouble condition present as an interfering signal.

[From NFPA 72 - 1990, 6-5.4.6 modified]

Chapter 4 Supervising Station Fire Alarm Systems

4-1 Scope. This chapter covers the requirements for the proper performance, installation, and operation of fire alarm systems between the protected premises and the continuously attended supervising station facility.

4-2 Communication Methods for Off-Premises Fire Alarm Systems.

NOTE: The requirements of Chapters 1, 3, 5, 6, and 7 shall apply to off-premises fire alarm systems unless they conflict with requirements of this section.

4-2.1 Scope. This section describes the requirements for the methods of communication between the protected premises and the supervising station. This includes the transmitter, transmission channel, and the signal receiving, processing, display, and recording equipment at the supervising station.

[New paragraphs and titles]

4-2.2 General.

[From NFPA 71, 4-1]

4-2.2.1 Applicable Requirements. The requirements of Sections 4-1, 4-3, 4-4, 4-5, 4-6, and 4-7 shall apply to active multiplex, including systems utilizing derived channels; digital alarm communicator systems, including digital alarm radio systems; McCulloh systems; two-way RF multiplex systems; and one-way radio alarm systems, except where they conflict with the requirements of this section.

[From NFPA 71, 4-1.1 modified, 5-1.1 modified, 6-1.1 modified, 7-1.1 modified, and 8-1.1 modified]

4-2.2.2 Equipment.

[From NFPA 71, 4-1.2]

4-2.2.2.1 Wiring, power supplies, and overcurrent protection shall comply with the requirements of 1-5.5.4 and 1-5.8.6.

[From NFPA 71, 4-1.2.1 modified, 7-1.2.1 modified, and 8-1.2.1 modified]

4-2.2.2.2 Exclusive of the transmission channel, grounding of fire alarm equipment shall be permitted.

[From NFPA 71, 4-1.2.2 modified]

4-2.2.2.3 Fire alarm system equipment and installations shall comply with Federal Communication Commission (FCC) rules and regulations, as applicable, concerning electromagnetic radiation; use of radio frequencies; and connection to the public switched telephone network of telephone equipment, systems, and protection apparatus.

[From NFPA 71, 5-1.3 modified, 8-1.1 modified; and NFPA 72, 8-7.1.3 modified]

4-2.2.2.4 Equipment shall be installed in compliance with NFPA 70, *National Electrical Code*, Article 810.

4-2.2.2.5 All external antennas shall be protected in order to minimize the possibility of damage by static discharge or lightning.

[From NFPA 71, 7-1.2.2 modified and 8-1.2.2 modified]

4-2.2.3 Adverse Conditions.

4-2.2.3.1 For active and two-way RF multiplex systems, the occurrence of an adverse condition on the transmission channel between a protected premises and the supervising station that will prevent the transmission of any status change signal shall be automatically indicated and recorded at the supervising station. This indication and record shall identify the affected portions of the system so that the supervising station operator can determine the location of the adverse condition by trunk or leg facility, or both.

[From NFPA 71, 4-3.1.2 modified, 7-3.1.2 modified, and 8-3.1.2 modified]

4-2.2.3.2 For a one-way radio alarm system, the system shall be supervised to ensure that at least two independent radio alarm repeater station receivers (RARSRs) are receiving signals for each radio alarm transmitter (RAT) during each 24-hour period. The occurrence of a failure to receive a signal by either RARSR shall be automatically indicated and recorded at the supervising station. The indication shall identify which RARSR has failed to receive such supervisory signals. It is not necessary for correctly received test signals to be indicated at the supervising station.

[From NFPA 71, 8-3.1.2 modified]

4-2.2.3.3 For active and two-way RF multiplex systems, restoration of normal service to the affected portions of the system shall be automatically recorded. When normal service is restored, the first status change of any initiating device circuit, or any initiating device directly connected to a signaling line circuit, or any combination that occurred at any of the affected premises during the service interruption shall also be recorded.

[From NFPA 71, 4-3.1.2 modified, 7-3.1.2 modified, and 8-3.1.2 modified]

Exception: This requirement does not apply to proprietary systems on contiguous properties.

[New paragraph]

4-2.2.4 Dual Control.

4-2.2.4.1 Dual control, where required, shall provide for redundancy in the form of a standby circuit or similar alternate means of transmitting signals over the primary trunk portion of a transmission channel. The same method of signal transmission shall be permitted to be used over separate routes, or different methods of signal transmission shall be permitted to be utilized. Public switched telephone network facilities shall be used only as the alternate method of transmitting signals.

4-2.2.4.2 Where utilizing facilities leased from a telephone company, that portion of the primary trunk facility between the supervising station and its serving wire center shall be permitted to be excepted from the separate routing requirement of the primary trunk facility. Dual control, where used, requires supervision as follows:

(a) Dedicated facilities, which are available full time and whose use is limited to signaling purposes as defined in this code, shall be exercised at least once every hour.

(b) Public switched telephone network facilities shall be exercised at least once every 24 hours.

[From NFPA 71, 4-3.1.3 modified and 7-3.1.3 modified]

4-2.3 Communication Methods.

4-2.3.1 Active Multiplex Transmission Systems.

[New titles]

4-2.3.1.1 The multiplex transmission channel terminates in a transmitter at the protected premises and in a system unit at the supervising station. The derived channel terminates in a transmitter at the protected premises and in derived channel equipment at a subsidiary station location or a telephone company wire center. The derived channel equipment at the subsidiary station location or a telephone company wire center selects or establishes the communication with the supervising station.

[From NFPA 71, 4-3.1 modified]

4-2.3.1.2* Operation of the transmission channel shall conform to the requirements of this code whether channels are private facilities, such as microwave, or leased facilities furnished by a communication utility company. Where private signal transmission facilities are utilized, the equipment necessary to transmit signals shall also comply with the requirements for duplicate equipment or replacement of critical components, as described in 4-2.4.2. The trunk transmission channels shall be dedicated facilities for the main channel. For Type 1 multiplex systems, the public switched telephone network facilities shall be permitted to be used for the alternate channel.

Exception: Derived channel scanners with no more than 32 legs shall be permitted to use the public switched telephone network for the main channel.

[From NFPA 71, 4-3.1.1 modified]

4-2.3.1.2.1 Derived channel signals shall be permitted to be transmitted over the leg facility, which shall be permitted to be shared by the telephone equipment under all normal on-hook and off-hook operating conditions.

[From NFPA 71, 4-3.1.1.1 modified]

4-2.3.1.2.2 Where used, the public switched telephone network shall be in compliance with the requirements of 4-2.3.2.

[From NFPA 71, 4-3.1.1.2 modified]

4-2.3.1.2.3 The maximum end-to-end operating time parameters allowed for an active multiplex system are as follows:

(a) The maximum allowable time lapse from the initiation of a single fire alarm signal until it is recorded at the supervising station shall not exceed 90 seconds. When any number of subsequent fire alarm signals occur at any rate, they shall be recorded at a rate no slower than one every 10 additional seconds.

(b)* The maximum allowable time lapse from the occurrence of an adverse condition in any transmission channel until recording of the adverse condition is started shall not exceed 90 seconds for Type 1 and Type 2 systems, and 200 seconds for Type 3 systems. (*See 4-2.3.1.3.*)

(c) In addition to the maximum operating time allowed for fire alarm signals, the requirements of one of the following paragraphs shall be met:

1. A system unit having more than 500 initiating device circuits shall be able to record not less than 50 simultaneous status changes in 90 seconds.

2. A system unit having fewer than 500 initiating device circuits shall be able to record not less than 10 percent of that total number of simultaneous status changes within 90 seconds.

[From NFPA 71, 4-2.1.3 modified]

4-2.3.1.3 System Classification. Active multiplex systems are divided into three categories based upon their ability to perform under adverse conditions of their transmission channels. System classifications are as follows:

(a) A Type 1 system shall have dual control as described in 4-2.2.4. An adverse condition on a trunk or leg facility shall not prevent the transmission of signals from any other trunk or leg facility, except those normally dependent on the portion of the transmission channel in which the adverse condition has occurred. An adverse condition limited to a leg facility shall not interrupt normal service on any trunk or other leg facility. The requirements of 4-2.2.1, 4-2.2.2, and 4-2.2.3 shall be met by Type 1 systems.

(b) A Type 2 system shall have the same requirements as a Type 1 system, except that dual control of the primary trunk facility shall not be required.

(c) A Type 3 system shall automatically indicate and record at the supervising station the occurrence of an adverse condition on the transmission channel between a protected premises and the supervising station. The requirements of 4-2.2, except for 4-2.2.4, shall be met.

[From NFPA 71, 4-3.1.4 modified]

4-2.3.1.4 System Loading Capacities. The capacities of active multiplex systems are based on the overall reliability of the signal receiving, processing, display, and recording equipment at the supervising and subsidiary stations, and the capability to transmit signals during adverse conditions of the signal transmission facilities. Table 4-2.3.1.4 establishes the allowable capacities.

[From NFPA 71, 4-4.1 modified]

4-2.3.1.5 Exceptions to Loading Capacities Listed in Table 4-2.3.1.4. Where the signal receiving, processing, display, and recording equipment is duplicated at the supervising station and a switch-over can be accomplished in not more than 30 seconds with no loss of signals during this period, the capacity of a system unit shall be unlimited.

[From NFPA 71, 4-4.2 modified]

4-2.3.2 Digital Alarm Communicator Systems.

[From NFPA 71, Chap. 5, and NFPA 72, 8-7]

4-2.3.2.1 Digital Alarm Communicator Transmitter (DACT).

[From NFPA 71, 5-2, and NFPA 72, 8-7.2]

4-2.3.2.1.1 A DACT shall be connected to the public switched telephone network upstream of any private telephone system at the protected premises. In addition, special attention is required to ensure that this connection shall be made only to a loop start telephone circuit and not to a ground start telephone circuit.

Exception: If public cellular telephone service is utilized as a secondary means of transmission, the requirements of this paragraph shall not apply.

[From NFPA 71, 5-2.1 modified, and NFPA 72, 8-7.2.1 modified]

Table 4-2.3.1.4

	System Type		
	Type 1	Type 2	Type 3
A. Trunks			
Maximum number of fire alarm service initiating device circuits per primary trunk facility	5120	1280	256
Maximum number of leg facilities for fire alarm service per primary trunk facility	512	128	64
Maximum number of leg facilities for all types of fire alarm service per secondary trunk facility*	128	128	128
Maximum number of all types of initiating device circuits per primary trunk facility in any combination*	10,240	2560	512
Maximum number of leg facilities for all types of fire alarm service per primary trunk facility in any combination*	1024	256	128
B. System Units at the Supervising Station			
Maximum number of all types of initiating device circuits per system unit*	10,240**	10,240**	10,240**
Maximum number of fire protecting buildings and premises per system unit	512**	512**	512**
Maximum number of fire fire alarm service initiating device circuits per system unit	5120**	5120**	5120**
C. Systems Emitting from Subsidiary Station	Same as B	Same as B	Same as B

*Includes every initiating device circuit, i.e., waterflow, fire alarm, supervisory, guard, burglary, hold-up, etc.
**Paragraph 4-2.3.1.5 applies.

[From NFPA 71, Table 4-4.1 modified]

4-2.3.2.1.2 All information exchanged between the DACT at the protected premises and the digital alarm communicator receiver (DACR) at the supervising or subsidiary station shall be by digital code or equivalent. Signal repetition, digital parity check, or some equivalent means of signal verification shall be used.

[From NFPA 71, 5-2.2 modified, and NFPA 72, 8-7.2.2 modified]

4-2.3.2.1.3* A DACT shall be capable of seizing the telephone line (going off-hook) at the protected premises, disconnecting an outgoing or incoming telephone call, and preventing its use for outgoing telephone calls until signal transmission has been completed. A DACT shall not be connected to a party line telephone facility.

[From NFPA 71, 5-2.3, and NFPA 72, 8-7.2.3]

4-2.3.2.1.4 A DACT shall have the means to satisfactorily obtain an available dial tone, dial the number(s) of the DACR, obtain verification that the DACR is ready to receive signals, transmit the signal, and receive acknowledgment that the DACR has accepted that signal. In no event shall the time from going off-hook to on-hook exceed 90 seconds per attempt.

[From NFPA 71, 5-2.4, and NFPA 72, 8-7.2.4]

4-2.3.2.1.5* A DACT shall have suitable means to reset and retry if the first attempt to complete a signal transmission sequence is unsuccessful. A failure to complete connection shall not prevent subsequent attempts to transmit an alarm if such alarm is generated from any other initiating device circuit or signaling line circuit, or both. Additional attempts shall be made until the signal transmission sequence has been completed to a minimum of five and a maximum of ten attempts.

If the maximum number of attempts to complete the sequence is reached, an indication of the failure shall be made at the premises.

[From NFPA 71, 5-2.5, and NFPA 72, 8-7.2.5]

4-2.3.2.1.6 A DACT shall be connected to two separate means of transmission at the protected premises. The DACT shall be capable of selecting the operable means of transmission in the event of failure of the other. The primary means of transmission shall be a telephone line (number) connected to the public switched network.

4-2.3.2.1.6.1 The secondary means of transmission shall be permitted to be one of the following:

(a) A one-way radio system utilized in accordance with 4-2.3.2.3.

(b) Public cellular telephone service. A verification signal shall be transmitted at least once a month.

(c) A telephone line (number).

[From NFPA 71, 5-2.6 modified, and NFPA 72, 8-7.2.6 modified]

4-2.3.2.1.6.2 The first transmission attempt shall utilize the primary means of transmission.

[New paragraph]

4-2.3.2.1.7* Failure of either of the telephone lines (numbers) at the protected premises shall be annunciated at the protected premises, and a trouble signal shall be transmitted to the supervising or subsidiary station over the other line (number). Transmission shall be initiated within 4 minutes of detection of the fault. If public cellular telephone service is used as the secondary means of transmission, loss of cellular service shall be considered a failure.

[From NFPA 71, 5-2.7 modified, and NFPA 72, 8-7.2.7 modified]

4-2.3.2.1.8 Each DACT shall be programmed to call a second DACR line (number) should the signal transmission sequence to the first called line (number) be unsuccessful.

[From NFPA 71, 5-2.8, and NFPA 72, 8-7.2.8]

4-2.3.2.1.9 If long distance telephone service (including WATS) is used, the second telephone number shall be provided by a different long distance service provider, where available.

[From NFPA 71, 5-2-8.1 modified]

4-2.3.2.1.10 Each DACT shall automatically initiate and complete a test signal transmission sequence to its associated DACR at least once every 24 hours. A successful signal transmission sequence of any other type within the same 24-hour period shall be considered sufficient to fulfill the requirement to verify the integrity of the reporting system, if signal processing is automated so that 24-hour delinquencies shall be individually acknowledged by supervising station personnel.

[From NFPA 71, 5-2.9, and NFPA 72, 8-7.2.9]

4-2.3.2.1.11* If DACTs are programmed to call a telephone line (number) that is call forwarded to the line (number) of the DACR, a means shall be implemented to verify the integrity of the call forwarding feature every 4 hours.

[New paragraph]

4-2.3.2.2 Digital Alarm Communicator Receiver (DACR).

[From NFPA 71, 5-3, and NFPA 72, 8-7.3]

4-2.3.2.2.1 Equipment.

[From NFPA 71, 5-3.1, and NFPA 72, 8-7.3.1]

4-2.3.2.2.1.1 Spare DACRs shall be provided in the supervising or subsidiary station and shall be able to be switched in place of a failed unit within 30 seconds after detection of failure.

NOTE: One spare DACR shall be permitted to serve as a backup for up to five DACRs in use.

[From NFPA 71, 5-3.1.1 modified, and NFPA 72, 8-7.3.1.1 modified]

4-2.3.2.2.1.2 The number of incoming telephone lines to a DACR shall be limited to eight lines.

Exception: Where the signal receiving, processing, display, and recording equipment at the supervising or subsidiary station is duplicated and a switchover can be accomplished in less than 30 seconds with no loss of signal during this period, the number of incoming lines to the unit is unlimited.

[From NFPA 71, 5-3.1.2, and NFPA 72, 8-7.3.1.2]

4-2.3.2.2.2 Transmission Channel.

[From NFPA 71, 5-3.3 modified, and NFPA 72, 8-7.3.3 modified]

4-2.3.2.2.2.1* The DACR equipment at the supervising or subsidiary station shall be connected to a minimum of two separate incoming telephone lines (numbers). If the lines (numbers) are in a single hunt group, they shall be individually accessible; otherwise, separate hunt groups are required. These lines (numbers) are to be used for no other purpose than receiving signals from DACTs. These lines (numbers) shall be unlisted.

[From NFPA 71, 5-3.3.1 modified, and NFPA 72, 8-7.3.3.1 modified]

4-2.3.2.2.2.2 Failure of any telephone line (number) connected to a DACR due to loss of line voltage shall be annunciated visually and audibly in the supervising station.

[From NFPA 71, 5-3.3.2 modified, and NFPA 72, 8-7.3.3.2 modified]

4-2.3.2.2.2.3* The loading capacity for a hunt group shall be in accordance with Table 4-2.3.2.2.2.3 or be capable of demonstrating a 90 percent probability of immediately answering the incoming call.

[From NFPA 71, 5-3.3.3 modified, and NFPA 72, 8-7.3.3.3 modified]

(a) Each supervised burglar alarm (open/close) or each suppressed guard tour transmitter shall reduce the allowable DACTs as follows:

1. up to a 4-line hunt group, by 10
2. up to a 5-line hunt group, by 7
3. up to a 6-line hunt group, by 6
4. up to a 7-line hunt group, by 5
5. up to an 8-line hunt group, by 4.

(b) Each guard tour transmitter shall reduce the allowable DACTs as follows:

1. up to a 4-line hunt group, by 30
2. up to a 5-line hunt group, by 21
3. up to a 6-line hunt group, by 18
4. up to a 7-line hunt group, by 15
5. up to an 8-line hunt group, by 12.

[From NFPA 71, Table 5-3.3.3 modified]

4-2.3.2.2.2.4* A signal shall be received on each individual incoming DACR line at least once every 24 hours.

[From NFPA 71, 5-3.3.4, and NFPA 72, 8-7.3.3.4]

4-2.3.2.2.2.5 The failure to receive a test signal from the protected premises shall be treated as a trouble signal. (*See 4-3.6.1.4.*)

[From NFPA 71, 5-3.3.5 modified, and NFPA 72, 8-7.3.3.5 modified]

Table 4-2.3.2.2.2.3

	Number of Lines in Hunt Group				
	1	2	3	4	5 to 8
System Loading at the Supervising Station					
With DACR lines processed in parallel					
Number of initiating circuits	N/A	5000	10,000	20,000	20,000
Number of DACTs*	N/A	500	1500	3000	3000
With DACR lines processed serially (put on hold, then answered one at a time)					
Number of initiating circuits	N/A	3000	5000	6000	6000
Number of DACTs*	N/A	300	800	1000	1000

*Table 4-2.3.2.2.2.3 is based on an average distribution of calls and an average connected time of 30 seconds for a message. The loading figures in the table presume that the lines are in a hunting group (i.e., DACT can access any available line). Note that a single-line DACR is NOT ACCEPTABLE (N/A) for any of the listed configurations.

4-2.3.2.3 Digital Alarm Radio System (DARS).

[From NFPA 71, 5-5]

4-2.3.2.3.1 In the event that any DACT signal transmission is unsuccessful, the information shall be transmitted by means of the digital alarm radio transmitter (DART). The DACT shall continue its normal transmission sequence as required by 4-2.3.2.1.5.

Exception: Simultaneous status change reporting by both the DACT and DART shall be permitted.

[From NFPA 71, 5-5.1 modified]

4-2.3.2.3.2 Failure of the telephone line at the protected premises shall result in a trouble signal being transmitted to the supervising station by means of the DART within 4 minutes of detection of the fault.

[From NFPA 71, 5-5.2 modified]

4-2.3.2.3.3 The DARS shall be capable of demonstrating a minimum of 90 percent probability of successfully completing each transmission sequence.

[From NFPA 71, 5-5.3]

4-2.3.2.3.4 Transmission sequences shall be repeated a minimum of five times. The DART transmission shall be permitted to be terminated in less than five sequences if the DACT successfully communicates to the DACR.

[From NFPA 71, 5-5.4 modified]

4-2.3.2.3.5 Each DART shall automatically initiate and complete a test signal transmission sequence to its associated digital alarm radio receiver (DARR) at least once every 24 hours. A successful DART signal transmission sequence of any other type within the same 24-hour period shall be considered sufficient to fulfill the requirement to test the integrity of the reporting system, if signal processing is automated so that 24-hour delinquencies must be individually acknowledged by supervising station personnel.

[From NFPA 71, 5-5.5]

4-2.3.2.4 Digital Alarm Radio Transmitter (DART). A DART shall transmit a digital code or equivalent by use of radio transmission to its associated digital alarm radio receiver (DARR). Signal repetition, digital parity check, or some equivalent means of signal verification shall be used. The DART shall comply with applicable FCC rules consistent with its operating frequency.

[From NFPA 71, 5-6 modified]

4-2.3.2.5 Digital Alarm Radio Receiver (DARR).

[From NFPA 71, 5-7]

4-2.3.2.5.1 Equipment.

[From NFPA 71, 5-7.1]

4-2.3.2.5.1.1 A spare DARR shall be provided in the supervising station and shall be able to be switched in place of a failed unit within 30 seconds after detection of failure.

[From NFPA 71, 5-7.1.1]

4-2.3.2.5.1.2 Facilities shall be provided at the supervising station for the following supervisory and control functions of subsidiary and repeater station radio receiving equipment. This shall be accomplished via a supervised circuit where the radio equipment is remotely located from the supervising or subsidiary station. The following conditions shall be supervised at the supervising station:

(a) Failure of ac power supplying the radio equipment

(b) Receiver malfunction

(c) Antenna and interconnecting cable malfunction

(d) Indication of automatic switchover of the DARR

(e) Data transmission line between the DARR and the supervising or subsidiary station.

[From NFPA 71, 5-7.1.2 modified]

4-2.3.2.6 Derived Local Channel.

4-2.3.2.6.1 When a DACT is connected to a telephone line (number) that is also supervised for adverse conditions by derived local channel, a second telephone line (number) shall not be required.

4-2.3.2.6.2 Failure of the telephone line (number) at the protected premises shall be automatically indicated and recorded at the supervising station in accordance with 4-2.2.3.

[New paragraphs and title]

4-2.3.3 McCulloh Systems.

[From NFPA 71, Chap. 6]

4-2.3.3.1 Transmitters.

[From NFPA 71, 6-2.1]

4-2.3.3.1.1 A coded alarm signal from a transmitter shall consist of not less than three complete rounds of the number or code transmitted.

[From NFPA 71, 6-2.1.1]

4-2.3.3.1.2* A coded fire alarm box shall produce not less than three signal impulses for each revolution of the coded signal wheel or equivalent device.

[From NFPA 71, 6-2.1.2 modified]

4-2.3.3.1.3 Circuit-adjusting means for emergency operating shall be permitted to either be automatic or be provided through manual operation upon receipt of a trouble signal.

[From NFPA 71, 6-2.2 modified]

4-2.3.3.1.4 Equipment shall be provided at the supervising or subsidiary station on all circuits extending from the supervising or subsidiary station utilized for McCulloh systems for making the following tests:

(a) Current on each circuit under normal conditions

(b) Current on each side of the circuit with the receiving equipment conditioned for an open circuit.

NOTE: The current readings in test (a) above should be compared with the normal readings to determine if a change in the circuit condition has occurred. A zero current reading in test (b) above indicates that the circuit is clear of a foreign ground.

[From NFPA 71, 6-2.3 modified]

4-2.3.3.2 Transmission Channels.

[From NFPA 71, 6-3 modified]

4-2.3.3.2.1 Circuits between the protected premises and the supervising or subsidiary station that are essential to the actuation or operation of devices initiating a signal indicative of fire shall be so arranged that the occurrence of a single break or single ground fault will not prevent transmission of an alarm.

Exception No. 1: Circuits wholly within the supervising or subsidiary station.

Exception No. 2: Carrier system portion of circuits.

[From NFPA 71, 6-3.1 modified]

4-2.3.3.2.2 The occurrence of a single break or a single ground fault on any circuit shall not of itself cause a false signal that may be interpreted as an alarm of fire. Where such single fault prevents the normal functioning of any circuit, its occurrence shall be indicated automatically at the supervising station by a trouble signal compelling attention and readily distinguishable from signals other than those indicative of an abnormal condition of supervised parts of a fire suppression system.

[From NFPA 71, 6-3.2 modified]

4-2.3.3.2.3 The circuits and devices shall be arranged to receive and record a signal readily identifiable as to location of origin, and provisions shall be made for equally identifiable transmission to the public fire service communication center.

[From NFPA 71, 6-3.3]

4-2.3.3.2.4 Multipoint transmission channels between the protected premises and the supervising or subsidiary station and within the protected premises, consisting of one or more coded transmitters and associated system unit(s), shall meet the requirements of either 4-2.3.3.2.5 or 4-2.3.3.2.6.

[From NFPA 71, 6-3.4 modified]

4-2.3.3.2.5 When end-to-end metallic continuity is present, proper signals shall be received from other points under any one of the following transmission channel fault conditions at one point on the line:

(a) Open

(b) Ground

(c)* Wire-to-wire short

(d) Open and ground.

[From NFPA 71, 6-3.4.1 modified]

4-2.3.3.2.6 When end-to-end metallic continuity is not present, the nonmetallic portion of transmission channels shall meet all of the following requirements:

(a) Two nonmetallic channels or one channel plus a means for immediate transfer to a standby channel shall be provided for each transmission channel, a maximum of eight transmission channels being associated with each standby channel, or over one channel, provided service is limited to one plant.

(b) The two nonmetallic channels (or one channel with standby arrangement) for each transmission channel shall be provided in one of the following ways, in descending order of preference:

1. Over separate facilities and separate routes
2. Over separate facilities in the same route
3. Over the same facilities in the same route.

(c) Failure of a nonmetallic channel or any portion thereof shall be indicated immediately and automatically in the supervising station.

(d) Proper signals shall be received from other points under any one of the following fault conditions at one point on the metallic portion of the transmission channel:

1. Open
2. Ground
3.* Wire-to-wire short.

[From NFPA 71, 6-3.4.2 modified]

4-2.3.3.3 Loading Capacity of McCulloh Circuits.

[From NFPA 71, 6-4 modified]

4-2.3.3.3.1 The number of transmitters connected to any transmission channel shall be limited to avoid interference.

The total number of code wheels or equivalent connected to a single transmission channel shall not exceed 250. Alarm signal transmission channels shall be reserved exclusively for fire alarm signal transmitting service, except as provided in 4-2.3.3.3.4.

[From NFPA 71, 6-4.1.1 modified]

4-2.3.3.3.2 The number of waterflow switches permitted to be connected to actuate a single transmitter shall not exceed five switches.

[From NFPA 71, 6-4.1.2]

4-2.3.3.3.3 The number of supervisory switches permitted to be connected to actuate a single transmitter shall not exceed 20.

[From NFPA 71, 6-4.1.3]

4-2.3.3.3.4 Combined alarm and supervisory transmission channels shall comply with the following:

(a) Where both sprinkler supervisory signals and fire or waterflow alarm signals are transmitted over the same transmission channel, provision shall be made to obtain either alarm signal precedence or sufficient repetition of the alarm signal to prevent the loss of any alarm signal.

(b) Other signal transmitters (burglar, industrial processes, etc.) on an alarm transmission channel shall not exceed five.

[From NFPA 71, 6-4.2 modified]

4-2.3.3.3.5* Where signals from manual fire alarm boxes and waterflow alarm transmitters within a building are transmitted over the same transmission channel and are operating at the same time, there shall be no interference with the fire box signals. Provision of the shunt noninterfering method of operation is acceptable for this performance.

[From NFPA 71, 6-4.3 modified]

4-2.3.3.3.6 One alarm transmission channel shall serve not more than 25 plants. A plant may consist of one or more buildings under the same ownership, and the circuit arrangement shall be such that an alarm signal will not be received from more than one transmitter within a plant at a time. If such noninterfering is not provided, each building shall be considered a plant.

[From NFPA 71, 6-4.4 modified]

4-2.3.3.3.7 One sprinkler supervisory transmission channel circuit shall serve not more than 25 plants. A plant may consist of one or more buildings under the same ownership.

[From NFPA 71, 6-4.5 modified]

4-2.3.3.3.8 Connections to a guard supervisory transmission channel or to a combination manual fire alarm and guard transmission channel shall be limited so that not more than 60 scheduled guard report signals will be transmitted in any 1-hour period. Patrol scheduling shall be such as to avoid interference between guard report signals.

[From NFPA 71, 6-4.6 modified]

4-2.3.4 Two-Way RF Multiplex Systems.

[From NFPA 71, Chap. 7]

4-2.3.4.1 The maximum end-to-end operating time parameters allowed for a two-way RF multiplex system are as follows:

(a) The maximum allowable time lapse from the initiation of a single fire alarm signal until it is recorded at the supervising station shall not exceed 90 seconds. When any number of subsequent fire alarm signals occur at any rate, they shall be recorded at a rate no slower than one every additional 10 seconds.

(b) The maximum allowable time lapse from the occurrence of an adverse condition in any transmission channel until recording of the adverse condition is started shall not exceed 90 seconds for Type 4 and Type 5 systems. (*See 4-2.3.4.4.*)

(c) In addition to the maximum operating time allowed for fire alarm signals, the requirements of one of the following paragraphs shall be met:

1. System units having more than 500 initiating device circuits shall be able to record not less than 50 simultaneous status changes in 90 seconds.

2. System units having fewer than 500 initiating device circuits shall be able to record not less than 10 percent of that total number of simultaneous status changes within 90 seconds.

[From NFPA 71, 7-2.1.3 modified]

4-2.3.4.2 Facilities shall be provided at the supervising station for the following supervisory and control functions of the supervising or subsidiary station, and repeater station radio transmitting and receiving equipment. This shall be accomplished via a supervised circuit where the radio equipment is remotely located from the system unit.

(a) The following conditions shall be supervised at the supervising station:

1. RF transmitter in use (radiating)
2. Failure of ac power supplying the radio equipment
3. RF receiver malfunction
4. Indication of automatic switchover.

(b) Independent deactivation of either RF transmitter shall be controlled from the supervising station.

[From NFPA 71, 7-2.1.4 modified]

4-2.3.4.3 Transmission Channel.

[From NFPA 71, 7-3 modified]

4-2.3.4.3.1 The RF multiplex transmission channel shall terminate in a RF transmitter/receiver at the protected premises and in a system unit at the supervising or subsidiary station.

[From NFPA 71, 7-3.1 modified]

4-2.3.4.3.2 Operation of the transmission channel shall conform to the requirements of this code whether channels are private facilities, such as microwave, or leased facilities furnished by a communication utility company. When private signal transmission facilities are utilized, the equipment necessary to transmit signals shall also comply with requirements for duplicate equipment or replacement of critical components, as described in 4-3.4.5.

[From NFPA 71, 7-3.1.1 modified]

4-2.3.4.4* Two-way RF multiplex systems are divided into two categories based upon their ability to perform under adverse conditions. System classifications are of two types.

(a) A Type 4 system shall have two or more control sites configured as follows:

1. Each site shall have a RF receiver interconnected to the supervising or subsidiary station by a separate channel.

2. The RF transmitter/receiver located at the protected premises shall be within transmission range of at least two RF receiving sites.

3. The system shall contain two RF transmitters, either:

(i) Located at one site with the capability of interrogating all of the RF transmitters/receivers on the premises, or

(ii) Dispersed with all of the RF transmitters/receivers on the premises having the capability to be interrogated by two different RF transmitters.

4. Each RF transmitter shall maintain a status that permits immediate use at all times. Facilities shall be provided in the supervising or subsidiary station to operate any off-line RF transmitter at least once every 8 hours.

5. Any failure of one of the RF receivers shall in no way interfere with the operation of the system from the other RF receiver. Failure of any receiver shall be annunciated at the supervising station.

6. A physically separate channel is required between each RF transmitter or RF receiver site, or both, and the system unit.

(b) A Type 5 system shall have a single control site configured as follows:

1. A minimum of one RF receiving site

2. A minimum of one RF transmitting site.

NOTE: The sites above can be co-located.

[From NFPA 71, 7-3.1.4 modified]

4-2.3.4.5 Loading Capacities.

[From NFPA 71, 7-4 modified]

4-2.3.4.5.1 The loading capacities of two-way RF multiplex systems are based on the overall reliability of the signal receiving, processing, display, and recording equipment at the supervising or subsidiary station and the capability to transmit signals during adverse conditions of the transmission channels. Table 4-2.3.4.5.1 establishes the allowable loading capacities.

[From NFPA 71, 7-4.1 modified]

4-2.3.4.5.2 Exceptions to Loading Capacities Listed in Table 4-2.3.4.5.1. Where the signal receiving, processing, display, and recording equipment is duplicated at the supervising station and a switch-over can be accomplished in not more than 30 seconds with no loss of signals during this period, the capacity of a system unit shall be unlimited.

[New paragraph]

Table 4-2.3.4.5.1

	System Type	
	Type 4	Type 5
A. Trunks		
Maximum number of fire alarm service initiating device circuits per primary trunk facility	5120	1280
Maximum number of leg facilities for fire alarm service per primary trunk facility	512	128
Maximum number of leg facilities for all types of fire alarm service per secondary trunk facility*	128	128
Maximum number of all types of initiating device circuits per primary trunk facility in any combination	10,240	2560
Maximum number of leg facilities for types of fire alarm service per primary trunk facility in any combination*	1024	256
B. System Units at the Supervising Station		
Maximum number of all types of initiating device circuits per system unit*	10,240**	10,240**
Maximum number of fire protected buildings and premises per system unit	512**	512**
Maximum number of fire alarm service initiating device circuits per system	5120**	5120**
C. Systems Emitting from Subsidiary Station	Same as B	Same as B

*Includes every initiating device circuit, i.e., waterflow, fire alarm supervisory, guard, burglary, hold up, etc.
**Paragraph 4-2.3.4.5.2 applies.

[From NFPA 71, Table 7-4.1 modified]

4-2.3.5 One-Way Private Radio Alarm Systems.

[From NFPA 71, Chap. 8 modified]

4-2.3.5.1 The requirements of this section for a radio alarm repeater station receiver (RARSR) shall be satisfied if signals from each radio alarm transmitter (RAT) are received and supervised, in accordance with this chapter, by at least two independently powered, independently operating, and separately located RARSR.

4-2.3.5.2* The end-to-end operating time parameters allowed for a one-way radio alarm system shall be as follows:

(a) There shall be a 90 percent probability that the time between the initiation of a single fire alarm signal until it is recorded at the supervising station shall not exceed 90 seconds.

(b) There shall be a 99 percent probability that the time between the initiation of a single fire alarm signal until it is recorded at the supervising station shall not exceed 180 seconds.

(c) There shall be a 99.999 percent probability that the time between the initiation of a single fire alarm signal until it is recorded at the supervising station shall not exceed 7.5 minutes (450 seconds), at which time the RAT shall cease transmitting.

When any number of subsequent fire alarm signals occur at any rate, they shall be recorded at an average rate no slower than one every additional 10 seconds.

(d) In addition to the maximum operating time allowed for fire signals, the system shall be able to record not less than 12 simultaneous status changes within 90 seconds at the supervising station.

[From NFPA 71, 8-2.1.3 modified]

4-2.3.5.3 Supervision.

4-2.3.5.3.1 Equipment shall be provided at the supervising station for the supervisory and control functions of the supervising or subsidiary station, and repeater station radio transmitting and receiving equipment. This shall be accomplished via a supervised circuit where the radio equipment is remotely located from the system unit. The following conditions shall be supervised at the supervising station:

(a) Failure of ac power supplying the radio equipment

(b) RF receiver malfunction

(c) Indication of automatic switchover (if applicable).

[From NFPA 71, 8-2.1.4 modified]

4-2.3.5.3.2 Protected Premises.

4-2.3.5.3.2.1 Interconnections between elements of transmitting equipment, including any antennas, shall be supervised to either cause an indication of failure at the protected premises or transmit a trouble signal to the supervising station.

4-2.3.5.3.2.2 Where these elements are physically separated, the wiring or cabling between them shall be protected by conduit.

[New paragraphs and title]

4-2.3.5.4 Transmission Channel.

[From NFPA 71, 8-3 modified]

4-2.3.5.4.1 The one-way RF transmission channel shall originate with a one-way RF transmitting device at the protected premises and shall terminate at the RF receiving system of a RARSR capable of receiving transmissions from such transmitting devices.

A receiving network transmission channel shall terminate at a RARSR at one end, and either with another RARSR or a radio alarm supervising station receiver (RASSR) at the other end.

[From NFPA 71, 8-3.1 modified]

4-2.3.5.4.2 Operation of receiving network transmission channels shall conform to the requirements of this code whether channels are private facilities, such as microwave, or leased facilities furnished by a communication utility company. Where private signal transmission facilities are utilized, the equipment necessary to transmit signals shall also comply with requirements for duplicate equipment or replacement of critical components as described in 4-2.4.2.

The system shall provide information indicating the quality of the received signal for each RARSR supervising each RAT in accordance with 4-2.3.5 and shall provide information at the supervising station if such signal quality falls below the minimum signal quality levels set forth in 4-2.3.5.

Each RAT shall be installed in such a manner so as to provide a signal quality over at least two independent one-way RF transmission channels, of the minimum quality level specified that satisfies the performance requirements in 4-2.2.2 and 4-2.4

[From NFPA 71, 8-3.1.1 modified]

4-2.3.5.5 Nonpublic one-way radio alarm systems shall be divided into two categories based upon the following number of RASSRs present in the system:

(a) A Type 6 system shall have one RASSR and at least two RARSRs.

(b) A Type 7 system shall have more than one RASSR and at least two RARSRs.

In a Type 7 system, if more than one RARSR is out of service and as a result any RATs are no longer being supervised, then the affected supervising station shall be notified.

In a Type 6 system, if any RARSR is out of service, a trouble signal shall be annunciated at the supervising station.

[From NFPA 71, 8-3.1.3 modified]

4-2.3.5.6 The loading capacities of one-way radio alarm systems are based on the overall reliability of the signal receiving, processing, display, and recording equipment at the supervising or subsidiary station and the capability to transmit signals during adverse conditions of the transmission channels. Table 4-2.3.5.6 establishes the allowable loading capacities.

[From NFPA 71, 8-4.1 modified]

4-2.3.5.7 Exceptions to Loading Capacities Listed in Table 4-2.3.5.6. Where the signal receiving, processing, display, and recording equipment is duplicated at the supervising station and a switch-over can be accomplished in not more than 30 seconds with no loss of signals during this period, the capacity of a system unit is unlimited.

[From NFPA 71, 8-4.2]

4-2.3.6 Directly-Connected Noncoded Systems.

[New title]

4-2.3.6.1 Circuits for transmission of alarm signals between the fire alarm control unit or the transmitter in the protected premises and the supervising station shall be arranged so as to comply with either of the following provisions:

(a) These circuits shall be arranged so that the occurrence of a single break or single ground fault will not prevent the transmission of an alarm signal. Circuits complying with this paragraph shall be automatically self-adjusting in the event of either a single break or a single ground fault and shall be automatically self-restoring in the event that the break or fault is corrected.

Table 4-2.3.5.6

	System Type	
	Type 6	Type 7
A. Radio Alarm Repeater Station Receiver (RARSR)		
Maximum number of fire alarm service initiating device circuits per RARSR	5120	5120
Maximum number of RATs for fire	512	512
Maximum number of all types of initiating device circuits per RARSR in any combination*	10,240	10,240
Maximum number of RATs for all types of fire alarm service per RARSR in any combination*†	1024	1024
B. System Units at the Supervising Station		
Maximum number of all types of initiating device circuits per system unit*	10,240**	10,240**
Maximum number of fire protected buildings and premises per system unit	512**	512**
Maximum number of fire alarm service initiating device circuits per system unit	5120**	5120**

*Includes every initiating device circuit, i.e., waterflow, fire alarm, supervisory, guard, burglary, hold-up, etc.

**Paragraph 4-2.3.5.7 applies.

†Each supervised BA (open/close) or each suppressed guard tour transmitter shall reduce the allowable RATs by 5.
Each guard tour transmitter shall reduce the allowable RATs by 15.
Each two-way protected premises radio transmitter shall reduce the allowable RATs by 2.

[From NFPA 71, Table 8-4.1 modified]

(b) These circuits shall be arranged so as to normally be isolated from ground (except for reference ground detection) and so that a single ground fault will not prevent the transmission of an alarm signal. Circuits complying with this paragraph shall be provided with a ground reference circuit so as to detect and indicate automatically the existence of a single ground fault, unless a multiple ground-fault condition that would prevent alarm operation will be indicated by an alarm or by a trouble signal.

[From NFPA 72, 8-6.1 modified]

4-2.3.6.2 Circuits for transmission of supervisory signals shall be separate from alarm circuits. These circuits within the protected premises and between the protected premises and the supervising station shall be arranged as described in 4-2.3.6.1(a) or 4-2.3.6.1(b).

Exception: Where the reception of alarm signals and supervisory signals at the same supervising station is permitted by the authority having jurisdiction, the supervisory signals do not interfere with the alarm signals, and alarm signals have priority, the same circuit between the protected premises and the supervising station shall be permitted to be used for alarm and supervisory signals.

[From NFPA 72, 8-6.2 modified]

4-2.3.6.3 The occurrence of a single break or a single ground fault on any circuit shall not of itself cause a false signal that may be interpreted as an alarm of fire.

[From NFPA 72, 4-2.2 modified]

4-2.3.6.4 The requirements of 4-2.3.6.1 and 4-2.3.6.2 shall not apply to the following circuits:

(a) Circuits wholly within the supervising station,

(b) Circuits wholly within the protected premises extending from one or more automatic fire detectors or other noncoded initiating devices other than water flow devices to a transmitter or control unit, or

(c) Power supply leads wholly within the building or buildings protected.

[From NFPA 72, 8-6.3 modified]

4-2.3.6.5 Loading Capacity of Circuits.

[From NFPA 72, 8-5]

4-2.3.6.5.1 The number of initiating devices connected to any signaling circuit and the number of plants that shall be permitted to be served by a signal circuit shall be determined by the authority having jurisdiction and shall not exceed the limitations specified in 4-2.3.6.5.

NOTE: A plant may consist of one or more buildings under the same ownership.

[From NFPA 72, 8-5.1 modified]

4-2.3.6.5.2 A single circuit shall not serve more than one plant.

[From NFPA 72, 8-5.4 modified]

NOTE: Where a single plant involves more than one gate entrance or involves a number of buildings, separate circuits may be required so that the alarm to the supervising station will indicate the area to which the fire department should be dispatched.

[From NFPA 72, 8-5.9 modified]

4-2.3.7 Private Microwave Radio Systems.

[From NFPA 72, 9-5 modified]

4-2.3.7.1 Where a private microwave radio is used as the transmission channel, appropriate supervised transmitting and receiving equipment shall be provided at supervising, subsidiary, and repeater stations.

[From NFPA 72, 9-5.1 modified]

4-2.3.7.2 Where more than 5 protected buildings or premises or 50 initiating devices or initiating device circuits are being serviced by a private radio carrier, the supervising, subsidiary, and repeater station radio facilities shall meet all of the following:

(a) Dual supervised transmitters, arranged for automatic switching from one to the other in case of trouble, shall be installed. Where the transmitters are located where someone is always on duty, switchboard facilities shall be permitted to be manually operated if the switching can be carried out within 30 seconds. Where the transmitters are located where no one is normally on duty, the circuit extending between the supervising station and the transmitters shall be a supervised circuit.

(b)* Transmitters shall be operated on a two-to-one time ratio basis within each 24 hours.

(c) Dual receivers shall be installed with a means for selecting a usable output from one of the two receivers. The failure of one shall in no way interfere with the operation of the other. Failure of either receiver shall be annunciated.

[From NFPA 72, 9-5.2 modified]

4-2.3.7.3 Means shall be provided at the supervising station for the supervision and control of supervising, subsidiary, and repeater station radio transmitting and receiving equipment. This shall be accomplished via a supervised circuit when the radio equipment is remote from the supervising station.

(a) The following conditions shall be supervised at the supervising station:

1. Transmitter in use (radiating)
2. Failure of ac power supplying the radio equipment
3. Receiver malfunction
4. Indication of automatic switchover.

(b) It shall be possible to independently deactivate either transmitter from the supervising station.

[From NFPA 72, 9-5.3 modified]

4-2.4 Display and Recording.

[New title]

4-2.4.1* Any status changes that occur in an initiating device or in any interconnecting circuits or equipment from the location of the initiating device(s) to the supervising station shall be presented in a form to expedite prompt operator interpretation. Status change signals shall provide the following information:

(a) *Type of Signal.* Identification of the type of signal to show whether it is an alarm, supervisory, delinquency, or trouble signal.

(b) *Condition.* Identification of the signal to differentiate between an initiation of an alarm, supervisory, delinquency, or trouble signal, and a restoration to normal from one or more of these conditions.

(c) *Location.* Identification of the point of origin of each status change signal.

[From NFPA 71, 4-2.1.1 modified, 5-3.2.1 modified, 5-7.2.1 modified, 7-2.1.1 modified, 8-2.1.1 modified; and NFPA 72, 8-7.3.2.1 modified]

4-2.4.2* If duplicate equipment for signal receiving, processing, display, and recording is not provided, the installed equipment shall be so designed that any critical assembly can be replaced from on-premises spares and the system restored to service within 30 minutes. A critical assembly is one in which a malfunction will prevent the receipt and interpretation of signals by the supervising station operator.

Exception: Proprietary and remote station systems.

[From NFPA 71, 4-1.2.3 modified, 7-1.2.3 modified, and 8-1.2.3 modified]

4-2.4.3* Any method of recording and display or indication of change of status signals shall be permitted, providing all of the following conditions are met:

(a) Each change of status signal requiring action to be taken by the operator shall result in an audible signal and not less than two independent methods of identifying the type, condition, and location of the status change.

(b) Each change of status signal shall be automatically recorded. The record shall provide the type of signal, condition, and location as required by 4-2.4.1 in addition to the time and date the signal was received.

(c) Failure of an operator to acknowledge or act upon a change of status signal shall not prevent subsequent alarm signals from being received, indicated or displayed, and recorded.

(d) Change of status signals requiring action to be taken by the operator shall be displayed or indicated in a manner that clearly differentiates them from those that have been acted upon and acknowledged.

(e) Each incoming signal to a DACR or DARR shall cause an audible signal that persists until manually acknowledged.

Exception: Test signals (see 4-2.3.2.1.10) received at a DACR or DARR shall be permitted to be excepted from this requirement.

[From NFPA 71, 4-2.1.2 modified, 5-3.2.2 modified, 5-7.2.2 modified, 7-2.1.2 modified, 8-2.1.2 modified; and NFPA 72, 8-7.3.2.2 modified]

4-2.5 Testing and Maintenance. Testing and maintenance of communication methods shall be in accordance with the requirements of Chapter 7.

[New paragraph]

4-3 Fire Alarm Systems for Central Station Service.

[From NFPA 71]

NOTE: The requirement of Chapters 1, 3, 5, 6, 7, and Section 4-2 shall apply to central station fire alarm systems unless they conflict with the requirements of this section.

[From NFPA 71, 1-2.5 modified]

4-3.1 Scope. This section describes the general requirements and use of fire alarm systems to provide central station service.

[From NFPA 71, 1-1.1 modified]

4-3.2 General.

[New title]

4-3.2.1 These systems include the central station physical plant, exterior communications channels, subsidiary stations, and signaling equipment located at the protected premises.

[From NFPA 71, 1-1.2 modified]

4-3.2.2* This section applies to central station service, which consists of the following elements: installation of fire alarm transmitters; alarm, guard, supervisory and trouble signal monitoring; retransmission; associated record keeping and reporting; testing and maintenance; and runner service. These services shall be provided under contract to a subscriber by one of the following:

(a) A listed central station that provides all of the elements of central station service with its own facilities and personnel.

(b) A listed central station that provides as a minimum the signal monitoring, retransmission, and associated record keeping and reporting with its own facilities and personnel and that may subcontract all or any part of the installation, testing and maintenance, and runner service.

(c) A listed fire alarm service — local company that provides the installation, and testing and maintenance with its own facilities and personnel and that subcontracts the monitoring, retransmission, and associated record keeping and reporting to a listed central station. The required runner service shall be provided by the listed fire alarm service — local company with its own personnel or the listed central station with its own personnel.

[From NFPA 71, 1-2.2 modified]

4-3.2.3 It shall be conspicuously indicated by the prime contractor that the fire alarm system providing service at a protected premises complies with all the requirements of this code by providing a means of third party verification, as specified in 4-3.2.3.1 or 4-3.2.3.2.

4-3.2.3.1 The installation shall be certificated.

4-3.2.3.1.1 Fire alarm systems providing service that complies with all requirements of this code shall be certified by the organization that has listed the central station, and a document attesting to this certification shall be located on or near the fire alarm system control unit or, if no control unit exists, on or near a fire alarm system component.

4-3.2.3.1.2 A central repository of issued certification documents, accessible to the authority having jurisdiction, shall be maintained by the organization that has listed the central station.

4-3.2.3.2 The installation shall be placarded.

4-3.2.3.2.1 Fire alarm systems providing service that complies with all requirements of this code shall be conspicuously marked by the central station to indicate compliance. The marking shall be by one or more securely affixed placards that meet the requirements of the organization that has listed the central station and requires the placard.

4-3.2.3.2.2 The placard(s) shall be 20 sq in. (130 cm^2) or larger, shall be located on or near the fire alarm system control unit or, if no control unit exists, on or near a fire alarm system component, and shall identify the central station by name and telephone number.

[From NFPA 71, 1-2.3.2]

4-3.2.4* Fire alarm system service not complying with all requirements of Section 4-3 shall not be designated as central station service.

[From NFPA 71, 1-2.4]

4-3.2.5* For the purpose of Section 4-3, the subscriber shall notify the prime contractor in writing of the identity of the authority(ies) having jurisdiction.

[From NFPA 71, 1-4.1 modified]

4-3.3 Supervising Station Facilities.

[From NFPA 71, 1-7 modified]

4-3.3.1 The central station building or that portion of a building occupied by a central station shall conform to the construction, fire protection, restricted access, emergency lighting, and power facilities requirements of the latest edition of ANSI/UL 827, *Central Stations for Watchman, Fire Alarm and Supervisory Service*.

[From NFPA 71, 1-6.2 modified]

4-3.3.2 Subsidiary station buildings or those portions of buildings occupied by subsidiary stations shall conform to the construction, fire protection, restricted access, emergency lighting, and power facilities requirements of the latest edition of ANSI/UL 827, *Central Stations for Watchman, Fire Alarm and Supervisory Service*.

4-3.3.2.1 All intrusion, fire, power, and environmental control systems for subsidiary station buildings shall be monitored by the central station in accordance with 4-3.3.

4-3.3.2.2 The subsidiary facility shall be inspected at least monthly by central station personnel for the purpose of verifying the operation of all supervised equipment, all telephones, battery conditions, and all fluid levels of batteries and generators.

4-3.3.2.3 In the event of the failure of equipment at the subsidiary station or the communication channel to the central station, a backup shall be operational within 90 seconds. Restoration of a failed unit shall be accomplished within 5 days.

4-3.3.2.4 There shall be continuous supervision of each communication channel between the subsidiary station and the central station.

4-3.3.2.5 When the communication channel between the subsidiary station and the supervising station fails, the communication shall be switched to an alternate path. Public switched telephone network facilities shall be used only as the alternate path.

4-3.3.2.6 In the subsidiary station, there shall be either a cellular telephone or an equivalent communication path that is independent of the telephone cable between the subsidiary station and the serving wire center.

4-3.3.2.7 A plan of action to provide for restoration of services specified by this code shall exist for each subsidiary station.

4-3.3.2.7.1 This plan shall provide for restoration of services within 4 hours of any impairment causing loss of signals from the subsidiary station to the central station.

4-3.3.2.7.2 There shall be an exercise to demonstrate the adequacy of the plan at least once a year.

4-3.4 Equipment.

[New paragraphs and title]

4-3.4.1 The central station and all subsidiary stations shall be so equipped to receive and record all signals in accordance with 4-2.4. Circuit-adjusting means for emergency operation shall be permitted to either be automatic or be provided through manual operation upon receipt of a trouble signal. Computer aided alarm and supervisory signal processing hardware and software shall be listed for the specific application.

[From NFPA 71, 1-7.1 modified]

4-3.4.2 Power supplies shall comply with the requirements of Chapter 1.

4-3.4.3 Transmission means shall comply with the requirements of Section 4-2.

[New paragraphs]

4-3.4.4* Two independent means shall be provided to retransmit a fire alarm signal to the appropriate public fire service communication center.

NOTE: The use of a universal emergency number 911 (public safety answering point) does not meet the intent of this code for the principal means of retransmission.

[From NFPA 71, 1-7.2 modified]

4-3.4.4.1 Where the principal means of retransmission is not equipped to permit the center to acknowledge receipt of each fire alarm report, both means shall be used to retransmit.

[From NFPA 71, 1-7.2.1 modified]

4-3.4.4.2* Where required by the authority having jurisdiction, one of the means shall be supervised so that interruption of retransmission circuit (channel) communication integrity will result in a trouble signal at the central station.

[From NFPA 71, 1-7.2.2 modified]

4-3.4.4.3 The retransmission means shall be tested in accordance with Chapter 7.

[From NFPA 71, 1-7.2.3 modified]

4-3.4.4.4 The retransmission signal and the time and date of retransmission shall be recorded at the central station.

[From NFPA 71, 1-7.2.4]

4-3.5 Personnel.

[New title]

4-3.5.1 The central station shall have sufficient personnel (a minimum of two persons) on duty at the central station at all times to ensure attention to signals received.

[From NFPA 71, 1-9.1 modified]

4-3.5.1.1 Operation and supervision shall be the primary functions of the operators, and no other interest or activity shall take precedence over the protective service.

[From NFPA 71, 1-9.1.2 modified]

4-3.6 Operations.

[New title]

4-3.6.1 Disposition of Signals.

[From NFPA 71, 1-10.2]

4-3.6.1.1 Alarm signals initiated by manual fire alarm boxes, automatic fire detectors, waterflow from the automatic sprinkler system, or actuation of other fire suppression systems or equipment shall be treated as fire alarms. The central station shall:

(a)* Immediately retransmit the alarm to the public fire service communication center

(b) Dispatch a runner or technician to the protected premises to arrive within 1 hour after receipt of signal when equipment needs to be manually reset by the prime contractor

(c) Notify the subscriber by the quickest available method

(d) Provide notice to the subscriber and/or authority having jurisdiction, if required.

Exception: When the alarm signal results from a prearranged test, it is not necessary to take the actions required by (a) and (c).

[From NFPA 71, 1-10.2.1 modified]

4-3.6.1.2 Upon failure to receive a guard's regular signal within a 15-minute maximum grace period, the central station shall:

(a) Communicate without unreasonable delay with personnel at the protected premises

(b) If communications cannot be established, dispatch a runner to the protected premises to arrive within 30 minutes of the delinquency

(c) Report all delinquencies to the subscriber and/or authority having jurisdiction, if required.

[From NFPA 71, 1-10.2.2 modified]

4-3.6.1.2.1 Failure of the guard to follow a prescribed route in transmitting signals shall be handled as a delinquency.

[From NFPA 71, 1-10.2.2.1]

4-3.6.1.3* Upon receipt of a supervisory signal from a sprinkler system, other fire suppression system, or other equipment, the central station shall:

(a)* Communicate immediately with person(s) designated by the subscriber

(b) Dispatch a runner or maintenance person (arrival time not to exceed 1 hour) to investigate, unless abnormal condition is restored to normal in accordance with a scheduled procedure determined by (a) above

(c) Notify the fire department and/or law enforcement agency, if required

(d) Notify the authority having jurisdiction when sprinkler systems or other fire suppression systems or equipment have been wholly or partially out of service for 8 hours

(e) When service has been restored, provide notice, if required, to the subscriber and/or the authority having jurisdiction as to the nature of the signal, time of occurrence, and restoration of service when equipment has been out of service for 8 hours or more.

Exception: When the supervisory signal results from a prearranged test, it is not necessary to take the actions required by (a), (c), and (e).

[From NFPA 71, 1-10.2.3 modified]

4-3.6.1.4 Upon receipt of trouble signals or other signals pertaining solely to matters of equipment maintenance of the fire alarm systems, the central station shall:

(a)* Communicate immediately with persons designated by the subscriber

(b) If necessary, dispatch personnel to arrive within 4 hours to initiate maintenance

(c) Provide notice, if required, to the subscriber and/or the authority having jurisdiction as to the nature of the interruption, time of occurrence, and restoration of service, when the interruption is more than 8 hours.

[From NFPA 71, 1-10.2.4 modified]

4-3.6.1.5 All test signals received shall be recorded to indicate date, time, and type.

(a) Test signals initiated by the subscriber, including those for the benefit of an authority having jurisdiction, shall be acknowledged by central station personnel whenever the subscriber or authority inquires.

(b)* Any test signal not received by the central station shall be investigated immediately and appropriate action taken to reestablish system integrity.

(c) The central station shall dispatch personnel to arrive within 1 hour when protected premises equipment must be manually reset after testing.

[From NFPA 71, 1-10.2.5 modified]

4-3.6.2 Record Keeping and Reporting.

[New title]

4-3.6.2.1 Complete records of all signals received shall be retained for at least 1 year.

[From NFPA 71, 1-4.5 modified]

4-3.6.2.2 The central station shall make arrangements to furnish reports of signals received to the authority having jurisdiction in a form acceptable to it.

[From NFPA 71, 1-10.1 modified]

4-3.7 Testing and Maintenance. Testing and maintenance for central station service shall be performed in accordance with Chapter 7.

[New paragraph]

4-4 Proprietary Supervising Station Systems.

NOTE: The requirements of Chapters 1, 3, 5, 6, 7, and Section 4-2 shall apply to proprietary fire alarm systems, except where they conflict with the requirements of this section.

[From NFPA 72, Chap. 9 modified]

4-4.1 Scope. Section 4-4 describes the operational procedures for the supervising facilities of proprietary fire alarm systems. It provides the minimum requirements for the facilities, equipment, personnel, operation, and testing and maintenance of the proprietary supervising station.

[New paragraph]

4-4.2 General.

[From NFPA 72, 9-2]

4-4.2.1 Proprietary supervising stations shall be located at the protected property and operated by trained, competent personnel in constant attendance who are responsible to the owner of the protected property. (*See 4-4.5.3.*)

4-4.2.2 The protected property shall be either a single property or noncontiguous properties under one ownership.

[New paragraphs]

4-4.2.3* Section 4-4 recognizes the interconnection of other systems to make the premises safer in the event of fire or other emergencies indicative of hazards to life or property.

[From NFPA 72, 9-1 modified]

4-4.3 Supervising Station Facilities.

[New title]

4-4.3.1 The proprietary supervising station shall be located in a fire-resistive, detached building or in a suitable cut-off room and shall not be near or exposed to the hazardous parts of the premises protected.

[From NFPA 72, 9-2.1 modified]

4-4.3.2 Access to the proprietary supervising station shall be restricted to those persons directly concerned with the implementation and direction of emergency action and procedure.

[From NFPA 72, 9-2.2 modified]

4-4.3.3 The proprietary supervising station, as well as remotely located power rooms for batteries or engine-driven generators, shall be provided with portable fire extinguishers that comply with the requirements of NFPA 10, *Standard for Portable Fire Extinguishers.*

4-4.3.4 The proprietary supervising station shall be provided with an automatic emergency lighting system. The emergency source shall be independent of the primary lighting source.

[New paragraphs]

4-4.3.5 Where 25 or more protected buildings or premises are connected to a subsidiary station, both of the following shall be provided at the subsidiary station:

(a) Automatic means for receiving and recording signals under emergency-staffing conditions

(b) A telephone.

[From NFPA 72, 9-6 modified]

4-4.4 Equipment.

4-4.4.1 This section shall apply to signal-receiving equipment in a proprietary supervising station.

[From NFPA 72, 9-7.1 modified]

4-4.4.2 Provision shall be made to designate the building in which a signal originates. The floor, section, or other subdivision of the building shall be designated at the proprietary supervising station or at the building protected, except that the authority having jurisdiction shall be permitted to waive this detailed designation where the area, height, or special conditions of occupancy make it unessential. This detailed designation shall utilize indicating appliances acceptable to the authority having jurisdiction.

[From NFPA 72, 9-7.3 modified]

4-4.4.3 The proprietary supervising station shall have, in addition to a recording device, two different means for alerting the operator when each signal is received indicating a change of state of any connected initiating device circuit. One of these shall be an audible signal and shall persist until manually acknowledged. This shall include the receipt of alarm signals, supervisory signals, and trouble signals including signals indicating restoration to normal.

[From NFPA 72, 9-8.1.1 modified]

4-4.4.4 Where suitable means is provided in the proprietary supervising station to readily identify the type of signal received, a common audible indicating appliance shall be permitted to be used for alarm, supervisory, and trouble indication.

[From NFPA 72, 9-8.1.2 modified]

4-4.4.5 At a proprietary supervising station, an audible trouble signal shall be permitted to be silenced provided the act of silencing it shall not prevent it from operating immediately upon receipt of a subsequent trouble signal.

[From NFPA 72, 9-8.1.3 modified]

4-4.4.6 All signals received by the proprietary supervising station that show a change in status shall be automatically and permanently recorded, including time and date of occurrence. This record shall be in a form that will expedite operator interpretation in accordance with any one of the following:

(a) In the event that a visual display is used that automatically provides change of status information for each individual signal, including type and location of occurrence, any form of automatic permanent visual record shall be acceptable. The recorded information shall include the content described above. The visual display shall show status information content at all times and shall be distinctly different after the operator has manually acknowledged each signal. Acknowledgment shall cause recorded information indicating time and date of acknowledgment.

(b) In the event that a visual display is not provided, signal content information shall be automatically recorded on duplicate permanent visual recording instruments.

One recording instrument shall be used for recording all incoming signals, while the other shall be used for fire, supervisory, and trouble signals only. Failure to acknowledge a signal shall not prevent subsequent signals from recording. Restoration of the signaling device to its prior or normal condition shall be recorded.

(c) In the event that a system combines the use of a sequential visual display and recorded permanent visual presentation, the signal content information shall be displayed and recorded. The visual information component shall be either retained on the display until manual acknowledgment or periodically repeated at intervals not greater than 5 seconds, for durations of 2 seconds each, until manually acknowledged. Each new displayed status change shall be accompanied by an audible indication that shall persist until manual acknowledgment of the signal is performed.

There shall be a means provided for the operator to redisplay status of initiating device circuits that have been acknowledged but not yet restored to a normal condition. If the system retains the signal on the visual display until manually acknowledged, subsequent recorded presentations shall not be inhibited upon failure to acknowledge. Fire alarm signals shall be segregated on a separate visual display in this configuration unless given priority status on the common visual display.

[From NFPA 72, 9-8.2 modified]

4-4.4.7 The maximum elapsed time from sensing a fire alarm at an initiating device or initiating device circuit until it is recorded or displayed at the proprietary supervising station shall not exceed 90 seconds.

[From NFPA 72, 9-8.3.1 modified]

4-4.4.8 To facilitate the prompt receipt of fire alarm signals from systems handling other types of signals that may produce multiple simultaneous status changes, the requirements of either of the following shall be met:

(a) In addition to the maximum processing time for a single alarm, the system shall record simultaneous status changes at a rate not slower than either a quantity of 50, or 10 percent of the total number of initiating device circuits connected, within 90 seconds, whichever number is smaller, without loss of any signal.

(b) In addition to the maximum processing time, the system shall display or record fire alarm signals at a rate not slower than one every 10 seconds, regardless of the rate or number of status changes occurring, without loss of any signals.

Exception: Where fire alarm, waterflow alarm, sprinkler supervisory signals, and their associated trouble signals are the only signals processed by the system, the rate of recording shall not be slower than one round of code every 30 seconds.

[From NFPA 72, 9-8.3.2]

4-4.4.9 Trouble signals required in 1-5.8 and their restoration to normal shall be automatically indicated and recorded at the proprietary supervising station within 200 seconds.

[From NFPA 72, 9-8.3.3 modified]

4-4.4.10 The recorded information for the occurrence of any trouble condition of signaling line circuit, leg facility, or trunk facility that prevents receipt of alarm signals at the proprietary supervising station shall be such that the operator is able to determine the presence of the trouble condition. Trouble conditions in a leg facility shall not affect or delay receipt of signals at the proprietary supervising station from other leg facilities on the same trunk facility.

[From NFPA 72, 9-9 modified]

4-4.5 Personnel.

[New title]

4-4.5.1 At least two operators, one of whom shall be permitted to be a runner, shall be on duty at all times.

Exception: Where the means for transmitting alarms to the fire department is automatic, at least one operator shall be on duty at all times.

4-4.5.2 When the runner is not in attendance at the proprietary supervising station, the runner shall establish two-way communications with the station at intervals not exceeding 15 minutes.

[From NFPA 72, 9-2.3 modified]

4-4.5.3 The primary duties of the operator(s) shall be to monitor signals, operate the system, and take such action as shall be required by the authority having jurisdiction. The operator(s) shall not be assigned any additional duties that would take precedence over the primary duties.

[From NFPA 72, 9-2.4]

4-4.6 Operations.

4-4.6.1 All communication and transmission channels between the proprietary supervising station and the protected premises master control unit (panel) shall be operated manually or automatically once every 24 hours to verify operation.

4-4.6.1.1 When a communication or transmission channel fails to operate, the operator shall immediately notify the person(s) identified by the owner or authority having jurisdiction.

[New paragraphs and title]

4-4.6.2 All operator controls at the proprietary supervising station(s) designated by the authority having jurisdiction shall be operated at each change of shift.

[From NFPA 72, 9-4 modified]

4-4.6.3 If operator controls fail, the operator shall immediately notify the person(s) identified by the owner or authority having jurisdiction.

[New paragraph]

4-4.6.4 Indication of a fire shall be promptly retransmitted to the public fire service communications center or other locations acceptable to the authority having jurisdiction, indicating the building or group of buildings from which the alarm has been received.

[From NFPA 72, 9-3.1]

4-4.6.5* The means of retransmission shall be acceptable to the authority having jurisdiction and shall be in accordance with Sections 4-3, 4-5, 4-6, or 4-7.

Exception: Secondary power supply capacity shall be as required in Chapter 1.

[From NFPA 72, 9-3.2 modified]

4-4.6.6* Retransmission by coded signals shall be confirmed by two-way voice communication indicating the nature of the alarm.

[From NFPA 72, 9-3.3 modified]

4-4.6.7 Dispositions of Signals.

[From NFPA 72, 9-10 modified]

4-4.6.7.1 Alarms. Upon receipt of a fire alarm signal, the proprietary supervising station operator shall initiate action to:

(a) Immediately notify the fire department, the plant fire brigade, and such other parties as the authority having jurisdiction may require

(b) Promptly dispatch a runner to the alarm location (Travel time shall not exceed 1 hour.)

(c) Restore the system to its normal operating condition as soon as possible after disposition of the cause of the alarm signal.

[From NFPA 72, 9-10.2 modified]

4-4.6.7.2 Guard's Tour Delinquency. If a regular signal is not received from a guard within a 15-minute maximum grace period, or if a guard fails to follow a prescribed route in transmitting the signals (if a prescribed route has been established), it shall be treated as a delinquency signal. When a guard's tour delinquency occurs, the proprietary supervising station operator shall initiate action to:

(a) Communicate at once with the protected areas or premises by telephone, radio, calling back over the system circuit, or other means acceptable to the authority having jurisdiction

(b) Dispatch a runner to investigate the delinquency, if communications with the guard cannot be promptly established. (Travel time shall not exceed one-half hour.)

[From NFPA 72, 9-10.3 modified]

4-4.6.7.3 Supervisory Signals. Upon receipt of sprinkler system and other supervisory signals, the proprietary supervising station operator shall initiate action to:

(a) Where required, communicate immediately with the designated person(s) to ascertain the reason for the signal

(b) Where required, dispatch a runner or maintenance person (travel time not to exceed 1 hour) to investigate, unless supervisory conditions are promptly restored to normal

(c) Where required, notify the fire department

(d) Where required, notify the authority having jurisdiction when sprinkler systems are wholly or partially out of service for 8 hours or more

(e) Where required, provide written notice to the authority having jurisdiction as to the nature of the signal, time of occurrence, and restoration of service, when equipment has been out of service for 8 hours or more.

[From NFPA 72, 9-10.4 modified]

4-4.6.7.4 Trouble Signals. Upon receipt of trouble signals or other signals pertaining solely to matters of equipment maintenance of the fire alarm system, the proprietary supervising station operator shall initiate action to:

(a) Where required, communicate immediately with the designated person(s) to ascertain reason for the signal

(b) Where required, dispatch a runner or maintenance person (travel time not to exceed 1 hour) to investigate

(c) Where required, notify the fire department

(d) Where required, notify the authority having jurisdiction when interruption of normal service will exist for 4 hours or more

(e) Where required, provide written notice to the authority having jurisdiction as to the nature of the signal, time of occurrence, and restoration of service, when equipment has been out of service for 8 hours or more.

[From NFPA 72, 9-3.4 modified and 9-10.5 modified]

4-4.6.8 Record Keeping and Reporting.

[New title]

4-4.6.8.1 Complete records of all signals received shall be retained for at least 1 year.

4-4.6.8.2 The proprietary supervising station shall make arrangements to furnish reports of signals received to the authority having jurisdiction, in a form acceptable to it.

[From NFPA 72, 9-10.1 modified]

4-4.7 Testing and Maintenance. Testing and maintenance of proprietary fire alarm systems shall be performed in accordance with Chapter 7.

[New paragraph]

4-5 Remote Supervising Station Fire Alarm Systems.

NOTE: The requirements of Chapters 1, 3, 5, 6, 7, and Section 4-2 shall apply to remote supervising station fire alarm systems, except where they conflict with the requirements of this section.

[From NFPA 72, Chap. 8 modified]

4-5.1 Scope. This section describes the installation, maintenance, testing, and use of a remote supervising station fire alarm system that serves properties under various ownership from a remote supervising station where trained competent personnel are in constant attendance. It covers the minimum requirements for the remote supervising station physical facilities, equipment, operating personnel, response, retransmission, signals, reports, and testing.

[From NFPA 72, 8-1.1 modified]

4-5.2 General.

[From NFPA 72, 8-2 modified]

4-5.2.1 Remote supervising station fire alarm systems provide an automatic audible and visible indication of alarm and, when required, of supervisory and trouble conditions at a location remote from the protected premises and a manual or automatic permanent record of these conditions.

[From NFPA 72, 8-2.1 modified]

4-5.2.2 This section does not require the use of audible signal notification appliances other than those required at the remote supervising station. If it is desired to provide fire alarm evacuation signals in the protected premises, the alarm signals, circuits, and controls shall comply with the provisions of Chapter 3 and Chapter 6 in addition to the provisions of this section.

[From NFPA 72, 8-2.6 modified]

4-5.2.3 The loading capacities of the remote supervising station equipment for any approved method of transmission shall be as designated in Section 4-2.

4-5.3* Supervising Station Facilities.

[New paragraph and title]

4-5.3.1 Where a remote supervising station connection is used to transmit an alarm signal, the signal shall be received at the public fire service communications center, at a fire station, or at the similar governmental agency that has a public responsibility for taking prescribed action to ensure response upon receipt of a fire alarm signal.

Exception: Where such an agency is unwilling to receive alarm signals or will permit the acceptance of another location by the authority having jurisdiction, such alternate location shall have personnel on duty at all times trained to receive the alarm signal and immediately retransmit it to the fire department.

[From NFPA 72, 8-2.2 modified]

4-5.3.2 Supervisory and trouble signals shall be handled at a constantly attended location having personnel on duty trained to recognize the type of signal received and to take prescribed action. This shall be permitted to be a location different from that at which alarm signals are received.

[From NFPA 72, 8-2.3 modified]

4-5.3.3 Where locations other than the public fire service communication center are used for the receipt of signals, access to receiving equipment shall be restricted in accordance with requirements of the authority having jurisdiction.

[From NFPA 72, 8-2.4 modified]

4-5.4 Equipment.

4-5.4.1 Signal-receiving equipment shall indicate receipt of each signal both audibly and visibly.

4-5.4.1.1 Audible signals shall meet the requirements of Chapter 6 for the private operating mode.

[New paragraphs and title]

4-5.4.1.2 Means for silencing alarm, supervisory, and trouble signals shall be provided and shall be so arranged that subsequent signals shall re-sound.

[From NFPA 72, 8-3.4 modified and 8-3.5 modified]

4-5.4.1.3 A trouble signal shall be received when the system or any portion of the system at the protected premises is placed in a bypass or test mode.

4-5.4.1.4 An audible and visible indication shall be provided upon restoration from any off-normal condition.

[New paragraphs]

4-5.4.1.5 Where suitable visible means are provided in the remote supervising station to readily identify the type of signal received, a common audible notification appliance shall be permitted to be used.

[From NFPA 72, 8-3.4 modified and 8-3.6 modified]

4-5.4.2 Power supplies shall comply with the requirements of Chapter 1.

Exception: In a remote supervising station fire alarm system where the alarm and supervisory signals are transmitted over a listed supervised one-way radio system, 24 hours of secondary (standby) power shall be permitted in lieu of 60 hours, as required in 1-5.2.5, at the radio alarm repeater station receivers (RARSR), provided that personnel are dispatched to arrive within 4 hours after detection of failure to initiate maintenance.

4-5.4.3 Transmission means shall comply with the requirements of Section 4-2.

[New paragraphs]

4-5.4.4 Retransmission of an alarm signal, where required, shall be by one of the following methods, listed in descending order of preference:

(a) A dedicated circuit that is independent of any switched telephone network. This circuit shall be permitted to be used for voice or data communication.

(b) A one-way (outgoing only) telephone at the remote supervising station that utilizes the public switched telephone network. This telephone shall be used primarily for voice transmission of alarms to a telephone at the public fire service communications center, which cannot be used for outgoing calls.

(c) A private radio system using the fire department frequency where permitted by the fire department.

(d) Other methods acceptable to the authority having jurisdiction.

[From NFPA 72, 8-3.2 modified]

4-5.5 Personnel. Sufficient personnel shall be available at all times to receive alarm signals at the remote supervising station and to take immediate appropriate action. Duties pertaining to other than operation of the remote supervising station receiving and retransmitting equipment shall be permitted subject to the approval of the authority having jurisdiction.

[From NFPA 72, 8-2.5 modified]

4-5.6 Operations.

[New title]

4-5.6.1 Where the remote supervising station is at a location other than the public fire service communication center, alarm signals shall be immediately retransmitted to the public fire service communications center.

[From NFPA 72, 8-3.1 modified]

4-5.6.2 Upon receipt of an alarm, supervisory, or trouble signal by the remote supervising station other than the public fire service communications center, it shall be the responsibility of the operator on duty to immediately notify the owner or the owner's designated representative.

[From NFPA 72, 8-3.3 modified]

4-5.6.3 A permanent record of the time, date, and location of all signals and restorations received; the action taken thereon; and the results of all tests shall be maintained for at least 1 year and made available to the authority having jurisdiction. These records shall be permitted to be made by manual means.

[New paragraph]

4-5.6.4 All operator controls at the remote supervising station shall be operated at the beginning of each shift or change in personnel, and the status of all off-normal conditions noted and recorded.

[From NFPA 72, 8-4 modified]

4-5.7 Testing and Maintenance. Testing and maintenance for remote supervising stations shall be performed in accordance with Chapter 7.

[New paragraph)

4-6 Public Fire Alarm Reporting Systems.

[From NFPA 1221, Chap. 4 modified]

4-6.1 Scope. This section covers the general requirements and use of public fire alarm reporting systems. These systems include the equipment necessary to effect the transmission and reception of fire alarms or other emergency calls from the public.

[New paragraph]

4-6.2 General Fundamentals.

[From NFPA 1221, 4-1.1 modified]

4-6.2.1 Where implemented at the option of the authority having jurisdiction, a public fire alarm reporting system shall be designed, installed, operated, and maintained to provide the maximum practicable reliability for transmission and receipt of fire alarms.

[From NFPA 1221, 4-1.1.1 modified]

4-6.2.2 It shall be permissible for a public fire alarm reporting system, as described herein, to be used for the transmission of other signals or calls of a public emergency nature, provided such transmission does not interfere with the transmission and receipt of fire alarms.

[From NFPA 1221, 4-1.1.3 modified]

4-6.2.3 Alarm systems shall be Type A or Type B. A Type A system shall be provided when the number of all alarms required to be transmitted over the dispatch circuits exceeds 2500 per year.

NOTE: Where a Type A system is required, automatic transmission of alarms from boxes by use of electronic equipment is permissible, only if the following requirements are satisfied:

(a) Reliable facilities are provided for the automatic receipt, storage, retrieval, and transmission of alarms in the order received; and

(b) Override capability is provided to the operator(s) so that manual transmission and dispatch facilities are instantly available.

[From NFPA 1221, 4-1.1.4 modified]

4-6.2.4 Any portion(s) of a public fire alarm reporting system used to effect the auxiliarized protection of a structure or multiple of structures shall be listed as compliant with Chapter 3 and Section 4-7.

[From NFPA 1221, 4-1.1.5 modified]

4-6.3 Management and Maintenance. (*See Chapter 7.*)

[From NFPA 1221, 4-1.2 modified]

4-6.4 Equipment and Installation.

[From NFPA 1221, 4-1.3]

4-6.4.1 Means for actuation of alarms by the public shall be conspicuous and readily accessible for easy operation.

[From NFPA 1221, 4-1.3.4 modified]

4-6.4.2 Public fire alarm reporting systems as defined in this chapter, shall, in their entirety, be subject to a complete operational acceptance test upon completion of system installation. Said test(s) shall be made in accordance with the requirements of the authority having jurisdiction. However, in no case shall the operational functions tested be less than those stipulated in Chapter 7. Like tests shall be performed on any alarm reporting devices as identified in this chapter that are added subsequent to the installation of the initial system.

4-6.4.3 Publicly accessible boxes shall be recognizable as such. Boxes shall have operating instructions plainly marked on the exterior surface.

[From NFPA 1221, 4-1.4.1.1 modified]

4-6.4.4 The actuating device shall be readily available and of such design and so located as to make the method of its use apparent.

[From NFPA 1221, 4-1.4.1.2 modified]

4-6.4.5 Publicly accessible boxes shall be as conspicuous as possible. Their color shall be distinctive.

[From NFPA 1221, 4-1.4.1.3]

4-6.4.6 All publicly accessible boxes mounted on support poles shall be identified by a wide band of distinctive colors or adequate signs placed 8 ft (2.44 m) above the ground and visible from all directions whenever possible.

[From NFPA 1221, 4-1.4.1.4 modified]

4-6.4.7* Indicating lights of a distinctive color, visible for at least 1500 ft (460 m), shall be installed over publicly accessible boxes in mercantile and manufacturing areas. Equipping the street light nearest the box with a distinctively colored light shall be acceptable.

[From NFPA 1221, 4-1.4.1.5 modified]

4-6.4.8 Boxes shall be securely mounted on poles, pedestals, or structural surfaces as directed by the authority having jurisdiction.

[From NFPA 1221, 4-1.4.1.8]

4-6.4.9 Concurrent operation of at least four boxes shall not result in the loss of an alarm.

[From NFPA 1221, 4-1.4.2.4]

4-6.5 Design of Boxes. (*See Chapter 5.*)

[From NFPA 1221, 4-1.4.2 modified]

4-6.6* Location of Boxes. Location of publicly accessible boxes shall be designated by the authority having jurisdiction. Schools, hospitals, nursing homes, and places of public assembly shall have a box located at or near the main entrance, as directed by the authority having jurisdiction.

[From NFPA 1221, 4-1.4.3 modified, 4-1.4.3.1 modified, 4-1.4.3.2 modified, and 4-1.4.3.3 modified]

4-6.7 Power Supply.

[From NFPA 1221, 4-1.5.3]

4-6.7.1 General.

[New title]

4-6.7.1.1 Batteries, motor-generators, or rectifiers shall be sufficient to supply all connected circuits without exceeding the capacity of any battery or overloading any generator or rectifier, so that circuits developing grounds or crosses with other circuits each may be supplied by an independent source to the extent required by 4-6.7.1.8(b).

[From NFPA 1221, 4-1.5.3.1.1.1 modified]

4-6.7.1.2 Provision shall be made in the operating room for supplying any circuit from any battery, generator, or rectifier. Enclosed fuses shall be provided at points where supplies for individual circuits are taken from common leads. Necessary switches, testing, and signal transmitting and receiving devices shall be provided to permit the isolation, control, and test of each circuit, to at least 10 percent of the total number of box and dispatch circuits, but never less than 2 circuits.

[From NFPA 1221, 4-1.5.3.1.1.2]

4-6.7.1.3 If common-current source systems are grounded, the ground shall not exceed 10 percent of resistance of any connected circuit and be located at one side of the battery. Visual and audible indicating devices shall be provided for each box and dispatch circuit to give immediate warning of ground leakage endangering operability.

[From NFPA 1221, 4-1.5.3.1.1.3]

4-6.7.1.4 Local circuits at communication centers shall be supplied either in common with box circuits or coded radio-receiving system circuits or by a separate power source. The source of power for local circuits required to operate the essential features of the system shall be supervised.

[From NFPA 1221, 4-1.5.3.2]

4-6.7.1.5 Visual and audible means to indicate a 15 percent or greater reduction of normal power supply (rated voltage) shall be provided.

[From NFPA 1221, 4-1.5.3.3]

4-6.7.1.6 The forms and arrangements of power supply shall be classified as described in the paragraphs below.

NOTE: If the electrical service/capacity of the equipment required under NFPA 1221, *Standard for the Installation, Maintenance, and Use of Public Fire Service Communication Systems*, 2-1.6, is adequate to satisfy the needs of equipment in Section 4.6, said equipment need not be duplicated.

[From NFPA 1221, 4-1.5.3.1 modified]

4-6.7.1.7 Form 2. These forms shall be permissible for Type A systems only. Box circuits shall be served in multiple by:

(a)* *Form 2A.* A rectifier or motor-generator powered from a single source of alternating current, with a floating storage battery having a 24-hour standby capacity.

(b)* *Form 2B.* A rectifier or motor-generator powered from two sources of alternating current, with a floating storage battery having a 4-hour standby capacity.

(c)* *Form 2C.* A duplicate rectifier or motor-generator powered from two sources of alternating current with transfer facilities to apply power from the secondary source to the system within 30 seconds (*see NFPA 1221, Standard for the Installation, Maintenance, and Use of Public Fire Service Communication Systems*). Each rectifier or motor-generator shall be capable of powering the entire system.

NOTE: For Forms 2A, 2B, and 2C, these arrangements are permissible but are not recommended where circuits are wholly or partly open-wire because of the possibility of trouble from multiple grounds.

[From NFPA 1221, 4-1.5.3.1.1 modified]

4-6.7.1.8 Form 3. Each box circuit or coded radio receiving system shall be served by:

(a)* *Form 3A.* A rectifier or motor-generator powered from a single source of alternating current with a floating storage battery having a 60-hour standby capacity.

(b)* *Form 3B.* A rectifier or motor-generator powered from two sources of alternating current with a floating storage battery having a 24-hour standby capacity.

[From NFPA 1221, 4-1.5.3.1.2 modified]

4-6.7.1.9 Form 4. Each box circuit or coded radio receiving system shall be served by:

(a)* *Form 4A.* An inverter powered from a common rectifier receiving power by a single source of alternating current with a floating storage battery having a 24-hour standby capacity.

(b)* *Form 4B.* An inverter powered from a common rectifier receiving power from two sources of alternating current with a floating storage battery having a 4-hour standby capacity.

NOTE: For Form 4A and Form 4B, it is permissible to distribute the system load between two or more common rectifiers and batteries.

(c)* *Form 4C.* A rectifier, converter, or motor-generator receiving power from two sources of alternating current with transfer facilities to apply power from the secondary source to the system within 30 seconds (*see NFPA 1221, Standard for the Installation, Maintenance, and Use of Public Fire Service Communication Systems*).

[From NFPA 1221, 4-1.5.3.1.3 modified]

4-6.7.2 Rectifiers, Converters, Inverters, and Motor-Generators.

[From NFPA 1221, 4-1.5.4]

4-6.7.2.1 Rectifiers shall be supplied through an isolating transformer taking energy from a circuit not to exceed 250 volts.

[From NFPA 1221, 4-1.5.4.1]

4-6.7.2.2 Complete, ready-to-use spare units or spare parts shall be available in reserve.

[From NFPA 1221, 4-1.5.4.2]

4-6.7.2.3 One spare rectifier shall be provided for each ten required for operation, but in no case less than one.

[From NFPA 1221, 4-1.5.4.3]

4-6.7.2.4 Leads from rectifiers or motor-generators, with storage battery floating, shall have fuses rated at not less than 1 amp and not more than 200 percent of maximum connected load. Where not provided with battery floating, the fuse shall be not less than 3 amps.

[From NFPA 1221, 4-1.5.4.4]

4-6.7.3 Engine-Driven Generator Sets.

[From NFPA 1221, 4-1.5.5]

4-6.7.3.1 The provisions of 4-6.7.3 shall apply to generators driven by internal combustion engines.

[From NFPA 1221, 4-1.5.5.1]

4-6.7.3.2 The installation of such units shall conform to the provisions of NFPA 37, *Standard for the Installation and Use of Stationary Combustion Engines and Gas Turbines*, and NFPA 110, *Standard for Emergency and Standby Power Systems*, except as restricted by the provisions of 4-6.7.3.

[From NFPA 1221, 4-1.5.5.2]

4-6.7.3.3 The engine-driven generator shall be located in an adequately ventilated cutoff area of the building housing the communication center equipment. The area housing the unit shall be used for no other purpose except storage of spare parts or equipment. Exhaust fumes shall be discharged directly outside the building.

[From NFPA 1221, 4-1.5.5.3]

4-6.7.3.4 Liquid fuel shall be stored in outside underground tanks and gravity feed shall not be used. Sufficient fuel shall be available for 24 hours of operation at full load if a reliable source of fuel supply is available, at any time, on 2 hours notice. If a source of supply is not reliable or readily available, or if special arrangements must be made for refueling as necessary, a supply sufficient for 48 hours of operation at full load shall be maintained.

[From NFPA 1221, 4-1.5.5.4 modified]

4-6.7.3.5 Liquefied petroleum gas and natural gas installations shall meet the requirements of NFPA 54, *National Fuel Gas Code*, and NFPA 58, *Standard for the Storage and Handling of Liquefied Petroleum Gases*.

[From NFPA 1221, 4-1.5.5.5]

4-6.7.3.6 The unit, as a minimum, shall be of sufficient capacity to supply power to operate all fire alarm facilities and emergency lighting of the operating rooms or communication building.

[From NFPA 1221, 4-1.5.5.6]

4-6.7.3.7 A separate storage battery on automatic float charger shall be provided for starting the engine-driven generator.

[From NFPA 1221, 4-1.5.5.7]

4-6.7.3.8 Where more than one engine-driven generator is provided, each shall be provided with a separate fuel line and transfer pump.

[From NFPA 1221, 4-1.5.5.8]

4-6.7.4 Float-Charged Batteries.

[From NFPA 1221, 4-1.5.6 modified]

4-6.7.4.1 Batteries shall be of the storage type; primary batteries (dry cells) shall not be used. All cells shall be of the sealed type. Lead-acid batteries shall be in jars of glass or other suitable transparent materials; other types of batteries shall be in containers suitable for the purpose.

[From NFPA 1221, 4-1.5.6.1]

4-6.7.4.2 Batteries shall be located in the same building as the operating equipment, preferably on the same floor, readily accessible for maintenance and inspection. The battery room shall be aboveground, except as permitted by NFPA 1221, *Standard for the Installation, Maintenance, and Use of Public Fire Service Communication Systems*, 2-1.1.2, and shall be ventilated to prevent accumulation of explosive gas mixtures; special ventilation is required only for unsealed cells.

[From NFPA 1221, 4-1.5.6.2 modified]

4-6.7.4.3 Batteries shall be mounted to provide effective insulation from the ground and from other batteries. The mounting shall be suitably protected against deterioration, and consideration shall be given to stability, especially in geographic areas subject to seismic disturbance.

[From NFPA 1221, 4-1.5.6.3]

4-6.8 Requirements for Metallic Systems and Metallic Interconnections.

[From NFPA 1221, 4-1.8]

4-6.8.1 Circuit Conductors.

[From NFPA 1221, 4-1.8.1 modified]

4-6.8.1.1 Wires shall be terminated so as to provide good electrical conductivity and to prevent breaking from vibration or stress.

[From NFPA 1221, 4-1.8.1.1]

4-6.8.1.2 Circuit conductors on terminal racks shall be identified and isolated from conductors of other systems whenever possible and shall be suitably protected from mechanical injury.

[From NFPA 1221, 4-1.8.1.2 modified]

4-6.8.1.3 Except as otherwise provided herein, exterior cable and wire shall conform to International Municipal Signal Association specifications or their equivalent.

[From NFPA 1221, 4-1.8.1.3]

4-6.8.1.4 If a municipal box is installed inside a building, it shall be placed as close as practical to the point of entrance of the circuit, and the exterior wire shall be installed in conduit or electrical metallic tubing, in accordance with Chapter 3 of NFPA 70, *National Electrical Code*.

Exception: This requirement shall not apply to coded radio box systems.

[From NFPA 1221, 4-1.8.1.4]

4-6.8.2 Cables.

[From NFPA 1221, 4-1.8.2]

4-6.8.2.1 General.

[From NFPA 1221, 4-1.8.2.1]

4-6.8.2.1.1 Cables that meet the requirements of NFPA 70, *National Electrical Code*, Article 310, for installation in wet locations shall be satisfactory for overhead or underground installation, except that direct-burial cable shall be specifically approved for the purpose.

[From NFPA 1221, 4-1.8.2.1(a)]

4-6.8.2.1.2 Paper or pressed pulp insulation shall not be considered satisfactory for an emergency service such as a fire alarm system, except that cables containing conductors with such insulation shall be acceptable if pressurized with dry air or nitrogen. Loss of pressure in cables shall be indicated by a visual or audible warning system located where someone who can interpret the pressure readings and who has authority to have the indicated abnormal condition corrected is in constant attendance.

[From NFPA 1221, 4-1.8.2.1(b) modified]

4-6.8.2.1.3 Natural rubber-sheathed cable shall not be used where it may be exposed to oil, grease, or other substances or conditions that may tend to deteriorate the cable sheath. Braided-sheathed cable shall be used only inside of buildings where run in conduit or metal raceways.

[From NFPA 1221, 4-1.8.2.1(c)]

4-6.8.2.1.4 Other municipally controlled signal wires shall be permitted to be installed in the same cable with fire alarm wires. Cables controlled by or containing wires of private signaling organizations shall be permitted to be used for fire alarm purposes only by permission of the authority having jurisdiction.

[From NFPA 1221, 4-1.8.2.1(d) modified]

4-6.8.2.1.5 Signaling wires that, because of the source of current supply, might introduce a hazard shall be protected and supplied as required for lighting circuits.

[From NFPA 1221, 4-1.8.2.1(e) modified]

4-6.8.2.1.6 All cables with all taps and splices made shall be tested for insulation resistance when installed, but before connection to terminals. Such tests shall indicate an insulation resistance of at least 200 megohms per mile between any one conductor and all others, the sheath, and ground.

[From NFPA 1221, 4-1.8.2.1(f)]

4-6.8.2.2 Underground Cables.

[From NFPA 1221, 4-1.8.2.2]

4-6.8.2.2.1 Underground cables in duct or direct burial shall be brought aboveground only at points where liability of mechanical injury or of disablement from heat incident to fires in adjacent buildings is minimized.

[From NFPA 1221, 4-1.8.2.2(a) modified]

4-6.8.2.2.2 Cables shall be in duct systems and manholes containing low-tension fire alarm system conductors only, except low-tension secondary power cables shall be permitted. If in duct systems or manholes containing power circuit conductors in excess of 250 volts to ground, fire alarm cables shall be located as far as possible from such power cables and shall be separated from them by a noncombustible barrier or by such other means as may be practicable to protect the fire alarm cables from injury.

[From NFPA 1221, 4-1.8.2.2(b) modified]

4-6.8.2.2.3 All cables installed in manholes shall be properly racked and marked for identification.

[From NFPA 1221, 4-1.8.2.2(c)]

4-6.8.2.2.4 All conduits or ducts entering buildings from underground duct systems shall be effectively sealed against moisture or gases entering the building.

[From NFPA 1221, 4-1.8.2.2(d)]

4-6.8.2.2.5 Cable joints shall be located only in manholes, fire stations, and other locations where proper accessibility is provided and where there is little liability of injury to the cable due to either falling walls or operations in the buildings. Cable joints shall be made to provide and maintain conductivity, insulation, and protection at least equal to that afforded by the cables that are joined. Cable ends shall be sealed against moisture.

[From NFPA 1221, 4-1.8.2.2(e)]

4-6.8.2.2.6 Direct-burial cable, without enclosure in ducts, shall be laid in grass plots, under sidewalks, or in other places where the ground is not apt to be opened for other underground construction. If splices are made, such splices shall, where practicable, be accessible for inspection and tests. Such cables shall be buried at least 18 in. (0.5 m) deep and, where crossing streets or other areas likely to be opened for other underground construction, shall be in duct or conduit or be covered by creosoted planking of at least 2 in. by 4 in. (50 mm by 100 mm) with half-round grooves, spiked or banded together after the cable is installed.

[From NFPA 1221, 4-1.8.2.2(f)]

4-6.8.2.3 Aerial Construction.

[From NFPA 1221, 4-1.8.3]

4-6.8.2.3.1 Fire alarm wires shall be run under all other wires except communication wires. Suitable precautions shall be provided where passing through trees, under bridges, over railroads, and at other places where injury or deterioration is possible. Wires and cables shall not be attached to a crossarm carrying electric light and power wires, except circuits carrying up to 220 volts for municipal communication use. Such 220-volt circuits shall be tagged or otherwise identified.

[From NFPA 1221, 4-1.8.3.1 modified]

4-6.8.2.3.2 Aerial cable shall be supported by messenger wire of adequate tensile strength, except as permitted in 4-6.8.2.3.3.

[From NFPA 1221, 4-1.8.3.2 modified]

4-6.8.2.3.3 Two-conductor cable shall be messenger-supported unless it has conductors of No. 20 AWG or larger size and has mechanical strength equivalent to No. 10 AWG hard-drawn copper.

[From NFPA 1221, 4-1.8.3.3]

4-6.8.2.3.4 Single wire shall meet International Municipal Signal Association specifications and shall not be smaller than No. 10 Roebling gauge if of galvanized iron or steel, No. 10 AWG if of hard-drawn copper, No. 12 AWG if of approved copper-covered steel, or No. 6 AWG if of aluminum. Span lengths shall not exceed manufacturers' recommendations.

[From NFPA 1221, 4-1.8.3.4 modified]

4-6.8.2.3.5 Wires to buildings shall contact only intended supports and shall enter through an approved weatherhead or suitable sleeves slanting upward and inward. Drip loops shall be formed on wires outside of buildings.

[From NFPA 1221, 4-1.8.3.5]

4-6.8.2.4 Leads Down Poles.

[From NFPA 1221, 4-1.8.4]

4-6.8.2.4.1 Leads down poles shall be protected against mechanical injury. Any metallic covering shall form a continuous conducting path to ground. Installation, in all cases, shall prevent water from entering the conduit or box.

[From NFPA 1221, 4-1.8.4.1 modified]

4-6.8.2.4.2 Leads to boxes shall have 600-volt insulation approved for wet locations, as defined in NFPA 70, *National Electrical Code*.

[From NFPA 1221, 4-1.8.4.2]

4-6.8.2.5 Wiring Inside Buildings.

[From NFPA 1221, 4-1.8.5]

4-6.8.2.5.1 At the communication center, conductors shall extend as directly as possible to the operating room in conduits, ducts, shafts, raceways, or overhead racks and troughs of a type of construction affording protection against fire and mechanical injury.

[From NFPA 1221, 4-1.8.5.1 modified]

4-6.8.2.5.2 All conductors inside buildings shall be in conduit, electrical tubing, metal molding, or raceways. Installation shall be in accordance with NFPA 70, *National Electrical Code*.

[From NFPA 1221, 4-1.8.5.2 modified]

4-6.8.2.5.3 Conductors shall have an approved insulation; the insulation or other outer covering shall be flame-retardant and moisture-resistant.

[From NFPA 1221, 4-1.8.5.3]

4-6.8.2.5.4 Conductors shall be installed as far as possible without joints. Splices shall be permitted only in junction or terminal boxes. Wire terminals, splices, and joints shall conform to NFPA 70, *National Electrical Code*.

[From NFPA 1221, 4-1.8.5.4 modified]

4-6.8.2.5.5 Conductors bunched together in a vertical run connecting two or more floors shall have a flame-retardant covering sufficient to prevent the carrying of fire from floor to floor. This requirement shall not apply if the conductors are encased in a metallic conduit or located in a fire-resistive shaft having fire stops at each floor.

[From NFPA 1221, 4-1.8.5.5]

4-6.8.2.5.6 Where cables or wiring are exposed to unusual fire hazards, they shall be properly protected.

[From NFPA 1221, 4-1.8.5.6]

4-6.8.2.5.7 Cable terminals and cross-connecting facilities shall be located in or adjacent to the operations room.

[From NFPA 1221, 4-1.8.5.7]

4-6.8.2.5.8 Where signal conductors and electric light and power wires are run in the same shaft, they shall be separated by at least 20 in. (50 mm), or either system shall be encased in a noncombustible enclosure.

[From NFPA 1221, 4-1.8.5.8]

4-6.9 Facilities for Signal Transmission.

[New title]

4-6.9.1 Circuits.

[From NFPA 1221, 4-2.1]

4-6.9.1.1 General.

[From NFPA 1221, 4-2.1.1]

4-6.9.1.1.1 ANSI/IEEE C2, *The National Electrical Safety Code*, shall be used as a guide for the installation of outdoor circuitry.

[From NFPA 1221, 4-2.1.1.1 modified, 4-3.2.1 modified, 4-4.1.1.1 modified, and 4-5.1.1.1 modified]

4-6.9.1.1.2 In all installations, first consideration shall be given to continuity of service. Particular attention shall be given to liability of mechanical injury; disablement from heat incident to a fire; injury by falling walls; and damage by floods, corrosive vapors, or other causes.

[From NFPA 1221, 4-2.1.1.2 modified, 4-3.2.1 modified, 4-4.1.1.2 modified, and 4-5.1.1.2 modified]

4-6.9.1.1.3 Open local circuits within single buildings are permitted in accordance with Chapter 3.

[From NFPA 1221, 4-2.1.1.3 modified, 4-4.1.1.3 modified, and 4-5.1.1.3 modified]

4-6.9.1.1.4 All circuits shall be so routed as to permit ready tracing of circuits for trouble.

[From NFPA 1221, 4-2.1.1.4, 4-4.1.1.4, and 4-5.1.1.4]

4-6.9.1.1.5 Circuits shall not pass over, under, through, or be attached to buildings or property not owned by or under the control of the authority having jurisdiction or the agency responsible for maintaining the system, except where the circuit is terminated in a box on the premises.

[From NFPA 1221, 4-2.1.1.5 modified, 4-4.1.1.5 modified, and 4-5.1.1.5 modified]

4-6.9.1.2 Box Circuits.

[From NFPA 1221, 4-2.1.2]

4-6.9.1.2.1 If a box is installed inside a building, it shall be placed as close as is practical to the point of entrance of the circuit, and the exterior wire shall be installed in conduit or electrical metallic tubing in accordance with Chapter 3 of NFPA 70, *National Electrical Code*.

[From NFPA 1221, 4-2.1.2.1 modified]

4-6.9.1.2.2 Accessible and reliable means, available only to the authority having jurisdiction or the agency responsible for maintaining the public fire alarm reporting system, shall be provided for disconnecting the auxiliary loop to the box inside the building, and definite notification shall be given to occupants of the building when the interior box is not in service.

[From NFPA 1221, 4-2.1.2.2 modified]

4-6.9.1.3 Tie Circuits.

[From NFPA 1221, 4-2.1.3 and 4-4.1.3]

4-6.9.1.3.1 A separate tie circuit shall be provided from the communication center to each subsidiary communication center.

[From NFPA 1221, 4-2.1.3.1 modified and 4-4.1.3.1 modified]

4-6.9.1.3.2 The tie circuit between the communication center and the subsidiary communication center shall not be used for any other purpose.

[From NFPA 1221, 4-4.1.3.2 modified]

4-6.9.1.3.3 In a Type B wire system, where all boxes in the system are of succession type, it shall be permissible to use the tie circuit as a dispatch circuit, to the extent permitted by NFPA 1221, *Standard for the Installation, Maintenance, and Use of Public Fire Service Communication Systems*.

[From NFPA 1221, 4-2.1.3.2 modified]

4-6.9.1.4* Circuit Protection.

[From NFPA 1221, 4-2.2, 4-4.2, and 4-5.2]

4-6.9.1.4.1 General.

[From NFPA 1221, 4-2.2.1, 4-4.2.1, and 4-5.2.1]

4-6.9.1.4.1.1 The protective devices shall be located close to or be combined with the cable terminals.

[From NFPA 1221, 4-2.2.1.1, 4-4.2.1.1, and 4-5.2.1.1]

4-6.9.1.4.1.2 Lightning arresters suitable for the purpose shall be provided. Lightning arresters shall be marked with the name of the manufacturer and model designation.

[From NFPA 1221, 4-2.2.1.2, 4-4.2.1.2, and 4-5.2.1.2]

4-6.9.1.4.1.3 All lightning arresters shall be connected to a suitable ground in accordance with NFPA 70, *National Electrical Code*.

[From NFPA 1221, 4-2.2.1.3, 4-4.2.1.3, and 4-5.2.1.3]

4-6.9.1.4.1.4 All fuses shall be plainly marked with their rated ampere capacity. All fuses rated over 2 amps shall be of the enclosed type.

[From NFPA 1221, 4-2.2.1.4, 4-4.2.1.4, and 4-5.2.1.4]

4-6.9.1.4.1.5 Circuit protection required at the communication center shall be provided in every building housing communication center equipment.

[From NFPA 1221, 4-2.2.1.5, 4-4.2.1.5, and 4-5.2.1.5]

4-6.9.1.4.1.6 Each conductor entering a fire station from partially or entirely aerial lines shall be protected by a lightning arrester.

[From NFPA 1221, 4-2.2.1.6, 4-4.2.1.6, and 4-5.2.1.6]

4-6.9.1.4.2 Communication Center.

[From NFPA 1221, 4-2.2.2 and 4-4.2.2]

4-6.9.1.4.2.1 All conductors entering the communication center shall be protected by the following devices, in the order named, starting from the exterior circuit:

(a) A fuse rated at 3 amps minimum to 7 amps maximum, and not less than 2000 volts

(b) A lightning arrester

(c) A fuse or circuit breaker, rated at $1/2$ amp.

[From NFPA 1221, 4-2.2.2.1, 4-4.2.2.1, and 4-5.2.2 modified]

4-6.9.1.4.2.2 The $1/2$-amp protection on the tie circuits shall be omitted at subsidiary communication centers.

[From NFPA 1221, 4-2.2.2.2 modified and 4-4.2.2.2 modified]

4-6.9.1.4.3 Protection on Aerial Construction.

[From NFPA 1221, 4-2.2.2.3, 4-4.2.2.3, and 4-5.2.2.3]

4-6.9.1.4.3.1 At junction points of open aerial conductors and cable, each conductor shall be protected by a lightning arrester of weatherproof type. There shall also be a connection between the lightning arrester ground, any metallic sheath, and messenger wire.

[From NFPA 1221, 4-2.2.3.1 modified, 4-4.2.3.1 modified, and 4-5.2.3.1 modified]

4-6.9.1.4.3.2 Aerial open-wire and non-messenger-supported 2-conductor cable circuits shall be protected by a lightning arrester at intervals of approximately 2000 ft (610 m).

[From NFPA 1221, 4-2.2.3.2, 4-4.2.3.2, and 4-5.2.3.2]

4-6.9.1.4.3.3 Lightning arresters, other than air-gap or self-restoring type, shall not be installed in fire alarm circuits.

[From NFPA 1221, 4-2.2.3.3 modified, 4-4.2.3.3 modified, and 4-5.2.3.3 modified]

4-6.9.1.4.3.4 All protective devices shall be accessible for maintenance and inspection.

[From NFPA 1221, 4-2.2.3.4, 4-4.2.3.4, and 4-5.2.3.4 modified]

4-6.10 Power.

[From NFPA 1221, 4-2.3 and 4-4.3]

4-6.10.1 Requirements for Constant-Current Systems.

[From NFPA 1221, 4-2.3.1 and 4-4.3.1]

4-6.10.1.1 Means shall be provided for manually regulating current in box circuits so that operating current is maintained within 10 percent of normal throughout changes in external circuit resistance from 20 percent above to 50 percent below normal.

[From NFPA 1221, 4-2.3.1.1 and 4-4.3.1.1]

4-6.10.1.2 The voltage supplied to maintain normal line current on box circuits shall not exceed 150 volts, measured under no-load conditions, and shall be such that the line current will not be reduced below safe operating value by the simultaneous operation of four boxes.

[From NFPA 1221, 4-2.3.1.2 and 4-4.3.1.2 modified]

4-6.10.1.3 Visual and audible means to indicate a 20 percent or greater reduction in the normal current in any alarm circuit shall be provided. All devices connected in series with any alarm circuit shall function properly when the alarm circuit current is reduced to 70 percent of normal.

[From NFPA 1221, 4-2.3.1.3 modified and 4-4.3.1.3 modified]

4-6.10.1.4 Sufficient meters shall be provided to indicate the current in any box circuit and the voltage of any power source. Meters used in common for several circuits shall be provided with cut-in devices designed to reduce the probability of cross-connecting circuits.

[From NFPA 1221, 4-2.3.1.4 and 4-4.3.1.4]

4-6.11 Receiving Equipment — Facilities for Receipt of Box Alarms.

[From NFPA 1221, 4-2.4]

4-6.11.1 General.

[From NFPA 1221, 4-2.4.3]

4-6.11.1.1 Alarms from boxes shall be automatically received and recorded at the communication center.

[From NFPA 1221, 4-2.4.3.1 and 4-4.5.4]

4-6.11.1.2 A permanent visual record and an audible signal shall be required to indicate the receipt of an alarm. The permanent record shall indicate the exact location from which the alarm is being transmitted.

NOTE: The audible signal device may be common to several box circuits and arranged so that the fire alarm operator can manually silence the signal temporarily by a self-restoring switch.

[From NFPA 1221, 4-2.4.3.2 modified and 4-4.5.5 modified]

4-6.11.1.3 Facilities shall be provided that will automatically record the date and time of receipt of each alarm, except that only the time need be automatically recorded in voice recordings.

[From NFPA 1221, 4-2.4.3.3 modified, 4-4.5.8 modified, and 4-5.5.8 modified]

4-6.11.2 Visual Recording Devices.

[From NFPA 1221, 4-2.4.1]

4-6.11.2.1 A device for producing a permanent graphic recording of all alarm, supervisory, trouble, and test signals received and/or retransmitted shall be provided at each communication center for each alarm circuit and tie circuit. If each circuit is served by a dedicated recording device, then the number of reserve recording devices required on site shall be equal to at least 5 percent of the circuits in service and in no case less than 1 percent. If two or more circuits are served by a common recording device, then a reserve recording device shall be available on site for each circuit connected to a common recorder.

[From NFPA 1221, 4-2.4.1.1 modified]

4-6.11.2.2 In a Type B wire system, one such device shall be installed in each fire station and at least one in the communication center.

[From NFPA 1221, 4-2.4.1.2 modified]

4-6.12 Supervision.

[From NFPA 1221, 4-2.5, 4-3.7, 4-4.7, and 4-5.7]

4-6.12.1 To ensure reliability, wired circuits upon which transmission and receipt of alarms depend shall be under constant electrical supervision to give prompt warning of conditions adversely affecting reliability.

[From NFPA 1221, 4-2.5.1 and 4-4.7.1]

4-6.12.2 The power supplied to all required circuits and devices of the system shall be supervised.

[From NFPA 1221, 4-2.5.2, 4-3.7.2, 4-4.7.2, and 4-5.7.1]

4-6.12.3 Trouble signals shall actuate a sounding device located where there is always a responsible person on duty.

[From NFPA 1221, 4-2.5.3, 4-3.7.3, 4-4.7.3, and 4-5.7.2]

4-6.12.4 Trouble signals shall be distinct from alarm signals and shall be indicated by both a visual light and an audible signal.

NOTE 1: The audible signal may be common to several supervised circuits.

NOTE 2: A switch for silencing the audible trouble signal is permitted if the visual signal remains operated until the silencing switch is restored to its normal position.

[From NFPA 1221, 4-2.5.4, 4-3.7.4, 4-4.7.4, and 4-5.7.3]

4-6.12.5 The audible signal shall be responsive to faults on any other circuits that may occur prior to restoration of the silencing switch to normal.

[From NFPA 1221, 4-2.5.5, 4-3.7.5, 4-4.7.5, and 4-5.7.4]

4-6.13 Coded Wired Reporting Systems.

4-6.13.1 For a Type B system, the effectiveness of noninterference and succession functions between box circuits shall be no less than between boxes in any one circuit. The disablement of any metallic box circuit shall cause a warning signal in all other circuits, and, thereafter, the circuit or circuits not otherwise broken shall be automatically restored to operative condition.

[From NFPA 1221, 4-2.1.2.3]

4-6.13.2 Box circuits shall be sufficient in number and so laid out that the areas that would be left without box protection in case of disruption of a circuit would not exceed that covered by 20 properly spaced boxes where all or any part of the circuit is of aerial open-wire, or 30 properly spaced boxes where the circuit is entirely in underground or messenger-supported cable.

[From NFPA 1221, 4-2.1.2.4]

4-6.13.3 Where all boxes on any individual circuit and associated equipment are designed and installed to provide for receipt of alarms through the ground in event of a break in the circuit, it is permissible for the circuit to serve twice the above figures for aerial open-wire and cable circuits, respectively.

[From NFPA 1221, 4-2.1.2.5 modified]

4-6.13.4 The installation of additional boxes in an area served by the number of properly spaced boxes indicated above shall not constitute geographical overloading of a circuit.

[From NFPA 1221, 4-2.1.2.6]

4-6.13.5 Sounding devices for signals shall be provided for box circuits.

NOTE 1: In a Type A system, it is satisfactory to use a common sounding device for more than one circuit, and it should be installed at the communication center.

NOTE 2: In a Type B system, a sounding device is to be installed in each fire station at the same location as the recording device for that circuit, except that at the communication center, a common sounding device is permitted.

[From NFPA 1221, 4-2.4.2.1]

4-6.14 Coded Radio Reporting Systems.

[From NFPA 1221, 4-3]

4-6.14.1 Radio Box Channel (Frequency).

[From NFPA 1221, 4-3.1]

4-6.14.1.1 The number of boxes permitted on a single frequency shall be governed by the following:

(a) For systems utilizing one-way transmission in which the individual box automatically initiates the required message (*see 4-6.14.1.4*) using circuitry integral to the boxes, not more than 500 boxes shall be permitted on a single frequency.

(b) For systems utilizing a two-way concept in which interrogation signals (*see 4-6.14.1.4*) are transmitted to the individual boxes from the communication center on the same frequency used for receipt of alarms, not more than 250 boxes shall be permitted on a single frequency. If interrogation signals are transmitted on a frequency different from that used for receipt of alarms, not more than 500 boxes shall be permitted on a single frequency.

(c) A specific frequency shall be designated for both fire and other fire-related or public safety alarm signals, and supervisory signals (test and tamper). All acknowledgment and other signals shall utilize a separate frequency.

[From NFPA 1221, 4-3.1.1 modified]

4-6.14.1.2 Where box message signals to the communication center or acknowledgment of message receipt signals from the communication center to the box are repeated, associated repeating facilities shall conform to the requirements indicated in NFPA 1221, *Standard for the Installation, Maintenance, and Use of Public Fire Service Communication Systems*, 3-4.1.2.

[From NFPA 1221, 4-3.1.2 modified]

4-6.14.1.3 All coded radio box systems shall provide constant monitoring of the frequency in use. Both an audible and visual indication of any sustained carrier signal (when in excess of 15 seconds' duration) shall be provided for each receiving system at the communication center.

[From NFPA 1221, 4-3.1.3 modified]

4-6.14.1.4 Each coded radio box shall automatically transmit a message at least once during each 24-hour period.

[From NFPA 1221, 4-3.6.1 modified]

4-6.14.2 Metallic Interconnections. Accessible and reliable means, available only to the agency responsible for maintaining the public fire alarm reporting system, shall be provided for disconnecting the auxiliary loop to the box inside the building, and definite notification shall be given to occupants of the building when the interior box is not in service.

[From NFPA 1221, 4-3.2.2 modified]

4-6.14.3 Receiving Equipment — Facilities for Receipt of Box Alarms.

[From NFPA 1221, 4-3.4]

4-6.14.3.1 Type A System.

[From NFPA 1221, 4-3.4.2]

4-6.14.3.1.1* For each frequency used, two separate receiving networks, each including an antenna, audible alerting device, receiver, power supply, signal processing equipment, a means of providing a permanent graphic recording of the incoming message that is both timed and dated, and other associated equipment shall be provided and shall be installed at the communication center. Facilities shall be so arranged that a failure of either receiving network will not affect the receipt of messages from boxes.

[From NFPA 1221, 4-3.4.2.1 modified]

4-6.14.3.1.2 Where the system configuration is such that a polling device is incorporated into the receiving network to allow remote/selective initiation of box tests (*see Chapter* 7), a separate such device shall be included in each of the two required receiving networks. Further, the polling devices shall be configured for automatic cycle initiation in their primary operating mode, capable of continuous self-monitoring, and integrated into the network(s) to provide automatic switchover and operational continuity in the event of failure of either device.

[From NFPA 1221, 4-3.4.2.2 modified]

4-6.14.3.1.3 Test signals from boxes shall not be required to include the date as part of their permanent recording, providing that the date is automatically printed on the recording tape at the beginning of each calendar day.

[From NFPA 1221, 4-3.4.2.3]

4-6.14.3.2 Type B System.

[From NFPA 1221, 4-3.4.3]

4-6.14.3.2.1 For each frequency used, a single complete receiving network shall be permitted in each fire station, providing the communication center conforms to 4-6.14.3.1.1. If the jurisdiction maintains in operation two or more alarm reception points, one receiving network shall be permitted to be at each alarm reception point.

[From NFPA 1221, 4-3.4.3.1 modified]

4-6.14.3.2.2 If alarm signals are transmitted to a fire station from the communication center using the coded radio-type receiving equipment in the fire station to receive and record the alarm message, a second receiving network conforming to 4-6.14.3.2.1 shall be provided at each fire station, and that receiving network shall employ a frequency other than that used for the receipt of box messages.

[From NFPA 1221, 4-3.4.3.2 modified]

4-6.14.4 Power. Power shall be provided in accordance with 4-6.7.

[From NFPA 1221, 4-3.5 modified]

4-6.14.5 Testing. (*See Chapter 7.*)

[New title]

4-6.14.6 Supervision. Radio repeaters upon which receipt of alarms depend shall be provided with dual receivers and transmitters. Failure of the primary transmitter or receiver shall cause an automatic switchover to the secondary receiver and transmitter.

Exception: If the repeater controls are located where someone is always on duty, manual switchover shall be permitted if it can be completed within 30 seconds.

[From NFPA 1221, 4-3.7.1 modified]

4-6.15 Telephone (Series) Reporting Systems.

[From NFPA 1221, 4-4]

4-6.15.1 A permanent visual recording device installed in the communication center shall be provided to record all incoming box signals. A spare recording device shall be provided for five or more box circuits.

[From NFPA 1221, 4-4.5.1]

4-6.15.2 A second visual means of identifying the calling box shall be provided.

[From NFPA 1221, 4-4.5.2]

4-6.15.3 Audible signals shall indicate all incoming calls from box circuits.

[From NFPA 1221, 4-4.5.3]

4-6.15.4 All voice transmissions from boxes for emergencies shall be recorded with the capability of instant playback.

[From NFPA 1221, 4-4.5.6]

4-6.15.5 A voice recording facility shall be provided for each operator handling incoming alarms to eliminate the possibility of interference.

[From NFPA 1221, 4-4.5.7]

4-6.15.6 Box circuits shall be sufficient in number and so laid out that the areas that would be left without box protection in case of disruption of a circuit would not exceed that covered by 20 properly spaced boxes where all or any part of the circuit is of aerial open-wire, or 30 properly spaced boxes where the circuit is entirely in underground or messenger-supported cable.

[From NFPA 1221, 4-4.1.2.1 modified]

4-6.15.7 Where all boxes on any individual circuit and associated equipment are designed and installed to provide for receipt of alarms through the ground in event of a break in the circuit, it shall be permissible for the circuit to serve twice the above figures for aerial open-wire and cable circuits, respectively.

[From NFPA 1221, 4-4.1.2.2]

4-6.15.8 The installation of additional boxes in an area served by the number of properly spaced boxes indicated above shall not constitute geographical overloading of a circuit.

[From NFPA 1221, 4-4.1.2.3]

4-6.16 Telephone (Parallel) Reporting Systems.

[From NFPA 1221, 4-5]

4-6.16.1 Box Circuits.

[From NFPA 1221, 4-5.1.2]

4-6.16.1.1 If a municipal box is installed inside a building, it shall be placed as close as practical to the point of entrance of the circuit, and the exterior wire shall be installed in conduit or electrical metallic tubing, in accordance with Chapter 3 of NFPA 70, *National Electrical Code*.

[From NFPA 1221, 4-5.1.2.1]

4-6.16.1.2 Accessible and reliable means, available only to the authority having jurisdiction or the agency responsible for maintaining the public fire alarm reporting system, shall be provided for disconnecting the box inside the building, and definite notification shall be given to occupants of the building when the interior box is not in service.

[From NFPA 1221, 4-5.1.2.2 modified]

4-6.16.1.3 A separate circuit shall be provided for each box.

[From NFPA 1221, 4-5.1.2.3]

4-6.16.1.4 Where a concentrator-identifier or similar device is employed, at least two tie circuits for the first 40 boxes connected shall be provided to the communication center. A tie circuit shall be provided for each 40 additional boxes, or fraction thereof, connected to the concentrator-identifier.

NOTE: These tie circuits are not to be used for any other purpose or function.

[From NFPA 1221, 4-5.1.3 modified]

4-6.16.1.5 Power shall be provided in accordance with Section 4-6.7

[From NFPA 1221, 4-5.3 modified]

4-6.16.2 Receiving Equipment — Facilities for Receipt of Box Alarms.

[From NFPA 1221, 4-5.5]

4-6.16.2.1 The box circuits shall be terminated:

(a) Directly on a console or switchboard located in the communication center, or

(b) In concentrator-identifier equipment located in a subsidiary communication center.

NOTE: The audible signal device may be common to several box circuits and arranged so that the operator can manually silence the signal temporarily with a self-restoring switch.

[From NFPA 1221, 4-5.5.1 modified]

4-6.16.2.2 All voice transmissions from boxes for emergencies shall be recorded with the capability of instant playback.

[From NFPA 1221, 4-5.5.6]

4-6.16.2.3 A means of voice recording shall be provided for each operator handling incoming alarms to eliminate the possibility of interference.

[From NFPA 1221, 4-5.5.7 modified]

4-6.16.2.4 Either a continuous line test or periodic (up to 6 minutes) automatic line tests shall detect an open, short, ground, or leakage condition. If one of these conditions occurs, a visual and audible trouble signal shall be actuated where there is an operator on duty.

[From NFPA 1221, 4-5.7.5]

4-7 Auxiliary Fire Alarm Systems.

NOTE: The requirements of Chapters 1, 3, 5, 6, 7, and Section 4-2 shall apply to auxiliary fire alarm systems, except where they conflict with the requirements of this section.

[From NFPA 72, Chap. 7 modified]

4-7.1 Scope. This section describes the equipment and circuits necessary to connect a protected premises (*see Chapter 3*) to a public fire alarm reporting system (*see Section 4-6*).

[From NFPA 72, 7-1 modified]

4-7.2 General.

[From NFPA 72, 7-2]

4-7.2.1 An auxiliary fire alarm system shall be used only in connection with a public fire alarm reporting system that is suitable for the service. A system satisfactory to the authority having jurisdiction shall be considered as meeting this requirement.

[From NFPA 72, 7-2.3]

4-7.2.2 Permission for the connection of an auxiliary fire alarm system to a public fire alarm reporting system and acceptance of the type of auxiliary transmitter, its actuating mechanism, circuits, and components connected thereto, shall be obtained from the authority having jurisdiction.

[From NFPA 72, 7-2.4 modified]

4-7.2.3 An auxiliary fire alarm system shall be maintained and supervised by a responsible person or corporation.

[From NFPA 72, 7-2.5 modified]

4-7.2.4 Section 4-7 does not require the use of audible alarm signals other than those necessary to operate the auxiliary fire alarm system. If it is desired to provide fire alarm evacuation signals in the protected property, the alarms, circuits, and controls shall comply with the provisions of Chapter 3, in addition to the provisions of Section 4-7.

[From NFPA 72, 7-2.6 modified]

4-7.3 Communication Center Facilities. The communication center facilities shall be in accordance with the requirements of Section 4-6.

4-7.4 Equipment.

[New paragraph and title]

4-7.4.1 Types of Systems. There are three types of auxiliary fire alarm systems in use, and these are described in (a), (b), and (c) below.

[From NFPA 72, 7-3]

(a)* The local energy type [Figure A-4-7.4.1(a)(1)] is electrically isolated from the public fire alarm reporting system and has its own power supply. The tripping of the transmitting device does not depend on the current in the system. In a wired circuit, whether or not the alarm will be received by the communication center if the circuit is accidently opened depends on the design of the transmitting device and the associated communication center equipment, i.e., whether or not the system is designed to receive alarms through manual or automatic ground operational facilities. In a radio box type system, whether or not the alarm will be received by the communication center depends on the proper operation of the radio transmitting and receiving equipment.

[From NFPA 72, 7-3(a) modified]

1. Local energy systems shall be permitted to be of coded or noncoded type.

[From NFPA 72, 7-6.2.1 modified]

2. Power supply sources for local energy systems shall conform to Chapter 1.

[From NFPA 72, 7-6.2.2 modified]

(b)* The shunt type [Figure A-4-7.4.1(b)(1)] is electrically connected to and is an integral part of the public fire alarm reporting system. A ground fault on the auxiliary circuit is a fault on the public fire alarm reporting system circuit, and an accidental opening of the auxiliary circuit will send a needless (or false) alarm to the communication center. An open circuit in the transmitting device trip coil will not be indicated either at the protected property or at the communication center; also, if an initiating device is operated, an alarm will not be transmitted but an open circuit indication will be given at the communications center. If a public fire alarm reporting system circuit is open when a connected shunt type system is operated, the transmitting device will not trip until the public fire alarm reporting system circuit returns to normal, at which time the alarm will be transmitted unless the auxiliary circuit is first returned to a normal condition.

A local system made into an auxiliary system by the addition of a relay whose coil is energized by a local power supply and whose normally closed contacts trip a shunt type master box shall not be permitted [Figure A-4-7.4.1(b)(2)].

[From NFPA 72, 7-3(b) modified]

1. Shunt systems shall be noncoded with respect to any remote electrical tripping or actuating devices.

[From NFPA 72, 7-6.1.1 modified]

2. All conductors of the shunt circuit shall be installed in accordance with Article 346, for rigid conduit, or Article 348, for electrical metallic tubing, of NFPA 70, *National Electrical Code.*

[From NFPA 72, 7-6.1.2]

3. Both sides of the shunt circuit shall be in the same conduit.

[From NFPA 72, 7-6.1.3]

4. Where an auxiliary transmitter is located within a private premise, it shall be installed in accordance with 4-6.9.1.

[From NFPA 72, 7-6.1.4 modified]

5. Where a shunt loop is used, it shall not exceed a length of 750 ft (230 m) and shall be in conduit.

[From NFPA 72, 7-6.1.5]

6. Conductors of the shunt circuits shall not be smaller than No. 14 AWG and shall be insulated as prescribed in NFPA 70, *National Electrical Code*, Article 310.

[From NFPA 72, 7-6.1.6]

7. The power for shunt-type systems shall be provided by the public fire alarm reporting system.

[From NFPA 72, 7-6.1.7 modified]

8. Additional design restrictions for shunt systems shall be found in laws or ordinances.

[From NFPA 72, 7-6.1.8 modified]

(c)* A parallel telephone type system [Figure A-4-7.4.1(c)] is a system in which alarms are transmitted over a circuit directly connected to the annunciating switchboard at the public fire service communication center and terminated at the protected property by an end-of-line device.

Such auxiliary systems are for connection to public fire alarm reporting systems of the type in which each alarm box annunciates at the communication center by individual circuit.

NOTE: The essential difference between the local energy or parallel telephone types and the shunt-type system is that accidental opening of the alarm initiating circuits will cause an alarm on the shunt type system only.

[From NFPA 72, 7-3(c) modified]

1. Parallel telephone systems shall be noncoded with respect to any remote electrical tripping or actuating devices.

[From NFPA 72, 7-6.3.1 modified]

2. Two methods of parallel telephone systems shall be permitted to be used:

(i) The circuits are extended beyond the entrance termination point to actuating devices with the supervisory device beyond the last actuating device in the circuit; or

(ii) The supervisory device for the circuit is located at the entrance termination point. The tripping relay shall be located immediately adjacent to the supervisory device and shall be connected thereto with conductors not smaller than No. 14 AWG in conduit.

[From NFPA 72, 7-6.3.2]

3. Nonvoice circuits connected to a parallel telephone system shall be indicated with distinctive and different color from voice circuits and shall be grouped in a reserved separate section of the receiving equipment with adequate written warning that no voice is to be expected on these alarms and that the fire department must be dispatched on alarm light indications.

[From NFPA 72, 7-6.3.3 modified]

4-7.4.2 The interface of the three types of auxiliary fire alarm systems with the four types of public fire alarm reporting systems shall be in accordance with Table 4-7.4.2.

Table 4-7.4.2

	Local Energy-Type	Shunt-Type	Parallel-Type
Coded Wired	Yes	Yes	No
Coded Radio	Yes	No	No
Telephone Series	Yes	No	No
Telephone Parallel	No	No	Yes

4-7.4.3 The application of the three types of auxiliary fire alarm systems shall be limited to the initiating devices specified in Table 4-7.4.3.

Table 4-7.4.3

	Local Energy-Type	Shunt-Type	Parallel-Type
Manual Fire Alarm	Yes	Yes	Yes
Waterflow or Actuation of Extinguishing System	Yes	Yes	Yes
Automatic Detection Devices	Yes	No	Yes

[New paragraphs and tables]

4-7.4.4 Location of Transmitting Devices.

[From NFPA 72, 7-4.2]

4-7.4.4.1 Auxiliary systems shall be arranged so that one auxiliary transmitter does not serve more than 100,000 sq ft (9290 m^2) total area, unless otherwise permitted by the authority having jurisdiction.

[From NFPA 72, 7-4.2.1 modified]

4-7.4.4.2 A separate auxiliary transmitter shall be provided for each building or where permitted by the authority having jurisdiction for each group of buildings of single ownership or occupancy.

[From NFPA 72, 7-4.2.2 modified]

4-7.4.4.3 The same box shall be permitted to be used as a public fire alarm reporting system box and as a transmitting device for an auxiliary system where permitted by the authority having jurisdiction, provided that the box is located at the outside of the entrance to the protected property.

NOTE: The fire department may require the box to be equipped with a signal light to differentiate between automatic and manual operation, unless local outside alarms at the protected property would serve the same purpose.

[From NFPA 72, 7-4.2.3 modified]

4-7.4.4.4 The transmitting device shall be located as required by the authority having jurisdiction.

[From NFPA 72, 7-4.2.4 modified]

4-7.4.4.5 The system shall be so designed and arranged that a single fault on the auxiliary system shall not jeopardize operation of the public fire alarm reporting system and shall not, in case of a single fault on either the auxiliary or public fire alarm reporting system, transmit a false alarm on either system.

Exception: Shunt systems. [See 4-7.4.1(b).]

[From NFPA 72, 7-4.7 modified]

4-7.5 Personnel. Personnel necessary to receive and act on signals from auxiliary fire alarm systems shall be in accordance with the requirements of Section 4-6 and NFPA 1221, *Standard for the Installation, Maintenance, and Use of Public Fire Service Communication Systems.*

4-7.6 Operations. Operations for auxiliary fire alarm systems shall be in accordance with the requirements of Section 4-6 and NFPA 1221, *Standard for the Installation, Maintenance, and Use of Public Fire Service Communication Systems.*

4-7.7 Testing and Maintenance. Testing and maintenance of auxiliary fire alarm systems shall be in accordance with the requirements of Chapter 7.

[New paragraphs]

Chapter 5 Initiating Devices

5-1 General.

5-1.1 Scope. This chapter covers minimum requirements for performance, selection, use, and location of automatic fire detection devices, sprinkler waterflow detectors, manually activated fire alarm stations, and supervisory signal initiating devices, including guard tour reporting used to ensure timely warning for the purposes of life safety and the protection of a building, space, structure, area, or object.

NOTE: For detector requirements in a household system, refer to Chapter 2.

[From NFPA 72E - 1990, 1-1 and 1-2.1 modified]

5-1.2 Application.

5-1.2.1 The material in this chapter is intended for use by persons knowledgeable in the application of fire detection and fire alarm systems/services.

[From NFPA 72E - 1990, 1-1.2 modified]

5-1.2.2 Automatic and manual initiating devices contribute to life safety, fire protection, and property conservation only when used in conjunction with other equipment. The interconnection of these devices with control equipment configurations, and power supplies or with output systems responding to external actuation is detailed elsewhere in this code and others.

[From NFPA 72E - 1990, 1-2.2 and 1-2.3 modified]

5-1.3 Installation and Required Location of Detection Devices.

[From NFPA 72E - 1990, 2-7 modified]

5-1.3.1 Where subject to mechanical damage, detectors shall be protected.

[From NFPA 72E - 1990, 2-7.1]

5-1.3.2 In all cases, detectors shall be supported independently of their attachment to the circuit conductors.

[From NFPA 72E - 1990, 2-7.2]

5-1.3.3 Detectors shall not be recessed in any way into the mounting surface, unless they have been tested and listed for such recessed mounting.

[From NFPA 72E - 1990, 2-7.3]

5-1.3.4 Detectors shall be installed in all areas where required by the appropriate NFPA standard or the authority having jurisdiction. Each installed detector shall be accessible for periodic maintenance and testing. Where total coverage is required, this shall include all rooms, halls, storage areas, basements, attics, lofts, spaces above suspended ceilings, and other subdivisions and accessible spaces, and inside all closets, elevator shafts, enclosed stairways, dumbwaiter shafts, and chutes. Inaccessible areas shall not be required to be protected by detectors unless they contain combustible material, in which case they shall be made accessible and be protected by detector(s).

Exception No. 1: Detectors may be omitted from combustible blind spaces where any of the following conditions prevail:

(a) Where the ceiling is attached directly to the underside of the supporting beams of a combustible roof or floor deck.

(b) Where the concealed space is entirely filled with a noncombustible insulation. In solid joist construction, the insulation need fill only the space from the ceiling to the bottom edge of the joist of the roof or floor deck.

(c) Where there are small concealed spaces over rooms, provided any space in question does not exceed 50 sq ft (4.6 m²) in area.

(d) In spaces formed by sets of facing studs or solid joists in walls, floors, or ceilings where the distance between the facing studs or solid joists is less than 6 in. (150 mm).

Exception No. 2: Detectors may be omitted from below open grid ceilings where all of the following conditions prevail:

(a) The openings of the grid are 1/4 in. (6.4 mm) or larger in the least dimension.

(b) The thickness of the material does not exceed the least dimension.

(c) The openings constitute at least 70 percent of the area of the ceiling material.

Exception No. 3: Concealed, accessible spaces above suspended ceilings, used as a return air plenum meeting the requirements of NFPA 90A, Standard for the Installation of Air Conditioning and Ventilating Systems, where equipped with smoke detection at each connection from the plenum to the central air handling system.

[From NFPA 72E - 1990, 2-7.4 modified]

5-1.3.5* Detectors shall be required underneath open loading docks or platforms and their covers, and for accessible underfloor spaces of buildings without basements.

Exception: By permission of the authority having jurisdiction, detectors may be omitted when all of the following conditions prevail:

(a) The space is not accessible for storage purposes or entrance of unauthorized persons and is protected against accumulation of windborne debris.

(b) The space contains no equipment such as steam pipes, electric wiring, shafting, or conveyors.

(c) The floor over the space is tight.

(d) No flammable liquids are processed, handled, or stored on the floor above.

[NFPA 72E - 1990, 2-7.5]

5-1.3.6 Where codes, standards, laws, or authorities having jurisdiction require the protection of selected areas only, the specified areas shall be protected in accordance with this code.

[From 72E, 2-7.6]

5-1.4* Connection to the Fire Alarm System.

[New title]

5-1.4.1 Duplicate terminals or leads, or equivalent, shall be provided on each initiating device for the express purpose of connecting into the fire alarm system to provide supervision of the connections. Such terminals or leads are necessary to ensure that the wire run is broken and that the individual connections are made to the incoming and outgoing leads or other terminals for signaling and power.

Exception: Initiating devices that provide equivalent supervision.

[From NFPA 72E - 1990, 2-7.7]

5-2 Heat-Sensing Fire Detectors.

[From NFPA 72E - 1990, Chap. 3]

5-2.1 Fire detectors that sense heat produced by burning substances are usually referred to as heat detectors. Heat is both the added energy that causes substances to rise in temperature as well as the energy produced by a burning substance.

[From NFPA 72E - 1990, 3-1, 3-1.1.1 modified]

5-2.2 Heat detectors shall be installed in all areas where required either by the appropriate NFPA standard or the authority having jurisdiction.

[From NFPA 72E, 3-1.1.2]

5-2.3 Operating Principles.

[From NFPA 72E - 1990, 3-2]

5-2.3.1 Fixed Temperature Detector.

[From NFPA 72E - 1990, 3-2.1]

5-2.3.1.1 A fixed temperature detector is a device that will respond when its operating element becomes heated to a predetermined level.

[From NFPA 72E - 1990, 2-2.1.1]

5-2.3.1.2 Thermal Lag. Where a fixed temperature device operates, the temperature of the surrounding air will always be higher than the operating temperature of the device itself. This difference between the operating temperature of the device and the actual air temperature is commonly referred to as thermal lag and is proportional to the rate at which the temperature is rising.

[From NFPA 72E - 1990, 3-2.1.2]

5-2.3.1.3 Typical examples of fixed temperature-sensing elements are:

(a) *Bimetallic.* A sensing element comprised of two metals having different coefficients of thermal expansion arranged so that the effect will be deflection in one direction when heated and in the opposite direction when cooled.

(b) *Electrical Conductivity.* A line-type or spot-type sensing element whose resistance varies as a function of temperature.

(c) *Fusible Alloy.* A sensing element of a special composition (eutectic) metal, which melts rapidly at the rated temperature.

(d) *Heat-Sensitive Cable.* A line-type device whose sensing element comprises, in one type, two current-carrying wires separated by heat-sensitive insulation that softens at the rated temperature, thus allowing the wires to make electrical contact. In another type, a single wire is centered in a metallic tube, and the intervening space filled with a substance that, at a critical temperature, becomes conductive, thus establishing electrical contact between the tube and the wire.

(e) *Liquid Expansion.* A sensing element comprising a liquid capable of marked expansion in volume in response to temperature increase.

[From NFPA 72E - 1990, 3-2.1.3]

5-2.3.2 Rate Compensation Detector.

[From NFPA 72E - 1990, 3-2.2]

5-2.3.2.1 A rate compensation detector is a device that will respond when the temperature of the air surrounding the device reaches a predetermined level, regardless of the rate of temperature rise.

[From NFPA 72E - 1990, 3-2.2.1]

5-2.3.2.2 A typical example is a spot-type detector with a tubular casing of a metal that tends to expand lengthwise as it is heated and an associated contact mechanism that will close at a certain point in the elongation. A second metallic element inside the tube exerts an opposing force on the contacts, tending to hold them open. The forces are balanced in such a way that on a slow rate of temperature rise, there is more time for heat to penetrate to the inner element, which inhibits contact closure until the total device has been heated to its rated temperature level. However, on a fast rate of temperature rise, there is not as much time for heat to penetrate to the inner element, which exerts less of an inhibiting effect so that contact closure is obtained when the total device has been heated to a lower level. This, in effect, compensates for thermal lag.

[From NFPA 72E - 1990, 3-2.2.2]

5-2.3.3 Rate-of-Rise Detector.

[From NFPA 72E - 1990, 3-2.3]

5-2.3.3.1 A rate-of-rise detector is a device that will respond when the temperature rises at a rate exceeding a predetermined amount.

[From NFPA 72E - 1990, 3-2.3.1]

5-2.3.3.2 Typical examples are:

(a) *Pneumatic Rate-of-Rise Tubing.* A line-type detector comprising small diameter tubing, usually copper, that is installed on the ceiling or high on the walls throughout the protected area. The tubing is terminated in a detector unit containing diaphragms and associated contacts set to actuate at a predetermined pressure. The system is sealed except for calibrated vents that compensate for normal changes in temperature.

(b) *Spot-Type Pneumatic Rate-of-Rise Detector.* A device consisting of an air chamber, diaphragm, contacts, and compensating vent in a single enclosure. The principle of operation is the same as that described in 5-2.3.3.2(a).

(c) *Thermoelectric Effect Detector.* A device whose sensing element comprises a thermocouple or thermopile unit that produces an increase in electric potential in response to an increase in temperature. This potential is monitored by associated control equipment, and an alarm is initiated when the potential increases at an abnormal rate.

(d) *Electrical Conductivity Rate-of-Change Detector.* A line-type or spot-type sensing element whose resistance changes due to a change in temperature. The rate of change of resistance is monitored by associated control equipment, and an alarm is initiated when the rate of temperature increase exceeds a preset value.

[From NFPA 72E - 1990, 3-2.3.2 modified]

5-2.4 Classification and Sensitivity.

[From NFPA 72E - 1990, 3-3 modified]

5-2.4.1 Heat detectors of the fixed-temperature or rate-compensated spot-pattern type shall be classified as to the temperature of operation and marked with the appropriate color code. (*See Table 5-2.4.1.*)

[From NFPA 72E - 1990, 3-3.1]

5-2.4.1.1 Where the overall color of a detector is the same as the color code marking required for that detector, either one of the following arrangements, applied in a contrasting color and visible after installation, shall be employed:

(a) A ring on the surface of the detector

(b) The temperature rating in numerals at least $^3/_8$ in. (9.5 mm) high.

[From NFPA 72E - 1990, 3-3.1.1]

Table 5-2.4.1

Temperature Classification	Temp. Rating Range °F	Temp. Rating Range °C	Max. Ceiling Temp. °F	Max. Ceiling Temp. °C	Color Code
Low*	100 to 134	39 to 57	20 below**	11	Uncolored
Ordinary	135 to 174	58 to 79	100	38	Uncolored
Intermediate	175 to 249	80 to 121	150	66	White
High	250 to 324	122 to 162	225	107	Blue
Extra High	325 to 399	163 to 204	300	149	Red
Very Extra High	400 to 499	205 to 259	375	191	Green
Ultra High	500 to 575	260 to 302	475	246	Orange

For SI Units: C = 5/9 (F −32).
*Intended only for installation in controlled ambient areas. Units shall be marked to indicate maximum ambient installation temperature.
**Maximum ceiling temperature has to be 20°F (11°C) or more below detector rated temperature.
NOTE: The difference between the rated temperature and the maximum ambient should be as small as possible to minimize the response time.

[From NFPA 72E - 1990, 3-3.1 modified]

5-2.4.2* A heat detector integrally mounted on a smoke detector shall be listed or approved for not less than 50-ft (15-m) spacing.

[From NFPA 74 - 1990, 4-3 modified]

5-2.5 Location.

[From NFPA 72E - 1990, 3-4]

5-2.5.1* Spot-type heat detectors shall be located on the ceiling not less than 4 in. (100 mm) from the side wall or on the side walls between 4 in. (100 mm) and 12 in. (300 mm) from the ceiling. (*See Figure A-5-2.5.1.*)

Exception No. 1: In the case of solid open joist construction, detectors shall be mounted at the bottom of the joists.

Exception No. 2: In the case of beam construction where beams are less than 12 in. (300 mm) in depth and less than 8 ft (2.4 m) on center, detectors may be installed on the bottom of beams.

[From NFPA 72E - 1990, 3-4.1]

5-2.5.2 Line-type heat detectors shall be located on the ceiling or on the side walls not more than 20 in. (500 mm) from the ceiling.

Exception No. 1: In the case of solid open joist construction, detectors shall be mounted at the bottom of the joists.

Exception No. 2: In the case of beam construction where beams are less than 12 in. (300 mm) in depth and less than 8 ft (2.4 m) on center, detectors may be installed on the bottom of beams.

[From NFPA 72E - 1990, 3-4.2 modified]

5-2.6* Temperature. Detectors having fixed-temperature or rate-compensated elements shall be selected in accordance with Table 5-2.4.1 for the maximum ceiling temperature that can be expected.

[From NFPA 72E - 1990, 3-4.3]

5-2.7* Spacing.

[From NFPA 72E - 1990, 3-5]

5-2.7.1* Smooth Ceiling Spacing. One of the following rules shall apply:

(a) The distance between detectors shall not exceed their listed spacing, and there shall be detectors within a distance of one-half the listed spacing, measured at a right angle, from all walls or partitions extending to within 18 in. (460 mm) of the ceiling; or

(b) All points on the ceiling shall have a detector within a distance equal to 0.7 times the listed spacing (0.7S). This will be useful in calculating locations in corridors or irregular areas.

[From NFPA 72E - 1990, 3-5.1]

5-2.7.1.1* Irregular Areas. For irregularly shaped areas, the spacing between detectors may be greater than the listed spacing, provided the maximum spacing from a detector to the furthest point of a side wall or corner within its zone of protection is not greater than 0.7 times the listed spacing. (*See Figure A-5-2.7.1.1.*)

[From NFPA 72E - 1990, 3-5.1.1]

5-2.7.1.2* High Ceilings. On ceilings 10 ft (3 m) to 30 ft (9.1 m) high, heat detector linear spacing shall be reduced in accordance with Table 5-2.7.1.2.

[From NFPA 72E - 1990, 3-5.1.2]

Table 5-2.7.1.2

Ceiling Height Above (ft)	Up to	Percent of Listed Spacing
0	10	100
10	12	91
12	14	84
14	16	77
16	18	71
18	20	64
20	22	58
22	24	52
24	26	46
26	28	40
28	30	34

For SI Units: 1 ft = 0.305 m.

Exception: Table 5-2.7.1.2 does not apply to the following detectors, which rely on the integration effect:

(a) Line-type electrical conductivity detectors. [See 5-2.3.1.3(b).]

(b) Pneumatic rate-of-rise tubing. [See 5-2.3.3.2(a).]

(c) Series connected thermoelectric effect detectors. [See 5-2.3.3.2(c).]

In these cases, the manufacturer's recommendations shall be followed for appropriate alarm point and spacing.

NOTE: Table 5-2.7.1.2 provides for spacing modifications to take into account different ceiling heights for generalized fire conditions. An alternative design method that allows a designer to take into account ceiling height, fire size, and ambient temperature is provided in Appendix B.

[From NFPA 72E, Table 3-5.1.2]

5-2.7.2* Solid Joist Construction. The spacing of heat detectors, where measured at right angles to the solid joists, shall not exceed 50 percent of the smooth ceiling spacing allowable under 5-2.7.1 and 5-2.7.1.1. (*See Figure A-5-2.7.2.*)

[From NFPA 72E - 1990, 3-5.2]

5-2.7.3* Beam Construction. A ceiling shall be treated as a smooth ceiling if the beams project no more than 4 in. (100 mm) below the ceiling. If the beams project more than 4 in. (100 mm) below the ceiling, the spacing of spot-type heat detectors at right angles to the direction of beam travel shall be not more than two-thirds the smooth ceiling spacing allowable under 5-2.7.1 and 5-2.7.1.1. If the beams project more than 18 in. (460 mm) below the ceiling and are more than 8 ft (2.4 m) on center, each bay formed by the beams shall be treated as a separate area.

[From NFPA 72E - 1990, 3-5.3]

5-2.7.4 Sloped Ceilings.

[From NFPA 72E - 1990, 3-5.4]

5-2.7.4.1* Peaked. A row of detectors shall first be spaced and located at or within 3 ft (0.9 m) of the peak of the ceiling, measured horizontally. The number and spacing of additional detectors, if any, shall be based on the horizontal projection of the ceiling in accordance with the type of ceiling construction. (*See Figure A-5-2.7.4.1.*)

[From NFPA 72E - 1990, 3-5.4.1]

5-2.7.4.2* Shed. Sloped ceilings having a rise greater than 1 ft in 8 ft (1 m in 8 m) horizontally shall have a row of detectors located on the ceiling within 3 ft (0.9 m) of the high side of the ceiling measured horizontally, spaced in accordance with the type of construction. Remaining detectors, if any, shall then be located in the remaining area on the basis of the horizontal projection of the ceiling. (*See Figure A-5-2.7.4.2.*)

[From NFPA 72E - 1990, 3-5.4.2]

5-2.7.4.3 For a roof slope of less than 30 degrees, all detectors shall be spaced utilizing the height at the peak. For a roof slope of greater than 30 degrees, the average slope height shall be used for all detectors other than those located in the peak.

[From NFPA 72E, 3-5.4.3]

5-3 Smoke-Sensing Fire Detectors.

[From NFPA 72E - 1990, Chap. 4]

5-3.1 General.

[From NFPA 72E - 1990, 4-1]

5-3.1.1* The purpose of Section 5-3 is to provide information to assist in design and installation of reliable early warning smoke detection systems for protection of life and property.

[From NFPA 72E - 1990, 4-1.1]

5-3.1.2 Section 5-3 covers general area application of smoke detectors in ordinary indoor locations.

[From NFPA 72E - 1990, 4-1.2]

5-3.1.3 For information on use of smoke detectors for control of smoke spread, refer to Section 5-11.

[From NFPA 72E - 1990, 4-1.2.1 modified]

5-3.1.4 For additional guidance in the application of smoke detectors for flaming fires of various sizes and growth rates in areas of various ceiling heights, refer to Appendix B.

[From NFPA 72E - 1990, 4-1.2.2]

5-3.2* Smoke detectors shall be installed in all areas where required either by the appropriate NFPA standard or by the authority having jurisdiction.

[From NFPA 72E - 1990, 4-1.3]

5-3.3 Principles of Detection.

[From NFPA 72E - 1990, 4-2]

5-3.3.1 Ionization Smoke Detection. Ionization smoke detection is based on the principle of using a small amount of radioactive material to ionize the air between two differentially charged electrodes. This gives the sensing chamber an effective measurable electrical conductance. Where smoke particles enter the ionization volume, they decrease the conductance of the air by reducing ion mobility. The conductance signal is processed and used to convey an alarm condition where the signal meets preset criteria.

[From NFPA 72E - 1990, 4-2.1 modified]

5-3.3.1.1 Ionization detection is more responsive to invisible (less than one micron in size) particles produced by most flaming fires. It is somewhat less responsive to the larger particles typical of most smoldering fires.

[From NFPA 72E - 1990, 4-2.1.1]

5-3.3.1.2 Smoke detectors utilizing the ionization principle are usually of the spot type.

[From NFPA 72E - 1990, 4-2.1.2]

5-3.3.2* Photoelectric Light-Scattering Smoke Detection. Photoelectric light-scattering smoke detection is based on the principle of a light source and a photosensitive sensor arranged so that the principal portion of rays from the light source do not normally fall on the photosensitive sensor. Where smoke particles enter the light path, some of the light is scattered by reflection and refraction onto the sensor. The scattered light signal is processed and used to convey an alarm condition where the signal meets preset criteria.

[From NFPA 72E - 1990, 4-2.2 modified]

5-3.3.2.1 Photoelectric light-scattering detection is more responsive to visible (more than one micron in size) particles produced by most smoldering fires. It is somewhat less responsive to the smaller particles typical of most flaming fires. It is also less responsive to black smoke than to lighter colored smoke.

[From NFPA 72E - 1990, 4-2.2.1 modified]

5-3.3.2.2 Smoke detectors utilizing the light-scattering principle are usually of the spot type.

[From NFPA 72E - 1990, 4-2.2.2]

5-3.3.3* Photoelectric Light Obscuration Smoke Detection. Photoelectric light obscuration smoke detection is based on the principle of reduction of light transmission between a light source and a photosensitive sensor onto which the principal portion of the source emissions are focused. Where smoke particles enter the light path, some of the light is scattered and some absorbed, thereby reducing the light reaching the receiving sensor. The receiving sensor signal is processed and used to convey an alarm condition where the signal meets preset criteria.

[From NFPA 72E - 1990, 4-2.3 modified]

5-3.3.3.1 The response of photoelectric light obscuration smoke detectors is usually not affected by the color of smoke.

[From NFPA 72E - 1990, 4-2.3.1]

5-3.3.3.2 Smoke detectors utilizing the light obscuration principle are usually of the line type. These detectors are commonly called projected beam smoke detectors.

[From NFPA 72E - 1990, 4-2.3.2]

5-3.3.4 Cloud Chamber Smoke Detection. Cloud chamber smoke detection is usually of the sampling type. An air sample is drawn from the protected areas into a high humidity chamber within the detector. After the humidity of the sample has been raised, the pressure is lowered slightly. If smoke particles are present, the moisture in the air condenses on them, forming a cloud in the chamber. The density of this cloud is then measured by a photoelectric principle. The density signal is processed and used to convey an alarm condition where the signal meets preset criteria.

[From NFPA 72E - 1990, 4-2.4 modified]

5-3.4 Sensitivity.

[From NFPA 72E - 1990, 4-2 modified]

5-3.4.1 Smoke detectors shall be marked with their normal production sensitivity (percent per foot obscuration), measured as required by the listing. The production tolerance around the normal sensitivity shall also be indicated.

[From NFPA 72E - 1990, 4-3.1 modified]

5-3.4.2 Smoke detectors that have provision for field adjustment of sensitivity shall have an adjustment range of not less than 0.6 percent per ft obscuration. If the means of adjustment is on the detector, a method shall be available to restore the detector to its factory calibration. Detectors that have provision for program controlled adjustment of sensitivity shall be permitted to only be marked with their programmable sensitivity range.

[From NFPA 72E - 1990, 4-3.1.1 modified]

5-3.5 Location and Spacing.

[From NFPA 72E - 1990, 4-4]

5-3.5.1* General. The location and spacing of smoke detectors shall result from an evaluation based on the guidelines detailed in this code and on engineering judgment. Ceiling shape and surfaces, ceiling height, configuration of contents, burning characteristics of combustible material present, ventilation, and the ambient environment are some of the conditions that shall be considered.

[From NFPA 72E - 1990, 4-4.1 modified]

5-3.5.1.1 Where the intent is to protect against a specific hazard, the detector(s) shall be permitted to be installed closer to the hazard in a position where the detector will readily intercept the smoke.

[From NFPA 72E - 1990, 4-4.1.1]

5-3.5.1.2* Stratification. The possible effect of smoke stratification at levels below the ceiling shall be considered.

[From NFPA 72E - 1990, 4-4.1.2]

5-3.5.2* Spot-Type Smoke Detectors. Spot-type smoke detectors shall be located on the ceiling not less than 4 in. (100 mm) from a sidewall to the near edge or, if on a sidewall, between 4 in. (100 mm) and 12 in. (300 mm) down from the ceiling to the top of the detector. (*See Figure A-5-2.1.*)

Exception No. 1: See 5-3.5.1.2.

Exception No. 2: See 5-3.5.6.

Exception No. 3: See 5-3.5.7.

[From NFPA 72E - 1990, 4-4.2]

5-3.5.2.1* To minimize dust contamination of smoke detectors where installed under raised room floors and similar spaces, they shall only be mounted in an orientation for which they have been listed. (*See Figure A-5-3.5.2.1.*)

[From NFPA 72E - 1990, 4-4.2.1]

5-3.5.3 Projected Beam-Type Smoke Detectors. Projected beam-type smoke detectors (*see 5-3.3.3.1*) shall normally be located with their projected beams parallel to the ceiling and in accordance with the manufacturer's documented instructions.

Exception No. 1: See 5-3.5.1.2.

Exception No. 2: Beams may be installed vertically or at any angle needed to afford protection of the hazard involved. (Example: Vertical beams through the open shaft area of a stairwell where there is a clear vertical space inside the handrails.)

[From NFPA 72E - 1990, 4-4.3 modified]

5-3.5.3.1 The beam length shall not exceed the maximum permitted by the equipment listing.

[From NFPA 72E - 1990, 4-4.3.1]

5-3.5.3.1.1 Where mirrors are used with projected beams, they shall be installed in accordance with the manufacturer's documented instructions.

[From NFPA 72E - 1990, 4-4.3.1.1 modified]

5-3.5.4 Sampling-Type Smoke Detector. Each sampling port of a sampling-type smoke detector shall be treated as a spot-type detector for the purpose of location and spacing. Maximum air sample transport time from the farthest sampling point shall not exceed 120 seconds.

[From NFPA 72E - 1990, 4-4.4 modified]

5-3.5.5 Smooth Ceiling Spacing.
[From NFPA 72E - 1990, 4-4.5]

5-3.5.5.1 Spot-Type Detectors. On smooth ceilings, spacing of 30 ft (9.1 m) shall be permitted to be used as a guide. In all cases, the manufacturer's documented instructions shall be followed. Other spacing shall be permitted to be used depending on ceiling height, different conditions, or response requirements. (*See Appendix B for detection of flaming fires.*)
[From NFPA 72E - 1990, 4-4.5.1 modified]

5-3.5.5.1.1* For smooth ceilings, all points on the ceiling shall have a detector within a distance equal to 0.7 times the selected spacing.
[From NFPA 72E - 1990, 4-4.5.1.1 modified]

5-3.5.5.2* Projected Beam-Type Detectors. For location and spacing of projected beam-type detectors, the manufacturer's documented installation instructions shall be followed. (*See Figure A-5-3.5.5.2.*)
[From NFPA 72E - 1990, 4-4.5.2 modified]

5-3.5.6* Solid Joist Construction.
[From NFPA 72E - 1990, 4-4.6]

5-3.5.6.1 Ceiling construction where joists are 8 in. (200 mm) or less in depth shall be considered equivalent to a smooth ceiling. Spot-type detectors shall be mounted on the bottom of the joists. (*See also 5-3.5.1.2.*)
[From NFPA 72E - 1990, 4-4.6.1]

5-3.5.6.2 If joists exceed 8 in. (200 mm) in depth, the spacing of spot-type detectors in the direction perpendicular to the joists shall be reduced by one third. If the projected light beams of line-type detectors run perpendicular to the joists, no spacing reduction shall be necessary; however, if the projected light beams are parallel to the joists, the spacing between light beams shall be reduced. Spot-type detectors shall be mounted on the bottom of the joists. (*See also 5-3.5.1.2.*)
[From NFPA 72E - 1990, 4-4.6.2]

5-3.5.7 Beam Construction.
[From NFPA 72E - 1990, 4-4.7]

5-3.5.7.1 Ceiling construction where beams are 8 in. (200 mm) or less in depth shall be considered equivalent to a smooth ceiling. (*See also 5-3.5.1.2.*)
[From NFPA 72E - 1990, 4-4.7.1]

5-3.5.7.2 If beams are over 8 in. (200 mm) in depth, the spacing of spot-type detectors in the direction perpendicular to the beams shall be reduced. The spacing of projected light beam detectors run perpendicular to the ceiling beams need not be reduced; however, if the projected light beams are run parallel to the ceiling beams, the spacing shall be reduced. (*See also 5-3.5.1.2.*)
[From NFPA 72E - 1990, 4-4.7.2]

5-3.5.7.3 If beams are less than 12 in. (305 mm) in depth and less than 8 ft (2.4 m) on center, spot-type detectors shall be permitted to be installed on the bottom of beams.
[From NFPA 72E - 1990, 4-4.7.3]

5-3.5.7.4* If the beams exceed 18 in. (460 mm) in depth and are more than 8 ft (2.4 m) on center, each bay shall be treated as a separate area requiring at least one spot-type or projected beam-type detector.
[From NFPA 72E - 1990, 4-4.7.4]

5-3.5.8 Sloped Ceilings.
[From NFPA 72E - 1990, 4-4.8]

5-3.5.8.1 Peaked. Detectors shall first be spaced and located within 3 ft (0.9 m) of the peak, measured horizontally. The number and spacing of additional detectors, if any, shall be based on the horizontal projection of the ceiling. (*See Figure A-5-2.7.4.1.*)
[From NFPA 72E - 1990, 4-4.8.1]

5-3.5.8.2 Shed. Detectors shall first be spaced and located within 3 ft (0.9 m) of the high side of the ceiling, measured horizontally. The number and spacing of additional detectors, if any, shall be based on the horizontal projection of the ceiling. (*See Figure A-5-2.7.4.2.*)
[From NFPA 72E - 1990, 4-4.8.2]

5-3.5.9 Raised Floors and Suspended Ceilings. In under-floor spaces and above-ceiling spaces that are not HVAC plenums, detector spacing shall be in accordance with Section 5-3.5.
[From NFPA 72E - 1990, 4-4.9]

5-3.5.10 Partitions. Where partitions extend upward to within 18 in. (460 mm) of the ceiling, they will not influence the spacing. Where the partition extends to within less than 18 in. (460 mm) of the ceiling, the effect of smoke travel shall be considered in reduction of spacing.
[From NFPA 72E - 1990, 4-4.10]

5-3.6 Heating, Ventilating, and Air Conditioning (HVAC).
[From NFPA 72E - 1990, 4-5]

5-3.6.1* In spaces served by air-handling systems, detectors shall not be located where air from supply diffusers could dilute smoke before it reaches the detectors. Detectors shall be located to intercept the air flow toward the return air opening(s). This may require additional detectors, since placing detectors only near return air openings may leave the balance of the area with inadequate protection when the air-handling system is shut down.
[From NFPA 72E - 1990, 4-5.1 modified]

5-3.6.2 In under-floor spaces and above-ceiling spaces that are used as HVAC plenums, detectors shall be listed for the anticipated environment. (*See 5-3.7.1.1.*) Detector spacings and locations shall be selected based upon anticipated airflow patterns and fire type.
[From NFPA 72E - 1990, 4-5.2 modified]

5-3.6.2.1 Detectors placed in environmental air ducts or plenums shall not be used as a substitute for open area detectors. (*See Section 5-11, Table A-5-3.7.1.1, A-5-11.1, and A-5-11.2.*) Where open area protection is required, 5-3.5 shall apply.

Smoke may not be drawn into the duct or plenums when the ventilating system is shut down. Further, when the ventilating system is operating, the detector(s) may be less responsive to a fire condition in the room of fire origin due to dilution by clean air.

[From NFPA 72E - 1990, 4-5.2.1 modified]

5-3.7 Special Considerations.

[From NFPA 72E - 1990, 4-6]

5-3.7.1 The selection and placement of smoke detectors shall take into consideration both the performance characteristics of the detector and the areas into which the detectors will be installed to prevent nuisance alarm or nonoperation after installation. Some of the considerations are as follows.

[From NFPA 72E - 1990, 4-6.1 modified]

5-3.7.1.1* The installation of smoke detectors shall take into consideration the range of environmental conditions present. Smoke detectors shall be intended for installation in areas where the normal ambient conditions are not likely to exceed the following:

(a) A temperature of 100°F (38°C), or fall below 32°F (0°C); or

(b) A relative humidity of 93 percent; or

(c) An air velocity of 300 fpm (1.5 mps).

Exception: Detectors specifically designed for use in ambients exceeding the limits of (a) through (c) and listed for the temperature, humidity, and air velocity conditions expected.

[From NFPA 72E - 1990, 4-6.1.1 modified]

5-3.7.1.2* To avoid nuisance alarms, the location of smoke detectors shall take into consideration normal sources of smoke, moisture, dust or fumes, and electrical or mechanical influences.

[From NFPA 72E - 1990, 4-6.1.2 modified]

5-3.7.1.3 Detectors shall not be installed until after the construction clean-up of all trades is complete and final.

Exception: Where required by the authority having jurisdiction for protection during construction.

Detectors that have been installed prior to final clean-up by all trades shall be cleaned or replaced per Chapter 7.

[From NFPA 72E - 1990, 4-6.1.3]

5-3.7.2 Spot-Type Detectors.

5-3.7.2.1 Smoke detectors having a fixed temperature element as part of the unit shall be selected in accordance with Table 5-2.4.1 for the maximum ceiling temperature that can be expected in service.

[From NFPA 72E - 1990, 4-6.2.1]

5-3.7.2.2* Holes in the back of a detector shall be covered by a gasket, sealant, or equivalent, and the detector shall be mounted so that air flow from inside or around the housing will not prevent the entry of smoke during a fire or test condition.

[From NFPA 72E - 1990, 4-6.2.2 modified]

5-3.7.3 Projected Beam-Type Detectors.

[From NFPA 72E - 1990, 4-6.3]

5-3.7.3.1 Projected beam-type detectors and mirrors shall be firmly mounted on stable surfaces so as to prevent false or erratic operation due to movement. The beam shall be so designed that small angular movements of the light source or receiver do not prevent operation due to smoke and do not cause nuisance alarms.

[From NFPA 72E - 1990, 4-6.3.1 modified]

5-3.7.3.2 Since the projected beam-type unit will not operate for alarm [but will give a trouble signal (*see A-5-3.3.3*)] where the light path to the receiver is abruptly interrupted or obscured, the light path shall be kept clear of opaque obstacles at all times.

[From NFPA 72E - 1990, 4-6.3.2]

5-3.7.4 Air Sampling-Type Detectors.

5-3.7.4.1* To ensure proper performance, a sampling pipe network shall be designed to include details of the sampling network based on and supported by sound fluid dynamic principles and calculations showing flow characteristics of the pipe network and for each sampling point.

5-3.7.4.2* Air sampling detectors shall give a trouble signal where the air flow is outside the manufacturer's specified range. The sampling ports and inline filter (if used) shall be kept clear in accordance with manufacturer's documented instructions.

5-3.7.4.3 Air sampling network piping and fittings shall be airtight and permanently fixed. Sampling piping shall be conspicuously identified as "SMOKE DETECTOR SAMPLING PIPE," with a warning not to disturb or alter.

[New paragraphs and title]

5-3.7.5* High Rack Storage. [*See Figures A-5-3.7.5(a) and (b).*] Detection systems are often installed in addition to suppression systems. Where smoke detectors are installed for early warning in high rack storage areas, it shall be necessary to consider installing detectors at several levels in the racks to ensure quicker response to smoke. Where detectors are installed to actuate a suppression system, see NFPA 231C, *Standard for Rack Storage of Materials.*

[From NFPA 72E - 1990, 4-6.4]

5-3.7.6 High Air Movement Areas.

[From NFPA 72E - 1990, 4-6.5]

5-3.7.6.1 General. The purpose and scope of 5-3.7.6 are to provide location and spacing guidance for smoke detectors in high air movement areas for early warning of fire.

Exception: Detectors provided for the control of smoke spread are covered by the requirements of Section 5-11.

[From NFPA 72E - 1990, 4-6.5.1]

5-3.7.6.2 Location. Smoke detectors shall not be located directly in the air stream of supply registers.

[From NFPA 72E - 1990, 4-6.5.3]

5-3.7.6.3 Spacing. Smoke detector spacing depends upon the movement of air within the room (including both supplied and recirculated air), which can be designated as minutes per air change or air changes per hour. Spacing shall be in accordance with Table 5-3.7.6.3 and Figure 5-3.7.6.3.

Exception: Air sampling or projected beam smoke detectors installed in accordance with the manufacturer's documented instructions.

[From NFPA 72E - 1990, 4-6.5.4 modified]

Table 5-3.7.6.3

Minutes/Air Change	Air Changes/Hour	Sq Ft/Detector
1	60	125
2	30	250
3	20	375
4	15	500
5	12	625
6	10	750
7	8.6	875
8	7.5	900
9	6.7	900
10	6	900

For SI Units: 1 sq ft = 0.0929 m^2.

[From NFPA 72E - 1990, 4-6.5.4(b)]

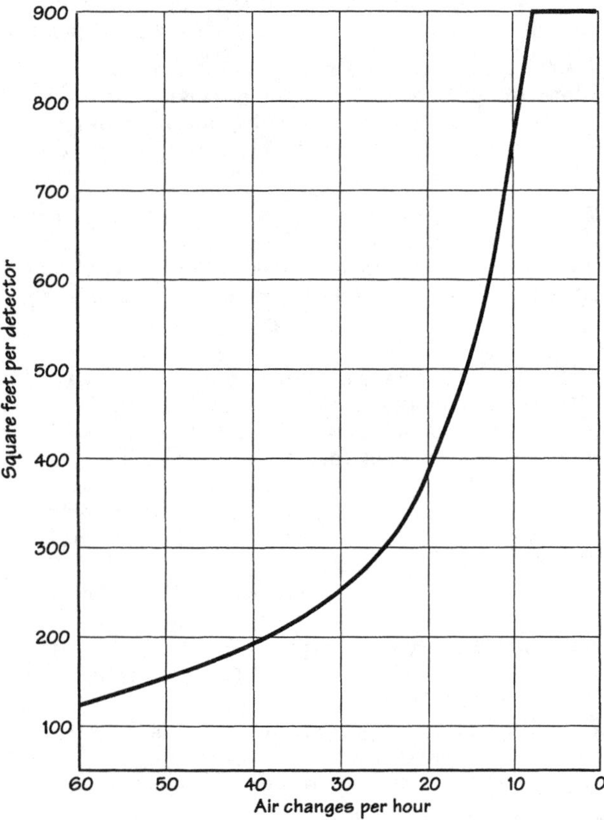

Figure 5-3.7.6.3 High air movement areas (not to be used for under-floor or above-ceiling spaces).

[From NFPA 72E - 1990, 4-6.5.4(a) modified]

5-4 Radiant Energy-Sensing Fire Detectors.

5-4.1 General.

5-4.1.1 The purpose and scope of Section 5-4 are to provide standards for the selection, location, and spacing of fire detectors that sense the radiant energy produced by burning substances. These detectors are categorized as flame detectors and spark/ember detectors.

[From NFPA 72E - 1990, 5-1.2 modified]

5-4.1.1.1 Flame Detectors. (*See 5-4.2.1, definition of Flame Detectors.*)

[From NFPA 72E - 1990, 2-2.1.3.1]

5-4.1.1.2 Spark/Ember Detectors. (*See 5-4.2.1, definition of Spark/Ember Detectors.*)

[From NFPA 72E - 1990, 2-2.1.3.2]

5-4.1.2 Radiant Energy. For the purpose of this code, radiant energy includes the electromagnetic radiation emitted as a by-product of the combustion reaction, which obeys the laws of optics. This includes radiation in the ultraviolet, visible, and infrared spectrum emitted by flames or glowing embers. These portions of the spectrum are distinguished by wavelengths as follows:

Ultraviolet	0.1 to 0.35 microns
Visible	0.36 to 0.75 microns
Infrared	0.76 to 220 microns

(1.0 micron = 1000 nanometers = 10,000 Angstroms)

[From NFPA 72E - 1990, 5-1.1 modified]

5-4.2 Definitions and Operating Principles.

[From NFPA 72E - 1990, 5-2]

5-4.2.1 Definitions.

[From NFPA 72E - 1990, 5-2.1]

Ember.* A particle of solid material that emits radiant energy due either to its temperature or the process of combustion on its surface. (*See definition of Spark.*)

[From NFPA 72E - 1990, 5-2.1.1 modified]

Field of View. The solid cone extending out from the detector within which the effective sensitivity of the detector is at least 50 percent of its on-axis, listed, or approved sensitivity.

[From NFPA 72E - 1990, 5-2.1.2]

Flame. A body or stream of gaseous material involved in the combustion process and emitting radiant energy at specific wavelength bands determined by the combustion chemistry of the fuel. In most cases, some portion of the emitted radiant energy is visible to the human eye.

[From NFPA 72E - 1990, 5-2.1.3]

Flame Detector Sensitivity. The distance along the optical axis of the detector at which the detector will detect a fire of specified size and fuel within a given time frame.

[From NFPA 72E - 1990, 5-2.1.5 modified]

Flame Detectors. Radiant energy fire detectors that are intended to detect flames and are designed to operate in environments where sunlight or other ambient lighting is assumed.

[From NFPA 72E - 1990, 5-2.1.4 modified]

Spark.* A moving ember.

[From NFPA 72E - 1990, 5-2.1.6]

Spark/Ember Detector Sensitivity. The number of watts (or fractions of watts) of radiant power from a point source radiator applied as a unit step signal at the wavelength of maximum detector sensitivity, necessary to produce an alarm signal from the detector within the specified response time.

[From NFPA 72E - 1990, 5-2.1.8]

Spark/Ember Detectors. Radiant energy fire detectors that are designed to detect sparks or embers, or both. These devices are normally intended to operate in dark environments and in the infrared part of the spectrum.

[From NFPA 72E - 1990, 5-2.1.7]

Wavelength.* The distance between the peaks of a sinusoidal wave. All radiant energy can be described as a wave having a wavelength. Wavelength serves as the unit of measure for distinguishing between different parts of the spectrum. Wavelengths are measured in microns (uM), nanometers (nM), or angstroms (Å).

[From NFPA 72E - 1990, 5-2.1.9 modified]

5-4.2.2 Operating Principles of Flame Detectors.

[From NFPA 72E - 1990, 5-2.2]

5-4.2.2.1 Ultraviolet flame detectors typically use a vacuum photodiode Geiger-Muller tube to detect the ultraviolet radiation that is produced by a flame. The photodiode allows a burst of current to flow for each ultraviolet photon that hits the active area of the tube. When the number of current bursts per unit time reaches a predetermined level, the detector initiates an alarm.

[From NFPA 72E - 1990, 5-2.2.1 modified]

5-4.2.2.2 A single wavelength infrared flame detector uses one of several different photocell types to detect the infrared emissions in a single wavelength band that are produced by a flame. These detectors generally include provisions to minimize alarms from commonly occurring infrared sources such as incandescent lighting or sunlight.

[From NFPA 72E - 1990, 5-2.2.2 modified]

5-4.2.2.3 An ultraviolet/infrared (UV/IR) flame detector senses ultraviolet radiation with a vacuum photodiode tube and a selected wavelength of infrared radiation with a photocell and uses the combined signal to indicate a fire. These detectors require both types of radiation to be present before an alarm signal is initiated.

[From NFPA 72E - 1990, 5-2.2.3 modified]

5-4.2.2.4 A multiple wavelength infrared (IR/IR) flame detector senses radiation at two or more narrow bands of wavelengths in the infrared spectrum. These detectors electronically compare the emissions between the band and initiate a signal where the relationship between the two bands indicates a fire.

[From NFPA 72E - 1990, 5-2.2.4 modified]

5-4.2.3 Operating Principles of Spark/Ember Detectors. A spark/ember-sensing detector usually uses a solid state photodiode or phototransistor to sense the radiant energy emitted by embers, typically between 0.5 and 2.0 microns in normally dark environments. These detectors can be made extremely sensitive (microwatts), and their response times can be made very short (microseconds).

[From NFPA 72E - 1990, 5-2.3 and 5-2.3.1 modified]

5-4.3 Fire Characteristics and Detector Selection.

[From NFPA 72E - 1990, 5-3]

5-4.3.1* The type and quantity of radiant energy-sensing fire detectors shall be determined based upon an analysis of the hazard, including the burning characteristics of the fuel, the fire growth rate, the environment, the ambient conditions, and the capabilities of the extinguishing media and equipment.

[From NFPA 72E - 1990, 5-3.1 modified]

5-4.3.2 The selection of the radiant energy-sensing detectors shall be based upon:

(a) The matching of the spectral response of the detector to the spectral emissions of the fire or fires to be detected; and

(b) Minimizing the possibility of spurious nuisance alarms from nonfire sources inherent to the hazard area. (*See A-5-4.3.1.*)

[From NFPA 72E - 1990, 5-6.1 modified]

5-4.4 Spacing Considerations.

[From NFPA 72E - 1990, 5-4]

5-4.4.1 General Rules.

[From NFPA 72E - 1990, 5-4.1]

5-4.4.1.1* Radiant energy-sensing fire detectors shall be employed consistent with the listing or approval and the inverse square law, which defines the fire size vs. distance curve for the detector.

[From NFPA 72E - 1990, 5-4.1.1]

5-4.4.1.2 Detectors shall be used in sufficient quantity and positioned so that no point requiring detection in the hazard area is obstructed or outside the field of view of at least one detector.

[From NFPA 72E - 1990, 5-4.1.2]

5-4.4.2 Spacing Considerations for Flame Detectors.

[From NFPA 72E - 1990, 5-4.2]

5-4.4.2.1* The location and spacing of detectors shall be the result of an engineering evaluation, taking into consideration:

(a) The size of the fire that is to be detected

(b) The fuel involved

(c) The sensitivity of the detector

(d) The field of view of the detector

(e) The distance between the fire and the detector

(f) The radiant energy absorption of the atmosphere

(g) The presence of extraneous sources of radiant emissions

(h) The purpose of the detection system

(i) The response time required.

[From NFPA 72E - 1990, 5-4.2.1 modified]

5-4.4.2.2 The system design shall specify the size of the flaming fire of given fuel that is to be detected.

[From NFPA 72E - 1990, 5-4.2.2 modified]

5-4.4.2.3* In applications where the fire to be detected could occur in an area not on the optical axis of the detector, the distance shall be reduced or detectors added to compensate for the angular displacement of the fire in accordance with the manufacturer's documented instructions.

[From NFPA 72E - 1990, 5-4.2.3 modified]

5-4.4.2.4* In applications in which the fire to be detected is of a fuel different than the test fuel used in the process of listing or approval, the distance between the detector and the fire shall be adjusted consistent with the fuel specificity of the detector as established by the manufacturer.

[From NFPA 72E - 1990, 5-4.2.4]

5-4.4.2.5 Since flame detectors are essentially line of sight devices, special care shall be taken to ensure that their ability to respond to the required area of fire in the zone that is to be protected will not be compromised by the presence of intervening structural members or other opaque objects or materials.

[From NFPA 72E - 1990, 5-4.2.5 and 5-5.1]

5-4.4.2.6* Provisions shall be made to sustain detector window clarity in applications where airborne particulates and aerosols coat the detector window between maintenance intervals and affect sensitivity.

[From NFPA 72E - 1990, 5-4.2.6 modified]

5-4.5 Spacing Considerations for Spark/Ember Detectors.

[From NFPA 72E - 1990, 5-4.3]

5-4.5.1* The location and spacing of detectors shall be the result of an engineering evaluation, taking into consideration:

(a) The size of the spark or ember that is to be detected

(b) The fuel involved

(c) The sensitivity of the detector

(d) The field of view of the detector

(e) The distance between the fire and the detector

(f) The radiant energy absorption of the atmosphere

(g) The presence of extraneous sources of radiant emissions

(h) The purpose of the detection systems

(i) The response time required.

[From NFPA 72E - 1990, 5-4.3.1 modified]

5-4.5.2* The system design shall specify the size of the spark or ember of given fuel that the detection system is to detect.

[From NFPA 72E - 1990, 5-4.3.2 modified]

5-4.5.3 Spark detectors shall be positioned so that all points within the cross section of the conveyance duct, conveyor, or chute where the detectors are located are within the field of view of at least one detector as defined in 5-4.2.1.

[From NFPA 72E - 1990, 5-4.3.3]

5-4.5.4 The location and spacing of the detectors shall be adjusted using the inverse square law, modified for the atmospheric absorption and the absorption of nonburning fuel suspended in the air in accordance with the manufacturer's documented instructions. (*See A-5-4.4.1.1.*)

[From NFPA 72E - 1990, 5-4.3.4 modified]

5-4.5.5* In applications where the sparks to be detected could occur in an area not on the optical axis of the detector, the distance shall be reduced or detectors added to compensate for the angular displacement of the fire in accordance with the manufacturer's documented instructions.

[From NFPA 72E - 1990, 5-4.3.5 modified]

5-4.5.6* Provisions shall be made to sustain the detector window clarity in applications where airborne particulates and aerosols coat the detector window and affect sensitivity.

[From NFPA 72E - 1990, 5-4.3.6 modified]

5-4.6 Other Considerations.

[From NFPA 72E - 1990, 5-6]

5-4.6.1 Radiant energy-sensing detectors shall be protected either by way of design or installation to ensure that optical performance is not compromised.

[From NFPA 72E - 1990, 5-6.2 modified]

5-4.6.2 Where necessary, radiant energy-sensing detectors shall be shielded or otherwise arranged to prevent action from unwanted radiant energy.

[From NFPA 72E - 1990, 5-6.3]

5-4.6.3 Where used in outdoor applications, radiant energy-sensing detectors shall be shielded or otherwise arranged in a fashion to prevent diminishing sensitivity by rain, snow, etc., and yet allow a clear field of vision of the hazard area.

[From NFPA 72E - 1990, 5-6.4 modified]

5-5 Gas-Sensing Fire Detectors.

[From NFPA 72E - 1990, Chap. 6]

5-5.1* The purpose of Section 5-5 is to provide information to assist in application and installation of fire detectors that sense gases produced by burning substances. These detectors are hereafter referred to as fire-gas detectors. This section covers general area application of fire-gas detectors in ordinary indoor locations.

[New paragraph]

5-5.2 Fire-gas detectors shall be installed in all areas where required either by the appropriate NFPA standard or by the authority having jurisdiction.

[From NFPA 72E - 1990, 6-1.1.3]

5-5.3 Fire-gas detectors shall respond to one or more of the gases produced by a fire. Gases are molecules without cohesion that are produced by a burning substance and are subject to oxidation or reduction.

[From NFPA 72E - 1990, 6-1.1.4]

5-5.4 Although some fire-gas detectors are capable of detecting combustible gases or vapors prior to ignition, such applications are not within the scope of this code.

5-5.5 Operating Principles.

[From NFPA 72E - 1990, 6-2]

5-5.5.1 Semiconductor. Fire-gas detectors of the semiconductor type respond to either oxidizing or reducing gases by creating electrical changes in the semiconductor. The subsequent conductivity change of the semiconductor causes actuation.

[From NFPA 72E - 1990, 6-2.1]

5-5.5.2 Catalytic Element. Fire-gas detectors of the catalytic element type contain a material that remains unchanged, but accelerates the oxidation of combustible gases. The resulting temperature rise of the element causes actuation.

[From NFPA 72E - 1990, 6-2.2]

5-5.6 Location and Spacing.

[From NFPA 72E - 1990, 6-3]

5-5.6.1* General. The location and spacing of fire-gas detectors shall result from an evaluation based on the guidelines detailed in this code and on engineering judgment. Ceiling shape and surfaces, ceiling height, configuration of contents, burning characteristics of combustible material present, ventilation, and the ambient environment are some of the conditions that shall be considered.

[From NFPA 72E - 1990, 6-3.1 modified]

5-5.6.1.1 Where the intent is to provide protection from a specific hazard, the detector(s) may be installed closer to the hazard in a position where the detector will readily intercept the fire gases.

[From NFPA 72E - 1990, 6-3.1.1]

5-5.6.1.2 Stratification. The possible effect of gas stratification at levels below the ceiling shall also be considered. (*See A-5-3.5.1.2.*)

[From NFPA 72E - 1990, 6-3.1.2]

5-5.6.2 Spot-type fire-gas detectors shall be located on the ceiling not less than 4 in. (100 mm) from a sidewall to the near edge or, if on a sidewall, between 4 in. (100 mm) and 12 in. (300 mm) down from the ceiling to the top of the detector. (*See Figure A-5-2.5.1.*)

Exception No. 1: See 5-5.6.1.2.

Exception No. 2: In the case of solid joist construction, detectors shall be mounted at the bottom of the joists.

Exception No. 3: In the case of beam construction where beams are less than 12 in. (300 mm) in depth and less than 8 ft (2.4 m) on center, detectors may be installed on the bottom of beams.

[From NFPA 72E - 1990, 6-3.2]

5-5.6.3* Each sampling port of a sampling-type fire-gas detector shall be treated as a spot-type detector for the purpose of location and spacing.

[From NFPA 72E - 1990, 6-3.3]

5-5.6.4 Smooth Ceiling Spacing.

[From NFPA 72E - 1990, 6-3.4]

5-5.6.4.1 Spot-Type Detectors. On smooth ceilings, spacing of 30 ft (9.1 m) shall be permitted to be used as a guide. In all cases, the manufacturer's recommendations shall be followed. Other spacing shall be permitted to be used depending on ceiling height, varying conditions, or response requirements.

[From NFPA 72E - 1990, 6-3.4.1]

5-5.6.5 Solid Joist Construction. (*See A-5-3.5.6.*)

[From NFPA 72E - 1990, 6-3.5]

5-5.6.5.1 Ceiling construction in which joists are 8 in. (200 mm) or less in depth shall be considered equivalent to a smooth ceiling. (*See also A-5-3.5.1.2.*)

[From NFPA 72E - 1990, 6-3.5.1]

5-5.6.5.2 If joists exceed 8 in. (200 mm) in depth, the spacing of spot-type detectors in the direction perpendicular to the joists shall be reduced. (*See also A-5-3.5.1.2.*)

[From NFPA 72E - 1990, 6-3.5.2]

5-5.6.6 Beam Construction.

[From NFPA 72E - 1990, 6-3.6]

5-5.6.6.1 Ceiling construction where beams are 8 in. (200 mm) or less in depth shall be considered equivalent to a smooth ceiling. (*See also A-5-3.5.1.2.*)

[From NFPA 72E - 1990, 6-3.6.1]

5-5.6.6.2 If beams are over 8 in. (200 mm) in depth, the spacing of spot-type detectors in the direction perpendicular to the beams shall be reduced. (*See also A-5-3.5.1.2.*)

[From NFPA 72E - 1990, 6-3.6.2]

5-5.6.6.3* If the beams exceed 18 in. (460 mm) in depth and are more than 8 ft (2.4 m) on center, each bay shall be treated as a separate area requiring at least one spot-type detector.

[From NFPA 72E - 1990, 6-3.6.3]

5-5.6.7 Sloped Ceilings.

[From NFPA 72E - 1990, 6-3.7]

5-5.6.7.1 Peaked. Detectors shall first be spaced and located within 3 ft (0.9 m) of the peak, measured horizontally. The number and spacing of additional detectors, if any, shall be based on the horizontal projection of the ceiling. (*See Figure A-5-2.7.4.1.*)

[From NFPA 72E - 1990, 6-3.7.1]

5-5.6.7.2 Shed. Detectors shall first be spaced and located within 3 ft (0.9 m) of the high side of the ceiling, measured horizontally. The number and spacing of additional detectors, if any, shall be based on the horizontal projection of the ceiling. (*See Figure A-5-2.7.4.2.*)

[From NFPA 72E - 1990, 6-3.7.2]

5-5.6.8 Suspended Ceilings. (*See 5-5.6.*)

[From NFPA 72E - 1990, 6-3.8]

5-5.6.9 Partitions. Where partitions extend upward to within 18 in. (460 mm) of the ceiling, they will not influence the spacing. Where the partition extends to within less than 18 in. (460 mm) of the ceiling, the effect on gas travel shall be considered in reduction of spacing.

[From NFPA 72E - 1990, 6-3.9]

5-5.7 Heating, Ventilating, and Air Conditioning (HVAC).

[From NFPA 72E - 1990, 6-4]

5-5.7.1* In spaces served by air-handling systems, detectors shall not be located where air from supply diffusers could dilute fire gases before they reach the detectors. Detectors shall be located to intercept the airflow toward the return air opening(s).

[From NFPA 72E - 1990, 6-4.1]

5-5.7.2 In under-floor spaces and above-ceiling spaces used as HVAC plenums, detectors shall be listed for the anticipated environment. (*See 5-3.7.1.1.*) Detector spacings and locations shall be selected based on anticipated air-flow patterns and fire types.

[From NFPA 72E - 1990, 6-4.2]

5-5.7.2.1 Detectors placed in environmental air ducts or plenums shall not be used as a substitute for open area detectors. (*See Section 5-11 and associated appendix material for related information.*) Where open area protection is required, 5-5.6 shall apply.

[From NFPA 72E - 1990, 6-4.2.1 modified]

5-5.8 Special Considerations.

[From NFPA 72E - 1990, 6-5]

5-5.8.1 The selection and placement of fire-gas detectors shall take into consideration both the performance characteristics of the detector and the areas into which the detectors will be installed to prevent nuisance alarm or nonoperation after installation. Some of the considerations are as follows.

[From NFPA 72E - 1990, 6-5.1]

5-5.8.1.1 Fire-gas detectors may alarm in nonfire situations due to certain human activities. The use of some aerosol sprays and hydrocarbon solvents are examples. Accordingly, considerable care shall be employed when installing fire-gas detectors. They shall not be installed where, under normal conditions, concentrations of detectable gases may be present. A garage is not a place to use fire-gas detectors for fire alarm purposes because the concentration of carbon monoxide may be high enough to trigger an alarm.

[From NFPA 72E - 1990, 6-5.1.1]

5-5.8.1.2 Fire-gas detectors having a fixed temperature element as part of the unit shall be selected in accordance with Table 5-2.4.1 for the maximum ceiling temperature that can be expected in service.

[From NFPA 72E - 1990, 6-5.1.2]

5-5.8.1.3* The installation of fire-gas detectors shall take into consideration the environmental condition of the area(s). (*See Table A-5-3.7.1.1.*) Fire-gas detectors are intended for installation in areas where the normal ambient conditions are not likely to exceed the following:

(a) A temperature of 100°F (38°C), or fall below 32°F (0°C); or

(b) A relative humidity outside the range of 10 to 93 percent; or

(c) An air velocity of 300 fpm (1.5 mps).

Exception: Detectors specifically designed for use in ambients exceeding the limits of (a) through (c) and listed for the temperature, humidity, and air velocity conditions expected.

[From NFPA 72E - 1990, 6-5.1.3]

5-6 Other Fire Detectors.

[From NFPA 72E - 1990, Chap. 7]

5-6.1 Detectors in the classification of "Other Fire Detectors" are those that operate on principles different from those described in 5-2.3, 5-3.3, 5-4.3, and 5-5.5. Such detectors shall be installed in all areas where they are required either by the appropriate NFPA standard or by the authority having jurisdiction.

[From NFPA 72E - 1990, 7-1]

5-6.2 Facilities for testing or metering or instrumentation to ensure adequate initial sensitivity and adequate retention thereof, relative to the protected hazard, shall be provided. These facilities shall be employed at regular intervals.

[From NFPA 72E - 1990, 7-1.1.2]

5-6.3 These detectors shall operate where subjected to the abnormal concentration of combustion effects that occur during a fire, such as water vapor, ionized molecules, or other phenomena for which they are designed. Detection is dependent upon the size and intensity of fire to provide the necessary amount of required products and related thermal lift, circulation, or diffusion for adequate operation.

[From NFPA 72E - 1990, 7-2.1]

5-6.4 Room sizes and contours, airflow patterns, obstructions, and other characteristics of the protected hazard shall be taken into account.

[From NFPA 72E - 1990, 7-2.2]

5-6.5 Location and Spacing.

[From NFPA 72E - 1990, 7-3]

5-6.5.1 The location and spacing of detectors shall be based on the principle of operation and an engineering survey of the conditions anticipated in service. The manufacturer's technical bulletin shall be consulted for recommended detector uses and locations.

[From NFPA 72E - 1990, 7-3.1]

5-6.5.2 Detectors shall not be spaced beyond their listed or approved maximums. Closer spacing shall be utilized where the structural or other characteristics of the protected hazard warrant.

[From NFPA 72E - 1990, 7-3.2]

5-6.5.3 Consideration shall be given to all factors with bearing on the location and sensitivity of the detectors, including structural features such as sizes and shapes of rooms and bays, their occupancies and uses, ceiling heights, ceiling and other obstructions, ventilation, ambient environment, stock piles, files, and fire hazard locations.

[From NFPA 72E - 1990, 7-3.3]

5-6.5.4 The overall situation shall be reviewed frequently to ensure that changes in structural or usage conditions that could interfere with fire detection are remedied.

[From NFPA 72E - 1990, 7-3.4]

5-6.6 Special Considerations. The selection and placement of detectors shall take into consideration both the performance characteristics of the detector and the areas into which the detectors will be installed to prevent nuisance alarm or nonoperation after installation.

[New paragraph]

5-7 Sprinkler Waterflow Alarm-Initiating Devices.

5-7.1 The provisions of Section 5-7 apply to devices that initiate an alarm indicating a flow of water in a sprinkler system.

[From NFPA 72, 3-4.1.1 modified]

5-7.2* Provisions shall be made to indicate the flow of water in a sprinkler system by an alarm signal within 90 seconds after flow of water at the alarm-initiating device equal to or greater than that from a single sprinkler of the smallest orifice size installed in the system. Movement of water due to waste, surges, or variable pressure shall not be indicated.

[From NFPA 72, 3-4.1.2 modified]

5-7.3 Piping between the sprinkler system and a pressure actuated alarm-initiating device shall be galvanized or of nonferrous metal or other approved corrosion resistant material, not less than $^3/_8$ in. (9.5 mm) nominal pipe size.

[From NFPA 71, 3-4.2.1 modified]

5-8 Detection of the Operation of Other Automatic Extinguishing Systems.

[From NFPA 71, 3-4.3 modified]

5-8.1* Provision shall be made to detect the operation of an automatic extinguishing system by means appropriate to the system, such as agent flow or agent pressure, by alarm-initiating devices installed in accordance with their individual listings.

[From NFPA 71, 3-4.3.1 modified]

5-9 Manually Actuated Alarm-Initiating Devices.

5-9.1 Manual fire alarm boxes shall be used only for fire alarm-initiating purposes. However, combination manual fire alarm boxes and guard's signaling stations shall be permitted.

[From NFPA 71, 3-1.1.1, and NFPA 72, 3-2.1 modified]

5-9.1.1 Mounting. Each manual fire alarm box shall be securely mounted. The operable part of each manual fire alarm box shall be not less than $3^1/_2$ ft (1.1 m) and not more than $4^1/_2$ ft (1.37 m) above floor level.

[From NFPA 72, 3-2.2, and NFPA 71, 3-4.1.1 modified]

5-9.1.2 Distribution. Manual fire alarm boxes shall be distributed throughout the protected area so that they are unobstructed, readily accessible, and located in the normal path of exit from the area as follows:

(a) At least one manual fire alarm box shall be provided on each floor.

(b) Additional manual fire alarm boxes shall be provided so that travel distance to the nearest fire alarm box will not be in excess of 200 ft (61 m) measured horizontally on the same floor.

(c) For systems employing automatic fire detectors or waterflow detection devices, at least one manual fire alarm box shall be provided to initiate a fire alarm signal. This manual fire alarm box shall be located where required by the authority having jurisdiction.

[From NFPA 72-1990, 3-2.3 modified and 3-2.4]

5-9.1.3* A coded manual fire alarm box shall produce at least three repetitions of the coded signal, each repetition to consist of at least three impulses.

[From NFPA 72, 2-4.3 modified]

5-9.2 Publicly Accessible Fire Service Boxes (Street Boxes).

[From NFPA 1221, 4-1.4 modified]

5-9.2.1 Street boxes, when in an abnormal condition, shall leave the circuit usable.

[From NFPA 1221, 4-1.4.2.1 modified]

5-9.2.2 Street boxes shall be designed so that recycling will not occur if a box actuating device is held in the actuating position and so that they will be ready to accept a new signal as soon as the actuating device is released.

[From NFPA 1221, 4-1.4.2.2 modified]

5-9.2.3 Street boxes, when actuated, shall give a visible or audible indication to the user that the box is operating or that the signal has been transmitted to the communication center.

NOTE: Where the operating mechanism of a box creates sufficient sound to be heard by the user, the requirements are satisfied.

[From NFPA 1221, 4-1.4.2.3 modified]

5-9.2.4 The street box housing shall protect the internal components from the weather.

[From NFPA 1221, 4-1.4.2.5 modified]

5-9.2.5 Doors on street boxes shall remain operable under adverse climatic conditions, including icing and salt spray.

[From NFPA 1221, 4.1.4.2.6 modified]

5-9.2.6 Street boxes shall be recognizable as such. Street boxes shall have instructions for use plainly marked on their exterior surfaces.

[From NFPA 1221, 4-1.4.1.1 modified]

5-9.2.7 Street boxes shall be securely mounted on poles, pedestals, or structural surfaces as directed by the authority having jurisdiction.

[From NFPA 1221, 4-1.4.1.8 modified]

5-9.2.8 Street boxes shall be as conspicuous as possible. Their color shall be distinctive, and they shall be visible from as many directions as possible. A wide band of distinctive colors visible over the tops of parked cars or adequate signs completely visible from all directions shall be applied to supporting poles.

[From NFPA 1221, 4-1.4.1.3 and 4-1.4.1.4 modified]

5-9.2.9* Location-designating lights of distinctive color, visible for at least 1500 ft (460 m) in all directions, shall be installed over street boxes. The street light nearest the street box, where equipped with a distinctively colored light, shall be acceptable.

[From NFPA 1221, 4-1.4.1.5 modified]

5-9.2.10 Street box cases and parts at any time accessible to users shall be of insulating materials or permanently and effectively grounded. All ground connections to street boxes shall comply with the requirements of NFPA 70, *National Electrical Code*, Article 250.

[From NFPA 1221, 4-1.4.1.6 and 4-1.4.1.7 modified]

5-9.2.11 If a street box is installed inside a structure, it shall be placed as close as is practical to the point of entrance of the circuit, and the exterior wire shall be installed in conduit or electrical metallic tubing in accordance with Chapter 3 of NFPA 70, *National Electrical Code*.

[From NFPA 1221, 4-2.1.2.1 modified]

5-9.2.12 Coded Radio Street Boxes.

[From NFPA 1221, 4-3.3]

5-9.2.12.1 Coded radio street boxes shall be designed and operated in compliance with all applicable rules and regulations of the FCC, as well as with the requirements established herein.

[From NFPA 1221, 4-3.3.1 modified]

5-9.2.12.2 Coded radio street boxes shall provide no less than three specific and individually identifiable functions to the communication center in addition to the street box number, and they shall be "test," "tamper," and "fire."

[From NFPA 1221, 4-3.3.2.1]

5-9.2.12.3* Coded radio street boxes shall transmit to the communication center no less than one repetition for "test," no less than one repetition for "tamper," and no less than three repetitions for "fire."

[From NFPA 1221, 4-3.3.2.2 modified]

5-9.2.12.4 Where multifunction coded radio street boxes are used to transmit to the communication center request(s) for emergency service or assistance in addition to those stipulated in 5-9.2.12.2, each such additional message function shall be individually identifiable.

[From NFPA 1221, 4-3.3.2.3]

5-9.2.12.5 Multifunction coded radio street boxes shall be so designed as to prevent the loss of supplemental or concurrently actuated messages.

[From NFPA 1221, 4-3.3.2.4 modified]

5-9.2.12.6 An actuating device held or locked in the activating position shall not prevent the activation and transmission of other messages.

[From NFPA 1221, 4-3.3.2.5 modified]

5-9.2.13 Power Source.

[From NFPA 1221, 4-3.3.3 modified]

5-9.2.13.1 Box primary power shall be permitted to be from a utility distribution system, a photovoltaic power system, user power, or be self-powered using either an integral battery or other stored energy source, as approved by the authority having jurisdiction.

[From NFPA 1221, 4-3.3.3.1]

5-9.2.13.2 Self-powered boxes shall have power for uninterrupted operation for not less than a period of 6 months. Self-powered boxes shall transmit a low power warning message to the communication center for at least 15 days prior to the time the power source will fail to operate the box. This message shall be part of all subsequent transmissions.

Use of a charger to extend the life of a self-powered box shall be permitted if the charger does not interfere with box operation. The box shall be capable of operation for not less than 6 months with the charger disconnected.

[From NFPA 1221, 4-3.3.3.2]

5-9.2.13.3 Boxes powered by a utility distribution system shall have an integral standby, sealed, rechargeable battery capable of powering box functions for at least 60 hours in the event of primary power failure. Transfer to standby battery power shall be automatic and without interruption to box operation. Where operating from primary power, the box shall be capable of operation with a dead or disconnected battery. A local trouble indication shall activate upon primary power failure. A battery charger shall be provided in compliance with 1-5.2.11.2, except as modified herein.

Where the primary power has failed, boxes shall transmit a power failure message to the communication center as part of subsequent test messages until primary power is restored. A low battery message shall be transmitted to the communication center where the remaining battery standby time is less than 54 hours.

[From NFPA 1221, 4-3.3.3.3]

5-9.2.13.4 Photovoltaic power systems shall provide box operation for not less than 6 months.

Photovoltaic power systems shall be supervised. The battery shall have power to sustain operation for a minimum period of 15 days without recharging. The box shall transmit a trouble message to the communication center when the charger has failed for more than 24 hours. This message shall be part of all subsequent transmissions. Where the remaining battery standby duration is less than 10 days, a low battery message shall be transmitted to the communication center.

[From NFPA 1221, 4-3.3.3.4]

5-9.2.13.5 User-powered boxes shall have an automatic self-test feature.

[From NFPA 1221, 4-3.3.3.5]

5-9.2.14 Design of Telephone Street Boxes (Series or Parallel).

[From NFPA 1221, 4-4.4 and 4-5.4 modified]

5-9.2.14.1 If a handset is used, the caps on the transmitter and receiver shall be secured to reduce the probability of the telephone street box being disabled due to vandalism.

[From NFPA 1221, 4-4.4.1 and 4-5.4.2 modified]

5-9.2.14.2 Telephone street boxes shall be designed to permit the communication center operator to determine whether or not the telephone street box has been restored to normal condition after use.

[From NFPA 1221, 4-4.4.2 and 4-5.4.1 modified]

5-10 Supervisory Signal-Initiating Devices.

[From NFPA 71, 3-4.4, and NFPA 72, 3-4]

5-10.1 Control Valve Supervisory Signal-Initiating Device. Two separate and distinct signals shall be initiated: one indicating movement of the valve from its normal position, and the other indicating restoration of the valve to its normal position. The off-normal signal shall be initiated during the first two revolutions of the hand wheel or during one-fifth of the travel distance of the valve control apparatus from its normal position. The off-normal signal shall not be restored at any valve position except normal.

[From NFPA 71, 3-4.4.2, and NFPA 72, 3-4.2.5 modified]

5-10.2 Pressure Supervisory Signal-Initiating Device. Two separate and distinct signals shall be initiated: one indicating that the required pressure has increased or decreased, and the other indicating restoration of the pressure to its normal value.

(a) A pressure tank supervisory signal-initiating device for a pressurized limited water supply, such as a pressure tank, shall indicate both high and low pressure conditions. A signal shall be initiated where the required pressure is increased or decreased 10 psi (70 kPa) from the normal pressure.

(b) A pressure supervisory signal-initiating device for a dry-pipe sprinkler system shall indicate both high and low pressure conditions. A signal shall be initiated where the pressure is increased or decreased 10 psi (70 kPa) from the normal pressure.

(c) A steam pressure supervisory signal-initiating device shall indicate a low pressure condition. A signal shall be initiated where the pressure reaches or exceeds 110 percent of the minimum operating pressure of the steam-operated equipment supplied.

(d) An initiating device for supervising the pressure of sources other than those specified in (a) through (c) shall be provided as required by the authority having jurisdiction.

[From NFPA 71, 3-4.4.3, and NFPA 72, 3-4.2.6 modified]

5-10.3 Water Level Supervisory Signal-Initiating Device. Two separate and distinct signals shall be initiated: one indicating that the required water level has been lowered or raised, and the other indicating restoration to the normal level.

(a) A pressure tank signal-initiating device shall indicate both high and low level conditions. A signal shall be obtained where the water level is lowered or raised 3 in. (76 mm) from the normal level.

(b) A supervisory signal-initiating device for other than pressure tanks shall initiate a low level signal where the water level is lowered 12 in. (300 mm) below the normal level.

[From NFPA 71, 3-4.4.4, and NFPA 72, 3-4.2.7 modified]

5-10.4 Water Temperature Supervisory Signal-Initiating Device. A temperature supervisory device for a water storage container exposed to freezing conditions shall initiate two separate and distinctive signals. One signal shall indicate that the temperature of the water has dropped to 40°F (4.4°C), and the other indicating restoration to a proper temperature.

[From NFPA 71, 3-4.4.5, and NFPA 72, 3-4.2.8 modified]

5-10.5 Room Temperature Supervisory Signal-Initiating Device. A room temperature supervisory device shall indicate the decrease in room temperature to 40°F (4.4°C) and its restoration to above 40°F (4.4°C).

[From NFPA 71, 3-4.4.7 modified]

5-11 Smoke Detectors for Control of Smoke Spread.

[From NFPA 72E - 1990, Chap. 9]

NOTE: See NFPA *101®*, *Life Safety Code®*, for definition of smoke compartment; NFPA 90A, *Standard for the Installation of Air Conditioning and Ventilating Systems*, for definition of duct systems; and NFPA 92A, *Recommended Practice for Smoke-Control Systems*, for definition of smoke zone.

[From NFPA 72E - 1990, 9-1 modified]

5-11.1* Section 5-11 covers installation and use of all types of smoke detectors to prevent smoke spread by initiating control of fans, dampers, doors, and other equipment. Detectors for this use shall be classified as:

(a) Area detectors that are installed in the related smoke compartments

(b) Detectors that are installed in the air duct systems.

[From NFPA 72E - 1990, 9-1.1]

5-11.2* Detectors that are installed in the air duct system per 5-11.1(b) shall not be used as a substitute for open area protection. Where open area protection is required, 5-3.5 shall apply.

[From NFPA 72E - 1990, 9-1.2 modified]

5-11.3 Smoke detectors in the related smoke compartment for open area protection are the preferred means to initiate control of smoke spread.

[From NFPA 72E - 1990, 9-1.3]

5-11.4 Purposes.

[From NFPA 72E - 1990, 9-2]

5-11.4.1 The purposes to which smoke detectors may be applied in order to initiate control of smoke spread are:

(a) Prevention of the recirculation of dangerous quantities of smoke within a building

(b) Selective operation of equipment to exhaust smoke from a building

(c) Selective operation of equipment to pressurize smoke compartments

(d) Operation of doors and dampers to close the openings in smoke compartments.

[From NFPA 72E - 1990, 9-2.1 modified]

5-11.4.2 To prevent the recirculation of dangerous quantities of smoke, a detector approved for air duct use shall be installed on the supply side of air handling systems in accordance with NFPA 90A, *Standard for the Installation of Air Conditioning and Ventilating Systems*, and 5-11.5.2.1.

[From NFPA 72E - 1990, 9-2.2]

5-11.4.3 To selectively initiate the operation of equipment to control smoke spread, the requirements of 5-11.5.2.2 shall apply.

[From NFPA 72E - 1990, 9-2.3]

5-11.4.4 Where detectors are used to initiate the operation of smoke doors, the requirements of 5-11.7 shall apply.

[From NFPA 72E - 1990, 9-2.4 modified]

5-11.4.5 Where duct detectors are used to initiate the operation of smoke dampers within ducts, the requirements of 5-11.6 shall apply.

[New paragraph]

5-11.5 Application.

[From NFPA 72E - 1990, 9-3]

5-11.5.1 Area Detectors Within Smoke Compartments. Area smoke detectors located within a smoke compartment for complete area coverage shall be permitted to be used to initiate control of smoke spread by operating doors, dampers, and other equipment where appropriate in the overall fire safety plan.

[From NFPA 72E - 1990, 9-3.1]

5-11.5.2 Smoke Detection for the Air Duct System.

[From NFPA 72E - 1990, 9-3.2]

5-11.5.2.1 Supply Air System. Where the detection of smoke in the supply air system is required by other NFPA standards, detector(s) listed for the air velocity present and located in the supply air duct downstream of both the fan and the filters shall be installed.

Exception No. 1: Where complete smoke detection is installed in the smoke compartment, installation of air duct detectors in the supply air system is not necessary if their function can be accomplished by the design of the area detection system.

Exception No. 2: Additional smoke detectors are not required to be installed in ducts where the air duct system passes through other smoke compartments not served by the duct.

[From NFPA 72E - 1990, 9-3.2.1 modified]

5-11.5.2.2* Return Air System. Where the detection of smoke in the return air system is required by other NFPA standards, detector(s) listed for the air velocity present shall be located at every return air opening within the smoke compartment, where the air leaves each smoke compartment, or in the duct system before the air enters the return air system common to more than one smoke compartment. [*See Figures A-5-11.5.2.2(a), (b), and (c).*]

Exception No. 1: Where complete smoke detection is installed in the smoke compartment, installation of air duct detectors in the return air system is not necessary if their function can be accomplished by the design of the area detection system.

Exception No. 2: Additional smoke detectors are not required to be installed in ducts where the air duct system passes through other smoke compartments not served by the duct.

[From NFPA 72E - 1990, 9-3.2.2]

5-11.6 Location and Installation of Detectors in Air Duct Systems.

[From NFPA 72E - 1990, 9-4]

5-11.6.1 Detectors shall be listed for the purpose.

[From NFPA 72E - 1990, 9-4.1]

5-11.6.2* Air duct detectors shall be securely installed in such a way as to obtain a representative sample of the air stream. This shall be permitted to be achieved by any of the following methods:

(a) Rigidly mounted within the duct

(b) Rigidly mounted to the wall of the duct with the sensing element protruding into the duct

(c) Outside the duct with rigidly mounted sampling tubes protruding into the duct

(d) Through the duct with projected light beam.

[From NFPA 72E - 1990, 9-4.2 modified]

5-11.6.3 Detectors shall be readily accessible for cleaning and shall be mounted in accordance with the manufacturer's recommendations. If necessary, access doors or panels shall be provided.

[From NFPA 72E - 1990, 9-4.3]

5-11.6.4 The location of all detectors in air duct systems shall be permanently and clearly identified and recorded.

[From NFPA 72E - 1990, 9-4.4]

5-11.6.5 Detectors mounted outside of a duct employing sampling tubes for transporting smoke from inside the duct to the detector shall be designed and installed to permit verification of airflow from the duct to the detector.

[From NFPA 72E - 1990, 9-4.5 modified]

5-11.6.6 Detectors shall be listed for proper operation over the complete range of air velocities, temperature, and humidity expected at the detector when the air handling system is operating.

[From NFPA 72E - 1990, 9-4.6 modified]

5-11.6.7 All penetrations of a return air duct in the vicinity of detectors installed on or in an air duct shall be sealed to prevent entrance of outside air and possible dilution or redirection of smoke within the duct.

[From NFPA 72E - 1990, 9-4.7]

5-11.7 Smoke Detectors for Door Release Service.

[From NFPA 72E - 1990, 9-5]

5-11.7.1 Smoke door release not initiated by a fire alarm system that includes smoke detectors protecting the areas on both sides of the door affected shall be accomplished by smoke detectors applied as specified in 5-11.7.

[From NFPA 72E - 1990, 9-5.1]

5-11.7.2 Smoke detectors listed or approved exclusively for door release service shall not be used for open area protection.

A smoke detector used concurrently for door release service and open area protection shall be acceptable if listed or approved for open area protection and installed in accordance with 5-3.5.

[From NFPA 72E - 1990, 9-5.2]

5-11.7.3 Smoke detectors shall be of the photoelectric, ionization, or other approved type.

[From NFPA 72E - 1990, 9-5.3]

5-11.7.4 Number of Detectors Required.

[From NFPA 72E - 1990, 9-5.4]

5-11.7.4.1 Where doors are to be closed in response to smoke flowing in either direction, the following rules shall apply.

[From NFPA 72E - 1990, 9-5.4.1]

5-11.7.4.1.1 Where the depth of wall section above the door is 24 in. (610 mm) or less, one ceiling-mounted detector shall be required on one side of the doorway only. (*See Figure 5-11.7.4.1.1, parts B and C.*)

[From NFPA 72E - 1990, 9-5.4.1.1]

5-11.7.4.1.2 Where the depth of wall section above the door is greater than 24 in. (610 mm), two ceiling-mounted detectors shall be required, one on each side of the doorway. (*See Figure 5-11.7.4.1.1, part F.*)

[From NFPA 72E - 1990, 9-5.4.1.2]

5-11.7.4.1.3 Where the depth of wall section above the door is 60 in. (1520 mm) or greater, additional detectors may be required as indicated by an engineering evaluation.

[From NFPA 72E - 1990, 9-5.4.1.3]

5-11.7.4.1.4 Where a detector is specifically listed for door frame mounting or where a listed combination or integral detector-door closer assembly is used, only one detector shall be required where installed in the manner recommended by the manufacturer.

[From NFPA 72E - 1990, 9-5.4.1.4]

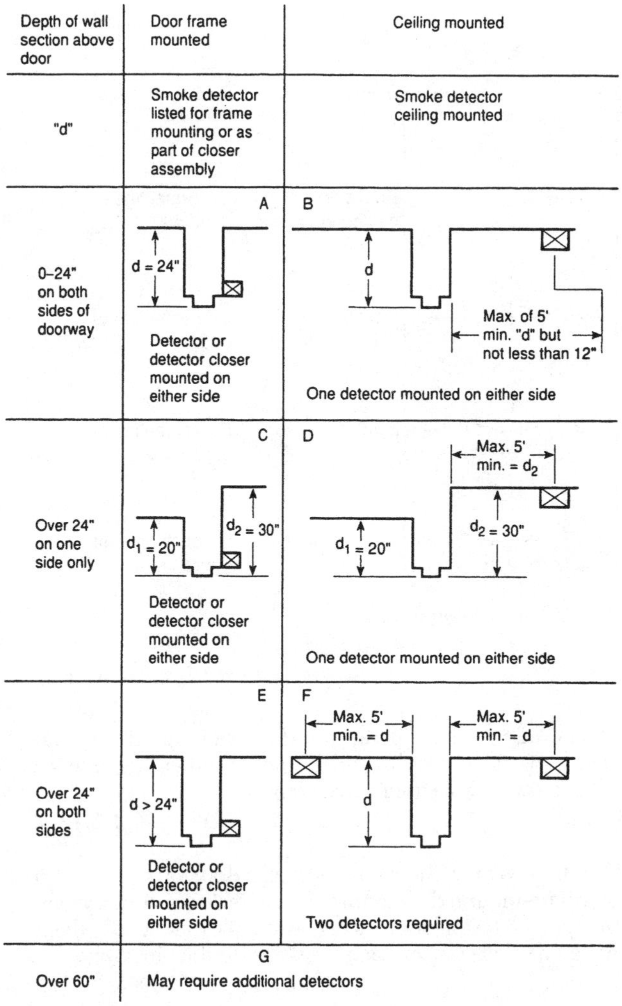

Depth of wall section above door	Door frame mounted	Ceiling mounted
"d"	Smoke detector listed for frame mounting or as part of closer assembly	Smoke detector ceiling mounted
0–24" on both sides of doorway	A d = 24" Detector or detector closer mounted on either side	B d Max. of 5' min. "d" but not less than 12" One detector mounted on either side
Over 24" on one side only	C d_1 = 20" d_2 = 30" Detector or detector closer mounted on either side	D Max. 5' min. = d_2 d_1 = 20" d_2 = 30" One detector mounted on either side
Over 24" on both sides	E d > 24" Detector or detector closer mounted on either side	F Max. 5' min. = d Max. 5' min. = d d Two detectors required
Over 60"	G May require additional detectors	

For SI Units: 1 in. = 25.4 mm; 1 ft = 0.305 m.

Figure 5-11.7.4.1.1

[From NFPA 72E - 1990, 9-5.4.1.1]

5-11.7.4.2 Where door release is intended to prevent smoke transmission from one space to another in one direction only, one detector located in the space to which smoke is to be confined shall suffice regardless of the depth of wall section above the door. Alternatively, a smoke detector conforming with 5-11.7.4.1.4 shall be used.

[From NFPA 72E - 1990, 9-5.4.2]

5-11.7.4.3 Where there are multiple doorways, additional ceiling-mounted detectors shall be required as follows.

[From NFPA 72E - 1990, 9-5.4.3]

5-11.7.4.3.1 Where the separation between doorways exceeds 24 in. (610 mm), each doorway shall be treated separately. (*See Figure 5-11.7.4.3.1.*)

[From NFPA 72E - 1990, 9-5.4.3.1]

5-11.7.4.3.2* Each group of three doorway openings shall be treated separately.

[From NFPA 72E - 1990, 9-5.4.3.2]

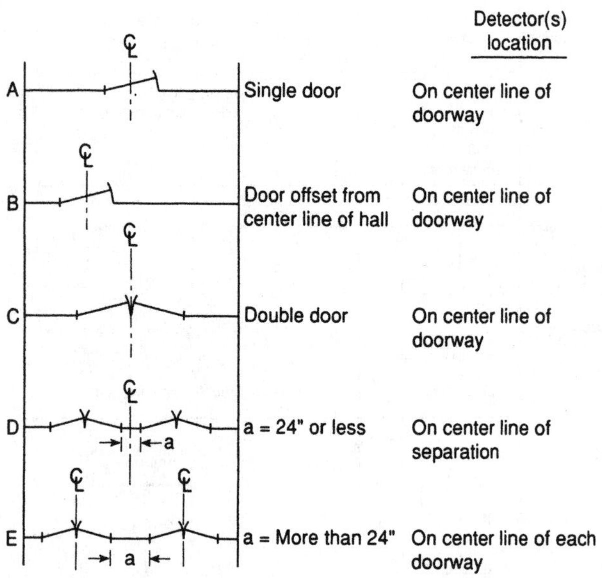

For SI Units: 1 in. = 25.4 mm.

Figure 5-11.7.4.3.1

[From NFPA 72E - 1990, 9-5.4.3.1]

5-11.7.4.3.3* Each group of doorway openings that exceeds 20 ft (6 m) in width measured at its overall extremes shall be treated separately.

[From NFPA 72E - 1990, 9-5.4.3.3]

5-11.7.4.4 Where there are multiple doorways and listed door frame-mounted detectors or where listed combination or integral detector-door closer assemblies are used, there shall be one detector for each single or double doorway.

[From NFPA 72E - 1990, 9-5.4.4]

5-11.7.4.4.1 A double doorway is a single opening that has no intervening wall space or door trim separating the two doors. (*See Figure 5-11.7.4.3.1.*)

[From NFPA 72E - 1990, 9-5.4.4.1]

5-11.7.5 Location.

[From NFPA 72E - 1990, 9-5.5]

5-11.7.5.1 Where ceiling-mounted smoke detectors are to be installed on a smooth ceiling for a single or double doorway, they shall be located as follows. (*See Figure 5-11.7.4.3.1.*)

(a) On the centerline of the doorway, and

(b) No more than 5 ft (1.5 m) measured along the ceiling and perpendicular to the doorway (*see Figure 5-11.7.4.1.1*), and

(c) No closer than shown in Figure 5-11.7.4.1.1, parts B, D, and F.

[From NFPA 72E - 1990, 9-5.5.1 modified]

5-11.7.5.2 Where ceiling-mounted detectors are to be installed in conditions other than those outlined in 5-11.7.5.1, engineering judgment is required.

[From NFPA 72E - 1990, 9-5.5.1]

Chapter 6 Notification Appliances for Fire Alarm Systems

6-1 Scope.

6-1.1 Minimum Requirements. This chapter covers minimum requirements for the performance, location, and mounting required for notification appliances for fire alarm systems for the purpose of evacuation or relocation of the occupants.

[From NFPA 72G, 1-2.1 modified]

6-1.2 Intended Use. These requirements are intended to be used with other NFPA standards that deal specifically with fire alarm, extinguishment, or control systems. Notification appliances for fire alarm systems add to fire protection by providing stimuli for initiating emergency action.

[From NFPA 72G, 1-2.2 modified]

6-1.3 All notification appliances or combinations thereof installed in conformity with this chapter shall be listed for the purpose for which they are used.

[From NFPA 72G, 3-4.2 modified]

6-1.4 These requirements are intended to address the reception of a notification signal and not its information content.

[From NFPA 72G, Chap. 2 modified]

6-1.5 Interconnection of Appliances. The interconnection of appliances, the control configurations, the power supply, and the use of the information provided by notification appliances for fire alarm systems are described in Chapter 1 and Chapter 3.

[From NFPA 72G, 1-2.3 modified]

6-2 General.

6-2.1 Definitions.

[New title]

Classification of Notification Signals. For the purpose of this chapter, notification signals for fire alarm systems are classified as listed below:

[From NFPA 72G, 2-1.1]

Coded. An audible or visible signal conveying several discrete bits or units of information. Notification signal examples are numbered strokes of an impact-type appliance and numbered flashes of a visible appliance.

[From NFPA 72G, 2-1.1.2]

Noncoded. An audible or visible signal conveying one discrete bit of information.

[From NFPA 72G, 2-1.1.1]

Noncoded Perceptually Constant. The continuous operation of a notification appliance (for example, a bell, horn, siren, or light) that is energized continuously.

[From NFPA 72G, 2-1.1.1.2]

Noncoded Perceptually Repetitious. The interrupted operation of a notification appliance (for example, a bell, horn, siren, or light) that is energized at a continuous uniform rate.

[From NFPA 72G, 2-1.1.1.3]

Noncoded Single Event. One stroke of an impact-type appliance or one flash of a strobe flash appliance. This should not be used for fire alarm purposes.

[From NFPA 72G, 2-1.1.1.1]

Textual. An audible or visible signal conveying a stream of information. An example of an audible textual signal is a voice message.

[From NFPA 72G, 2-1.1.3]

General Audible. Labeled ratings are in accordance with ANSI S12.31, *Precision Methods for the Determination of Sound Power Levels of Broad Band Noise Sources in Reverberation Rooms*, and ANSI S12.32, *Precision Methods for the Determination of Sound Power Levels of Discrete Frequency and Narrow Band Noise Sources in Reverberation Rooms*, unless otherwise noted.

[From NFPA 72G, 2-2.1]

General/Notification. Audible or visible signals used for alerting the general public or specific individuals responsible for implementation and direction of emergency action.

[From NFPA 72G, 2-2.3 modified]

General Visible. Definitions are in accordance with IES RP-16, *Nomenclature and Definitions for Illuminating Engineering*, unless otherwise noted.

[From NFPA 72G, 2-2.2]

Operating Mode, Private. Audible or visible signaling only to those persons directly concerned with the implementation and direction of emergency action initiation and procedure in the area protected by the fire alarm system.

[From NFPA 72G, 2-3.2]

Operating Mode, Public. Audible or visible signaling to occupants or inhabitants of the area protected by the fire alarm system.

[From NFPA 72G, 2-3.1]

6-2.2 Nameplates.

[From NFPA 72G, 2-4]

6-2.2.1 The notification appliances shall include on their nameplates reference to electrical requirements and rated audible or visible performance, or both, as defined by the listing authority.

[From NFPA 72G, 2-4.1]

6-2.2.2 The audible appliances shall include on their nameplates reference to their parameters or reference to installation documents (supplied with the appliance) that include the parameters in accordance with 6-3.1. The visible appliances shall include on their nameplates reference to their parameters or reference to installation documents (supplied with the appliance) that include the parameters in accordance with 6-4.2.1.

6-2.3 Physical Construction. All material for audible, textual, and visible appliances shall be moisture-, fire-, and climate-resistant in accordance with the stated purpose and shall be designed and fabricated to render them damage- and tamper-resistant.

[From NFPA 72G, 4-3.1, 5-3.1, 7-3.1 modified, and NFPA 72 - 1990, 2-4.8.3 modified]

6-2.4 Where subject to obvious mechanical damage, appliances shall be suitably protected.

[From NFPA 72G, 3-5.1]

6-2.5 Appliances shall be supported, in all cases, independently of their attachments to the circuit conductors.

[From NFPA 72G, 3-5.2]

6-3 Audible Characteristics.

6-3.1* Public Mode.

6-3.1.1 Audible signals intended for operation in the public mode shall have a sound level of not less than 75 dBA at 10 ft (3 m) or more than 130 dBA at the minimum hearing distance from the audible appliance.

[From NFPA 72G, 3-1.1.1]

6-3.1.2 To ensure that audible public mode signals are clearly heard, it shall be required that their sound level be at least 15 dBA above the average ambient sound level or 5 dBA above the maximum sound level having a duration of at least 60 seconds (whichever is greater), measured 5 ft (1.5 m) above the floor in the occupiable area.

[From NFPA 72G, 4-2-1]

6-3.1.3 Temporary sound sources not normally found continuously in the occupied area need not be considered in measuring maximum sound level. The average ambient sound level is the root mean square, A-weighted sound pressure measured over a 24-hour period.

6-3.1.4 An average sound level greater than 115 dBA shall require the use of a visible signal appliance(s) in accordance with Section 6-4.

6-3.1.5 Each section of a floor divided by a required 2-hour rated fire wall shall be considered as a separate area.

[From NFPA 72 - 1990, A-10-4.6.2 modified]

NOTE: The typical average ambient sound level should be considered.

6-3.2 Private Mode. Audible signals intended for operation in the private mode shall have a sound level of not less than 45 dBA at 10 ft (3 m) or more than 130 dBA at the minimum hearing distance from the audible appliance. An average sound level greater than 115 dBA requires the use of a visible signal appliance(s) in accordance with Section 6-4.

[From NFPA 72G, 3-1.1.2]

6-3.3 Audibility. The sound level of an installed audible signal shall be adequate to perform its intended function and shall meet the requirements of the authority having jurisdiction or other applicable standards.

[From NPFA 72G, 3-1.1.3]

6-3.4 Mechanical Equipment Rooms. Where audible appliances are installed in mechanical equipment rooms, the average ambient sound level that shall be used for design guidance is at least 85 dBA for all occupancies.

[From NFPA 72G, 3-1.1.4]

6-3.5 Sleeping Areas.

6-3.5.1 Where audible appliances are installed to signal sleeping areas, the maximum of 15 dBA above the average ambient sound or a minimum of 70 dBA shall be provided.

6-3.5.2 Sound level measurements at any point within the sleeping areas shall be the maximum of 15 dbA above the average ambient sound or a minimum of 70 dbA.

6-3.6 Noncoded Audible Signal Appliances. The purpose and scope of 6-3.6 is to provide requirements for location and spacing of noncoded audible appliances.

[From NFPA 72G, 4-1.1]

6-3.7 Location of Audible Signal Appliances. Where ceiling heights permit, wall-mounted appliances shall have their tops at heights above the finished floors of not less than 90 in. (2.30 m) and below the finished ceilings of not less than 6 in. (0.15 m). This shall not preclude ceiling-mounted or recessed appliances.

[From NFPA 72G, 4-4.1]

Exception: Combination audible/visible appliances installed in sleeping areas shall comply with 6-4.4.3.

6-3.7.1 Where combination audible/visible appliances are installed, the location of the installed appliance shall be determined by the requirements of 6-4.4.

Exception: Where the combination audible/visible appliance serves as an integral part of a smoke detector, the mounting location shall be in accordance with Chapter 2.

[New paragraphs]

6-4 Visible Characteristics, Public Mode.

6-4.1 There are two methods of visible signaling. These are methods in which the message of notification of an emergency condition is conveyed by direct viewing of the illuminating appliance or by means of illumination of the surrounding area.

[From NFPA 72G, 3-2.1.1 and 3-2.1.2]

NOTE: One method of determining compliance with Section 6-4 is that the product be listed in accordance with UL 1971, *Signaling Applications for the Hearing Impaired.*

[New paragraph]

6-4.2 Light Pulse Characteristics. The flash rate shall not exceed three flashes per second nor be less than one flash every three seconds.

[From NFPA 72G, 3-2.3.1]

6-4.2.1 A maximum pulse duration shall be 0.2 sec with a maximum duty cycle of 40 percent. The pulse duration is defined as the time interval between initial and final points of 10 percent of maximum signal.

[From NFPA 72G, 3-2.3.2]

6-4.2.2 The light source color shall be clear or nominal white and shall not exceed 1000 candela (cd) (effective intensity).

[From NFPA 72G, 3-2.3.3]

6-4.3 Appliance Photometrics. Visible notification appliances used in the public mode shall be located so that the operating effect of the appliance can be seen by the intended viewers and shall be of a type, size, intensity, and number so that the viewer can discern when they have been illuminated, regardless of the viewer's orientation.

[From NFPA 72G, 3-2.4.1]

6-4.4 Appliance Location. Wall-mounted appliances shall have their bottoms at heights above the finished floor of not less than 80 in. (2-m) and no greater than 96 in. (2.4 m). Ceiling-mounted appliances shall be installed per Table 6-4.4.1(b).

[From NFPA 72G, 5-2.1.1]

Exception: Appliances installed in sleeping areas shall comply with 6-4.4.3.

[New paragraph]

6-4.4.1* Spacing Allocation for Rooms.

6-4.4.1.1 Spacing shall be in accordance with Figure 6-4.4.1 and Tables 6-4.4.1(a) and (b). A maximum separation between appliances shall not exceed 100 ft (30 m).

6-4.4.1.2 If a room configuration is not square, the square room size that will entirely encompass the room or subdivide the room into multiple squares shall be used.

6-4.4.2* Spacing Allocation for Corridors.

6-4.4.2.1 Table 6-4.4.2 applies to corridors not exceeding 20 ft (6.1 m) wide. For corridors greater than 20 ft (6.1 m) wide, refer to Figure 6-4.4.1 and Tables 6-4.4.1(a) and (b). In a corridor application, visible appliances shall be rated not less than 15 cd.

6-4.4.2.2 The visible appliances shall be located no more than 15 ft (4.57 m) from the end of the corridor with a separation no greater than 100 ft (30.4 m) between appliances. Where there is an interruption of the concentrated viewing path, such as a fire door, an elevation change, or any other obstruction, the area shall be considered as a separate corridor.

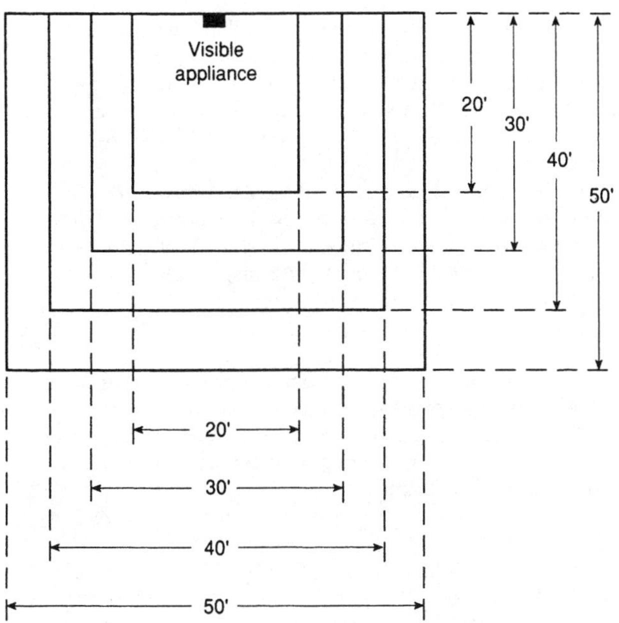

Figure 6-4.4.1 Room spacing allocation for wall-mounted visible appliances.

Note: The above is based on locating the visible signaling appliance at the halfway distance of the longest wall. In square rooms with appliances not centered or nonsquare rooms, the effective intensity (cd) from one visible signaling appliance shall be determined by maximum room size dimensions obtained either by the distance to the farthest wall or by double the distance to the farthest adjacent wall, whichever is greater, as shown in Table 6-4.4.1(a).

Table 6-4.4.1(a) Room Spacing Allocation for Wall-Mounted Visible Appliances

	Minimum Required Light Output, Candela (cd) (Effective Intensity)		
Maximum Room Size	One Light Per Room (cd)	Two Lights per Room (Located on Opposite Walls) (cd)	Four Lights per Room One Light per Wall) (cd)
20' × 20'	15	-	-
30' × 30'	30	15	-
40' × 40'	60	30	15
50' × 50'	95	60	30
60' × 60'	135	95	30
70' × 70'	185	110	60
80' × 80'	-	140	60
90' × 90'	-	180	95
100' × 100'	-	-	95
110' × 110'	-	-	135
120' × 120'	-	-	160
130' × 130'	-	-	185

6-4.4.3* Sleeping Areas.

6-4.4.3.1 Smoke detectors shall be installed in accordance with the applicable requirements of Chapter 2 and Chapter 5.

6-4.4.3.2 Table 6-4.4.3 applies to sleeping areas having no linear dimension greater than 16 ft (4.87 m). For larger rooms, the visible notification appliance shall be located within 16 ft (4.87 m) of the pillow.

Table 6-4.4.1(b) Room Spacing Allocation for Ceiling-Mounted Visible Appliances

	Minimum Required Light Output, Candels (cd) (Effective Intensity)	
Maximum Room Size	Maximum Ceiling Height	One Light (cd)
20' × 20'	10'	15
30' × 30'	10'	30
40' × 40'	10'	60
50' × 50'	10'	95
20' × 20'	20'	30
30' × 30'	20'	45
40' × 40'	20'	80
50' × 50'	20'	115
20' × 20'	30'	55
30' × 30'	30'	75
40' × 40'	30'	115
50' × 50'	30'	150

NOTE 1: Where ceiling heights exceed 30 ft, visible signaling appliances shall be suspended at or below 30 ft or wall-mounted in accordance with Table 6-4.4.1(a).

NOTE 2: The above is based on locating the visible signaling appliance at the center of the room. Where it is not located at the center of the room, the effective intensity (cd) shall be determined by doubling the distance from the appliance to the farthest wall to obtain the maximum room size.

Table 6-4.4.2 Corridor Spacing Allocation for Wall-Mounted Visible Appliances

Corridor Length (ft)	Minimum Number of 15-cd Visible Appliances Required
0 - 30	1
31 - 130	2
131 - 230	3
231 - 330	4
331 - 430	5
431 - 530	6

Table 6-4.4.3 Effective Intensity Requirements for Sleeping Area

Visible Notification Appliance Distance from Ceiling to Top of Lens	Intensity
greater than or equal to 24"	110 cd
less than 24"	177 cd

6-4.4.4 Where visible appliances are required, a minimum of one appliance shall be installed in the concentrated viewing path such as might be experienced in such areas as classrooms, theater stages, etc.

[From NFPA 72G, 5-2.1.4]

6-5 Visible Characteristics, Private Mode. Visible signals used in the private mode shall be adequate for their intended purpose.

[From NFPA 72G, 3-3.1]

6-6 Supplementary Visible Signaling Method. A supplementary visible appliance is intended to augment an audible or visible signal.

[From NFPA 72G, 3-2.2.1]

6-6.1 A supplementary visible appliance shall comply with its marked rated performance.

[From NFPA 72G, 3-2.2.2]

6-6.2 Supplementary visible notification appliances shall be permitted to be located less than 80 in. (2 m) above the floor.

[From NFPA 72G, 5-2.1.5]

6-7 Coded Appliance Characteristics. All requirements for noncoded appliances shall be met. In addition, the appliances shall differentiate several bits or units of information from all other information conveyed by that appliance.

[From NFPA 72G, 6-1.1]

6-8 Textual Audible Appliances.

6-8.1 Performance. The textual appliance shall reproduce normal voice frequencies.

6-8.2 Loudspeaker Appliance. The sound level in dBA of the loudspeaker appliance evacuation tone signals of the particular mode installed shall comply with all the requirements in 6-3.1.

[From NFPA 72G, 7-2.1.1]

6-8.3 Location of Loudspeaker Appliances. Where ceiling heights permit, wall-mounted loudspeaker appliances shall have their tops at heights above the finished floors of not less than 90 in. (2.30 m) and below the finished ceilings of not less than 6 in. (0.15 m). This does not preclude ceiling-mounted or recessed appliances.

[From NFPA 72G, 7-4.1]

6-8.3.1 Where loudspeaker/visible appliances are installed, the height of the installed appliance shall comply with 6-4.4.

Exception: Combination loudspeaker/visible appliances installed in sleeping areas shall comply with 6-4.4.3.

[New paragraphs]

6-8.4 Telephone Appliance. The telephone appliance shall be in accordance with EIA Tr 41.3, *Telephones*.

6-8.5 Location of Telephone Appliances. Wall-mounted telephone appliances or related jacks shall be of convenient heights not to exceed 66 in. (1.7 m), except that where accessible to the general public, one telephone appliance per location should be no higher than 54 in. (1.37 m) with clear access to the wall at least 30 in. (0.76 m) wide.

[From NFPA 72G, 7-4.2]

6-9 Textual Visible Appliances.

[New title]

6-9.1 The temporary textual visible appliance shall be a nonstorage display that produces either visible alphanumerics subtending a character angle to the observing eye of not less than 10 minutes of arc or visible pictorial images.

[From NFPA 72G, 8-2.1]

6-9.1.1 The alphanumeric display shall have an equivalent minimum 7 by 5 matrix character definition, a minimum grey scale contrast as defined by 10 shades of grey, and a character retentivity from $^1/_2$ minute to 5 minutes.

[From NFPA 72G, 8-2.1.1]

6-9.1.2 The pictorial display shall have a minimum of 250 line scan per frame, a minimum of 250 points per line scan, each arranged on a scale of 10 shades of grey, and shall have 30 frames per second. The display shall have an aspect ratio of 1:1.33.

[From NFPA 72G, 8-2.1.2]

6-9.1.3 The permanent textual visible appliance shall be a storage display that produces retrieved alphanumerics or retrieved pictorial images defined in accordance with 6-9.1. The retrieval time for the permanent textual visible appliance shall be not less than 1 year.

[From NFPA 72G, 8-2.2]

6-9.2 Location. All textual visible appliances in the private mode shall be located in rooms accessible only to those persons directly concerned with the implementation and direction of emergency action initiation and procedure in the areas protected by the fire alarm system.

[From NFPA 72G, 8-4.1]

Exception: In the lobby of a building where required by the authority having jurisdiction.

[From NFPA 72G, 8-4.1 Exception]

Chapter 7 Inspection, Testing, and Maintenance

7-1 General.

7-1.1 This chapter covers the requirements for the inspection, testing, and maintenance of the fire alarm systems described in Chapters 3 and 4 and for their initiation and notification components described in Chapters 5 and 6. The testing and maintenance requirements for household fire warning equipment are located in Chapter 2.

[New paragraph]

7-1.1.1 Inspection, testing, and maintenance programs shall satisfy the requirements of this code and the equipment manufacturer's instructions.

[From NFPA 72E, 8-1.2 modified]

7-1.1.2 Nothing in this chapter is intended to prevent the use of other test methods or testing devices, provided these other methods or devices are equivalent in effectiveness and safety and meet the intent of the requirements of this chapter.

[From NFPA 72, 1-3.2, and NFPA 72H, 1-1.3 modified]

7-1.2 The owner or his designated representative shall be responsible for inspection, testing, and maintenance of the system and alterations or additions to this system. Delegation of responsibility shall be in writing, with a copy of such delegation made available to the authority having jurisdiction.

[From NFPA 72E, 8-1.3, 8-1.3.1; and NFPA 72, 2-5.4 modified]

7-1.2.1 Inspection, testing, or maintenance shall be permitted to be done by a person or organization other than the owner when conducted under a written contract. Delegation of responsibility shall be in writing, with a copy of such delegation made available to the authority having jurisdiction.

[From NFPA 72, 2-5.4, and NFPA 1221, 2-1.11.2 modified]

7-1.2.2 Service personnel shall be qualified and experienced in the inspection, testing, and maintenance of fire alarm systems. Examples of qualified personnel shall be permitted to include but are not limited to:

(a) Factory trained and certified

(b) National Institute for Certification in Engineering Technologies Fire Alarm certified

(c) International Municipal Signaling Association Fire Alarm certified

(d) Certified by state or local authority

(e) Trained and qualified personnel employed by an organization listed by a national testing laboratory for the servicing of fire alarm systems.

[From NFPA 72, 2-5.4; NFPA 72E, 8-1.3.2 and A-8-1.3.2 modified]

7-1.3 Before proceeding with any testing, all persons and facilities who would receive an alarm, supervisory, or trouble signal, and building occupants, shall be notified to prevent unnecessary response. At the conclusion of testing, those previously notified (and others necessary) shall be further notified that testing has been concluded.

[From NFPA 71, 1-9.5(a), (h), (i); NFPA 72H, 2-2.1, 4-1; NFPA 72G, 9-1.3; and NFPA 72E, 8-1.4 modified]

7-1.3.1 The owner or his designated representative and service personnel shall coordinate system testing to prevent interruption of critical building systems or equipment.

[New paragraph]

7-1.4 Prior to system maintenance or testing, the system certificate and the information regarding the system and system alterations including specifications, wiring diagrams, and floor plans shall be made available by the owner or designated representative to the service personnel.

[From NFPA 72, 2-2.1 and 2-2.2 modified]

7-1.5 Special Hazards Systems and Equipment. Special hazards systems and equipment shall include but not be limited to preaction and deluge sprinkler systems, Halon systems, carbon dioxide systems, dry chemical systems, foam systems, and fire pump controllers.

7-1.5.1 Where a special hazards system has its own control unit that is connected to and monitored by a protected premises fire alarm system, testing shall be limited to the point of interface.

7-1.5.2 Where the special hazards system does not have its own control unit and the protected premises fire alarm system is used to provide complete control of the special hazards equipment, testing shall include verification of the simulated release of the extinguishing agent or activation of the fire pump controls.

7-1.5.3 Only qualified service personnel familiar with the special hazards system and equipment used shall be permitted to perform the required tests.

7-1.6 System Reacceptance Testing. Reacceptance test shall be performed after system components are added or deleted; after any modification, repair, or adjustment to system hardware or wiring; or after any change to software. All components, circuits, system operations, or software functions known to be affected by the change or identified by a means that indicates the system operational changes shall be 100 percent tested. In addition, 10 percent of initiating devices that are not directly affected by the change, up to a maximum of 50 devices, shall also be tested and proper system operation verified.

7-2 Test Methods.

7-2.1* Central Stations. The installation shall be inspected at the request of the authority having jurisdiction for complete information regarding the system, including specifications, wiring diagrams, and floor plans having been submitted for approval prior to installation of equipment and wiring.

[From NFPA 71, 1-4.1(b)]

7-2.1.1 The installation shall be inspected to ensure all devices, combinations of devices, and equipment constructed and installed shall be approved for the purpose for which they are intended.

[From NFPA 71, 1-4.2]

7-2.2* Fire alarm systems and other systems and equipment that may be associated with fire alarm systems and accessory equipment shall be tested according to Table 7-2.2.

[From NFPA 72H, 4-1 modified]

7-3 Inspection and Testing Frequency.

7-3.1 Visual Inspection.

7-3.1.1 Visual inspection shall be performed in accordance with the schedules in this chapter or more frequently where required by the authority having jurisdiction. The visual inspection shall be made to ensure that there are no changes that would affect equipment performance, such as building modifications, occupancy hazards, and environmental effects.

Exception: Items in areas that are inaccessible for safety considerations due to continuous process operations, energized electrical equipment, etc., shall be inspected during each scheduled shutdown but not more than every 18 months.

7-3.1.2 Where automatic testing is performed at a frequency of not less than weekly by a remotely monitored fire alarm control unit specifically listed for this application, the visual inspection frequency shall be permitted to be extended to annually. (*See Table 7-3.1.*)

[From NFPA 72E, 8-3.2 modified]

Table 7-2.2 Test Methods

DEVICE	METHOD
1. Control Equipment:	
a. Functions	All functions of the system, including operation of the system in various alarm and trouble modes for which it is designed (e.g., open circuit, grounded circuits, power outage, etc.), shall be tested in accordance with the manufacturer's instructions. [From NFPA 72, 2-5.1, and NFPA 72H, 7-1.3 modified]
b. Fuses	Remove fuse and verify rating and supervision. [From NFPA 72H, 4-1]
c. Interfaced Equipment	Integrity of single or multiple circuits providing interface between two or more control panels shall be verified. Interfaced equipment connections shall be tested by operating or simulating operation of the equipment being supervised. Signals required to be transmitted shall be verified at the control panel. [New paragraphs]
d. Lamps and LEDs	Lamps and LEDs shall be illuminated.
e. Primary (Main) Power Supply	All secondary (standby) power shall be disconnected and tested under maximum load, including all alarm appliances requiring simultaneous operation. All secondary (standby) power shall be reconnected at end of test. For redundant power supplies, each shall be tested separately. [From NFPA 72H, 4-1]
2. Engine-Driven Generator	If an engine-driven generator dedicated to the fire alarm system is used as a required power source, operation of the generator shall be verified in accordance with NFPA 110, *Standard for Emergency and Standby Power Systems,* by the building owner. [From NFPA 72, 2-5.2.3 modified]
3. Secondary (Standby) Power Supply	Disconnect all primary (main) power supplies and verify that required trouble indication for loss of primary power occurs. Measure or verify system's standby and alarm current demand and, using manufacturer's data, verify whether batteries are adequate to meet standby and alarm requirements. Operate general alarm systems for a minimum of five minutes and emergency voice communication systems for a minimum of fifteen minutes. Reconnect primary (main) power supply at end of test. [From NFPA 72H, 4-1, and NFPA 72, 5-3.3]
4. Uninterrupted Power Supply (UPS)	If a UPS system dedicated to the fire alarm system is used as a required power source, verify the operation of the UPS system in accordance with NFPA 111, *Standard on Stored Electrical Energy Emergency and Standby Power Systems,* by the building owner. [From NFPA 71, 2-2.3.7 modified]
5. Batteries — General Tests:	
a. Visual Inspection	Inspect batteries for corrosion or leakage. Check and ensure tightness of connections. If necessary, clean and coat the battery terminals or connections. Visually inspect electrolyte level in lead acid batteries.
b. Battery Replacement	Batteries shall be replaced in accordance with the recommendations of the alarm equipment manufacturer, or when the recharged battery voltage or current falls below the manufacturer's recommendations.
c. Charger Test	Check operation of battery charger in accordance with charger test for the specific type of battery. [From NFPA 72H, 4-1 modified]
d. Discharge Test	With the battery charger disconnected, load test the batteries following the manufacturer's recommendations. The voltage level shall not fall below the levels specified. [From NFPA 71, 2-2.3.7 modified] *Exception: An artificial load equal to the full fire alarm load connected to the battery shall be permitted to be utilized in conducting this test.* [New paragraph]

Table 7-2.2 Test Methods (cont.)

DEVICE	METHOD
e. Load Voltage Test	With the battery charger disconnected, measure the terminal voltage while supplying the maximum load required by its application. [From NFPA 71, 2-2.5.3, and NFPA 72H 4-1 modified] The voltage level shall not fall below the levels specified for the specific type of battery. If the voltage falls below the level specified, corrective action shall be taken and the batteries retested. [From NFPA 71, 2-2.5.3 modified] *Exception: An artificial load equal to the full fire alarm load connected to the battery shall be permitted to be utilized in conducting this test.* [New paragraph]
f. Open Circuit Voltage	With the battery charger disconnected, measure the open circuit voltage of the battery. [From NFPA 72H, 4-1 modified]
6. Battery Tests (Specific Types):	
a. Primary Batteries:	
1. Load Voltage Test*	The maximum load for a No. 6 primary battery shall not be more than 2 amperes per cell. An individual (1.5-volt) cell shall be replaced when a load of 1 ohm reduces the voltage below 1 volt. A 6-volt assembly shall be replaced where a test load of 4 ohms reduces the voltage below 4 volts. [From NFPA 71, A-2-2.5]
b. Lead-Acid Type:	
1. Charger Test	With the batteries fully charged and connected to the charger, measure the voltage across the batteries with a voltmeter. The voltage shall be 2.30 volts per cell +/− .02 volts (at 25°C) or as specified by the equipment manufacturer. [New paragraph]
2. Load Voltage Test*	Under load, the battery shall not fall below 2.05 volts per cell. [From NFPA 71, 2-2.3.7 modified]
3. Specific Gravity	The specific gravity of the liquid in the pilot cell or all of the cells shall be measured as required. The specific gravity shall be within the range specified by the manufacturer. Although the specified specific gravity may vary from manufacturer to manufacturer, a range of 1.205 - 1.220 is typical for regular lead acid batteries, while 1.240 - 1.260 is typical for high performance batteries. A hydrometer that only shows a pass or fail condition of the battery and does not indicate the specific gravity shall not be used since such a reading does not give a true indication of the battery condition.
c. Nickel-Cadmium Type:	
1. Charger Test	With the batteries fully charged and connected to the charger, place an amp meter in series with the battery under charge. The charging current shall be in accordance with the manufacturer's recommendations for the type of battery used. In the absence of specific information, this usually is 1/30 to 1/25 of the battery rating. (Example: 4000mAh × 1/25 = 160ma charging current at 25°C.) [New paragraphs]
2. Load Voltage Test*	Under load, the float voltage for the entire battery shall be 1.42 volts per cell nominal. If possible, cells shall be measured individually. [From NFPA 1221, 2-1.10.2.2, 3-1.5.3.2, and 4-1.6.2.3 modified]
d. Sealed Lead-Acid Type:	
1. Charger Test	With the batteries fully charged and connected to the charger, measure the voltage across the batteries with a voltmeter. The voltage should be 2.30 volts per cell +/− .02 volts (at 25°C) or as specified by the equipment manufacturer. [New paragraph]
2. Load Voltage Test*	Under load, the float voltage shall not fall below 2.05 volts per cell. [From NFPA 71, 2-2.3.7; NFPA 1221, 2-1.10.2.2 and 3-1.5.3.2 modified]
7. Public Reporting System Tests	In addition to the tests and inspection required above, the following requirements shall apply. Manual tests of the power supply for public reporting circuits shall be made and recorded atleast once during each 24-hour period. Such tests shall include: (a) Current strength of each circuit. Changes in current of any circuit, amounting to 10 percent of normal current, shall be investigated immediately.

Table 7-2.2 Test Methods (cont.)

DEVICE	METHOD
	(b) Voltage across terminals of each circuit, inside of terminals of protective devices. Changes in voltage of any circuit, amounting to 10 percent of normal voltage, shall be investigated immediately. (c) Voltage between ground and circuits. Where this test shows a reading in excess of 50 percent of that shown in test (b) above, the trouble shall be immediately located and cleared; readings in excess of 25 percent shall be given early attention. These readings shall be taken with a voltmeter of not more than 100-ohms resistance per volt. NOTE 1: The voltmeter sensitivity has been changed from 1000 ohms per volt to 100 ohms per volt so that false ground readings (caused by induced voltages) will be minimized. NOTE 2: Systems in which each circuit is supplied by an independent current source (Forms 3 and 4) will require tests between ground and each side of each circuit. Common current source systems (Form 2) will require voltage tests between ground and each terminal of each battery and other current source. (d) A ground current reading shall be acceptable in lieu of (c) above. When this method of testing is used, all grounds showing a current reading in excess of 5 percent of the normal line current shall given immediate attention. (e) Voltage across terminals of common battery, on switchboard side of fuses. (f) Voltage between common battery terminals and ground. Abnormal ground readings shall be investigated immediately. NOTE: Tests (e) and (f) apply only to those systems using a common battery. If more than one common battery is used, each common battery is to be tested.
8. Transient Suppressors	Lightning protection equipment shall be inspected and maintained per manufacturer's specifications. Additional inspections shall be required after any lightning strikes. Equipment located in moderate to severe areas outlined in NFPA 780, *Lightning Protection Code*, Appendix I, shall be inspected semi-annually and after any lightning strikes.
9. Control Panel Trouble Signals:	
a. Audible and Visual	Verify operation of panel trouble signals and ring back feature for systems using a trouble silencing switch that requires resetting.
b. Disconnect Switches	When control unit (panel) has disconnect or isolating switches, verify that each switch performs its intended function and a trouble signal is received when a supervised function is disconnected.
c. Ground-Fault Monitoring Circuit	When system has ground detection feature, verify that a ground fault indication is given whenever any installation conductor is grounded.
d. Transmission of Signals to Off-Premises Location	Actuate an appropriate initiating device and verify that alarm signal is received at the off-premises location. Create a trouble condition and verify that a trouble signal is received at the off-premises location. [New paragraphs] Actuate a supervisory device and verify that a supervisory signal is received at the off-premises location. If transmission carrier is capable of operation under a single or multiple fault condition, activate an initiating device during such fault condition and verify that a trouble signal is received at the off-premises location in addition to the alarm signal.
10. Remote Annunciators	Verify for proper operation and confirm proper identification. Where provided, verify proper operation under a fault condition.
11. Conductors/Metallic:	
a. Stray Voltage	All installation conductors shall be tested with a volt/ohm meter to verify that there are no stray (unwanted) voltages between installation conductors or between installation conductors and ground. Unless a different threshold is specified in the system manufacturer's documentation, the maximum allowable stray voltage shall not exceed 1 volt ac/dc. [From NFPA 72H, 2-2.2]
b. Ground Faults	All installation conductors other than those intentionally and permanently grounded shall be tested for isolation from ground per the manufacturer's recommendations. [From NFPA 72H, 2-2.3]

Table 7-2.2 Test Methods (cont.)

DEVICE	METHOD
c. Short Circuit Faults	All installation conductors other than those intentionally connected together shall be tested for conductor-to-conductor isolation per the manufacturer's recommendations. These same circuits shall be tested conductor-to-ground, also. [From NFPA 72H, 2-2.4]
d. Loop Resistance	With each initiating and indicating circuit installation conductor pair short-circuited at the far end, measure and record the resistance of each circuit. Verify that the loop resistance does not exceed the manufacturer's specified limits. [From NFPA 72H, 2-2.5]
12. Conductors/Non-Metallic:	
a. Circuits' Integrity	Test each initiating device, indicating appliance, and signaling line circuit to confirm that the integrity of installation conductors are being properly supervised.
b. Fiber Optics	The fiber optic transmission line shall be tested in accordance with the manufacturer's instructions or by the use of an optical power meter, or an optical time domain reflectometer to measure the relative power lost of the line. This relative figure for each fiber optic line shall be recorded in the fire alarm control panel. If the power level drops 2 percent or more from the figure recorded during the initial acceptance test, the transmission line, section thereof, or connectors shall be repaired and/or replaced by a qualified technician to bring the line back into compliance with an accepted transmission level per manufacturer's recommendations.
c. Supervision	Introduction of a fault in any supervised circuit shall result in a suitable trouble indication at the control unit. One connection shall be opened at no less than 10 percent of the initiating device, indicating appliance, and signaling line circuits. [From NFPA 72H, 2-3.2 modified] Test each initiating device, indicating appliance, and signaling line circuit for proper alarm response. [From NFPA 72H, 2-3.2]
13. Initiating Devices:	NOTE: See Table 3-6.1 for description of circuit performance and capacity.
a. Electromechanical Releasing Device:	
1. Nonrestorable-Type Link	Remove the fusible link and operate the associated device to ensure proper operation. Lubricate any moving parts as necessary.
2. Restorable-Type Link	Remove the fusible link and operate the associated device to ensure proper operation. Lubricate any moving parts as necessary. [New paragraphs] NOTE: Fusible thermal link detectors are commonly used to close fire doors and fire dampers. They can be actuated by the presence of external heat, which causes a solder element in the link to fuse, and by an electric thermal device which, when energized, generates heat within the body of the link, causing the link to fuse and separate.
b. Extinguishing System Alarm Switch	Mechanically or electrically operate the switch and verify receipt of signal by the control panel. [From NFPA 72H, 4-1]
c. Fire-Gas and Other Detectors	Fire-gas detectors and other fire detectors shall be tested as prescribed by the manufacturer and as necessary for the application. [From NFPA 72E, 8-3.6]
d. Heat Detectors:	
1. Fixed-Temperature and/or Rate-of-Rise or Rate-of-Compensation, Restorable Line or Spot Type (Except Pneumatic Tube)	Heat test with a heat source per manufacturer's recommendations for response within 1 minute. Precaution should be taken to avoid damage to the nonrestorable fixed-temperature element of a combination rate-of-rise/fixed-temperature element.
2. Fixed-Temperature, Nonrestorable Line Type	Do not heat test. Test mechanically and electrically for function. Measure and record loop resistance. Investigate changes from acceptance test.
3. Fixed-Temperature, Nonrestorable Spot Type	After 15 years, replace all devices or laboratory test two detectors per 100. Replace the two detectors with new devices. If a failure occurs on any of the detectors removed, additional detectors shall be removed and tested to determine either a general problem involving faulty detectors or a localized problem involving one or two defective detectors. [From NFPA 72E, 8-3.3.1 modified]
4. Nonrestorable (General)	Do not heat test. Test mechanically and electrically for function.
5. Restorable Line Type, Pneumatic Tube Only	Heat source (where test chambers are in circuit) or pressure pump. [From NFPA 72H, 4-1, and NFPA 72E, 8-2.3]

Table 7-2.2 Test Methods (cont.)

DEVICE	METHOD
e. Fire Alarm Boxes	Operate per manufacturer's instruction. For key operated pre-signal fire alarm boxes, test both pre-signal and general alarm circuit.
f. Radiant Energy Fire Detectors	Flame detectors and spark/ember detectors shall be tested in accordance with the manufacturer's instructions to determine that each detector is operative. [From NFPA 72E, 8-3.5.1] Flame detector and spark/ember detector sensitivity shall be determined using either: (a) A calibrated test method, or (b) The manufacturer's calibrated sensitivity test instrument, or (c) Listed control panel arranged for the purpose, or (d) Other calibrated sensitivity test method acceptable to the authority having jurisdiction that is directly proportional to the input signal from a fire consistent with the detector listing or approval. Detectors found to be outside of the approved range of sensitivity shall be replaced or adjusted to bring them into the approved range if designed to be field adjustable. Flame detector and spark/ember detector sensitivity shall not be determined using a light source that administers an unmeasured quantity of radiation at an undefined distance from the detector. [From NFPA 72E, 8-3.5.2]
g. Smoke Detectors:	
1. All Types	The detectors shall be tested in place to ensure smoke entry into the sensing chamber and an alarm response. Testing with smoke or listed aerosol acceptable to the manufacturer, or other means acceptable to the detector manufacturer shall be permitted as one acceptable test method. [From NFPA 72E, 8-2.4.1.1] Ensure that each smoke detector is within its listed and marked sensitivity range by testing using either: (a) A calibrated test method, or (b) The manufacturer's calibrated sensitivity test instrument, or (c) Listed control equipment arranged for the purpose, or (d) Other calibrated sensitivity test method acceptable to the authority having jurisdiction. NOTE: The detector sensitivity cannot be tested or measured using any spray device that administers an unmeasured concentration of aerosol into the detector. [From NFPA 72E, 8-2.4.2]
2. Air Sampling:	
Wilson Cloud Chamber	Per manufacturer's recommended test methods, including verification of sampling from each method.
Photoelectric-Type	Verify detector alarm response through the end sampling port on each pipe run, as well as verifying air flow through all other ports.
3. Duct-Type	Air duct detectors shall be tested or inspected to ensure that the device will sample the air stream. The test shall be made in accordance with the manufacturer's instructions. [From NFPA 72E, 8-3.4.3 modified]
4. Projected Beam-Type	The detector shall be tested by introducing smoke, other aerosol, or an optical filter into the beam path. [From NFPA 72E, 8-2.4.1.2]
5. Smoke Detector with Built-in Thermal Element	Operate both portions of the detector independently as described for the respective devices. [New paragraph]
6. Smoke Detectors with Control Output Functions	When individual fire detectors are used to control the operation of equipment as permitted by 3-7.1, the control capability shall remain operable even if all of the initiating devices connected to the sameinitiating circuit are in an alarm state.
h. Initiating Devices, Supervisory:	
1. Control Valve Switch	Operate valve and verify signal receipt within the first two revolutions of the hand wheel or within one-fifth of the travel distance, or manufacturer's specifications.
2. High or Low Air Pressure Switch	Operate switch and verify that receipt of signal is obtained where the required pressure is increased or decreased 10 psi from the required pressure level. [From NFPA 71, 3-4.4.3 modified]

Table 7-2.2 Test Methods (cont.)

DEVICE	METHOD
3. Room Temperature Switch	Operate switch and verify receipt of signal to indicate the decrease in room temperature to 40°F (4.4°C) and its restoration to above 40°F (4.4°C). [From NFPA 71, 3-4.4.7 modified]
4. Water Level Switch	Operate switch and verify the receipt of signal indicating the water level raised or lowered 3 in. (76.2 mm) from the required level within a pressure tank, or 12 in. (305 mm) from the required level of a nonpressure tank, and its restoral to required level. [From NFPA 71, 3-4.4.4 modified]
5. Water Temperature Switch	Operate switch and verify receipt of signal to indicate the decrease in water temperature to 40°F (4.4°C) and its restoration to above 40°F (4.4°C). [From NFPA 71, 3-4.4.7 modified]
i. Waterflow Device:	
1. Mechanical, Electrosonic, or Pressure Type	Flow water through an inspector's test connection indicating the flow of water equal to that from a single sprinkler of the smallest orifice size installed in the system for wet-pipe systems, or an alarm test bypass connection for dry-pipe, pre-action, or deluge systems in accordance with NFPA 25, *Standard for the Inspection, Testing, and Maintenance of Water-Based Fire Protection Systems.* [From NFPA 71, 1-9.5 and 3-4.2.1; NFPA 72, 2-5.3 and 3-4.1.2 modified]
14. Alarm Notification Appliances:	
a. Audible	Measure sound pressure level with sound level meter meeting ANSI S-1.4a, *Sound Level Meters,* Type 2 requirements. Measure and record levels throughout protected area. [From NFPA 72G, 9-2.1 modified]
b. Speakers	Measure sound pressure level with sound level meter meeting ANSI S-1.4a, *Sound Level Meters,* Type 2 requirements. Measure and record levels throughout protected area. [From NFPA 72G, 9-1.2 modified] Verify voice clarity. [From NFPA 72H, 4-1]
c. Visible	Test in accordance with manufacturer's instructions. Verify device locations are per approved layout and confirm that no floor plan changes affect the approved layout. [From NFPA 72G, 9-2.2 modified]
15. Special Hazard Equipment:	
a. Abort Switch (IRI-Type)	Operate abort switch. Verify correct sequence and operation.
b. Abort Switch (Recycle-Type)	Operate abort switch. Verify correct matrix develops with each sensor operated.
c. Abort Switch (Special-Type)	Operate abort switch. Verify correct sequence and operation in accordance with authority having jurisdiction. Note sequence on as-built drawings or in owner's manual.
d. Cross Zone Detection Circuit	Operate one sensor or detector on each zone. Verify that correct sequence occurs with operation of first zone and then with operation of second zone.
e. Matrix Type Circuit	Operate all sensors in system. Verify correct matrix develops with each sensor operated.
f. Release Solenoid Circuit	Use solenoid with equal current requirements. Verify operation of solenoid.
g. Squibb Release Circuit	Use AGI flashbulb or other test light acceptable to the manufacturer. Verify operation of flashbulb or light.
h. Verified, Sequential, or Counting Zone Circuit	Operate required sensors at a minimum of four locations in circuit. Verify correct sequence with both the first and second detector in alarm.
i. All Above Devices and/or Circuits	Verify supervision of circuits by creating an open circuit. Note specific trouble indications.
16. Transmission and Receiving Equipment, Off Premises:	
a. All Equipment	Verify all system functions and features in accordance with manufacturer's instructions. Remove primary power, actuate an initiating device, and verify that the initiating device signal is received at the monitoring station. On completion of test, restore system to normal. Where test jacks are used, the first and last tests shall be made without the use of the test jack.
b. Transmitters—Digital Alarm Communicator Systems (DACS)	Verify that the failure of the primary transmission path at the protected premises shall result in a trouble signal being transmitted via the secondary path to the monitoring station within 4 minutes of the detection of the fault.

Table 7-2.2 Test Methods (cont.)

DEVICE	METHOD
1. DACT	See 7-4.4.1.
	Verify the DACT is connected to two separate lines (numbers) at the protected premises.
	In turn, disconnect each telephone line at the protected premises and verify local annunciation and that trouble signals are transmitted to the monitoring station over the other line (number). Transmission shall be initiated within 4 minutes of the detection of the fault.
2. DACR	Verify that the DACR equipment is connected to a minimum of two separate incoming telephone lines (numbers). Verify that if the lines (numbers) are in a single hunt group, they are individually accessible.
	Use 7-4.4.2(b).
	Use 7-4.4.2(c).
	Use 7-4.4.2(d).
3. DARR	Verify supervision of the following conditions at the monitoring station:
	(a) Failure of ac power supplying the radio equipment
	(b) Receiver malfunction
	(c) Antenna and interconnecting cable malfunction
	(d) Indication of automatic switchover of the DARR
	(e) Data transmission line between the DARR and the monitoring station.
4. McCulloh Systems	Verify that signals are received during one of the following signaling line fault conditions:
	(a) Open
	(b) Ground
	(c) Wire-to-wire short
	(d) Open and ground.
17. Emergency Communication Equipment:	
a. Amplifier/Tone Generators	Verification of proper switching and operation of backup equipment.
b. Call-in Signal Silence	Operate function and verify receipt of proper visual and audible signals at control panel.
c. Off-hook Indicator (Ring Down)	Install phone set or remove phone from hook and verify receipt of signal at control panel.
d. Phone Jacks	Visual inspection and initiate communication path through jack.
e. Phone Set	Activate each phone set and verify proper operation.
f. System Performance	Operate system with a minimum of any five handsets simultaneously. Verify acceptable voice quality and clarity. [New paragraphs]
18. Interface Equipment	Interface equipment connections shall be tested by operating or simulating the equipment being supervised. Signals required to be transmitted shall be verified at the control panel. Test frequency for interface equipment shall be the same as the frequency required by the applicable NFPA standard(s) for the equipment being supervised.
19. Guard's Tour Equipment	Test the device in accordance with manufacturer's specifications.
20. Special Procedures:	
a. Alarm Verification	Verify time delay and alarm response for smoke detector circuits identified as having alarm verification. [From NFPA 72H, 5-1.1 modified]
b. Multiplex Systems	Verify communication between sending and receiving units under both normal and standby power. [From NFPA 72H, 6-1.1 modified]
	Verify communication between sending and receiving units under open circuit and short-circuit trouble conditions. [From NFPA 72H, 6-1.2 modified]
	Verify communication between sending and receiving units in all directions when multiple communication pathways are provided. [From NFPA 72H, 6-1.6 modified]
	When redundant central control equipment is provided, verify switchover and all required functions and operations of secondary control equipment. [From NFPA 72H, 6-1.6.2 modified]
	Verify all system functions and features in accordance with manufacturer's instructions. [From NFPA 72H, 6-1.7 modified]

Table 7-3.1 Visual Inspection Frequencies

		Init./Reaccpt.	Monthly	Quarterly	Semiann.	Ann.
1.	**Alarm Indicating Appliances — Supervised**	X			X	
2.	**Batteries**					
	a. Lead-Acid	X	X			
	b. Nickel-Cadmium	X			X	
	c. Primary (Dry Cell)	X	X			
	d. Sealed Lead-Acid	X			X	
3.	**Control Equipment: Fire Alarm Systems Monitored for Alarm, Supervisory, Trouble Signals**					
	a. Fuses	X				X
	b. Interfaced Equipment	X				X
	c. Lamps and LEDs	X				X
	d. Primary (Main) Power Supply	X				X
4.	**Control Equipment: Fire Alarm Systems Unmonitored for Alarm, Supervisory, Trouble Signals**					
	a. Fuses	X				X
	b. Interfaced Equipment	X				X
	c. Lamps and LEDs	X				X
	d. Primary (Main) Power Supply	X				X
5.	**Control Panel Trouble Signals**	X			X	
6.	**Emergency Voice/Alarm Communications Equipment**	X			X	
7.	**Fiber Optic Cable Connections**	X				X
8.	**Guard's Tour Equipment**	X			X	
9.	**Initiating Devices**					
	a. Air Sampling	X			X	
	b. Duct Detectors	X			X	
	c. Electromechanical Releasing Device	X			X	
	d. Extinguishing System Switches	X			X	
	e. Fire Alarm Boxes	X			X	
	f. Heat Detectors	X			X	
	g. Radiant Energy Fire Detectors	X			X	
	h. Smoke Detectors	X			X	
	i. Supervisory Signal Devices	X		X		
	j. Waterflow Devices	X		X		
10.	**Interface Equipment**	X			X	
11.	**Remote Annunciators**	X			X	
12.	**Special Procedures**	X			X	
13.	**Transient Suppressors**	X			X	
14.	**Transmission and Receiving Equipment — Off Premises**					
	a. All Equipment	X			X	
	b. DACT — Telephone Line	X			X	
	c. DACR — Telephone Line	X	X			
	d. DACR — Signal Receipt	X (DAILY)				

7-3.2* Testing. Testing hall be performed in accordance with the schedules in this chapter or more frequently where required by the authority having jurisdiction. Where automatic testing is performed at least weekly by a remotely monitored fire alarm control unit specifically listed for the application, the manual testing frequency shall be permitted to be extended to annually. (*See Table 7-3.2.*)

[From NFPA 72H, 4-1 modified]

Exception: Devices in areas that are inaccessible for safety considerations, such as continuous process operations, shall be tested during scheduled shutdowns at intervals approved by the authority having jurisdiction.

[New]

7-3.2.1* Detector sensitivity shall be checked within 1 year after installation and every alternate year thereafter. After the second required calibration test, if sensitivity tests indicate that the detector has remained within its listed and marked sensitivity range, the length of time between calibration tests shall be permitted to be extended not to exceed 5 years. If the frequency is extended, records of detector-caused unwanted alarms and subsequent trends of these alarms shall be maintained. In zone or in areas where unwanted alarms show any increase over the previous year, calibration tests shall be performed.

To ensure that each smoke detector is within its listed and marked sensitivity range, it shall be tested using either:

(a) A calibrated test method, or

(b) The manufacturer's calibrated sensitivity test instrument, or

(c) Listed control equipment arranged for the purpose, or

(d) A smoke detector/control unit arrangement whereby the detector causes a signal at the control unit where its sensitivity is outside its acceptable sensitivity range, or

(e) Other calibrated sensitivity test method acceptable to the authority having jurisdiction.

Detectors found to have a sensitivity outside the listed and marked sensitivity range shall be cleaned and recalibrated or replaced.

Exception: Detectors listed as field adjustable may be either adjusted within the listed and marked sensitivity range, cleaned, and recalibrated, or replaced.

The detector sensitivity shall not be tested or measured using any device that administers an unmeasured concentration of smoke or other aerosol into the detector.

7-3.2.2 Test frequency of interfaced equipment shall be the same as specified by the applicable NFPA standards for the equipment being supervised.

7-3.3 Single-station smoke detectors shall be inspected, tested, and maintained as specified by Chapter 2.

[New]

7-3.4 Test of all circuits extending from the central station shall be made at intervals of not more than 24 hours.

7-4 Maintenance.

[From NFPA 72H, 4-1]

7-4.1 Fire alarm system equipment shall be periodically maintained in accordance with manufacturer's instructions. The frequency of maintenance will depend on the type of equipment and the local ambient conditions.

7-4.2 Any accumulation of dust and dirt may adversely effect device and appliance performance. The frequency of cleaning will depend on the type of equipment and the local ambient conditions.

[From NFPA 72E, 8-4.1, and NFPA 72G, 9-4.1 modified]

7-4.3 All apparatus requiring rewinding or resetting to maintain normal operation shall be restored to normal as promptly as possible after each test and alarm and kept in normal condition for operation. All test signals received shall be recorded to indicate date, time, and type.

[From NFPA 71, 1-5.4]

7-4.4 The retransmission means as defined in Section 4-3 shall be tested at intervals of not more than 12 hours. The retransmission signal and the time and date of the retransmission shall be recorded in the central station.

Exception: Where the retransmission means is the public switched telephone network, it need only be tested weekly to confirm its operation to each public fire service communications center.

[From NFPA 71, 1-7.2.4]

7-4.4.1 Digital Alarm Communicator Transmitter (DACT).

[New]

(a) Verify the DACT is capable of seizing the telephone line (going off-hook) at the protected premises, disconnecting an outgoing or incoming telephone call, and preventing its use for outgoing calls until signal transmission is completed.

[From NFPA 71, 5-1]

(b) Verify the DACT has the means to satisfactorily obtain an available dial tone, dial the number(s) of the DACR, obtain verification that the DACR is ready to receive signals, transmit the signal, and receive acknowledgment that the DACR has accepted the signal. In no event shall the time from going off-hook to on-hook exceed 90 seconds per attempt.

(c) Verify the DACT has a suitable means to reset and retry if the first attempt to complete a signal transmission sequence is unsuccessful. A failure to complete connection shall not prevent subsequent attempts to transmit an alarm if such alarm is generated from any other initiating device circuit. Additional attempts shall be made until the signal transmission sequence has been completed to a minimum of five and a maximum of ten attempts.

(d) If the maximum number of attempts to complete the sequence is reached, an indication of the failure shall be made at the premises.

(e) Verify the DACT is connected to two separate lines (numbers) at the protected premise by disconnecting the primary phone line of the DACT. The DACT trouble signal shall be transmitted within the time specified in accordance with 7-4.4.1(a). Operate an initiating device to test the secondary transmission of the DACT. The DACT shall be capable of selecting the operable line (number) in the event of failure in either (line number).

(f) Failure of either of the telephone lines (numbers) at the protected premises shall be annunciated at the protected premises, and a trouble signal shall be transmitted to the central station over the other line (number). Transmission shall be initiated within 4 minutes of the detection of the fault.

[New paragraphs]

Table 7-3.2 Testing Frequencies

	Init./Reaccpt.	Monthly	Quarterly	Semiann.	Ann.	Table 7-2.2 Reference
1. Alarm Notification Appliances						14
a. Audible Devices	X				X	
b. Speakers	X				X	
c. Visible Devices	X				X	
2. Batteries — Central Station Facilities						
a. Lead-Acid Type						6b
1. Charger Test (Replace battery as needed.)	X				X	
2. Discharge Test (30 min.)	X	X				
3. Load Voltage Test	X	X				
4. Specific Gravity	X			X		
b. Nickel-Cadmium Type						6c
1. Charger Test (Replace battery as needed.)	X		X			
2. Discharge Test (30 min.)	X				X	
3. Load Voltage Test	X				X	
c. Sealed Lead-Acid Type	X	X				6d
1. Charger Test (Replace battery as needed.)		X	X			
2. Discharge Test (30 min.)	X	X				
3. Load Voltage Test	X	X				
3. Batteries — Fire Alarm Systems						
a. Lead-Acid Type						6b
1. Charger Test (Replace battery as needed.)	X				X	
2. Discharge Test (30 min.)	X			X		
3. Load Voltage Test	X			X		
4. Specific Gravity	X			X		
b. Nickel-Cadmium Type						6c
1. Charger Test (Replace battery as needed.)	X				X	
2. Discharge Test (30 min.)	X				X	
3. Load Voltage Test	X			X		
c. Primary Type (Dry Cell)						6a
1. Load Voltage Test	X	X				
d. Sealed Lead-Acid Type						6d
1. Charger Test (Replace battery every 4 years.)	X				X	
2. Discharge Test (30 min.)	X				X	
3. Load Voltage Test	X			X		
4. Batteries — Public Fire Alarm Reporting Systems	X (DAILY)					
Voltage tests in accordance with Table 7-2.2, Public Reporting System Tests, paragraphs (a) - (f).						
a. Lead-Acid Type						6b
1. Charger Test (Replace battery as needed.)	X				X	
2. Discharge Test (2 hours)	X		X			
3. Load Voltage Test	X		X			
4. Specific Gravity	X			X		
b. Nickel-Cadmium Type						6c
1. Charger Test (Replace battery as needed.)	X				X	
2. Discharge Test (2 hours)	X				X	
3. Load Voltage Test	X		X			
c. Sealed Lead-Acid Type						6d
1. Charger Test (Replace battery as needed.)	X				X	
2. Discharge Test (2 hours)	X				X	
3. Load Voltage Test	X		X			
5. Conductors/Metallic	X					11
6. Conductors/Nonmetallic	X					12

Table 7-3.2 Testing Frequencies (cont.)

		Init./Reaccpt.	Monthly	Quarterly	Semiann.	Ann.	Table 7-2.2 Reference
7.	**Control Equipment: Fire Alarm Systems Monitored for Alarm, Supervisory, Trouble Signals**						1, 7 and 16
	a. Functions	X				X	
	b. Fuses	X				X	
	c. Interfaced Equipment	X				X	
	d. Lamps and LEDs	X				X	
	e. Primary (Main) Power Supply	X				X	
	f. Transponders	X				X	
8.	**Control Equipment: Fire Alarm Systems Unmonitored for Alarm, Supervisory, Trouble Signals**						1
	a. Functions	X		X			
	b. Fuses	X		X			
	c. Interfaced Equipment	X		X			
	d. Lamps and LEDs	X		X			
	e. Primary (Main) Power Supply	X		X			
	f. Transponders	X		X			
9.	**Control Unit Trouble Signals**	X				X	9
10.	**Emergency Voice/Alarm Communications Equipment**	X				X	17
11.	**Engine-Driven Generator**	X (WEEKLY)					
12.	**Fiber Optic Cable Power**	X				X	19
13.	**Guard's Tour Equipment**	X				X	
14.	**Initiating Devices**						13
	a. Duct Detectors	X				X	
	b. Electromechanical Releasing Device	X				X	
	c. Extinguishing System Switches	X				X	
	d. Fire-Gas and Other Detectors	X				X	
	e. Heat Detectors	X				X	
	f. Fire Alarm Boxes	X				X	
	g. Radiant Energy Fire Detectors	X				X	
	h. Smoke Detectors - Functional	X				X	
	i. Smoke Detectors - Sensitivity (*See 7-3.2.1.*)						
	j. Supervisory Signal Devices	X		X			
	k. Waterflow Devices	X		X			
15.	**Interface Equipment**	X				X	18
16.	**Off-Premises Transmission Equipment**	X		X			
17.	**Remote Annunciators**	X				X	10
18.	**Retransmission Equipment**	X (*See 7-3.4.*)					
19.	**Special Hazard Equipment**	X				X	15
20.	**Special Procedures**	X				X	20
21.	**System and Receiving Equipment — Off-Premises**						16
	a. Operational						
	1. Functional — All	X				X	
	2. Transmitters — WF & Supervisory	X		X			
	3. Transmitters — All Others	X				X	
	4. Receivers	X	X				
	b. Standby Loading — All Receivers	X	X				
	c. Standby Power						
	1. Receivers — All	X	X				
	2. Transmitters — All	X				X	
	d. Telephone Line — All Receivers	X	X				
	e. Telephone Line — All Transmitters	X				X	

NOTE: For testing addressable and analog described devices, which are normally affixed to either a single molded assembly or twist lock type affixed to a base, TESTING SHALL BE DONE UTILIZING THE SIGNALING STYLE CIRCUITS (Styles 0.5 through 7). The addressable term was determined by the Technical Committee in Formal Interpretation 79-8 on NFPA 72D and Formal Interpretation 87-1 on NFPA 72A. Analog type detectors shall be tested with the same criteria.

[From NFPA 72H, 4-1 modified]

7-4.4.2 Digital Alarm Communicator Receiver (DACR).

(a) Verify that at least two separate incoming telephone lines are in a hunt group and are individually accessible. These lines shall be used for no other purpose than receiving signals from DACTs. These lines (numbers) shall be unlisted.

(b) The failure of any telephone line (number) connected to the DACR due to loss of line voltage shall be annunciated visually and audibly in the central station.

(c) The loading capacity for hunt group shall be in accordance to Table 4-2.3.2.2.2.3 or be capable of demonstrating a 90 percent probability of immediately answering the incoming call.

(d) Verify a signal is received on each individual incoming DARC line at least once every 24 hours.

(e) The verification of the 24-hour DARC line test should be done early enough in the day to allow repairs to be made by the telephone company.

7-4.4.3 Digital Alarm Radio System (DARS).

(a) When DARS is used, verify that when any DACT signal transmission is unsuccessful, the information is transmitted by means of the DART. The DACT shall continue its normal transmission as required.

(b) The failure of the telephone line at the protected premises shall result in a trouble signal being transmitted to the central station by means of the DART within 4 minutes of the detection of the fault.

(c) Each DART shall automatically initiate and complete a test transmission sequence to its associated DARR at least once every 24 hours. A successful DART signal transmission sequence of any other type shall be considered sufficient to fulfill the requirement to test integrity of the reporting system, if signal processing is automated so that 24-hour delinquencies must be acknowledged by central station personnel.

[From NFPA 71, 5-5]

7-4.4.3.1 Digital Alarm Radio Receiver (DARR).

Verify supervision in the central station of the following conditions:

(a) Failure of ac power supplying the radio equipment

(b) Receiver malfunction

(c) Antenna and interconnecting cable malfunction

(d) Indication of automatic switchover of the DARR

(e) Data transmission line between the DARR and the central station.

[From NFPA 71, 5-7]

7-4.4.3.2 McCulloh Systems.

Verify that when end-to-end metallic continuity is present, proper signals shall be received From other points under one of the following signaling line fault conditions at one point in the line:

(a) Open

(b) Ground

(c) Wire-to-wire short

(d) Open group.

[From NFPA 71, 6-1]

7-5 Records.

[From NFPA 71, 1-10 modified]

7-5.1 Record of Inspection. A permanent record of all inspections, testing, and maintenance shall be provided, which includes the following information of periodic tests and all the applicable information requested in Figure 7-5.1.

(a) Date

(b) Test frequency

(c) Name of property

(d) Address

(e) Name of person performing inspection, maintenance, and/or tests, affiliation, business address, and telephone number

(f) Approving agency's(ies') name, address, and representative

(g) Designation of the detector(s) tested ("Tests performed in accordance with Section ____________.")

(h) Functional test of detectors

(i) Check of all smoke detectors

(j) Loop resistance for all fixed temperature line type heat detectors

(k) Other tests as required by equipment manufacturers

(l) Other tests as required by the authority having jurisdiction

(m) Signatures of tester and approved authority representative.

[New paragraphs]

7-5.2 Permanent Records. After successful completion of acceptance tests satisfactory to the authority having jurisdiction, a set of reproducible as-built installation drawings, operation and maintenance manuals, and a written sequence of operation shall be provided to the building owner or his designated representative. In addition, inspection, testing, and maintenance reports shall be provided for the owner or a designated representative. It shall be the responsibility of the owner to maintain these records for the life of system and to keep them available for examination by any authority having jurisdiction. Paper or electronic media shall be acceptable.

[From NFPA 72, 10-2.4, and NFPA 72H, 2-1 modified]

7-5.3 Where off-premise monitoring is provided, records of signals, tests, and operations recorded at the monitoring center shall be maintained for not less than 12 months. Upon request, a hardcopy record shall be available for examination by the authority having jurisdiction. Paper or electronic media shall be acceptable.

[From NFPA 71, 1-4.5 modified]

7-5.4 Where the operation of a device, circuit, control panel function, or special hazard system interface is simulated, it shall be noted on the certificate that the operation was simulated and who it was simulated by.

[New paragraph]

INSPECTION AND TESTING FORM

DATE: ______________

TIME: ______________

SERVICE ORGANIZATION

NAME: ______________

ADDRESS: ______________

REPRESENTATIVE: ______________

LICENSE NO.: ______________

TELEPHONE: ______________

PROPERTY NAME (USER)

NAME: ______________

ADDRESS: ______________

OWNER CONTRACT: ______________

TELEPHONE: ______________

MONITORING ENTITY

CONTACT: ______________

TELEPHONE: ______________

MONITORING ACCOUNT REF. NO.: ______________

APPROVING AGENCY

CONTACT: ______________

TELEPHONE: ______________

TYPE TRANSMISSION

[ ] - McCulloh
[ ] - Multiplex
[ ] - Digital
[ ] - Reverse Priority
[ ] - RF
[ ] - Other (Specify)

SERVICE

[ ] - Weekly
[ ] - Monthly
[ ] - Quarterly
[ ] - Semi-Annually
[ ] - Annually
[ ] - Other (Specify)

____

____

PANEL MANUFACTURE: ______________ MODEL NO.: ______________

CIRCUIT STYLES: ______________

NO. OF CIRCUITS: ______________

SOFTWARE REV.: ______________

LAST DATE SYSTEM HAD ANY SERVICE PERFORMED: ______________

LAST DATE THAT ANY SOFTWARE OR CONFIGURATION WAS REVISED: ______________

ALARM INITIATING DEVICES AND CIRCUIT INFORMATION

QTY OF	CIRCUIT STYLE	
______	______	MANUAL STATIONS
______	______	ION DETECTORS
______	______	PHOTO DETECTORS
______	______	DUCT DETECTORS
______	______	HEAT DETECTORS
______	______	WATERFLOW SWITCHES
______	______	SUPERVISORY SWITCHES
______	______	OTHER: (SPECIFY) ______________

Figure 7-5.1 Inspection and Testing Form.

[New figure]

ALARM INDICATING APPLIANCES AND CIRCUIT INFORMATION

QTY OF	CIRCUIT STYLE	
________	________	BELLS
________	________	HORNS
________	________	CHIMES
________	________	STROBES
________	________	SPEAKERS
________	________	OTHER: (SPECIFY) ________________
________	________	________________________

NO. OF ALARM INDICATING CIRCUITS: ____________________

ARE CIRCUITS SUPERVISED? [ ] YES [ ] NO

SUPERVISORY SIGNAL INITIATING DEVICES AND CIRCUIT INFORMATION

QTY OF	CIRCUIT STYLE	
________	________	BUILDING TEMP.
________	________	SITE WATER TEMP.
________	________	SITE WATER LEVEL
________	________	FIRE PUMP POWER
________	________	FIRE PUMP RUNNING
________	________	FIRE PUMP AUTO POSITION
________	________	FIRE PUMP OR PUMP CONTROLLER TROUBLE
________	________	FIRE PUMP RUNNING
________	________	GENERATOR IN AUTO POSITION
________	________	GENERATOR OR CONTROLLER TROUBLE
________	________	SWITCH TRANSFER
________	________	GENERATOR ENGINE RUNNING
________	________	OTHER: ________________
		________________________

SIGNALING LINE CIRCUITS

Quantity and style (See NFPA 72, Table 3-6.1) of signaling line circuits connected to system:

Quantity ________________ Style(s) ________________

SYSTEM POWER SUPPLIES

a. Primary (Main): Nominal Voltage ____________, Amps ____________

Overcurrent Protection: Type ____________, Amps ____________

Location (Panel Number): ________________________

Disconnecting Means Location: ________________________

Figure 7-5.1 Inspection and Testing Form. (cont.)

[New figure]

b. Secondary (Standby):

______________ Storage Battery: Amp-Hr. Rating ______________

Calculated capacity to operate system, in hours: ______ 24 ______ 60 ______

_______ Engine-driven generator dedicated to fire alarm system:

Location of fuel storage: ______________

TYPE BATTERY

[ ] Dry Cell

[ ] Nickel Cadmium

[ ] Sealed Lead-Acid

[ ] Lead-Acid

[ ] Other (Specify) ______________

c. Emergency or standby system used as a backup to primary power supply, instead of using a secondary power supply:

_______ Emergency system described in NFPA 70, Article 700

_______ Legally required standby described in NFPA 70, Article 701

_______ Optional standby system described in NFPA 70, Article 702, which also meets the performance requirements of Article 700 or 701.

PRIOR TO ANY TESTING

NOTIFICATIONS ARE MADE:	YES	NO	WHO	TIME
MONITORING ENTITY	[ ]	[ ]	______	______
BUILDING OCCUPANTS	[ ]	[ ]	______	______
BUILDING MANAGEMENT	[ ]	[ ]	______	______
OTHER (SPECIFY)	[ ]	[ ]	______	______
AHJ (NOTIFIED) OF ANY IMPAIRMENTS	[ ]	[ ]		

SYSTEM TESTS AND INSPECTIONS

TYPE	VISUAL	FUNCTIONAL	COMMENTS
CONTROL PANEL	[ ]	[ ]	______
INTERFACE EQ.	[ ]	[ ]	______
LAMPS/LEDS	[ ]	[ ]	______
FUSES	[ ]	[ ]	______
PRIMARY POWER SUPPLY	[ ]	[ ]	______
TROUBLE SIGNALS	[ ]	[ ]	______
DISCONNECT SWITCHES	[ ]	[ ]	______
GROUND FAULT MONITORING	[ ]	[ ]	______

SECONDARY POWER

TYPE	VISUAL	FUNCTIONAL	COMMENTS
BATTERY CONDITION	[ ]		______
LOAD VOLTAGE		[ ]	______
DISCHARGE TEST		[ ]	______
CHARGER TEST		[ ]	______
SPECIFIC GRAVITY		[ ]	______

Figure 7-5.1 Inspection and Testing Form. (cont.)

[New figure]

TRANSIENT SUPPRESSORS	[ ]		________
REMOTE ANNUNCIATORS	[ ]	[ ]	________
NOTIFICATION APPLIANCES			
AUDIBLE	[ ]	[ ]	________
VISUAL	[ ]	[ ]	________
SPEAKERS	[ ]	[ ]	________
VOICE CLARITY	[ ]		________

INITIATING AND SUPERVISORY DEVICE TESTS AND INSPECTIONS

LOC. & S/N	DEVICE TYPE	VISUAL CHECK	FUNCTIONAL TEST	FACTORY SETTING	MEAS. SETTING	PASS	FAIL
____	____	[ ]	[ ]	____	____	[ ]	[ ]
____	____	[ ]	[ ]	____	____	[ ]	[ ]
____	____	[ ]	[ ]	____	____	[ ]	[ ]
____	____	[ ]	[ ]	____	____	[ ]	[ ]
____	____	[ ]	[ ]	____	____	[ ]	[ ]
____	____	[ ]	[ ]	____	____	[ ]	[ ]

COMMENTS: ____
____
____
____

EMERGENCY COMMUNICATIONS EQUIPMENT	**VISUAL**	**FUNCTIONAL**	**COMMENTS**
PHONE SET	[ ]	[ ]	________
PHONE JACKS	[ ]	[ ]	________
OFF-HOOK INDICATOR	[ ]	[ ]	________
AMPLIFIER(S)	[ ]	[ ]	________
TONE GENERATOR(S)	[ ]	[ ]	________
CALL IN SIGNAL	[ ]	[ ]	________
SYSTEM PERFORMANCE	[ ]	[ ]	________

	VISUAL	**DEVICE OPERATION**	**SIMULATED OPERATION**
INTERFACE EQUIPMENT			
(SPECIFY) ________	[ ]	[ ]	[ ]
(SPECIFY) ________	[ ]	[ ]	[ ]
(SPECIFY) ________	[ ]	[ ]	[ ]
SPECIAL HAZARD SYSTEMS			
(SPECIFY) ________	[ ]	[ ]	[ ]
(SPECIFY) ________	[ ]	[ ]	[ ]
(SPECIFY) ________	[ ]	[ ]	[ ]

Figure 7-5.1 Inspection and Testing Form. (cont.)

[New figure]

SPECIAL PROCEDURES: ____

____

____

____

COMMENTS: ____

____

____

____

ON/OFF PREMISES MONITORING:

	YES	NO	TIME	COMMENTS
ALARM SIGNAL	[ ]	[ ]	________	________
ALARM RESTORAL	[ ]	[ ]	________	________
TROUBLE SIGNAL	[ ]	[ ]	________	________
SUPERVISORY SIGNAL	[ ]	[ ]	________	________
SUPERVISORY RESTORAL	[ ]	[ ]	________	________

NOTIFICATIONS THAT TESTING IS COMPLETE:	**YES**	**NO**	**WHO**	**TIME**
BUILDING MANAGEMENT	[ ]	[ ]	________	________
MONITORING AGENCY	[ ]	[ ]	________	________
BUILDING OCCUPANTS	[ ]	[ ]	________	________
OTHER (SPECIFY)	[ ]	[ ]	________	________

THE FOLLOWING DID NOT OPERATE CORRECTLY: ____

____

____

____

SYSTEM RESTORED TO NORMAL OPERATION: DATE ________ TIME ________

THIS TESTING WAS PERFORMED IN ACCORDANCE WITH APPLICABLE NFPA STANDARDS.

NAME OF INSPECTOR: ____

DATE: __________ TIME: __________

SIGNATURE: ____

NAME OF OWNER OR REPRESENTATIVE: ____

DATE: __________ TIME: __________

SIGNATURE: ____

Figure 7-5.1 Inspection and Testing Form. (cont.)

[New figure]

Chapter 8 Referenced Publications

8-1 The following documents or portions thereof are referenced within this code and should be considered part of the requirements of this document. The edition indicated for each reference is the current edition as of the date of the NFPA issuance of this document.

8-1.1 NFPA Publications. National Fire Protection Association, 1 Batterymarch Park, P.O. Box 9101, Quincy, MA 02269-9101.

NFPA 10, *Standard for Portable Fire Extinguishers,* 1990 edition.

NFPA 13, *Standard for the Installation of Sprinkler Systems,* 1991 edition.

NFPA 13D, *Standard for the Installation of Sprinkler Systems in One- and Two-Family Dwellings and Mobile Homes,* 1991 edition.

NFPA 13R, *Standard for the Installation of Sprinkler Systems in Residential Occupancies Up to and Including Four Stories in Height,* 1991 edition.

NFPA 20, *Standard for the Installation of Centrifugal Fire Pumps,* 1993 edition.

NFPA 25, *Standard for the Inspection, Testing, and Maintenance of Water-Based Fire Protection Systems,* 1992 edition.

NFPA 37, *Standard for the Installation and Use of Stationary Combustion Engines and Gas Turbines,* 1990 edition.

NFPA 54, *National Fuel Gas Code,* 1992 edition.

NFPA 58, *Standard for the Storage and Handling of Liquefied Petroleum Gases,* 1992 edition.

NFPA 70, *National Electrical Code,* 1993 edition.

NFPA 90A, *Standard for the Installation of Air Conditioning and Ventilating Systems,* 1993 edition.

NFPA 110, *Standard for Emergency and Standby Power Systems,* 1993 edition.

NFPA 601, *Standard on Guard Service in Fire Loss Prevention,* 1992 edition.

NFPA 780, *Lightning Protection Code,* 1992 edition.

NFPA 1221, *Standard for the Installation, Maintenance, and Use of Public Fire Service Communication Systems,* 1991 edition.

8-1.2 ANSI Publications. American National Standards Institute, 1430 Broadway, New York, NY 10036.

ANSI A-58.1-1982, *Building Code Requirements for Minimum Design Loads in Buildings and Other Structures.*

ANSI S-1.4a-1985, *Specifications for Sound Level Meters.*

ANSI S3.41-1990, *Audible Emergency Evacuation Signals.*

ANSI S12.31-1980, *Precision Methods for the Determination of Sound Power Levels of Broad Band Noise Sources in Reverberation Rooms.*

ANSI S12.32-1980, *Precision Methods for the Determination of Sound Power Levels of Discrete Frequency and Narrow Band Noise Sources in Reverberation Rooms.*

ANSI/ASME A17.1, *Safety Code for Elevators and Escalators.*

ANSI/IEEE C2, *The National Electrical Safety Code.*

ANSI/UL 217, *Single and Multiple Station Smoke Detectors, Third Edition.*

ANSI/UL 268, *Smoke Detectors for Fire Protective Signaling Systems, Second Edition.*

ANSI/UL 827-1988, *Central Stations for Watchman, Fire Alarm and Supervisory Service.*

8-1.3 EIA Publication. Electronic Industries Association, 2001 I Street NW, Washington, DC 20006.

EIA Tr 41.3, *Telephones.*

8-1.4 IES Publication. Illuminating Engineering Society of North America, 345 East 47th Street, New York, NY 10017.

IES RP-16-1987, *Nomenclature and Definitions for Illuminating Engineering.*

Appendix A Explanatory Material

This Appendix is not a part of the requirements of this NFPA document, but is included for information purposes only.

A-1-2.1 In determining the performance criteria of circuits, consult the performance and capacity tables in Chapters 3 and 4. On modifying an existing system, the system should be tested to determine the style of each circuit for the proper description and understanding of the system.

[From NFPA 72 - 1990, A-1-2.1 modified]

A-1-5.2.6(c) An engine-driven generator without standby battery supplement is not assumed to be capable of reliable power transfer within 30 seconds of a primary power loss.

[From NFPA 71, A-2-2.1.6(c)]

A-1-5.2.6.1 UPS equipment often contains an internal bypass arrangement to supply the load directly from the line. These internal bypass arrangements are a potential source of failure. UPS equipment also requires periodic maintenance. It is therefore necessary to provide a means of promptly and safely bypassing and isolating the UPS equipment from all power sources while maintaining continuity of power supply to the equipment normally supplied by the UPS.

[From NFPA 71, A-2-2.1.8]

A-1-5.2.9 Rechargeable-(Storage-)Type Batteries. The following newer types of rechargeable batteries are normally used in protected premises applications:

(a) *Vented Lead-Acid, Gelled, or Starved Electrolyte Battery.* This rechargeable-type battery is generally used in place of primary batteries in applications having a relatively high current drain or requiring extended standby capability of much lower currents. Nominal voltage of a single cell is 2 volts, and the battery is available in multiples of 2 volts (2, 4, 6, 12, etc.). Batteries should be stored according to manufacturer's recommendations.

(b) *Nickel-Cadmium Battery.* The sealed-type nickel-cadmium battery generally used in applications where the battery current drain during a power outage is low to moderate (typically up to a few hundred milliamperes) and is fairly constant. Nickel-cadmium batteries are also available in much larger capacities for other applications. The nominal voltage per cell is 1.42 volts (12.78, 25.56, etc.). Batteries in storage can be stored in any state of charge for indefinite periods. However, a battery in storage will lose capacity (will self-discharge) according to storage time and temperature. Typically, batteries stored more than 1 month will require an 8- to 14-hour charge period to restore capacity. In service, the battery should receive a continuous constant charging current sufficient to keep it fully charged (typically, the charge rate equals $^1/_{10}$ to $^1/_{20}$ of the ampere-hour rating of the battery). Because batteries are made up of individual cells connected in series, the possibility exists that during deep discharge one or more cells that may be low in capacity will reach complete discharge prior to other cells. The cells with remaining life tend to charge the depleted cells, causing a polarity reversal resulting in permanent battery damage. This condition can be determined by measuring the open cell voltage of a fully charged battery (voltage should be a minimum of 1.28 volts per cell multiplied by the number of cells). Voltage depression effect is a minor change in discharge voltage level caused by constant current charging below the system discharge rate.

In some applications of nickel-cadmium batteries (for example, battery-powered shavers) a memory characteristic also exists. Specifically, if the battery is discharged for 1 minute a day, day after day, followed by a recharge, an attempt to have it operate for 5 minutes will not result in obtaining the rated ampere-hour output. The reason for this is that the battery has developed a 1-minute discharge memory.

(c) *Sealed Lead-Acid Battery.* In a sealed lead-acid battery, the electrolyte is totally absorbed by the separators, and no venting normally occurs. Gas evolved during recharge is internally recombined, resulting in minimal loss of capacity life. A high-pressure vent, however, is provided to avoid damage under abnormal conditions. Other battery characteristics are comparable to those described under A-1-5.2.11(a).

[From NFPA 71, A-2-2.3]

A-1-5.2.9.2(d) Batteries are trickle charged if they are off-line and waiting to be put under load in the event of a loss of power.

Float-charge batteries are fully charged and connected across the output of the rectifiers to smooth the output and serve as a standby source of power in the event of a loss of line power.

[From NFPA 71, A-2-2.3.4(d)]

A-1-5.2.11 Maximum Load. The maximum normal load of a No. 6 primary battery should not be more than 2 amperes per cell. No. 6 batteries should be replaced under the following conditions:

(a) An individual primary battery cell rated 1 volt should be replaced when a test load of 1 ohm reduces the potential below 1 volt.

(b) A unit assembly of primary battery cells rated 6 volts should be replaced when a test load of 4 ohms reduces the potential of the unit below 4 volts.

[From NFPA 71, A-2-2.5]

A-1-5.4.2.1 Coded Alarm Signal Designations. The following suggested coded signal assignment for buildings having four floors and multiple basements is provided as a guide:

Location	Coded Signal
4th floor	2-4
3rd Floor	2-3
2nd Floor	2-2
1st Floor	2-1
Basement	3-1
Sub-Basement	3-2

[From NFPA 72 - 1990, A-2-4.3]

A-1-5.4.7(b) A tamper switch, low pressure switch, or other device intended to cause a supervisory signal when actuated should not be connected in series with the end-of-line supervisory device of initiating device circuits unless a distinctive signal, different from a trouble signal, is indicated.

[From NFPA 72 - 1990, A-2-4.10(b)]

A-1-5.5.1(a) This requirement does not preclude transfer to secondary supply at less than 85 percent of nominal primary voltage as long as the requirements of 1-5.2.6 are met.

[From NFPA 72 - 1990, A-2-3.1(a)]

A-1-5.5.4 Wiring and Equipment. The installation of all fire alarm system wiring should take into account the fire alarm system manufacturer's published installation instructions and the limitations of the applicable product listings or approvals.

[From NFPA 72 - 1990, A-2-1.4]

A-1-5.8.5.1 Backup amplifying and evacuation signal-generating equipment is recommended with automatic transfer upon primary equipment failure to ensure prompt restoration of service in the event of equipment failure.

A-1-7.2.1 The requirements of Chapter 7 should be used to perform the installation wiring and operational acceptance tests required when completing the certificate of compliance.

[From NFPA 72, A-2-2.2 modified]

A-1-7.2.2(a) The owner's manual and installation instructions should include the following:

(a) A detailed narrative description of the system inputs, evacuation signaling, ancillary functions, annunciation, intended sequence of operations, expansion capability, application considerations, and limitations.

(b) Operator instructions for basic system operations, including alarm acknowledgment, system reset, interpreting system output (LEDs, CRT display, and printout), operation of manual evacuation signaling and ancillary function controls, changing printer paper, etc.

(c) A detailed description of routine maintenance and testing as required and recommended and as would be provided under a maintenance contract, including testing and maintenance instructions for each type of device installed. This information should include the following:

1. A listing of the individual system components that require periodic testing and maintenance
2. Step-by-step instructions detailing the requisite testing and maintenance procedures and the intervals at which those procedures shall be performed, for each type of device installed
3. A schedule that correlates the testing and maintenance procedures required by paragraph (2) above with the listing required by paragraph (1) above.

(d) Detailed troubleshooting instructions for each trouble condition generated from the monitored field wiring, including opens, grounds, loop failures, etc. These instructions should include a list of all trouble signals annunciated by the system, a description of the condition(s) that will cause those trouble signals, and step-by-step instructions describing how to isolate those problems and correct them (or call for service, as appropriate).

(e) A service directory, including a list of names and telephone numbers for those who should be called to obtain service on the system. [From NFPA 72 - 1990, A-2-2.3(a)]

A-2 Household Fire Warning Protection.

(a) *Fire Danger in the Home.* Fire is the third leading cause of accidental death. Residential occupancies account for most fire fatalities, and most of these deaths occur at night during the sleeping hours.

Most fire injuries also occur in the home. Of the 300,000 Americans who are injured by fire every year, nearly 50,000 lie in hospitals for a period ranging from 6 weeks to 2 years. Many never resume normal lives.

The chances are that the average family will experience one serious fire every generation.

(b) *Fire Safety in the Home.* This code is intended to provide reasonable fire safety for persons in family living units. Reasonable fire safety can be produced through a three-point program:

1. Minimizing fire hazards
2. Providing a fire warning system
3. Having and practicing an escape plan.

(c) *Minimizing Life Safety Hazards.* This code cannot protect all persons at all times. For instance, the application of this code may not protect against the three traditional fire killers:

1. Smoking in bed
2. Leaving children home alone
3. Cleaning with flammable liquids such as gasoline.

But Chapter 2 can lead to reasonable safety from fire when the three items under A-2(b) are observed.

(d) *Fire Warning System.* There are two extremes of fire to which household fire warning equipment must respond. One is the rapidly developing, high heat fire. The other is the slow, smoldering fire. Either can produce smoke and toxic gases.

Household fires are especially dangerous at night when the occupants are asleep. Fires produce smoke and deadly gases that can overcome occupants while they are asleep. Further, dense smoke reduces visibility. Most fire casualties are victims of smoke and gas inhalation rather than burns. To warn against a fire, Chapter 2 requires smoke detectors in accordance with 2-2.1.1.1 and recommends heat or smoke detectors in all other major areas. (*See 2-2.1.1.1.*)

(e) *Family Escape Plan.* There often may be very little time between detection of a fire and the time it becomes deadly. This interval may be as little as 1 or 2 minutes. Thus, this code requires detection means to give a family some advance warning of the development of conditions that will become dangerous to life within a short period of time. Such warning, however, may be wasted unless the family has planned in advance for rapid exit from their residence. Therefore, in addition to the fire warning system, this code requires exit plan information to be furnished.

Planning and practicing for fire conditions with focus on rapid exit from the residence are important. Drills should be held so that all family members know what to do. Each person should plan for the possibility that exit out of the bedroom window may be necessary. An exit out of the residence without requiring the opening of a bedroom door is essential.

(f) *Special Provisions for the Disabled.* For special circumstances where life safety of some occupant(s) depends upon prompt rescue by others, the fire warning system should include means of prompt, automatic notification to those who are to be depended upon for rescue.

[From NFPA 74 - 1989, Appendix C]

A-2-1.1 Chapter 2 does not attempt to cover all equipment, methods, and requirements that may be necessary or advantageous for the protection of lives and property from fire.

This is what is known as a "minimum code" and it provides a number of requirements related to household fire warning equipment that are deemed to be the practical and necessary minimum for average conditions at the present state-of-the-art.

[From NFPA 74 - 1989, A-1-1]

A-2-2.1.1 Experience has shown that all hostile fires in family living units generate smoke to a greater or lesser degree. The same statement can be made with respect to heat buildup from fires. But the results of full-scale experiments conducted over the past several years in the U.S., using typical fires in family living units, indicate that detectable quantities of smoke precede detectable levels of heat in nearly all cases. In addition, slowly developing, smoldering fires may produce smoke and toxic gases without a significant increase in the room's temperature. Again, the results of experiments indicate that detectable quantities of smoke precede the development of hazardous atmospheres in nearly all cases.

For the above reasons, the required protection in this code utilizes smoke detectors as the primary life safety equipment that provides a reasonable level of protection against fire.

Of course, it is possible to install a lesser number of detectors than required in this code. It may be argued that the installation of only one fire detector, be it a smoke or heat detector, offers some life-saving potential. While this is true, it is the opinion of the committee that developed Chapter 2 that the smoke detector requirements as stated in 2-2.1.1 are the minimum that should be considered.

The installation of additional detectors of either the smoke or heat type should result in a higher degree of protection. Adding detectors to rooms that are normally closed off from the required detectors will increase the escape time because the fire need not build to a higher level needed to force smoke out of the closed room to the required detector. As a consequence, it is recommended that the householder consider the installation of additional fire protection devices. But it should be understood that Chapter 2 does not require additional detectors over and above those called for in 2-2.1.1.

A-2-2.2 At times, depending upon conditions, the audibility of detection devices may be seriously impaired to occupants within the bedroom area. For instance, there may be a noisy window air conditioner or room humidifier that may generate an ambient noise level of 55 dBA or higher. The detection devices' alarms must be able to penetrate through the closed doors and be heard over the bedroom's noise levels with sufficient intensity to awaken sleeping occupants therein. Test data indicate that detection devices having sound pressure ratings of 85 dBA of 10 ft (3 m) and installed outside the bedrooms can produce about 15 dBA over ambient noise levels of 55 dBA in the bedrooms. This should be sufficient to awaken the average sleeping person.

Detectors located remote from the bedroom area may not be loud enough to awaken the average person. In such cases, it is recommended that detectors be interconnected in such a way that the operation of the remote detector will cause an alarm of sufficient intensity to penetrate the bedrooms. The interconnection may be accomplished by the installation of a fire detection system, by the wiring together of multiple station alarm devices, or by the use of line carrier or radio frequency transmitters/receivers.

[From NFPA 74 - 1989, A-2-2]

A-2-2.2.2 The use of the distinctive three-pulse temporal pattern fire alarm evacuation signal required by 3-7.2(a) had previously been recommended for this purpose by this code since 1979. It has since been adopted as both an American National Standard (ANSI S3.41, *Audible Emergency Evacuation Signal*) and an International Standard (ISO 8201, *Audible Emergency Evacuation Signal*).

Copies of both of these standards are available from the Standards Secretariat, Acoustical Society of America, 335 East 45th Street, New York, NY 10017-3483. Telephone 212-661-9404 ext. 562.

The standard fire alarm evacuation signal is a three-pulse temporal pattern using any appropriate sound. The pattern consists of an "on" phase (a) lasting 0.5 second ± 10 percent followed by an "off" phase (b) lasting 0.5 second ± 10 percent, for three successive "on" periods, which is then followed by an "off" phase (c) lasting 1.5 seconds ± 10 percent. [*See Figures A-2-2.2.2(a) and (b).*] The signal should be repeated for a period appropriate for the purposes of evacuation of the building, but for not less than 180 seconds. A single-stroke bell or chime sounded at "on" intervals lasting 1 second ± 10 percent, with a 2-second ± 10 percent "off" interval after each third "on" stroke, is acceptable. [*See Figure A-2-2.2.2(c).*]

The minimum repetition time may be manually interrupted.

[New paragraphs]

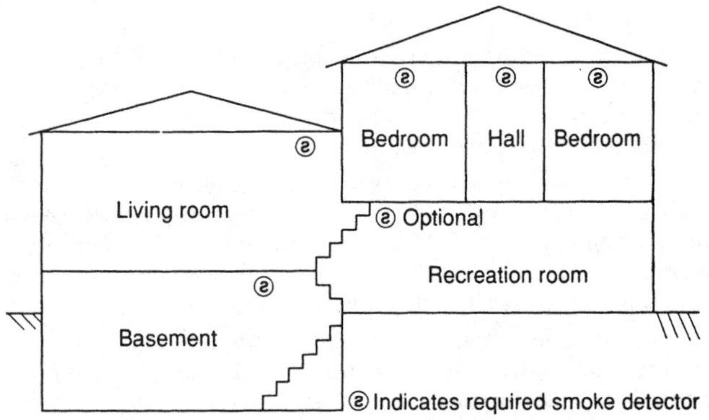

Figure A-2-2.1.1.2 Split level arrangement. Smoke detectors are required where shown. Smoke detectors are optional if door is not provided between living and recreation rooms.

[From NFPA 74 - 1989, A-2-1.1]

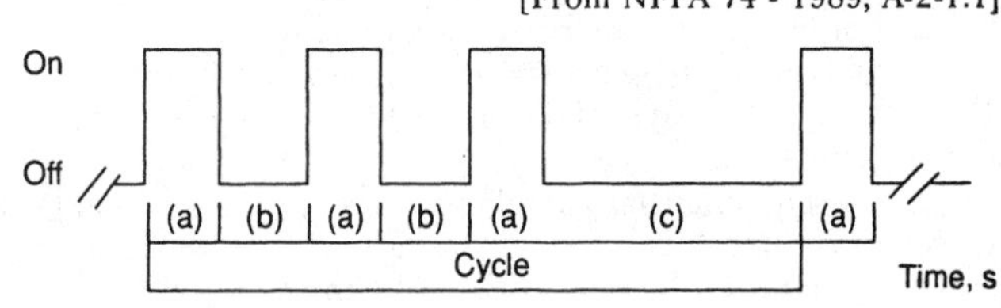

Figure A-2-2.2.2(a) Temporal pattern parameters.

[From NFPA 72 - 1990, Figure A-2-4.10(a)(1)]

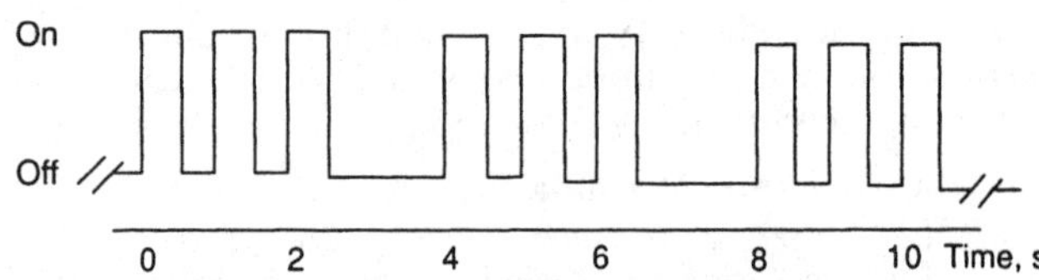

Figure A-2-2.2.2(b) Temporal pattern imposed on signaling appliances that emit a continuous signal while energized.

[From NFPA 72 - 1990, Figure A-2-4.10(a)(2)]

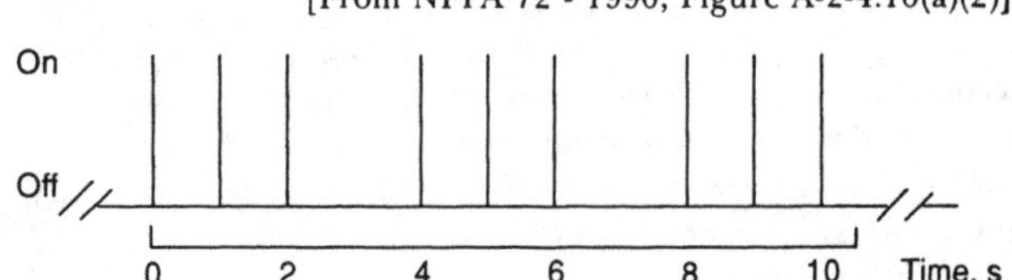

Figure A-2-2.2.2(c) Temporal pattern imposed on a single stroke bell or chime.

[From NFPA 72 - 1990, Figure A-2-4.10(a)(3)]

A-2-4.3 The linear space rating is the maximum allowable distance between heat detectors. The linear space rating is also a measure of their response time to a standard test fire when tested at the same distance. The higher the rating, the faster the response time. This code recognizes only those heat detectors with ratings of 50 ft (15 m) or more.

[From NFPA 74 - 1989, A-4-3]

A-2-4.3.1 A heat detector with a temperature rating somewhat in excess of the highest normally expected ambient temperature is specified in order to avoid the possibility of premature operation of the heat detector to nonfire conditions.

Some areas or rooms of the family living unit can experience ambient temperatures considerably higher than in the normally occupied living spaces. Examples are unfinished attics, the space near hot air registers, and some furnace rooms. This fact should be considered in the selection of the appropriate temperature rating for fixed temperature heat detectors to be installed in these areas or rooms.

[From NFPA 74 - 1989, A-4-3.1]

A-2-5.1.2.1 One of the common problems associated with residential smoke detectors is the unwanted alarms that are usually triggered by products of combustion from cooking, smoking, or other household particulates. While an alarm for such a condition would be anticipated and tolerated by the occupant of a family living unit through routine living experience, the alarm would not be acceptable if it also sounded alarms in other family living units or in common use spaces. Unwanted alarms from cooking are a very common occurrence, and inspection authorities should be aware of the ramifications that could result if the coverage is extended beyond the limits of the family living unit.

[From NFPA 74 - 1989, A-5-1.2.1]

A-2-5.2 One of the most critical factors of any fire alarm system is the location of the fire detecting devices. This appendix is not a technical study. It is an attempt to state some fundamentals on detector location. For simplicity, only those types of detectors recognized by Chapter 2, i.e., smoke and heat detectors, will be discussed. In addition, special problems requiring engineering judgment, such as locations in attics and in rooms with high ceilings, will not be covered.

[From NFPA 74 - 1989, B-1.1]

A-2-5.2.1 Smoke Detection.

(a) *Where to Locate the Required Smoke Detectors in Existing Construction.* The major threat from fire in a family living unit is at night when everyone is asleep. The principal threat to persons in sleeping areas comes from fires in the remainder of the unit; therefore, smoke detector(s) are best located between the bedroom areas and the rest of the unit. In units with only one bedroom area on one floor, the smoke detector should be located as shown in Figure A-2-5.2.1(a).

In family living units with more than one bedroom area or with bedrooms on more than one floor, more than one smoke detector will be needed, as shown in Figure A-2.5.2.1(b).

In addition to smoke detectors outside of the sleeping areas, Chapter 2 requires the installation of a smoke detector on each additional story of the family living unit, including the basement. These installations are shown in Figure A-2-5.2.1(c). The living area smoke detector should be installed in the living room and/or near the stairway to the upper level. The basement smoke detector should be installed in close proximity to the stairway leading to the floor above. If installed on an open-joisted ceiling, the detector should be placed on the bottom of the joists. The detector should be positioned relative to the stairway so as to intercept smoke coming from a fire in the basement before the smoke enters the stairway.

[From NFPA 74 - 1989, B-2]

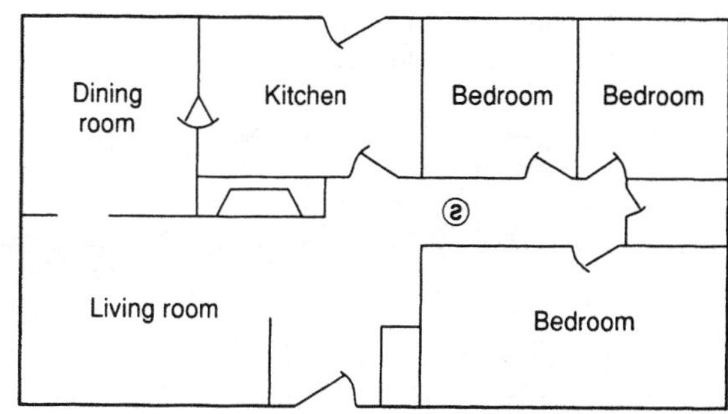

Figure A-2-5.2.1(a) A smoke detector should be located between the sleeping area and the rest of the family living unit.

[From NFPA 74, Figure B-2.1.1]

(b) *Where to Locate the Required Smoke Detectors in New Construction.* All of the smoke detectors specified in (a) for existing construction are required, and, in addition, a smoke detector is required in each bedroom.

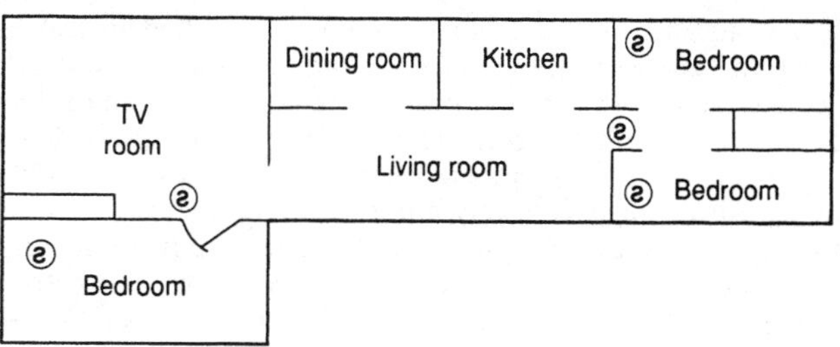

Figure A-2-5.2.1(b) In family living units with more than one sleeping area, a smoke detector should be provided to protect each sleeping area in addition to detectors required in bedrooms.

[From NFPA 74, Figure B-2.1.2]

(c) *Are More Smoke Detectors Desirable?* The required number of smoke detectors may not provide reliable early warning protection for those areas separated by a door from the areas protected by the required smoke detectors. For this reason, it is recommended that the householder consider the use of additional smoke detectors for those areas for increased protection. The additional areas include: basement, bedrooms, dining room, furnace room, utility room, and hallways not protected by the required smoke detectors. The installation of smoke detectors in kitchens, attics (finished or unfinished), or in garages is not normally recommended, as these locations occasionally experience conditions that may result in improper operation.

A-2-5.2.1.6 Smoke Detector Mounting — Dead Air Space. The smoke from a fire generally rises to the ceiling, spreads out across the ceiling surface, and begins to bank down from the ceiling. The corner where the ceiling and

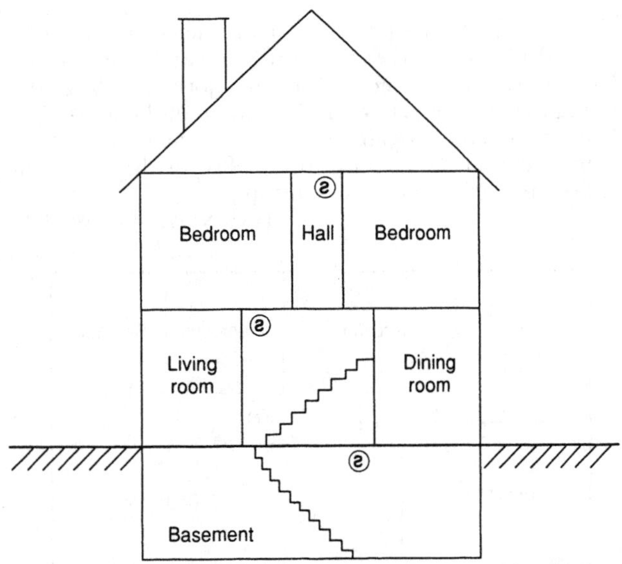

Figure A-2-5.2.1(c) A smoke detector should be located on each story.
[From NFPA 74, Figure B-2.1.3]

wall meet is an air space into which the smoke may have difficulty penetrating. In most fires, this dead air space measures about 4 in. (0.1 m) along the ceiling from the corner and about 4 in. (0.1 m) down the wall as shown in Figure A-2-5.2.2(b). Detectors should not be placed in this dead air space.

[From NFPA 74 - 1989, B-2]

Smoke and heat detectors should be installed in those locations recommended by the manufacturer, except in those cases where the space above the ceiling is open to the outside and little or no insulation is present over the ceiling. Such cases result in the ceiling being excessively cold in the winter or excessively hot in the summer. Where the ceiling is significantly different in temperature from the air space below, smoke and heat has difficulty reaching the ceiling and a detector that may be placed there. In this situation, placement of the detector on a side wall, with the top 4 in. to 12 in. (0.1 m to 0.3 m) from the ceiling, is preferred.

The situation described above for uninsulated or poorly insulated ceilings may also exist, but to a lesser extent, with outside walls. While the recommendation is to place the smoke detector on a side wall, if the side wall is an exterior wall with little or no insulation, then an interior wall should be selected. It should be recognized that the condition of inadequately insulated ceilings and walls can exist in multifamily housing (apartments), single-family housing, and mobile homes.

In those family living units employing radiant heating in the ceiling, the wall location is the preferred location. Radiant heating in the ceiling can create a hot-air, boundary layer along the ceiling surface, which can seriously restrict the movement of smoke and heat to a ceiling-mounted detector.

[From NFPA 74 - 1989, A-5-2.1.6]

A-2-5.2.2 Heat Detection.

(a) *General.* While Chapter 2 does not require heat detectors as part of the basic protection scheme, it is recommended that the householder consider the use of additional heat detectors for the same reasons presented under A-2-5.2.1(c). The additional areas lending themselves to protection with heat detectors are: kitchen, dining room, attic (finished or unfinished), furnace room, utility room, basement, and integral or attached garage. For bedrooms, the installation of a smoke detector is preferable to the installation of a heat detector for protection of the occupants from fires in their bedrooms.

(b) *Heat Detector Mounting — Dead Air Space.* Heat from a fire rises to the ceiling, spreads out across the ceiling surface, and begins to bank down from the ceiling. The corner where the ceiling and the wall meet is an air space into which heat has difficulty in penetrating. In most fires, this dead air space measures about 4 in. (0.1 m) along the ceiling from the corner and 4 in. (0.1 m) down the wall as shown in Figure A-2-5.2.2(b). Heat detectors should not be placed in this dead air space.

The placement of the detector is critical if maximum speed of fire detection is desired. Thus, a logical location for a detector is the center of the ceiling. At this location, the detector is closest to all areas of the room.

If the detector cannot be located in the center of the ceiling, an off-center location may be used on the ceiling.

The next logical location for mounting detectors is on the side wall. Any detector mounted on the side wall should be located as near as possible to the ceiling. A detector mounted on the side wall should have the top of the detector between 4 in. and 12 in. (0.1 m and 0.3 m) from the ceiling.

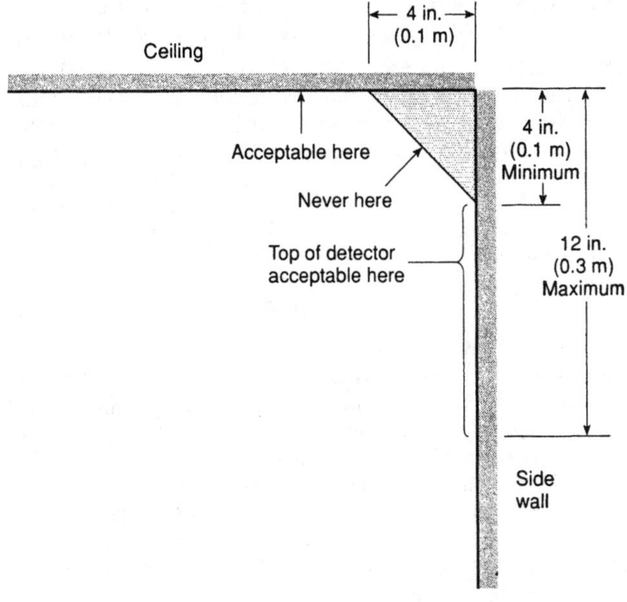

NOTE: Measurements shown are to the closest edge of the detector.
Figure A-2-5.2.2(b) Example of proper mounting for detectors.
[From NFPA 74, Figure B-3.2.1]

(c) *The Spacing of Detectors.* In a room too large for protection by a single detector, several detectors should be used. It is important that they be properly located so all parts of the room are covered. For further information on the spacing of detectors see Chapter 5.

(d) *When the Distance Between Detectors Should Be Further Reduced.* The distance between detectors is based on data obtained from the spread of heat across a smooth ceiling. If the ceiling is not smooth, then the placement of the detector will have to be tailored to the situation.

For instance, with open wood joists heat travels freely down the joist channels so that the maximum distance between detectors [50 ft (15 m)] can be used. Heat, however, has trouble spreading across the joists, so the distance in this direction should be one-half the distance allowed between detectors, as shown in Figure A-2-5.2.2(d), and the distance to the wall is reduced to $12^1/_2$ ft (3.8 m). Since $^1/_2 \times$ 50 ft (15 m) is 25 ft (7.6 m), the distance between detectors across open wood joists should not exceed 25 ft (7.6 m), as shown in Figure A-2-5.2.2(d), and the distance to the wall is reduced [$^1/_2 \times$ 25 ft (7.6 m)] to 12.5 ft (3.8 m). Paragraph 2-5.2.2.4 requires that detectors be mounted on the bottom of the joists and not up in joist channels.

Walls, partitions, doorways, ceiling beams, and open joists interrupt the normal flow of heat, thus creating new areas to be protected.

[From NFPA 74 - 1989, B-3]

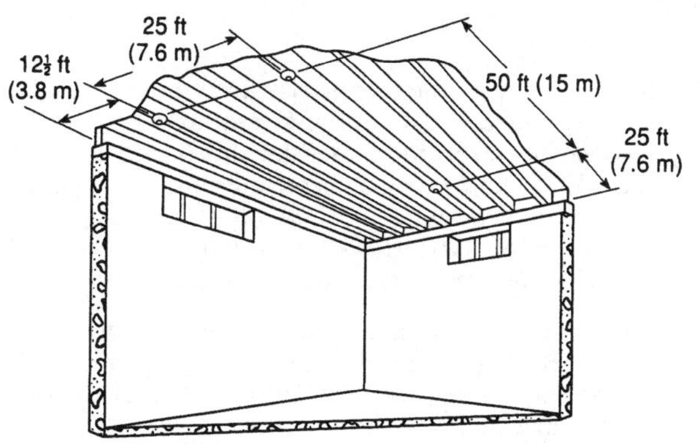

Figure A-2-5.2.2(d) Open joists, attics, and extra high ceilings are some of the areas that require special knowledge for installation.

[From NFPA 74, Figure B-3.4.2]

A-2-5.2.2.3 The same comments apply here as under A-2-5.2.1.6.

[From NFPA 74 - 1989, A-5-2.2.3]

A-2-5.2.2.5 In addition to the special requirements for heat detectors installed on ceilings with exposed joists, reduced spacing may also be required due to other structural characteristics of the protected area, possible drafts, or other conditions that may affect detector operation.

[From NFPA 74 - 1989, A-5-2.2.5]

A-2-6.1 Good fire protection requires that the equipment be periodically maintained. If the householder is unable to perform the required maintenance, a maintenance agreement should be considered.

[From NFPA 74 - 1989, A-6-1]

A-2-6.2 It is a good practice to establish a specific schedule for these tests.

[From NFPA 74 - 1989, A-6-2]

A-3-2.4 This requirement is intended to limit damage to a fire alarm system, resulting from a fire, to the area in which the fire occurs. The concern is maintaining the operability of the system in areas beyond, but threatened by, the fire.

Conformance to this requirement may entail that:

(a) Where common risers or trunk circuits are used:

1. Separately routed, redundant risers or trunk circuits be provided, arranged so that one or more circuit faults on one riser or trunk circuit causes the system to automatically switch over to its associated, alternate circuit without loss of function. This capability should permit full system operation with a damaged or severed riser or trunk circuit.

2. Primary and alternate conductors for redundant circuits be separated by 2-hour fire resistive construction.

(b) Where multiple individual circuits are routed in a common riser, conduit, raceway, cable, bundle of conductors, or other arrangement resulting in close physical proximity and resultant susceptibility to common misfortune, such circuits be Class A, capable of full operation over a single open or single ground fault.

(c) Where Class A circuits are required, that they be installed so that the supply and return conductors are routed separately. Supply and return risers should be separated by at least 2-hour rated fire construction.

[New paragraphs]

A-3-4.1 Class A and Class B circuit designations have been added to this edition of the code because they are still preferred by some specifiers and authorities having jurisdiction to the style designations introduced into the code in the late 1970s. The committee had discontinued the use of the Class A and Class B designations because, with the introduction of signaling line circuits, they were no longer adequate for describing the required performance of new technology systems under all fault conditions.

Class A circuits are considered more reliable than Class B circuits because they remain fully operational during the occurrence of a single open or a single ground fault,while Class B circuits only remain operational up to the location of an open fault. However, neither Class A nor Class B circuits remain operational during a wire-to-wire short.

For both Class A and Class B initiating device circuits, a wire-to-wire short was permitted to cause an alarm on the system on the rationale that a wire-to-wire short was the result of a double fault (e.g., both circuit conductors have to become grounded), while the code only considered the consequences of single faults. For many applications, an alarm caused by a wire-to-wire short is unacceptable and being limited to a simple Class A designation was not adequate. Introducing the style designation made it possible to specify the exact performance required during a variety of possible fault conditions.

A more serious problem existed for signaling line circuits. Though a Class A signaling line circuit remains fully operational during the occurrence of a single open or single ground fault, a wire-to-wire short disables the entire circuit. The risk of such a catastrophic failure was not acceptable to many system designers, users, and authorities having jurisdiction. Here again, introducing the style designation made it possible to specify either full system operation during a wire-to-wire short (Style 7), or performance in between that of a Style 7 and a minimum function Class A circuit (Style 2).

As revised, the specifier now can simply specify a circuit as either Class A or Class B where system performance during wire-to-wire shorts is of no concern, or by the appropriate style designation where the system performance during a wire-to-wire short and other multiple fault conditions is of concern.

A-3-4.2 Where installed within the protected premises, the integrity and reliability of the interconnecting signaling paths (circuits) are influenced by the following:

(a) The transmission media utilized

(b) The length of the circuit conductors

(c) The total building area covered by and the quantity of initiating devices and notification appliances connected to a single circuit

(d) The nature of the hazard present within the protected premises

(e) The functional requirements of the system necessary to provide the level of protection desired by the system.

A-3-5.1 and A-3-6.1 Using Tables 3-5.1 and 3-6.1:

(a) Determine whether the initiating devices are:

1. Directly connected to the initiating device circuit

2. Directly connected to a signaling line circuit interface on a signaling line circuit

3. Directly connected to an initiating device circuit, which in turn is connected to a signaling line circuit interface on a signaling line circuit.

(b) Determine the style of signaling performance required. The columns marked A through Eα in Table 3-5.1, and 0.5 through 7α in Table 3-6.1 are arranged in ascending order of performance and capacities.

(c) Upon determining the style of the system, the charts singularly or together will specify the maximum number of devices, equipment, premises, and buildings allowed to be incorporated into an actual protected premises installation.

(d) In contrast, where the number of devices, equipment, premises, and buildings (in addition to signaling ability) in an installation is known, a required system style can be determined.

(e) The prime purpose of the tables is to enable identification of minimum performance for styles of initiating device circuits and signaling line circuits. It is not the intention that the styles be construed as grades. That is, a Style 3 system is not better than a Style 2, or vice versa. In fact, a particular style may better provide adequate and reliable signaling for an installation than a more complex style number. The quantities tabulated under each style do, unfortunately, tend to imply that one style is better than the one to its left. The increased quantities for the higher style numbers are based on the ability to signal an alarm during an abnormal condition in addition to signaling the same abnormal condition.

(f) The tables allow users, designers, manufacturers, and the authority having jurisdiction to identify minimum performance of present and future systems by determining the trouble and alarm signals received at the control unit for the specified abnormal conditions.

(g) The overall system reliability is considered to be equal from style to style when the capacities are at the maximum allowed.

(h) Upon determining the style of the system, the tables indicate the maximum number of devices, equipment, protected buildings, etc., allowed to be incorporated into an actual installation for a protected premises fire alarm system.

(i) The number of automatic fire detectors connected to an initiating device circuit is limited by good engineering practice. If a large number of detectors are connected to one initiating device circuit covering a widespread area, pinpointing the source of alarm becomes difficult and time consuming.

On certain types of detectors, a trouble signal results from faults in the detector. Where this occurs with a large number of detectors on an initiating device circuit, locating the faulty detector also becomes difficult and time consuming.

[From NFPA 72 - 1990, A-2-6.2 and A-2-7.2 modified]

A-3-7.2(a) The use of the distinctive three-pulse temporal pattern fire alarm evacuation signal required by 3-7.2(a) had previously been recommended for this purpose by this code since 1979. It has since been adopted as both an American National Standard (ANSI S3.41, *Audible Emergency Evacuation Signal*) and an International Standard (ISO 8201, *Audible Emergency Evacuation Signal*).

Copies of both of these standards are available from the Standards Secretariat, Acoustical Society of America, 335 East 45th Street, New York, NY 10017-3483. Telephone 212-661-9404 ext. 562.

The standard fire alarm evacuation signal is a three-pulse temporal pattern using any appropriate sound. The pattern consists of an "on" phase (a) lasting 0.5 second ± 10 percent followed by an "off" phase (b) lasting 0.5 second ± 10 percent, for three successive "on" periods, which is then followed by an "off" phase (c) lasting 1.5 seconds ± 10 percent. [*See Figures A-3-7.2(a)(1) and (2).*] The signal should be repeated for a period appropriate for the purposes of evacuation of the building, but for not less than 180 seconds. A single-stroke bell or chime sounded at "on" intervals lasting 1 second ± 10 percent, with a 2-second ± 10 percent "off" interval after each third "on" stroke, is acceptable. [*See Figure A-3-7.2(a)(3).*]

The minimum repetition time may be manually interrupted.

[New paragraphs]

A-3-8.2.3 The alarm verification feature should not be used as a substitute for proper detector location/applications or regular system maintenance. Alarm verification features are intended to reduce the frequency of false alarms caused by transient conditions. They are not intended to compensate for design errors or lack of maintenance.

A-3-8.3.4 The bypass means is intended to enable automatic or manual day/night/weekend operation.

[From NFPA 72 - 1990, A-3-3.6.5]

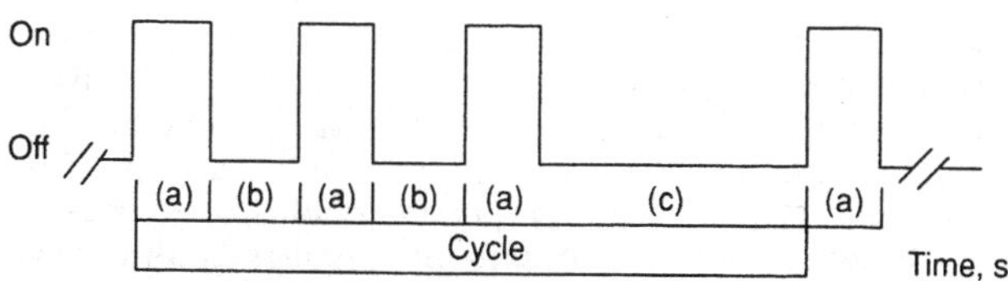

Figure A-3-7.2(a)(1) Temporal pattern parameters.
[From NFPA 72 - 1990, Figure A-2-4.10(a)(1)]

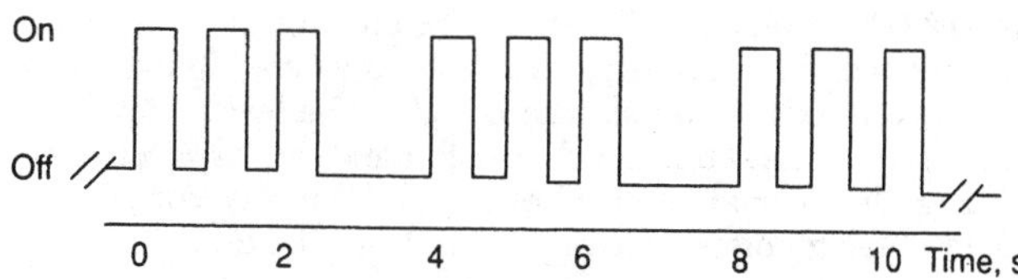

Figure A-3-7.2(a)(2) Temporal pattern imposed on signaling appliances that emit a continuous signal while energized.
[From NFPA 72 - 1990, Figure A-2-4.10(a)(2)]

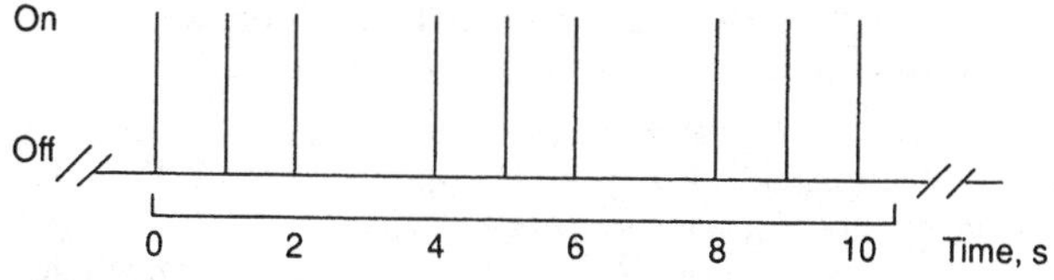

Figure A-3-7.2(a)(3) Temporal pattern imposed on a single stroke bell or chime.
[From NFPA 72 - 1990, Figure A-2-4.10(a)(3)]

A-3-8.4 Embossed plastic tape, pencil, ink, crayon, etc., should not be considered a permanently attached placard.
[From NFPA 72 - 1990, A-3-3.7]

A-3-8.7.2 Supervisory systems are not intended to provide indication of design, installation, or functional defects in the supervised systems or system components and are not a substitute for regular testing of those systems in accordance with the applicable standard.

Supervised conditions should include but not be limited to:

(a) Control valves $1^1/_2$ in. (38.1 mm) or larger

(b) Pressure:
- Dry pipe system air
- Pressure tank air
- Preaction system supervisory air
- Steam for flooding systems
- Public water

(c) Water tanks:
- Level
- Temperature

(d) Building temperature (including valve closet, fire pump house, etc.)

(e) Fire pumps:
- Electric:
  - Running (alarm or supervisory)
  - Power failure
  - Phase reversal
- Engine-driven:
  - Running (alarm or supervisory)
  - Failure to start
  - Controller off "automatic"
  - Trouble (low oil, high temperature, overspeed, etc.)
- Steam turbine:
  - Running (alarm or supervisory)
  - Steam pressure
  - Steam control valves

(f) Fire suppression systems appropriate to the system employed.

[New paragraphs]

A-3-8.11.2 Sealing or locking such a valve in the open position or removing the handle from the valve does not meet the intent of this requirement.

A-3-8.14.1 The provisions of this section apply to the types of equipment used in common for fire alarm systems (such as fire alarm, sprinkler supervisory, or guard's tour service) and for other systems (such as burglar alarm or coded paging systems) and to methods of circuit wiring common to both types of systems.
[From NFPA 72 - 1990, A-3-4.3.2]

A-3-8.15.1 Dedicated fire alarm system control units are required for elevator recall by 3-8.15.1 in order that the elevator recall systems be monitored for integrity and have primary and secondary power meeting the requirements of this code.

The control unit used for this purpose should be located in an area that is normally occupied and should have audible and visible indicators to annunciate supervisory (elevator recall) and trouble conditions; however, no form of general occupant notification or evacuation signal is required or intended by 3-8.15.1.

[New paragraph]

A-3-8.15.4 It is recommended that the installation be in accordance with the following figures. Use Figure A-3-8.15.4(a) when the elevator is installed at the same time as the building fire alarm system. Use Figure A-3-8.15.4(b) when the elevator is installed after the building fire alarm system.
[From NFPA 72 - 1990, A-3-7.3.5(a) and (b)]

A-3-8.16.1 A lower response time index is intended to provide detector response prior to the sprinkler, since a lower temperature rating alone may not provide earlier response. The listed spacing rating of the heat detector should be 25 ft (7.6 m) or greater.

A-3-8.16.3 Care should be taken to ensure that elevator power will not be interrupted due to water pressure surges in the sprinkler system.

A-3-10.6 Automatic fire suppression systems referred to in 3-10.6 include, but are not limited to, preaction and deluge sprinkler systems, carbon dioxide systems, halon systems, and dry chemical systems.

[New paragraphs]

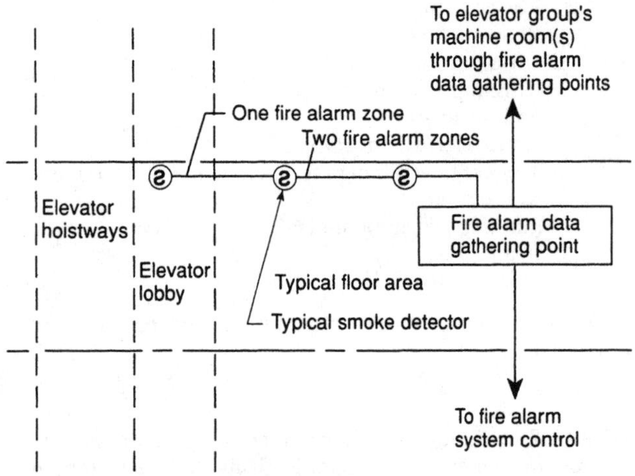

Figure A-3-8.15.4(a) Elevator zone — elevator and fire alarm system installed at same time.

[From NFPA 72 - 1990, Figure A-3-7.3.5(a)]

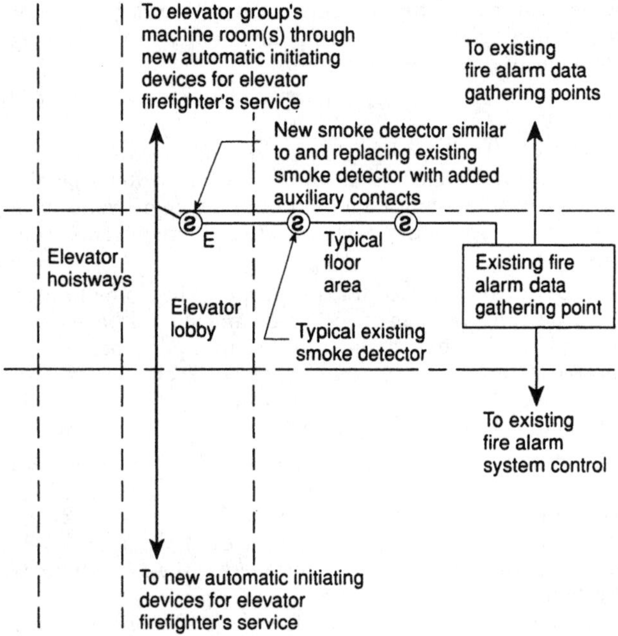

Figure A-3-8.15.4(b) Elevator zone — elevator installed after fire alarm system.

[From NFPA 72 - 1990, Figure A-3-7.3.5(b)]

A-3-11 This code contemplates field installations interconnecting two or more listed control units, possibly from different manufacturers, which together fulfill the requirements of this code.

Such an arrangement should preserve the reliability, adequacy, and integrity of all alarm, supervisory, and trouble signals and interconnecting circuits intended to be in accordance with the provisions of this code.

Where interconnected control units are in separate buildings, consideration should be given to protecting the interconnecting wiring from electrical and radio frequency interference.

[New paragraphs]

A-3-12.4.1 It is not the intention that emergency voice/alarm communications service be limited to English-speaking populations. Emergency messages should be provided in the language of the predominant building population. Where there is a possibility of isolated groups that do not speak the predominant language, multilingual messages should be provided. It is expected that small groups of transients unfamiliar with the predominant language will be picked up in the traffic flow in the time of emergency, and are not likely to be in an isolated situation.

[From NFPA 72 - 1990, A-10-4.1]

A-3-12.4.6.2 Placement of loudspeakers should give consideration to interference with normal use of emergency telephones and microphones in the area.

A-3-12.6.3 Consideration should be given to the type of fire fighters' telephone handset used in areas where high ambient noise levels exist or areas where high noise levels may exist during a fire condition. Push-to-talk handsets, handsets containing directional microphones, or handsets containing other suitable noise-canceling features may be used.

A-3-13 Special Requirements for Low Power Radio (Wireless) Systems.

(a) The term "wireless" has been replaced with "low power radio" to eliminate potential confusion with other transmission media such as optical fiber cables.

(b) Low power radio devices are required to comply with the applicable low power requirements of Title 47, *Code of Federal Regulations*, Part 15.

[New paragraphs]

A-4-2.3.1.2 Where derived channels are used, normal operating conditions of the telephone equipment will not inhibit or impair the successful transmission of signals. These normal conditions include, but are not limited to, the following:

(a) Intraoffice calls with a transponder on the originating end

(b) Intraoffice calls with a transponder on the terminating end

(c) Intraoffice calls with transponders on both ends

(d) Receipt and origination of long-distance calls

(e) Calls to announcement circuits

(f) Permanent signal receiver off-hook tone

(g) Ringing with no answer, with transponder on either the originating or the receiving end

(h) Calls to tone circuits, i.e., service tone, test tone, busy, and/or reorder

(i) Simultaneous with voice source

(j) Simultaneous with data source

(k) Tip and ring reversal

(l) Cable identification equipment.

[From NFPA 71, A-4-3.1]

A-4-2.3.1.2.3(b) Derived channel systems comprise Type 1 and Type 2 systems only.

[From NFPA 71, A-4-2.1.3(b)]

A-4-2.3.2.1.3 In order to give the DACT the ability to disconnect an incoming call to the protected premises, telephone service must be of the type that provides for timed-release disconnect. In some telephone systems (step-by-step offices), timed-release disconnect may not be provided.

[From NFPA 71, A-5-2.3, and NFPA 72, A-8-7.2.3]

A-4-2.3.2.1.5 A DACT may be programmed to originate calls to the DACR telephone lines (numbers) in any alternating sequence. The sequence can consist of single or multiple calls to one DACR telephone line (number), followed by single or multiple calls to a second DACR telephone line (number), or any combination thereof that is consistent with the minimum/maximum attempt requirements in 4-2.3.2.1.5.

[From NFPA 71, A-5-2.5 modified, and NFPA 72, A-8-7.2.5 modified]

A-4-2.3.2.1.7 Most failures of a telephone line may be detected by supervising the presence of the telephone line voltage. A loss of voltage indicates failure. Where the telephone line is also used for telephone communication, the voltage will drop when the telephone is in use. The presence of current will also indicate a normal line condition during this period.

[From NFPA 71, A-5-2.7, and NFPA 72, A-8-7.2.7]

A-4-2.3.2.1.11 Since call forwarding requires equipment at a telephone company central office that might occasionally interrupt the call forwarding feature, a signal should be initiated whereby the integrity of the forwarded telephone line (number) that is being called by DACTs is verified every 4 hours. This may be accomplished by a single DACT either in service or used solely for verification that automatically initiates and completes a transmission sequence to its associated DACR every 4 hours. A successful signal transmission sequence of any other type within the same 4-hour period should be considered sufficient to fulfill this requirement.

Call forwarding should not be confused with WATS or 800 service. The latter, differentiated by dialing the 800 prefix, is a dedicated service used mainly for its toll-free feature; all calls are pre-determined to terminate at a fixed telephone line (number) or to a dedicated line.

[New paragraphs]

A-4-2.3.2.2.2.1 The timed-release disconnect considerations as outlined in A-4-2.3.2.1.3 apply to the telephone lines (numbers) connected to a DACR at the supervising station.

It may be necessary to consult with appropriate telephone service personnel to ensure that numbers assigned to the DACR can be individually accessed even though they may be connected in rotary (a hunt group).

[From NFPA 71, A-5-3.3.1 modified, and NFPA 72, A-8-7.3.3.1 modified]

A-4-2.3.2.2.2.3 In determining system loading, Table 4-2.3.2.2.2.3 may be used, or it may be demonstrated that there is a 90 percent probability of incoming line availability. Table 4-2.3.2.2.2.3 is based on an average distribution of calls and an average connected time of 30 seconds for a message. Therefore, when it is proposed to use Table 4-2.3.2.2.2.3 to determine system loading, if any factors are disclosed that will extend DACR connect time so as to increase the average connect time, this will dictate that the alternate method of determining system loading be used. Higher (or possibly lower) loadings may be appropriate in some applications. Some factors that may increase (or decrease) the capacity of a hunt group are listed below.

(a) Shorter (or longer) average message transmission time.

(b) The use of audio monitoring (listen-in) slow scan video or other similar equipment may significantly increase the connected time for a signal and reduce effective hunt group capacity.

(c) The clustering of active burglar alarm signals may generate high peak loads at certain hours.

(d) Inappropriate scheduling of 24-hour test signals may generate excessive peak loads.

Demonstration of a 90-percent probability of incoming line availability can be accomplished by the following in-service monitoring of line activity:

1. Incoming lines are assigned to telephone hunt groups. When a DACT calls the main number of a hunt group, it can connect to any currently available line in that hunt group.

2. The receiver continuously monitors the "available" status of each line. A line is available if it is waiting for an incoming call. A line is unavailable for any of the following reasons:

(i) Currently processing a call

(ii) Line in trouble

(iii) Audio monitoring (listen-in) in progress

(iv) Any other condition that makes the line input unable to accept calls.

3. The receiver monitors the "available" status of the hunt group. A hunt group is available if any line in it is available.

4. A message is emitted by the receiver if a hunt group is unavailable for more than 1 minute in 10. This message references the hunt group and the degree of overload.

[From NFPA 71, A-5-3.3.3 modified, and NFPA 72, A-8-7.3.3.3 modified]

A-4-2.3.2.2.2.4 The verification of the 24-hour DACR line test should be done early enough in the day to allow repairs to be made by the telephone company.

[From NFPA 71, A-5-3.3.4, and NFPA 72, A-8-7.3.3.4]

A-4-2.3.3.1.2 The following suggested coded signal assignments for a building having four floors and basements are provided as a guide:

Location	Coded Signal
4th Floor	2-4
3rd Floor	2-3
2nd Floor	2-2
1st Floor	2-1
Basement	3-1
Sub-Basement	3-2

[From NFPA 71, A-6-2.1.2, and NFPA 72, A-2-4.3 modified]

A-4-2.3.3.2.5(c) Though rare, it is understood that the occurrence of a wire-to-wire short on the primary trunk facility near the supervising station could disable the transmission system without immediate detection.

[From NFPA 71, A-6-3.4.1(c) modified]

A-4-2.3.3.2.6(d)(3) Though rare, it is understood that the occurrence of a wire-to-wire short on the primary trunk facility near the supervising station could disable the transmission system without immediate detection.

[From NFPA 71, A-6-3.4.2(d)(3) modified]

A-4-2.3.3.3.5 Verify by test at time of system acceptance.

[From NFPA 71, A-6-4.3.1]

A-4-2.3.4.4 The intent of the plurality of control sites is to safeguard against damage caused by lightning and to minimize the effect of interference on the receipt of signals.

[From NFPA 71, A-7-3.1.4]

A-4-2.3.5.2 It is intended that each RAT communicate with two or more independently located RARSRs. The location of such RARSRs should be such that they do not share common facilities.

NOTE: All probability calculations required for the purposes of Chapter 4 should be made in accordance with established communications procedures, should assume the maximum channel loading parameters specified, and should further assume that 25 RATs are actively in alarm and are being received by each RARSR.

[From NFPA 71, A-8-1.2.3 modified]

A-4-2.3.7.2(b) Transmitters should be operated alternately, 16 hours on, 16 hours off.

[From NFPA 72, A-9-5.2(b)]

A-4-2.4.1 The signal information may be provided in coded form. Records may be used to interpret these codes.

[From NFPA 71, A-5-3.2.1, and NFPA 72, A-8-7.3.2.1]

A-4-2.4.2 In order to expedite repairs, it is recommended that spare modules, such as printed circuit boards, CRT displays, printers, etc., be stocked at the supervising station.

[From NFPA 71, A-4-1.2.3 modified and A-7-1.2.3 modified]

A-4-2.4.3 For all forms of transmission, the maximum time to process an alarm signal should be 90 seconds. The maximum time to process a supervisory signal should be 4 minutes. The time to process an alarm or supervisory signal is defined as that time from which a signal is received to the time that retransmission or subscriber contact is initiated.

When the level of traffic in a supervising station system reaches a magnitude such that delayed response is possible, even though the loading tables or loading formulas of this code are not exceeded, it is envisioned that it will be necessary to employ an enhanced method of processing.

For example, in a system where a single DACR instrument provided fire and burglar alarm service is connected to multiple telephone lines, it is conceivable that during certain periods of the day, fire alarm signals may be delayed by the security signaling traffic such as opening and closing signals. Such an enhanced system would be one that, upon receipt of signal would:

(a) Automatically process the signals, differentiating between those that require immediate response by supervising station personnel and those that need only be logged

(b) Automatically provide relevant subscriber information to assist supervising station personnel in their response

(c) Maintain a timed, unalterable log of the signals received and the response of supervising station personnel to such signals.

[From NFPA 71, A-1-7.1 modified]

A-4-3.2.2 There are related types of contract service that often are provided from or controlled by a central station, but that are neither anticipated by nor consistent with the provisions of 4-3.2.2. Although 4-3.2.2 does not preclude such arrangements, a central station company is expected to recognize, provide for, and preserve the reliability, adequacy, and integrity of those supervisory and alarm services intended to be in accordance with the provisions of 4-3.2.2.

[From NFPA 71, A-1-2.2 modified]

A-4-3.2.4 It is the responsibility of the prime contractor to remove all compliance markings (certification markings or placards) when a service contract goes into effect that conflicts in any way with the requirements of 4-3.2.4.

[From NFPA 71, A-1-2.4 modified]

A-4-3.2.5 The prime contractor should be aware of statutes, public agency regulations, or certifications regarding fire alarm systems that may be binding on the subscriber. The prime contractor should identify for the subscriber which agencies could be an authority having jurisdiction and, where possible, advise the subscriber of any requirements or approvals being mandated by these agencies.

The subscriber has the responsibility for notifying the prime contractor of those private organizations that are being designated as an authority having jurisdiction. The subscriber also has the responsibility to notify the prime contractor of changes in the authority having jurisdiction, such as where there is a change in insurance companies. Although the responsibility is primarily the subscriber's, the prime contractor should also take responsibility to seek out these "private" authorities having jurisdiction through the subscriber. The prime contractor has the responsibility for maintaining current records on the authority(ies) having jurisdiction for each protected premises.

The most prevalent public agency involved as an authority having jurisdiction with regard to fire alarm systems is the local fire department or fire prevention bureau. These are normally city or county agencies with statutory authority and may be required to approve fire alarm system installations. At the state level, the fire marshal's office would be most likely to serve as the public regulatory agency.

The most prevalent private organizations involved as authorities having jurisdiction are insurance companies. Others include insurance rating bureaus, insurance brokers and agents, and private consultants. It is important to note that these organizations have no statutory authority and become authorities having jurisdiction only when designated by the subscriber.

With both public and private concerns to satisfy, it is not uncommon to find multiple authorities having jurisdiction involved with a particular protected premises. It is necessary to identify all authorities having jurisdiction in order to obtain all the necessary approvals for a central station fire alarm system's installation.

[From NFPA 71, A-1-4.1 modified]

A-4-3.4.4 Two telephone lines at the central station connected to the public switched telephone network, each having its own telephone instrument connected, and two telephone numbers available at the public fire service communication center to which a central station operator may retransmit an alarm meets the intent of this requirement.

[New paragraph]

A-4-3.4.4.2 The following methods have been used successfully for supervising retransmission circuits (channels):

(a) An electrically supervised circuit (channel) provided with suitable code sending and automatic recording equipment.

(b) A supervised circuit (channel) providing suitable voice transmitting, receiving, and automatic recording equipment. The circuit may be a telephone circuit that:

1. Cannot be used for any other purpose;

2. Is provided with a two-way ring down feature for supervision between the fire department communications center and the central station;

3. Is provided with terminal equipment located on the premises at each end; and

4. Is provided with 24-hour standby power provided.

Exception: Local on-premises circuits need not be supervised.

(c) Radio facilities using transmissions over a supervised channel with supervised transmitting and receiving equipment. Circuit continuity ensured at intervals not exceeding 8 hours by any means is satisfactory.

[From NFPA 71, A-1-7.2.2 modified]

A-4-3.6.1.1(a) Use of the term "immediately" in this context is intended to mean "without unreasonable delay." Routine handling should take a maximum of 90 seconds from receipt of an alarm signal by the central station until the initiation of retransmission to the public fire service communication center.

[New paragraph]

A-4-3.6.1.3 It is anticipated that the central station will first attempt to notify designated personnel at the protected premises. When such notification cannot be made, it may be appropriate to notify law enforcement and/or the fire department. For example, if a valve supervisory signal is received where protected premises are not occupied, it may be appropriate to notify police.

[From NFPA 71, A-1-10.2.3 modified]

A-4-3.6.1.3(a) Use of the term "immediately" in this context is intended to mean "without unreasonable delay." Routine handling should take a maximum of 4 minutes from receipt of a supervisory signal by the central station until initiation of communication with person(s) designated by the subscriber.

[New paragraph]

A-4-3.6.1.4(a) Use of the term "immediately" in this context is intended to mean "without unreasonable delay." Routine handling should take a maximum of 4 minutes from receipt of a trouble signal by the central station until initiation of the investigation by telephone.

[New paragraph]

A-4-3.6.1.5(b) Use of the term "immediately" in this context is intended to mean "without unreasonable delay." Routine handling should take a maximum of 4 minutes from receipt of a trouble signal by the central station until initiation of the investigation by telephone.

[From NFPA 71, A-1-10.2.5(b) modified]

A-4-4.2.3 The following functions are in Appendix A to provide guidelines for utilizing building systems and equipment in addition to proprietary fire alarm equipment to provide life safety and property protection.

Building functions that may be initiated or controlled during a fire alarm condition include, but are not limited to, the following:

(a) Elevator operation consistent with ANSI A17.1, *Safety Code for Elevators, Dumbwaiters, Escalators, and Moving Walks*.

(b) Unlocking stairwell and exit doors. Refer to NFPA 80, *Standard for Fire Doors and Fire Windows*, and NFPA *101*, *Life Safety Code*.

(c) Release of fire and smoke dampers. Refer to NFPA 90A, *Standard for the Installation of Air Conditioning and Ventilating Systems*, and NFPA 90B, *Standard for the Installation of Warm Air Heating and Air Conditioning Systems*.

(d) Monitoring and initiating of self-contained automatic fire extinguishing systems and equipment. Refer to NFPA 11, *Standard for Low Expansion Foam and Combined Agent Systems*; NFPA 11A, *Standard for Medium- and High-Expansion Foam Systems*; NFPA 12, *Standard on Carbon Dioxide Extinguishing Systems*; NFPA 12A, *Standard on Halon 1301 Fire Extinguishing Systems*; NFPA 12B, *Standard on Halon 1211 Fire Extinguishing Systems*; NFPA 13, *Standard for the Installation of Sprinkler Systems*; NFPA 14, *Standard for the Installation of Standpipe and Hose Systems*; NFPA 15, *Standard for Water Spray Fixed Systems for Fire Protection*; and NFPA 17, *Standard for Dry Chemical Extinguishing Systems*.

(e) Lighting control necessary to provide essential illumination during fire alarm conditions. Refer to NFPA 70, *National Electrical Code*, and NFPA *101*, *Life Safety Code*.

(f) Emergency shutoff of hazardous gas.

(g) Control of building environmental heating, ventilating, and air conditioning equipment to provide smoke control. Refer to NFPA 90A, *Standard for the Installation of Air Conditioning and Ventilating Systems*.

(h) Control of process, data processing, and similar equipment as necessary during fire alarm conditions.

[From NFPA 72, A-9-1]

A-4-4.6.5 It is the intent of this code that the operator within the proprietary supervising station should have a secure means of immediately retransmitting any signal indicative of a fire to the public fire department communication center. Automatic retransmission using an approved method installed in accordance with Sections 4-3, 4-4, 4-5, 4-6, and 4-7 is no doubt the best method for proper retransmission. However, a manual means may be used, consisting of either a manual connection following the requirements of Sections 4-3, 4-5, and 4-7, or, for proprietary supervising stations serving only contiguous properties, in the form of a municipal fire alarm box installed within 50 ft (15 m) of the proprietary supervising station in accordance with Section 4-6.

[From NFPA 72, A-9-3.2]

A-4-4.6.6 No matter what type of retransmission facility is used, telephone communication between the proprietary supervising station and the fire department should be available at all times and should not depend on a switchboard operator.

[From NFPA 72, A-9-3.3]

A-4-5.3 As a minimum, the room or rooms containing the remote supervising station equipment should have a 1-hour fire rating, and the entire structure should be protected by an alarm system complying with Chapter 3.

[New paragraph]

A-4-6.4.7 Indicating Lights.

(a) Current supply for designating lamps at street boxes should preferably be secured at lamp locations from the local electric utility company.

(b) Alternating current power may be superimposed on metallic fire alarm circuits for supplying designating lamps or for control or actuation of equipment devices for fire alarm or other emergency signals, provided:

1. Voltages between any wire and ground or between one wire and any other wire of the system shall not exceed 150 volts; the total resultant current in any line circuit shall not exceed 1/4 amp.

2. Coupling capacitors, transformers, chokes, coils, etc., shall be rated for 600-volt working voltage and have a breakdown voltage of at least twice the working voltage plus 1000 volts.

3. There is not interference with fire alarm service under any conditions.

[From NFPA 1221 - 1991, A-4-1.4.1.5 modified]

A-4-6.6 If the intent is for complete coverage, then it will not be necessary to travel in excess of one block or 500 ft (150 m) to reach a box. In residential areas, it will not be necessary to travel in excess of 2 blocks or 800 ft (240 m) to reach a box.

[From NFPA 1221, 4-1.4.3.2 modified]

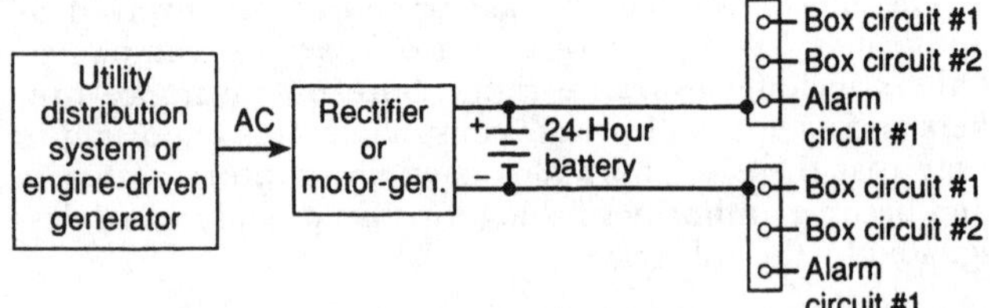

Figure A-4-6.7.1.7(a) Form 2A.
[From NFPA 1221, Figure B-4-1.5.3.1.1(a)]

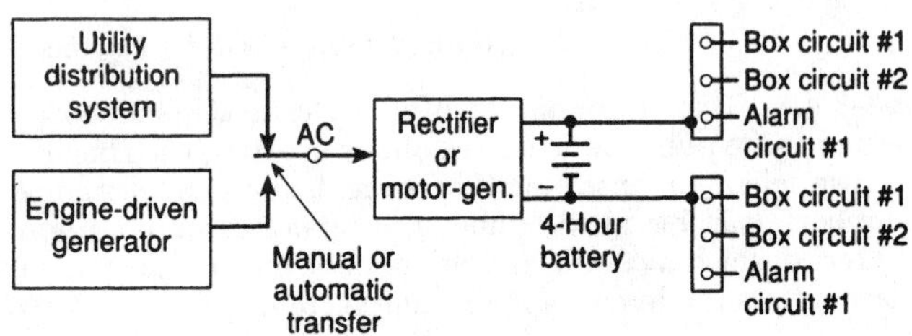

Figure A-4-6.7.1.7(b)(1) Form 2B-1.
[From NFPA 1221, Figure B-4-1.5.3.1.1(b)(1)]

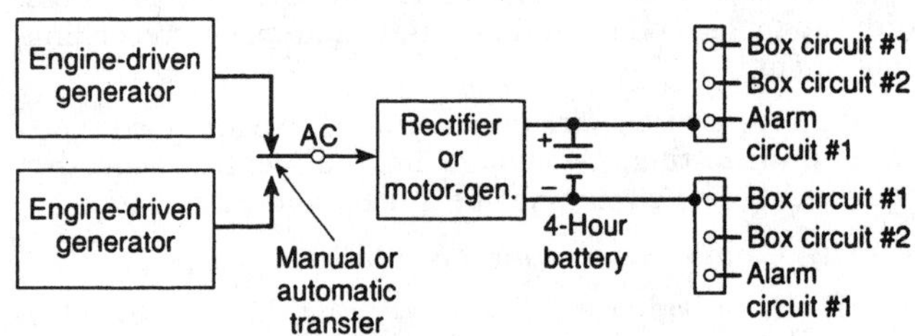

Figure A-4-6.7.1.7(b)(2) Form 2B-2.
[From NFPA 1221, Figure B-4-1.5.3.1.1(b)(2)]

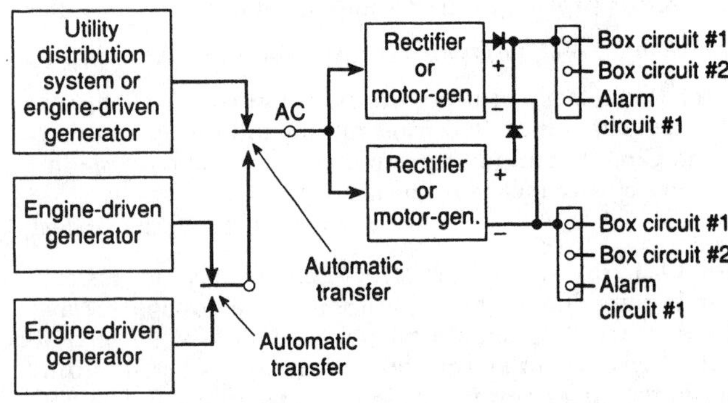

Figure A-4-6.7.1.7(c) Form 2C.
[From NFPA 1221, Figure B-4-1.5.3.1.1(c)]

A-4-6.9.1.4 All requirements for circuit protection do not apply to coded radio reporting systems. These systems do not use metallic circuits.

[New paragraph]

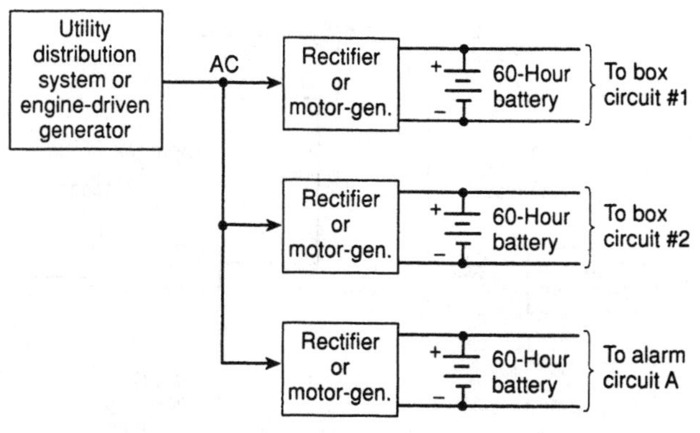

Figure A-4-6.7.1.8(a) Form 3A.
[From NFPA 1221, Figure B-4-1.5.3.1.2(a)]

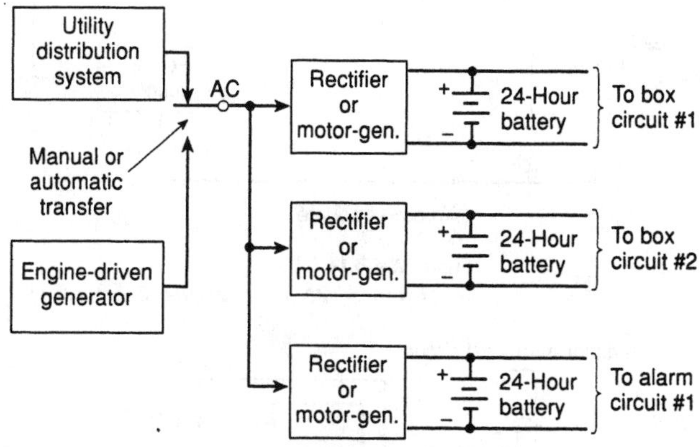

Figure A-4-6.7.1.8(b)(1) Form 3B-1.
[From NFPA 1221, Figure B-4-1.5.3.1.2(b)(1)]

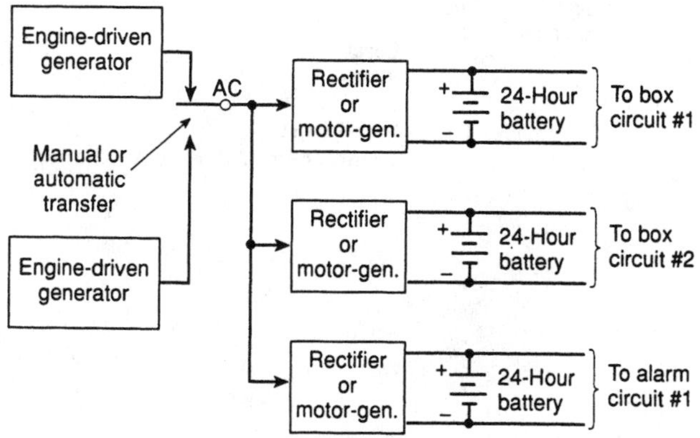

Figure A-4-6.7.1.8(b)(2) Form 3B-2.
[From NFPA 1221, Figure B-4-1.5.3.1.2(b)(2)]

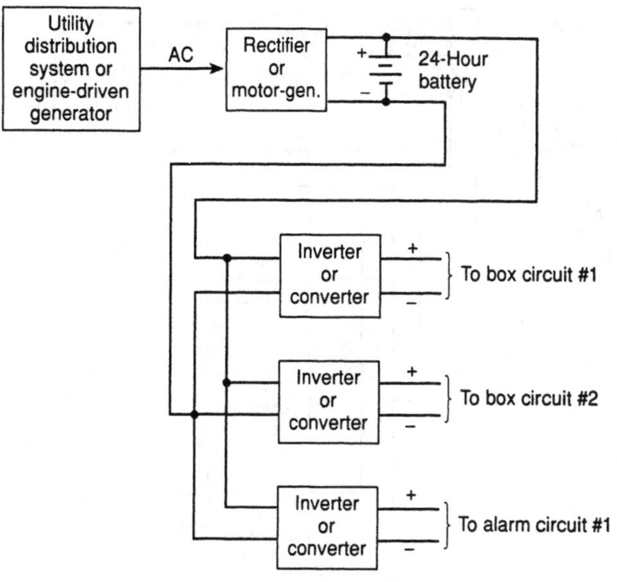

Figure A-4-6.7.1.9(a) Form 4A.
[From NFPA 1221, Figure B-4-1.5.3.1.3(a)]

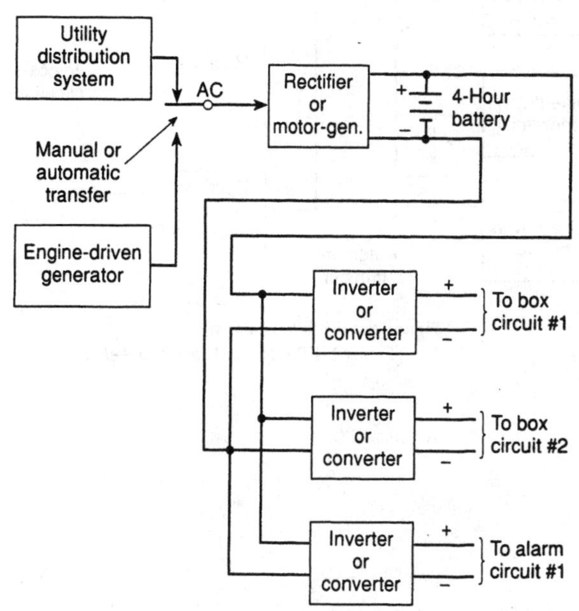

Figure A-4-6.7.1.9(b)(1) Form 4B-1.
[From NFPA 1221, Figure B-4-1.5.3.1.3(b)(1)]

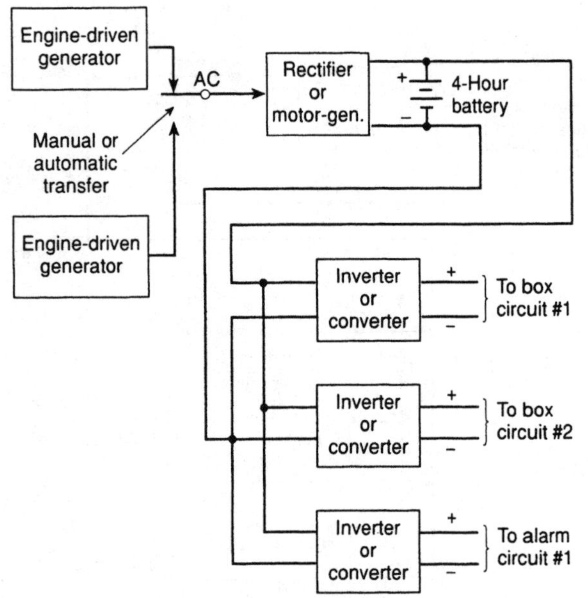

Figure A-4-6.7.1.9(b)(2) Form 4B-2.
[From NFPA 1221, Figure B-4-1.5.3.1.3(b)(2)]

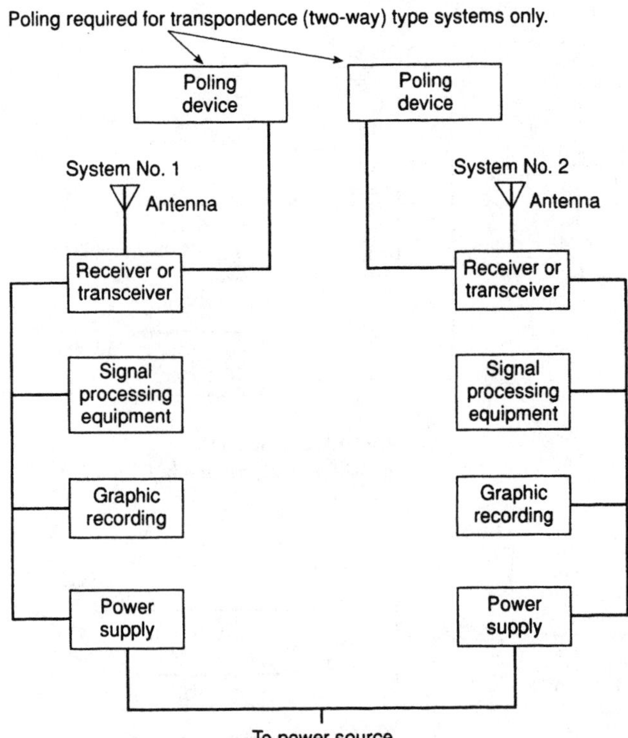

Figure A-4-6.14.3.1.1
[From NFPA 1221, Figure B-4-3.4.2.1]

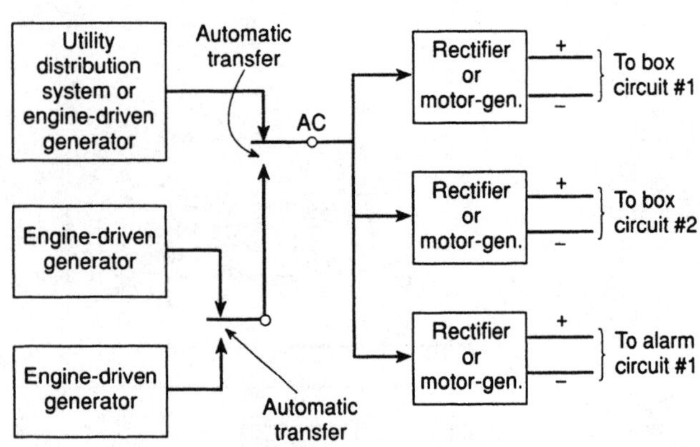

Figure A-4-6.7.1.9(c) Form 4C.
[From NFPA 1221, Figure B-4-1.5.3.1.3(c)]

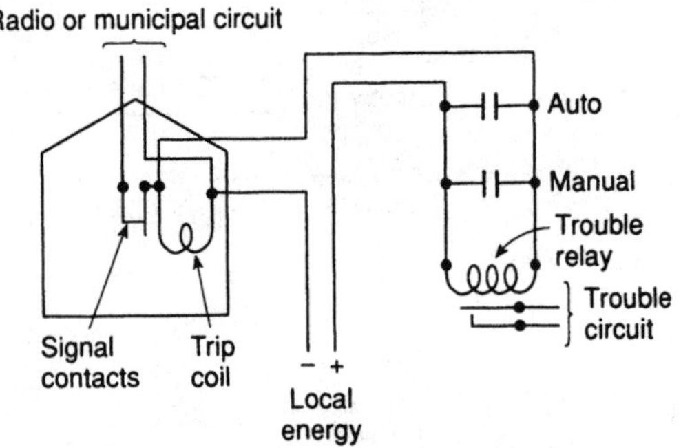

Figure A-4-7.4.1(a)(1)
[From NFPA 72, Figure A-7-3(a)(1)]

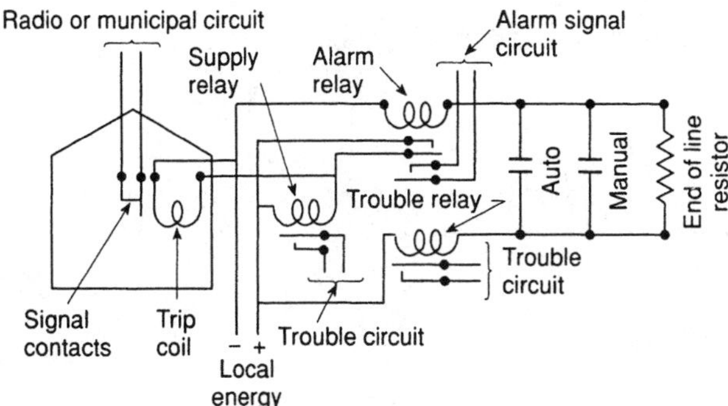

Figure A-4-7.4.1(a)(2)
[From NFPA 72, Figure A-7-3(a)(2)]

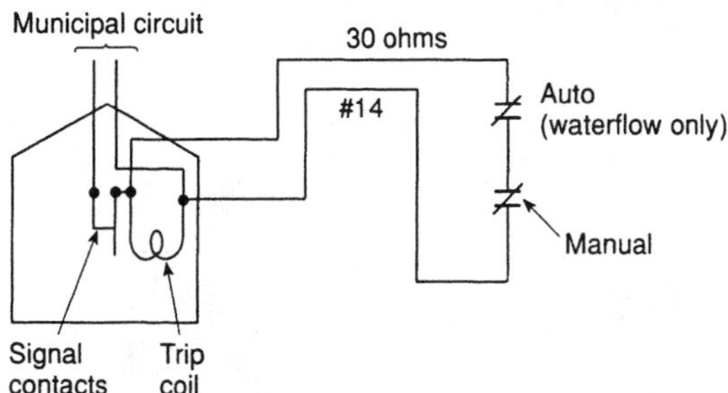

Figure A-4-7.4.1(b)(1)
[From NFPA 72, Figure A-7-3(b)(1)]

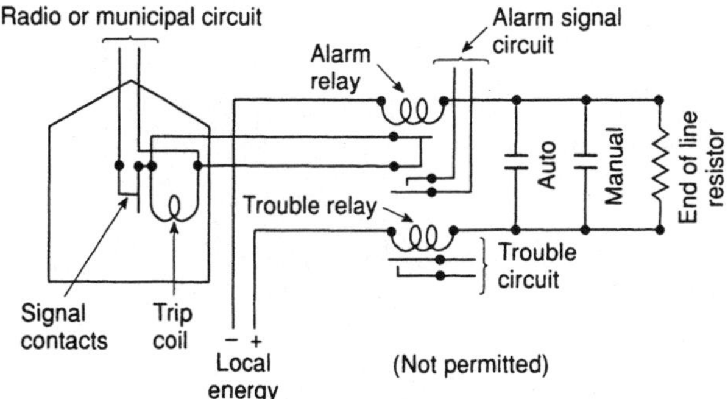

Figure A-4-7.4.1(b)(2)
[From NFPA 72, Figure A-7-3(b)(2)]

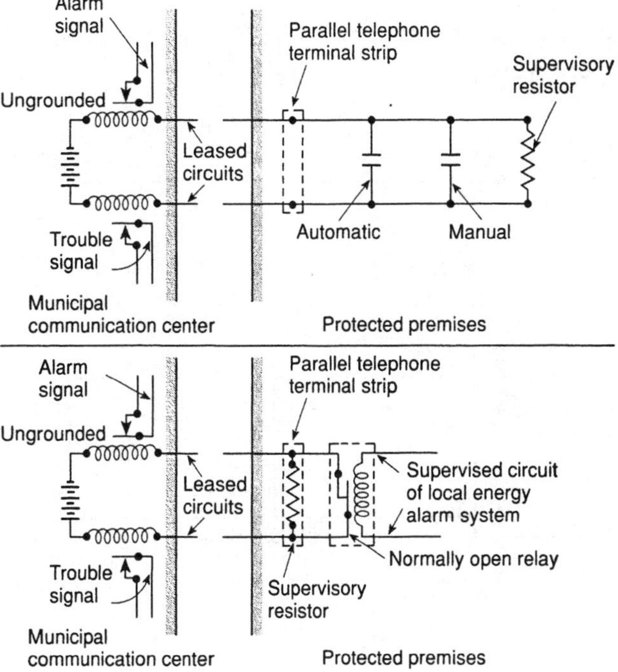

Figure A-4-7.4.1(c)
[From NFPA 72, Figure A-7-3(c)]

A-5-1.3.5 Detectors may be required under large benches, shelves, or tables, and inside cupboards or other enclosures.

[From NFPA 72E - 1990, 2-7.5]

A-5-1.4 Refer to Figures A-5-1.4(a) and (b) for proper connections of automatic fire detectors to fire alarm systems initiating device circuits and power supply circuits.

[From NFPA 72E - 1990, A-2-7.7]

A-5-2.4.2 The linear space rating is the maximum allowable distance between heat detectors. The linear space rating is also a measure of the heat detector response time to a standard test fire where tested at the same distance. The higher the rating, the faster the response time. This code recognizes only those heat detectors with ratings of 50 ft (15 m) or more.

[From NFPA 74, A-4-3]

A-5-2.6 A heat detector with a temperature rating somewhat in excess of the highest normally expected ambient temperature is specified in order to avoid the possibility of premature operation of the heat detector to nonfire conditions.

[From NFPA 74, A-4-3.1]

A-5-2.7 In addition to the special requirements for heat detectors installed on ceilings with exposed joists, reduced spacing may also be required due to other structural characteristics of the protected area, possible drafts, or other conditions that may affect detector operation.

[From NFPA 74, A-5-2.2.5]

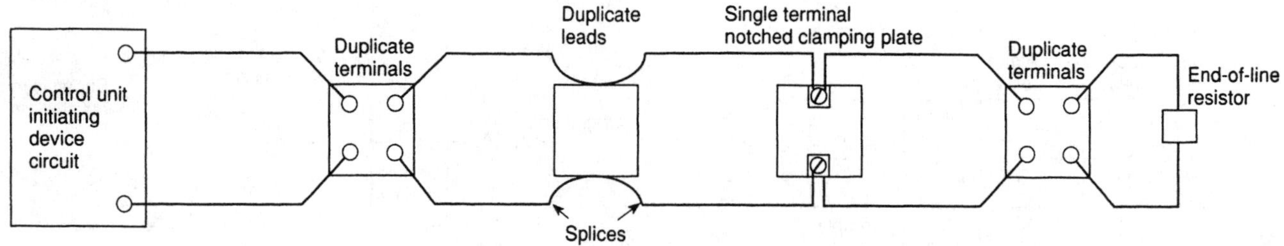

Correct wiring method – Two wire detectors

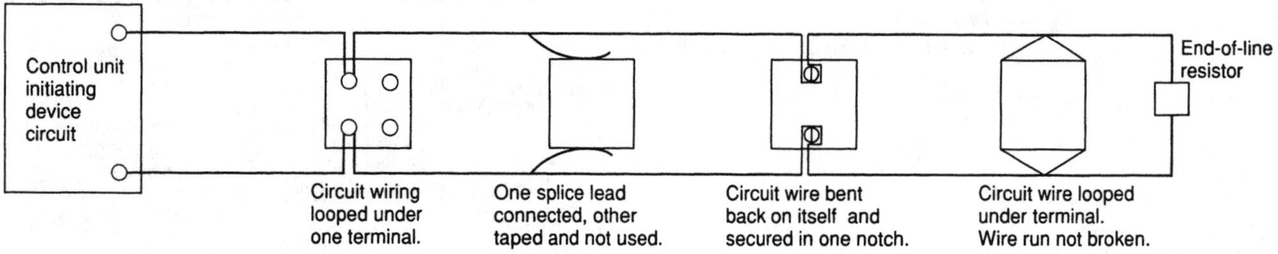

Incorrect wiring method – Two wire detectors

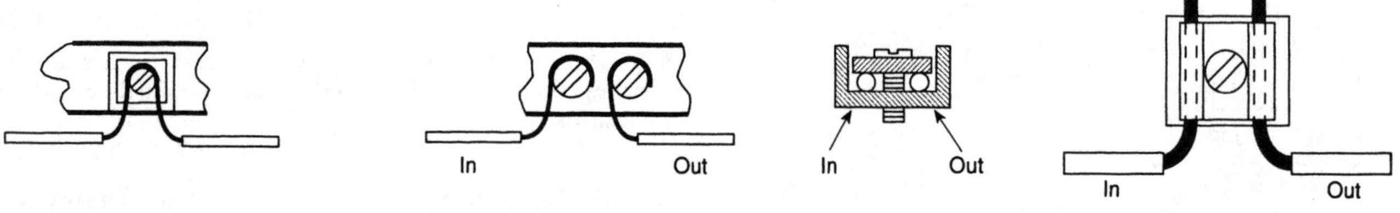

Figure A-5-1.4(a) Correct wiring methods — four-wire detectors with separate power supply.

[From NFPA 72E - 1990, A-2-7.7(a)]

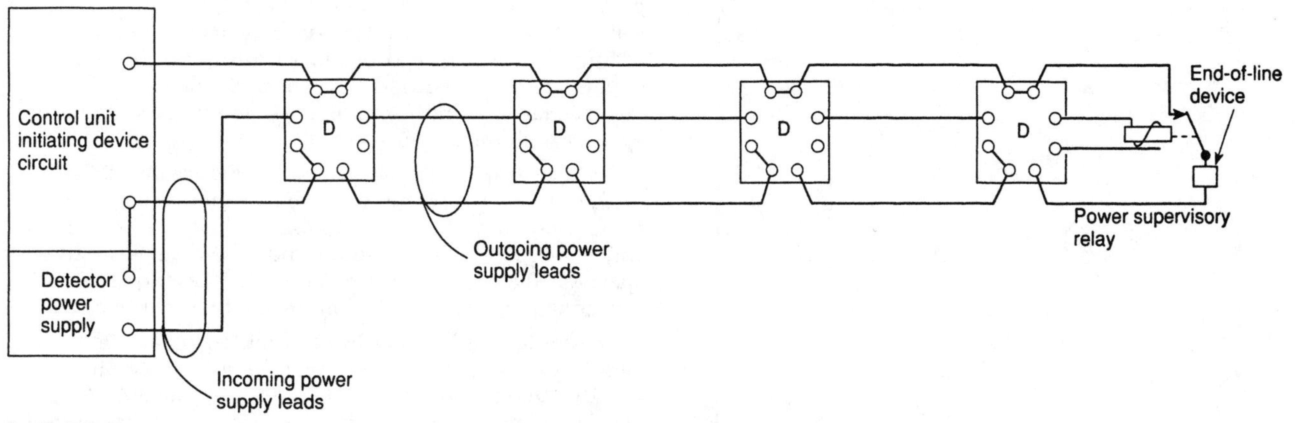

D = Detector

Illustrates 4-wire smoke detector employing a 3-wire connecting arrangement. One side of power supply is connected to one side of initiating device circuit. Wire run broken at each connection to smoke detector to provide supervision.

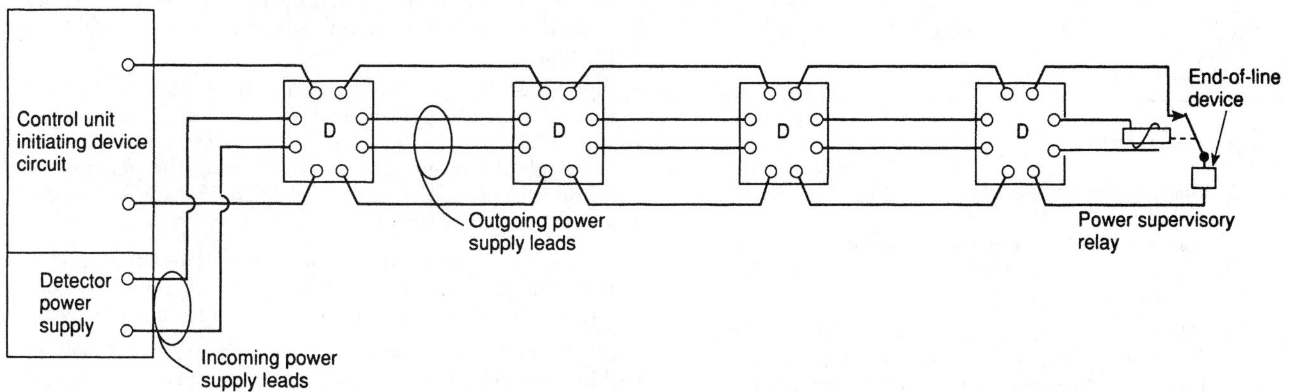

D = Detector

Illustrates 4-wire smoke detector employing a 4-wire connecting arrangement. Incoming and outgoing leads or terminals for both initiating device and power supply connections. Wire run broken at each connection to provide supervision.

Figure A-5-1.4(b)

[From NFPA 72E - 1990, Figure A-2-7.7(b)]

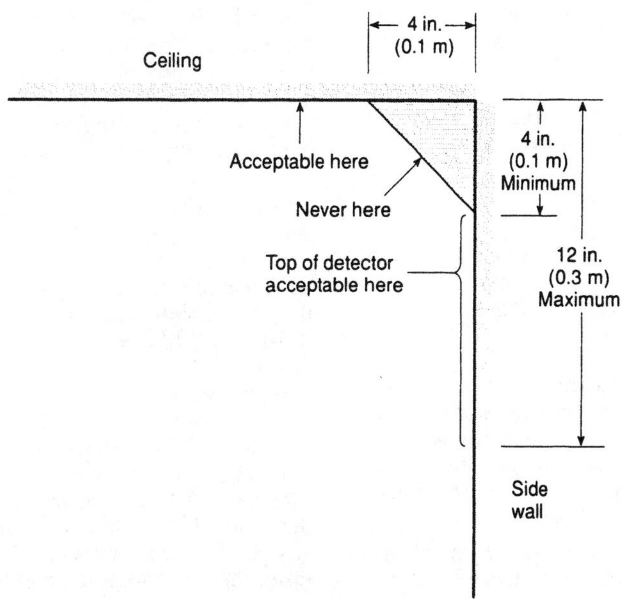

NOTE: Measurements shown are to the closest edge of the detector.

Figure A-5-2.5.1 Example of proper mounting for detectors.

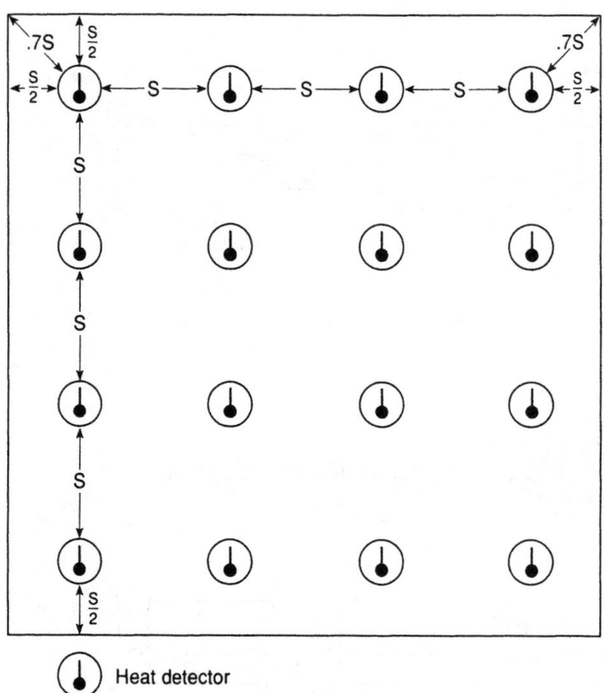

Figure A-5-2.7.1(a) Spot-type heat detectors.
[From NFPA 72E - 1990, Figure A-3-4.1]

A-5-2.7.1 Maximum linear spacings on smooth ceilings for spot-type heat detectors are determined by full-scale fire tests. These tests assume that the detectors are to be installed in a pattern of one or more squares, each side of which equals the maximum spacing as determined in the test. This is illustrated in Figure A-5-2.7.1(a). The detectors to be tested are placed at one corner of the square, which is the furthest distance it can be from the fire while still within the square. Thus the distance from the detector ("D") to the fire ("F") is always the test spacing multiplied by 0.7 and can be set up in the following tables:

Test Spacing	Maximum Test Distance from Fire to Detector (0.7 × D)
50 × 50 ft	35 ft
40 × 40 ft	28 ft
30 × 30 ft	21 ft
25 × 25 ft	17.5 ft
20 × 20 ft	14 ft
15 × 15 ft	10.5 ft

For SI Units: 1 ft = 0.305 m.

Once the correct maximum test distance has been determined, then it is valid to interchange the positions of the fire ("F") and the detector ("D"). The detector is now in the middle of the square, and what the listing actually says is that the detector is adequate to detect a fire that occurs anywhere within that square — even out to the farthest corner.

In laying out detector installations, designers speak in terms of rectangles, as building areas are generally rectangular in shape. The pattern of heat spread from a fire source, however, is not rectangular in shape. On a smooth ceiling, heat will spread out in all directions, in an ever-expanding circle. Thus, the coverage of a detector is not in fact a square, but rather a circle whose radius is the linear spacing multiplied by 0.7.

This is graphically illustrated in Figure A-5-2.7.1(b). With the detector as the center, by rotating the square, an infinite number of squares can be laid out, the corners of which will plot a circle whose radius is 0.7 times the listed spacing. The detector will cover any of these squares and, consequently, any point within the confines of the circle.

So far this explanation has considered squares and circles. In practical applications, very few areas turn out to be exactly square, and circular areas are rare indeed. Designers deal generally with rectangles of odd dimensions and corners of rooms or areas formed by wall intercepts, where spacing to one wall is less than one-half the listed spacing. To simplify the rest of this explanation, consider the use of a detector with a listed spacing of 30 ft by 30 ft (9.1 m by 9.1 m). The principles derived will be equally applicable to other types.

Figure A-5-2.7.1(c) illustrates the derivation of this concept. A detector is placed in the center of a circle with a radius of 21 ft (0.7 × 30 ft) [6.4 m (0.7 × 9.1 m)]. A series of rectangles with one dimension less than the permissible maximum of 30 ft (9.1 m) is constructed within the circle. The following conclusions can be drawn:

(a) As the smaller dimension decreases, the longer dimension can be increased beyond the linear maximum spacing of the detector with no loss in detection efficiency.

(b) A single detector will cover any area that will fit within the circle. For a rectangle, a single properly located detector will suffice if the diagonal of the rectangle does not exceed the diameter of the circle.

(c) Relative detector efficiency will actually be increased, because the area coverage in sq ft is always less than the 900 sq ft (83.6 m^2) permissible if the full 30 ft by 30 ft (9.1 m by 9.1 m) square were to be utilized. The principle illustrated here allows equal linear spacing between the detector and the fire, with no recognition for the effect of reflection from walls or partitions, which in narrow rooms or corridors will be of additional benefit. For detectors that are not centered, the longer dimension should always be used in laying out the radius of coverage.

Areas so large that they exceed the rectangular dimensions given in Figure A-5-2.7.1(c) require additional detectors. Often proper placement of detectors can be facilitated by breaking down the area into multiple rectangles of the dimensions that fit most appropriately. [*See Figure A-5-2.7.1(d).*] For example, see Figure A-5-2.7.1(c). A corridor 10 ft (3 m) wide and up to 82 ft (25 m) long can be covered with two 30-ft (9.1-m) detectors. An area 40 ft (12.2 m) wide and up to 74 ft (22.6 m) long can be covered with four detectors. Irregular areas will take more careful planning to make sure that no spot on the ceiling is more than 21 ft (6.4 m) away from a detector. These points can be determined by striking arcs from the remote corner. Where any part of the area lies beyond the circle with a radius of 0.7 times the listed spacings, additional detectors are required.

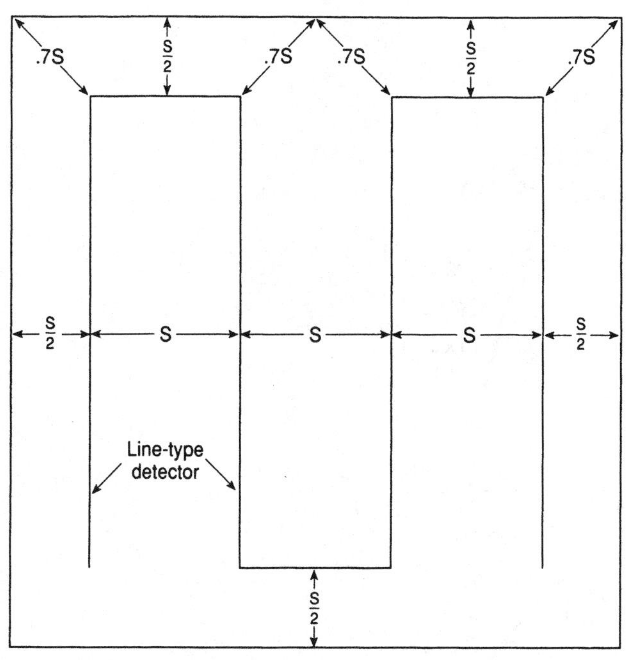

Figure A-5-2.7.1(b) Line-type detectors — spacing layouts, smooth ceiling.
[From NFPA 72E - 1990, Figure A-3-5.1]

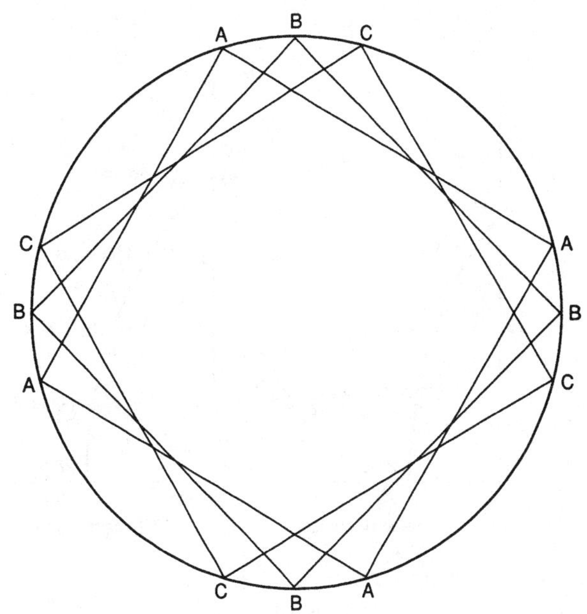

Figure A-5-2.7.1(d) A detector will cover any square laid out in the confines of a circle whose radius is 0.7 times the listed spacing.
[From NFPA 72E - 1990, A-3-5.1(b)]

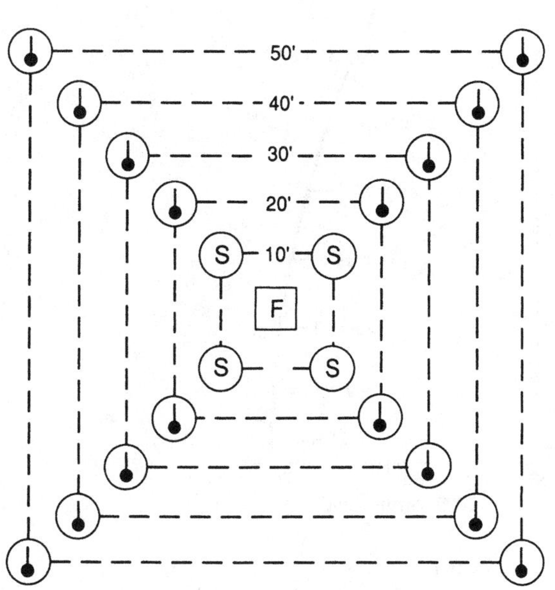

Legend

F –Test fire, denatured alcohol, 190-proof. Pan located approximately 3 ft (0.9 m) above floor.
(S) –Indicates normal sprinkler spacings on 10-ft (3-m) schedules.
–Indicates normal heat detector spacing on various spacing schedules.

For SI Units: 1 ft = 0.305 m.

Figure A-5-2.7.1(c) Fire test layout.
[From NFPA 72E - 1990, A-3-5.1(a)]

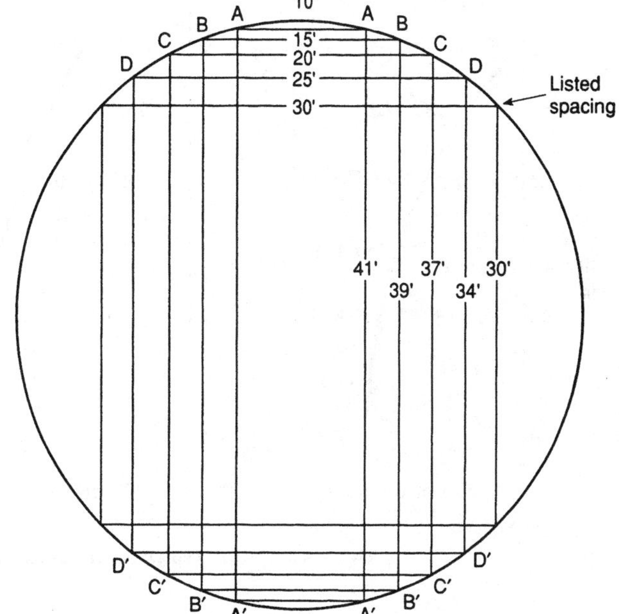

Rectangle A = 10' x 41' = 410 sq ft
B = 15' x 39' = 585 sq ft
C = 20' x 37' = 740 sq ft
D = 25' x 34' = 850 sq ft
Listed spacing = 30' x 30' = 900 sq ft

For SI Units: 1 ft = 0.305 m.

Figure A-5-2.7.1(e) Detector spacing, rectangular areas.
[From NFPA 72E - 1990, Figure A-3-5.1(c)]

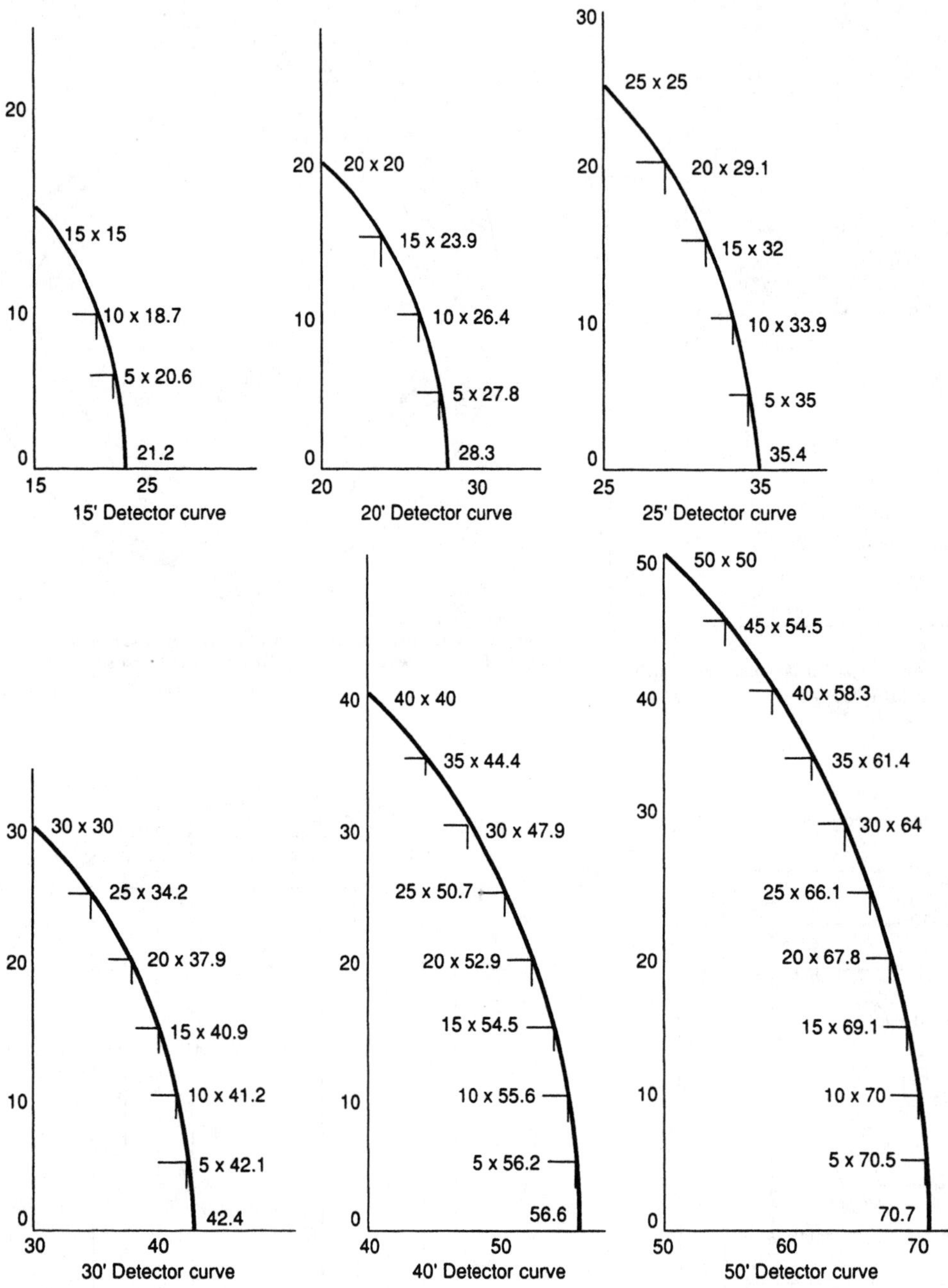

For SI Units: 1 ft = 0.305 m.

Figure A-5-2.7.1(f) Typical rectangles for detector curves of 15 - 50 ft.

[From NFPA 72E - 1990, Figure A-3-5.1(d)]

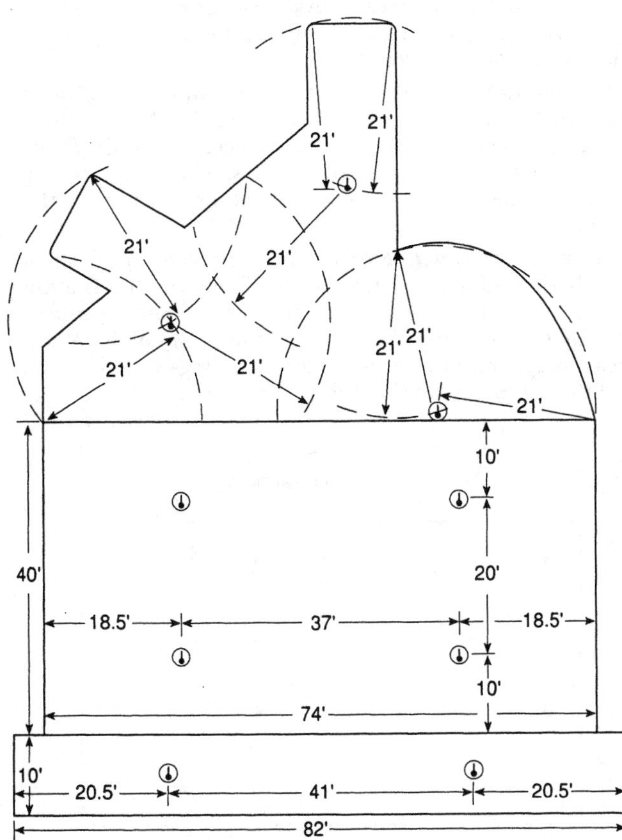

For SI Units: 1 ft = 0.305 m.

Figure A-5-2.7.1.1 Detector spacing layout, irregular areas.
[From NFPA 72E - 1990, Figure A-3-5.1.1]

A-5-2.7.1.2 Both 5-2.7.1.2 and Table 5-2.7.1.2 are constructed to provide essentially the equivalent detector performance on higher ceilings [to 30 ft (9.1 m) high)] as that which would exist with detectors on a 10-ft (3-m) ceiling.

The Fire Detection Institute Fire Test Report (*see references in Appendix C*), used as a basis for Table 5-2.7.1.2, does not include data on integration-type detectors. Pending development of such data, the manufacturer's recommendations provide guidance.

[From NFPA 72E - 1990, A-3-5.1.2]

A-5-2.7.3 Location and spacing of heat detectors should consider beam depth, ceiling height, beam spacing, and fire size.

(a) If the ratio of beam depth (D) to ceiling height (H) (D/H) is greater than 0.10 and the ratio of beam spacing (W) to ceiling height (H) (W/H) is greater than 0.40, heat detectors should be located in each beam pocket.

(b) If either the ratio of beam depth to ceiling height (D/H) is less than 0.10 or the ratio of beam spacing to ceiling height (W/H) is less than 0.40, heat detectors should be installed on the bottom of the beams.

[From NFPA 72E - 1990, A-3-5.3]

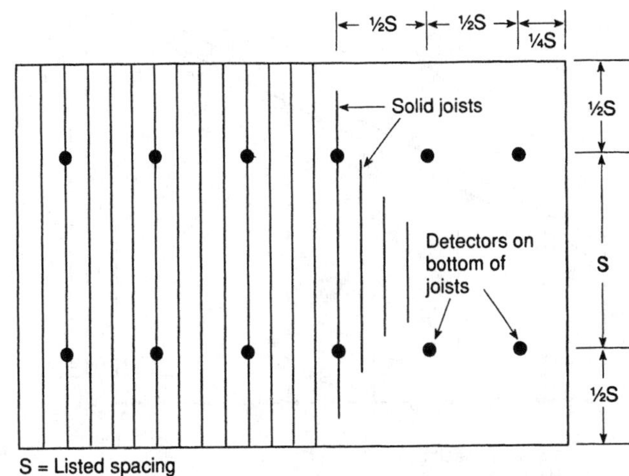

Figure A-5-2.7.2 Detector spacing layout, solid joist construction.
[From NFPA 72E - 1990, A-3-5.2]

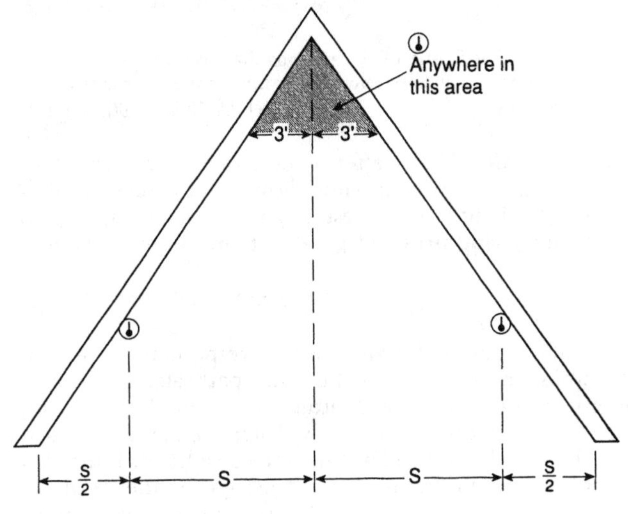

For SI Units: 1 ft = 0.305 m.

Figure A-5-2.7.4.1 Detector spacing layout, sloped ceilings (peaked type).
[From NFPA 72E - 1990, A-3-5.4.1]

A-5-3.1.1 The addition of a heat detector to a smoke detector does not enhance its performance as an early warning device.

[From NFPA 72E - 1990, A-4-1.1]

A-5-3.2 The person designing an installation should keep in mind that in order for a smoke detector to respond, the smoke must travel from the point of origin to the detector. In evaluating any particular building or location, likely fire locations should first be determined. From each of these points of origin, paths of smoke travel should be determined. Wherever practical, actual field tests should be conducted. The most desired location for smoke detectors would be the common points of intersection of smoke travel from fire locations throughout the building.

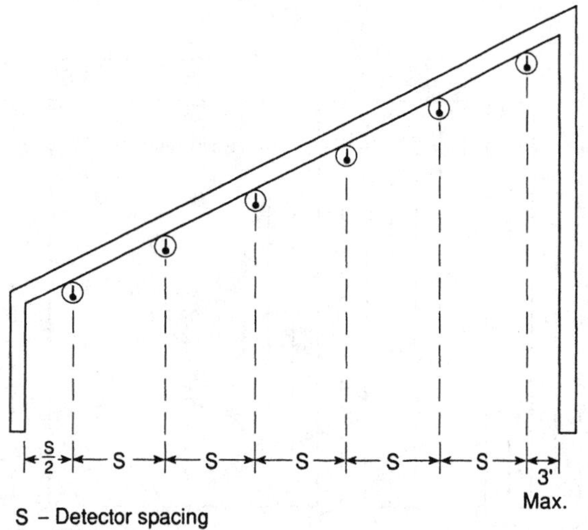

For SI Units: 1 ft = 0.305 m.

Figure A-5-2.7.4.2 Detector spacing layout, sloped ceilings (shed type).

[From NFPA 72E - 1990, A-3-5.4.2]

NOTE: This is one of the reasons that specific spacing is not assigned to smoke detectors by the testing laboratories.

[From NFPA 72E - 1990, A-4-1.3]

A-5-3.3.2 Most light-scattering detectors use a high intensity pulsed light source with silicon photodiode or phototransistor light sensors, resulting in excellent response to most smoldering fires and good response to most flaming fires.

[From NFPA 72E - 1990, A-4-2.2]

A-5-3.3.3 Projected beam detectors respond to the sum of the smoke obscuration in the beam path along its entire length between the transmitting unit and the receiving unit. A reduction in the received light initiates an alarm signal. A total and sudden loss of received light initiates a trouble signal indicating beam blockage or the need for service. Some projected beam detectors have signal-processing circuits to compensate for transient conditions and the effect of dust on sensitivity.

[From NFPA 72E - 1990, A-4-2.3]

A-5-3.5.1 For operation, all types of smoke detectors depend on smoke entering the sensing chamber or light beam. Where sufficient concentration is present, operation is obtained. Since the detectors are usually mounted on the ceiling, response time depends on the nature of the fire. A hot fire will rapidly drive the smoke up to the ceiling. A smoldering fire, such as in a sofa, produces little heat; therefore, the time for smoke to reach the detector will be increased.

[From NFPA 72E - 1990, A-4-4.1]

A-5-3.5.1.2 Stratification. Stratification of air in a room may hinder air containing smoke particles or gaseous combustion products from reaching ceiling-mounted smoke or fire-gas detectors.

Stratification occurs when air containing smoke particles or gaseous combustion products is heated by smoldering or burning material and, becoming less dense than surrounding cooler air, rises until it reaches a level at which there is no longer a difference in temperature between it and the surrounding air.

Stratification may also occur when evaporative coolers are used, because moisture introduced by these devices may condense on smoke, causing it to fall toward the floor. Therefore, to ensure rapid response, smoke detectors may need to be installed on sidewalls or at locations below the ceiling.

In installations where detection of smoldering or small fires is desired and where the possibility of stratification exists, consideration should be given to mounting a portion of the detectors below the ceiling. In high ceiling areas, projected beam-type or air sampling-type detectors at different levels should also be considered.

[From NFPA 72E - 1990, A-4-4.1.2]

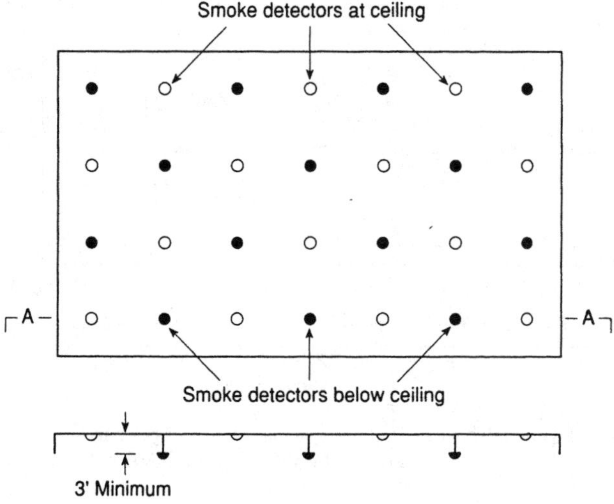

For SI Units: 1 ft = 0.305 m.

Figure A-5-3.5.1.2 Smoke detector layout accounting for stratification.

[From NFPA 72E - 1990, Figure A-4-4.1.2]

A-5-3.5.2 In high ceiling areas, such as atriums, where spot-type smoke detectors are not accessible for periodic maintenance and testing, projected beam-type or air sampling-type detectors should be considered where access can be provided.

[From NFPA 72E - 1990, A-4-4.2]

A-5-3.5.5.1.1 This will be useful in calculating locations in corridors or irregular areas. (*See A-5-2.7.1 and Figure A-5-2.7.1.1.*) For irregularly shaped areas, the spacing between detectors may be greater than the selected spacing, provided the maximum spacing from a detector to the farthest point of a sidewall or corner within its zone of protection is not greater than 0.7 times the selected spacing (0.7S). (*See Figure A-5-2.7.1.1.*)

[New paragraph]

A-5-3.5.5.2 On smooth ceilings, a spacing of not more than 60 ft (18.3 m) between projected beams and not more than one-half that spacing between a projected beam and a

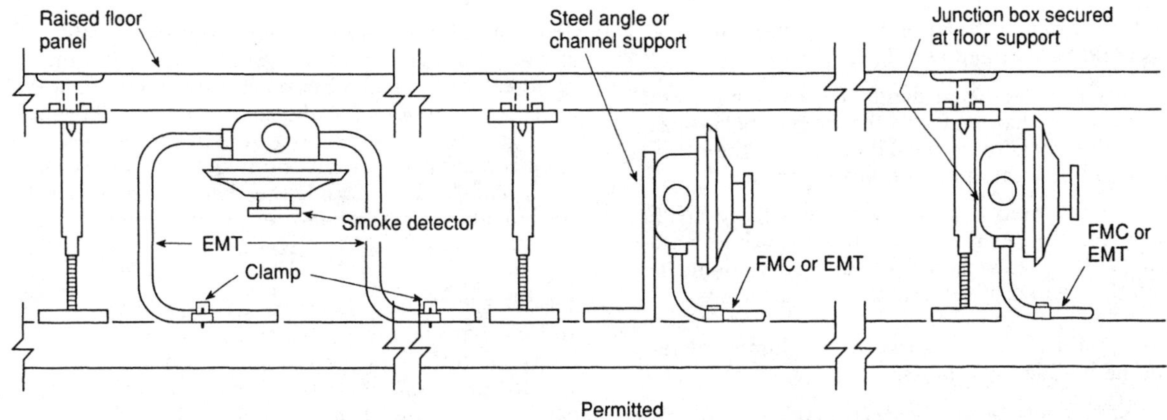

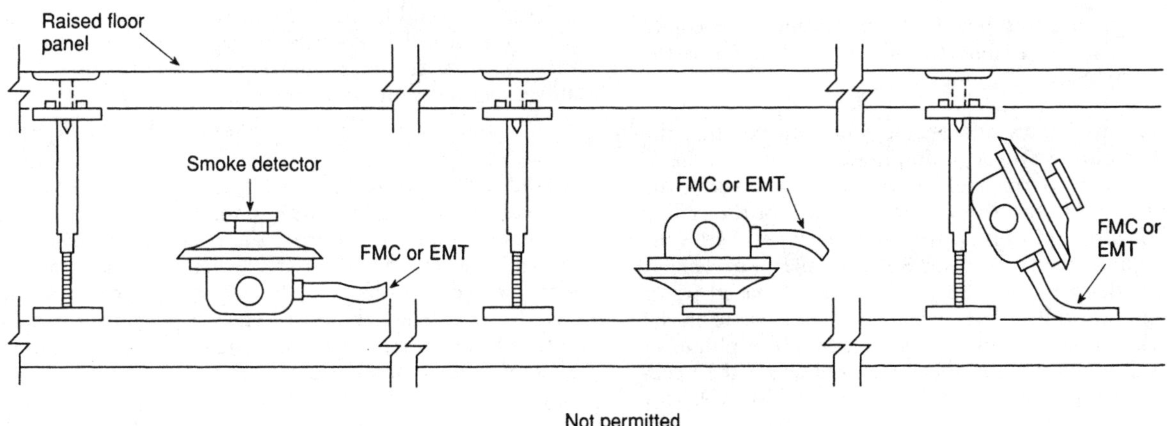

Figure A-5-3.5.2.1 Mounting installations, permitted (top) and not permitted (bottom).

[From NFPA 72E - 1990, Figure A-4-4.3.1.1]

sidewall (wall parallel to the beam travel) may be used as a guide. Other spacing may be determined depending on ceiling height, airflow characteristics, and response requirements.

In some cases, the light beam projector will be mounted on one end wall, with the light beam receiver mounted on the opposite wall. However, it is also permissible to suspend the projector and receiver from the ceiling at a distance from the end walls not exceeding one-quarter the selected spacing. For an illustration of this, see Figure A-5-3.5.5.2.

[From NFPA 72E - 1990, A-4-4.5.2]

A-5-3.5.6 Detectors are placed at reduced spacings at right angles to joists or beams in an attempt to ensure that detection time is equivalent to that which would be experienced on a flat ceiling. It takes longer for the combustion products (smoke or heat) to travel at right angles to beams or joists, because of the phenomenon wherein a plume from a relatively hot fire with significant thermal lift tends to fill the pocket between each beam or joist before moving to the next one.

Though it is true that this phenomenon may not be significant in a small smoldering fire where there is only enough thermal lift to cause stratification at the bottom of the joists, reduced spacing is still recommended to ensure that detection time is equivalent to that which would exist on a flat ceiling, even in the hotter type of fire.

[From NFPA 72E - 1990, A-4-4.6]

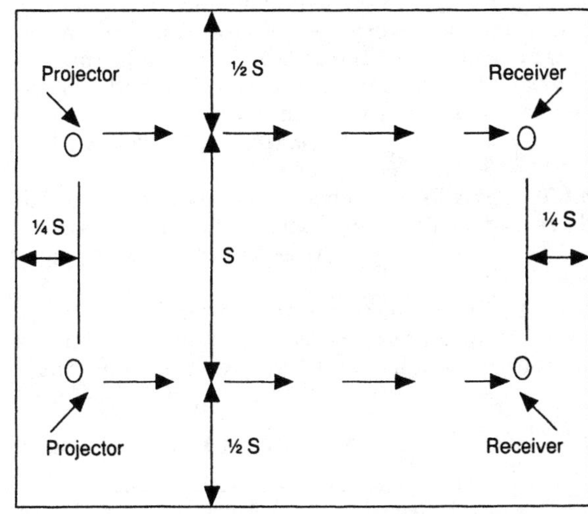

Figure A-5-3.5.5.2 Maximum distance that ceiling-suspended light projector and receiver may be positioned from end wall is ¼ selected spacing (S).

[From NFPA 72E - 1990, Figure A-4-4.5.2]

A-5-3.5.7.4 To detect flaming fires (strong plumes), detectors should be installed as follows:

(a) If the ratio of the beam depth (D) to ceiling height (H) (D/H) is greater than 0.10 and the ratio of beam spacing (W) to ceiling height (H) (W/H) is greater than 0.40, detectors should be located in each beam pocket.

(b) If either the ratio of beam depth to ceiling height (D/H) is less than 0.10 or the ratio of beam spacing to ceiling height (W/H) is less than 0.40, detectors should be installed on the bottom of the beams.

To detect smoldering fires (weak or no plumes), detectors should be installed as follows:

(a) If air mixing into beam pockets is good (e.g., air-flow parallel to long beams) and condition (a) exists as above, detector should be located in each beam pocket.

(b) If air mixing into beam pockets is limited or condition (b) exists as above, detectors should be located on the bottom of the beams.

Research on plumes and ceiling jets indicates that the radius of a plume where it impinges on the ceiling is approximately 20 percent of the ceiling height above the fire source (p. 2H) and the minimum depth of the ceiling jet (at its turning point) is approximately 10 percent of the ceiling height above the fire source (y. 0.10H). For ceilings with beams deeper than the jet depth and spaced wider than the plume width, detectors will respond faster in the beam pocket because they will be in either the plume or ceiling jet. For ceilings with beams of less depth than ceiling jet or spaced closer than the plume width, detector response will not be enhanced by placing detectors in each beam pocket, and the detectors may perform better on (for spot-type detectors) or below (for beam detectors) the bottom of the beams.

Where plumes are weak, ventilation and mixing into the beam pockets will determine detector response. Where beams are closely spaced and airflow is perpendicular to the beam, mixing into the beam pocket is limited and detectors will perform better on or below the bottom of the beams.

[From NFPA 72E - 1990, A-4-4.7.4]

A-5-3.6.1 Detectors should not be located in a direct air-flow nor closer than 3 ft (900 mm) from an air supply diffuser.

[From NFPA 72E - 1990, A-4-5.1]

A-5-3.7.1.1 Product-listing standards include tests for temporary excursions beyond normal limits. In addition to temperature, humidity, and velocity variations, smoke detectors should operate reliably under such common environmental conditions as mechanical vibration, electrical interference, and other environmental influences. Tests for these conditions are also conducted by the testing laboratories in their listing program. In those cases in which environmental conditions approach the limits shown in Table A-5-3.7.1.1, consult the detector manufacturer for additional information and recommendations.

[From NFPA 72E - 1990, A-4-6.1.1)

A-5-3.7.1.2 Smoke detectors may be affected by electrical and mechanical influences and by aerosols and particulate matter found in protected spaces. Location of detectors should be such that the influences of aerosols and particulate matter from sources such as those in Table A-5-3.7.1.2(a) are minimized. Similarly, the influences of electrical and mechanical factors shown in Table A-5-3.7.1.2(b) should be minimized. While it may not be possible to totally isolate environmental factors, an awareness of these factors during system layout and design will favorably affect detector performance.

[From NFPA 72E - 1990, A-4-6.1.2]

A-5-3.7.2.2 Airflow through holes in the rear of a smoke detector may interfere with smoke entry to the sensing chamber. Similarly, air from the conduit system may flow around the outside edges of the detector and again interfere with smoke reaching the sensing chamber. Additionally, holes in the rear of a detector provide a means for entry of dust, dirt, and insects, each of which can adversely affect the detector's performance.

[From NFPA 72E - 1990, A-4-6.2.2]

A-5-3.7.4.1 Air Sampling-Type Detectors. A single pipe network has a shorter transport time than a multiple pipe network of similar length pipe; however, a multiple pipe system provides a faster smoke transport time than a single pipe system of the same total length. As the number of sampling holes in a pipe increases, the smoke transport time increases. Where practical, pipe run lengths in a multiple pipe system should be nearly equal or the system should be otherwise pneumatically balanced.

A-5-3.7.4.2 The air sampling-type detector system should be able to withstand dusty environments by either air filtering or electronic discrimination of particle size. The detector should be capable of providing optimal time delays of alarm outputs to eliminate nuisance alarms due to transient smoke conditions. The detector should also provide facilities for the connection of monitoring equipment for

Table A-5-3.7.1.1 Environmental Conditions that Influence Detector Response

Detection Protection	Air Velocity >300′/min	Atm. Pressure Above Sea Level	>3000′ Humidity >93%	Temp. <32°F >100°F	Color of Smoke
Ion	X	X	X	X	O
Photo	O	O	X	X	X
Beam	O	O	X	X	O
Air Sampling	O	O	X	X	O

X = May affect detector response.
O = Generally does not affect detector response.

[From NFPA 72E - 1990, Table A-4-6.1.4]

Table A-5-3.7.1.2(a) Common Sources of Aerosols and Particulate Matter Moisture

Moisture	
Live steam	Excessive tobacco smoke
Steam tables	Heat treating
Showers	Corrosive atmospheres
Humidifiers	Dust or lint
Slop sink	Linen/bedding handling
Humid outside air	Sawing, drilling, and grinding
Water spray	Pneumatic transport
	Textile and agricultural processing
Combustion Products and Fumes	
Cooking equipment	**Engine Exhaust**
Ovens	
Dryers	Gasoline forklift trucks
Fireplaces	Diesel trucks and locomotives
Exhaust hoods	Engines not vented to the outside
Cutting, welding, and brazing	
	Heating element with abnormal conditions
Machining	
Paint spray	Dust accumulations
Curing	Improper exhaust
Chemical fumes	Incomplete combustion
Cleaning fluids	

[From NFPA 72E, Table A-4-6.1.5(a)]

Table A-5-3.7.1.2(b) Sources of Electrical and Mechanical Influences on Smoke Detectors

Electrical Noise and Transients	Airflow
Vibration or shock	Gusts
Radiation	Excessive velocity
Radio frequency	Power supply
Intense light	
Lightning	
Electrostatic discharge	

[From NFPA 72E, Table A-4-6.1.5(b)]

the recording of background smoke level information necessary in setting alert and alarm levels and delays.

[New paragraphs]

A-5-3.7.5 High Rack Storage. For most effective detection of fire in high rack storage areas, detectors should be located on the ceiling above each aisle and at intermediate levels in the racks. This is necessary to detect smoke that may be trapped in the racks at an early stage of fire development, when insufficient thermal energy is released to carry the smoke to the ceiling. Earliest detection of smoke is achieved by locating the intermediate level detectors adjacent to alternate pallet sections as shown in Figures A-5-3.7.5(a) and (b). Detector manufacturer's recommendations and engineering judgment should be followed for specific installations.

A protected beam-type detector may be used in lieu of a single row of individual spot-type smoke detectors.

[From NFPA 72E - 1990, A-4-6.4]

Sampling ports of an air sampling-type detector may be located above each aisle to provide coverage equivalent to the location of spot-type detectors. Manufacturer's recommendations and engineering judgment should be followed for specific installation.

[New paragraph]

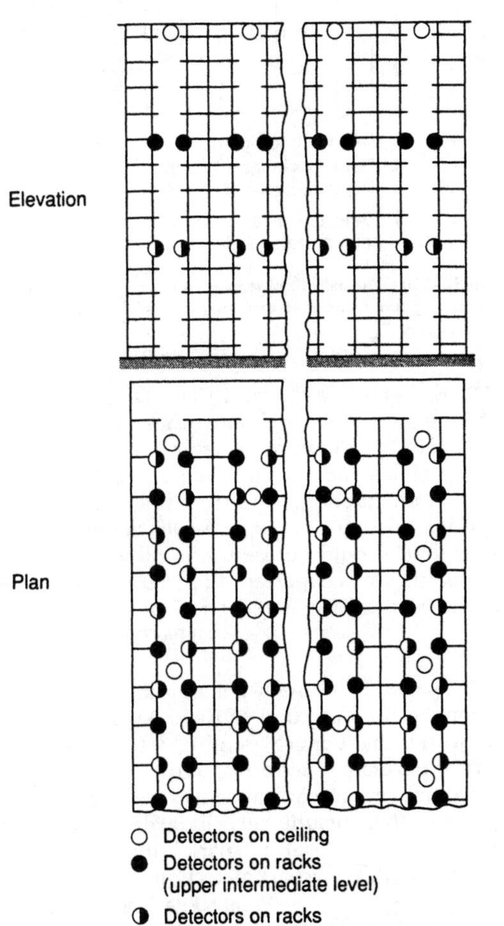

Figure A-5-3.7.5(a) For solid storage (closed rack) in which transverse and longitudinal flue spaces are irregular or nonexistent, as for slatted or solid shelved storage.

[From NFPA 72E - 1990, Figure A-4-6.1.8(a)]

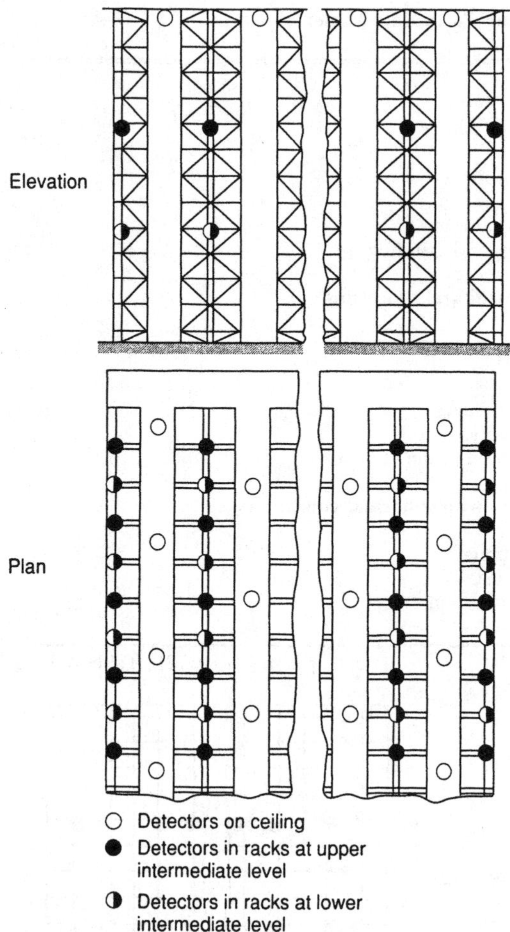

Figure A-5-3.7.5(b) For palletized storage (open rack) or no shelved storage in which regular transverse and longitudinal flue spaces are maintained.

[From NFPA 72E - 1990, Figure A-4-6.1.8(b)]

A-5-4.2.1 Ember. Class A and Class D combustibles will burn as embers under conditions where the typical flame associated with fire does not necessarily exist. This glowing combustion yields radiant emissions in radically different parts of the radiant energy spectrum than flaming combustion. Specialized detectors, specifically designed to detect those emission, should be used in applications where this type of combustion is expected. In general, flame detectors are not intended for the detection of embers.

[From NFPA 72E - 1990, A-5-2.1.1]

A-5-4.2.1 Spark. The overwhelming majority of applications involving the detection of Class A and Class D combustibles with radiant energy-sensing detectors involves the transport of particulate solid materials through pneumatic conveyor ducts or mechanical conveyors. It is common in the industries that include such hazards to call a moving piece of burning material a "spark" and systems for the detection of such fires "spark detection systems."

[From NFPA 72E - 1990, A-5-2.1.6]

A-5-4.2.1 Wavelength. The concept of wavelength is extremely important in selecting the proper detector for a particular application. There is a precise interrelation between the wavelength of light being emitted from a flame and the combustion chemistry producing the flame. Specific sub-atomic, atomic, and molecular events yield radiant energy of specific wavelengths. For example, ultraviolet photons are emitted as the result of the complete loss of electrons or very large changes in electron energy levels. During combustion, molecules are violently torn apart by the chemical reactivity of oxygen, and electrons are released in the process, recombining at drastically lower energy levels, thus giving rise to ultraviolet radiation. Visible radiation is generally the result of smaller changes in electron energy levels within the molecules of fuel, flame intermediates, and products of combustion. Infrared radiation comes from the vibration of molecules or parts of molecules when they are in the superheated state associated with combustion. Each chemical compound exhibits a group of wavelengths at which it is resonant. These wavelengths constitute the chemical's infrared spectrum, which is usually unique to that chemical.

This interrelationship between wavelength and combustion chemistry affects the relative performance of various types of detectors to various fires.

[From NFPA 72E - 1990, A-5-2.1.9]

A-5-4.3.1 The radiant energy from a flame or spark/ember is comprised of emissions in various bands of the ultraviolet, visible, and infrared portions of the spectrum. The relative quantities of radiation emitted in each part of the spectrum are determined by the fuel chemistry, the temperature, and the rate of combustion. The detector should be matched to the characteristics of the fire.

Almost all materials that participate in flaming combustion will emit ultraviolet radiation to some degree during flaming combustion, whereas only carbon-containing fuels will emit significant radiation at the 4.35 micron (carbon dioxide) band used by many detector types to detect a flame.

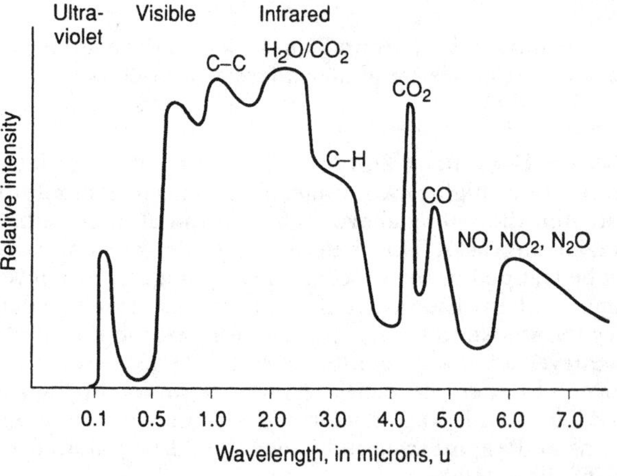

Figure A-5-4.3.1 Spectrum of a "typical" flame (free burning gasoline).

[New]

The radiant energy emitted from an ember is determined primarily by the fuel temperature (Plank's Law Emissions) and the emissivity of the fuel. Radiant energy from an ember is primarily infrared and, to a lesser degree, visible in wavelength. In general, embers do not emit ultraviolet energy in significant quantities (0.1 percent of total emissions) until the ember achieves temperatures of 2000°K (1727°C or 3240°F). In most cases, the emissions will be included in the band of 0.8 to 2.0 microns, corresponding to temperatures of approximately 750°F (398°C) to 1830°F (1000°C).

Most radiant energy detectors have some form of qualification circuitry within them that uses time to help distinguish between spurious, transient signals and legitimate fire alarms. These circuits become very important when one considers the anticipated fire scenario and the ability of the detector to respond to that anticipated fire. For example, a detector that utilizes an integration circuit or a timing circuit to respond to the flickering light from a fire may not respond well to a deflagration resulting from the ignition of accumulated combustible vapors and gases, or where the fire is a spark that is traveling up to 100 meters per second past the detector. Under these circumstances, a detector that has a high speed response capability would be most appropriate. On the other hand, in applications where the development of the fire will be slower, a detector that utilizes time for the confirmation of repetitive signals would be appropriate. Consequently, the fire growth rate should be considered in selecting the detector. The detector performance should be selected to respond to the anticipated fire.

The radiant emissions are not the only criteria to be considered. The medium between the anticipated fire and the detector is also very important. Different wavelengths of radiant energy are absorbed with varying degrees of efficiency by materials suspended in the air or that may accumulate on the optical surfaces of the detector. Generally, aerosols and surface deposits reduce the sensitivity of the detector. The detection technology utilized should take into account those normally occurring aerosols and surface deposits to minimize the reduction of system response between maintenance intervals. Note that the smoke evolved from the combustion of middle and heavy fraction petroleum distillates is highly absorptive in the ultraviolet end of the spectrum. Where using this type of detection, the system should be designed to minimize the interference of smoke on the response of the detection system.

The environment and ambient conditions anticipated in the area to be protected will impact on the choice of detector. All detectors have limitations on the range of ambient temperatures over which they will respond, consistent with their tested or approved sensitivities. The designer should make certain that the detector is compatible with the range of ambient temperatures anticipated in the area in which it is installed. In addition, rain, snow, and ice will attenuate both ultraviolet and infrared radiation to varying degrees. Where anticipated, provisions should be made to protect the detector from accumulations of these materials on the optical surfaces.

[From NFPA 72E - 1990, A-5-3.1 modified]

A-5-4.4.1.1 All optical detectors respond according to the following theoretical equation:

$$S = \frac{Kpe^{\zeta d}}{d^2}$$

Where:

k = proportionality constant for the detector
p = radiant power emitted by the fire
e = Naperian logarithm base (2.7183)
ζ = the extinction coefficient of air
d = the distance between the fire and the detector
S = radiant power reaching the detector.

The sensitivity (S) would typically be measured in nanowatts. This equation yields a family of curves similar to the one shown in Figure A-5-4.4.1.1.

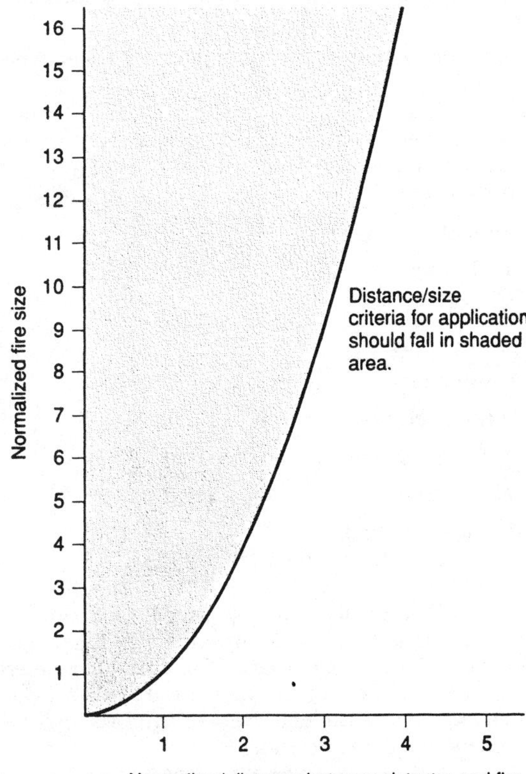

Figure A-5-4.4.1.1 Generalized fire size vs. distance.
[From NFPA 72E - 1990, A-5-4.1.1]

The curve defines the maximum distance at which the detector consistently detects a fire of defined size and fuel. Detectors should only be employed in the shaded area beneath the curve.

Under the best of conditions, with no atmospheric absorption, the radiant power reaching the detector is reduced by a factor of four if the distance between the detector and the fire is doubled. For the consumption of the atmospheric extinction, the exponential term, Zeta (ς) is added to the equation. Zeta is a measure of the clarity of the air at the wavelength under consideration. Zeta will be affected by humidity, dust, and any other contaminants in the air that are absorbent at the wavelength in question. Zeta generally has values between −.001 and −.1 for normal ambient air.

[From NFPA 72E - 1990, A-5-4.1.1 modified]

A-5-4.4.2.1 The types of application for which flame detectors are suitable are:

(a) High ceiling, open spaced buildings such as warehouses and aircraft hangers

(b) Outdoor or semi-outdoor areas where winds or draughts may prevent smoke reaching a heat or smoke detector

(c) Risks where rapidly developing flaming fires may occur, such as aircraft hàngers, petrochemical production, storage and transfer areas, natural gas installations, paint shops, solvent areas, etc.

(d) Spot protection of high fire risk machinery or installations, often coupled with an automatic gas extinguishing system

(e) Environments that are unsuitable for other types of detectors.

Some extraneous sources of radiant emissions that have been identified as interfering with the stability of flame detectors include:

(a) Sunlight

(b) Lightning

(c) X-rays

(d) Gamma rays

(e) Cosmic rays

(f) Ultraviolet radiation from arc welding

(g) Electromagnetic interference (EMI, RFI)

(h) Hot objects

(i) Artificial lighting.

[From NFPA 72E - 1990, A-5-4.2.1 modified]

A-5-4.4.2.3 The greater the angular displacement of the fire from the optical axis of the detector, the larger the fire must become before it is detected. This phenomenon establishes the field of view of the detector. Figure A-5-4.4.2.3 shows an example of the effective sensitivity versus angular displacement of a flame detector.

[From NFPA 72E - 1990, A-5-4.2.3 modified]

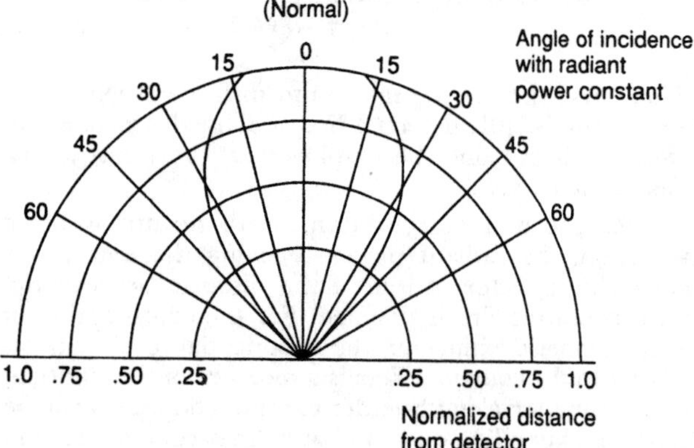

Figure A-5-4.4.2.3 Normalized sensitivity vs. angular displacement.
[From NFPA 72E - 1990, A-5-4.2.3]

A-5-4.4.2.4 Virtually all radiant energy-sensing detectors exhibit some kind of fuel specificity. Different fuels when burned at uniform rates (joules/second or watts) will emit different levels of radiant power in the ultraviolet, visible, and infrared portions of the spectrum. Under free-burn conditions, a fire of given surface area but of different fuels will burn at different rates (joules/second or watts) and emit varying levels of radiation in each of the major portions of the spectrum. Most radiant energy detectors designed to detect flame are qualified based upon a defined fire under specific conditions. Where employing these detectors for fuels other than the defined fire, the designer should make certain that the appropriate adjustments to the maximum distance between the detector and the fire are made consistent with the fuel specificity of the detector.

[From NFPA 72E - 1990, A-5-4.2.4]

A-5-4.4.2.6 The means by which this requirement has been satisfied include:

(a) Lens clarity monitoring and cleaning where a contaminated lens signal is rendered

(b) Lens air purge.

[From NFPA 72E - 1990, A-5-4.2.6]

A-5-4.5.1 Spark/ember detectors are installed primarily to detect sparks and embers that may, if allowed to continue to burn, precipitate a much larger fire or explosion. Spark/ember detectors are typically mounted on some form of duct or conveyor, monitoring the fuel as it passes by. Usually, it is necessary to enclose the portion of the conveyor where the detectors are located as these devices generally require a dark environment. Extraneous sources of radiant emissions that have been identified as interfering with the stability of spark/ember detectors include:

(a) Ambient light

(b) Electromagnetic interference (EMI, RFI)

(c) Electrostatic discharge in the fuel stream.

[From NFPA 72E - 1990, A-5-4.3.1 modified]

A-5-4.5.2 There is a minimum ignition power (watts) for all combustible dusts. If the spark or ember is incapable of delivering that quantity of power to the adjacent combustible material (dust), an expanding dust fire will not occur. The minimum ignition power is determined by the fuel chemistry, fuel particle size, fuel concentration in air, and ambient conditions such as temperature and humidity.

[From NFPA 72E - 1990, A-5-4.3.2]

A-5-4.5.5 The greater the displacement of the fire from the optical axis of the detector, the larger the fire must become before it is detected. This phenomenon establishes the field of view of the detector. Figure A-5-4.4.2.3 shows an example of the effective sensitivity versus angular displacement of a flame detector.

[From NFPA 72E-1990, A-5-4.3.5]

A-5-4.5.6 The means by which this requirement has been satisfied include:

(a) Lens clarity monitoring and cleaning where a contaminated lens signal is rendered

(b) Lens air purge.

[From NFPA 72E - 1990, A-5-4.3.6]

A-5-5.1 Many gases may be produced by a fire. Fire-gas detectors are instruments that are triggered into alarm by one or more fire gases. Fire-gas detectors need not be able to differentiate among the various fire gases. Depending on the material being burned and the oxygen supply available, the quantity and composition of gases given off can vary greatly.

If ordinary cellulosic material such as wood or paper is burned with an abundance of oxygen, the gases given off are primarily carbon dioxide and water vapor. If, however, the same material is burned or smolders with a limited supply of oxygen, a host of additional gases will be evolved.

[From NFPA 72E - 1990, A-6-1.1.1]

A-5-5.6.1 Fire-gas detectors depend on fire gases reaching the sensing element. Where sufficient concentration is present, operation is obtained. Since the detectors are usually mounted on or near the ceiling, response time depends on the nature of the fire. A hot fire will drive fire gases up to the ceiling more rapidly. A smoldering fire produces little heat, and, therefore, the detection time will be increased.

[From NFPA 72E - 1990, A-6-3.1]

A-5-5.6.3 Gas transport to the sensor of a fire-gas detector may occur by diffusion where migration results from concentration gradients or by sampling if pumps, fans, or aspirators are employed.

[From NFPA 72E - 1990, A-6-3.3]

A-5-5.6.6.3 Location and spacing of fire-gas detectors should consider beam depth, ceiling height, beam spacing, and anticipated fire type and location. For ceiling configurations where mixing of air into beam pockets is inhibited by ventilation systems, detectors will perform better if installed on the bottom of beams.

To detect flaming fires (strong plumes), detectors should be installed as follows:

(a) If the ratio of the beam depth (D) to ceiling height (H) (D/H) is greater than 0.10 and the ratio of beam spacing (W) to ceiling height (H) (W/H) is greater than 0.40, detectors should be located in each beam pocket.

(b) If either ratio of beam depth to ceiling height (D/H) is less than 0.10 or the ratio of beam spacing to ceiling height (W/H) is less than 0.40, detectors should be installed on the bottom of the beams.

To detect smoldering fires (weak or no plumes), detectors should be installed as follows:

(a) If air mixing into beam pockets is good (e.g., air-flow parallel to long beams) and condition (a) exists as above, a detector should be located in each beam pocket.

(b) If air mixing into beam pockets is limited or condition (b) exists as above, detectors should be located on the bottom of the beams.

[From NFPA 72E - 1990, A-6-3.6.3]

A-5-5.7.1 Detectors should not be located in a direct airflow nor closer than 3 ft (900 mm) from an air supply diffuser.

[From NFPA 72E - 1990, A-6-4.1]

A-5-5.8.1.3 Product-listing standards include tests for temporary excursions beyond normal limits. In addition to temperature, humidity, and velocity variations, fire-gas detectors should operate reliably under such common environmental conditions as mechanical vibration, electrical interference, and other environmental influences. These conditions are also included in tests conducted by the listing agencies.

[From NFPA 72E - 1990, A-6-5.1.3]

A-5-7.2 The waterflow device should be field adjusted so that an alarm will be initiated in no more than 90 seconds after a sustained flow of at least 10 gpm (40 L/min).

Features that should be investigated to minimize alarm response time include elimination of trapped air in the sprinkler system piping, use of an excess pressure pump, use of pressure drop alarm-initiating devices, or a combination thereof.

Care should be taken when choosing waterflow alarm-initiating devices for hydraulically calculated looped systems and those systems using small orifice sprinklers. Such systems may incorporate a single point flow significantly less than 10 gpm (40 L/min). In such cases, additional waterflow alarm-initiating devices or use of pressure drop-type waterflow alarm-initiating devices may be necessary.

Care should be taken, where choosing waterflow alarm initiating devices for sprinklers utilizing on-off sprinklers, to ensure that an alarm will be initiated in the event of a waterflow condition. On-off sprinklers open at a predetermined temperature and close when the temperature reaches a predetermined lower temperature. With certain types of fires, waterflow may occur in a series of short bursts of 10 to 30 seconds' duration each. An alarm-initiating device with retard may not detect waterflow under these conditions. It is recommended that an excess pressure system or one that operates on pressure drop be considered to facilitate waterflow detection on sprinkler systems utilizing on-off sprinklers.

Excess pressure systems may be used with or without alarm valves. The following is a description of one type of excess pressure system with an alarm valve.

An excess pressure system with an alarm valve consists of an excess pressure pump with pressure switches to control the operation of the pump. The inlet of the pump is connected to the supply side of the alarm valve, and the outlet is connected to the sprinkler system. The pump control pressure switch is of the differential type, maintaining the sprinkler system pressure above the main pressure by a constant amount. Another switch monitors low sprinkler system pressure to initiate a supervisory signal in the event of a failure of the pump or other malfunction. An additional pressure switch may be used to stop pump operation in the event of a deficiency in water supply. Another pressure switch is connected to the alarm outlet of the alarm valve to initiate a waterflow alarm signal when waterflow exists. This type of system also inherently prevents false alarms due to water surges. The sprinkler retard chamber should be eliminated to enhance the detection capability of the system for short duration flows.

[From NFPA 72, A-3-4.1.2, and NFPA 71, A-3-4.2.1 modified]

A-5-8.1 Appropriate means may involve:

(a) Foam systems: Flow of water

(b) Pump activation

(c) Differential pressure detectors

(d) Halon: Pressure detector

(e) Carbon dioxide: Pressure detector.

In any case, an alarm that activates the extinguishing system may be initiated from the detection system.

[From NFPA 71, A-3-4.3]

A-5-9.1.3 Coded Signal Designations. The following suggested coded signal assignment for buildings having four floors and multiple basements is provided as a guide:

Location	Coded Signal
4th Floor	2-4
3rd Floor	2-3
2nd Floor	2-2
1st Floor	2-1
Basement	3-1
Sub-Basement	3-2

[New paragraph and table]

A-5-9.2.9 Current supply for location-designating lights at street boxes should preferably be secured at lamp locations from the local electric utility company.

Alternating current power may be superimposed on metallic fire alarm circuits for supplying designating lamps, or for control or actuation of equipment devices for fire alarm or other emergency signals, provided:

(a) Voltage between any wire and ground or between one wire and any other wire of the system shall not exceed 150 volts. The total resultant current in any line circuit shall not exceed 1/4 amp.

(b) Coupling capacitors, transformers, choke, coils, etc., shall be rated for 600-volt working voltage and have a breakdown voltage of at least twice the working voltage plus 1000 volts.

(c) There is no interference with fire alarm service under any conditions.

[From NFPA 1221, A-4-1.4.1.5]

A-5-9.2.12.3 FCC Rules and Regulations, Vol. V, Part 90, March 1979: "Except for test purposes, each transmission must be limited to a maximum of 2 seconds and may be automatically repeated not more than two times at spaced intervals within the following 30 seconds; thereafter, the authorized cycle may not be reactivated for 1 minute."

[From NFPA 1221, A-4-3.3.2.2 modified]

A-5-11.1 Smoke detectors located in the open area(s) are preferred to duct-type detectors because of the dilution effect in air ducts. Active smoke management systems installed in accordance with NFPA 92A, *Recommended Practice for Smoke-Control Systems,* or NFPA 92B, *Guide for Smoke Management Systems in Malls, Atria, and Large Areas,* should be controlled by total coverage open area detection.

[From NFPA 72E - 1990, A-9-1.1 modified]

A-5-11.2 Dilution of smoke-laden air by clean air from other parts of the building or dilution by outside air intakes may allow high densities of smoke in a single room with no appreciable smoke in the air duct at the detector location. Smoke may not be drawn from open areas where air conditioning systems or ventilating systems are shut down.

[From NFPA 72E - 1990, A-9-1.2(a) and (b)]

A-5-11.5.2.2 Detectors listed for the air velocity present may be installed at the opening where the return air enters the common return air system. The detectors should be installed up to 12 in. (0.3 m) in front of or behind the opening and spaced according to the following opening dimensions [*see Figure A-5-11.5.2.2(a)*]:

(a) *Width.*

1. Up to 36 in. (914 mm) — One detector centered in opening

2. Up to 72 in. (1829 mm) — Two detectors located at the 1/4-points of the opening

3. Over 72 in. (1829 mm) — One additional detector for each full 24 in. of opening.

(b) *Depth.* The number and spacing of the detector(s) in the depth (vertical) of the opening should be the same as those given for the width (horizontal) above.

(c) *Orientation.* Detectors should be oriented in the most favorable position for smoke entry with respect to the direction of air flow. The path of a projected beam-type detector across the return air openings should be considered equivalent in coverage to a row of individual detectors.

[From NFPA 72E - 1990, A-9-3.2.2]

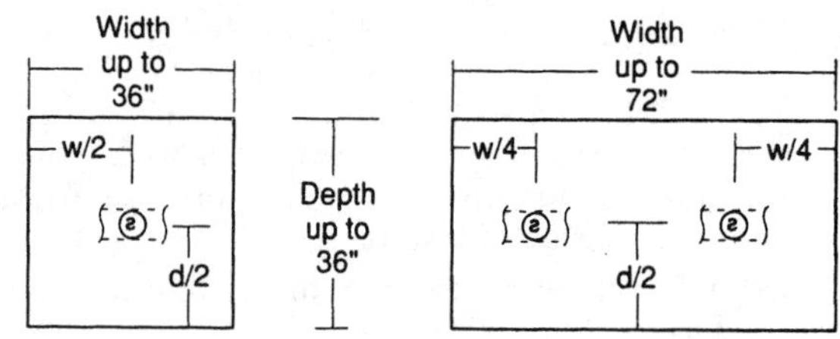

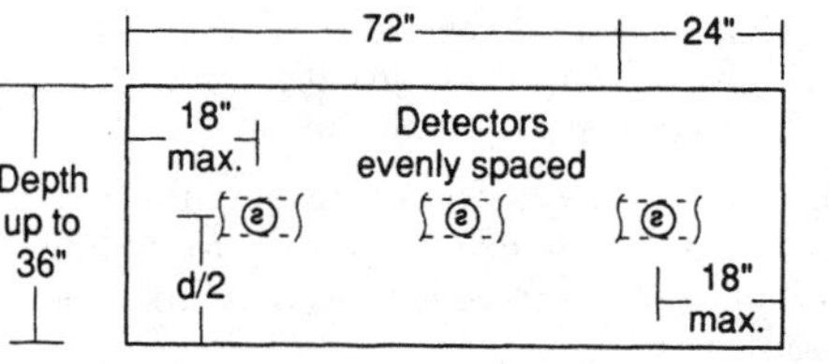

Figure A-5-11.5.2.2(a) Location of smoke detector(s) in return air systems for selective operation of equipment.

[From NFPA 72E - 1990, A-9-3.2.2(a)]

A-5-11.6.2 Where duct detectors are used to initiate the operation of smoke dampers, they should be located so that the detector is between the last inlet or outlet upstream of the damper and the first inlet or outlet downstream of the damper.

In order to obtain a representative sample, stratification and dead air space should be avoided. Such conditions may be caused by return duct openings, sharp turns or connections, as well as by long, uninterrupted straight runs. For this reason, duct smoke detectors should be located in the zone between 6 and 10 duct equivalent diameters of straight, uninterrupted run. In return air systems, the requirements of 5-11.5.2.2 take precedence over these considerations. [*See Figure A-5-11.6.2(b).*]

[New paragraph]

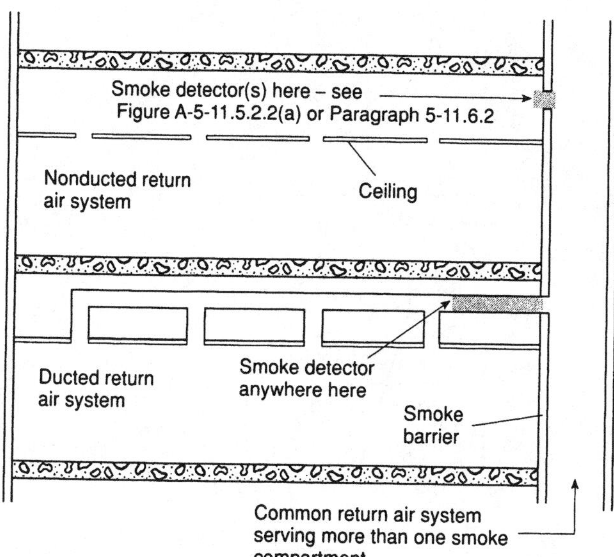

Figure A-5-11.5.2.2(b) Location of smoke detector(s) in return air systems for selective operation of equipment.

[From NFPA 72E - 1990, A-9-3.2.2(b) and A-9-3.2.2]

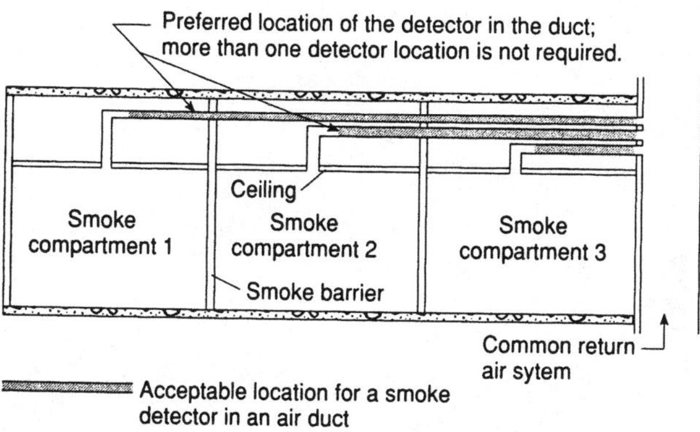

Figure A-5-11.5.2.2(c) Detector location in a duct that passes through smoke compartments not served by the duct.

[From NFPA 72E - 1990, A-9-3.2.2(c)]

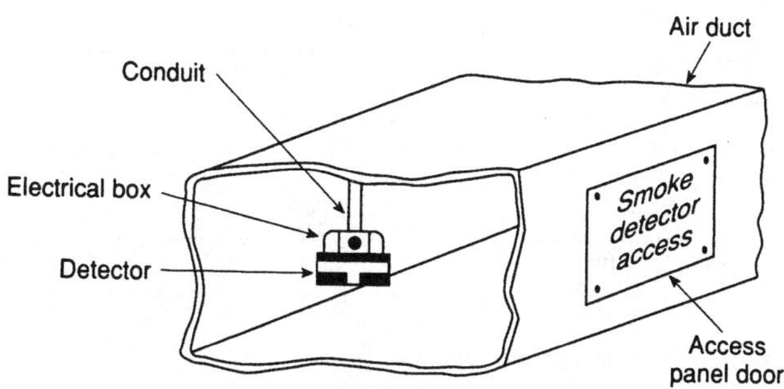

Figure A-5-11.6.2(a) Pendant mounting air duct installation.

[From NFPA 72E - 1990, A-9-4.8(a)]

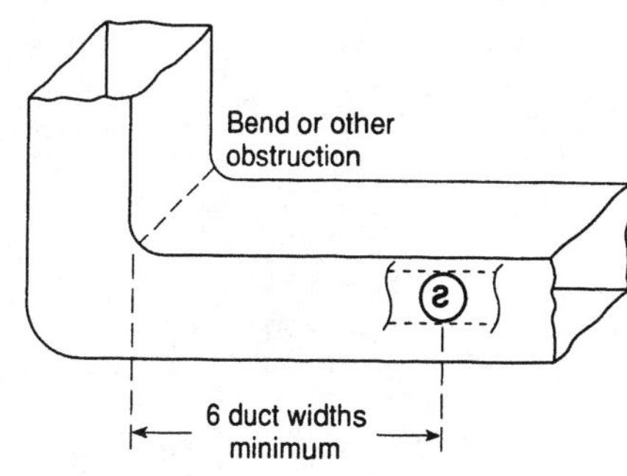

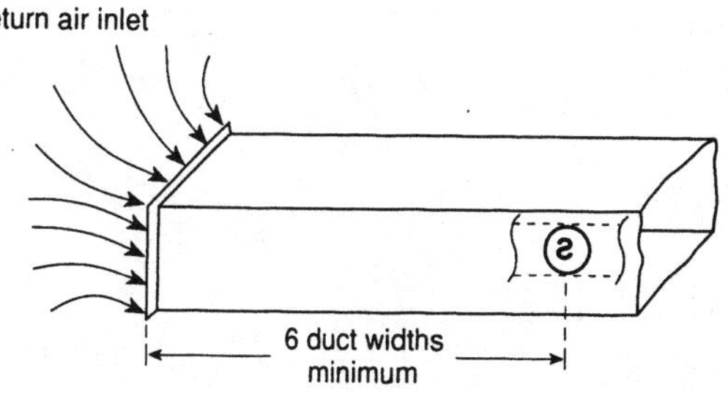

Figure A-5-11.6.2(b) Typical duct detector placement.

[From NFPA 72E - 1990, A-9-4.8(b) modified]

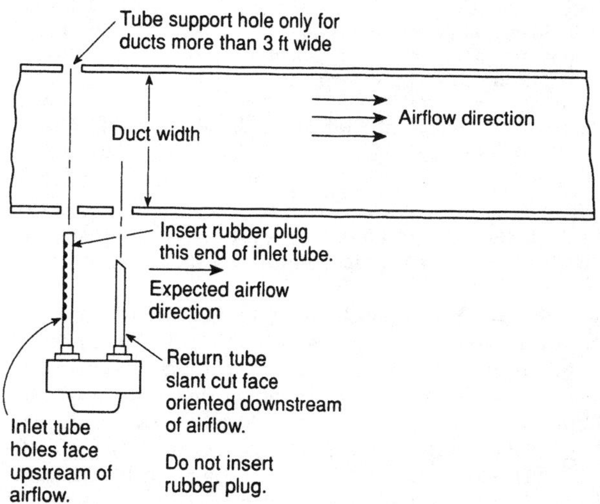

Figure A-5-11.6.2(c) Inlet tube orientation.

[From NFPA 72E - 1990, A-9-4.8(c)]

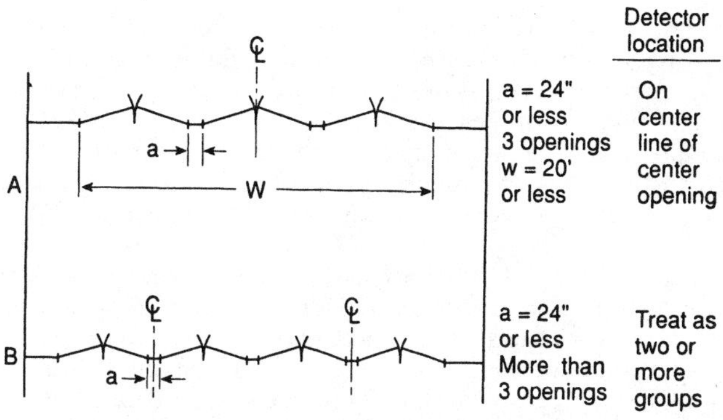

For SI Units: 1 in. = 25.4 mm; 1 ft = 0.305 m.

Figure A-5-11.7.4.3.2

[From NFPA 72E - 1990, A-9-5.4.3.2]

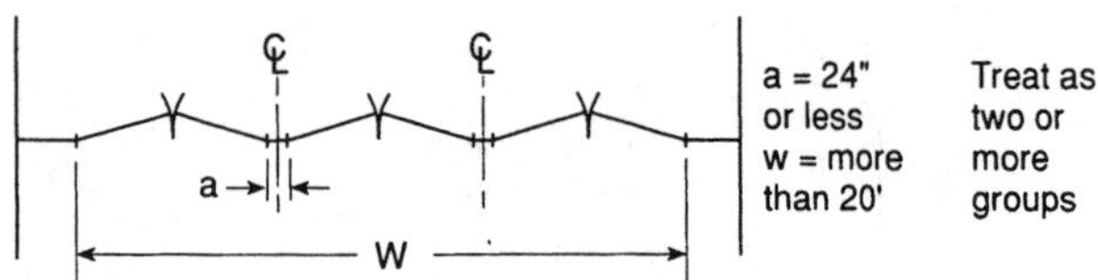

For SI Units: 1 in. = 25.4 mm; 1 ft = 0.305 m.

Figure A-5-11.7.4.3.3

[From NFPA 72E - 1990, A-9-5.4.3.3]

A-6-3.1 The typical average ambient sound level for the following occupancies are intended only for design guidance purposes:

Locations	Average Ambient Sound Level
Business occupancies	55 dBA
Educational occupancies	45 dBA
Industrial occupancies	80 dBA
Institutional occupancies	50 dBA
Mercantile occupancies	40 dBA
Piers and water-surrounded structures	40 dBA
Places of assembly	55 dBA
Residential occupancies	35 dBA
Storage occupancies	30 dBA
Thoroughfares, high density urban	70 dBA
Thoroughfares, medium density urban	55 dBA
Thoroughfares, rural and suburban	40 dBA
Tower occupancies	35 dBA
Underground structures and windowless buildings	40 dBA
Vehicles and vessels	50 dBA

[From NFPA 72G, 3-1.1.4]

The typical average ambient sound levels noted should not be used in lieu of actual sound level measurements.

A-6-4.4.1 Areas so large that they exceed the rectangular dimensions given in Figures A-6-4.4.1(a), (b), and (c) require additional appliances. Often, proper placement of appliances can be facilated by breaking down the area into multiple squares and dimensions that fit most appropriately. [*See Figures A-6-4.4.1(a), (b), (c), and (d).*] An area 40 ft (12.2 m) wide and 74 ft (22.6 m) long can be covered with two 60-cd appliances. Irregular areas will take more careful planning to make sure that at least one 15-cd appliance is installed per 20 ft by 20 ft (6.09 m by 6.09 m) room.

[New paragraph]

A-6-4.4.3 Effective intensity is the conventional method of equating the brightness of a flashing light to that of a steady burning light as seen by a human observer. The units of effective intensity are expressed in candelas. For example, a flashing light that has an effective intensity of 15 candelas has the same apparent brightness to an observer as a 15-candela steady burning light source.

A-7-2.1 Where the authority having jurisdiction strongly suspects significant deterioration or otherwise improper operation by a central station, a surprise inspection to test the operation of the central station may be made but requires extreme precaution. This test will be conducted without advising the central station, but the public fire service communication center must definitely be contacted

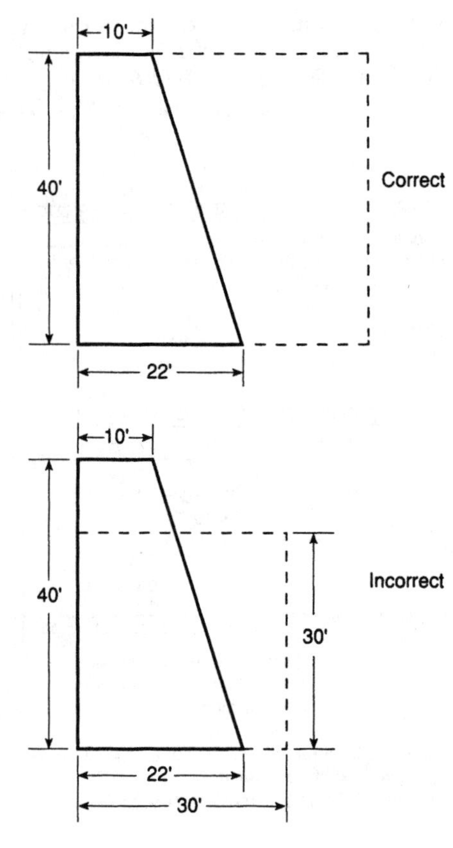

Figure A-6-4.4.1(a)

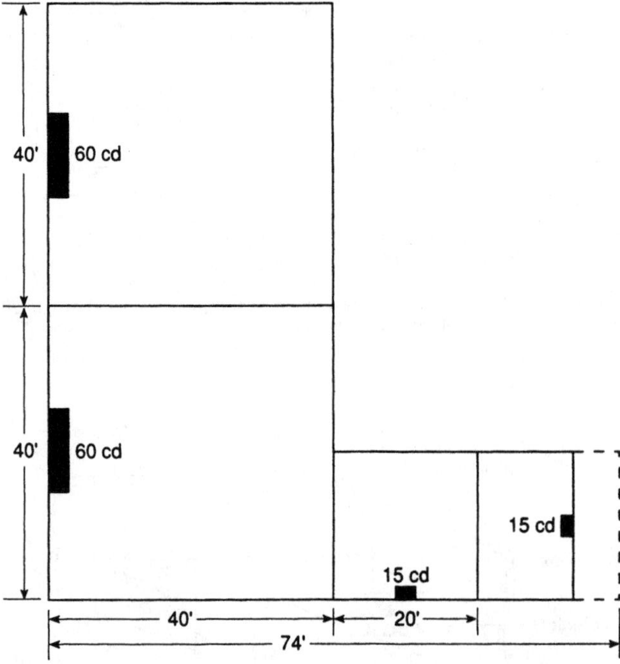

NOTE: Dashed lines represent imaginary walls.

Figure A-6-4.4.1(b) Room spacing allocation for ceiling-mounted visible appliances.

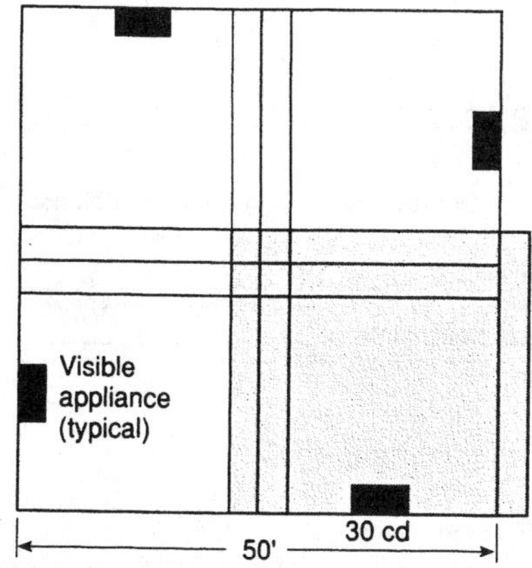

Figure A-6-4.4.1(c) Room spacing allocation — correct.

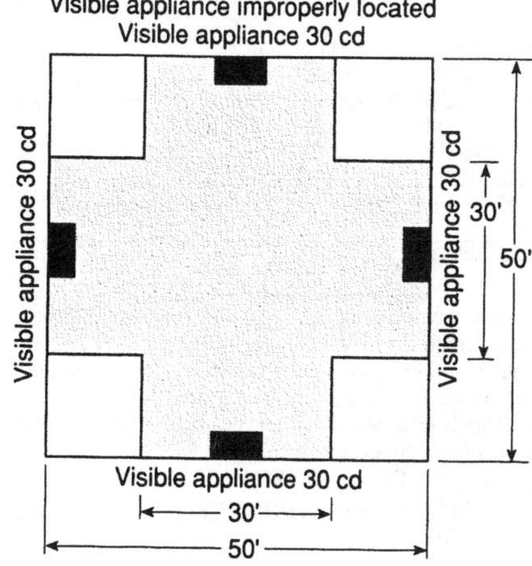

NOTE: See Table 6-4.4.1(a) for correction.

Figure A-6-4.4.1(d) Room spacing allocation — incorrect.

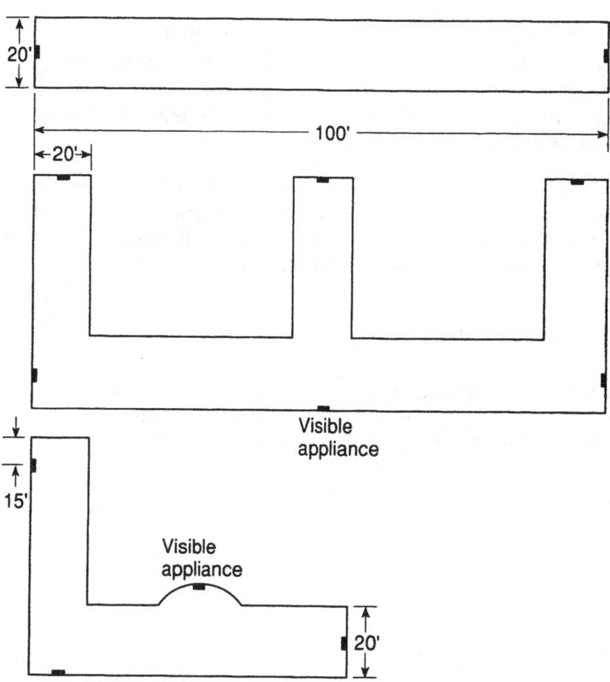

Figure A-6-4.4.2 Corridor and elevator area spacing allocation.

when manual, waterflow alarms, or automatic fire detection systems are tested so that the fire department will not respond. In addition, persons normally receiving calls for supervisory alarms should be notified when gate valves, pump power, etc., are tested. Confirmation of the authenticity of the test procedure is recommended and should be a matter for resolution between plant management and the central station.

[From NFPA 71, 1-9.5]

A-7-2.2 Test Methods. The following wiring diagrams are representative of typical circuits encountered in the field and are not intended to be all-inclusive.

The noted styles are as indicated in Table 3-5.1, 3-6.1, 3-7.1, and 4-2.3.2.2.2.3.

The noted systems are as indicated in NFPA 170, *Standard for Firesafety Symbols.*

Since ground-fault detection is not required for all circuits, tests for ground-fault detection should be limited to those circuits equipped with ground-fault detection.

An individual point-identifying (addressable) initiating device operates on a signaling line circuit and not on a Style A, B, C, D, or E (Class B and Class A) initiating device circuit.

All of the following initiating device circuits are illustrative of either alarm or supervisory signaling. Alarm and supervisory initiating devices are not permitted on the same initiating device circuit.

In addition to losing its ability to receive an alarm from an initiating device located beyond an open fault, a Style A (Class B) initiating device circuit also loses its ability to receive an alarm when a single ground fault is present.

Style C and Style E (Class B and Class A) initiating device circuits can discriminate between an alarm condition and a wire-to-wire short. In these circuits, a wire-to-wire short provides a trouble indication. However, a wire-to-wire short will prevent alarm operation. Shorting-type initiating devices cannot be used without an additional current or voltage limiting element.

Directly connected system smoke detectors, commonly referred to as two-wire detectors, should be listed as being electrically and functionally compatible with the control unit and the specific subunit or module to which they are connected. If the detectors and the units or modules are not compatible, it is possible that, during an alarm condition, the detector's visible indicator will illuminate, but no change of state to the alarm condition will occur at the control unit. Incompatibility can also prevent proper system operation at extremes of operating voltage, temperature, and other environmental conditions.

If two or more two-wire detectors with integral relays are connected to a single initiating device circuit and their relay contacts are used to control essential building functions (e.g., fan shutdown, elevator recall, etc.), it should be clearly noted that the circuit may be capable of supplying only enough energy to support one detector/relay combination in an alarm mode. If control of more than one building function is required, each detector/relay combination used to control separate functions should be connected to separate initiating device circuits, or they should be connected to an initiating device circuit that will provide adequate power to permit all the detectors connected to the circuit to be in the alarm mode simultaneously. During acceptance and reacceptance testing, this feature should always be tested and verified.

A speaker is an alarm indicating appliance, and, when used in the following diagrams, the principle of operation and supervision is the same as for other audible alarm indicating appliances (e.g., bells, horns, etc.).

Wiring Diagrams.

NOTE: Where testing circuits, verify the correct wiring size, insulation type, and conductor fill in accordance with the requirements in NFPA 70, *National Electrical Code*.

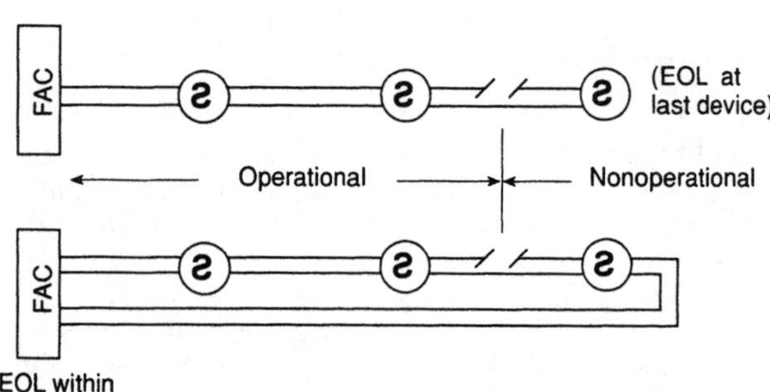

Disconnect conductor at device or control unit, then reconnect. Temporarily connect a ground to either leg of conductors, then remove ground. Both operations should indicate audible and visual trouble with subsequent restoral at control unit. Conductor-to-conductor short should initiate alarm, Style A and Style B (Class B) indicate trouble Style C (Class B). Style A (Class B) will not initiate alarm while in trouble condition.

Figure A-7-2.2(a)

[From NFPA 72H, Figure 7-2 modified]

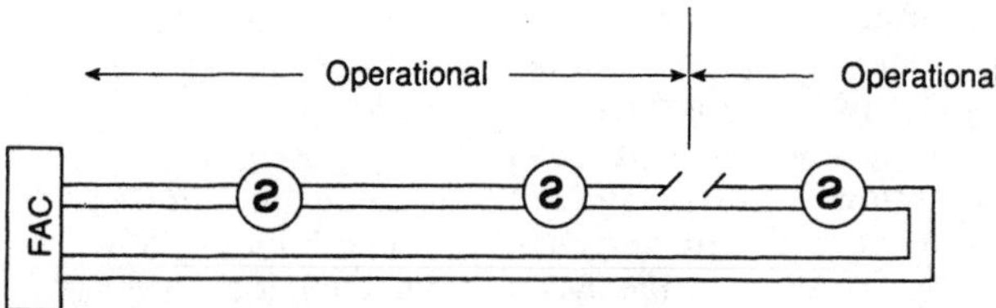

Disconnect a conductor at a device mid-point in the circuit. Operate a device on either side of device with disconnected conductor. Reset control unit and reconnect conductor. Repeat test with a ground applied to either conductor in place of the disconnected conductor. Both operations should indicate audible and visual trouble, then alarm or supervisory indication with subsequent restoral.

Figure A-7-2.2(b)

[From NFPA 72H, Figure 7-3 modified]

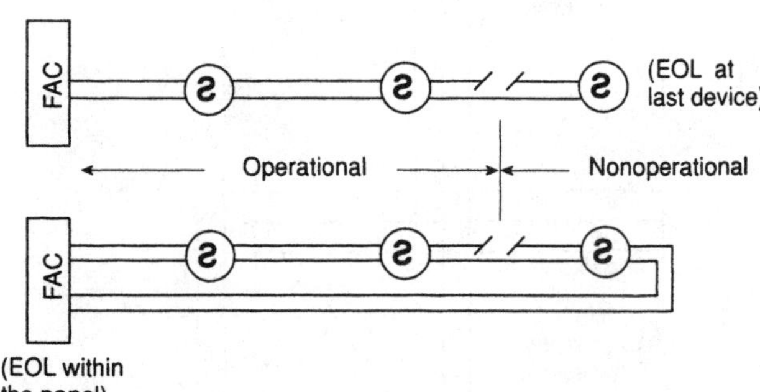

Remove smoke detector if installed with plug-in base or disconnect conductor beyond first device from control unit. Activate smoke detector per manufacturer's recommendations between control unit and circuit break. Restore detector and/or circuit. Control unit should indicate trouble where fault occurs and alarm where detectors are activated between the break and the control unit.

Figure A-7-2.2(c)

[From NFPA 72H, Figure 7-4 modified]

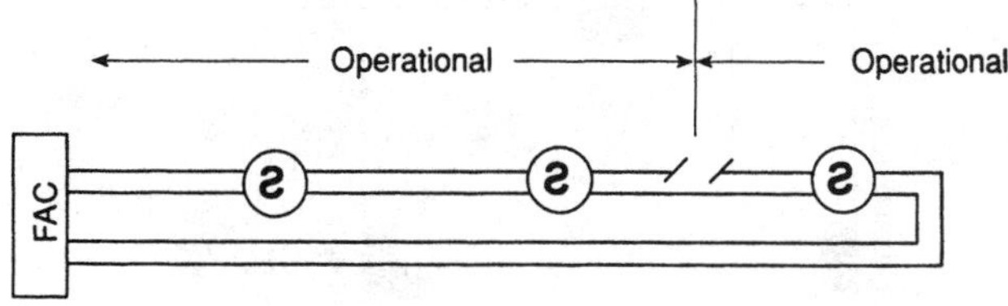

Disconnect conductor at a smoke detector or remove if installed with a plug-in base mid-point in the circuit. Operate a device on either side of device with the fault. Reset control unit and reconnect conductor or detector. Repeat test with a ground applied to either conductor in place of the disconnected conductor or removed device. Both operations should indicate audible and visual trouble, then alarm indication with subsequent restoral.

Figure A-7-2.2(d)

[From NFPA 72H, Figure 7-5 modified]

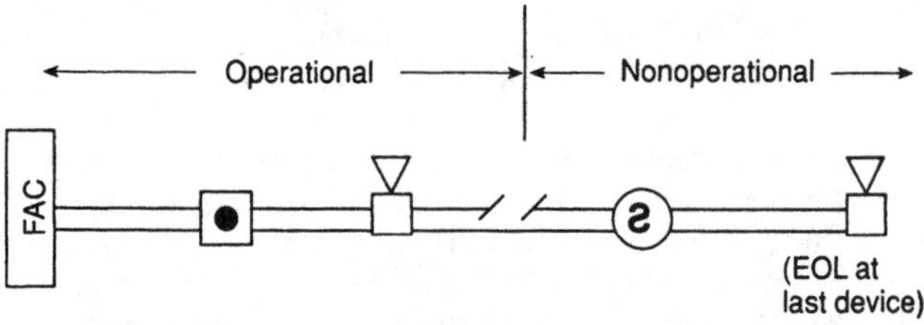

Disconnect a conductor either at indicating or initiating device. Activate initiating device between fault and control unit. Activate additional smoke detectors between device first activated and control unit. Restore circuit, initiating devices, and control unit. Confirm that all indicating appliances on the circuit operate from the control unit up to the fault and that all smoke detectors tested and their associated ancillary functions, if any, operated.

Figure A-7-2.2(e)

[From NFPA 72H, Figure 7-6 modified]

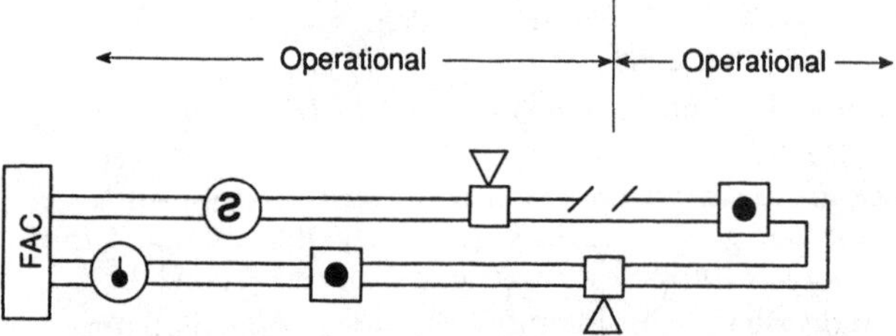

Testing of the circuit is similar to that described above. Confirm all indicating appliances operate on either side of fault.

Figure A-7-2.2(f)

[From NFPA 72H, Figure 7-7 modified]

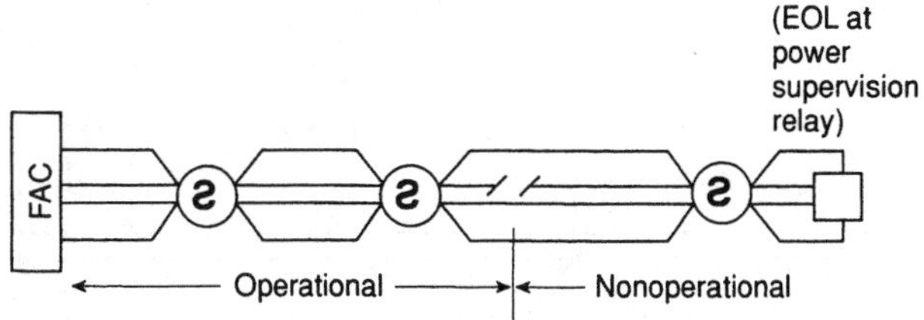

Testing of the circuit is similar to that described in A-7-2.2(c) and A-7-2.2(d). Disconnect a leg of the power supply circuit beyond the first device on the circuit. Activate initiating device between fault and control unit. Restore circuits, initiating devices, and control unit. Audible and visual trouble should indicate at the control unit where either initiating or power circuit is faulted. All initiating devices between the circuit fault and the control unit should activate. In addition, removal of a smoke detector from a plug-in type base can also break the power supply circuit. When circuits contain various powered and nonpowered devices on the same initiating circuit, verify that the nonpowered devices beyond the power circuit fault can still initiate an alarm. A return loop should be brought back to the last powered device and the power supervisory relay to incorporate into the end-of-line device.

Figure A-7-2.2(g)

[From NFPA 72H, Figure 7-8 modified]

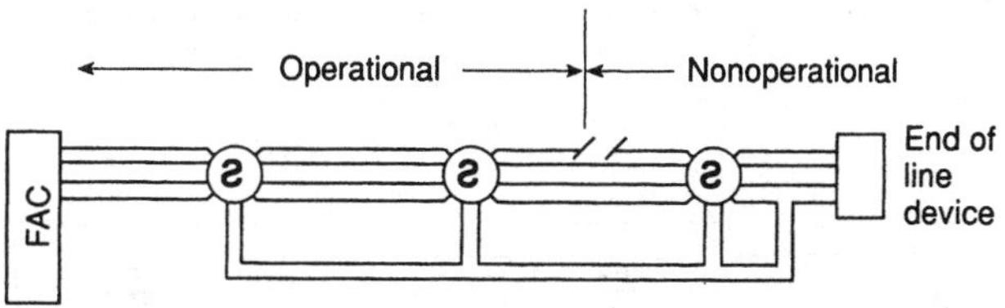

Testing of the circuit is similar to that described in A-7-2.2(c) with the addition of a power circuit.

Figure A-7-2.2(h)

[From NFPA 72H, Figure 7-9 modified]

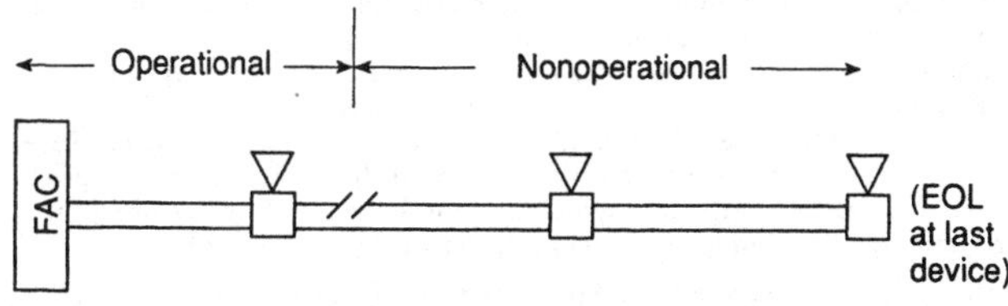

Testing of the indicating appliances connected to Style W and Style Y (Class B) is similar to that described in A-7-2.2(c).

Figure A-7-2.2(i)

[From NFPA 72H, Figure 7-13 modified]

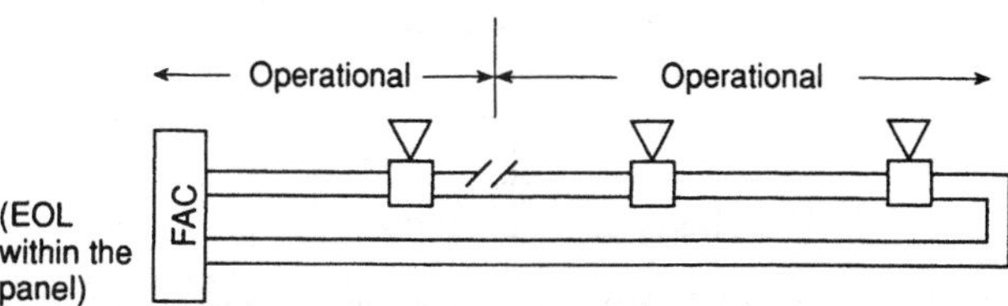

Testing of the indicating appliances connected to Style X and Style Z (Class B and Class A) is similar to that described in A-7-2.2(d).

Figure A-7-2.2(j)

[From NFPA 72H, Figure 7-10.2 modified]

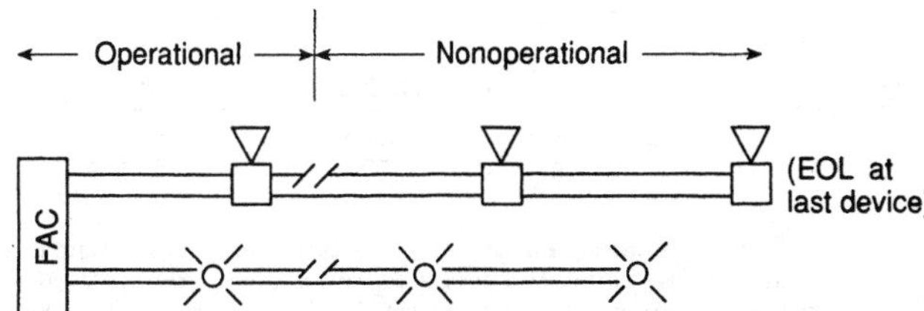

Testing of the indicating appliances connected to Style X and Style Z (Class B and Class A) is similar to that described in A-7-2.2(d).

Figure A-7-2.2(k)

[From NFPA 72H, Figure 7-11]

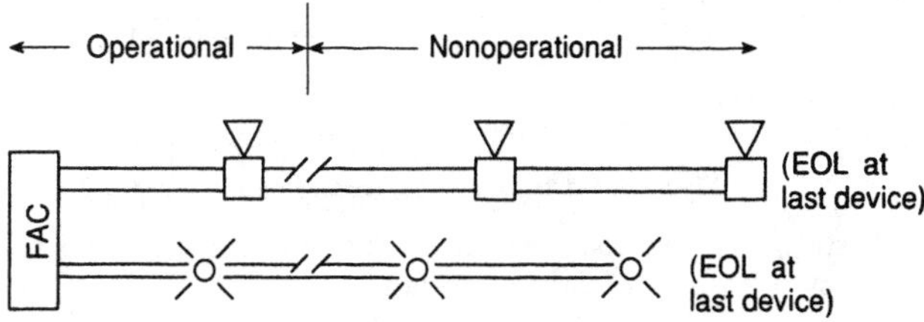

Testing of the indicating appliances connected to Style X and Style Z (Class B and Class A) is similar to that described in A-7-2.2(d).

Figure A-7-2.2(l)

[From NFPA 72H, Figure 7-12]

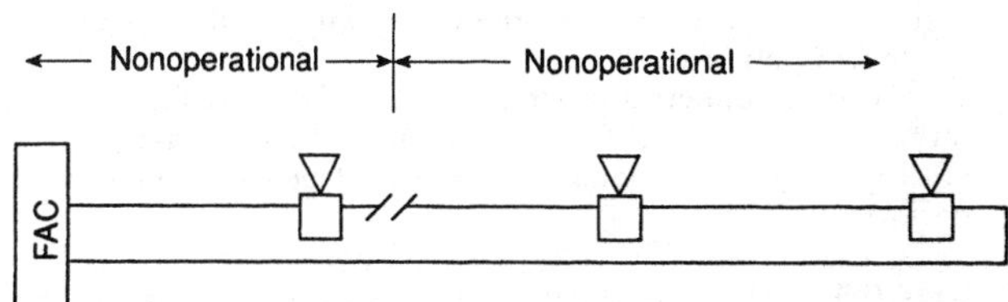

An open fault in the circuit wiring should cause a trouble condition.

Figure A-7-2.2(m)

[From NFPA 72H, Figure 7-13]

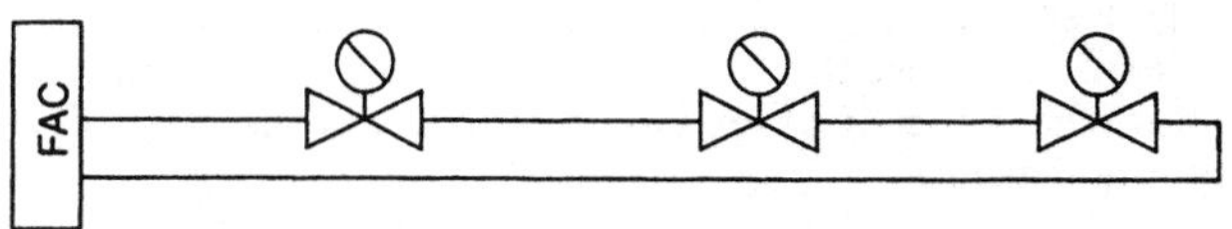

An open fault in the circuit wiring of operation of the valve switch (or any supervisory signal device) should cause a trouble condition.

Figure A-7-2.2(n)

[From NFPA 72H, Figure 7-14]

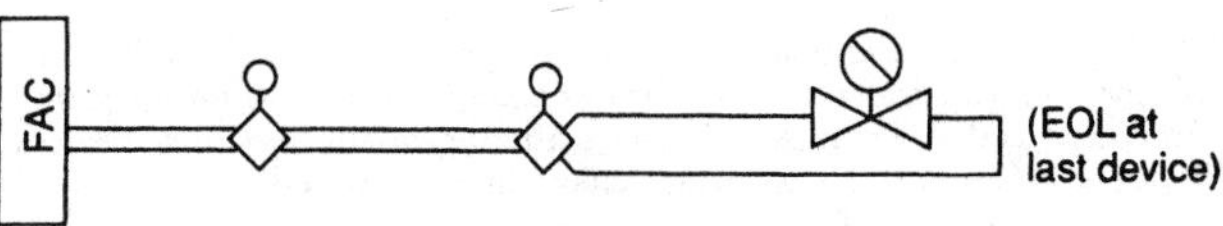

An open fault in the circuit wiring or operation of the valve switch should cause a trouble signal.

Figure A-7-2.2(o)

[From NFPA 72H, Figure 7-15)

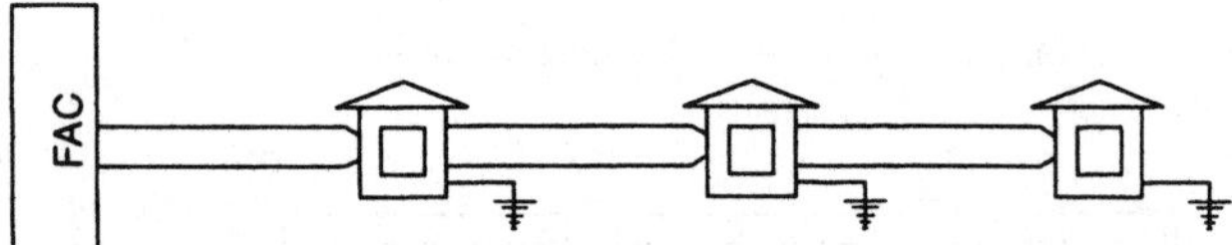

Disconnect a leg of municipal circuit at master box. Verify alarm sent to public communication center. Disconnect leg of auxiliary circuit. Verify trouble condition on control unit. Restore circuits. Activate control unit and send alarm signal to communication center. Verify control unit in trouble condition until master box reset.

Figure A-7-2.2(p)

[From NFPA 72H, Figure 7-17]

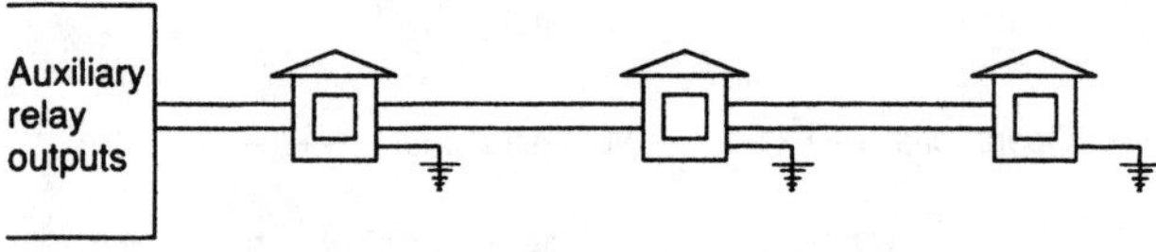

Figure A-7-2.2(q) Self-explanatory test.

Testing of supervised remote relays to be conducted in same manner as indicating appliances.

Circuit Styles.

NOTE: Some testing laboratories and authorities having jurisdiction permit systems to be classified as a Style 7 (Class A) by the application of two circuits of the same style operating in parallel. An example of this is to take two series circuits, either Style 0.5 or Style 1.0 (Class B), and operate them in parallel. The logic being that should a condition occur on one of the circuits, the remaining parallel circuit would be operative.

In order to understand the principles of the circuit, perform alarm receipt capability on a single circuit and indicate on the certificate of completion the style type based on the performance.

Style 0.5. This signaling circuit operates as a series circuit in performance. This is identical to the historical series audible signaling circuits. Any type of break or ground in one of the conductors or the internal of the multiple interface device, and the total circuit is rendered operative.

To test and verify this type of circuit, either lift a conductor or place an earth ground on a conductor or a terminal point where the signaling circuit attaches to the multiplex interface device.

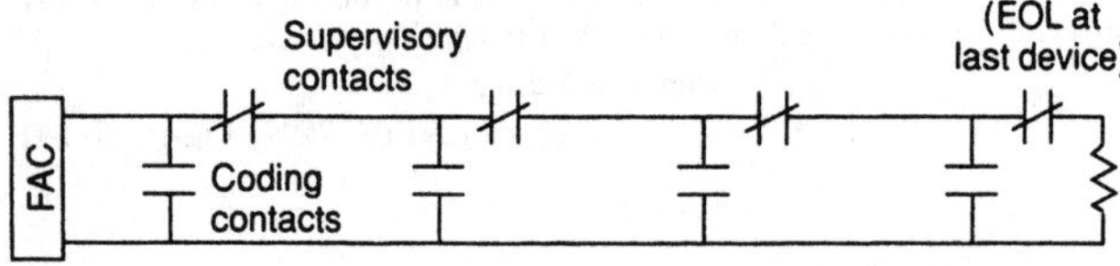

Style 0.5(a) functions so that when a box is operated, the supervisory contacts open, making the succeeding devices nonoperative while the operating box sends a coded signal. Any alarms occurring in any successive devices will not be received at the receiving station during this period.

Figure A-7-2.2(r) Style 0.5(a) (Class B) series.

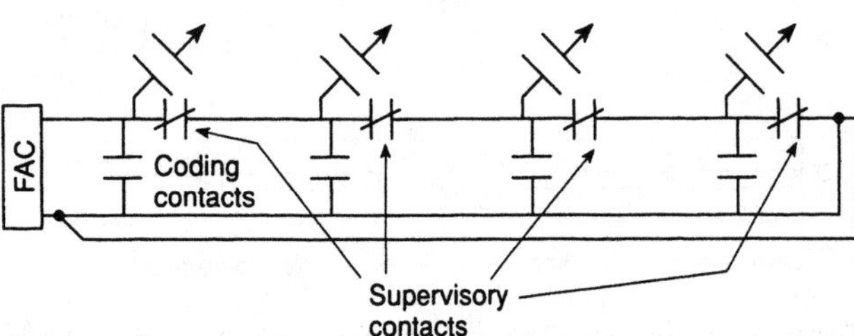

The contact closes when the device is operated and remains closed to shut out the remainder of the system until the code is complete.

Figure A-7-2.2(s) Style 0.5(b) (Class B) shunt.

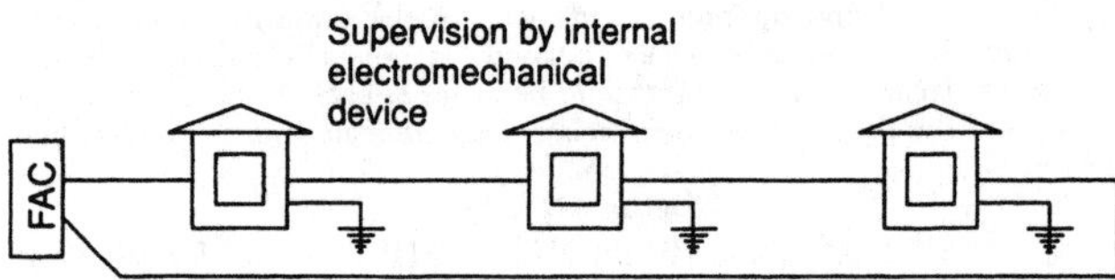

An open or ground fault on the circuit should cause a trouble condition at the control unit.

Figure A-7-2.2(t) Style 0.5(c) (Class B) positive supervised successive.

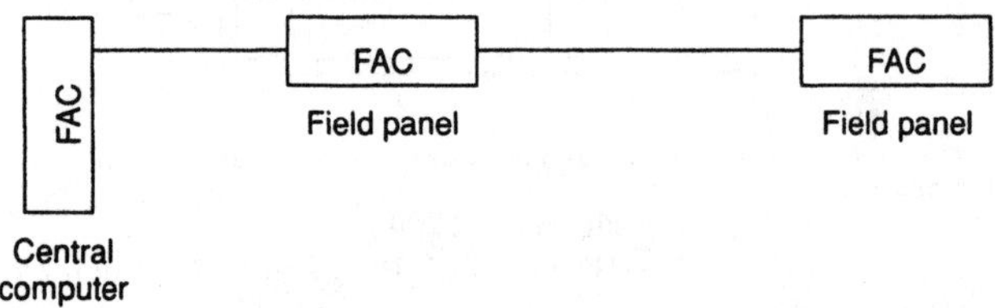

This is a series circuit identical to diagram for Style 0.5, except that the fire alarm system hardware has enhanced performance. A single earth ground can be placed on a conductor or multiplex interface device, and the circuit and hardware still have alarm operability.

If a conductor break or an internal fault occurs in the pathway of the circuit conductors, the entire circuit becomes inoperative.

To verify alarm receipt capability and the resulting trouble signal, place an earth ground on one of the conductors or at the point where the signaling circuit attaches to the multiplex interface device. Then place one of the transmitters or an initiating devices into alarm.

Figure A-7-2.2(u) Style 1.0 (Class B).

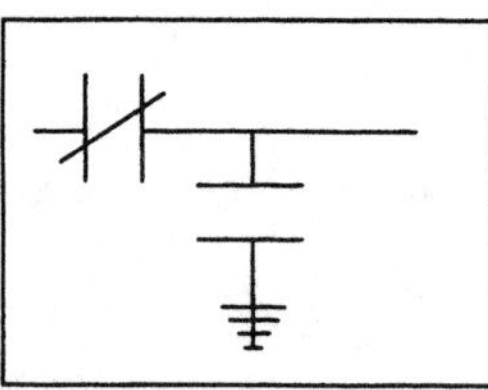

Figure A-7-2.2(v) Typical transmitter layout.

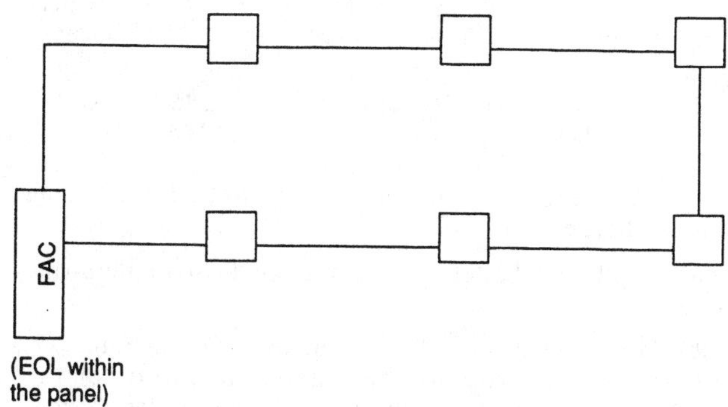

This is the central station McCulloh redundant type circuit and has alarm receipt capability on either side of a single break.

(a) To test, lift one of the conductors and operate a transmitter or initiating device on each side of the break. This activity should be repeated for each conductor.

(b) Place an earth ground on a conductor and operate a single transmitter or initiating device to verify alarm receipt capability and trouble condition for each conductor.

(c) Repeat the instructions of (a) and (b) at the same time and verify alarm receipt capability and that a trouble condition results.

Figure A-7-2.2(w) Typical McCulloh loop.

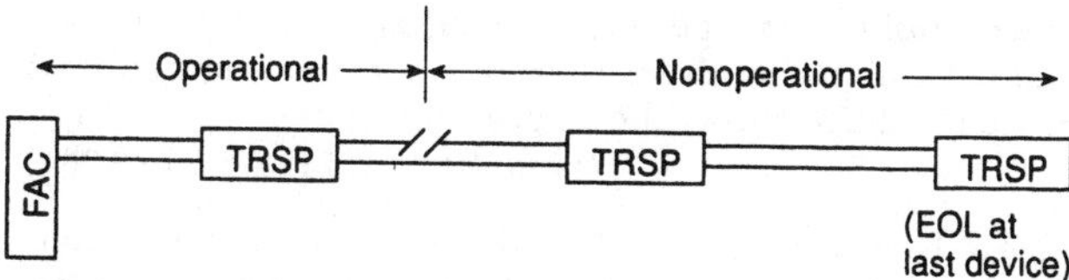

TRSP = Transponder

This is a parallel circuit whose multiplex interface devices transmit signal and operating power over the same conductors. The multiplex interface devices may be operable up to the point of a single break. Verify by lifting a conductor and causing an alarm condition on one of the units between the central alarm unit and the break. Either lift a conductor to verify the trouble condition or place an earth ground on the conductors. Test for all the valuations shown on the signaling table.

On ground fault testing verify alarm receipt capability by actuating a multiplex interface initiating device or a transmitter.

Figure A-7-2.2(x) Style 3.0 (Class B).

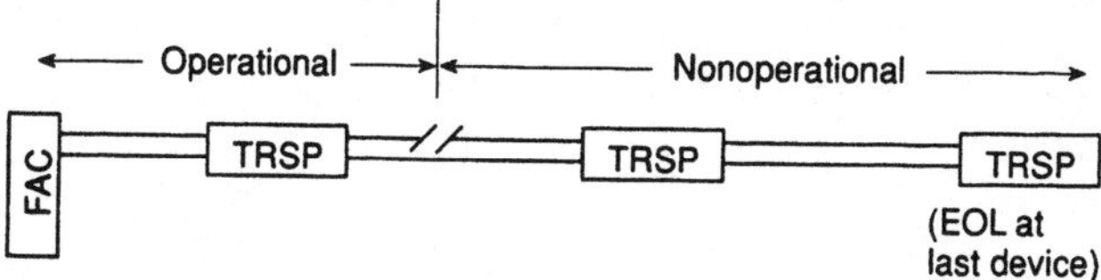

Repeat the instructions for Style 3.0 (Class B) and verify the trouble conditions by either lifting a conductor or placing a ground on the conductor.

Figure A-7-2.2(y) Style 3.5 (Class B).

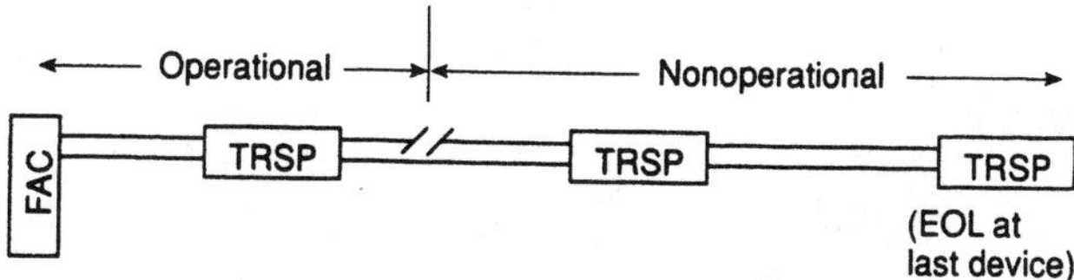

Repeat the instructions for Style 3.0 (Class B) and include a loss of carrier if the signal is being used.

Figure A-7-2.2(z) Style 4.0 (Class B).

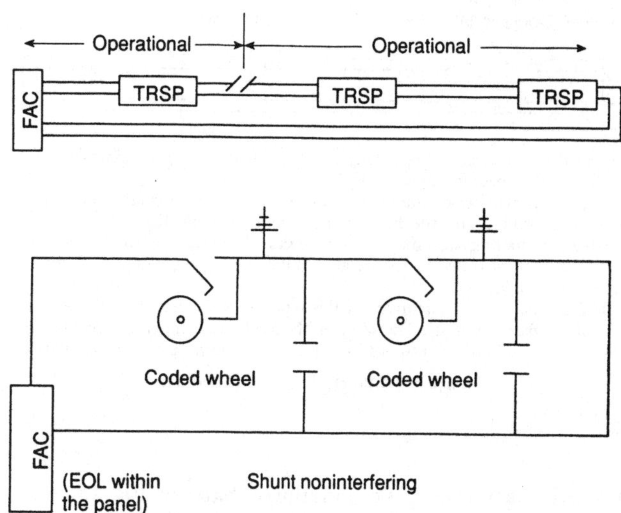

Repeat the instructions for Style 3.5 (Class B). Verify alarm receipt capability while lifting a conductor by actuating a multiple interface device or transmitter on each side of the break.

Figure A-7-2.2(aa) Style 4.5 (Class B).

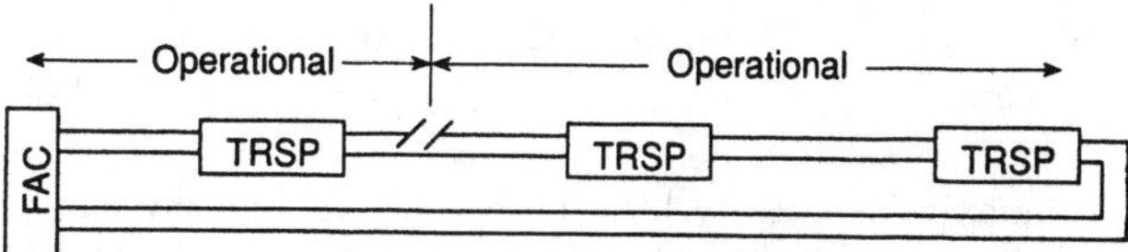

Verify the alarm receipt capability and trouble annunciation by lifting a conductor and actuating a multiplex interfacing device or a transmitter on each side of the break. For the earth ground verification, place an earth ground and certify alarm receipt capability and trouble annunciation by actuating a single multiplex interfacing device or a transmitter.

Figure A-7-2.2(bb) Style 5.0 (Class A).

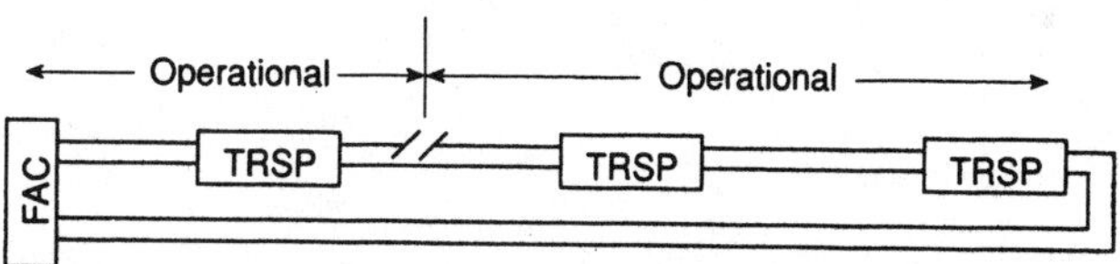

Repeat the instructions for Style 2.0 (Class A) [(a) through (c)]. Verify the remaining steps for trouble annunciation for the various combinations.

Figure A-7-2.2(cc) Style 6.0 (Class A).

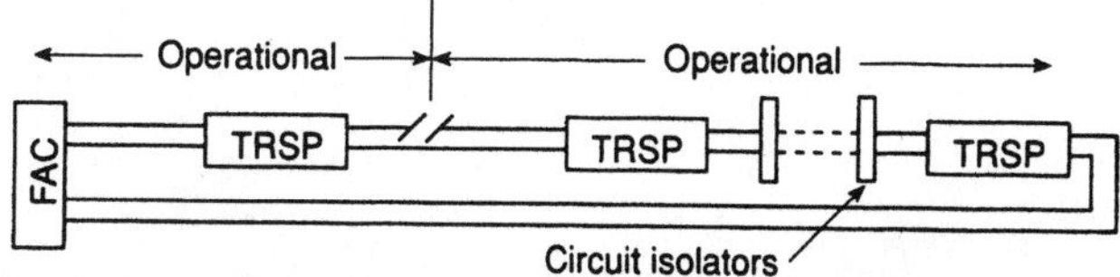

For the portions of the circuits electrically located between the monitoring points of circuit isolators, follow the instructions for a Style 7.0 (Class A) circuit. It should be clearly noted that the alarm receipt capability for remaining portions of the circuit protection isolators is not the capability of the circuit, but permissible with enhanced system capabilities.

Figure A-7-2.2(dd) Style 6.0 (with circuit isolators) (Class A).

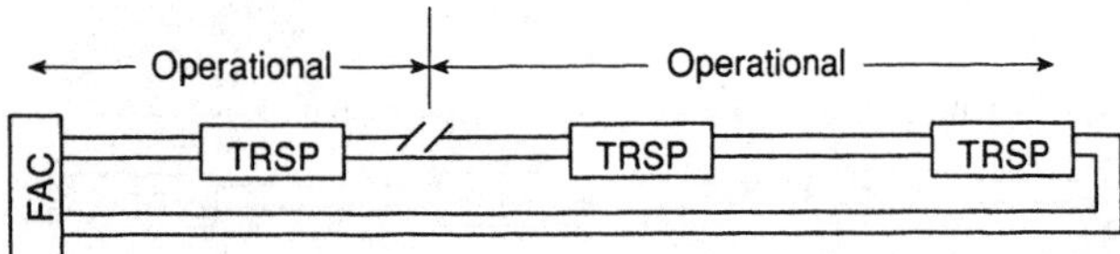

Repeat the instructions for testing of Style 6.0 (Class A) for alarm receipt capability and trouble annunciation.
NOTE 1: A portion of the circuit between the alarm processor or central supervising station and the first circuit isolator does not have alarm receipt capability in the presence of a wire-to-wire short. The same is true for the portion of the circuit from the last isolator to the alarm processor or the central supervising station.
NOTE 2: Some manufacturers of this type of equipment have isolators as part of the base assembly. Therefore in the field this component may not be readily observable without the assistance of the manufacturer's representative.

Figure A-7-2.2(ee) Style 7.0 (Class A).

A-7-3.2 Batteries. To maximize battery life, nickel-cadmium batteries should be charged as follows:

Float Voltage	1.42 Volts/Cell + .01 volts
High Rate Voltage	1.58 Volts/Cell + .07 – 0.00 volts

NOTE: High and low gravity voltages are (+) 0.07 volts and (–) 0.03 volts respectively.

[From NFPA 1221, 2-1.10.2.2, 3-1.5.3.2, and 4-1.6.2.3]

To maximize battery life, the battery voltage for lead-acid cells should be maintained within the limits shown in the following table:

Float Voltage	High Gravity Battery (Lead Calcium)	Low Gravity Battery (Lead Antimony)
Maximum	2.25 Volts/Cell	2.17 Volts/Cell
Minimum	2.20 Volts/Cell	2.13 Volts/Cell
High Rate Voltage		2.33 Volts/Cell

The following procedure is recommended for checking state of charge for nickel-cadmium batteries:

(a) Switch the battery charger from float to high-rate mode.

(b) The current, as indicated on the charger ammeter, will immediately rise to the maximum output of the charger, and the battery voltage, as shown on the charger voltmeter, will start to rise at the same time.

(c) The actual value of the voltage rise is unimportant since it depends on many variables; the length of time it takes for the voltage to rise is the important factor.

(d) If, for example, the voltage rises rapidly in a few minutes, then holds steady at the new value, the battery was fully charged. At the same time, the current will drop to slightly above its original value.

(e) In contrast, if the voltage rises slowly and the output current remains high, the high-rate charge should be continued until the voltage remains constant. Such a condition is an indication that the battery was not fully charged, and the float voltage should be increased slightly.

[From NFPA 1221, A-2-1.10.2.2(b)]

A-7-3.2.1 It is suggested that the annual test can be conducted in segments so that all devices are tested annually.

[New paragraph]

Appendix B Engineering Guide for Automatic Fire Detector Spacing

[From NFPA 72E-1990, Appendix C modified]

This Appendix is not a part of the requirements of this NFPA document, but is included for information purposes only.

B-1 Introduction.

B-1.1 Scope. This appendix provides information intended to supplement Chapter 5 and includes a procedure for determining heat detector spacing based on the size and rate of growth of fire to be detected, various ceiling heights, and ambient temperature. The effects of ceiling height and the size and rate of growth of a flaming fire on smoke detector spacing are also treated. A procedure for analyzing the response of existing heat detection systems is also presented.

B-1.1.1 This appendix utilizes the results of fire research funded by the Fire Detection Institute to provide test data and analysis to the NFPA Technical Committee on Detection Devices. (*See reference 10 in Appendix C.*)

B-1.1.2 This appendix is based on full-scale fire tests in which all fires were geometrically growing flaming fires.

B-1.1.3 The tables and graphs in this appendix were produced using test data and data correlations for wood fuels having a total heat of combustion of about 20,900 kJ/kg and a convective heat release rate fraction equal to 75 percent of the total heat release rate. Users should refer to references 12 and 13 in Appendix C for fuels or burning conditions substantially different from these conditions.

[From NFPA 72E - 1990, Appendix C]

B-1.1.4 The guidance applicable to smoke detectors is limited to a theoretical analysis based on the flaming fire test data and is not intended to address the detection of smoldering fires.

B-1.2 Purpose. The purpose of this appendix is to assist fire alarm system engineers concerned with spacing and response of heat or smoke detectors.

B-1.2.1 Design. This appendix provides a method for modifying the listed spacing of both rate-of-rise and fixed-temperature heat detectors required to achieve detector response to a geometrically growing flaming fire at a specific fire size, taking into account the height of the ceiling on which the detectors are mounted and the fire safety objectives for the space. This procedure also permits modification of listed spacing of fixed temperature heat detectors to account for variation of ambient temperature (T_o) from standard test conditions.

[From NFPA 72E - 1990, Appendix C modified]

B-1.2.2 Analysis. This appendix may be used to estimate the fire size that can be detected by an existing array of listed heat detectors installed at a given spacing for a given ceiling height in known ambient conditions.

[From NFPA 72E - 1990, C-5-2]

B-1.2.3 This appendix is also intended to explain the effect of rate of fire growth and fire size of a flaming fire, as well as the effect of ceiling height on the spacing and response of smoke detectors.

[From NFPA 72E - 1990, C-5-2.2 modified]

B-1.2.4 This methodology utilizes theories of fire development, fire plume dynamics, and detector performance, which are the major factors influencing detector response. However, it does not consider several lesser phenomena that, in general, are unlikely to have significant influence. A discussion of ceiling drag, heat loss to the ceiling, radiation to the detector from a fire, re-radiation of heat from a detector to its surroundings, and the heat of fusion of eutectic materials in fusible elements of heat detectors and their possible limitations on the design method are provided in references 4, 11, and 14 in Appendix C.

[From NFPA 72E - 1990, C-5-2.3]

B-1.3 Relationship to Listed Spacings. Listed spacings for heat detectors are based on relatively large fires (approximately 1200 Btu/sec), burning at a constant rate. [The listed spacing is based on the distance from a fire at which an ordinary degree heat detector actuates prior to operation of a 160°F (71°C) sprinkler installed at a 10-ft (3-m) spacing.] [*See Figure A-5-2.7.1(a).*]

Design spacing for this type of fire can be determined using the material in Chapter 5.

When smaller or larger fires and varying growth rates must be considered, the designer may use the material presented by this appendix.

[From NFPA 72E - 1990, Appendix C modified]

B-1.4 Required Data. The following data are required to use the methods in this appendix for either analysis or design.

B-1.4.1 Analysis.

T_o	Ambient temperature
H	Ceiling height or clearance above fuel
T_s	Detector operating temperature (heat detectors only)
ΔT_s/min	Rate of temperature change set point for rate-of-rise heat detectors
RTI	Response time index for the detector (heat detectors only) or its listed spacing
α or t_g	Fuel fire intensity coefficient or t_g, the fire growth time
S	The actual installed spacing of the existing detectors

B-1.4.2 Design.

T_o	Ambient temperature
H	Ceiling height or clearance above fuel
T_s	Detector operating temperature (heat detectors only)
ΔT_s/min	Rate of temperature change set point for rate-of-rise heat detectors
RTI	Response time index for the detector (heat detectors only) or its listed spacing
α or t_g	Fuel fire intensity coefficient or t_g, the fire growth time
Q_d or t_d	The threshold fire size at which response must occur or the time to detector response

B-1.4.3 The terms and data listed above are defined in more detail in the following sections.

[From NFPA 72E - 1990, Appendix C]

B-2 Fire Development and Ceiling Height Considerations.

B-2.1 General. The purpose of this section is to discuss the effects of ceiling height and the selection of a threshold fire size that may be used as the basis for determination of type and spacing of automatic fire detectors in a specific situation.

[From NFPA 72E - 1990, Appendix C modified]

B-2.1.1 A detector will ordinarily operate sooner in detecting the fire if it is nearer the fire.

[From NFPA 72E - 1990, B-1-1]

B-2.1.2 Generally, height is the most important single dimension where ceiling heights exceed 16 ft (4.9 m).

[From NFPA 72E - 1990, B-1-2]

B-2.1.3 As smoke and heat rise from a fire, they tend to spread in the general form of an inverted cone. Therefore, the concentration within the cone varies inversely as a variable exponential function of the distance from the source. This effect is very significant in the early stages of a fire, because the angle of the cone is wide. As a fire intensifies, the angle of the cone narrows and the significance of the effect of height is lessened.

[From NFPA 72E - 1990, B-1-3]

B-2.1.4 High Ceilings. As the ceiling height increases, a larger-size fire is required to actuate the same detector in the same time. In view of this, it is mandatory that the designer of a fire detection system calling for heat detectors consider the size of the fire and rate of heat release that may be permitted to develop before detection is ultimately obtained.

[From NFPA 72E - 1990, B-1-4]

B-2.1.5 The most sensitive detectors suitable for the maximum ambient temperature at heights above 30 ft (9.1 m) should be employed.

[From NFPA 72E - 1990, B-1-5]

B-2.1.6 Spacing recommended by testing laboratories for the location of detectors is an indication of their relative sensitivity. This applies with each detection principle; however, detectors operating on various physical principles have different inherent sensitivities to different types of fires and fuels.

[From NFPA 72E - 1990, B-1-6]

B-2.1.7 Reduction of listed spacing may be required for any of the following purposes:

(a) Faster response of the device to a fire

(b) Response of the device to a smaller fire

(c) Accommodation to room geometry

(d) Other special considerations, such as air movement, or ceiling or other obstructions.

[From NFPA 72E - 1990, B-1-7]

B-2.2 Fire Development.

B-2.2.1 Fire development will vary depending on the combustion characteristics of the fuels involved and the physical configuration of the fuels. After ignition, most fires grow in an accelerating pattern.

B-2.2.2 Fire Size.

B-2.2.2.1 Fires can be characterized by their rate of heat release, measured in terms of the number of Btus per second (kW) generated. Typical maximum heat release rates, Q_m, for a number of different fuels and fuel configurations are provided in Tables B-2.2.2.1(a) and (b).

In Table B-2.2.2.1(a):

$$Q_m = q_A$$

Where:

Q_m = the maximum or peak heat release rate in Btu/sec

q = the heat release rate density per unit floor area in Btu/sec/ft^2

A = the floor area of the fuel in ft^2.

[From NFPA 72E - 1990, Appendix C modified]

B-2.2.2.2 Example. A particular hazard analysis is to be based on a fire scenario involving a 10-ft by 10-ft stack of wood pallets 5 ft high. Approximately what peak heat release rate can be expected?

From Table B-2.2.2.1(a), the heat release rate density (q) for 5-ft high wood pallets is about 330 Btu/sec/ft^2.

The area is 10 ft by 10 ft = 100 ft^2.

$Q_m = q_A = 330 \times 100 = 33{,}000$ Btu/sec.

The fire would have a medium to fast fire growth rate reaching 1000 Btu/sec in about 90 to 190 seconds.

[From NFPA 72E - 1990, Appendix C]

B-2.2.2.3 The National Institute of Standards and Technology (former National Bureau of Standards) has developed a large-scale calorimeter for measuring the heat release rates of burning furniture. Two reports issued by NIST (*see references 3 and 13 in Appendix C*) describe the apparatus and data collected during two test series.

Test data from 40 furniture calorimeter tests have been used to independently verify the power-law fire growth model, $Q = \alpha t^2$. (*See reference 14 in Appendix C.*) Here Q is the instantaneous heat release rate, α is the fire intensity coefficient, and t is time. The fire growth time, t_g, is arbitrarily defined as the time after established burning when the fire would reach a burning rate of 1000 Btu/sec. In terms of t_g:

$$\alpha = 1000/t_g^2 \text{ Btu/sec}^3$$

$$\alpha = 1055/t_g^2 \text{ kW/sec}^2$$

and

$$Q = (1000/t_g^2)t^2 \text{ Btu/sec}$$

$$Q = (1055/t_g^2)t^2 \text{ kW.}$$

Graphs of heat release data from the 40 furniture calorimeter tests can be found in reference 8. Best fit power-law fire growth curves have been superimposed on the graphs. Data from the best fit curves can be used with this appendix to design or analyze fire detection systems that must respond to similar items burning under a flat ceiling. Table B-2.2.2.3 is a summary of that data.

Table B-2.2.2.1(a) Maximum Heat Release Rates

	Warehouse Materials	Growth Time (tg) (sec)	Heat Release Density (q)	Classification (s = slow, m = medium, f = fast)
1.	Wood pallets, stack, $1^1/_2$ ft high (6-12% moisture)	150-310	110	f-m
2.	Wood pallets, stack, 5 ft high (6-12% moisture)	90-190	330	f-m
3.	Wood pallets, stack, 10 ft high (6-12% moisture)	80-110	600	f
4.	Wood pallets, stack, 16 ft high (6-12% moisture)	75-105	900	f
5.	Mail bags, filled, stored 5 ft high	190	35	m
6.	Cartons, compartmented, stacked 15 ft high	60	200	f
7.	Paper, vertical rolls, stacked 20 ft high	15-28	—	†
8.	Cotton (also PE, PE/Cot, Acrylic/Nylon/PE), garments in 12-ft high rack	20-42	—	†
9.	Cartons on pallets, rack storage, 15-30 ft high	40-280	—	f-m
10.	Paper products, densely packed in cartons, rack storage, 20 ft high	470	—	s
11.	PE letter trays, filled, stacked 5 ft high on cart	190	750	m
12.	PE trash barrels in cartons, stacked 15 ft high	55	250	f
13.	FRP shower stalls in cartons, stacked 15 ft high	85	110	f
14.	PE bottles, packed in Item 6	85	550	f
15.	PE bottles in cartons, stacked 15 ft high	75	170	f
16.	PE pallets, stacked 3 ft high	130	—	f
17.	PE pallets, stacked 6-8 ft high	30-55	—	f
18.	PU mattress, single, horizontal	110	—	f
19.	PE insulation board, rigid foam, stacked 15 ft high	8	170	†
20.	PS jars, packed in Item 6	55	1200	f
21.	PS tubs nested in cartons, stacked 14 ft high	105	450	f
22.	PS toy parts in cartons, stacked 15 ft high	110	180	f
23.	PS insulation board, rigid, stacked 14 ft high	7	290	†
24.	PVC bottles, packed in Item 6	9	300	†
25.	PP tubs, packed in Item 6	10	390	†
26.	PP and PE film in rolls, stacked 14 ft high	40	350	†
27.	Distilled spirits in barrels, stacked 20 ft high	23-40	—	†
28.	Methyl alcohol	—	65	—
29.	Gasoline	—	200	—
30.	Kerosene	—	200	—
31.	Diesel oil	—	180	—

For SI Units: 1 ft = 0.305 m.
NOTE: The heat release rates per unit floor area are for fully involved combustibles, assuming 100 percent combustion efficiency. The growth times shown are those required to exceed 1000 Btu/sec heat release rate for developing fires assuming 100 percent combustion efficiency.
(PE = polyethylene; PS = polystyrene; PVC = polyvinyl chloride; PP = polypropylene; PU = polyurethane; FRP = fiberglass-reinforced polyester.)
†Fire growth rate exceeds design data.

[From NFPA 72E - 1990, Appendix C modified]

Table B-2.2.2.1(b) Maximum Heat Release Rates from Fire Detection Institute Analysis

Materials	Approximate Values Btu/sec
Medium wastebasket with milk cartons	100
Large barrel with milk cartons	140
Upholstered chair with polyurethane foam	350
Latex foam mattress (heat at room door)	1200
Furnished living room (heat at open door)	4000-8000

For reference, the table contains the test numbers used in the original NIST reports. The virtual time of origin, t_v, is the time at which the fires began to obey the power-law fire growth model. Prior to t_v, the fuels may have smoldered but did not burn vigorously with an open flame. The model curves are then predicted by:

$$Q = \alpha(t - t_v)^2 \text{ Btu/sec or kW}$$

$$Q = (1000/t_g^2)(t - t_v)^2 \text{ Btu/sec}$$

$$Q = (1055/t_g^2)(t - t_v)^2 \text{ kW.}$$

Figure B-2.2.2.3 is an example of actual test data with a power-law curve superimposed. This shows how the model may be used to approximate the growth phase of the fire.

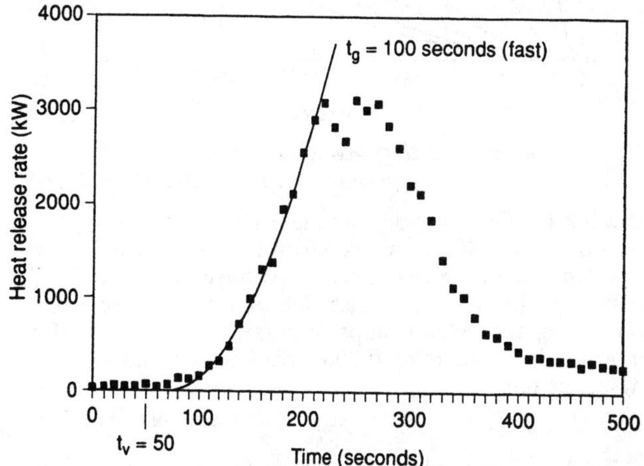

Figure B-2.2.2.3 Test 38, foam sofa.

[From NFPA 72E - 1990, Appendix C]

For tests 19, 21, 29, 42, and 67, different power-law curves were used to model the initial and the latter realms of burning. In examples such as these, engineers must choose the fire growth parameter that best describes the realm of burning that the detection system is being designed to respond to.

In addition to heat release rate data, the original NIST reports contain data on particulate conversion and radiation from the test specimens. These data can be used to determine the threshold fire size (heat release rate) at which tenability becomes endangered or when additional fuel packages might become involved in the fire.

[From NFPA 72E - 1990, C-5-2.2.2 modified]

B-2.2.2.4 A fire detection system can be designed to detect a fire at a certain size in terms of its heat release rate. This is called the threshold fire size (Q_d). The threshold size is the rate of heat release at which detection is desired.

[From NFPA 72E - 1990, C-2.2.3]

B-2.2.3 Fire Growth.

B-2.2.3.1 A second important consideration concerning fire development is the time (t_g) it takes for fire to reach a given heat release rate. Table B-2.2.2.1(a) and Table B-2.2.2.3 provide the times required to reach a heat release rate of 1000 Btu/sec (1055 kW) for a variety of materials in various configurations.

B-2.2.3.2 For purposes of this appendix, fires are classified as being either slow-, medium-, or fast-developing. (*See Figure B-2.2.3.2.*)

[From NFPA 72E - 1990, Appendix C modified]

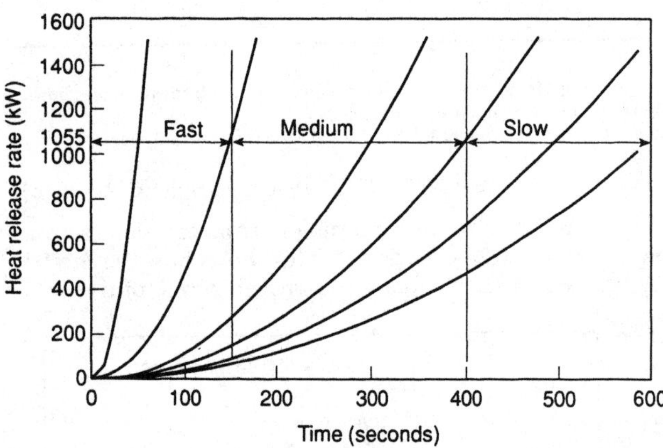

Figure B-2.2.3.2 Power-law heat release rates.

[From NFPA 72E - 1990, Appendix C]

B-2.2.3.2.1 The slow-developing fire is defined as one that would take 400 or more seconds (6 minutes, 40 seconds) from the time that established burning occurs until the fire reaches a heat release rate of 1000 Btu/sec (1055 kW). Using the relationships discussed in B-2.2.2.3, this corresponds to an α of 0.0062 Btu/sec^3 or less (0.0066 kW/sec^2 or less).

[From NFPA 72E - 1990, Appendix C modified]

B-2.2.3.2.2 The medium-developing fire is one that would take 150 seconds (2 minutes, 30 seconds) or more and less than 400 seconds (6 minutes, 40 seconds) from the time that established burning occurs until the fire reaches a heat release rate of 1000 Btu/sec (1055 kW). Using the relationships discussed in B-2.2.2.3, this corresponds to $0.0444 \leq \alpha < 0.0062$ Btu/sec^3 ($0.0469 \leq \alpha < 0.0066$ kW/sec^2).

B-2.2.3.2.3 The fast-developing fire is one that would take less than 150 seconds (2 minutes, 30 seconds) from the time that established burning occurs until the fire reaches a heat release rate of 1000 Btu/sec (1055 kW). Using the relationships discussed in B-2.2.2.3, this corresponds to an α greater than 0.0444 Btu/sec^3 (0.0469 kW/sec^2).

B-2.2.3.3 The design fires used in this guide grow according to the following equation: $Q = (1000/t_g^2)t^2$ [where Q is the heat release rate in Btu/sec; t_g is the fire growth time (149 sec = fast, 150–399 sec = medium, 400 sec = slow); and t_g is the time, in seconds, after established burning occurs].

B-2.2.4 Selection of Fire Size. The selection of threshold fire size, Q_d, should be based on an understanding of the characteristics of a specified space and fire safety objectives for that space.

For example, in a particular installation it may be desirable to detect a typical wastebasket fire. Table B-2.2.2.1(b) includes data for a fire involving a comparable array of combustibles, specifically milk cartons in a wastebasket. Such a fire is indicated to produce a peak heat release rate of 100 Btu/sec.

B-2.3 Ceiling Height.

B-2.3.1 The Fire Detection Institute data are based on the height of the ceiling above the fire. In this guide, it is recommended that the designer use the actual distance from floor to ceiling, since the ceiling height will thereby be more conservative and actual detector response will improve when the potential fuel in a room is above floor level.

B-2.3.2 Where the designer desires to consider the height of the potential fuel in the room, the distance between the fuel and the ceiling should be used in place of the ceiling height in the tables and graphs. This should be considered only where the minimum height of the potential fuel is always constant, and where the concept is acceptable to the authority having jurisdiction.

B-2.3.3 The procedures presented in this appendix are based on an analysis of test data for ceiling heights up to 30 ft (9.1 m). No data was analyzed for ceilings greater than 30 ft (9.1 m); therefore, in such installations, engineering judgment and manufacturer's recommendations should be used.

B-3 Heat Detector Spacing.

B-3.1 General.

B-3.1.1 This section discusses procedures for determination of installed spacing of listed heat detectors used to detect flaming fires.

B-3.1.2 The determination of the installed spacing of heat detectors using these procedures adjusts the listed spacing to reflect the effects of ceiling height, threshold fire size, rate of fire development, and, for fixed temperature detectors, the ambient temperature and the temperature rating of the detector.

B-3.1.3 Other factors that will affect detector response, such as beams and joists, are treated in Chapter 5.

Table B-2.2.2.3 Furniture Heat Release Rates

Test No.	Item/Mass/Description	Growth Time (t_g) (sec)	Classification (s = slow, m = medium, f = fast)	Alpha (α) (kW/sec²)	Virtual time (t_v) (sec)	Maximum Heat Release Rates (kW)
Test 15	Metal wardrobe, 41.4 kg (total)	50	f	0.4220	10	750
Test 18	Chair F33 (trial loveseat), 39.2 kg	400	s	0.0066	140	950
Test 19	Chair F21, 28.15 kg (initial)	175	m	0.0344	110	350
Test 19	Chair F21, 28.15 kg (later)	50	f	0.4220	190	2000
Test 21	Metal wardrobe, 40.8 kg (total) (initial)	250	m	0.0169	10	250
Test 21	Metal wardrobe, 40.8 kg (total) (average)	120	f	0.0733	60	250
Test 21	Metal wardrobe, 40.8 kg (total) (later)	100	f	0.1055	30	140
Test 22	Chair F24, 28.3 kg	350	m	0.0086	400	700
Test 23	Chair F23, 31.2 kg	400	s	0.0066	100	700
Test 24	Chair F22, 31.9 kg	2000	s	0.0003	150	300
Test 25	Chair F26, 19.2 kg	200	m	0.0264	90	800
Test 26	Chair F27, 29.0 kg	200	m	0.0264	360	900
Test 27	Chair F29, 14.0 kg	100	f	0.1055	70	1850
Test 28	Chair F28, 29.2 kg	425	s	0.0058	90	700
Test 29	Chair F25, 27.8 kg (later)	60	f	0.2931	175	700
Test 29	Chair F25, 27.8 kg (initial)	100	f	0.1055	100	2000
Test 30	Chair F30, 25.2 kg	60	f	0.2931	70	950
Test 31	Chair F31 (loveseat), 39.6 kg	60	F	0.2931	145	2600
Test 37	Chair F31 (loveseat), 40.4 kg	80	f	0.1648	100	2750
Test 38	Chair F32 (sofa), 51.5 kg	100	f	0.1055	50	3000
Test 39	1/2-in. plywood wardrobe with fabrics, 68.5 kg	35	†	0.8612	20	3250
Test 40	1/2-in. plywood wardrobe with fabrics, 68.32 kg	35	†	0.8612	40	3500
Test 41	1/8-in. plywood wardrobe with fabrics, 36.0 kg	40	†	0.6594	40	6000
Test 42	1/8-in. plywood wardrobe with fire-retardant int. fin. (initial growth)	70	f	0.2153	50	2000
Test 42	1/8-in. plywood wardrobe with fire-retardant int. fin. (later growth)	30	†	1.1722	100	5000
Test 43	Repeat of 1/2-in. plywood wardrobe, 67.62 kg	30	†	1.1722	50	3000
Test 44	1/8-in. plywood wardrobe with fire-retardant latex paint, 37.26 kg	90	f	0.1302	30	2900
Test 45	Chair F21, 28.34 kg	100	f	0.1055	120	2100
Test 46	Chair F21, 28.34 kg	45	†	0.5210	130	2600
Test 47	Chair, adj. back metal frame, foam cushions, 20.82 kg	170	m	0.0365	30	250
Test 48	Easy chair C07, 11.52 kg	175	m	0.0344	90	950
Test 49	Easy chair F-34, 15.68 kg	200	m	0.0264	50	200
Test 50	Chair, metal frame, minimum cushion, 16.52 kg	200	m	0.0264	120	3000
Test 51	Chair, molded fiberglass, no cushion, 5.28 kg	120	f	0.0733	20	35
Test 52	Molded plastic patient chair, 11.26 kg	275	m	0.0140	2090	700
Test 53	Chair, metal frame, padded seat and back, 15.54 kg	350	m	0.0086	50	280
Test 54	Loveseat, metal frame, foam cushions, 27.26 kg	500	s	0.0042	210	300
Test 56	Chair, wood frame, latex foam cushions, 11.2 kg	500	s	0.0042	50	85
Test 57	Loveseat, wood frame, foam cushions, 54.6 kg	350	m	0.0086	500	1000
Test 61	Wardrobe, 3/4-in. particleboard, 120.33 kg	150	m	0.0469	0	1200
Test 62	Bookcase, plywood with aluminum frame, 30.39 kg	65	f	0.2497	40	25
Test 64	Easy chair, molded flexible urethane frame, 15.98 kg	1000	s	0.0011	750	450
Test 66	Easy chair, 23.02 kg	76	f	0.1827	3700	600
Test 67	Mattress and boxspring, 62.36 kg (later)	350	m	0.0086	400	500
Test 67	Mattress and boxspring, 62.36 kg (initial)	1100	s	0.0009	90	400

For SI Units: 1 ft = 0.305 m; 1000 Btu/sec = 1055 kW; 1 lb = 0.456kg.
†Fire growth exceeds design data.

[From NFPA 72E - 1990, Table C-5-2.2.2 modified]

B-3.1.4 The difference between the rated temperature of a fixed temperature detector (T_s) and the maximum ambient temperature (T_o) at the ceiling should be as small as possible. To reduce unwanted alarms, the difference between operating temperature and ambient temperature should be not less than 20°F (11°C).

B-3.1.5 Listed rate-of-rise heat detectors are designed to activate at a nominal rate of temperature rise of 15°F (8°C) per minute.

B-3.1.6 The listed spacing of a detector is an indicator of the detector's sensitivity. Given the same temperature rating, a detector listed for a 50-ft (15.2-m) spacing is more sensitive than one listed for a 20-ft (6.1-m) spacing.

B-3.1.7 Where using combination detectors incorporating both fixed temperature and rate-of-rise heat detection principles to detect a geometrically growing fire, the data herein for rate-of-rise detectors should be used in selecting an installed spacing because the rate-of-rise principle controls the response.

B-3.1.8 Rate-compensated detectors are not specifically covered by this guide. However, a conservative approach to predicting their performance is to use the fixed temperature heat detector guidance contained herein.

B-3.2 Fixed-Temperature Heat Detector Spacing.

B-3.2.1 Tables B-3.2.2 and B-3.2.4(a) through (y) are to be used to determine the installed spacing of fixed-temperature heat detectors. The analytical basis for the tables is presented in a later section of this appendix. This section describes how the tables are to be used.

B-3.2.1.1 Except for ceiling height, the nearest value shown in the tables will provide sufficient accuracy for these calculations. Interpolation is allowable but not necessary except for ceiling height.

B-3.2.2 Given the detector's listed spacing and the detector's rated temperature (T_s), use Table B-3.2.2 to find the detector time constant (τ_0). The time constant is a measure of the detector's sensitivity. (*See B-3.3.*)

[From NFPA 72E - 1990, Appendix C modified]

B-3.2.2.1 Response time index (RTI) can also be used to describe the sensitivity of a fixed temperature heat detector. (*See Section B-4.*)

B-3.2.3 Estimate the minimum ambient temperature (T_o) expected at the ceiling of the space to be protected. Calculate the temperature change (ΔT) of the detector required for detection ($\Delta T = T_s - T_o$).

B-3.2.3.1 Selection of the minimum ambient temperature requires engineering judgment. Use of the absolute minimum ambient temperature will result in the most conservative designs. This is true because it is then assumed that the detector must absorb enough energy to raise its temperature from the low ambient value up to its operating temperature. A review of historical data may show very low ambient temperatures that occur relatively infrequently, such as every one hundred years or so.

Depending on actual design considerations, it may be more prudent to use an average minimum ambient temperature. In any case, a sensitivity analysis should be performed to determine the effect of changing the ambient temperature on the design results.

[From NFPA 72E - 1990, Appendix C]

Table B-3.2.2 Time Constants (τ_0) for Any Listed Heat Detector*

Listed Spacing (ft)	ULI 128°	135°	145°	160°	170°	196°	FMRC All Temps.
10	400	330	262	195	160	97	196
15	250	190	156	110	89	45	110
20	165	135	105	70	52	17	70
25	124	100	78	48	32		48
30	95	80	61	36	22		36
40	71	57	41	18			
50	59	44	30				
70	36	24	9				

NOTE 1: These time constants are based on an analysis of the Underwriters Laboratories Inc. and Factory Mutual listing test procedures. Plunge test (*see reference 8 in Appendix C*) results performed on the detector to be used will give a more accurate time constant. See Section B-5 for a further discussion of detector time constants.

NOTE 2: These time constants can be converted to response time index (RTI) values by multiplying by $\sqrt{5}$ ft/sec. (*See B-3-3.*)

*At a reference velocity of 5 ft/sec.

[From NFPA 72E - 1990, C-5-2.2.1]

B-3.2.4 Having determined the detector's sensitivity (time constant or RTI) (*see B-3.2.2*), the temperature change of the detector required for detection (*see B-3.2.3*), the threshold fire size (*see B-3.2.2*), the fire growth rate (*see B-3.2.3*), and the ceiling height, use Tables B-3.2.4(a) through (y) to determine the required installed spacing. Table B-3.2.4 is an index to the tables.

[From NFPA 72E - 1990, Appendix C modified]

Table B-3.2.4 Design Tables Index

	Threshold Fire Size (Btu/sec) Q_d	Fire Growth Period (sec) t_g	Alpha (Btu/sec^3) α
Table B-3.2.4(a)	250	50	0.400
Table B-3.2.4(b)	250	150	0.044
Table B-3.2.4(c)	250	300	0.011
Table B-3.2.4(d)	250	500	0.004
Table B-3.2.4(e)	250	600	0.003
Table B-3.2.4(f)	500	50	0.400
Table B-3.2.4(g)	500	150	0.044
Table B-3.2.4(h)	500	300	0.011
Table B-3.2.4(i)	500	500	0.004
Table B-3.2.4(j)	500	600	0.003
Table B-3.2.4(k)	750	50	0.400
Table B-3.2.4(l)	750	150	0.044
Table B-3.2.4(m)	750	300	0.011
Table B-3.2.4(n)	750	500	0.004
Table B-3.2.4(o)	750	600	0.003
Table B-3.2.4(p)	1000	50	0.400
Table B-3.2.4(q)	1000	150	0.044
Table B-3.2.4(r)	1000	300	0.011
Table B-3.2.4(s)	1000	500	0.004
Table B-3.2.4(t)	1000	600	0.003
Table B-3.2.4(u)	2000	50	0.400
Table B-3.2.4(v)	2000	150	0.044
Table B-3.2.4(w)	2000	300	0.011
Table B-3.2.4(x)	2000	500	0.004
Table B-3.2.4(y)	2000	600	0.003

[From NFPA 72E - 1990, Appendix C modified]

Table B-3.2.4(a)
Q_d, Threshold Fire Size at Response: 250 Btu/sec
t_g: 50 seconds to 1000 Btu/sec
α: 0.400 Btu/sec^3

τ	RTI	ΔT	CEILING HEIGHT IN FEET						
			4.0	8.0	12.0	16.0	20.0	24.0	28.0
			INSTALLED SPACING OF DETECTORS						
25	56	40	7	5	2	0	0	0	0
25	56	60	6	3	1	0	0	0	0
25	56	80	5	2	0	0	0	0	0
25	56	100	4	2	0	0	0	0	0
25	56	120	4	1	0	0	0	0	0
25	56	140	3	1	0	0	0	0	0
50	112	40	5	3	1	0	0	0	0
50	112	60	4	2	0	0	0	0	0
50	112	80	3	1	0	0	0	0	0
50	112	100	3	0	0	0	0	0	0
50	112	120	2	0	0	0	0	0	0
50	112	140	2	0	0	0	0	0	0
75	168	40	4	2	0	0	0	0	0
75	168	60	3	1	0	0	0	0	0
75	168	80	2	0	0	0	0	0	0
75	168	100	2	0	0	0	0	0	0
75	168	120	2	0	0	0	0	0	0
75	168	140	1	0	0	0	0	0	0
100	224	40	3	1	0	0	0	0	0
100	224	60	2	0	0	0	0	0	0
100	224	80	2	0	0	0	0	0	0
100	224	100	1	0	0	0	0	0	0
100	224	120	1	0	0	0	0	0	0
100	224	140	1	0	0	0	0	0	0
125	280	40	3	0	0	0	0	0	0
125	280	60	2	0	0	0	0	0	0
125	280	80	1	0	0	0	0	0	0
125	280	100	1	0	0	0	0	0	0
125	280	120	0	0	0	0	0	0	0
125	280	140	0	0	0	0	0	0	0
150	335	40	2	0	0	0	0	0	0
150	335	60	2	0	0	0	0	0	0
150	335	80	1	0	0	0	0	0	0
150	335	100	0	0	0	0	0	0	0
150	335	120	0	0	0	0	0	0	0
150	335	140	0	0	0	0	0	0	0
175	391	40	2	0	0	0	0	0	0
175	391	60	1	0	0	0	0	0	0
175	391	80	1	0	0	0	0	0	0
175	391	100	0	0	0	0	0	0	0
175	391	120	0	0	0	0	0	0	0
175	391	140	0	0	0	0	0	0	0
200	447	40	2	0	0	0	0	0	0
200	447	60	1	0	0	0	0	0	0
200	447	80	0	0	0	0	0	0	0
200	447	100	0	0	0	0	0	0	0
200	447	120	0	0	0	0	0	0	0
200	447	140	0	0	0	0	0	0	0
225	503	40	2	0	0	0	0	0	0
225	503	60	1	0	0	0	0	0	0
225	503	80	0	0	0	0	0	0	0
225	503	100	0	0	0	0	0	0	0
225	503	120	0	0	0	0	0	0	0
225	503	140	0	0	0	0	0	0	0
250	559	40	2	0	0	0	0	0	0
250	559	60	0	0	0	0	0	0	0
250	559	80	0	0	0	0	0	0	0
250	559	100	0	0	0	0	0	0	0
250	559	120	0	0	0	0	0	0	0
250	559	140	0	0	0	0	0	0	0
275	615	40	1	0	0	0	0	0	0
275	615	60	0	0	0	0	0	0	0
275	615	80	0	0	0	0	0	0	0
275	615	100	0	0	0	0	0	0	0
275	615	120	0	0	0	0	0	0	0
275	615	140	0	0	0	0	0	0	0
300	671	40	1	0	0	0	0	0	0
300	671	60	0	0	0	0	0	0	0
300	671	80	0	0	0	0	0	0	0
300	671	100	0	0	0	0	0	0	0
300	671	120	0	0	0	0	0	0	0
300	671	140	0	0	0	0	0	0	0
325	727	40	1	0	0	0	0	0	0
325	727	60	0	0	0	0	0	0	0
325	727	80	0	0	0	0	0	0	0
325	727	100	0	0	0	0	0	0	0
325	727	120	0	0	0	0	0	0	0
325	727	140	0	0	0	0	0	0	0
350	783	40	1	0	0	0	0	0	0
350	783	60	0	0	0	0	0	0	0
350	783	80	0	0	0	0	0	0	0
350	783	100	0	0	0	0	0	0	0
350	783	120	0	0	0	0	0	0	0
350	783	140	0	0	0	0	0	0	0
375	839	40	0	0	0	0	0	0	0
375	839	60	0	0	0	0	0	0	0
375	839	80	0	0	0	0	0	0	0
375	839	100	0	0	0	0	0	0	0
375	839	120	0	0	0	0	0	0	0
375	839	140	0	0	0	0	0	0	0
400	894	40	0	0	0	0	0	0	0
400	894	60	0	0	0	0	0	0	0
400	894	80	0	0	0	0	0	0	0
400	894	100	0	0	0	0	0	0	0
400	894	120	0	0	0	0	0	0	0
400	894	140	0	0	0	0	0	0	0

NOTE: Detector time constant at a reference velocity of 5 ft/sec.
For SI Units: 1 ft = 0.305 m
1000 BTU/sec = 1055 kW

Table B-3.2.4(b)
Q_d, Threshold Fire Size at Response: 250 Btu/sec
t_g: 150 Seconds to 1000 Btu/sec
α: 0.044 Btu/sec^3

τ	RTI	ΔT	CEILING HEIGHT IN FEET						
			4.0	8.0	12.0	16.0	20.0	24.0	28.0
			INSTALLED SPACING OF DETECTORS						
25	56	40	15	12	9	6	3	0	0
25	56	60	12	9	6	3	0	0	0
25	56	80	10	7	4	1	0	0	0
25	56	100	9	6	2	0	0	0	0
25	56	120	8	4	1	0	0	0	0
25	56	140	7	4	1	0	0	0	0
50	112	40	11	9	6	3	1	0	0
50	112	60	9	6	3	1	0	0	0
50	112	80	7	5	2	0	0	0	0
50	112	100	6	4	1	0	0	0	0
50	112	120	6	3	1	0	0	0	0
50	112	140	5	2	0	0	0	0	0
75	168	40	9	7	4	2	0	0	0
75	168	60	7	5	2	0	0	0	0
75	168	80	6	3	1	0	0	0	0
75	168	100	5	3	0	0	0	0	0
75	168	120	4	2	0	0	0	0	0
75	168	140	4	1	0	0	0	0	0
100	224	40	8	6	3	1	0	0	0
100	224	60	6	4	2	0	0	0	0
100	224	80	5	3	1	0	0	0	0
100	224	100	4	2	0	0	0	0	0
100	224	120	4	1	0	0	0	0	0
100	224	140	3	1	0	0	0	0	0
125	280	40	7	5	2	1	0	0	0
125	280	60	5	3	1	0	0	0	0
125	280	80	4	2	0	0	0	0	0
125	280	100	4	1	0	0	0	0	0
125	280	120	3	1	0	0	0	0	0
125	280	140	3	0	0	0	0	0	0
150	335	40	6	4	2	0	0	0	0
150	335	60	5	2	1	0	0	0	0
150	335	80	4	2	0	0	0	0	0
150	335	100	3	1	0	0	0	0	0
150	335	120	3	0	0	0	0	0	0
150	335	140	2	0	0	0	0	0	0
175	391	40	6	3	1	0	0	0	0
175	391	60	4	2	0	0	0	0	0
175	391	80	3	1	0	0	0	0	0
175	391	100	3	1	0	0	0	0	0
175	391	120	2	0	0	0	0	0	0
175	391	140	2	0	0	0	0	0	0
200	447	40	5	3	1	0	0	0	0
200	447	60	4	2	0	0	0	0	0
200	447	80	3	1	0	0	0	0	0
200	447	100	3	0	0	0	0	0	0
200	447	120	2	0	0	0	0	0	0
200	447	140	2	0	0	0	0	0	0
225	503	40	5	3	1	0	0	0	0
225	503	60	4	2	0	0	0	0	0
225	503	80	3	1	0	0	0	0	0
225	503	100	2	0	0	0	0	0	0
225	503	120	2	0	0	0	0	0	0
225	503	140	2	0	0	0	0	0	0
250	559	40	5	2	0	0	0	0	0
250	559	60	3	1	0	0	0	0	0
250	559	80	3	0	0	0	0	0	0
250	559	100	2	0	0	0	0	0	0
250	559	120	2	0	0	0	0	0	0
250	559	140	1	0	0	0	0	0	0
275	615	40	4	2	0	0	0	0	0
275	615	60	3	1	0	0	0	0	0
275	615	80	2	0	0	0	0	0	0
275	615	100	2	0	0	0	0	0	0
275	615	120	2	0	0	0	0	0	0
275	615	140	1	0	0	0	0	0	0
300	671	40	4	2	0	0	0	0	0
300	671	60	3	1	0	0	0	0	0
300	671	80	2	0	0	0	0	0	0
300	671	100	2	0	0	0	0	0	0
300	671	120	1	0	0	0	0	0	0
300	671	140	1	0	0	0	0	0	0
325	727	40	4	2	0	0	0	0	0
325	727	60	3	1	0	0	0	0	0
325	727	80	2	0	0	0	0	0	0
325	727	100	2	0	0	0	0	0	0
325	727	120	1	0	0	0	0	0	0
325	727	140	1	0	0	0	0	0	0
350	783	40	4	2	0	0	0	0	0
350	783	60	3	0	0	0	0	0	0
350	783	80	2	0	0	0	0	0	0
350	783	100	2	0	0	0	0	0	0
350	783	120	1	0	0	0	0	0	0
350	783	140	1	0	0	0	0	0	0
375	839	40	3	1	0	0	0	0	0
375	839	60	2	0	0	0	0	0	0
375	839	80	2	0	0	0	0	0	0
375	839	100	1	0	0	0	0	0	0
375	839	120	1	0	0	0	0	0	0
375	839	140	0	0	0	0	0	0	0
400	894	40	3	1	0	0	0	0	0
400	894	60	2	0	0	0	0	0	0
400	894	80	2	0	0	0	0	0	0
400	894	100	1	0	0	0	0	0	0
400	894	120	1	0	0	0	0	0	0
400	894	140	0	0	0	0	0	0	0

NOTE: Detector time constant at a reference velocity of 5 ft/sec.
For SI Units: 1 ft = 0.305 m
1000 BTU/sec = 1055 kW

Table B-3.2.4(c)
Q_d, Threshold Fire Size at Response: 250 Btu/sec
t_g: 300 Seconds to 1000 Btu/sec
α: 0.011 Btu/sec^3

τ	RTI	ΔT	CEILING HEIGHT IN FEET						
			4.0	8.0	12.0	16.0	20.0	24.0	28.0
			INSTALLED SPACING OF DETECTORS						
25	56	40	21	18	14	10	6	3	0
25	56	60	17	13	9	5	2	0	0
25	56	80	14	10	6	3	0	0	0
25	56	100	12	8	4	1	0	0	0
25	56	120	11	7	3	0	0	0	0
25	56	140	10	6	2	0	0	0	0
50	112	40	17	4	11	7	4	2	0
50	112	60	13	0	7	4	1	0	0
50	112	80	11	8	5	2	0	0	0
50	112	100	10	6	3	0	0	0	0
50	112	120	8	5	2	0	0	0	0
50	112	140	8	4	1	0	0	0	0
75	168	40	14	1	8	6	3	1	0
75	168	60	11	8	5	3	1	0	0
75	168	80	9	6	3	1	0	0	0
75	168	100	8	5	2	0	0	0	0
75	168	120	7	4	1	0	0	0	0
75	168	140	6	3	1	0	0	0	0
100	224	40	12	10	7	4	2	0	0
100	224	60	10	7	4	2	0	0	0
100	224	80	8	5	3	1	0	0	0
100	224	100	7	4	2	0	0	0	0
100	224	120	6	3	1	0	0	0	0
100	224	140	5	3	0	0	0	0	0
125	280	40	11	9	6	3	1	0	0
125	280	60	9	6	3	1	0	0	0
125	280	80	7	4	2	0	0	0	0
125	280	100	6	3	1	0	0	0	0
125	280	120	5	3	1	0	0	0	0
125	280	140	5	2	0	0	0	0	0
150	335	40	10	8	5	3	1	0	0
150	335	60	8	5	3	1	0	0	0
150	335	80	6	4	2	0	0	0	0
150	335	100	6	3	1	0	0	0	0
150	335	120	5	2	0	0	0	0	0
150	335	140	4	2	0	0	0	0	0
175	391	40	9	7	4	2	1	0	0
175	391	60	7	5	2	1	0	0	0
175	391	80	6	3	1	0	0	0	0
175	391	100	5	3	1	0	0	0	0
175	391	120	4	2	0	0	0	0	0
175	391	140	4	1	0	0	0	0	0
200	447	40	9	6	4	2	0	0	0
200	447	60	7	4	2	0	0	0	0
200	447	80	5	3	1	0	0	0	0
200	447	100	5	2	0	0	0	0	0
200	447	120	4	2	0	0	0	0	0
200	447	140	3	1	0	0	0	0	0

τ	RTI	ΔT	CEILING HEIGHT IN FEET						
			4.0	8.0	12.0	16.0	20.0	24.0	28.0
			INSTALLED SPACING OF DETECTORS						
225	503	40	8	6	3	2	0	0	0
225	503	60	6	4	2	0	0	0	0
225	503	80	5	3	1	0	0	0	0
225	503	100	4	2	0	0	0	0	0
225	503	120	4	1	0	0	0	0	0
225	503	140	3	1	0	0	0	0	0
250	559	40	8	5	3	1	0	0	0
250	559	60	6	3	1	0	0	0	0
250	559	80	5	2	0	0	0	0	0
250	559	100	4	2	0	0	0	0	0
250	559	120	3	1	0	0	0	0	0
250	559	140	3	1	0	0	0	0	0
275	615	40	7	5	3	1	0	0	0
275	615	60	6	3	1	0	0	0	0
275	615	80	4	2	0	0	0	0	0
275	615	100	4	1	0	0	0	0	0
275	615	120	3	1	0	0	0	0	0
275	615	140	3	0	0	0	0	0	0
300	671	40	7	5	2	1	0	0	0
300	671	60	5	3	1	0	0	0	0
300	671	80	4	2	0	0	0	0	0
300	671	100	3	1	0	0	0	0	0
300	671	120	3	1	0	0	0	0	0
300	671	140	3	0	0	0	0	0	0
325	727	40	7	4	2	0	0	0	0
325	727	60	5	3	1	0	0	0	0
325	727	80	4	2	0	0	0	0	0
325	727	100	3	1	0	0	0	0	0
325	727	120	3	1	0	0	0	0	0
325	727	140	2	0	0	0	0	0	0
350	783	40	6	4	2	0	0	0	0
350	783	60	5	2	1	0	0	0	0
350	783	80	4	2	0	0	0	0	0
350	783	100	3	1	0	0	0	0	0
350	783	120	3	0	0	0	0	0	0
350	783	140	2	0	0	0	0	0	0
375	839	40	6	4	2	0	0	0	0
375	839	60	4	2	0	0	0	0	0
375	839	80	4	1	0	0	0	0	0
375	839	100	3	1	0	0	0	0	0
375	839	120	2	0	0	0	0	0	0
375	839	140	2	0	0	0	0	0	0
400	894	40	6	3	2	0	0	0	0
400	894	60	4	2	0	0	0	0	0
400	894	80	3	1	0	0	0	0	0
400	894	100	3	1	0	0	0	0	0
400	894	120	2	0	0	0	0	0	0
400	894	140	2	0	0	0	0	0	0

NOTE: Detector time constant at a reference velocity of 5 ft/sec.
For SI Units: 1 ft = 0.305 m
1000 BTU/sec = 1055 kW

Table B-3.2.4(d)
Q_d, Threshold Fire Size at Response: 250 Btu/sec
t_g: 500 Seconds to 1000 Btu/sec
α: 0.004 Btu/sec³

			CEILING HEIGHT IN FEET						
τ	RTI	ΔT	4.0	8.0	12.0	16.0	20.0	24.0	28.0
			INSTALLED SPACING OF DETECTORS						
25	56	40	26	22	17	13	9	5	1
25	56	60	20	16	11	7	3	0	0
25	56	80	17	12	8	4	0	0	0
25	56	100	15	10	5	1	0	0	0
25	56	120	13	8	4	0	0	0	0
25	56	140	11	7	2	0	0	0	0
50	112	40	21	18	14	11	7	4	1
50	112	60	17	13	9	6	2	0	0
50	112	80	14	10	6	3	0	0	0
50	112	100	12	8	4	1	0	0	0
50	112	120	11	7	3	0	0	0	0
50	112	140	9	6	2	0	0	0	0
75	168	40	18	15	12	9	6	3	0
75	168	60	14	11	8	5	2	0	0
75	168	80	12	9	5	2	0	0	0
75	168	100	10	7	4	1	0	0	0
75	168	120	9	6	2	0	0	0	0
75	168	140	8	5	1	0	0	0	0
100	224	40	16	14	10	7	4	0	0
100	224	60	13	10	7	4	1	0	0
100	224	80	11	8	4	2	0	0	0
100	224	100	9	6	3	0	0	0	0
100	224	120	8	5	2	0	0	0	0
100	224	140	7	4	1	0	0	0	0
125	280	40	15	12	9	6	4	1	0
125	280	60	12	9	6	3	1	0	0
125	280	80	10	7	4	1	0	0	0
125	280	100	8	5	2	0	0	0	0
125	280	120	7	4	1	0	0	0	0
125	280	140	6	3	1	0	0	0	0
150	335	40	14	11	8	5	3	1	0
150	335	60	11	8	5	3	1	0	0
150	335	80	9	6	3	1	0	0	0
150	335	100	8	5	2	0	0	0	0
150	335	120	7	4	1	0	0	0	0
150	335	140	6	3	1	0	0	0	0
175	391	40	13	10	7	5	2	1	0
175	391	60	10	7	4	2	0	0	0
175	391	80	8	5	3	1	0	0	0
175	391	100	7	4	2	0	0	0	0
175	391	120	6	3	1	0	0	0	0
175	391	140	5	3	0	0	0	0	0
200	447	40	12	9	7	4	2	1	0
200	447	60	9	7	4	2	0	0	0
200	447	80	8	5	2	1	0	0	0
200	447	100	6	4	1	0	0	0	0
200	447	120	6	3	1	0	0	0	0
200	447	140	5	2	0	0	0	0	0

			CEILING HEIGHT IN FEET						
τ	RTI	ΔT	4.0	8.0	12.0	16.0	20.0	24.0	28.0
			INSTALLED SPACING OF DETECTORS						
225	503	40	11	9	6	4	2	0	0
225	503	60	9	6	4	1	0	0	0
225	503	80	7	5	2	0	0	0	0
225	503	100	6	3	1	0	0	0	0
225	503	120	5	3	1	0	0	0	0
225	503	140	5	2	0	0	0	0	0
250	559	40	11	8	6	3	1	0	0
250	559	60	8	6	3	1	0	0	0
250	559	80	7	4	2	0	0	0	0
250	559	100	6	3	1	0	0	0	0
250	559	120	5	2	0	0	0	0	0
250	559	140	4	2	0	0	0	0	0
275	615	40	10	8	5	3	1	0	0
275	615	60	8	5	3	1	0	0	0
275	615	80	6	4	2	0	0	0	0
275	615	100	5	3	1	0	0	0	0
275	615	120	5	2	0	0	0	0	0
275	615	140	4	2	0	0	0	0	0
300	671	40	10	1	0	0	7	5	3
300	671	60	7	0	0	0	5	3	1
300	671	80	6	0	0	0	4	1	0
300	671	100	5	0	0	0	3	1	0
300	671	120	4	0	0	0	2	0	0
300	671	140	4	0	0	0	2	0	0
325	727	40	9	1	0	0	7	4	2
325	727	60	7	0	0	0	5	2	1
325	727	80	6	0	0	0	3	1	0
325	727	100	5	0	0	0	2	0	0
325	727	120	4	0	0	0	2	0	0
325	727	140	4	0	0	0	1	0	0
350	783	40	9	1	0	0	6	4	2
350	783	60	7	0	0	0	4	2	0
350	783	80	6	0	0	0	3	1	0
350	783	100	5	0	0	0	2	0	0
350	783	120	4	0	0	0	2	0	0
350	783	140	3	0	0	0	1	0	0
375	839	40	9	0	0	0	6	4	2
375	839	60	6	0	0	0	4	2	0
375	839	80	5	0	0	0	3	1	0
375	839	100	4	0	0	0	2	0	0
375	839	120	4	0	0	0	2	0	0
375	839	140	3	0	0	0	1	0	0
400	894	40	8	0	0	0	6	4	2
400	894	60	6	0	0	0	4	2	0
400	894	80	5	0	0	0	3	1	0
400	894	100	4	0	0	0	2	0	0
400	894	120	4	0	0	0	1	0	0
400	894	140	3	0	0	0	1	0	0

NOTE: Detector time constant at a reference velocity of 5 ft/sec.
For SI Units: 1 ft = 0.305 m
1000 BTU/sec = 1055 kW

Table B-3.2.4(e)
Q_d, Threshold Fire Size at Response: 250 Btu/sec
t_g: 600 Seconds to 1000 Btu/sec
α: 0.003 Btu/sec^3

			CEILING HEIGHT IN FEET						
τ	RTI	ΔT	4.0	8.0	12.0	16.0	20.0	24.0	28.0
			INSTALLED SPACING OF DETECTORS						
25	56	40	28	23	18	14	9	5	2
25	56	60	22	17	12	8	4	0	0
25	56	80	18	13	8	4	0	0	0
25	56	100	15	10	6	2	0	0	0
25	56	120	13	8	4	0	0	0	0
25	56	140	12	7	3	0	0	0	0
50	112	40	23	19	15	12	8	4	1
50	112	60	18	14	10	6	3	0	0
50	112	80	15	11	7	3	0	0	0
50	112	100	13	9	5	1	0	0	0
50	112	120	11	7	3	0	0	0	0
50	112	140	10	6	2	0	0	0	0
75	168	40	20	17	13	10	7	3	1
75	168	60	16	12	9	5	2	0	0
75	168	80	13	10	6	3	0	0	0
75	168	100	11	8	4	1	0	0	0
75	168	120	10	6	3	0	0	0	0
75	168	140	9	5	2	0	0	0	0
100	224	40	18	15	12	9	5	3	0
100	224	60	14	11	8	4	2	0	0
100	224	80	12	8	5	2	0	0	0
100	224	100	10	7	4	1	0	0	0
100	224	120	9	5	2	0	0	0	0
100	224	140	8	5	1	0	0	0	0
125	280	40	16	14	10	7	5	2	0
125	280	60	13	10	7	4	1	0	0
125	280	80	11	8	4	2	0	0	0
125	280	100	9	6	3	0	0	0	0
125	280	120	8	5	2	0	0	0	0
125	280	140	7	4	1	0	0	0	0
150	335	40	15	12	9	7	4	2	0
150	335	60	12	9	6	3	1	0	0
150	335	80	10	7	4	1	0	0	0
150	335	100	8	5	3	0	0	0	0
150	335	120	7	4	2	0	0	0	0
150	335	140	7	4	1	0	0	0	0
175	391	40	14	11	9	6	3	1	0
175	391	60	11	8	5	3	1	0	0
175	391	80	9	6	3	1	0	0	0
175	391	100	8	5	2	0	0	0	0
175	391	120	7	4	1	0	0	0	0
175	391	140	6	3	1	0	0	0	0
200	447	40	13	11	8	5	3	1	0
200	447	60	10	8	5	2	1	0	0
200	447	80	8	6	3	1	0	0	0
200	447	100	7	4	2	0	0	0	0
200	447	120	6	4	1	0	0	0	0
200	447	140	6	3	1	0	0	0	0
225	503	40	12	10	7	5	2	1	0
225	503	60	10	7	4	2	0	0	0
225	503	80	8	5	3	1	0	0	0
225	503	100	7	4	2	0	0	0	0
225	503	120	6	3	1	0	0	0	0
225	503	140	5	3	0	0	0	0	0
250	559	40	12	9	7	4	2	1	0
250	559	60	9	7	4	2	0	0	0
250	559	80	8	5	2	1	0	0	0
250	559	100	6	4	1	0	0	0	0
250	559	120	6	3	1	0	0	0	0
250	559	140	5	2	0	0	0	0	0
275	615	40	11	9	6	4	2	0	0
275	615	60	9	6	4	1	0	0	0
275	615	80	7	5	2	0	0	0	0
275	615	100	6	3	1	0	0	0	0
275	615	120	5	3	1	0	0	0	0
275	615	140	5	2	0	0	0	0	0
300	671	40	11	8	6	3	1	0	0
300	671	60	8	6	3	1	0	0	0
300	671	80	7	4	2	0	0	0	0
300	671	100	6	3	1	0	0	0	0
300	671	120	5	2	0	0	0	0	0
300	671	140	4	2	0	0	0	0	0
325	727	40	10	8	5	3	1	0	0
325	727	60	8	5	3	1	0	0	0
325	727	80	6	4	2	0	0	0	0
325	727	100	6	3	1	0	0	0	0
325	727	120	5	2	0	0	0	0	0
325	727	140	4	2	0	0	0	0	0
350	783	40	10	7	5	3	1	0	0
350	783	60	8	5	3	1	0	0	0
350	783	80	6	4	2	0	0	0	0
350	783	100	5	3	1	0	0	0	0
350	783	120	5	2	0	0	0	0	0
350	783	140	4	2	0	0	0	0	0
375	839	40	10	7	5	3	1	0	0
375	839	60	7	5	3	1	0	0	0
375	839	80	6	3	1	0	0	0	0
375	839	100	5	3	1	0	0	0	0
375	839	120	4	2	0	0	0	0	0
375	839	140	4	1	0	0	0	0	0
400	894	40	9	7	4	2	1	0	0
400	894	60	7	5	2	1	0	0	0
400	894	80	6	3	1	0	0	0	0
400	894	100	5	2	0	0	0	0	0
400	894	120	4	2	0	0	0	0	0
400	894	140	4	1	0	0	0	0	0

NOTE: Detector time constant at a reference velocity of 5 ft/sec.
For SI Units: 1 ft = 0.305 m
1000 BTU/sec = 1055 kW

Table B-3.2.4(f)
Q_d, Threshold Fire Size at Response: 500 Btu/sec
t_g: 50 Seconds to 1000 Btu/sec
α: 0.400 Btu/sec^3

τ	RTI	ΔT	CEILING HEIGHT IN FEET						
			4.0	8.0	12.0	16.0	20.0	24.0	28.0
			INSTALLED SPACING OF DETECTORS						
25	56	40	13	11	8	5	2	1	0
25	56	60	11	8	5	3	1	0	0
25	56	80	9	6	4	1	0	0	0
25	56	100	8	5	3	1	0	0	0
25	56	120	7	4	2	0	0	0	0
25	56	140	7	4	1	0	0	0	0
50	112	40	10	7	5	2	1	0	0
50	112	60	8	5	3	1	0	0	0
50	112	80	7	4	2	0	0	0	0
50	112	100	6	3	1	0	0	0	0
50	112	120	5	3	0	0	0	0	0
50	112	140	5	2	0	0	0	0	0
75	168	40	8	6	3	1	0	0	0
75	168	60	6	4	2	0	0	0	0
75	168	80	5	3	1	0	0	0	0
75	168	100	4	2	0	0	0	0	0
75	168	120	4	2	0	0	0	0	0
75	168	140	3	1	0	0	0	0	0
100	224	40	7	4	2	0	0	0	0
100	224	60	5	3	1	0	0	0	0
100	224	80	4	2	0	0	0	0	0
100	224	100	4	1	0	0	0	0	0
100	224	120	3	1	0	0	0	0	0
100	224	140	3	0	0	0	0	0	0
125	280	40	6	4	2	0	0	0	0
125	280	60	5	2	0	0	0	0	0
125	280	80	4	2	0	0	0	0	0
125	280	100	3	1	0	0	0	0	0
125	280	120	3	0	0	0	0	0	0
125	280	140	2	0	0	0	0	0	0
150	335	40	5	3	1	0	0	0	0
150	335	60	4	2	0	0	0	0	0
150	335	80	3	1	0	0	0	0	0
150	335	100	3	0	0	0	0	0	0
150	335	120	2	0	0	0	0	0	0
150	335	140	2	0	0	0	0	0	0
175	391	40	5	3	1	0	0	0	0
175	391	60	4	2	0	0	0	0	0
175	391	80	3	1	0	0	0	0	0
175	391	100	2	0	0	0	0	0	0
175	391	120	2	0	0	0	0	0	0
175	391	140	2	0	0	0	0	0	0
200	447	40	5	2	0	0	0	0	0
200	447	60	3	1	0	0	0	0	0
200	447	80	3	0	0	0	0	0	0
200	447	100	2	0	0	0	0	0	0
200	447	120	2	0	0	0	0	0	0
200	447	140	1	0	0	0	0	0	0

τ	RTI	ΔT	CEILING HEIGHT IN FEET						
			4.0	8.0	12.0	16.0	20.0	24.0	28.0
			INSTALLED SPACING OF DETECTORS						
225	503	40	4	2	0	0	0	0	0
225	503	60	3	1	0	0	0	0	0
225	503	80	2	0	0	0	0	0	0
225	503	100	2	0	0	0	0	0	0
225	503	120	2	0	0	0	0	0	0
225	503	140	1	0	0	0	0	0	0
250	559	40	4	2	0	0	0	0	0
250	559	60	3	1	0	0	0	0	0
250	559	80	2	0	0	0	0	0	0
250	559	100	2	0	0	0	0	0	0
250	559	120	1	0	0	0	0	0	0
250	559	140	1	0	0	0	0	0	0
275	615	40	4	2	0	0	0	0	0
275	615	60	3	0	0	0	0	0	0
275	615	80	2	0	0	0	0	0	0
275	615	100	2	0	0	0	0	0	0
275	615	120	1	0	0	0	0	0	0
275	615	140	1	0	0	0	0	0	0
300	671	40	3	1	0	0	0	0	0
300	671	60	2	0	0	0	0	0	0
300	671	80	2	0	0	0	0	0	0
300	671	100	1	0	0	0	0	0	0
300	671	120	1	0	0	0	0	0	0
300	671	140	0	0	0	0	0	0	0
325	727	40	3	1	0	0	0	0	0
325	727	60	2	0	0	0	0	0	0
325	727	80	2	0	0	0	0	0	0
325	727	100	1	0	0	0	0	0	0
325	727	120	1	0	0	0	0	0	0
325	727	140	0	0	0	0	0	0	0
350	783	40	3	1	0	0	0	0	0
350	783	60	2	0	0	0	0	0	0
350	783	80	2	0	0	0	0	0	0
350	783	100	1	0	0	0	0	0	0
350	783	120	0	0	0	0	0	0	0
350	783	140	0	0	0	0	0	0	0
375	839	40	3	1	0	0	0	0	0
375	839	60	2	0	0	0	0	0	0
375	839	80	1	0	0	0	0	0	0
375	839	100	1	0	0	0	0	0	0
375	839	120	0	0	0	0	0	0	0
375	839	140	0	0	0	0	0	0	0
400	894	40	3	0	0	0	0	0	0
400	894	60	2	0	0	0	0	0	0
400	894	80	1	0	0	0	0	0	0
400	894	100	1	0	0	0	0	0	0
400	894	120	0	0	0	0	0	0	0
400	894	140	0	0	0	0	0	0	0

NOTE: Detector time constant at a reference velocity of 5 ft/sec.
For SI Units: 1 ft = 0.305 m
1000 BTU/sec = 1055 kW

B-3.2.4(g)
Q_d, Threshold Fire Size at Response: 500 Btu/sec
t_g: 150 Seconds to 1000 Btu/sec
α: 0.044 Btu/sec^3

τ	RTI	ΔT	CEILING HEIGHT IN FEET						
			4.0	8.0	12.0	16.0	20.0	24.0	28.0
			INSTALLED SPACING OF DETECTORS						
25	56	40	24	22	18	15	11	8	5
25	56	60	20	17	13	10	6	3	0
25	56	80	17	14	10	6	3	0	0
25	56	100	15	11	8	4	1	0	0
25	56	120	13	10	6	3	0	0	0
25	56	140	12	8	5	1	0	0	0
50	112	40	19	16	14	11	8	5	2
50	112	60	15	13	10	7	4	1	0
50	112	80	13	10	7	4	2	0	0
50	112	100	11	9	5	3	0	0	0
50	112	120	10	7	4	1	0	0	0
50	112	140	9	6	3	1	0	0	0
75	168	40	16	14	11	8	5	3	1
75	168	60	13	10	8	5	2	1	0
75	168	80	11	8	5	3	1	0	0
75	168	100	10	7	4	2	0	0	0
75	168	120	8	6	3	1	0	0	0
75	168	140	8	5	2	0	0	0	0
100	224	40	14	12	9	6	4	2	1
100	224	60	11	9	6	4	2	0	0
100	224	80	10	7	4	2	0	0	0
100	224	100	8	6	3	1	0	0	0
100	224	120	7	5	2	0	0	0	0
100	224	140	7	4	2	0	0	0	0
125	280	40	13	10	8	5	3	1	0
125	280	60	10	8	5	3	1	0	0
125	280	80	8	6	3	1	0	0	0
125	280	100	7	5	2	1	0	0	0
125	280	120	6	4	2	0	0	0	0
125	280	140	6	3	1	0	0	0	0
150	335	40	12	9	7	4	2	1	0
150	335	60	9	7	4	2	1	0	0
150	335	80	8	5	3	1	0	0	0
150	335	100	7	4	2	0	0	0	0
150	335	120	6	3	1	0	0	0	0
150	335	140	5	3	1	0	0	0	0
175	391	40	11	8	6	4	2	0	0
175	391	60	8	6	4	2	0	0	0
175	391	80	7	5	2	1	0	0	0
175	391	100	6	4	2	0	0	0	0
175	391	120	5	3	1	0	0	0	0
175	391	140	5	2	0	0	0	0	0
200	447	40	10	8	5	3	1	0	0
200	447	60	8	5	3	1	0	0	0
200	447	80	7	4	2	0	0	0	0
200	447	100	6	3	1	0	0	0	0
200	447	120	5	2	1	0	0	0	0
200	447	140	4	2	0	0	0	0	0

τ	RTI	ΔT	CEILING HEIGHT IN FEET						
			4.0	8.0	12.0	16.0	20.0	24.0	28.0
			INSTALLED SPACING OF DETECTORS						
225	503	40	9	7	5	3	1	0	0
225	503	60	7	5	3	1	0	0	0
225	503	80	6	4	2	0	0	0	0
225	503	100	5	3	1	0	0	0	0
225	503	120	5	2	0	0	0	0	0
225	503	140	4	2	0	0	0	0	0
250	559	40	9	7	4	2	1	0	0
250	559	60	7	5	2	1	0	0	0
250	559	80	6	3	1	0	0	0	0
250	559	100	5	3	1	0	0	0	0
250	559	120	4	2	1	0	0	0	0
250	559	140	4	2	0	0	0	0	0
275	615	40	8	6	4	2	0	0	0
275	615	60	7	4	2	0	0	0	0
275	615	80	5	3	1	0	0	0	0
275	615	100	5	2	0	0	0	0	0
275	615	120	4	2	0	0	0	0	0
275	615	140	3	1	0	0	0	0	0
300	671	40	8	6	3	2	0	0	0
300	671	60	6	4	2	0	0	0	0
300	671	80	5	3	1	0	0	0	0
300	671	100	4	2	0	0	0	0	0
300	671	120	4	2	0	0	0	0	0
300	671	140	3	1	0	0	0	0	0
325	727	40	8	5	3	1	0	0	0
325	727	60	6	4	2	0	0	0	0
325	727	80	5	3	1	0	0	0	0
325	727	100	4	2	0	0	0	0	0
325	727	120	3	1	0	0	0	0	0
325	727	140	3	1	0	0	0	0	0
350	783	40	7	5	3	1	0	0	0
350	783	60	6	3	1	0	0	0	0
350	783	80	5	2	0	0	0	0	0
350	783	100	4	2	0	0	0	0	0
350	783	120	3	1	0	0	0	0	0
350	783	140	3	1	0	0	0	0	0
375	839	40	7	5	3	1	0	0	0
375	839	60	5	3	1	0	0	0	0
375	839	80	4	2	0	0	0	0	0
375	839	100	4	2	0	0	0	0	0
375	839	120	3	1	0	0	0	0	0
375	839	140	3	0	0	0	0	0	0
400	894	40	7	4	2	1	0	0	0
400	894	60	5	3	1	0	0	0	0
400	894	80	4	2	0	0	0	0	0
400	894	100	3	1	0	0	0	0	0
400	894	120	3	1	0	0	0	0	0
400	894	140	3	0	0	0	0	0	0

NOTE: Detector time constant at a reference velocity of 5 ft/sec.
For SI Units: 1 ft = 0.305 m
1000 BTU/sec = 1055 kW

Table B-3.2.4(h)
Q_d, Threshold Fire Size at Response: 500 Btu/sec
t_g: 300 Seconds to 1000 Btu/sec
α: 0.011 Btu/sec^3

τ	RTI	ΔT	CEILING HEIGHT IN FEET						
			4.0	8.0	12.0	16.0	20.0	24.0	28.0
			INSTALLED SPACING OF DETECTORS						
25	56	40	34	30	25	21	17	13	9
25	56	60	27	23	18	14	10	6	2
25	56	80	23	18	14	9	5	2	0
25	56	100	20	15	11	7	3	0	0
25	56	120	18	13	8	4	1	0	0
25	56	140	16	11	7	3	0	0	0
50	112	40	27	24	21	17	14	10	7
50	112	60	22	18	15	11	8	4	1
50	112	80	18	15	11	8	4	1	0
50	112	100	16	12	9	5	2	0	0
50	112	120	14	11	7	3	0	0	0
50	112	140	13	9	5	2	0	0	0
75	168	40	23	21	18	14	11	8	5
75	168	60	19	16	13	9	6	3	1
75	168	80	16	13	9	6	3	1	0
75	168	100	14	11	7	4	1	0	0
75	168	120	12	9	6	3	0	0	0
75	168	140	11	8	4	1	0	0	0
100	224	40	21	18	15	12	9	6	4
100	224	60	17	14	11	8	5	2	0
100	224	80	14	11	8	5	2	0	0
100	224	100	12	9	6	3	1	0	0
100	224	120	11	8	5	2	0	0	0
100	224	140	10	7	4	1	0	0	0
125	280	40	19	16	14	11	8	5	3
125	280	60	15	12	10	7	4	2	0
125	280	80	13	10	7	4	2	0	0
125	280	100	11	8	5	3	1	0	0
125	280	120	10	7	4	2	0	0	0
125	280	140	9	6	3	1	0	0	0
150	335	40	17	15	12	10	7	4	2
150	335	60	14	11	8	6	3	1	0
150	335	80	12	9	6	4	1	0	0
150	335	100	10	7	5	2	0	0	0
150	335	120	9	6	3	1	0	0	0
150	335	140	8	5	3	1	0	0	0
175	391	40	16	14	11	9	6	4	2
175	391	60	13	10	8	5	3	1	0
175	391	80	11	8	5	3	1	0	0
175	391	100	9	7	4	2	0	0	0
175	391	120	8	6	3	1	0	0	0
175	391	140	7	5	2	0	0	0	0
200	447	40	15	13	10	8	5	3	1
200	447	60	12	10	7	4	2	1	0
200	447	80	10	8	5	3	1	0	0
200	447	100	9	6	4	1	0	0	0
200	447	120	8	5	3	1	0	0	0
200	447	140	7	4	2	0	0	0	0

τ	RTI	ΔT	CEILING HEIGHT IN FEET						
			4.0	8.0	12.0	16.0	20.0	24.0	28.0
			INSTALLED SPACING OF DETECTORS						
225	503	40	14	12	10	7	5	3	1
225	503	60	11	9	6	4	2	0	0
225	503	80	10	7	4	2	1	0	0
225	503	100	8	6	3	1	0	0	0
225	503	120	7	5	2	1	0	0	0
225	503	140	6	4	2	0	0	0	0
250	559	40	14	11	9	6	4	2	1
250	559	60	11	8	6	3	2	0	0
250	559	80	9	6	4	2	0	0	0
250	559	100	8	5	3	1	0	0	0
250	559	120	7	4	2	0	0	0	0
250	559	140	6	4	1	0	0	0	0
275	615	40	13	11	8	6	4	2	1
275	615	60	10	8	5	3	1	0	0
275	615	80	9	6	4	2	0	0	0
275	615	100	7	5	3	1	0	0	0
275	615	120	6	4	2	0	0	0	0
275	615	140	6	3	1	0	0	0	0
300	671	40	12	10	8	5	3	2	0
300	671	60	10	7	5	3	1	0	0
300	671	80	8	6	3	1	0	0	0
300	671	100	7	5	2	1	0	0	0
300	671	120	6	4	2	0	0	0	0
300	671	140	6	3	1	0	0	0	0
325	727	40	12	10	7	5	3	1	0
325	727	60	9	7	5	2	1	0	0
325	727	80	8	5	3	1	0	0	0
325	727	100	7	4	2	0	0	0	0
325	727	120	6	3	1	0	0	0	0
325	727	140	5	3	1	0	0	0	0
350	783	40	12	9	7	4	3	1	0
350	783	60	9	7	4	2	1	0	0
350	783	80	7	5	3	1	0	0	0
350	783	100	6	4	2	0	0	0	0
350	783	120	6	3	1	0	0	0	0
350	783	140	5	3	1	0	0	0	0
375	839	40	11	9	6	4	2	1	0
375	839	60	9	6	4	2	0	0	0
375	839	80	7	5	3	1	0	0	0
375	839	100	6	4	2	0	0	0	0
375	839	120	5	3	1	0	0	0	0
375	839	140	5	2	0	0	0	0	0
400	894	40	11	8	6	4	2	1	0
400	894	60	8	6	4	2	0	0	0
400	894	80	7	4	2	1	0	0	0
400	894	100	6	3	1	0	0	0	0
400	894	120	5	3	1	0	0	0	0
400	894	140	5	2	0	0	0	0	0

NOTE: Detector time constant at a reference velocity of 5 ft/sec.
For SI Units: 1 ft = 0.305 m
1000 BTU/sec = 1055 kW

Table B-3.2.4(i)
Q_d, Threshold Fire Size at Response: 500 Btu/sec
t_g: 500 Seconds to 1000 Btu/sec
α: 0.004 Btu/sec^3

τ	RTI	ΔT	CEILING HEIGHT IN FEET 4.0	8.0	12.0	16.0	20.0	24.0	28.0
			INSTALLED SPACING OF DETECTORS						
25	56	40	41	35	30	25	20	16	11
25	56	60	32	26	21	16	12	7	3
25	56	80	27	21	16	11	7	3	0
25	56	100	23	17	12	8	4	0	0
25	56	120	20	15	10	5	1	0	0
25	56	140	18	13	8	3	0	0	0
50	112	40	34	30	26	22	18	14	10
50	112	60	27	23	18	14	10	6	3
50	112	80	23	18	14	10	6	2	0
50	112	100	20	15	11	7	3	0	0
50	112	120	17	13	9	5	1	0	0
50	112	140	16	11	7	3	0	0	0
75	168	40	30	26	23	19	15	12	8
75	168	60	24	20	16	13	9	5	2
75	168	80	20	16	12	9	5	2	0
75	168	100	17	14	10	6	2	0	0
75	168	120	15	11	8	4	1	0	0
75	168	140	14	10	6	2	0	0	0
100	224	40	27	24	20	17	14	10	7
100	224	60	21	18	15	11	8	4	2
100	224	80	18	15	11	8	4	1	0
100	224	100	16	12	9	5	2	0	0
100	224	120	14	10	7	5	3	0	0
100	224	140	13	9	5	2	0	0	0
125	280	40	25	22	19	15	12	9	6
125	280	60	20	17	13	10	7	4	1
125	280	80	16	13	10	7	4	1	0
125	280	100	14	11	8	5	2	0	0
125	280	120	13	9	6	3	0	0	0
125	280	140	11	8	5	2	0	0	0
150	335	40	23	20	17	14	11	8	5
150	335	60	18	15	12	9	6	3	1
150	335	80	15	12	9	6	3	1	0
150	335	100	13	10	7	4	1	0	0
150	335	120	12	9	5	3	0	0	0
150	335	140	11	7	4	1	0	0	0
175	391	40	21	19	16	13	10	7	4
175	391	60	17	14	11	8	5	3	1
175	391	80	14	11	8	5	3	1	0
175	391	100	12	9	6	3	1	0	0
175	391	120	11	8	5	2	0	0	0
175	391	140	10	7	4	1	0	0	0
200	447	40	20	18	15	12	9	6	4
200	447	60	16	13	10	7	5	2	1
200	447	80	13	11	8	5	2	0	0
200	447	100	12	9	6	3	1	0	0
200	447	120	10	7	4	2	0	0	0
200	447	140	9	6	3	1	0	0	0
225	503	40	19	17	14	11	8	6	3
225	503	60	15	13	10	7	4	2	0
225	503	80	13	10	7	4	2	0	0
225	503	100	11	8	5	3	1	0	0
225	503	120	10	7	4	2	0	0	0
225	503	140	9	6	3	1	0	0	0
250	559	40	18	16	13	10	8	5	3
250	559	60	14	12	9	6	4	2	0
250	559	80	12	9	7	4	2	0	0
250	559	100	10	8	5	2	1	0	0
250	559	120	9	6	4	1	0	0	0
250	559	140	8	6	3	1	0	0	0
275	615	40	17	15	12	10	7	5	2
275	615	60	14	11	8	6	3	1	0
275	615	80	12	9	6	3	1	0	0
275	615	100	10	7	5	2	0	0	0
275	615	120	9	6	3	1	0	0	0
275	615	140	8	5	3	1	0	0	0
300	671	40	17	14	12	9	6	4	2
300	671	60	13	11	8	5	3	1	0
300	671	80	11	8	6	3	1	0	0
300	671	100	10	7	4	2	0	0	0
300	671	120	8	6	3	1	0	0	0
300	671	140	8	5	2	0	0	0	0
325	727	40	16	14	11	9	6	4	2
325	727	60	13	10	8	5	3	1	0
325	727	80	11	8	5	3	1	0	0
325	727	100	9	7	4	2	0	0	0
325	727	120	8	5	3	1	0	0	0
325	727	140	7	5	2	0	0	0	0
350	783	40	16	13	11	8	6	3	2
350	783	60	12	10	7	5	2	1	0
350	783	80	10	8	5	3	1	0	0
350	783	100	9	6	4	2	0	0	0
350	783	120	8	5	3	1	0	0	0
350	783	140	7	4	2	0	0	0	0
375	839	40	15	13	10	8	5	3	1
375	839	60	12	9	7	4	2	1	0
375	839	80	10	7	5	2	1	0	0
375	839	100	8	6	3	1	0	0	0
375	839	120	7	5	2	1	0	0	0
375	839	140	7	4	2	0	0	0	0
400	894	40	14	12	10	7	5	3	1
400	894	60	11	9	6	4	2	1	0
400	894	80	9	7	4	2	1	0	0
400	894	100	8	6	3	1	0	0	0
400	894	120	7	5	2	1	0	0	0
400	894	140	6	4	2	0	0	0	0

NOTE: Detector time constant at a reference velocity of 5 ft/sec.
For SI Units: 1 ft = 0.305 m
1000 BTU/sec = 1055 kW

Table B-3.2.4(j)
Q_d, Threshold Fire Size at Response: 500 Btu/sec
t_g: 600 Seconds to 1000 Btu/sec
α: 0.003 Btu/sec^3

τ	RTI	ΔT	CEILING HEIGHT IN FEET						
			4.0	8.0	12.0	16.0	20.0	24.0	28.0
			INSTALLED SPACING OF DETECTORS						
25	56	40	43	37	31	26	21	17	12
25	56	60	34	27	22	17	12	8	4
25	56	80	28	22	16	12	7	3	0
25	56	100	24	18	13	8	4	0	0
25	56	120	21	15	10	6	1	0	0
25	56	140	19	13	8	4	0	0	0
50	112	40	36	32	27	23	19	15	11
50	112	60	29	24	20	15	11	7	3
50	112	80	24	19	15	10	6	2	0
50	112	100	21	16	11	7	3	0	0
50	112	120	18	14	9	5	1	0	0
50	112	140	17	12	7	3	0	0	0
75	168	40	32	29	25	21	17	13	9
75	168	60	26	22	18	14	10	6	3
75	168	80	21	17	13	9	6	2	0
75	168	100	19	14	10	6	3	0	0
75	168	120	17	12	8	4	1	0	0
75	168	140	15	11	7	3	0	0	0
100	224	40	29	26	22	19	15	12	8
100	224	60	23	20	16	12	9	5	2
100	224	80	19	16	12	8	5	2	0
100	224	100	17	13	9	6	2	0	0
100	224	120	15	11	7	4	1	0	0
100	224	140	14	10	6	2	0	0	0
125	280	40	27	24	20	17	14	10	7
125	280	60	21	18	15	11	8	5	2
125	280	80	18	15	11	8	4	1	0
125	280	100	16	12	9	5	2	0	0
125	280	120	14	10	7	3	1	0	0
125	280	140	12	9	5	2	0	0	0
150	335	40	25	22	19	16	13	9	6
150	335	60	20	17	14	10	7	4	1
150	335	80	17	14	10	7	4	1	0
150	335	100	15	11	8	5	2	0	0
150	335	120	13	10	6	3	0	0	0
150	335	140	12	8	5	2	0	0	0
175	391	40	23	21	18	15	12	8	6
175	391	60	19	16	13	9	6	3	1
175	391	80	16	13	9	6	3	1	0
175	391	100	14	10	7	4	1	0	0
175	391	120	12	9	6	3	0	0	0
175	391	140	11	8	4	2	0	0	0
200	447	40	22	19	17	14	11	8	5
200	447	60	18	15	12	9	6	3	1
200	447	80	15	12	9	6	3	1	0
200	447	100	13	10	7	4	1	0	0
200	447	120	11	8	5	2	0	0	0
200	447	140	10	7	4	1	0	0	0

τ	RTI	ΔT	CEILING HEIGHT IN FEET						
			4.0	8.0	12.0	16.0	20.0	24.0	28.0
			INSTALLED SPACING OF DETECTORS						
225	503	40	21	18	16	13	10	7	4
225	503	60	17	14	11	8	5	3	1
225	503	80	14	11	8	5	3	1	0
225	503	100	12	9	6	3	1	0	0
225	503	120	11	8	5	2	0	0	0
225	503	140	10	7	4	1	0	0	0
250	559	40	20	18	15	12	9	6	4
250	559	60	16	13	10	7	5	2	1
250	559	80	13	11	8	5	2	0	0
250	559	100	12	9	6	3	1	0	0
250	559	120	10	7	4	2	0	0	0
250	559	140	9	6	3	1	0	0	0
275	615	40	19	17	14	11	8	6	3
275	615	60	15	13	10	7	4	2	0
275	615	80	13	10	7	4	2	0	0
275	615	100	11	8	5	3	1	0	0
275	615	120	10	7	4	2	0	0	0
275	615	140	9	6	3	1	0	0	0
300	671	40	18	16	13	11	8	5	3
300	671	60	15	12	9	6	4	2	0
300	671	80	12	10	7	4	2	0	0
300	671	100	11	8	5	2	1	0	0
300	671	120	9	7	4	1	0	0	0
300	671	140	8	6	3	1	0	0	0
325	727	40	18	15	13	10	7	5	3
325	727	60	14	11	9	6	4	2	0
325	727	80	12	9	6	4	2	0	0
325	727	100	10	7	5	2	1	0	0
325	727	120	9	6	4	1	0	0	0
325	727	140	8	5	3	1	0	0	0
350	783	40	17	15	12	9	7	4	2
350	783	60	13	11	8	6	3	1	0
350	783	80	11	9	6	3	1	0	0
350	783	100	10	7	4	2	0	0	0
350	783	120	9	6	3	1	0	0	0
350	783	140	8	5	2	1	0	0	0
375	839	40	17	14	12	9	6	4	2
375	839	60	13	11	8	5	3	1	0
375	839	80	11	8	6	3	1	0	0
375	839	100	9	7	4	2	0	0	0
375	839	120	8	6	3	1	0	0	0
375	839	140	7	5	2	0	0	0	0
400	894	40	16	14	11	9	6	4	2
400	894	60	13	10	7	5	3	1	0
400	894	80	11	8	5	3	1	0	0
400	894	100	9	6	4	2	0	0	0
400	894	120	8	5	3	1	0	0	0
400	894	140	7	5	2	0	0	0	0

NOTE: Detector time constant at a reference velocity of 5 ft/sec.
For SI Units: 1 ft = 0.305 m
1000 BTU/sec = 1055 kW

Table B-3.2.4(k)
Q_d, Threshold Fire Size at Response: 750 Btu/sec
t_g: 50 Seconds to 1000 Btu/sec
α: 0.400 Btu/sec^3

τ	RTI	ΔT	CEILING HEIGHT IN FEET						
			4.0	8.0	12.0	16.0	20.0	24.0	28.0
			INSTALLED SPACING OF DETECTORS						
25	56	40	18	15	13	10	7	4	2
25	56	60	15	12	9	6	4	1	0
25	56	80	13	10	7	4	2	0	0
25	56	100	11	9	6	3	1	0	0
25	56	120	10	7	4	2	0	0	0
25	56	140	9	6	4	1	0	0	0
50	112	40	14	11	9	6	3	2	0
50	112	60	11	9	6	3	1	0	0
50	112	80	9	7	4	2	0	0	0
50	112	100	8	6	3	1	0	0	0
50	112	120	7	5	2	0	0	0	0
50	112	140	7	4	2	0	0	0	0
75	168	40	11	9	6	4	2	0	0
75	168	60	9	7	4	2	0	0	0
75	168	80	8	5	3	1	0	0	0
75	168	100	7	4	2	0	0	0	0
75	168	120	6	3	1	0	0	0	0
75	168	140	5	3	1	0	0	0	0
100	224	40	10	7	5	3	1	0	0
100	224	60	8	5	3	1	0	0	0
100	224	80	7	4	2	0	0	0	0
100	224	100	6	3	1	0	0	0	0
100	224	120	5	3	1	0	0	0	0
100	224	140	4	2	0	0	0	0	0
125	280	40	9	6	4	2	0	0	0
125	280	60	7	5	2	1	0	0	0
125	280	80	6	3	1	0	0	0	0
125	280	100	5	3	1	0	0	0	0
125	280	120	4	2	0	0	0	0	0
125	280	140	4	2	0	0	0	0	0
150	335	40	8	6	3	1	0	0	0
150	335	60	6	4	2	0	0	0	0
150	335	80	5	3	1	0	0	0	0
150	335	100	4	2	0	0	0	0	0
150	335	120	4	2	0	0	0	0	0
150	335	140	3	1	0	0	0	0	0
175	391	40	7	5	3	1	0	0	0
175	391	60	6	3	1	0	0	0	0
175	391	80	5	2	0	0	0	0	0
175	391	100	4	2	0	0	0	0	0
175	391	120	3	1	0	0	0	0	0
175	391	140	3	1	0	0	0	0	0
200	447	40	7	4	2	1	0	0	0
200	447	60	5	3	1	0	0	0	0
200	447	80	4	2	0	0	0	0	0
200	447	100	4	1	0	0	0	0	0
200	447	120	3	1	0	0	0	0	0
200	447	140	3	0	0	0	0	0	0

τ	RTI	ΔT	CEILING HEIGHT IN FEET						
			4.0	8.0	12.0	16.0	20.0	24.0	28.0
			INSTALLED SPACING OF DETECTORS						
225	503	40	6	4	2	0	0	0	0
225	503	60	5	3	1	0	0	0	0
225	503	80	4	2	0	0	0	0	0
225	503	100	3	1	0	0	0	0	0
225	503	120	3	1	0	0	0	0	0
225	503	140	2	0	0	0	0	0	0
250	559	40	6	4	2	0	0	0	0
250	559	60	4	2	0	0	0	0	0
250	559	80	4	2	0	0	0	0	0
250	559	100	3	1	0	0	0	0	0
250	559	120	3	0	0	0	0	0	0
250	559	140	2	0	0	0	0	0	0
275	615	40	6	3	1	0	0	0	0
275	615	60	4	2	0	0	0	0	0
275	615	80	3	1	0	0	0	0	0
275	615	100	3	1	0	0	0	0	0
275	615	120	2	0	0	0	0	0	0
275	615	140	2	0	0	0	0	0	0
300	671	40	5	3	1	0	0	0	0
300	671	60	4	2	0	0	0	0	0
300	671	80	3	1	0	0	0	0	0
300	671	100	3	0	0	0	0	0	0
300	671	120	2	0	0	0	0	0	0
300	671	140	2	0	0	0	0	0	0
325	727	40	5	3	1	0	0	0	0
325	727	60	4	2	0	0	0	0	0
325	727	80	3	1	0	0	0	0	0
325	727	100	2	0	0	0	0	0	0
325	727	120	2	0	0	0	0	0	0
325	727	140	2	0	0	0	0	0	0
350	783	40	5	3	1	0	0	0	0
350	783	60	4	1	0	0	0	0	0
350	783	80	3	1	0	0	0	0	0
350	783	100	2	0	0	0	0	0	0
350	783	120	2	0	0	0	0	0	0
350	783	140	2	0	0	0	0	0	0
375	839	40	5	2	0	0	0	0	0
375	839	60	3	1	0	0	0	0	0
375	839	80	3	0	0	0	0	0	0
375	839	100	2	0	0	0	0	0	0
375	839	120	2	0	0	0	0	0	0
375	839	140	1	0	0	0	0	0	0
400	894	40	4	2	0	0	0	0	0
400	894	60	3	1	0	0	0	0	0
400	894	80	2	0	0	0	0	0	0
400	894	100	2	0	0	0	0	0	0
400	894	120	2	0	0	0	0	0	0
400	894	140	1	0	0	0	0	0	0

NOTE: Detector time constant at a reference velocity of 5 ft/sec.
For SI Units: 1 ft = 0.305 m
1000 BTU/sec = 1055 kW

Table B-3.2.4(1)
Q_d, Threshold Fire Size at Response: 750 Btu/sec
t_g: 150 Seconds to 1000 Btu/sec
α: 0.044 Btu/sec^3

τ	RTI	ΔT	CEILING HEIGHT IN FEET						
			4.0	8.0	12.0	16.0	20.0	24.0	28.0
			INSTALLED SPACING OF DETECTORS						
25	56	40	32	29	26	22	18	15	11
25	56	60	26	23	19	15	12	8	4
25	56	80	23	19	15	11	8	4	1
25	56	100	20	16	12	8	5	1	0
25	56	120	18	14	10	6	3	0	0
25	56	140	16	12	8	5	1	0	0
50	112	40	25	23	20	17	14	11	8
50	112	60	21	18	15	12	8	5	3
50	112	80	18	15	12	8	5	2	0
50	112	100	16	13	9	6	3	1	0
50	112	120	14	11	8	4	2	0	0
50	112	140	13	10	6	3	1	0	0
75	168	40	22	19	17	14	11	8	5
75	168	60	18	15	12	9	6	4	1
75	168	80	15	12	9	6	4	1	0
75	168	100	13	10	7	5	2	0	0
75	168	120	12	9	6	3	1	0	0
75	168	140	11	8	5	2	0	0	0
100	224	40	19	17	14	12	9	6	4
100	224	60	16	13	10	8	5	3	1
100	224	80	13	11	8	5	3	1	0
100	224	100	12	9	6	3	1	0	0
100	224	120	10	8	5	2	1	0	0
100	224	140	9	7	4	1	0	0	0
125	280	40	17	15	13	10	7	5	3
125	280	60	14	12	9	6	4	2	1
125	280	80	12	9	7	4	2	0	0
125	280	100	10	8	5	3	1	0	0
125	280	120	9	7	4	2	0	0	0
125	280	140	8	6	3	1	0	0	0
150	335	40	16	14	11	9	6	4	2
150	335	60	13	10	8	5	3	1	0
150	335	80	11	8	6	3	1	0	0
150	335	100	9	7	4	2	1	0	0
150	335	120	8	6	3	1	0	0	0
150	335	140	8	5	3	1	0	0	0
175	391	40	15	13	10	8	5	3	2
175	391	60	12	9	7	5	2	1	0
175	391	80	10	8	5	3	1	0	0
175	391	100	9	6	4	2	0	0	0
175	391	120	8	5	3	1	0	0	0
175	391	140	7	4	2	0	0	0	0
200	447	40	14	12	9	7	4	3	1
200	447	60	11	9	6	4	2	1	0
200	447	80	9	7	4	2	1	0	0
200	447	100	8	6	3	1	0	0	0
200	447	120	7	5	2	1	0	0	0
200	447	140	6	4	2	0	0	0	0
225	503	40	13	11	8	6	4	2	1
225	503	60	10	8	6	3	2	0	0
225	503	80	9	6	4	2	0	0	0
225	503	100	8	5	3	1	0	0	0
225	503	120	7	4	2	0	0	0	0
225	503	140	6	4	1	0	0	0	0
250	559	40	12	10	8	5	3	2	0
250	559	60	10	7	5	3	1	0	0
250	559	80	8	6	4	2	0	0	0
250	559	100	7	5	2	1	0	0	0
250	559	120	6	4	2	0	0	0	0
250	559	140	6	3	1	0	0	0	0
275	615	40	12	10	7	5	3	1	0
275	615	60	9	7	5	3	1	0	0
275	615	80	8	5	3	1	0	0	0
275	615	100	7	4	2	1	0	0	0
275	615	120	6	4	2	0	0	0	0
275	615	140	5	3	1	0	0	0	0
300	671	40	11	9	7	4	3	1	0
300	671	60	9	7	4	2	1	0	0
300	671	80	7	5	3	1	0	0	0
300	671	100	6	4	2	0	0	0	0
300	671	120	6	3	1	0	0	0	0
300	671	140	5	3	1	0	0	0	0
325	727	40	11	9	6	4	2	1	0
325	727	60	9	6	4	2	1	0	0
325	727	80	7	5	3	1	0	0	0
325	727	100	6	4	2	0	0	0	0
325	727	120	5	3	1	0	0	0	0
325	727	140	5	2	1	0	0	0	0
350	783	40	10	8	6	4	2	1	0
350	783	60	8	6	4	2	0	0	0
350	783	80	7	4	2	1	0	0	0
350	783	100	6	3	2	0	0	0	0
350	783	120	5	3	1	0	0	0	0
350	783	140	5	2	0	0	0	0	0
375	839	40	10	8	5	3	2	0	0
375	839	60	8	6	3	2	0	0	0
375	839	80	6	4	2	0	0	0	0
375	839	100	6	3	1	0	0	0	0
375	839	120	5	3	1	0	0	0	0
375	839	140	4	2	0	0	0	0	0
400	894	40	10	7	5	3	2	0	0
400	894	60	8	5	3	1	0	0	0
400	894	80	6	4	2	0	0	0	0
400	894	100	5	3	1	0	0	0	0
400	894	120	5	2	1	0	0	0	0
400	894	140	4	2	0	0	0	0	0

NOTE: Detector time constant at a reference velocity of 5 ft/sec.
For SI Units: 1 ft = 0.305 m
1000 BTU/sec = 1055 kW

Table B-3.2.4(m)
Q_d, Threshold Fire Size at Response: 750 Btu/sec
t_g: 300 Seconds to 1000 Btu/sec
α: 0.011 Btu/sec^3

			CEILING HEIGHT IN FEET						
τ	RTI	ΔT	4.0	8.0	12.0	16.0	20.0	24.0	28.0
			INSTALLED SPACING OF DETECTORS						
25	56	40	43	39	34	30	25	21	17
25	56	60	35	30	25	21	16	12	8
25	56	80	30	24	20	15	11	6	3
25	56	100	26	21	16	11	7	3	0
25	56	120	23	18	13	9	4	1	0
25	56	140	21	15	11	6	2	0	0
50	112	40	36	32	29	25	21	17	14
50	112	60	29	25	21	17	14	10	6
50	112	80	24	21	17	13	9	5	2
50	112	100	21	17	13	10	6	2	0
50	112	120	19	15	11	7	3	0	0
50	112	140	17	13	9	5	2	0	0
75	168	40	31	28	25	22	18	15	11
75	168	60	25	22	18	15	12	8	5
75	168	80	21	18	14	11	7	4	1
75	168	100	19	15	12	8	5	2	0
75	168	120	17	13	10	6	3	0	0
75	168	140	15	12	8	4	1	0	0
100	224	40	28	25	22	19	16	13	10
100	224	60	22	19	16	13	10	7	4
100	224	80	19	16	13	10	6	3	1
100	224	100	17	14	10	7	4	1	0
100	224	120	15	12	8	5	2	0	0
100	224	140	14	10	7	4	1	0	0
125	280	40	25	23	20	17	14	11	8
125	280	60	20	18	15	12	9	6	3
125	280	80	17	14	11	8	5	3	1
125	280	100	15	12	9	6	3	1	0
125	280	120	14	11	7	4	2	0	0
125	280	140	12	9	6	3	1	0	0
150	335	40	23	21	18	15	13	10	7
150	335	60	19	16	13	10	8	5	2
150	335	80	16	13	10	7	5	2	0
150	335	100	14	11	8	5	3	1	0
150	335	120	13	10	7	4	1	0	0
150	335	140	11	8	5	3	0	0	0
175	391	40	22	20	17	14	11	9	6
175	391	60	18	15	12	9	7	4	2
175	391	80	15	12	9	7	4	2	0
175	391	100	13	10	7	5	2	0	0
175	391	120	12	9	6	3	1	0	0
175	391	140	11	8	5	2	0	0	0
200	447	40	21	18	16	13	10	8	5
200	447	60	17	14	11	9	6	4	2
200	447	80	14	11	9	6	3	1	0
200	447	100	12	10	7	4	2	0	0
200	447	120	11	8	5	3	1	0	0
200	447	140	10	7	4	2	0	0	0

			CEILING HEIGHT IN FEET						
τ	RTI	ΔT	4.0	8.0	12.0	16.0	20.0	24.0	28.0
			INSTALLED SPACING OF DETECTORS						
225	503	40	20	17	15	12	9	7	5
225	503	60	16	13	11	8	5	3	1
225	503	80	13	11	8	5	3	1	0
225	503	100	12	9	6	4	2	0	0
225	503	120	10	8	5	2	1	0	0
225	503	140	9	7	4	2	0	0	0
250	559	40	19	16	14	11	9	6	4
250	559	60	15	12	10	7	5	3	1
250	559	80	13	10	7	5	3	1	0
250	559	100	11	8	6	3	1	0	0
250	559	120	10	7	4	2	1	0	0
250	559	140	9	6	4	1	0	0	0
275	615	40	18	16	13	10	8	6	3
275	615	60	14	12	9	7	4	2	1
275	615	80	12	9	7	4	2	1	0
275	615	100	10	8	5	3	1	0	0
275	615	120	9	7	4	2	0	0	0
275	615	140	8	6	3	1	0	0	0
300	671	40	17	15	12	10	7	5	3
300	671	60	14	11	9	6	4	2	1
300	671	80	11	9	6	4	2	1	0
300	671	100	10	7	5	3	1	0	0
300	671	120	9	6	4	2	0	0	0
300	671	140	8	5	3	1	0	0	0
325	727	40	16	14	12	9	7	5	3
325	727	60	13	11	8	6	3	2	0
325	727	80	11	9	6	4	2	0	0
325	727	100	10	7	5	2	1	0	0
325	727	120	8	6	3	1	0	0	0
325	727	140	8	5	3	1	0	0	0
350	783	40	16	14	11	9	6	4	2
350	783	60	13	10	8	5	3	1	0
350	783	80	11	8	6	3	1	0	0
350	783	100	9	7	4	2	1	0	0
350	783	120	8	6	3	1	0	0	0
350	783	140	7	5	2	1	0	0	0
375	839	40	15	13	11	8	6	4	2
375	839	60	12	10	7	5	3	1	0
375	839	80	10	8	5	3	1	0	0
375	839	100	9	6	4	2	0	0	0
375	839	120	8	5	3	1	0	0	0
375	839	140	7	5	2	1	0	0	0
400	894	40	15	13	10	8	5	3	2
400	894	60	12	9	7	5	3	1	0
400	894	80	10	7	5	3	1	0	0
400	894	100	8	6	4	2	0	0	0
400	894	120	7	5	3	1	0	0	0
400	894	140	7	4	2	0	0	0	0

NOTE: Detector time constant at a reference velocity of 5 ft/sec.
For SI Units: 1 ft = 0.305 m
1000 BTU/sec = 1055 kW

Table B-3.2.4(n)
Q_d, Threshold Fire Size at Response: 750 Btu/sec
t_g: 500 Seconds to 1000 Btu/sec
α: 0.004 Btu/sec^3

			CEILING HEIGHT IN FEET						
τ	RTI	ΔT	4.0	8.0	12.0	16.0	20.0	24.0	28.0
			INSTALLED SPACING OF DETECTORS						
25	56	40	52	45	39	34	29	24	20
25	56	60	41	34	28	23	18	14	9
25	56	80	34	28	22	17	12	8	4
25	56	100	29	23	18	13	8	4	0
25	56	120	26	20	14	10	5	1	0
25	56	140	23	17	12	7	3	0	0
50	112	40	44	40	35	30	26	22	18
50	112	60	35	30	26	21	17	12	8
50	112	80	30	25	20	15	11	7	3
50	112	100	26	21	16	12	7	3	0
50	112	120	23	18	13	9	5	1	0
50	112	140	21	16	11	7	3	0	0
75	168	40	39	35	31	27	24	20	16
75	168	60	31	27	23	19	15	11	7
75	168	80	26	22	18	14	10	6	3
75	168	100	23	19	15	10	7	3	0
75	168	120	20	16	12	8	4	1	0
75	168	140	18	14	10	6	2	0	0
100	224	40	35	32	29	25	21	18	14
100	224	60	28	25	21	17	14	10	6
100	224	80	24	20	16	13	9	5	2
100	224	100	21	17	13	10	6	2	0
100	224	120	19	15	11	7	4	0	0
100	224	140	17	13	9	5	2	0	0
125	280	40	32	30	26	23	20	16	13
125	280	60	26	23	19	16	12	9	6
125	280	80	22	19	15	12	8	5	2
125	280	100	19	16	12	9	5	2	0
125	280	120	17	14	10	7	3	0	0
125	280	140	16	12	8	5	2	0	0
150	335	40	30	28	25	21	18	15	12
150	335	60	24	21	18	15	11	8	5
150	335	80	21	17	14	11	7	4	1
150	335	100	18	15	11	8	5	2	0
150	335	120	16	13	9	6	3	0	0
150	335	140	15	11	8	4	1	0	0
175	391	40	28	26	23	20	17	14	10
175	391	60	23	20	17	14	10	7	4
175	391	80	19	16	13	10	7	4	1
175	391	100	17	14	11	7	4	1	0
175	391	120	15	12	9	5	2	0	0
175	391	140	14	10	7	4	1	0	0
200	447	40	27	24	22	18	16	12	10
200	447	60	22	19	16	13	10	7	4
200	447	80	18	15	12	9	6	3	1
200	447	100	16	13	10	7	4	1	0
200	447	120	14	11	8	5	2	0	0
200	447	140	13	10	7	4	1	0	0

			CEILING HEIGHT IN FEET						
τ	RTI	ΔT	4.0	8.0	12.0	16.0	20.0	24.0	28.0
			INSTALLED SPACING OF DETECTORS						
225	503	40	26	23	20	17	14	12	9
225	503	60	20	18	15	12	9	6	3
225	503	80	17	14	11	8	6	3	1
225	503	100	15	12	9	6	3	1	0
225	503	120	13	11	7	4	2	0	0
225	503	140	12	9	6	3	1	0	0
250	559	40	24	22	19	16	14	11	8
250	559	60	19	17	14	11	8	5	3
250	559	80	16	14	11	8	5	3	1
250	559	100	14	12	9	6	3	1	0
250	559	120	13	10	7	4	2	0	0
250	559	140	12	9	6	3	1	0	0
275	615	40	23	21	18	16	13	10	7
275	615	60	19	16	13	10	8	5	3
275	615	80	16	13	10	7	5	2	1
275	615	100	14	11	8	5	3	1	0
275	615	120	12	9	7	4	1	0	0
275	615	140	11	8	5	3	1	0	0
300	671	40	22	20	18	15	12	9	7
300	671	60	18	15	13	10	7	5	2
300	671	80	15	13	10	7	4	2	0
300	671	100	13	11	8	5	2	1	0
300	671	120	12	9	6	3	1	0	0
300	671	140	11	8	5	2	0	0	0
325	727	40	22	19	17	14	11	9	6
325	727	60	17	15	12	9	7	4	2
325	727	80	15	12	9	6	4	2	0
325	727	100	13	10	7	5	2	1	0
325	727	120	11	9	6	3	1	0	0
325	727	140	10	7	5	2	0	0	0
350	783	40	21	19	16	13	11	8	6
350	783	60	17	14	12	9	6	4	2
350	783	80	14	12	9	6	4	2	0
350	783	100	12	10	7	4	2	0	0
350	783	120	11	8	5	3	1	0	0
350	783	140	10	7	4	2	0	0	0
375	839	40	20	18	16	13	10	8	5
375	839	60	16	14	11	8	6	3	2
375	839	80	14	11	8	6	3	1	0
375	839	100	12	9	7	4	2	0	0
375	839	120	11	8	5	3	1	0	0
375	839	140	10	7	4	2	0	0	0
400	894	40	20	17	15	12	10	7	5
400	894	60	16	13	11	8	5	3	1
400	894	80	13	11	8	5	3	1	0
400	894	100	11	9	6	4	2	0	0
400	894	120	10	8	5	3	1	0	0
400	894	140	9	7	4	2	0	0	0

NOTE: Detector time constant at a reference velocity of 5 ft/sec.
For SI Units: 1 ft = 0.305 m
1000 BTU/sec = 1055 kW

Table B-3.2.4(o)
Q_d, Threshold Fire Size at Response: 750 Btu/sec
t_g: 600 Seconds to 1000 Btu/sec
α: 0.003 Btu/sec^3

τ	RTI	ΔT	CEILING HEIGHT IN FEET						
			4.0	8.0	12.0	16.0	20.0	24.0	28.0
			INSTALLED SPACING OF DETECTORS						
25	56	40	55	47	41	35	30	25	21
25	56	60	43	36	29	24	19	14	10
25	56	80	36	28	23	18	13	8	4
25	56	100	31	24	18	13	9	4	0
25	56	120	27	20	15	10	6	1	0
25	56	140	24	18	12	8	3	0	0
50	112	40	47	42	37	32	28	23	19
50	112	60	37	32	27	22	18	13	9
50	112	80	31	26	21	16	12	8	4
50	112	100	27	22	17	12	8	4	0
50	112	120	24	19	14	9	5	1	0
50	112	140	22	16	11	7	3	0	0
75	168	40	42	38	34	29	25	21	17
75	168	60	33	29	25	20	16	12	8
75	168	80	28	24	19	15	11	7	3
75	168	100	24	20	15	11	7	3	0
75	168	120	22	17	13	9	5	1	0
75	168	140	20	15	11	6	3	0	0
100	224	40	38	35	31	27	23	19	16
100	224	60	30	27	23	19	15	11	7
100	224	80	26	22	18	14	10	6	3
100	224	100	22	18	14	10	7	3	0
100	224	120	20	16	12	8	4	1	0
100	224	140	18	14	10	6	2	0	0
125	280	40	35	32	29	25	22	18	14
125	280	60	28	25	21	17	14	10	7
125	280	80	24	20	16	13	9	6	2
125	280	100	21	17	13	10	6	3	0
125	280	120	19	15	11	7	4	1	0
125	280	140	17	13	9	5	2	0	0
150	335	40	33	30	27	23	20	17	13
150	335	60	26	23	20	16	13	9	6
150	335	80	22	19	15	12	8	5	2
150	335	100	19	16	12	9	5	2	0
150	335	120	17	14	10	7	3	0	0
150	335	140	16	12	8	5	2	0	0
175	391	40	31	28	25	22	19	15	12
175	391	60	25	22	18	15	12	9	5
175	391	80	21	18	14	11	8	4	2
175	391	100	18	15	12	8	5	2	0
175	391	120	16	13	10	6	3	0	0
175	391	140	15	11	8	5	1	0	0
200	447	40	29	27	24	21	17	14	11
200	447	60	23	21	17	14	11	8	5
200	447	80	20	17	14	10	7	4	1
200	447	100	17	14	11	8	4	2	0
200	447	120	15	12	9	6	3	0	0
200	447	140	14	11	7	4	1	0	0
225	503	40	28	26	23	19	16	13	10
225	503	60	22	20	17	13	10	7	4
225	503	80	19	16	13	10	7	4	1
225	503	100	16	13	10	7	4	1	0
225	503	120	15	12	8	5	2	0	0
225	503	140	13	10	7	4	1	0	0
250	559	40	27	24	21	18	15	12	10
250	559	60	21	19	16	13	10	7	4
250	559	80	18	15	12	9	6	3	1
250	559	100	16	13	10	7	4	1	0
250	559	120	14	11	8	5	2	0	0
250	559	140	13	10	7	4	1	0	0
275	615	40	26	23	20	18	15	12	9
275	615	60	21	18	15	12	9	6	4
275	615	80	17	15	12	9	6	3	1
275	615	100	15	12	9	6	3	1	0
275	615	120	13	11	7	5	2	0	0
275	615	140	12	9	6	3	1	0	0
300	671	40	25	22	20	17	14	11	8
300	671	60	20	17	14	11	8	6	3
300	671	80	17	14	11	8	5	3	1
300	671	100	15	12	9	6	3	1	0
300	671	120	13	10	7	4	2	0	0
300	671	140	12	9	6	3	1	0	0
325	727	40	24	22	19	16	13	10	8
325	727	60	19	16	14	11	8	5	3
325	727	80	16	13	10	8	5	2	1
325	727	100	14	11	8	5	3	1	0
325	727	120	12	10	7	4	2	0	0
325	727	140	11	8	5	3	1	0	0
350	783	40	23	21	18	15	13	10	7
350	783	60	18	16	13	10	7	5	3
350	783	80	15	13	10	7	5	2	1
350	783	100	13	11	8	5	3	1	0
350	783	120	12	9	6	4	1	0	0
350	783	140	11	8	5	3	1	0	0
375	839	40	22	20	17	15	12	9	7
375	839	60	18	15	13	10	7	5	2
375	839	80	15	12	10	7	4	2	0
375	839	100	13	10	8	5	0	1	0
375	839	120	12	9	6	3	1	0	0
375	839	140	11	8	5	2	0	0	0
400	894	40	22	19	17	14	11	9	6
400	894	60	17	15	12	9	7	4	2
400	894	80	15	12	9	6	4	2	0
400	894	100	13	10	7	5	2	1	0
400	894	120	11	9	6	3	1	0	0
400	894	140	10	7	5	2	0	0	0

NOTE: Detector time constant at a reference velocity of 5 ft/sec.
For SI Units: 1 ft = 0.305 m
1000 BTU/sec = 1055 kW

Table B-3.2.4(p)
Q_d, Threshold Fire Size at Response: 1000 Btu/sec
t_g: 50 Seconds to 1000 Btu/sec
α: 0.400 Btu/sec^3

τ	RTI	ΔT	CEILING HEIGHT IN FEET						
			4.0	8.0	12.0	16.0	20.0	24.0	28.0
			INSTALLED SPACING OF DETECTORS						
25	56	40	22	20	17	14	11	8	5
25	56	60	18	16	13	10	7	4	2
25	56	80	16	13	10	7	4	2	0
25	56	100	14	11	8	5	3	0	0
25	56	120	13	10	7	4	1	0	0
25	56	140	12	9	6	3	1	0	0
50	112	40	17	15	12	9	7	4	2
50	112	60	14	11	9	6	4	2	0
50	112	80	12	9	7	4	2	0	0
50	112	100	11	8	5	3	1	0	0
50	112	120	10	7	4	2	0	0	0
50	112	140	9	6	3	1	0	0	0
75	168	40	14	12	9	7	4	2	1
75	168	60	12	9	7	4	2	1	0
75	168	80	10	7	5	3	1	0	0
75	168	100	9	6	4	2	0	0	0
75	168	120	8	5	3	1	0	0	0
75	168	140	7	4	2	0	0	0	0
100	224	40	12	10	8	5	3	1	0
100	224	60	10	8	5	3	1	0	0
100	224	80	8	6	4	2	0	0	0
100	224	100	7	5	3	1	0	0	0
100	224	120	7	4	2	0	0	0	0
100	224	140	6	4	1	0	0	0	0
125	280	40	11	9	6	4	2	1	0
125	280	60	9	7	4	2	1	0	0
125	280	80	8	5	3	1	0	0	0
125	280	100	7	4	2	0	0	0	0
125	280	120	6	3	1	0	0	0	0
125	280	140	5	3	1	0	0	0	0
150	335	40	0	8	5	3	2	0	0
150	335	60	8	6	3	2	0	0	0
150	335	80	7	4	2	0	0	0	0
150	335	100	6	3	2	0	0	0	0
150	335	120	5	3	1	0	0	0	0
150	335	140	5	2	0	0	0	0	0
175	391	40	9	7	5	3	1	0	0
175	391	60	7	5	3	1	0	0	0
175	391	80	6	4	2	0	0	0	0
175	391	100	5	3	1	0	0	0	0
175	391	120	5	2	0	0	0	0	0
175	391	140	4	2	0	0	0	0	0
200	447	40	9	6	4	2	1	0	0
200	447	60	7	5	2	1	0	0	0
200	447	80	6	3	1	0	0	0	0
200	447	100	5	3	1	0	0	0	0
200	447	120	4	2	0	0	0	0	0
200	447	140	4	2	0	0	0	0	0
225	503	40	8	6	4	2	0	0	0
225	503	60	6	4	2	0	0	0	0
225	503	80	5	3	1	0	0	0	0
225	503	100	5	2	0	0	0	0	0
225	503	120	4	2	0	0	0	0	0
225	503	140	3	1	0	0	0	0	0
250	559	40	8	5	3	1	0	0	0
250	559	60	6	4	2	0	0	0	0
250	559	80	5	3	1	0	0	0	0
250	559	100	4	2	0	0	0	0	0
250	559	120	4	2	0	0	0	0	0
250	559	140	3	1	0	0	0	0	0
275	615	40	7	5	3	1	0	0	0
275	615	60	6	3	1	0	0	0	0
275	615	80	5	2	0	0	0	0	0
275	615	100	4	2	0	0	0	0	0
275	615	120	3	1	0	0	0	0	0
275	615	140	3	1	0	0	0	0	0
300	671	40	7	5	3	1	0	0	0
300	671	60	5	3	1	0	0	0	0
300	671	80	4	2	0	0	0	0	0
300	671	100	4	2	0	0	0	0	0
300	671	120	3	1	0	0	0	0	0
300	671	140	3	1	0	0	0	0	0
325	727	40	7	4	2	1	0	0	0
325	727	60	5	3	1	0	0	0	0
325	727	80	4	2	0	0	0	0	0
325	727	100	3	1	0	0	0	0	0
325	727	120	3	1	0	0	0	0	0
325	727	140	3	0	0	0	0	0	0
350	783	40	6	4	2	0	0	0	0
350	783	60	5	3	1	0	0	0	0
350	783	80	4	2	0	0	0	0	0
350	783	100	3	1	0	0	0	0	0
350	783	120	3	1	0	0	0	0	0
350	783	140	2	0	0	0	0	0	0
375	839	40	6	4	2	0	0	0	0
375	839	60	5	2	0	0	0	0	0
375	839	80	4	2	0	0	0	0	0
375	839	100	3	1	0	0	0	0	0
375	839	120	3	0	0	0	0	0	0
375	839	140	2	0	0	0	0	0	0
400	894	40	6	4	2	0	0	0	0
400	894	60	4	2	0	0	0	0	0
400	894	80	3	1	0	0	0	0	0
400	894	100	3	1	0	0	0	0	0
400	894	120	2	0	0	0	0	0	0
400	894	140	2	0	0	0	0	0	0

NOTE: Detector time constant at a reference velocity of 5 ft/sec.
For SI Units: 1 ft = 0.305 m
1000 BTU/sec = 1055 kW

Table B-3.2.4(q)
Q_d, Threshold Fire Size at Response: 1000 Btu/sec
t_g: 150 Seconds to 1000 Btu/sec
α: 0.044 Btu/sec³

τ	RTI	ΔT	CEILING HEIGHT IN FEET						
			4.0	8.0	12.0	16.0	20.0	24.0	28.0
			INSTALLED SPACING OF DETECTORS						
25	56	40	39	36	32	28	25	21	17
25	56	60	32	28	24	21	17	13	9
25	56	80	27	24	20	16	12	8	4
25	56	100	24	20	16	12	8	4	1
25	56	120	22	18	14	10	6	2	0
25	56	140	20	16	12	8	4	0	0
50	112	40	31	29	26	22	19	16	13
50	112	60	25	23	19	16	13	9	6
50	112	80	22	19	15	12	9	6	3
50	112	100	19	16	13	9	6	3	0
50	112	120	17	14	11	7	4	1	0
50	112	140	16	13	9	6	2	0	0
75	168	40	27	24	22	19	16	13	10
75	168	60	22	19	16	13	10	7	4
75	168	80	19	16	13	10	7	4	2
75	168	100	16	14	11	7	4	2	0
75	168	120	15	12	9	6	3	1	0
75	168	140	13	10	7	4	2	0	0
100	224	40	24	22	19	16	13	10	8
100	224	60	19	17	14	11	8	6	3
100	224	80	16	14	11	8	5	3	1
100	224	100	14	12	9	6	3	1	0
100	224	120	13	10	7	5	2	0	0
100	224	140	12	9	6	3	1	0	0
125	280	40	21	19	17	14	11	9	6
125	280	60	17	15	12	10	7	4	2
125	280	80	15	12	10	7	4	2	1
125	280	100	13	10	8	5	3	1	0
125	280	120	12	9	6	4	1	0	0
125	280	140	11	8	5	3	1	0	0
150	335	40	20	18	15	13	10	7	5
150	335	60	16	14	11	8	6	4	2
150	335	80	14	11	9	6	3	2	0
150	335	100	12	9	7	4	2	1	0
150	335	120	11	8	5	3	1	0	0
150	335	140	10	7	4	2	1	0	0
175	391	40	18	16	14	11	9	6	4
175	391	60	15	13	10	7	5	3	1
175	391	80	13	10	8	5	3	1	0
175	391	100	11	9	6	4	2	0	0
175	391	120	10	7	5	2	1	0	0
175	391	140	9	6	4	2	0	0	0
200	447	40	17	15	13	10	8	5	3
200	447	60	14	12	9	7	4	2	1
200	447	80	12	9	7	4	2	1	0
200	447	100	10	8	5	3	1	0	0
200	447	120	9	7	4	2	1	0	0
200	447	140	8	6	3	1	0	0	0

τ	RTI	ΔT	CEILING HEIGHT IN FEET						
			4.0	8.0	12.0	16.0	20.0	24.0	28.0
			INSTALLED SPACING OF DETECTORS						
225	503	40	16	14	12	9	7	5	3
225	503	60	13	11	8	6	4	2	1
225	503	80	11	9	6	4	2	1	0
225	503	100	10	7	5	3	1	0	0
225	503	120	9	6	4	2	0	0	0
225	503	140	8	5	3	1	0	0	0
250	559	40	16	13	11	9	6	4	2
250	559	60	12	10	8	5	3	2	0
250	559	80	11	8	6	3	2	0	0
250	559	100	9	7	4	2	1	0	0
250	559	120	8	6	3	1	0	0	0
250	559	140	7	5	3	1	0	0	0
275	615	40	15	13	10	8	6	4	2
275	615	60	12	10	7	5	3	1	0
275	615	80	10	8	5	3	1	0	0
275	615	100	9	6	4	2	0	0	0
275	615	120	8	5	3	1	0	0	0
275	615	140	7	5	2	1	0	0	0
300	671	40	14	12	10	7	5	3	2
300	671	60	11	9	7	4	2	1	0
300	671	80	10	7	5	3	1	0	0
300	671	100	8	6	4	2	0	0	0
300	671	120	7	5	3	1	0	0	0
300	671	140	7	4	2	0	0	0	0
325	727	40	14	12	9	7	5	3	1
325	727	60	11	9	6	4	2	1	0
325	727	80	9	7	4	2	1	0	0
325	727	100	8	6	3	1	0	0	0
325	727	120	7	5	2	1	0	0	0
325	727	140	6	4	2	0	0	0	0
350	783	40	13	11	9	6	4	2	1
350	783	60	10	8	6	4	2	1	0
350	783	80	9	6	4	2	1	0	0
350	783	100	8	5	3	1	0	0	0
350	783	120	7	4	2	1	0	0	0
350	783	140	6	4	2	0	0	0	0
375	839	40	13	11	8	6	4	2	1
375	839	60	10	8	5	3	2	0	0
375	839	80	8	6	4	2	0	0	0
375	839	100	7	5	3	1	0	0	0
375	839	120	6	4	2	0	0	0	0
375	839	140	6	3	1	0	0	0	0
400	894	40	12	10	8	5	3	2	1
400	894	60	10	7	5	3	1	0	0
400	894	80	8	6	4	2	0	0	0
400	894	100	7	5	3	1	0	0	0
400	894	120	6	4	2	0	0	0	0
400	894	140	6	3	1	0	0	0	0

NOTE: Detector time constant at a reference velocity of 5 ft/sec.
For SI Units: 1 ft = 0.305 m
1000 BTU/sec = 1055 kW

Table B-3.2.4(r)
Q_d, Threshold Fire Size at Response: 1000 Btu/sec
t_g: 300 Seconds to 1000 Btu/sec
α: 0.011 Btu/sec^3

τ	RTI	ΔT	CEILING HEIGHT IN FEET						
			4.0	8.0	12.0	16.0	20.0	24.0	28.0
			INSTALLED SPACING OF DETECTORS						
25	56	40	52	47	42	37	32	28	23
25	56	60	42	36	31	26	22	17	13
25	56	80	35	30	25	20	15	11	7
25	56	100	31	25	20	15	11	7	3
25	56	120	28	22	17	12	8	4	0
25	56	140	25	19	14	10	5	1	0
50	112	40	43	40	36	32	28	24	20
50	112	60	35	31	27	23	19	15	11
50	112	80	30	25	21	17	13	9	5
50	112	100	26	22	18	13	9	6	2
50	112	120	23	19	15	11	7	3	0
50	112	140	21	17	12	8	4	1	0
75	168	40	37	35	31	28	24	21	17
75	168	60	30	27	24	20	16	13	9
75	168	80	26	22	19	15	11	8	4
75	168	100	23	19	15	12	8	5	1
75	168	120	20	17	13	9	6	2	0
75	168	140	19	15	11	7	4	1	0
100	224	40	34	31	28	25	22	18	15
100	224	60	27	24	21	18	14	11	8
100	224	80	23	20	17	13	10	7	4
100	224	100	20	17	14	10	7	4	1
100	224	120	18	15	12	8	5	2	0
100	224	140	17	13	10	6	3	0	0
125	280	40	31	29	26	23	19	16	13
125	280	60	25	22	19	16	13	10	7
125	280	80	21	18	15	12	9	6	3
125	280	100	19	16	13	9	6	3	1
125	280	120	17	14	10	7	4	1	0
125	280	140	15	12	9	6	3	0	0
150	335	40	29	27	24	21	18	15	12
150	335	60	23	21	18	15	12	9	6
150	335	80	20	17	14	11	8	5	2
150	335	100	17	14	11	8	5	3	1
150	335	120	16	13	10	6	4	1	0
150	335	140	14	11	8	5	2	0	0
175	391	40	27	25	22	19	16	13	11
175	391	60	22	19	16	13	10	8	5
175	391	80	18	16	13	10	7	4	2
175	391	100	16	13	10	8	5	2	0
175	391	120	15	12	9	6	3	1	0
175	391	140	13	10	7	4	2	0	0
200	447	40	25	23	21	18	15	12	9
200	447	60	20	18	15	12	10	7	4
200	447	80	17	15	12	9	6	4	2
200	447	100	15	13	10	7	4	2	0
200	447	120	14	11	8	5	3	1	0
200	447	140	12	10	7	4	2	0	0

τ	RTI	ΔT	CEILING HEIGHT IN FEET						
			4.0	8.0	12.0	16.0	20.0	24.0	28.0
			INSTALLED SPACING OF DETECTORS						
225	503	40	24	22	19	17	14	11	9
225	503	60	19	17	14	11	9	6	4
225	503	80	16	14	11	8	6	3	1
225	503	100	14	12	9	6	4	2	0
225	503	120	13	10	7	5	2	1	0
225	503	140	12	9	6	3	1	0	0
250	559	40	23	21	18	16	13	10	8
250	559	60	18	16	13	11	8	5	3
250	559	80	16	13	10	8	5	3	1
250	559	100	14	11	8	6	3	1	0
250	559	120	12	10	7	4	2	0	0
250	559	140	11	8	6	3	1	0	0
275	615	40	22	20	17	15	12	9	7
275	615	60	18	15	13	10	7	5	3
275	615	80	15	12	10	7	5	2	1
275	615	100	13	11	8	5	3	1	0
275	615	120	12	9	6	4	2	0	0
275	615	140	11	8	5	3	1	0	0
300	671	40	21	19	16	14	11	9	6
300	671	60	17	15	12	9	7	4	2
300	671	80	14	12	9	7	4	2	1
300	671	100	13	10	7	5	3	1	0
300	671	120	11	9	6	3	1	0	0
300	671	140	10	8	5	3	1	0	0
325	727	40	20	18	16	13	11	8	6
325	727	60	16	14	11	9	6	4	2
325	727	80	14	11	9	6	4	2	1
325	727	100	12	10	7	4	2	1	0
325	727	120	11	8	6	3	1	0	0
325	727	140	10	7	5	2	1	0	0
350	783	40	20	18	15	13	10	8	5
350	783	60	16	13	11	8	6	4	2
350	783	80	13	11	8	6	3	2	0
350	783	100	12	9	7	4	2	1	0
350	783	120	10	8	5	3	1	0	0
350	783	140	9	7	4	2	1	0	0
375	839	40	19	17	14	12	9	7	5
375	839	60	15	13	10	8	5	3	2
375	839	80	13	10	8	5	3	1	0
375	839	100	11	9	6	4	2	0	0
375	839	120	10	7	5	3	1	0	0
375	839	140	9	6	4	2	0	0	0
400	894	40	18	16	14	11	9	7	4
400	894	60	15	12	10	7	5	3	1
400	894	80	12	10	7	5	3	1	0
400	894	100	11	8	6	3	2	0	0
400	894	120	10	7	5	2	1	0	0
400	894	140	9	6	4	2	0	0	0

NOTE: Detector time constant at a reference velocity of 5 ft/sec.
For SI Units: 1 ft = 0.305 m
1000 BTU/sec = 1055 kW

Table B-3.2.4(s)
Q_d, Threshold Fire Size at Response: 1000 Btu/sec
t_g: 500 Seconds to 1000 Btu/sec
α: 0.004 Btu/sec^3

τ	RTI	ΔT	CEILING HEIGHT IN FEET 4.0	8.0	12.0	16.0	20.0	24.0	28.0
			INSTALLED SPACING OF DETECTORS						
25	56	40	62	54	48	42	37	31	27
25	56	60	49	41	35	29	24	19	15
25	56	80	41	33	27	22	17	12	8
25	56	100	35	28	22	17	12	8	4
25	56	120	31	24	18	13	9	4	0
25	56	140	28	21	16	11	6	2	0
50	112	40	53	48	43	38	33	29	24
50	112	60	42	37	32	27	22	18	14
50	112	80	35	30	25	20	16	11	7
50	112	100	31	25	20	16	11	7	3
50	112	120	27	22	17	12	8	4	0
50	112	140	25	19	14	10	6	2	0
75	168	40	47	43	39	35	31	26	22
75	168	60	38	33	29	25	20	16	12
75	168	80	32	27	23	19	14	10	6
75	168	100	28	23	19	14	10	6	3
75	168	120	25	20	16	11	7	3	0
75	168	140	22	18	13	9	5	1	0
100	224	40	43	40	36	32	28	24	20
100	224	60	34	31	27	23	19	15	11
100	224	80	29	25	21	17	13	9	6
100	224	100	25	21	17	13	9	6	2
100	224	120	23	19	15	11	7	3	0
100	224	140	21	16	12	8	5	1	0
125	280	40	39	37	33	30	26	22	19
125	280	60	32	28	25	21	17	14	10
125	280	80	27	23	20	16	12	9	5
125	280	100	24	20	16	12	9	5	2
125	280	120	21	17	14	10	6	3	0
125	280	140	19	15	11	8	4	1	0
150	335	40	37	34	31	28	24	21	17
150	335	60	30	27	23	20	16	13	9
150	335	80	25	22	18	15	11	8	5
150	335	100	22	19	15	12	8	5	2
150	335	120	20	16	13	9	6	2	0
150	335	140	18	14	11	7	4	1	0
175	391	40	35	32	29	26	23	19	16
175	391	60	28	25	22	18	15	12	8
175	391	80	24	20	17	14	10	7	4
175	391	100	21	18	14	11	7	4	1
175	391	120	19	15	12	8	5	2	0
175	391	140	17	13	10	7	3	1	0
200	447	40	33	30	28	24	21	18	15
200	447	60	26	24	20	17	14	11	8
200	447	80	22	19	16	13	10	7	4
200	447	100	20	17	13	10	7	4	1
200	447	120	18	14	11	8	5	2	0
200	447	140	16	13	9	6	3	1	0

τ	RTI	ΔT	CEILING HEIGHT IN FEET 4.0	8.0	12.0	16.0	20.0	24.0	28.0
			INSTALLED SPACING OF DETECTORS						
225	503	40	31	29	26	23	20	17	14
225	503	60	25	22	19	16	13	10	7
225	503	80	21	18	15	12	9	6	3
225	503	100	19	16	13	9	6	3	1
225	503	120	17	14	10	7	4	2	0
225	503	140	15	12	9	6	3	0	0
250	559	40	30	28	25	22	19	16	13
250	559	60	24	21	18	15	12	9	7
250	559	80	20	18	15	11	8	6	3
250	559	100	18	15	12	9	6	3	1
250	559	120	16	13	10	7	4	1	0
250	559	140	14	11	8	5	2	0	0
275	615	40	29	27	24	21	18	15	12
275	615	60	23	20	18	15	12	9	6
275	615	80	20	17	14	11	8	5	3
275	615	100	17	14	11	8	5	3	1
275	615	120	15	12	9	6	4	1	0
275	615	140	14	11	8	5	2	0	0
300	671	40	28	25	23	20	17	14	11
300	671	60	22	20	17	14	11	8	5
300	671	80	19	16	13	10	7	5	2
300	671	100	16	14	11	8	5	2	1
300	671	120	15	12	9	6	3	1	0
300	671	140	13	10	7	5	2	0	0
325	727	40	27	25	22	19	16	13	11
325	727	60	21	19	16	13	10	8	5
325	727	80	18	16	13	10	7	4	2
325	727	100	16	13	10	7	5	2	0
325	727	120	14	11	8	6	3	1	0
325	727	140	13	10	7	4	2	0	0
350	783	40	26	24	21	18	15	13	10
350	783	60	21	18	15	13	10	7	5
350	783	80	18	15	12	9	7	4	2
350	783	100	15	13	10	7	4	2	0
350	783	120	14	11	8	5	3	1	0
350	783	140	12	10	7	4	2	0	0
375	839	40	25	23	20	18	15	12	9
375	839	60	20	18	15	12	9	7	4
375	839	80	17	14	12	9	6	4	2
375	839	100	15	12	9	7	4	2	0
375	839	120	13	11	8	5	3	1	0
375	839	140	12	9	6	4	1	0	0
400	894	40	24	22	20	17	14	11	9
400	894	60	19	17	14	12	9	6	4
400	894	80	16	14	11	8	6	3	1
400	894	100	14	12	9	6	4	2	0
400	894	120	13	10	7	5	2	1	0
400	894	140	12	9	6	4	1	0	0

NOTE: Detector time constant at a reference velocity of 5 ft/sec.
For SI Units: 1 ft = 0.305 m
1000 BTU/sec = 1055 kW

Table B-3.2.4(t)
Q_d, Threshold Fire Size at Response: 1000 Btu/sec
t_g: 600 Seconds to 1000 Btu/sec
α: 0.003 Btu/sec³

τ	RTI	ΔT	CEILING HEIGHT IN FEET						
			4.0	8.0	12.0	16.0	20.0	24.0	28.0
			INSTALLED SPACING OF DETECTORS						
25	56	40	65	56	50	43	38	33	28
25	56	60	51	43	36	30	25	20	15
25	56	80	42	34	28	23	18	13	8
25	56	100	36	29	23	17	13	8	4
25	56	120	32	25	19	14	9	5	1
25	56	140	29	21	16	11	6	2	0
50	112	40	56	51	45	40	35	30	26
50	112	60	45	39	33	28	23	19	14
50	112	80	37	31	26	21	16	12	8
50	112	100	33	26	21	16	12	7	3
50	112	120	29	23	18	13	8	4	0
50	112	140	26	20	15	10	6	2	0
75	168	40	50	46	42	37	32	28	24
75	168	60	40	35	31	26	22	17	13
75	168	80	34	29	24	20	15	11	7
75	168	100	30	25	20	15	11	7	3
75	168	120	26	21	17	12	8	4	0
75	168	140	24	19	14	10	5	2	0
100	224	40	46	43	38	34	30	26	22
100	224	60	37	33	28	24	20	16	12
100	224	80	31	27	23	18	14	10	6
100	224	100	27	23	18	14	10	6	3
100	224	120	24	20	15	11	7	3	0
100	224	140	22	17	13	9	5	1	0
125	280	40	43	40	36	32	28	24	21
125	280	60	34	31	27	23	19	15	11
125	280	80	29	25	21	17	13	10	6
125	280	100	25	21	17	13	10	6	2
125	280	120	23	19	15	11	7	3	0
125	280	140	21	16	12	8	5	1	0
150	335	40	40	37	34	30	26	23	19
150	335	60	32	29	25	21	18	14	11
150	335	80	27	24	20	16	12	9	5
150	335	100	24	20	16	13	9	5	2
150	335	120	21	17	14	10	6	3	0
150	335	140	19	15	12	8	4	1	0
175	391	40	38	35	32	28	25	21	18
175	391	60	30	27	24	20	17	13	10
175	391	80	26	22	19	15	12	8	5
175	391	100	22	19	15	12	8	5	2
175	391	120	20	17	13	9	6	3	0
175	391	140	18	15	11	7	4	1	0
200	447	40	36	33	30	27	24	20	17
200	447	60	29	26	22	19	16	12	9
200	447	80	24	21	18	14	11	8	4
200	447	100	21	18	15	11	8	4	2
200	447	120	19	16	12	9	5	2	0
200	447	140	17	14	10	7	4	1	0

τ	RTI	ΔT	CEILING HEIGHT IN FEET						
			4.0	8.0	12.0	16.0	20.0	24.0	28.0
			INSTALLED SPACING OF DETECTORS						
225	503	40	34	32	29	26	22	19	16
225	503	60	27	25	21	18	15	12	8
225	503	80	23	20	17	14	10	7	4
225	503	100	20	17	14	11	7	4	1
225	503	120	18	15	12	8	5	2	0
225	503	140	17	13	10	6	3	1	0
250	559	40	33	30	27	24	21	18	15
250	559	60	26	23	20	17	14	11	8
250	559	80	22	19	16	13	10	7	4
250	559	100	19	16	13	10	7	4	1
250	559	120	17	14	11	8	5	2	0
250	559	140	16	13	9	6	3	1	0
275	615	40	31	29	26	23	20	17	14
275	615	60	25	23	19	16	13	10	7
275	615	80	21	18	15	12	9	6	3
275	615	100	19	16	13	9	6	3	1
275	615	120	17	14	11	7	4	2	0
275	615	140	15	12	9	6	3	0	0
300	671	40	30	28	25	22	19	16	13
300	671	60	24	22	19	16	13	10	7
300	671	80	21	18	15	12	9	6	3
300	671	100	18	15	12	9	6	3	1
300	671	120	16	13	10	7	4	1	0
300	671	140	15	12	8	5	3	0	0
325	727	40	29	27	24	21	18	15	13
325	727	60	23	21	18	15	12	9	6
325	727	80	20	17	14	11	8	5	3
325	727	100	17	15	12	8	6	3	1
325	727	120	16	13	10	7	4	1	0
325	727	140	14	11	8	5	2	0	0
350	783	40	28	26	23	21	18	15	12
350	783	60	23	20	17	14	11	9	6
350	783	80	19	17	14	11	8	5	3
350	783	100	17	14	11	8	5	3	1
350	783	120	15	12	9	6	3	1	0
350	783	140	14	11	8	5	2	0	0
375	839	40	28	25	23	20	17	14	11
375	839	60	22	19	17	14	11	8	5
375	839	80	19	16	13	10	7	5	2
375	839	100	16	14	11	8	5	2	1
375	839	120	15	12	9	6	3	1	0
375	839	140	13	10	7	5	2	0	0
400	894	40	27	25	22	19	16	13	11
400	894	60	21	19	16	13	10	8	5
400	894	80	18	15	13	10	7	4	2
400	894	100	16	13	10	7	5	2	1
400	894	120	14	11	8	6	3	1	0
400	894	140	13	10	7	4	2	0	0

NOTE: Detector time constant at a reference velocity of 5 ft/sec.
For SI Units: 1 ft = 0.305 m
1000 BTU/sec = 1055 kW

Table B-3.2.4(u)
Q_d, Threshold Fire Size at Response: 2000 Btu/sec
t_g: 50 Seconds to 1000 Btu/sec
α: 0.400 Btu/sec^3

τ	RTI	ΔT	CEILING HEIGHT IN FEET						
			4.0	8.0	12.0	16.0	20.0	24.0	28.0
			INSTALLED SPACING OF DETECTORS						
25	56	40	35	33	31	28	25	21	18
25	56	60	30	27	24	21	18	15	11
25	56	80	26	23	20	17	14	10	7
25	56	100	23	21	17	14	11	7	4
25	56	120	21	18	15	12	8	5	2
25	56	140	20	17	13	10	7	3	1
50	112	40	28	26	23	21	18	15	12
50	112	60	23	21	18	15	13	10	7
50	112	80	20	18	15	12	9	6	4
50	112	100	18	15	13	10	7	4	2
50	112	120	16	14	11	8	5	3	1
50	112	140	15	12	10	7	4	2	0
75	168	40	24	22	19	17	14	11	9
75	168	60	20	17	15	12	9	7	4
75	168	80	17	15	12	9	7	4	2
75	168	100	15	13	10	7	5	3	1
75	168	120	14	11	8	6	3	1	0
75	168	140	13	10	7	5	2	1	0
100	224	40	21	19	17	14	11	9	6
100	224	60	17	15	13	10	7	5	3
100	224	80	15	13	10	7	5	3	1
100	224	100	13	11	8	6	3	2	0
100	224	120	12	10	7	4	2	1	0
100	224	140	11	8	6	3	2	0	0
125	280	40	19	17	15	12	10	7	5
125	280	60	16	13	11	8	6	4	2
125	280	80	13	11	9	6	4	2	1
125	280	100	12	10	7	5	2	1	0
125	280	120	11	8	6	3	2	0	0
125	280	140	10	7	5	3	1	0	0
150	335	40	18	16	13	11	8	6	4
150	335	60	14	12	10	7	5	3	1
150	335	80	12	10	7	5	3	1	0
150	335	100	11	8	6	4	2	0	0
150	335	120	10	7	5	3	1	0	0
150	335	140	9	6	4	2	0	0	0
175	391	40	16	14	12	9	7	5	3
175	391	60	13	11	9	6	4	2	1
175	391	80	11	9	7	4	2	1	0
175	391	100	10	8	5	3	1	0	0
175	391	120	9	7	4	2	1	0	0
175	391	140	8	6	3	2	0	0	0
200	447	40	15	13	11	8	6	4	2
200	447	60	12	10	8	5	3	2	0
200	447	80	11	8	6	4	2	1	0
200	447	100	9	7	5	3	1	0	0
200	447	120	8	6	4	2	0	0	0
200	447	140	8	5	3	1	0	0	0
225	503	40	15	12	10	8	5	3	2
225	503	60	12	9	7	5	3	1	0
225	503	80	10	8	5	3	2	0	0
225	503	100	9	6	4	2	1	0	0
225	503	120	8	5	3	1	0	0	0
225	503	140	7	5	3	1	0	0	0
250	559	40	14	12	9	7	5	3	2
250	559	60	11	9	6	4	2	1	0
250	559	80	9	7	5	3	1	0	0
250	559	100	8	6	4	2	0	0	0
250	559	120	7	5	3	1	0	0	0
250	559	140	7	4	2	1	0	0	0
275	615	40	13	11	9	6	4	2	1
275	615	60	10	8	6	4	2	1	0
275	615	80	9	7	4	2	1	0	0
275	615	100	8	5	3	2	0	0	0
275	615	120	7	5	2	1	0	0	0
275	615	140	6	4	2	0	0	0	0
300	671	40	13	10	8	6	4	2	1
300	671	60	10	8	5	3	2	0	0
300	671	80	8	6	4	2	1	0	0
300	671	100	7	5	3	1	0	0	0
300	671	120	7	4	2	1	0	0	0
300	671	140	6	4	2	0	0	0	0
325	727	40	12	10	8	5	3	2	1
325	727	60	10	7	5	3	1	0	0
325	727	80	8	6	4	2	0	0	0
325	727	100	7	5	3	1	0	0	0
325	727	120	6	4	2	0	0	0	0
325	727	140	6	3	1	0	0	0	0
350	783	40	12	9	7	5	3	2	0
350	783	60	9	7	5	3	1	0	0
350	783	80	8	5	3	2	0	0	0
350	783	100	7	4	2	1	0	0	0
350	783	120	6	4	2	0	0	0	0
350	783	140	5	3	1	0	0	0	0
375	839	40	11	9	7	4	3	1	0
375	839	60	9	7	4	2	1	0	0
375	839	80	7	5	3	1	0	0	0
375	839	100	6	4	2	0	0	0	0
375	839	120	6	3	2	0	0	0	0
375	839	140	5	3	1	0	0	0	0
400	894	40	11	9	6	4	2	1	0
400	894	60	9	6	4	2	1	0	0
400	894	80	7	5	3	1	0	0	0
400	894	100	6	4	2	0	0	0	0
400	894	120	5	3	1	0	0	0	0
400	894	140	5	3	1	0	0	0	0

NOTE: Detector time constant at a reference velocity of 5 ft/sec.
For SI Units: 1 ft = 0.305 m
1000 BTU/sec = 1055 kW

Table B-3.2.4(v)
Q_d, Threshold Fire Size at Response: 2000 Btu/sec
t_g: 150 Seconds to 1000 Btu/sec
α: 0.044 Btu/sec³

τ	RTI	ΔT	CEILING HEIGHT IN FEET 4.0	8.0	12.0	16.0	20.0	24.0	28.0
			INSTALLED SPACING OF DETECTORS						
25	56	40	60	57	53	49	44	40	36
25	56	60	50	46	41	37	32	28	23
25	56	80	43	38	34	29	25	20	16
25	56	100	38	33	28	24	19	15	11
25	56	120	34	29	25	20	15	11	7
25	56	140	31	26	21	17	13	8	4
50	112	40	49	47	44	40	37	33	30
50	112	60	40	38	34	31	27	23	19
50	112	80	35	32	28	24	21	17	13
50	112	100	31	28	24	20	16	12	9
50	112	120	28	24	21	17	13	9	6
50	112	140	26	22	18	14	10	7	3
75	168	40	43	41	38	35	32	28	25
75	168	60	35	33	30	26	23	20	16
75	168	80	30	28	24	21	18	14	11
75	168	100	27	24	21	17	14	10	7
75	168	120	24	21	18	14	11	8	4
75	168	140	22	19	16	12	9	5	2
100	224	40	38	36	34	31	28	25	22
100	224	60	31	29	26	23	20	17	14
100	224	80	27	25	22	18	15	12	9
100	224	100	24	21	18	15	12	9	6
100	224	120	22	19	16	13	9	6	3
100	224	140	20	17	14	11	7	4	2
125	280	40	35	33	31	28	25	22	19
125	280	60	29	27	24	21	18	15	12
125	280	80	25	22	19	16	13	11	8
125	280	100	22	19	16	13	10	7	5
125	280	120	20	17	14	11	8	5	3
125	280	140	18	15	12	9	6	4	1
150	335	40	32	31	28	26	23	20	17
150	335	60	27	24	22	19	16	13	10
150	335	80	23	20	18	15	12	9	6
150	335	100	20	18	15	12	9	6	4
150	335	120	18	16	13	10	7	4	2
150	335	140	17	14	11	8	5	3	1
175	391	40	30	29	26	24	21	18	15
175	391	60	25	23	20	17	15	12	9
175	391	80	21	19	16	14	11	8	6
175	391	100	19	16	14	11	8	6	3
175	391	120	17	15	12	9	6	4	2
175	391	140	16	13	10	7	5	2	1
200	447	40	29	27	25	22	19	17	14
200	447	60	23	21	19	16	13	11	8
200	447	80	20	18	15	12	10	7	5
200	447	100	18	15	13	10	7	5	3
200	447	120	16	14	11	8	5	3	1
200	447	140	15	12	9	7	4	2	1

τ	RTI	ΔT	CEILING HEIGHT IN FEET 4.0	8.0	12.0	16.0	20.0	24.0	28.0
			INSTALLED SPACING OF DETECTORS						
225	503	40	27	26	23	21	18	15	13
225	503	60	22	20	18	15	12	10	7
225	503	80	19	17	14	11	9	6	4
225	503	100	17	14	12	9	7	4	2
225	503	120	15	13	10	7	5	3	1
225	503	140	14	11	9	6	4	2	0
250	559	40	26	24	22	19	17	14	12
250	559	60	21	19	16	14	11	9	6
250	559	80	18	16	13	11	8	6	4
250	559	100	16	14	11	8	6	4	2
250	559	120	14	12	9	7	4	2	1
250	559	140	13	11	8	5	3	1	0
275	615	40	25	23	21	18	16	13	11
275	615	60	20	18	16	13	11	8	6
275	615	80	17	15	13	10	7	5	3
275	615	100	15	13	10	8	5	3	2
275	615	120	14	11	9	6	4	2	1
275	615	140	12	10	7	5	3	1	0
300	671	40	24	22	20	17	15	12	10
300	671	60	19	17	15	12	10	7	5
300	671	80	17	14	12	9	7	5	3
300	671	100	15	12	10	7	5	3	1
300	671	120	13	11	8	6	3	2	0
300	671	140	12	10	7	5	2	1	0
325	727	40	23	21	19	16	14	11	9
325	727	60	19	17	14	12	9	7	5
325	727	80	16	14	11	9	6	4	2
325	727	100	14	12	9	7	4	2	1
325	727	120	13	10	8	5	3	1	0
325	727	140	11	9	7	4	2	1	0
350	783	40	22	20	18	16	13	11	8
350	783	60	18	16	13	11	9	6	4
350	783	80	15	13	11	8	6	4	2
350	783	100	13	11	9	6	4	2	1
350	783	120	12	10	7	5	3	1	0
350	783	140	11	9	6	4	2	1	0
375	839	40	22	20	17	15	12	10	8
375	839	60	17	15	13	10	8	6	4
375	839	80	15	13	10	8	5	3	2
375	839	100	13	11	8	6	4	2	1
375	839	120	12	9	7	5	3	1	0
375	839	140	11	8	6	3	2	0	0
400	894	40	21	19	17	14	12	9	7
400	894	60	17	15	12	10	8	5	3
400	894	80	14	12	10	7	5	3	2
400	894	100	13	10	8	5	3	2	1
400	894	120	11	9	6	4	2	1	0
400	894	140	10	8	5	3	2	0	0

NOTE: Detector time constant at a reference velocity of 5 ft/sec.
For SI Units: 1 ft = 0.305 m
1000 BTU/sec = 1055 kW

Table B-3.2.4(w)
Q_d, Threshold Fire Size at Response: 2000 Btu/sec
t_g: 300 Seconds to 1000 Btu/sec
α: 0.011 Btu/sec^3

τ	RTI	ΔT	CEILING HEIGHT IN FEET						
			4.0	8.0	12.0	16.0	20.0	24.0	28.0
			INSTALLED SPACING OF DETECTORS						
25	56	40	79	73	66	60	55	49	44
25	56	60	64	56	50	44	39	33	29
25	56	80	54	46	40	34	29	24	20
25	56	100	47	40	33	28	23	18	14
25	56	120	42	35	29	23	18	14	9
25	56	140	38	31	25	20	15	10	6
50	112	40	67	63	58	54	49	44	40
50	112	60	54	49	45	40	35	30	26
50	112	80	46	41	36	31	27	22	18
50	112	100	41	35	30	26	21	17	12
50	112	120	36	31	26	21	17	13	8
50	112	140	33	28	23	18	14	9	5
75	168	40	59	56	52	48	44	40	36
75	168	60	48	44	40	36	32	28	24
75	168	80	41	37	33	29	24	20	16
75	168	100	36	32	28	23	19	15	11
75	168	120	33	28	24	20	15	11	7
75	168	140	30	25	21	17	12	9	5
100	224	40	53	51	48	44	41	37	33
100	224	60	43	40	37	33	29	25	22
100	224	80	37	34	30	26	22	19	15
100	224	100	33	29	25	22	18	14	10
100	224	120	30	26	22	18	14	10	7
100	224	140	27	23	19	15	11	8	4
125	280	40	49	47	44	41	37	34	31
125	280	60	40	37	34	31	27	23	20
125	280	80	34	31	28	24	21	17	14
125	280	100	30	27	23	20	16	13	9
125	280	120	27	24	20	17	13	9	6
125	280	140	25	22	18	14	11	7	4
150	335	40	46	44	41	38	35	32	28
150	335	60	37	35	32	28	25	22	18
150	335	80	32	29	26	23	19	16	12
150	335	100	28	25	22	19	15	12	8
150	335	120	26	22	19	15	12	9	5
150	335	140	23	20	17	13	10	6	3
175	391	40	43	41	39	36	33	29	26
175	391	60	35	33	30	27	23	20	17
175	391	80	30	28	24	21	18	15	11
175	391	100	27	24	21	17	14	11	8
175	391	120	24	21	18	14	11	8	5
175	391	140	22	19	16	12	9	6	3
200	447	40	41	39	37	34	31	28	25
200	447	60	33	31	28	25	22	19	16
200	447	80	29	26	23	20	17	14	10
200	447	100	25	22	19	16	13	10	7
200	447	120	23	20	17	14	10	7	4
200	447	140	21	18	15	11	8	5	2

τ	RTI	ΔT	CEILING HEIGHT IN FEET						
			4.0	8.0	12.0	16.0	20.0	24.0	28.0
			INSTALLED SPACING OF DETECTORS						
225	503	40	39	37	35	32	29	26	23
225	503	60	32	30	27	24	21	18	15
225	503	80	27	25	22	19	16	13	10
225	503	100	24	21	18	15	12	9	6
225	503	120	22	19	16	13	10	7	4
225	503	140	20	17	14	11	8	5	2
250	559	40	37	36	33	30	28	25	22
250	559	60	30	28	25	23	19	17	14
250	559	80	26	24	21	18	15	12	9
250	559	100	23	20	17	14	11	8	6
250	559	120	21	18	15	12	9	6	3
250	559	140	19	16	13	10	7	4	2
275	615	40	36	34	32	29	26	23	20
275	615	60	29	27	24	21	18	16	13
275	615	80	25	23	20	17	14	11	8
275	615	100	22	19	17	14	11	8	5
275	615	120	20	17	14	11	8	6	3
275	615	140	18	15	12	9	7	4	2
300	671	40	35	33	30	28	25	22	19
300	671	60	28	26	23	20	18	15	13
300	671	80	24	22	19	16	13	10	8
300	671	100	21	19	16	13	10	7	5
300	671	120	19	16	14	11	8	5	3
300	671	140	17	15	12	9	6	4	1
325	727	40	33	32	29	27	24	21	18
325	727	60	27	25	22	20	17	14	11
325	727	80	23	21	18	15	12	10	7
325	727	100	20	18	15	12	10	7	4
325	727	120	18	16	13	10	7	5	2
325	727	140	17	14	11	8	6	3	1
350	783	40	32	31	28	26	23	20	17
350	783	60	26	24	21	19	16	13	11
350	783	80	22	20	17	15	12	9	7
350	783	100	20	17	15	12	9	6	4
350	783	120	18	15	12	10	7	4	2
350	783	140	16	14	11	8	5	3	1
375	839	40	31	30	27	25	22	19	16
375	839	60	25	23	21	18	15	13	10
375	839	80	22	19	17	14	11	9	6
375	839	100	19	17	14	11	9	6	4
375	839	120	17	15	12	9	6	4	2
375	839	140	16	13	10	8	5	3	1
400	894	40	30	29	26	24	21	18	16
400	894	60	25	23	20	17	15	12	9
400	894	80	21	19	16	13	11	8	5
400	894	100	19	16	13	11	8	6	3
400	894	120	17	14	11	9	6	4	2
400	894	140	15	13	10	7	5	2	1

NOTE: Detector time constant at a reference velocity of 5 ft/sec.
For SI Units: 1 ft = 0.305 m
1000 BTU/sec = 1055 kW

Table B-3.2.4(x)
Q_d, Threshold Fire Size at Response: 2000 Btu/sec
t_g: 500 Seconds to 1000 Btu/sec
α: 0.004 Btu/sec^3

			CEILING HEIGHT IN FEET						
τ	RTI	ΔT	4.0	8.0	12.0	16.0	20.0	24.0	28.0
			INSTALLED SPACING OF DETECTORS						
25	56	40	92	82	74	67	60	54	49
25	56	60	72	62	55	48	42	36	31
25	56	80	61	51	43	37	32	26	22
25	56	100	52	43	36	30	25	20	15
25	56	120	46	37	31	25	20	15	10
25	56	140	42	33	27	21	16	11	7
50	112	40	81	74	68	62	56	51	46
50	112	60	64	57	51	45	40	35	30
50	112	80	54	47	41	35	30	25	20
50	112	100	47	40	34	29	23	19	14
50	112	120	42	35	29	24	19	14	10
50	112	140	38	31	25	20	15	11	6
75	168	40	73	68	63	58	53	48	43
75	168	60	58	53	47	42	37	33	28
75	168	80	49	44	38	33	28	24	19
75	168	100	43	37	32	27	22	18	13
75	168	120	39	33	27	22	18	13	9
75	168	140	35	29	24	19	14	10	6
100	224	40	67	63	58	54	50	45	41
100	224	60	54	49	45	40	35	31	27
100	224	80	46	41	36	31	27	23	18
100	224	100	40	35	30	26	21	17	13
100	224	120	36	31	26	21	17	13	9
100	224	140	33	27	23	18	14	10	6
125	280	40	62	59	55	51	47	43	38
125	280	60	50	46	42	38	33	29	25
125	280	80	43	38	34	30	25	21	17
125	280	100	37	33	29	24	20	16	12
125	280	120	34	29	25	20	16	12	8
125	280	140	31	26	22	17	13	9	5
150	335	40	58	55	52	48	44	40	36
150	335	60	47	44	40	36	32	28	24
150	335	80	40	36	32	28	24	20	16
150	335	100	35	31	27	23	19	15	11
150	335	120	32	27	23	19	15	11	8
150	335	140	29	25	20	16	12	9	5
175	391	40	55	53	49	46	42	38	35
175	391	60	44	41	38	34	30	26	23
175	391	80	38	34	31	27	23	19	15
175	391	100	33	30	26	22	18	14	11
175	391	120	30	26	22	18	15	11	7
175	391	140	27	23	20	16	12	8	4
200	447	40	52	50	47	44	40	36	33
200	447	60	42	39	36	32	29	25	21
200	447	80	36	33	29	26	22	18	15
200	447	100	32	28	25	21	17	14	10
200	447	120	29	25	21	18	14	10	7
200	447	140	26	22	19	15	11	8	4
225	503	40	50	48	45	42	38	35	31
225	503	60	40	38	34	31	27	24	20
225	503	80	35	31	28	24	21	17	14
225	503	100	30	27	24	20	16	13	9
225	503	120	27	24	20	17	13	10	6
225	503	140	25	21	18	14	11	7	4
250	559	40	48	46	43	40	37	33	30
250	559	60	39	36	33	30	26	23	19
250	559	80	33	30	27	23	20	17	13
250	559	100	29	26	23	19	16	12	9
250	559	120	26	23	20	16	13	9	6
250	559	140	24	21	17	14	10	7	4
275	615	40	46	44	41	38	35	32	29
275	615	60	37	35	32	28	25	22	19
275	615	80	32	29	26	22	19	16	13
275	615	100	28	25	22	18	15	12	8
275	615	120	25	22	19	15	12	9	5
275	615	140	23	20	16	13	10	6	3
300	671	40	45	43	40	37	34	31	27
300	671	60	36	34	31	27	24	21	18
300	671	80	31	28	25	22	18	15	12
300	671	100	27	24	21	18	14	11	8
300	671	120	24	21	18	15	11	8	5
300	671	140	22	19	16	13	9	6	3
325	727	40	43	41	39	36	33	30	26
325	727	60	35	32	30	26	23	20	17
325	727	80	30	27	24	21	18	14	11
325	727	100	26	23	20	17	14	11	8
325	727	120	24	21	17	14	11	8	5
325	727	140	22	19	15	12	9	6	3
350	783	40	42	40	37	35	31	28	25
350	783	60	34	31	29	26	22	19	16
350	783	80	29	26	23	20	17	14	11
350	783	100	25	23	19	16	13	10	7
350	783	120	23	20	17	14	11	7	5
350	783	140	21	18	15	12	8	5	3
375	839	40	41	39	36	33	30	27	24
375	839	60	33	31	28	25	22	19	16
375	839	80	28	25	22	19	16	13	10
375	839	100	25	22	19	16	13	10	7
375	839	120	22	19	16	13	10	7	4
375	839	140	20	17	14	11	8	5	2
400	894	40	40	38	35	32	29	27	24
400	894	60	32	30	27	24	21	18	15
400	894	80	27	25	22	19	16	13	10
400	894	100	24	21	18	15	12	9	6
400	894	120	22	19	16	13	10	7	4
400	894	140	20	17	14	11	8	5	2

NOTE: Detector time constant at a reference velocity of 5 ft/sec.
For SI Units: 1 ft = 0.305 m
1000 BTU/sec = 1055 kW

Table B-3.2.4(y)
Q_d, Threshold Fire Size at Response: 2000 Btu/sec
t_g: 600 Seconds to 1000 Btu/sec
α: 0.003 Btu/sec^3

			CEILING HEIGHT IN FEET						
τ	RTI	ΔT	4.0	8.0	12.0	16.0	20.0	24.0	28.0
			INSTALLED SPACING OF DETECTORS						
25	56	40	96	85	78	68	62	56	50
25	56	60	75	64	56	49	43	37	32
25	56	80	63	52	44	38	32	27	22
25	56	100	54	44	37	31	25	20	15
25	56	120	48	38	31	25	20	15	11
25	56	140	43	34	27	21	16	12	7
50	112	40	86	78	71	64	58	53	48
50	112	60	68	60	53	47	41	36	31
50	112	80	57	49	42	36	31	26	21
50	112	100	49	41	35	29	24	19	15
50	112	120	44	36	30	24	19	15	10
50	112	140	40	32	26	21	16	11	7
75	168	40	78	72	66	61	55	50	45
75	168	60	62	56	50	44	39	34	29
75	168	80	52	46	40	34	30	25	20
75	168	100	46	39	33	28	23	19	14
75	168	120	41	34	28	23	19	14	10
75	168	140	37	30	25	20	15	11	6
100	224	40	72	67	62	57	52	48	43
100	224	60	57	52	47	42	37	32	28
100	224	80	49	43	38	33	28	24	19
100	224	100	43	37	32	27	22	18	13
100	224	120	38	32	27	22	18	13	9
100	224	140	35	29	24	19	14	10	6
125	280	40	67	63	59	54	50	45	41
125	280	60	54	49	45	40	35	31	27
125	280	80	46	41	36	31	27	23	18
125	280	100	40	35	30	26	21	17	13
125	280	120	36	31	26	21	17	13	9
125	280	140	33	27	23	18	14	10	6
150	335	40	63	60	56	52	47	43	39
150	335	60	51	47	42	38	34	30	26
150	335	80	43	39	34	30	26	22	18
150	335	100	38	33	29	25	20	16	12
150	335	120	34	29	25	21	16	12	8
150	335	140	31	26	22	17	13	9	5
175	391	40	60	57	53	49	45	41	37
175	391	60	48	44	41	36	32	28	24
175	391	80	41	37	33	29	25	21	17
175	391	100	36	32	28	24	19	15	12
175	391	120	32	28	24	20	16	12	8
175	391	140	29	25	21	17	13	9	5
200	447	40	57	54	51	47	43	40	36
200	447	60	46	43	39	35	31	27	23
200	447	80	39	35	32	28	24	20	16
200	447	100	34	30	26	23	19	15	11
200	447	120	31	27	23	19	15	11	7
200	447	140	28	24	20	16	12	8	5

			CEILING HEIGHT IN FEET						
τ	RTI	ΔT	4.0	8.0	12.0	16.0	20.0	24.0	28.0
			INSTALLED SPACING OF DETECTORS						
225	503	40	54	52	49	45	42	38	34
225	503	60	44	41	37	34	30	26	22
225	503	80	37	34	30	26	23	19	15
225	503	100	33	29	25	22	18	14	11
225	503	120	30	26	22	18	14	11	7
225	503	140	27	23	19	15	12	8	4
250	559	40	52	50	47	43	40	36	33
250	559	60	42	39	36	32	29	25	21
250	559	80	36	33	29	25	22	18	15
250	559	100	32	28	24	21	17	14	10
250	559	120	28	25	21	17	14	10	7
250	559	140	26	22	19	15	11	8	4
275	615	40	50	48	45	42	39	35	32
275	615	60	41	38	35	31	28	24	21
275	615	80	35	32	28	25	21	18	14
275	615	100	30	27	24	20	17	13	10
275	615	120	27	24	20	17	13	10	6
275	615	140	25	22	18	14	11	7	4
300	671	40	49	47	44	40	37	34	30
300	671	60	39	37	33	30	27	23	20
300	671	80	33	31	27	24	20	17	13
300	671	100	29	26	23	19	16	12	9
300	671	120	26	23	20	16	13	9	6
300	671	140	24	21	17	14	10	7	4
325	727	40	47	45	42	39	36	33	29
325	727	60	38	35	32	29	26	22	19
325	727	80	32	30	26	23	20	16	13
325	727	100	29	25	22	19	15	12	9
325	727	120	26	22	19	16	12	9	6
325	727	140	23	20	17	13	10	7	3
350	783	40	46	44	41	38	35	32	28
350	783	60	37	34	31	28	25	22	18
350	783	80	31	29	25	22	19	16	12
350	783	100	28	25	21	18	15	12	8
350	783	120	25	22	18	15	12	9	5
350	783	140	23	20	16	13	9	6	3
375	839	40	44	42	40	37	34	31	27
375	839	60	36	33	30	27	24	21	18
375	839	80	31	28	25	21	18	15	12
375	839	100	27	24	21	18	14	11	8
375	839	120	24	21	18	15	11	8	5
375	839	140	22	19	16	12	9	6	3
400	894	40	43	41	39	36	33	30	26
400	894	60	35	32	30	26	23	20	17
400	894	80	30	27	24	21	18	14	11
400	894	100	26	23	20	17	14	11	8
400	894	120	23	21	17	14	11	8	5
400	894	140	21	18	15	12	9	6	3

NOTE: Detector time constant at a reference velocity of 5 ft/sec.
For SI Units: 1 ft = 0.305 m
1000 BTU/sec = 1055 kW

B-3.2.5 Installed spacings listed as zero in the tables indicate that the detector chosen will not respond within the design objectives.

[From NFPA 72E - 1990, Appendix C]

B-3.2.6 Example.

Input:

Ceiling height: 8 ft (2.4 m)

Detector type: Fixed temperature 135°F (57°C)

UL listed spacing: 30 ft (9.1 m)

Fire:

Q_d: 500 Btu/sec (527 kW)

Fire growth rate: Slow

t_g: 600 sec

α: 0.003 Btu/sec^3

Environmental conditions:

T_o: 55°F (12.8°C)

Required installed spacing:

From Table B-3.2.2, the detector time constant (τ_o) is 80 seconds.

$(RTI = 80\sqrt{5} = 180\ ft^{1/2}\ sec^{1/2})$

$\Delta T = T_s - T_o = 135 - 55 = 80°F$

From Table B-3.2.4(j):

For τ_o = 75 sec — spacing = 17 ft

For τ_o = 100 sec — spacing = 16 ft

By interpolation:

Spacing = 17 - [(17–16/80–75/100–75)] = 16.8, round to 17.0 ft

NOTE: Interpolation for τ_o = 80 seconds was not required, but was included for demonstration. If the ceiling height is 16 ft, the required spacing would be 8.8 ft. Using the detector in the above example, at a ceiling height of 28 ft, no practical spacing would ensure detection of the fire at the threshold fire size of 500 Btu/sec. A more sensitive detector would need to be used. Alternatively, the design objectives could be changed to accept a larger fire. These results clearly illustrate the need to consider ceiling height in the design of a detection system.

For SI Units: 1 ft = 0.305 m.

[From NFPA 72E - 1990, C-3-2.5 modified]

B-3.3 Rate-of-Rise Heat Detector Spacing.

B-3.3.1 Tables B-3.3.2(a) and B-3.3.2(b) are to be used to determine the installed spacing of rate-of-rise heat detectors. The analytical basis for the tables is presented in Section B-6. This section shows how the tables are to be used.

B-3.3.2 Table B-3.3.2(a) provides installed spacings for rate-of-rise heat detectors required to achieve detection for a specific threshold for size, fire growth rate, and ceiling height. This table may be used directly to determine installed spacings for 50-ft (15.2-m) listed spacing detectors.

[From NFPA 72E - 1990, C-5-3.4 modified]

B-3.3.2.1 Tables B-3.3.2(a) and B-3.3.2(b) use the following values for t_g:

Fast fire growth rate, t_g = 150 seconds

Medium fire growth rate, t_g = 300 seconds

Slow fire growth rate, t_g = 600 seconds.

[From NFPA 72E - 1990, Appendix C]

B-3.3.3 For rate-of-rise heat detectors with a listed spacing of other than 50 ft (15.2 m), installed spacing obtained from Table B-3.3.2(a) must be multiplied by the modifier shown in Table B-3.3.2(b) for the appropriate listed spacing and fire growth rate. This takes into account the difference in sensitivity between the detector and a 50-ft (15.2-m) listed detector.

B-3.3.4 Having determined the threshold fire size (*see B-2.2.2*), the fire growth rate (*see B-2.2.3*), the detector's listed spacing, and the ceiling height, use Table B-3.3.2(a) to determine the corrected spacing for 50-ft (15.2-m) listed detectors. Use Table B-3.3.2(b) to determine the spacing modifier. Find the required installed spacing by multiplying the corrected spacing by the spacing modifier.

[From NFPA 72E - 1990, Appendix C modified]

B-3.3.5 Example.

Input:

Ceiling height: 12 ft (3.7 m)

Detector type: Combination rate-of-rise, fixed temperature 30-ft (9.1-m) listed spacing

Q_d: 500 Btu/sec

Fire growth rate: Medium

Spacing:

From Table B-3.3.2(a), installed spacing = 18 ft (5.5 m)

From Table B-3.3.2(b), spacing modifier = 0.86

Installed spacing = 18 × 0.86 = 15.5 ft (4.7 m)

NOTE: This answer may be rounded to either 15 ft (4.6 m) or 16 ft (4.9 m). Use of 15 ft (4.6 m) would be slightly conservative. However, depending on field conditions, use of 16 ft (4.9 m) may fit the space better.

[From NFPA 72E - 1990, C-5-3.4 modified]

B-3.4 Design Curves.

B-3.4.1 The design curves [Figures B-3.4.1 (a) through (i)] may also be used to determine the installed spacings of heat detectors. However, they are not as comprehensive as the tables, because the tables include additional fire growth rates, fire sizes, and detector sensitivities.

B-3.4.1.1 Fixed-Temperature Heat Detectors. Figures B-3.4.1(a) through (f) can be used directly to determine the installed spacing for fixed-temperature heat detectors having listed spacings of 30 ft and 50 ft (9.1 m and 15.2 m), respectively, where the difference between the detectors' rated temperature (T_s) and the ambient temperature (T_o) is 65°F (36°C). When ΔT is not 65°F (36°C), tables previously discussed in B-3.3 should be used.

[From NFPA 72E - 1990, Appendix C modified]

B-3.4.1.2 Rate-of-Rise Heat Detectors. Figures B-3.4.1(g), (h), and (i) can be used directly to determine the installed spacing for rate-of-rise heat detectors having a listed spacing of 50 ft (15.2 m).

B-3.3.2(a) **Installed Spacings for Rate-of-Rise Heat Detectors (Threshold Fire Size and Growth Rate)**

Ceiling Height (ft)	Q_d = 1000 Btu/sec			Q_d = 750 Btu/sec			Q_d = 500 Btu/sec			Q_d = 250 Bru/sec			Q_d = 100 Btu/sec		
	s	m	f	s	m	f	s	m	f	s	m	f	s	m	f
4	28	32	32	26	28	27	22	24	23	16	17	16	11	11	10
5	27	31	31	25	27	27	21	23	22	15	16	15	10	10	9
6	26	30	31	24	26	27	20	22	22	15	15	15	9	9	9
7	25	29	30	23	26	26	19	21	21	14	14	14	9	9	8
8	24	29	30	22	25	26	18	21	21	13	13	14	8	8	8
9	23	28	29	21	24	25	17	20	20	12	13	13	7	7	7
10	22	27	29	20	23	25	16	19	20	12	12	13	7	7	7
11	21	27	28	18	23	24	15	19	19	11	12	12	6	6	6
12	20	26	26	17	22	24	15	18	19	10	11	12	5	5	5
13	19	25	27	16	22	23	14	18	18	9	11	11	5	5	5
14	18	24	27	15	21	22	13	17	18	9	10	11		4	
15	16	24	26	14	20	21	12	17	17	8	10	10			
16	15	23	25	13	19	21	11	16	16	7	9	10			
17	14	22	25	12	19	20	10	15	16	6	9	9			
18	13	22	24	11	18	20	9	14	15		8	8			
19	12	21	23	10	17	19	8	14	14		8	8			
20	11	20		9	16	19	7	13	14		7	7			
21	10	19		8	15	18		12	13		7				
22	9	19		7	15	17		12	13		6				
23	8	18			14	17		11	12		5				
24		17			13	16		11	11		5				
25		16			12	15		10	10		4				
26		15			12	15		9	10						
27		14			11	14		9							
28		13			11	13		8							
29		13			10			8							
30		12			10			7							

s = slow fire, m = medium fire, f = fast fire.

Table B-3.3.2(b) Spacing Modifiers for Rate-of-Rise Heat Detectors

Listed Spacing (ft)	Fire Growth Rate Slow	Medium	Fast
15	0.57	0.55	0.45
20	0.72	0.63	0.62
25	0.84	0.78	0.76
30	0.92	0.86	0.85
40	0.98	0.96	0.95
50	1.00	1.00	1.00
70	1.00	1.01	1.02

For SI Units: 1 ft = 0.305 m.

B-3.4.2 To use the curves, the same format must be followed as with tables. The designer must first determine how large a fire can be tolerated before detection can occur. This is the threshold fire size, Q_d. Curves are presented, in most cases, for values of Q_d = 1000, 750, 500, 250, and 100 Btu/sec (1055, 791, 527, 264, and 105 kW). Interpolation between values of Q_d on a given graph is allowable. Table B-2.2.2.1(a) and Table B-2.2.2.3 also contain examples of various fuels and their fire growth rates under specified conditions.

[From NFPA 72E - 1990, C-3-4.1.3 modified]

B-3.4.3 Once a threshold size and expected fire growth rate have been selected, an installed detector spacing can be obtained from Figures B-3.4.1(a) through (i) for a certain detector's listed spacing, ambient temperature, and ceiling height. As in B-3.2.6, to determine the installed spacing of 135°F (57°C) fixed temperature heat detectors with a listed spacing of 30 ft (9.1 m) and to detect a slowly developing fire at a threshold fire size of 500 Btu/sec (527 kW) in a room 10 ft (3 m) high with an ambient temperature of 70°F (21°C), the following procedure is used.

[From NFPA 72E - 1990, C-3-4.1.4 modified]

B-3.4.3.1 Example 1.

Input:

Ceiling height: 10 ft (3 m)

Detector type: Fixed temperature 135°F (57°C)

UL listed spacing: 30 ft (9.1 m)

Fire:

Q_d: 500 Btu/sec (527 kW)

Fire growth rate: Slow

t_g: 600 sec

Environmental conditions:

T_o: 70°F (21°C)

ΔT = 135 - 70 = 65°F (36°C)

Required installed spacing:

From Figure B-3.4.1(a), use an installed spacing of 18 ft (5.2 m) (17.5 ft rounded to 18 ft).

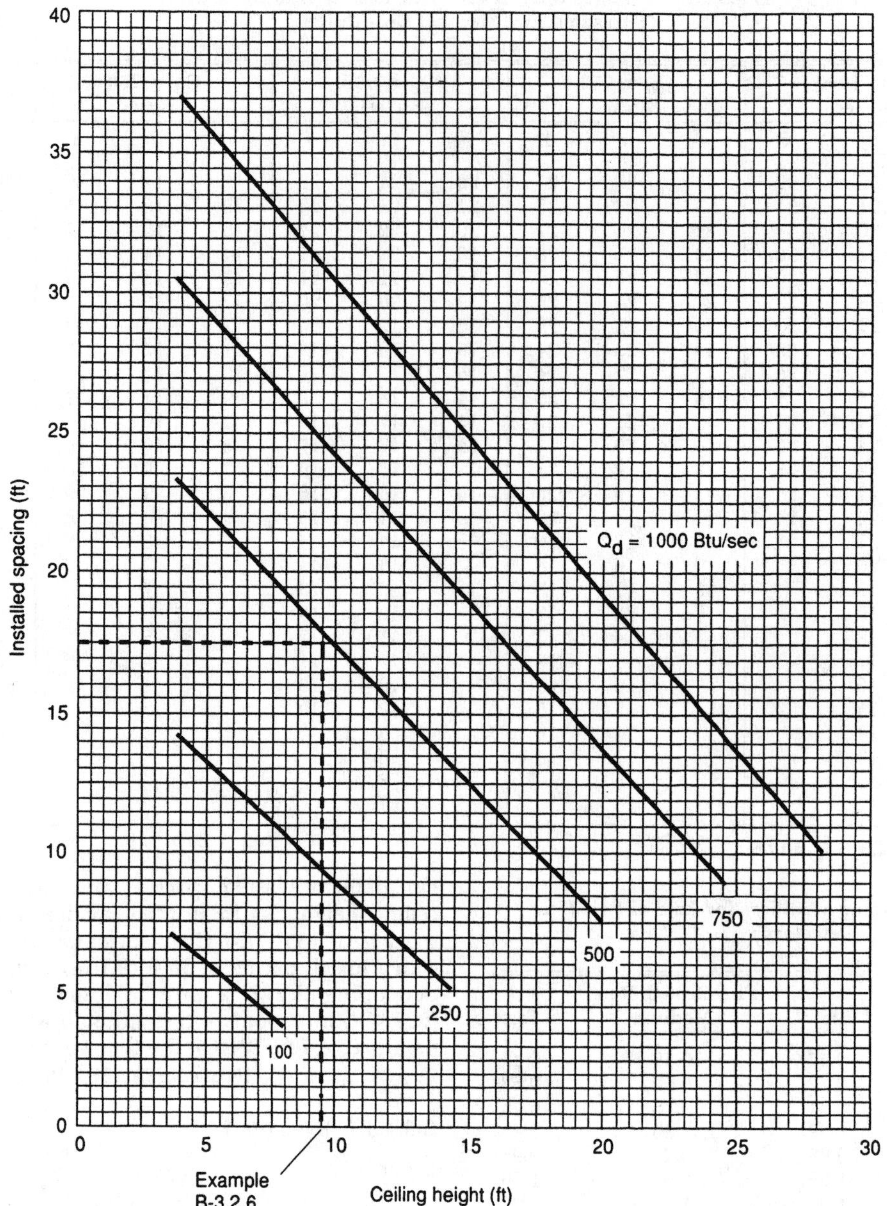

Figure B-3.4.1(a) Heat detector, fixed temperature, 30-ft (9.1-m) listed spacing, slow fire. ΔT = 65°F (36.1°C).

[From NFPA 72E - 1990, Appendix C modified]

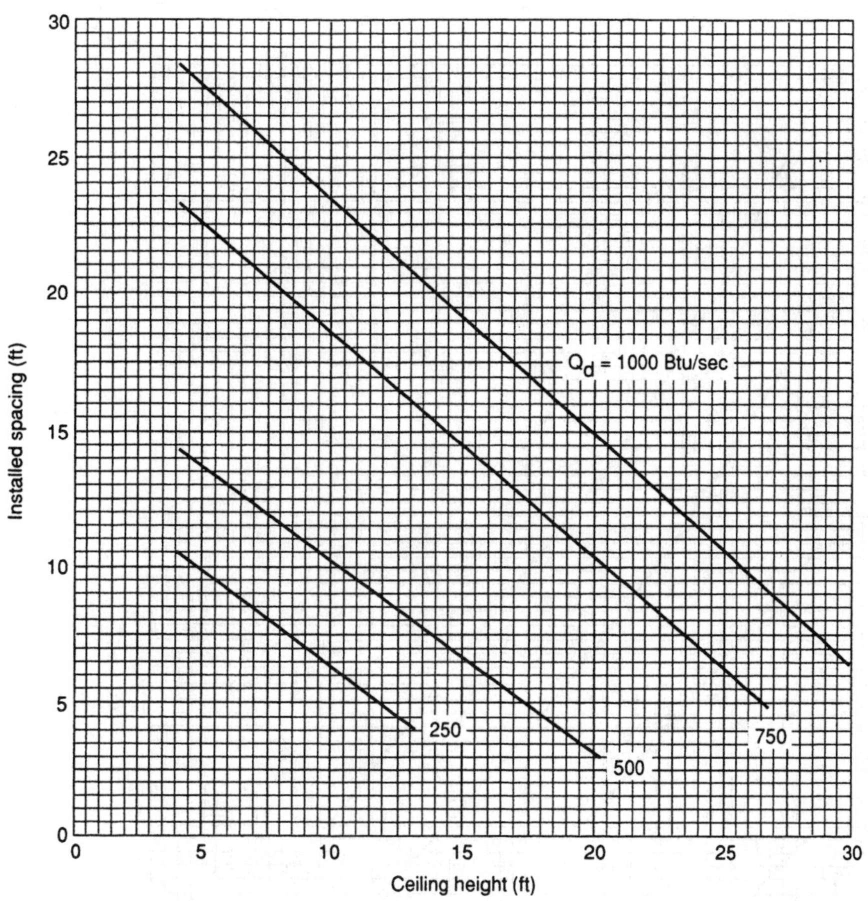

Figure B-3.4.1(b) Heat detector, fixed temperature, 30-ft (9.1-m) listed spacing, medium fire. ΔT = 65°F (36°C).

[From NFPA 72E - 1990, Appendix C modified]

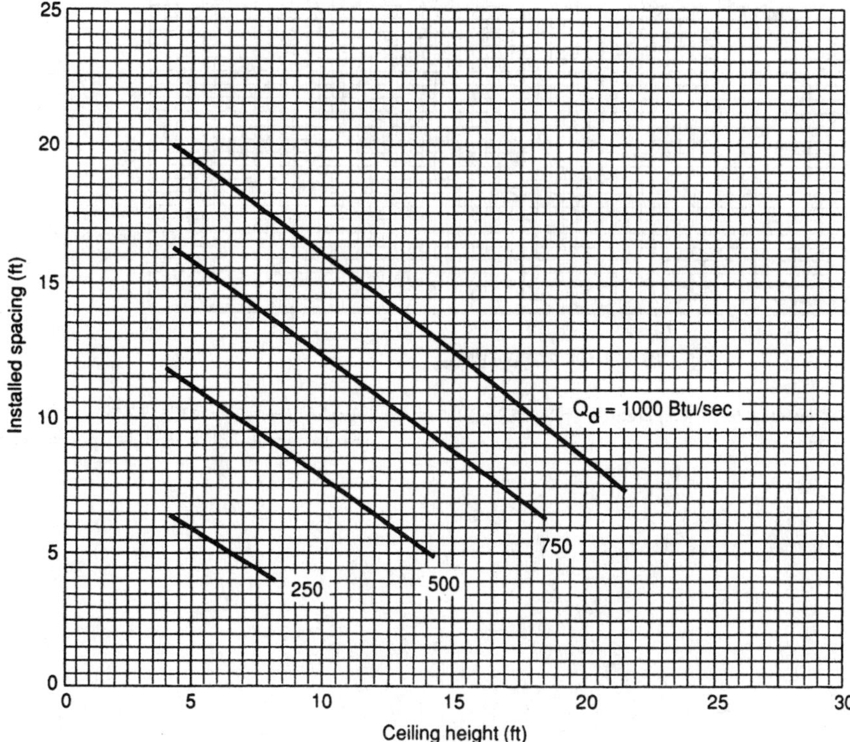

Figure B-3.4.1(c) Heat detector, fixed temperature, 30-ft (9.1-m) listed spacing, fast fire. ΔT = 65°F (36°C).

[From NFPA 72E - 1990, Appendix C modified]

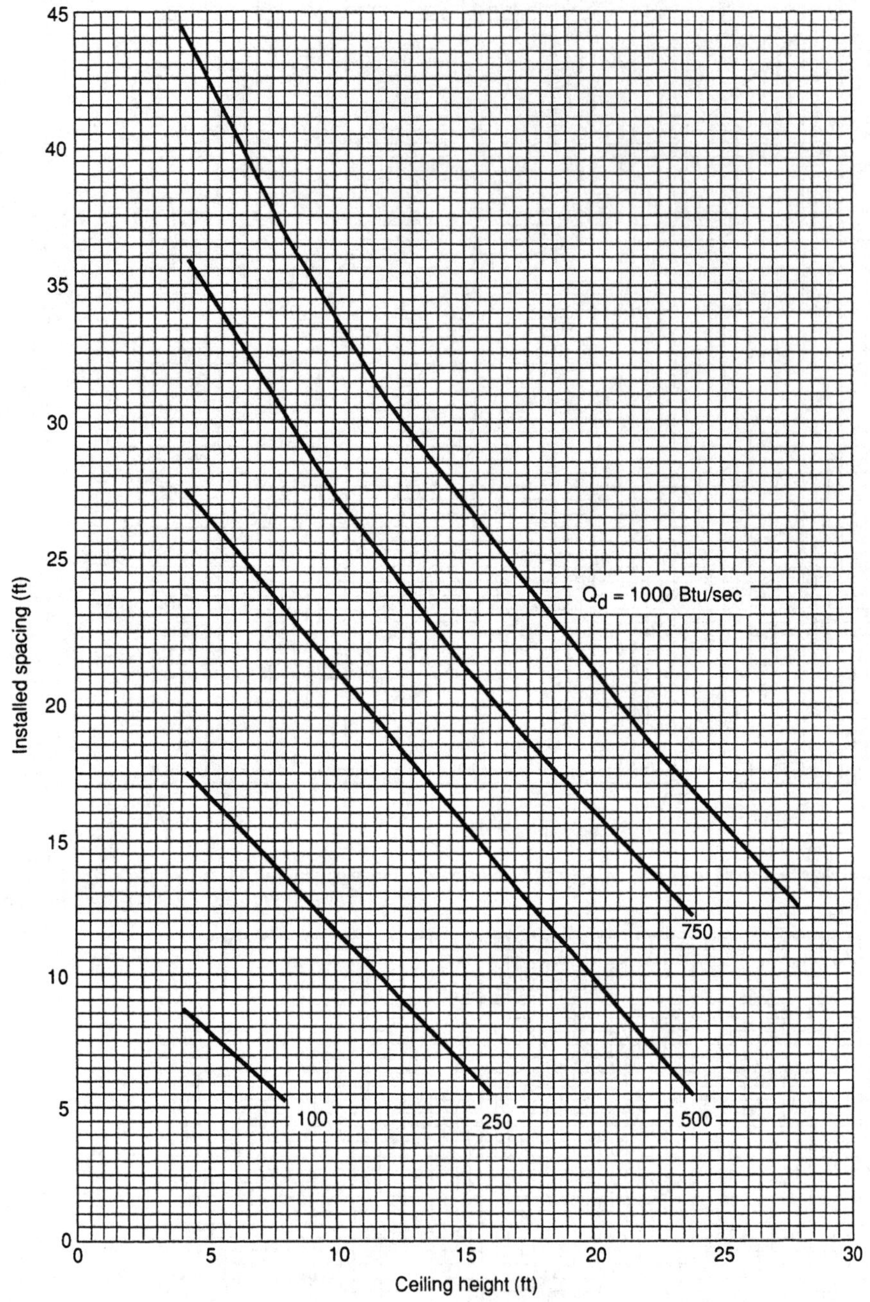

Figure B-3.4.1(d) Heat detector, fixed temperature, 50-ft (15.2-m) listed spacing, slow fire. ΔT = 65°F (36°C).

[From NFPA 72E - 1990, Appendix C modified]

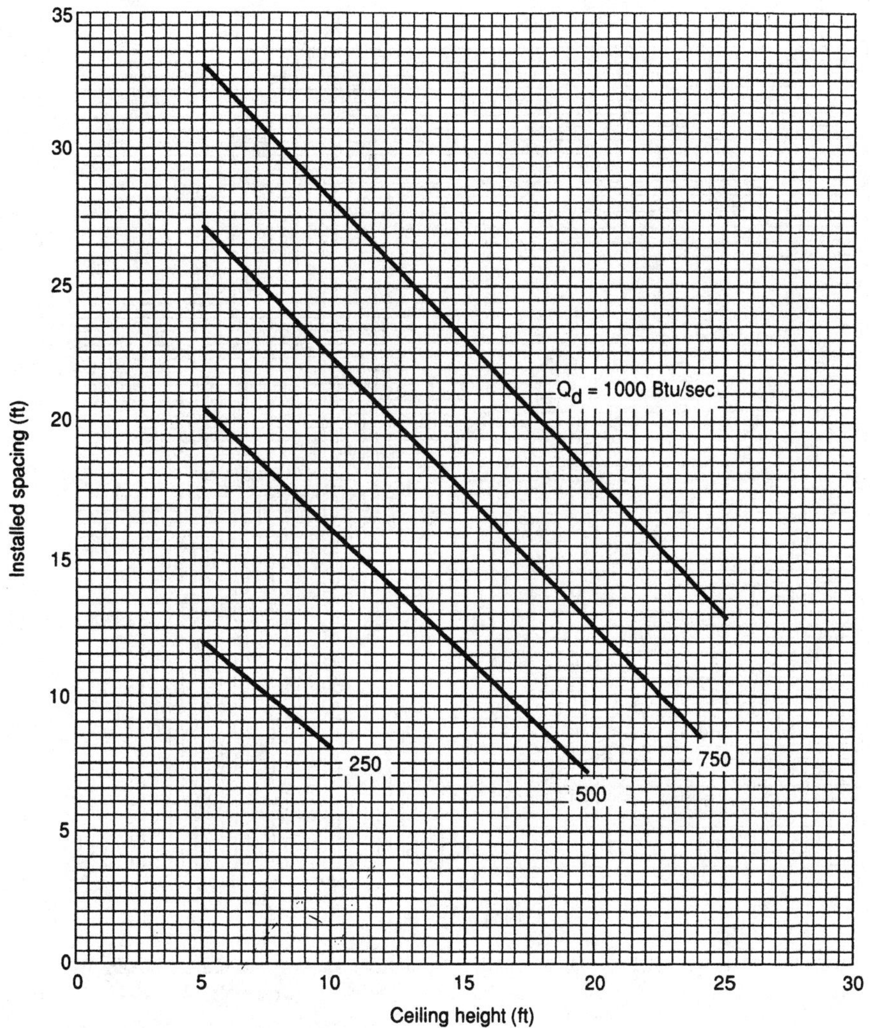

Figure B-3.4.1(e) Heat detector, fixed temperature, 50-ft (15.2-m) listed spacing, medium fire. ΔT = 65°F (36°C).

[From NFPA 72E - 1990, Appendix C modified]

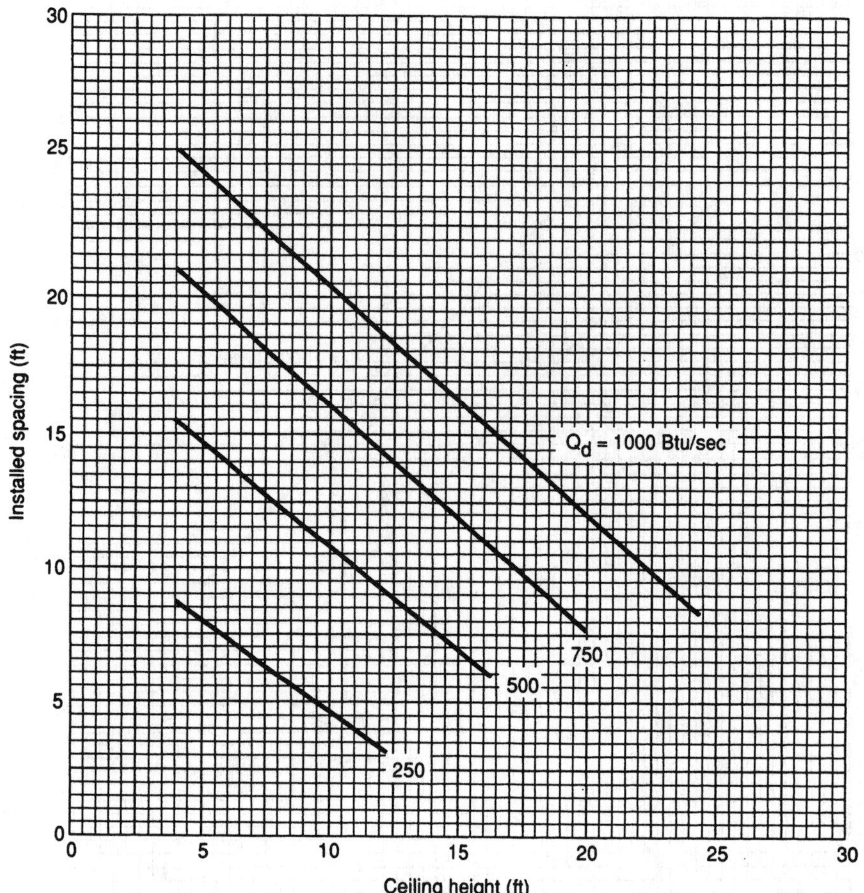

Figure B-3.4.1(f) Heat detector, fixed temperature, 50-ft (15.2-m) listed spacing, fast fire. ΔT = 65°F (36°C).

[From NFPA 72E - 1990, Appendix C modified]

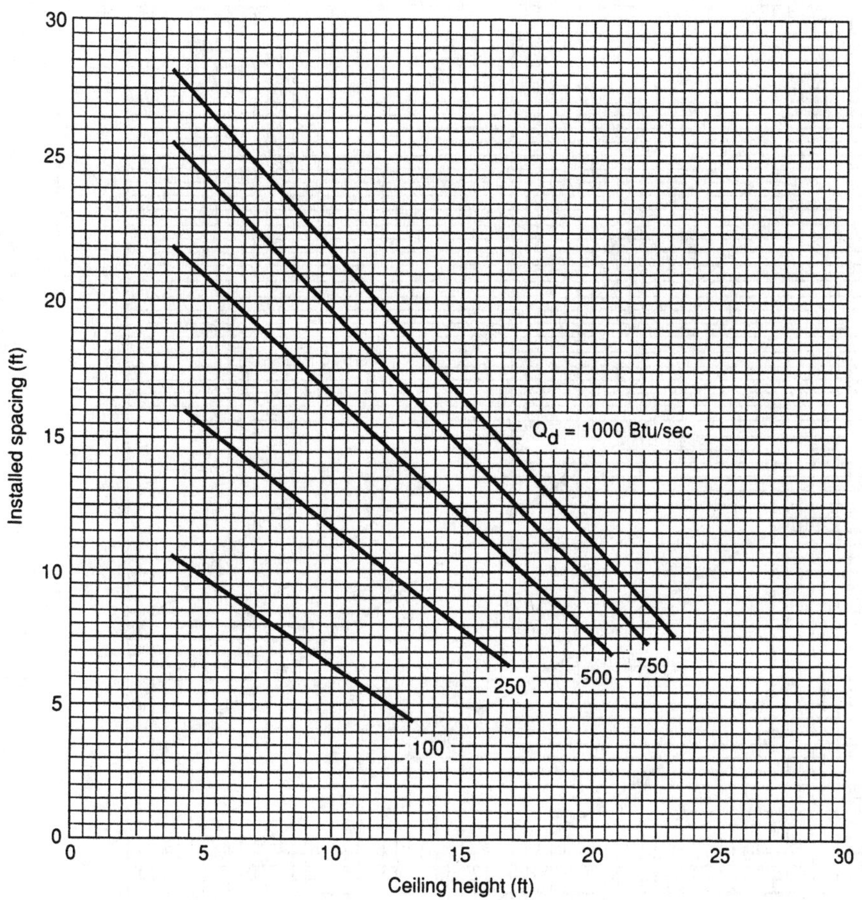

Figure B-3.4.1(g) Heat detector, rate-of-rise, 50-ft (15.2-m) listed spacing, slow fire.
[From NFPA 72E - 1990, Appendix C modified]

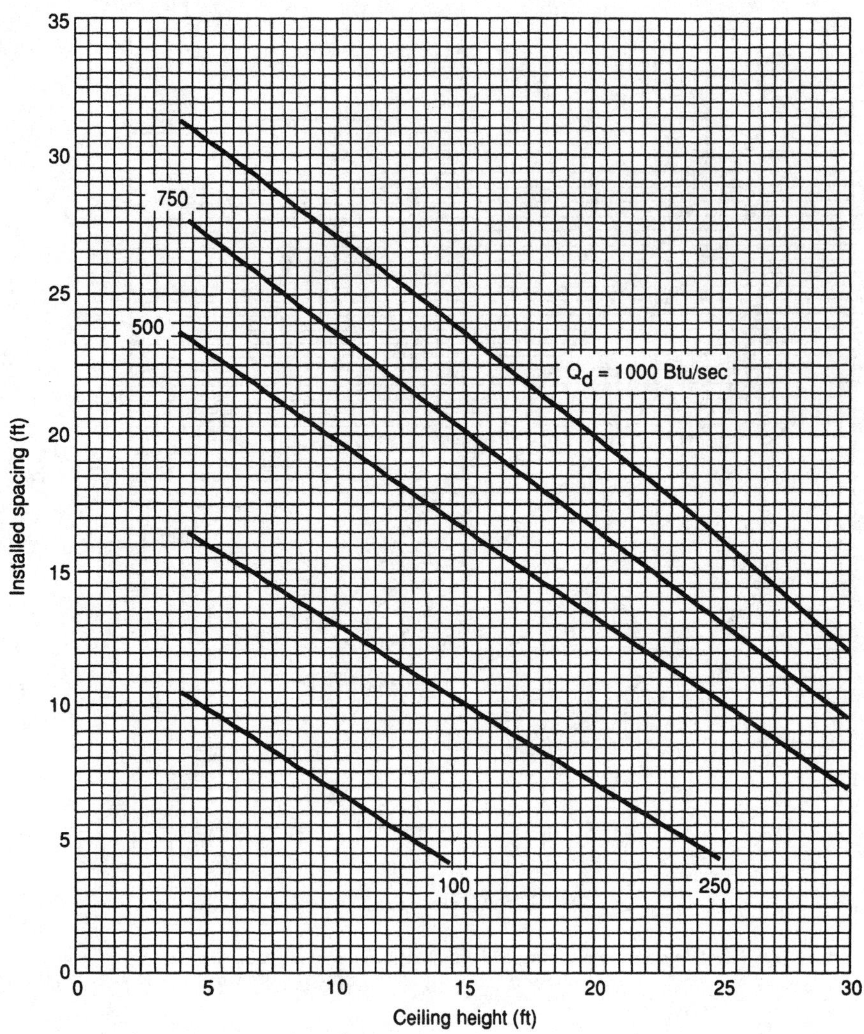

Figure B-3.4.1(h) Heat detector, rate-of-rise, 50-ft (15.2-m) listed spacing, medium fire.

[From NFPA 72E - 1990, Appendix C modified]

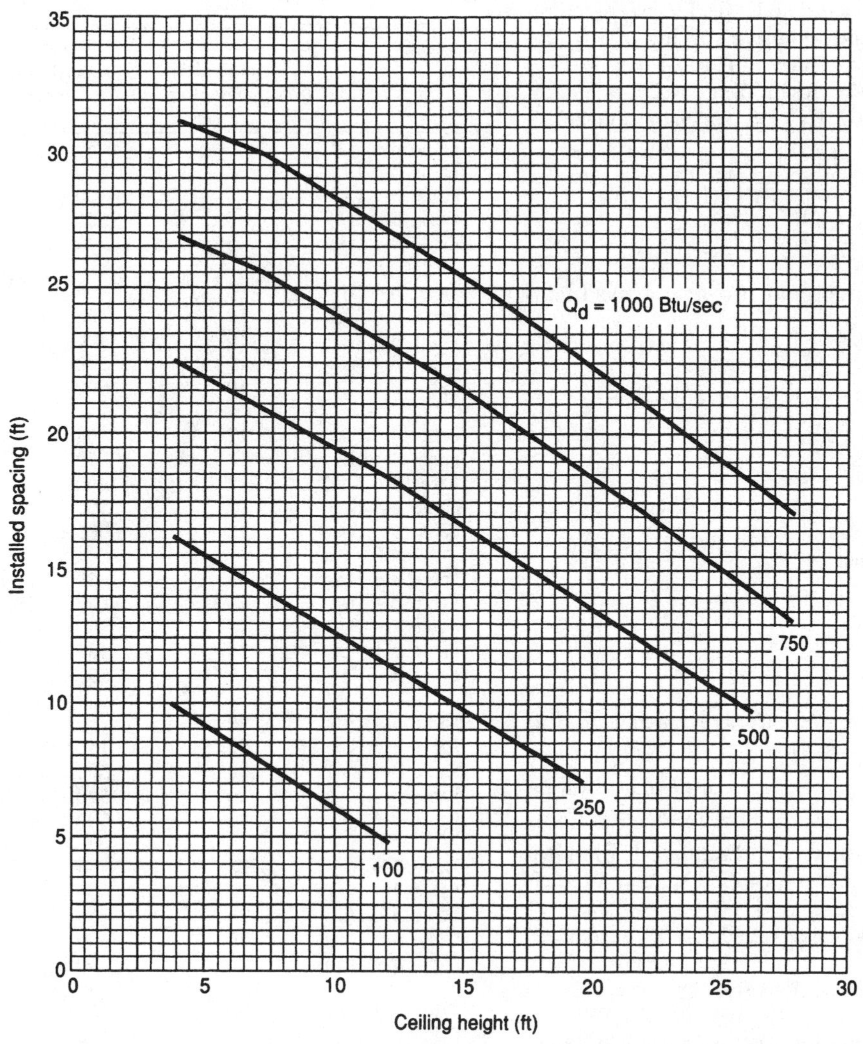

Figure B-3.4.1(i) Heat detector, rate-of-rise, 50-ft (15.2-m) listed spacing, fast fire.

[From NFPA 72E - 1990, Appendix C modified]

Note that if the ceiling height is 15 ft (4.6 m), the same graph gives an installed spacing of 12 ft (3.5 m). A ceiling height of 20 ft (6.1 m) would require a spacing of 8 ft (2.4 m). This change in spacing clearly illustrates the need to consider ceiling height in the design of a detection system.

[From NFPA 72E - 1990, Appendix C modified]

B-3.4.3.2 Example 2.

Input:

Ceiling height: 10 ft (3 m)

Detector type: Combination rate-of-rise and fixed temperature

UL listed spacing: 50 ft (15.2 m)

Fire:

Q_d: 500 Btu/sec (527 kW)

Fire growth rate: Fast

t_g: 150 sec

Environmental conditions:

T_o: 70°F (21°C)

ΔT: 65°F (36°C)

Spacing:

From Figure B-3.4.1(i), use an installed spacing of 20 ft (5.8 m) (19.5 ft rounded to 20 ft).

A 30-ft (9.1-m) fixed temperature detector would require a 7.5-ft (2.5-m) spacing.

If the fire growth rate was slow, as in Example 1, the rate-of-rise detector would require an installed spacing of 16 ft (4.88 m).

[From NFPA 72E - 1990, C-3-4.1.5 modified]

B-4 Analysis of Existing Heat Detection Systems.

B-4.1 Tables B-4.1(a) through (nn) can be used to determine the size fire (heat release rate) that existing fixed-temperature heat detection systems will respond to. Table B-4.1 is an index to Tables B-4.1(a) through (nn).

The use of the analysis tables is similar to that described for new designs. The difference is that the spacing of the existing detectors must be known. An estimate of the fire intensity coefficient (α) or the fire growth time (t_g) must also be made for the fuel that is expected to burn.

[From NFPA 72E - 1990, Appendix C modified]

Table B-4.1 Analysis Tables Index

	Installed Spacing (ft)	Fire Growth Rate (sec) τ_g	Alpha (Btu/sec^3) α
Table B-4.1(a)	8	50	0.400
Table B-4.1(b)	8	150	0.044
Table B-4.1(c)	8	300	0.011
Table B-4.1(d)	8	500	0.004
Table B-4.1(e)	8	600	0.003
Table B-4.1(f)	10	50	0.400
Table B-4.1(g)	10	150	0.044
Table B-4.1(h)	10	300	0.011
Table B-4.1(i)	10	500	0.004
Table B-4.1(j)	10	600	0.003
Table B-4.1(k)	12	50	0.400
Table B-4.1(l)	12	150	0.044
Table B-4.1(m)	12	300	0.011
Table B-4.1(n)	12	500	0.004
Table B-4.1(o)	12	600	0.003
Table B-4.1(p)	15	50	0.400
Table B-4.1(q)	15	150	0.044
Table B-4.1(r)	15	300	0.011
Table B-4.1(s)	15	500	0.004
Table B-4.1(t)	15	600	0.003
Table B-4.1(u)	20	50	0.400
Table B-4.1(v)	20	150	0.044
Table B-4.1(w)	20	300	0.011
Table B-4.1(x)	20	500	0.004
Table B-4.1(y)	20	600	0.003
Table B-4.1(z)	25	50	0.400
Table B-4.1(aa)	25	150	0.044
Table B-4.1(bb)	25	300	0.011
Table B-4.1(cc)	25	500	0.004
Table B-4.1(dd)	25	600	0.003
Table B-4.1(ee)	30	50	0.400
Table B-4.1(ff)	30	150	0.044
Table B-4.1(gg)	30	300	0.011
Table B-4.1(hh)	30	500	0.004
Table B-4.1(ii)	30	600	0.003
Table B-4.1(jj)	50	50	0.400
Table B-4.1(kk)	50	150	0.044
Table B-4.1(ll)	50	300	0.011
Table B-4.1(mm)	50	500	0.004
Table B-4.1(nn)	50	600	0.003

[From NFPA 72E - 1990, Appendix C modified]

Table B-4.1(a)
Installed Spacing of Heat Detector: 8 feet
t_g: 50 Seconds to 1000 Btu/sec
α: 0.400 Btu/sec^3

			CEILING HEIGHT IN FEET						
τ	RTI	ΔT	4.0	8.0	12.0	16.0	20.0	24.0	28.0
			FIRE SIZE AT DETECTOR RESPONSE (BTU/SEC)						
25	56	40	300	402	535	668	832	1016	1219
25	56	60	368	508	687	877	1106	1365	1657
25	56	80	450	618	838	1102	1381	1722	2110
25	56	100	512	716	985	1308	1661	2090	2585
25	56	120	573	815	1132	1517	1949	2473	3082
25	56	140	654	919	1282	1730	2265	2870	3601
50	112	40	422	571	755	926	1136	1366	1614
50	112	60	546	738	976	1211	1496	1811	2157
50	112	80	642	883	1181	1484	1846	2251	2699
50	112	100	754	1033	1383	1752	2194	2692	3248
50	112	120	865	1179	1582	2018	2542	3138	3810
50	112	140	928	1305	1773	2318	2895	3592	4386
75	168	40	542	722	908	1137	1389	1659	1948
75	168	60	702	932	1219	1492	1826	2193	2589
75	168	80	813	1111	1472	1824	2245	2710	3217
75	168	100	931	1289	1718	2146	2656	3221	3844
75	168	120	1016	1451	1955	2464	3063	3733	4475
75	168	140	1149	1629	2193	2778	3470	4247	5115
100	224	40	625	841	1101	1332	1614	1920	2246
100	224	60	802	1087	1427	1742	2122	2535	2978
100	224	80	944	1305	1728	2128	2604	3125	3687
100	224	100	1050	1503	2012	2501	3074	3703	4388
100	224	120	1222	1723	2298	2867	3537	4276	5088
100	224	140	1360	1925	2573	3226	3995	4849	5791
125	280	40	729	967	1208	1501	1820	2160	2519
125	280	60	912	1238	1622	1972	2394	2850	3337
125	280	80	1036	1472	1959	2409	2936	3508	4123
125	280	100	1233	1730	2294	2830	3461	4150	4895
125	280	120	1398	1968	2614	3240	3976	4782	5661
125	280	140	1561	2201	2926	3642	4484	5411	6246
150	335	40	793	1066	1340	1664	2013	2384	2775
150	335	60	979	1362	1797	2187	2649	3145	3674
150	335	80	1185	1656	2186	2673	3247	3868	4533
150	335	100	1378	1933	2554	3138	3825	4570	5373
150	335	120	1568	2201	2911	3590	4389	5259	6202
150	335	140	1757	2462	3257	4033	4944	5942	7027
175	391	40	882	1175	1468	1818	2195	2595	3016
175	391	60	1046	1483	1965	2391	2890	3425	3993
175	391	80	1301	1819	2397	2923	3542	4210	4923
175	391	100	1520	2127	2802	3431	4170	4970	5827
175	391	120	1734	2423	3193	3923	4782	5713	6718
175	391	140	1947	2712	3573	4405	5382	6447	7601
200	447	40	925	1257	1586	1964	2369	2797	3247
200	447	60	1168	1625	2136	2587	3121	3692	4298
200	447	80	1415	1977	2599	3162	3825	4537	5295
200	447	100	1658	2313	3040	3711	4501	5352	6262
200	447	120	1897	2637	3464	4242	5158	6148	7212
200	447	140	2133	2952	3875	4761	5802	6932	8152
225	503	40	968	1337	1754	2111	2537	2991	3468
225	503	60	1254	1747	2294	2774	3342	3949	4590
225	503	80	1527	2129	2794	3392	4096	4851	5653
225	503	100	1794	2494	3268	3980	4819	5720	6681
225	503	120	2057	2845	3724	4549	5520	6567	7689
225	503	140	2317	3185	4168	5104	6206	7400	8683
250	559	40	1011	1417	1865	2247	2698	3177	3681
250	559	60	1339	1866	2447	2955	3556	4197	4873
250	559	80	1637	2278	2982	3614	4358	5155	5999
250	559	100	1928	2669	3489	4241	5126	6076	7087
250	559	120	2215	3046	3890	4842	5870	6972	8150
250	559	140	2499	3412	4356	5431	6597	7852	9197
275	615	40	1093	1513	1981	2380	2854	3358	3887
275	615	60	1424	1982	2596	3131	3763	4437	5147
275	615	80	1746	2422	3165	3829	4612	5449	6334
275	615	100	2061	2840	3618	4488	5424	6421	7479
275	615	120	2371	3242	4128	5129	6209	7365	8597
275	615	140	2679	3633	4622	5753	6977	8291	9697
300	671	40	1151	1595	2089	2508	3005	3533	4087
300	671	60	1507	2096	2740	3301	3964	4670	5413
300	671	80	1853	2563	3259	4032	4859	5735	6661
300	671	100	2192	3007	3820	4734	5714	6756	7862
300	671	120	2526	3434	4359	5409	6540	7748	9033
300	671	140	2859	3849	4881	6066	7346	8718	10183
325	727	40	1208	1677	2194	2633	3152	3704	4282
325	727	60	1589	2207	2804	3461	4160	4898	5672
325	727	80	1959	2701	3428	4236	5100	6014	6978
325	727	100	2322	3171	4018	4973	5996	7084	8234
325	727	120	2680	3623	4585	5682	6862	8121	9457
325	727	140	3038	4061	5133	6371	7706	9135	10657
350	783	40	1265	1756	2297	2754	3296	3871	4472
350	783	60	1671	2315	2937	3623	4352	5119	5925
350	783	80	2064	2836	3592	4435	5335	6287	7289
350	783	100	2451	3331	4211	5207	6272	7403	8599
350	783	120	2834	3808	4805	5949	7177	8485	9872
350	783	140	3218	4270	5380	6669	8058	9542	11121
375	839	40	1321	1835	2398	2874	3437	4034	4658
375	839	60	1751	2422	3069	3782	4539	5336	6172
375	839	80	2169	2969	3753	4630	5565	6553	7592
375	839	100	2579	3489	4401	5436	6543	7716	8955
375	839	120	2987	3990	5021	6210	7486	8842	10279
375	839	140	3303	4445	5620	6961	8403	9941	11575
400	894	40	1377	1912	2423	2982	3574	4193	4840
400	894	60	1831	2527	3197	3937	4723	5549	6415
400	894	80	2272	3100	3911	4821	5791	6814	7890
400	894	100	2707	3645	4586	5660	6807	8023	9304
400	894	120	3141	4169	5233	6466	7788	9192	10677
400	894	140	3456	4640	5857	7247	8741	10332	12020

NOTE: Detector time constant at a reference velocity of 5 ft/sec.
For SI Units: 1 ft = 0.305 m
1000 BTU/sec = 1055 kW

Table B-4.1(b)
Installed Spacing of Heat Detector: 8 feet
t_g: 50 Seconds to 1000 Btu/sec
α: 0.044 Btu/sec³

τ	RTI	ΔT	CEILING HEIGHT IN FEET 4.0	8.0	12.0	16.0	20.0	24.0	28.0
			FIRE SIZE AT DETECTOR RESPONSE (BTU/SEC)						
25	56	40	118	167	232	311	400	507	631
25	56	60	154	226	322	440	584	752	952
25	56	80	194	286	415	579	781	1026	1309
25	56	100	228	346	512	726	993	1319	1699
25	56	120	263	409	614	883	1221	1633	2118
25	56	140	299	473	721	1049	1462	1969	2573
50	112	40	171	237	320	410	517	638	775
50	112	60	224	317	435	574	728	913	1126
50	112	80	281	397	550	735	949	1205	1504
50	112	100	329	474	666	901	1185	1516	1912
50	112	120	377	552	785	1074	1428	1846	2347
50	112	140	424	630	906	1254	1683	2202	2808
75	168	40	216	296	395	498	620	756	906
75	168	60	283	395	533	683	861	1063	1291
75	168	80	352	492	668	876	1107	1381	1696
75	168	100	413	585	803	1063	1360	1714	2125
75	168	120	472	678	939	1255	1622	2063	2578
75	168	140	531	770	1076	1451	1901	2427	3055
100	224	40	255	349	462	577	713	863	1027
100	224	60	343	467	622	788	983	1202	1446
100	224	80	416	578	776	996	1254	1548	1880
100	224	100	488	685	929	1214	1530	1904	2333
100	224	120	559	792	1081	1424	1811	2273	2806
100	224	140	636	898	1234	1637	2101	2656	3301
125	280	40	291	397	523	650	799	962	1140
125	280	60	391	532	704	885	1097	1333	1593
125	280	80	476	657	877	1114	1392	1705	2056
125	280	100	558	779	1046	1342	1690	2086	2534
125	280	120	647	899	1214	1571	1992	2476	3029
125	280	140	723	1017	1382	1813	2300	2878	3543
150	335	40	325	443	581	719	880	1056	1246
150	335	60	435	593	781	976	1204	1456	1733
150	335	80	531	732	971	1226	1523	1855	2224
150	335	100	634	869	1157	1473	1842	2259	2728
150	335	120	720	999	1340	1719	2164	2671	3245
150	335	140	805	1128	1522	1967	2491	3093	3780
175	391	40	357	486	637	784	957	1145	1347
175	391	60	478	650	854	1063	1307	1574	1866
175	391	80	584	803	1061	1332	1649	1999	2386
175	391	100	694	952	1262	1598	1989	2427	2915
175	391	120	790	1094	1460	1861	2330	2860	3456
175	391	140	892	1236	1656	2125	2675	3301	4011
200	447	40	396	530	676	846	1031	1230	1444
200	447	60	519	705	924	1146	1405	1687	1995
200	447	80	646	873	1148	1435	1769	2138	2543
200	447	100	752	1031	1363	1718	2129	2588	3096
200	447	120	870	1188	1576	1998	2490	3042	3660
200	447	140	959	1337	1785	2277	2852	3503	4236

τ	RTI	ΔT	CEILING HEIGHT IN FEET 4.0	8.0	12.0	16.0	20.0	24.0	28.0
			FIRE SIZE AT DETECTOR RESPONSE (BTU/SEC)						
225	503	40	425	570	726	906	1102	1312	1538
225	503	60	558	759	992	1227	1500	1797	2119
225	503	80	693	939	1231	1533	1885	2271	2694
225	503	100	809	1108	1461	1833	2265	2744	3272
225	503	120	926	1274	1686	2130	2645	3220	3859
225	503	140	1026	1434	1909	2425	3025	3700	4456
250	559	40	453	608	774	964	1170	1392	1628
250	559	60	596	810	1041	1304	1591	1902	2239
250	559	80	738	1002	1311	1629	1997	2401	2841
250	559	100	876	1185	1556	1946	2397	2896	3444
250	559	120	982	1358	1794	2258	2795	3392	4053
250	559	140	1107	1531	2029	2567	3192	3891	4671
275	615	40	480	645	820	1021	1237	1469	1716
275	615	60	646	863	1103	1379	1680	2005	2355
275	615	80	783	1063	1389	1722	2107	2527	2984
275	615	100	921	1256	1647	2054	2525	3043	3611
275	615	120	1039	1440	1898	2382	2941	3560	4242
275	615	140	1177	1624	2146	2706	3355	4078	4881
300	671	40	507	681	865	1075	1301	1543	1801
300	671	60	680	911	1163	1452	1766	2105	2469
300	671	80	827	1123	1445	1811	2213	2650	3123
300	671	100	967	1325	1736	2161	2650	3187	3774
300	671	120	1109	1523	2000	2503	3083	3723	4427
300	671	140	1246	1715	2260	2842	3514	4261	5087
325	727	40	533	717	909	1129	1365	1616	1884
325	727	60	714	959	1222	1524	1851	2203	2580
325	727	80	881	1184	1517	1899	2317	2770	3259
325	727	100	1014	1393	1823	2264	2772	3328	3933
325	727	120	1169	1601	2100	2622	3222	3884	4608
325	727	140	1314	1803	2371	2974	3670	4440	5288
350	783	40	559	751	952	1181	1426	1688	1965
350	783	60	747	1005	1280	1594	1933	2298	2688
350	783	80	917	1239	1589	1986	2418	2887	3392
350	783	100	1072	1462	1885	2365	2892	3466	4089
350	783	120	1228	1679	2197	2737	3359	4041	4786
350	783	140	1380	1890	2480	3104	3822	4615	5486
375	839	40	584	785	994	1232	1486	1757	2045
375	839	60	780	1050	1336	1662	2014	2391	2795
375	839	80	953	1294	1658	2070	2518	3002	3523
375	839	100	1122	1528	1967	2464	3009	3601	4242
375	839	120	1286	1754	2292	2851	3492	4195	4960
375	839	140	1446	1975	2587	3231	3971	4787	5681
400	894	40	609	818	1036	1282	1545	1826	2122
400	894	60	813	1094	1392	1729	2093	2483	2899
400	894	80	989	1348	1726	2153	2615	3114	3651
400	894	100	1171	1593	2048	2562	3123	3733	4393
400	894	120	1343	1829	2359	2962	3623	4346	5132
400	894	140	1511	2058	2692	3356	4118	4956	5872

NOTE: Detector time constant at a reference velocity of 5 ft/sec.
For SI Units: 1 ft = 0.305 m
1000 BTU/sec = 1055 kW

Table B-4.1(c)
Installed Spacing of Heat Detector: 8 feet
t_g: 300 Seconds to 1000 Btu/sec
α: 0.011 Btu/sec^3

τ	RTI	ΔT	CEILING HEIGHT IN FEET 4.0	8.0	12.0	16.0	20.0	24.0	28.0
			FIRE SIZE AT DETECTOR RESPONSE (BTU/SEC)						
25	56	40	70	104	152	211	285	374	477
25	56	60	95	149	223	321	443	592	767
25	56	80	122	196	302	442	620	838	1099
25	56	100	148	246	387	575	815	1110	1463
25	56	120	174	299	479	719	1027	1405	1858
25	56	140	201	354	576	873	1253	1721	2283
50	112	40	101	144	200	267	345	439	547
50	112	60	136	200	284	389	517	668	849
50	112	80	172	257	372	520	703	926	1187
50	112	100	205	315	465	661	906	1206	1560
50	112	120	239	374	563	811	1124	1508	1963
50	112	140	273	437	666	970	1356	1830	2399
75	168	40	127	178	242	318	402	502	616
75	168	60	170	245	339	453	586	746	931
75	168	80	215	311	438	595	786	1012	1280
75	168	100	255	378	540	745	998	1303	1661
75	168	120	296	445	646	903	1223	1612	2072
75	168	140	336	514	756	1069	1461	1942	2510
100	224	40	150	209	281	361	455	561	682
100	224	60	201	286	390	514	654	821	1013
100	224	80	253	361	500	667	864	1099	1374
100	224	100	300	436	611	827	1088	1397	1764
100	224	120	347	511	725	993	1322	1714	2183
100	224	140	393	587	843	1167	1568	2055	2628
125	280	40	171	237	317	403	504	618	745
125	280	60	230	323	437	567	719	893	1093
125	280	80	289	408	557	736	941	1184	1466
125	280	100	342	490	678	906	1173	1493	1867
125	280	120	395	573	801	1081	1420	1819	2294
125	280	140	447	656	926	1262	1674	2163	2748
150	335	40	192	264	350	443	551	671	805
150	335	60	261	360	482	619	780	963	1170
150	335	80	322	451	612	801	1015	1267	1557
150	335	100	381	542	742	981	1258	1587	1969
150	335	120	440	631	873	1166	1511	1923	2406
150	335	140	497	721	1006	1356	1778	2276	2867
175	391	40	211	289	383	481	596	723	863
175	391	60	287	394	525	670	839	1030	1245
175	391	80	353	493	664	859	1087	1348	1646
175	391	100	419	591	803	1055	1341	1679	2070
175	391	120	482	687	943	1248	1603	2025	2517
175	391	140	545	784	1083	1447	1875	2387	2987
200	447	40	229	314	413	518	639	772	919
200	447	60	311	426	566	719	896	1095	1318
200	447	80	384	533	715	918	1156	1427	1733
200	447	100	454	638	862	1119	1421	1770	2169
200	447	120	523	741	1010	1328	1694	2126	2626
200	447	140	596	844	1158	1535	1974	2497	3106

τ	RTI	ΔT	CEILING HEIGHT IN FEET 4.0	8.0	12.0	16.0	20.0	24.0	28.0
			FIRE SIZE AT DETECTOR RESPONSE (BTU/SEC)						
225	503	40	247	337	443	553	680	820	973
225	503	60	335	458	606	766	951	1158	1389
225	503	80	413	572	763	976	1223	1503	1819
225	503	100	489	684	919	1186	1499	1858	2267
225	503	120	569	794	1075	1406	1782	2225	2735
225	503	140	639	902	1230	1621	2072	2605	3224
250	559	40	264	360	471	587	720	866	1025
250	559	60	357	488	644	811	1005	1220	1458
250	559	80	441	610	811	1032	1289	1578	1902
250	559	100	522	728	975	1252	1576	1945	2363
250	559	120	607	844	1138	1474	1868	2322	2842
250	559	140	682	959	1301	1705	2167	2712	3341
275	615	40	280	382	499	620	759	911	1076
275	615	60	380	518	681	856	1057	1280	1525
275	615	80	469	646	856	1086	1352	1651	1984
275	615	100	555	771	1028	1316	1650	2029	2457
275	615	120	643	893	1199	1546	1953	2418	2948
275	615	140	723	1014	1369	1779	2261	2817	3456
300	671	40	297	403	520	652	797	955	1126
300	671	60	401	546	717	899	1108	1338	1591
300	671	80	496	682	901	1140	1415	1722	2064
300	671	100	593	813	1081	1378	1723	2113	2550
300	671	120	679	941	1259	1617	2035	2512	3052
300	671	140	763	1067	1436	1858	2352	2921	3571
325	727	40	317	425	546	684	834	998	1174
325	727	60	422	574	753	941	1157	1395	1656
325	727	80	522	716	945	1192	1476	1792	2143
325	727	100	623	854	1132	1439	1795	2194	2641
325	727	120	713	988	1317	1687	2116	2604	3155
325	727	140	802	1119	1502	1936	2442	3023	3684
350	783	40	332	445	571	714	871	1040	1222
350	783	60	443	602	787	982	1206	1451	1719
350	783	80	548	750	987	1242	1535	1861	2220
350	783	100	653	894	1182	1499	1865	2274	2731
350	783	120	747	1033	1375	1755	2196	2694	3256
350	783	140	841	1171	1566	2012	2531	3123	3795
375	839	40	347	465	596	744	906	1081	1269
375	839	60	463	629	821	1023	1253	1506	1781
375	839	80	573	783	1029	1292	1594	1928	2296
375	839	100	682	933	1232	1558	1933	2353	2820
375	839	120	781	1078	1431	1822	2274	2784	3356
375	839	140	885	1221	1629	2086	2618	3222	3906
400	894	40	362	485	620	774	941	1121	1314
400	894	60	483	655	846	1062	1300	1560	1842
400	894	80	604	817	1070	1341	1651	1994	2371
400	894	100	710	971	1280	1615	2001	2430	2907
400	894	120	814	1122	1486	1888	2351	2872	3454
400	894	140	919	1270	1690	2160	2704	3320	4015

NOTE: Detector time constant at a reference velocity of 5 ft/sec.
For SI Units: 1 ft = 0.305 m
1000 BTU/sec = 1055 kW

Table B-4.1(d)
Installed Spacing of Heat Detector: 8 feet
t_g: 500 Seconds to 1000 Btu/sec
α: 0.004 Btu/sec³

			CEILING HEIGHT IN FEET						
τ	RTI	ΔT	4.0	8.0	12.0	16.0	20.0	24.0	28.0
			FIRE SIZE AT DETECTOR RESPONSE (BTU/SEC)						
25	56	40	49	78	118	171	237	318	413
25	56	60	70	116	183	272	385	523	689
25	56	80	91	158	256	386	553	759	1005
25	56	100	113	203	336	513	740	1020	1357
25	56	120	136	252	422	651	944	1306	1741
25	56	140	160	304	515	799	1163	1613	2154
50	112	40	70	104	148	204	273	355	453
50	112	60	96	149	220	312	427	568	735
50	112	80	124	196	297	431	601	809	1058
50	112	100	150	246	381	562	792	1075	1415
50	112	120	178	298	471	703	1000	1365	1803
50	112	140	206	353	567	855	1222	1676	2221
75	168	40	87	126	176	236	309	393	493
75	168	60	120	178	255	351	470	612	782
75	168	80	152	231	338	476	649	860	1109
75	168	100	184	286	427	612	845	1131	1471
75	168	120	215	343	521	757	1057	1425	1867
75	168	140	247	402	621	912	1283	1740	2289
100	224	40	103	147	201	266	341	430	533
100	224	60	141	205	288	389	512	658	830
100	224	80	179	264	378	521	698	912	1163
100	224	100	214	324	472	661	898	1188	1530
100	224	120	250	386	571	811	1114	1486	1928
100	224	140	286	449	674	970	1345	1805	2354
125	280	40	118	166	225	295	374	466	573
125	280	60	160	231	319	426	552	702	878
125	280	80	203	295	415	564	746	961	1218
125	280	100	243	360	515	711	952	1245	1590
125	280	120	282	427	619	865	1173	1548	1993
125	280	140	322	494	727	1028	1407	1871	2423
150	335	40	131	184	248	320	404	501	611
150	335	60	179	255	349	462	592	747	926
150	335	80	226	325	452	607	793	1013	1273
150	335	100	270	395	557	759	1005	1300	1650
150	335	120	313	466	666	918	1231	1610	2058
150	335	140	356	537	778	1085	1469	1937	2492
175	391	40	144	201	269	345	434	535	649
175	391	60	196	278	378	496	631	790	973
175	391	80	247	353	487	648	837	1063	1327
175	391	100	295	428	597	806	1058	1356	1711
175	391	120	342	503	711	971	1289	1669	2123
175	391	140	389	579	828	1142	1532	2004	2562
200	447	40	157	217	290	370	463	568	685
200	447	60	213	300	405	526	668	832	1020
200	447	80	268	380	520	688	882	1113	1381
200	447	100	320	460	637	852	1107	1413	1771
200	447	120	370	539	755	1022	1346	1731	2189
200	447	140	421	620	877	1199	1594	2067	2633
225	503	40	169	233	310	394	491	599	721
225	503	60	232	321	432	558	705	873	1065
225	503	80	288	406	553	727	926	1162	1435
225	503	100	343	490	675	897	1158	1469	1832
225	503	120	397	574	799	1073	1403	1792	2254
225	503	140	451	659	925	1254	1656	2134	2703
250	559	40	181	249	329	417	518	630	756
250	559	60	247	342	458	588	740	914	1110
250	559	80	307	432	584	765	970	1211	1488
250	559	100	366	520	712	941	1208	1524	1892
250	559	120	424	609	841	1122	1455	1853	2320
250	559	140	480	697	971	1309	1717	2200	2774
275	615	40	192	264	348	439	544	660	789
275	615	60	263	362	483	618	775	953	1154
275	615	80	326	456	615	798	1012	1258	1541
275	615	100	388	549	748	984	1257	1578	1951
275	615	120	449	642	882	1171	1510	1914	2386
275	615	140	509	734	1017	1362	1773	2266	2844
300	671	40	203	278	366	461	569	690	823
300	671	60	277	381	507	647	809	992	1198
300	671	80	345	481	645	834	1053	1305	1593
300	671	100	410	578	783	1026	1305	1632	2010
300	671	120	474	674	922	1219	1564	1974	2451
300	671	140	541	770	1062	1415	1833	2331	2915
325	727	40	214	292	384	482	594	719	855
325	727	60	292	400	531	676	843	1030	1240
325	727	80	362	504	675	869	1094	1351	1644
325	727	100	431	606	818	1063	1352	1685	2069
325	727	120	498	706	961	1266	1617	2033	2516
325	727	140	568	806	1106	1467	1892	2396	2985
350	783	40	224	306	401	503	619	747	887
350	783	60	306	419	555	704	875	1068	1282
350	783	80	380	527	704	903	1134	1397	1694
350	783	100	452	633	852	1104	1398	1738	2126
350	783	120	522	737	1000	1312	1670	2092	2580
350	783	140	594	841	1149	1518	1949	2460	3055
375	839	40	235	320	419	523	643	774	918
375	839	60	320	437	577	731	907	1104	1324
375	839	80	397	550	732	937	1173	1442	1744
375	839	100	472	659	885	1143	1444	1790	2184
375	839	120	545	767	1038	1357	1722	2150	2644
375	839	140	619	875	1191	1569	2007	2524	3125
400	894	40	245	333	435	543	666	801	949
400	894	60	333	455	600	758	939	1141	1364
400	894	80	414	572	760	970	1212	1486	1794
400	894	100	492	685	918	1182	1489	1841	2241
400	894	120	572	798	1075	1396	1773	2208	2707
400	894	140	645	908	1233	1619	2063	2588	3194

NOTE: Detector time constant at a reference velocity of 5 ft/sec.
For SI Units: 1 ft = 0.305 m
1000 BTU/sec = 1055 kW

Table B-4.1(e)
Installed Spacing of Heat Detector: 8 feet
t_g: 600 Seconds to 1000 Btu/sec
α: 0.003 Btu/sec^3

			CEILING HEIGHT IN FEET						
τ	RTI	ΔT	4.0	8.0	12.0	16.0	20.0	24.0	28.0
			FIRE SIZE AT DETECTOR RESPONSE (BTU/SEC)						
25	56	40	44	71	110	160	225	303	397
25	56	60	63	108	173	259	370	505	668
25	56	80	83	148	244	372	536	738	980
25	56	100	104	192	323	497	721	997	1328
25	56	120	126	240	408	633	922	1279	1709
25	56	140	149	291	499	780	1139	1584	2119
50	112	40	62	93	135	188	254	334	429
50	112	60	86	135	203	292	404	542	705
50	112	80	111	180	278	409	575	779	1024
50	112	100	136	228	360	537	763	1042	1376
50	112	120	161	279	448	676	968	1328	1761
50	112	140	188	332	542	826	1188	1636	2175
75	168	40	77	112	158	215	284	365	462
75	168	60	106	160	233	325	440	579	744
75	168	80	136	210	312	446	614	821	1066
75	168	100	165	262	398	578	807	1088	1425
75	168	120	194	316	489	720	1015	1378	1813
75	168	140	224	373	586	872	1238	1689	2231
100	224	40	91	130	180	241	312	396	495
100	224	60	124	184	261	357	475	616	784
100	224	80	158	238	346	483	654	863	1110
100	224	100	191	295	436	619	851	1134	1471
100	224	120	224	353	531	765	1062	1428	1866
100	224	140	257	413	631	920	1288	1742	2287
125	280	40	103	147	201	265	339	427	528
125	280	60	141	206	288	388	510	653	824
125	280	80	180	265	378	520	695	905	1155
125	280	100	216	326	472	660	895	1181	1520
125	280	120	252	388	571	810	1110	1478	1916
125	280	140	289	451	675	968	1340	1796	2341
150	335	40	115	162	220	288	366	456	561
150	335	60	158	227	313	419	542	690	863
150	335	80	200	291	409	556	734	947	1200
150	335	100	239	355	508	701	939	1229	1570
150	335	120	279	421	611	854	1158	1530	1970
150	335	140	318	488	718	1016	1391	1851	2398
175	391	40	127	177	239	309	391	485	593
175	391	60	173	247	338	448	575	727	903
175	391	80	218	315	439	591	774	989	1246
175	391	100	261	384	543	741	983	1274	1620
175	391	120	304	454	650	898	1206	1581	2024
175	391	140	347	524	761	1064	1443	1906	2456
200	447	40	138	192	257	330	416	513	624
200	447	60	187	266	362	476	607	763	942
200	447	80	237	339	468	625	810	1031	1291
200	447	100	283	412	576	780	1027	1321	1670
200	447	120	329	485	688	942	1255	1630	2078
200	447	140	374	559	802	1111	1495	1961	2513
225	503	40	148	205	274	351	440	541	654
225	503	60	202	284	385	504	639	798	981
225	503	80	254	362	496	658	848	1073	1336
225	503	100	303	438	609	818	1070	1368	1720
225	503	120	352	515	725	985	1302	1681	2132
225	503	140	401	593	843	1158	1546	2013	2572
250	559	40	158	219	291	371	463	567	684
250	559	60	215	302	407	528	670	832	1019
250	559	80	271	384	524	691	885	1114	1380
250	559	100	323	464	641	856	1110	1414	1770
250	559	120	375	545	761	1027	1350	1732	2187
250	559	140	426	626	884	1204	1598	2069	2630
275	615	40	168	232	307	390	486	593	713
275	615	60	231	320	429	554	700	866	1056
275	615	80	287	405	550	723	921	1155	1425
275	615	100	343	490	673	893	1152	1460	1820
275	615	120	397	574	797	1069	1397	1783	2241
275	615	140	451	658	923	1250	1649	2123	2689
300	671	40	178	244	323	409	508	619	742
300	671	60	244	337	451	579	729	900	1093
300	671	80	303	426	577	754	957	1195	1469
300	671	100	362	514	703	930	1193	1506	1869
300	671	120	419	602	831	1110	1440	1834	2296
300	671	140	475	690	962	1295	1699	2178	2747
325	727	40	187	257	339	428	530	644	770
325	727	60	256	353	471	604	758	933	1130
325	727	80	319	447	602	782	992	1234	1512
325	727	100	380	538	733	965	1234	1551	1919
325	727	120	440	630	865	1150	1485	1884	2350
325	727	140	499	721	999	1340	1746	2233	2806
350	783	40	196	269	354	446	551	668	797
350	783	60	269	370	492	628	786	965	1166
350	783	80	334	467	627	811	1026	1273	1555
350	783	100	398	562	763	1000	1274	1596	1968
350	783	120	461	657	899	1190	1530	1934	2404
350	783	140	523	751	1037	1384	1796	2287	2864
375	839	40	205	281	369	464	572	692	824
375	839	60	281	386	512	652	814	997	1201
375	839	80	349	486	652	841	1060	1312	1598
375	839	100	416	585	792	1035	1313	1640	2016
375	839	120	481	683	932	1229	1574	1983	2458
375	839	140	549	781	1073	1427	1844	2341	2922
400	894	40	214	292	383	481	592	715	851
400	894	60	292	401	531	675	841	1028	1236
400	894	80	364	506	676	869	1094	1350	1640
400	894	100	433	608	820	1065	1352	1684	2065
400	894	120	501	709	964	1268	1618	2032	2511
400	894	140	571	810	1110	1470	1893	2395	2981

NOTE: Detector time constant at a reference velocity of 5 ft/sec.
For SI Units: 1 ft = 0.305 m
1000 BTU/sec = 1055 kW

Table B-4.1(f)
Installed Spacing of Heat Detector: 10 feet
t_g: 50 Seconds to 1000 Btu/sec
α: 0.400 Btu/sec^3

τ	RTI	ΔT	CEILING HEIGHT IN FEET 4.0	8.0	12.0	16.0	20.0	24.0	28.0
			FIRE SIZE AT DETECTOR RESPONSE (BTU/SEC)						
25	56	40	376	499	623	779	956	1152	1366
25	56	60	486	641	811	1027	1273	1550	1860
25	56	80	570	769	1013	1271	1591	1957	2371
25	56	100	675	902	1193	1517	1916	2377	2906
25	56	120	751	1024	1371	1766	2249	2814	3465
25	56	140	827	1146	1551	2040	2593	3268	4050
50	112	40	552	692	904	1084	1306	1550	1813
50	112	60	712	895	1171	1418	1723	2059	2426
50	112	80	828	1106	1391	1738	2129	2561	3038
50	112	100	945	1282	1633	2055	2531	3064	3658
50	112	120	1035	1446	1905	2371	2936	3575	4292
50	112	140	1177	1626	2143	2685	3343	4094	4942
75	168	40	673	890	1088	1331	1598	1885	2191
75	168	60	885	1157	1418	1744	2104	2495	2916
75	168	80	1000	1370	1725	2136	2590	3086	3625
75	168	100	1174	1602	2024	2518	3066	3670	4333
75	168	120	1330	1822	2315	2893	3538	4255	5047
75	168	140	1484	2037	2602	3264	4010	4843	5769
100	224	40	801	1051	1276	1554	1858	2183	2528
100	224	60	985	1337	1662	2037	2446	2885	3356
100	224	80	1195	1623	2026	2494	3005	3560	4158
100	224	100	1389	1893	2375	2934	3550	4221	4951
100	224	120	1581	2155	2714	3365	4086	4877	5742
100	224	140	1771	2411	3046	3790	4618	5532	6537
125	280	40	908	1193	1447	1759	2097	2457	2837
125	280	60	1130	1528	1889	2307	2761	3246	3763
125	280	80	1364	1853	2303	2823	3389	3998	4652
125	280	100	1595	2164	2699	3319	3997	4732	5525
125	280	120	1822	2466	3083	3803	4594	5456	6392
125	280	140	2046	2759	3458	4277	5183	6175	7257
150	335	40	971	1308	1605	1949	2320	2713	3127
150	335	60	1257	1702	2101	2560	3055	3583	4144
150	335	80	1528	2070	2564	3132	3749	4410	5117
150	335	100	1794	2421	3004	3681	4418	5213	6067
150	335	120	2055	2760	3430	4214	5072	6002	7006
150	335	140	2314	3089	3845	4737	5716	6782	7939
175	391	40	1035	1419	1755	2130	2531	2954	3400
175	391	60	1381	1869	2303	2800	3335	3903	4505
175	391	80	1688	2277	2811	3426	4091	4801	5558
175	391	100	1988	2666	3294	4025	4818	5670	6582
175	391	120	2284	3042	3760	4606	5527	6521	7591
175	391	140	2577	3406	4214	5173	6223	7361	8590
200	447	40	1151	1552	1902	2302	2732	3185	3661
200	447	60	1503	2030	2495	3029	3601	4209	4851
200	447	80	1844	2477	3047	3706	4417	5175	5980
200	447	100	2179	2903	3571	4353	5201	6108	7076
200	447	120	2509	3313	4076	4980	5962	7019	8151
200	447	140	2837	3712	4567	5591	6709	7917	9215
225	503	40	1234	1667	2041	2468	2925	3406	3911
225	503	60	1622	2186	2681	3249	3858	4503	5183
225	503	80	1998	2671	3274	3976	4731	5535	6386
225	503	100	2367	3132	3838	4670	5569	6529	7551
225	503	120	2731	3577	4380	5340	6382	7499	8692
225	503	140	3096	3911	4902	5994	7178	8452	9818
250	559	40	1317	1778	2175	2628	3111	3620	4152
250	559	60	1740	2337	2860	3461	4105	4786	5503
250	559	80	2150	2859	3494	4237	5035	5882	6778
250	559	100	2553	3355	4096	4976	5925	6936	8011
250	559	120	2953	3739	4669	5689	6787	7963	9215
250	559	140	3267	4270	5234	6384	7631	8970	10402
275	615	40	1398	1886	2305	2783	3291	3826	4386
275	615	60	1855	2484	3033	3667	4345	5061	5813
275	615	80	2300	3042	3707	4489	5329	6219	7159
275	615	100	2737	3485	4340	5272	6270	7331	8456
275	615	120	3175	3975	4954	6027	7181	8413	9723
275	615	140	3488	4440	5548	6761	8070	9472	10968
300	671	40	1478	1992	2432	2933	3467	4027	4613
300	671	60	1970	2628	3202	3867	4578	5328	6115
300	671	80	2448	3221	3915	4735	5615	6547	7529
300	671	100	2922	3687	4584	5560	6605	7716	8890
300	671	120	3301	4199	5231	6356	7563	8850	10217
300	671	140	3705	4696	5858	7129	8498	9962	11520
325	727	40	1557	2096	2555	3079	3637	4222	4834
325	727	60	2084	2769	3367	4063	4805	5588	6409
325	727	80	2596	3397	4117	4975	5894	6866	7889
325	727	100	3106	3883	4821	5842	6933	8090	9313
325	727	120	3489	4421	5501	6677	7937	9278	10699
325	727	140	3919	4945	6160	7488	8915	10439	12059
350	783	40	1635	2198	2676	3222	3804	4413	5049
350	783	60	2196	2908	3528	4253	5027	5842	6696
350	783	80	2744	3476	4308	5209	6166	7178	8241
350	783	100	3291	4076	5052	6117	7253	8456	9726
350	783	120	3675	4639	5765	6991	8302	9695	11170
350	783	140	4130	5189	6456	7839	9323	10905	12585
375	839	40	1713	2298	2794	3362	3966	4600	5260
375	839	60	2308	3044	3685	4440	5244	6090	6976
375	839	80	2891	3636	4501	5438	6433	7483	8586
375	839	100	3366	4257	5279	6386	7566	8814	10130
375	839	120	3858	4853	6024	7298	8659	10104	11631
375	839	140	4339	5428	6745	8183	9723	11362	13100
400	894	40	1790	2396	2909	3499	4126	4782	5466
400	894	60	2419	3178	3840	4622	5457	6334	7251
400	894	80	3038	3793	4691	5662	6694	7782	8923
400	894	100	3522	4440	5501	6649	7872	9165	10527
400	894	120	4040	5062	6278	7599	9009	10504	12083
400	894	140	4546	5662	7029	8519	10115	11810	13606

NOTE: Detector time constant at a reference velocity of 5 ft/sec.
For SI Units: 1 ft = 0.305 m
1000 BTU/sec = 1055 kW

Table B-4.1(g)
Installed Spacing of Heat Detector: 10 feet
t_g: 150 Seconds to 1000 Btu/sec
α: 0.044 Btu/sec^3

τ	RTI	ΔT	CEILING HEIGHT IN FEET 4.0	8.0	12.0	16.0	20.0	24.0	28.0
			FIRE SIZE AT DETECTOR RESPONSE (BTU/SEC)						
25	56	40	152	209	280	362	461	576	709
25	56	60	205	284	389	519	671	856	1071
25	56	80	252	358	502	683	904	1164	1473
25	56	100	298	435	621	858	1151	1504	1912
25	56	120	345	514	746	1044	1416	1864	2385
25	56	140	392	595	877	1241	1696	2247	2890
50	112	40	221	296	380	481	596	727	872
50	112	60	297	398	525	669	841	1040	1268
50	112	80	362	496	664	860	1097	1374	1695
50	112	100	426	593	805	1064	1366	1730	2154
50	112	120	490	691	950	1269	1649	2107	2645
50	112	140	561	791	1098	1482	1952	2506	3166
75	168	40	277	369	467	584	715	861	1021
75	168	60	372	495	635	803	995	1212	1456
75	168	80	454	614	807	1022	1280	1576	1913
75	168	100	535	731	971	1245	1574	1957	2397
75	168	120	622	848	1135	1472	1879	2355	2908
75	168	140	697	963	1302	1713	2194	2772	3446
100	224	40	328	435	545	677	823	983	1158
100	224	60	439	582	738	926	1136	1371	1632
100	224	80	537	720	926	1171	1450	1766	2122
100	224	100	641	857	1122	1418	1770	2174	2633
100	224	120	730	990	1307	1667	2098	2596	3168
100	224	140	819	1121	1492	1920	2434	3034	3726
125	280	40	383	487	617	763	923	1097	1286
125	280	60	501	662	835	1040	1268	1520	1799
125	280	80	625	822	1044	1310	1611	1947	2322
125	280	100	729	973	1249	1580	1956	2382	2862
125	280	120	831	1121	1467	1850	2307	2828	3421
125	280	140	935	1268	1670	2123	2665	3288	4002
150	335	40	426	543	685	844	1017	1204	1406
150	335	60	559	738	925	1147	1392	1662	1957
150	335	80	694	914	1155	1442	1762	2119	2513
150	335	100	812	1081	1380	1733	2133	2581	3082
150	335	120	930	1246	1602	2025	2507	3052	3667
150	335	140	1034	1406	1839	2317	2886	3535	4271
175	391	40	467	595	750	920	1106	1306	1521
175	391	60	628	798	1011	1249	1511	1797	2108
175	391	80	760	1002	1261	1567	1907	2283	2697
175	391	100	899	1186	1504	1880	2302	2772	3295
175	391	120	1013	1362	1744	2192	2699	3268	3906
175	391	140	1146	1540	1981	2503	3099	3773	4534
200	447	40	506	646	811	994	1191	1403	1631
200	447	60	678	866	1093	1347	1625	1927	2254
200	447	80	825	1086	1362	1687	2047	2442	2874
200	447	100	966	1284	1623	2021	2465	2957	3501
200	447	120	1109	1477	1880	2352	2884	3478	4138
200	447	140	1247	1667	2133	2682	3305	4005	4790
225	503	40	544	694	871	1064	1273	1497	1737
225	503	60	727	931	1173	1441	1734	2052	2395
225	503	80	895	1170	1460	1803	2181	2595	3046
225	503	100	1034	1378	1738	2157	2623	3136	3701
225	503	120	1195	1587	2011	2507	3063	3680	4634
225	503	140	1345	1790	2280	2856	3504	4230	5040
250	559	40	580	742	928	1132	1352	1588	1840
250	559	60	775	994	1250	1532	1840	2173	2531
250	559	80	948	1246	1555	1915	2311	2743	3212
250	559	100	1116	1473	1849	2289	2775	3310	3895
250	559	120	1279	1694	2138	2658	3237	3878	4585
250	559	140	1440	1909	2422	3024	3698	4450	5284
275	615	40	616	787	984	1198	1429	1676	1939
275	615	60	822	1055	1324	1621	1943	2290	2663
275	615	80	1001	1322	1647	2024	2438	2888	3375
275	615	100	1187	1564	1958	2417	2924	3479	4085
275	615	120	1362	1797	2261	2804	3406	4070	4800
275	615	140	1534	2025	2560	3187	3887	4664	5523
300	671	40	663	832	1038	1263	1504	1762	2036
300	671	60	880	1115	1397	1707	2043	2405	2792
300	671	80	1065	1398	1736	2130	2561	3028	3533
300	671	100	1256	1652	2063	2542	3069	3644	4270
300	671	120	1443	1898	2382	2946	3571	4258	5010
300	671	140	1625	2138	2695	3346	4071	4873	5757
325	727	40	695	875	1091	1325	1577	1845	2130
325	727	60	918	1172	1467	1791	2141	2516	2918
325	727	80	1123	1471	1823	2234	2681	3166	3687
325	727	100	1325	1738	2166	2664	3210	3805	4451
325	727	120	1522	1996	2499	3085	3732	4441	5216
325	727	140	1716	2249	2827	3502	4252	5078	5986
350	783	40	727	918	1142	1387	1648	1927	2222
350	783	60	957	1229	1537	1873	2236	2626	3041
350	783	80	1179	1542	1909	2335	2799	3300	3839
350	783	100	1392	1822	2266	2783	3348	3963	4628
350	783	120	1600	2093	2614	3222	3890	4621	5418
350	783	140	1805	2330	2955	3655	4428	5279	6211
375	839	40	758	959	1193	1447	1718	2007	2312
375	839	60	996	1304	1605	1954	2330	2733	3162
375	839	80	1234	1589	1992	2434	2914	3432	3987
375	839	100	1459	1880	2364	2900	3484	4118	4802
375	839	120	1678	2161	2726	3355	4045	4798	5616
375	839	140	1894	2434	3081	3804	4601	5476	6431
400	894	40	789	1000	1242	1505	1787	2085	2400
400	894	60	1035	1359	1671	2032	2422	2837	3280
400	894	80	1289	1657	2074	2532	3027	3561	4132
400	894	100	1524	1959	2461	3014	3617	4269	4973
400	894	120	1754	2251	2837	3486	4197	4971	5810
400	894	140	1982	2536	3205	3951	4771	5669	6648

NOTE: Detector time constant at a reference velocity of 5 ft/sec.
For SI Units: 1 ft = 0.305 m
1000 BTU/sec = 1055 kW

Table B-4.1(h)
Installed Spacing of Heat Detector: 10 feet
t_g: 300 Seconds to 1000 Btu/sec
α: 0.011 Btu/sec^3

τ	RTI	ΔT	CEILING HEIGHT IN FEET 4.0	8.0	12.0	16.0	20.0	24.0	28.0
			FIRE SIZE AT DETECTOR RESPONSE (BTU / SEC)						
25	56	40	91	131	183	249	330	424	537
25	56	60	126	187	271	379	513	675	863
25	56	80	160	246	367	524	720	957	1234
25	56	100	195	309	471	682	947	1268	1645
25	56	120	230	377	582	853	1193	1605	2091
25	56	140	267	448	701	1036	1456	1967	2574
50	112	40	131	180	241	313	399	500	616
50	112	60	179	250	344	459	597	762	956
50	112	80	224	322	451	615	816	1054	1338
50	112	100	269	395	565	782	1051	1377	1758
50	112	120	314	470	684	960	1305	1723	2213
50	112	140	359	549	810	1150	1575	2092	2700
75	168	40	164	222	293	371	465	572	694
75	168	60	224	306	410	532	679	851	1050
75	168	80	279	389	530	703	909	1155	1444
75	168	100	333	473	654	881	1158	1485	1874
75	168	120	386	558	784	1068	1420	1839	2338
75	168	140	440	645	918	1266	1697	2220	2833
100	224	40	194	260	335	424	526	640	769
100	224	60	265	357	471	602	757	937	1143
100	224	80	328	451	604	784	1001	1255	1550
100	224	100	391	545	739	977	1258	1596	1991
100	224	120	453	639	879	1175	1534	1959	2464
100	224	140	519	735	1022	1380	1821	2344	2967
125	280	40	222	296	377	474	583	705	841
125	280	60	302	404	528	667	832	1020	1234
125	280	80	374	508	673	863	1090	1353	1656
125	280	100	445	612	820	1065	1360	1706	2108
125	280	120	514	716	969	1278	1642	2079	2591
125	280	140	587	820	1122	1493	1938	2473	3103
150	335	40	248	329	417	521	637	766	909
150	335	60	366	448	577	729	903	1100	1321
150	335	80	417	563	739	939	1176	1448	1759
150	335	100	495	676	897	1153	1458	1814	2224
150	335	120	577	789	1056	1372	1752	2199	2718
150	335	140	651	901	1218	1603	2058	2602	3239
175	391	40	273	361	455	566	689	825	975
175	391	60	370	490	627	789	972	1177	1407
175	391	80	458	615	796	1012	1259	1541	1860
175	391	100	544	737	971	1237	1554	1920	2339
175	391	120	631	858	1140	1468	1859	2316	2844
175	391	140	712	979	1311	1703	2175	2730	3375
200	447	40	301	386	491	609	739	882	1038
200	447	60	401	531	676	846	1038	1251	1489
200	447	80	497	665	856	1082	1339	1631	1959
200	447	100	595	796	1042	1319	1647	2023	2452
200	447	120	684	925	1220	1560	1964	2432	2969
200	447	140	771	1053	1400	1806	2290	2856	3510
225	503	40	323	415	526	650	787	936	1099
225	503	60	432	570	723	901	1101	1324	1570
225	503	80	535	713	914	1150	1417	1718	2056
225	503	100	639	853	1103	1399	1738	2125	2563
225	503	120	734	990	1299	1650	2066	2545	3092
225	503	140	828	1125	1487	1906	2403	2980	3645
250	559	40	345	443	560	690	833	989	1159
250	559	60	461	608	768	955	1163	1394	1649
250	559	80	572	759	969	1215	1493	1804	2151
250	559	100	682	907	1168	1476	1826	2224	2672
250	559	120	783	1052	1374	1738	2166	2656	3214
250	559	140	888	1196	1572	2003	2514	3103	3778
275	615	40	366	470	593	729	878	1041	1217
275	615	60	490	644	812	1007	1224	1463	1725
275	615	80	613	806	1024	1280	1567	1888	2244
275	615	100	723	961	1232	1551	1913	2321	2780
275	615	120	831	1113	1439	1823	2264	2766	3334
275	615	140	938	1264	1655	2098	2622	3223	3910
300	671	40	387	496	624	767	922	1091	1273
300	671	60	518	680	855	1058	1283	1530	1800
300	671	80	647	850	1077	1342	1639	1969	2335
300	671	100	763	1012	1294	1624	1997	2416	2885
300	671	120	883	1173	1510	1907	2360	2873	3453
300	671	140	988	1330	1725	2191	2728	3342	4040
325	727	40	407	521	656	804	965	1140	1328
325	727	60	546	715	897	1107	1340	1595	1873
325	727	80	680	892	1128	1403	1710	2050	2425
325	727	100	803	1063	1355	1696	2080	2510	2989
325	727	120	925	1230	1579	1989	2454	2979	3570
325	727	140	1038	1395	1803	2283	2833	3459	4168
350	783	40	427	546	686	840	1007	1188	1382
350	783	60	572	749	937	1156	1396	1659	1945
350	783	80	713	934	1179	1463	1779	2128	2513
350	783	100	842	1113	1415	1766	2161	2602	3091
350	783	120	967	1287	1647	2069	2546	3083	3685
350	783	140	1092	1459	1879	2372	2935	3574	4295
375	839	40	446	571	716	875	1048	1235	1435
375	839	60	606	774	977	1203	1451	1722	2016
375	839	80	745	976	1228	1521	1847	2205	2599
375	839	100	886	1162	1473	1835	2241	2692	3192
375	839	120	1009	1342	1714	2148	2637	3185	3798
375	839	140	1141	1521	1953	2460	3036	3688	4421
400	894	40	465	595	745	910	1089	1281	1487
400	894	60	631	807	1017	1250	1505	1784	2085
400	894	80	776	1016	1277	1579	1913	2281	2684
400	894	100	920	1209	1530	1903	2319	2781	3291
400	894	120	1055	1397	1780	2225	2726	3286	3910
400	894	140	1190	1582	2027	2547	3136	3800	4544

NOTE: Detector time constant at a reference velocity of 5 ft/sec.
For SI Units: 1 ft = 0.305 m
1000 BTU/sec = 1055 kW

Table B-4.1(i)
Installed Spacing of Heat Detector: 10 feet
t_g: 500 Seconds to 1000 Btu/sec
α: 0.004 Btu/sec³

τ	RTI	ΔT	CEILING HEIGHT IN FEET 4.0	8.0	12.0	16.0	20.0	24.0	28.0
			FIRE SIZE AT DETECTOR RESPONSE (BTU / SEC)						
25	56	40	65	98	143	202	274	362	465
25	56	60	92	146	222	322	447	598	775
25	56	80	121	200	312	458	643	867	1133
25	56	100	150	258	410	609	861	1166	1530
25	56	120	181	320	516	773	1098	1493	1963
25	56	140	214	386	630	950	1352	1844	2430
50	112	40	91	130	179	241	316	405	510
50	112	60	127	186	266	369	495	649	828
50	112	80	162	246	361	511	698	924	1191
50	112	100	198	309	464	666	920	1229	1593
50	112	120	235	376	574	835	1162	1561	2031
50	112	140	272	447	692	1015	1422	1917	2506
75	168	40	114	158	212	279	356	449	556
75	168	60	158	223	308	415	545	699	882
75	168	80	199	290	410	564	754	981	1251
75	168	100	241	359	519	725	982	1293	1660
75	168	120	283	431	634	898	1228	1630	2103
75	168	140	326	506	756	1082	1492	1991	2580
100	224	40	134	183	243	312	395	491	602
100	224	60	185	257	348	460	592	751	937
100	224	805	233	330	458	616	810	1040	1313
100	224	100	280	406	572	783	1044	1356	1727
100	224	120	328	484	693	961	1295	1700	2176
100	224	140	376	564	819	1150	1563	2065	2657
125	280	40	153	207	272	345	432	533	647
125	280	60	210	288	386	501	640	803	992
125	280	80	264	369	503	667	863	1099	1375
125	280	100	317	451	624	841	1106	1421	1795
125	280	120	370	534	751	1024	1362	1768	2250
125	280	140	422	619	882	1218	1635	2141	2736
150	335	40	171	229	297	377	468	572	690
150	335	60	234	318	422	542	686	853	1046
150	335	80	293	405	546	717	918	1158	1437
150	335	100	351	493	674	897	1165	1486	1864
150	335	120	409	582	807	1087	1430	1838	2324
150	335	140	466	673	944	1285	1707	2213	2815
175	391	40	187	250	322	407	503	611	733
175	391	60	257	346	456	582	731	903	1100
175	391	80	321	440	588	762	971	1216	1499
175	391	100	384	534	723	953	1225	1551	1933
175	391	120	447	629	861	1148	1494	1909	2398
175	391	140	512	725	1004	1352	1780	2289	2895
200	447	40	204	271	347	435	536	648	774
200	447	60	279	374	489	620	774	951	1152
200	447	80	348	474	629	809	1023	1273	1561
200	447	100	416	574	770	1007	1285	1616	2002
200	447	120	483	674	915	1209	1560	1980	2473
200	447	140	552	775	1062	1419	1848	2365	2975

τ	RTI	ΔT	CEILING HEIGHT IN FEET 4.0	8.0	12.0	16.0	20.0	24.0	28.0
			FIRE SIZE AT DETECTOR RESPONSE (BTU / SEC)						
225	503	40	219	291	370	463	568	685	815
225	503	60	300	400	518	657	817	998	1204
225	503	80	374	507	668	854	1074	1329	1622
225	503	100	446	612	816	1056	1343	1680	2070
225	503	120	518	717	966	1268	1625	2051	2548
225	503	140	591	823	1120	1484	1919	2441	3055
250	559	40	234	310	393	490	599	720	854
250	559	60	320	426	549	693	858	1045	1255
250	559	80	399	538	706	898	1124	1385	1683
250	559	100	476	649	861	1107	1401	1743	2139
250	559	120	555	760	1017	1323	1689	2121	2623
250	559	140	628	870	1176	1548	1990	2517	3135
275	615	40	249	328	415	517	630	755	893
275	615	60	339	451	578	728	898	1090	1305
275	615	80	423	569	743	941	1173	1440	1742
275	615	100	505	685	904	1157	1458	1806	2206
275	615	120	588	801	1066	1379	1753	2190	2697
275	615	140	665	916	1231	1611	2059	2593	3216
300	671	40	266	343	437	542	659	788	930
300	671	60	358	475	607	762	938	1135	1355
300	671	80	447	599	755	983	1221	1493	1801
300	671	100	533	720	947	1207	1513	1868	2273
300	671	120	619	841	1115	1435	1815	2259	2772
300	671	140	701	961	1285	1668	2128	2668	3296
325	727	40	280	361	458	567	688	821	967
325	727	60	377	499	636	796	976	1178	1403
325	727	80	470	628	810	1024	1269	1546	1860
325	727	100	564	755	988	1255	1568	1929	2340
325	727	120	650	880	1162	1489	1877	2327	2845
325	727	140	735	1005	1338	1729	2196	2742	3376
350	783	40	293	378	479	592	717	854	1003
350	783	60	395	522	664	829	1014	1221	1451
350	783	80	493	657	844	1064	1315	1598	1917
350	783	100	591	789	1024	1302	1622	1989	2406
350	783	120	681	919	1209	1543	1938	2394	2919
350	783	140	770	1048	1389	1788	2263	2816	3456
375	839	40	306	394	499	616	744	885	1039
375	839	60	413	544	691	861	1051	1263	1498
375	839	80	515	685	878	1104	1360	1649	1974
375	839	100	616	822	1064	1348	1675	2048	2471
375	839	120	710	957	1254	1596	1998	2461	2991
375	839	140	803	1091	1440	1847	2329	2889	3535
400	894	40	319	410	519	639	772	916	1074
400	894	60	431	567	718	893	1088	1305	1544
400	894	80	537	712	911	1143	1405	1700	2030
400	894	100	642	854	1102	1394	1728	2107	2536
400	894	120	740	994	1299	1648	2057	2527	3063
400	894	140	836	1132	1490	1905	2395	2692	3614

NOTE: Detector time constant at a reference velocity of 5 ft/sec.
For SI Units: 1 ft = 0.305 m
1000 BTU/sec = 1055 kW

Table B-4.1(j)
Installed Spacing of Heat Detector: 10 feet
t_g: 600 Seconds to 1000 Btu/sec
α: 0.003 Btu/sec³

τ	RTI	ΔT	CEILING HEIGHT IN FEET 4.0	8.0	12.0	16.0	20.0	24.0	28.0
			FIRE SIZE AT DETECTOR RESPONSE (BTU / SEC)						
25	56	40	58	89	133	190	260	346	446
25	56	60	84	136	210	307	429	577	752
25	56	80	110	188	298	442	623	843	1105
25	56	100	139	244	394	591	838	1139	1498
25	56	120	168	305	499	753	1073	1463	1928
25	56	140	200	371	611	927	1325	1811	2391
50	112	40	81	116	163	222	295	381	483
50	112	60	114	170	246	346	469	619	795
50	112	80	146	226	338	485	668	890	1153
50	112	100	179	287	439	637	887	1191	1550
50	112	120	214	352	547	803	1126	1519	1987
50	112	140	249	420	662	981	1382	1871	2454
75	168	40	100	140	191	254	328	417	521
75	168	60	140	201	282	384	510	661	839
75	168	80	178	264	379	528	714	938	1203
75	168	100	216	329	484	685	937	1244	1605
75	168	120	256	398	596	855	1180	1576	2043
75	168	140	295	470	715	1036	1440	1932	2515
100	224	40	118	162	218	283	361	452	559
100	224	60	164	230	316	422	550	704	884
100	224	80	207	298	419	572	760	985	1253
100	224	100	250	369	529	734	988	1297	1660
100	224	120	294	443	645	907	1235	1633	2103
100	224	140	338	519	767	1091	1498	1994	2579
125	280	40	134	183	242	311	393	487	596
125	280	60	186	257	348	459	590	746	930
125	280	80	234	332	458	615	806	1034	1304
125	280	100	282	408	573	782	1040	1349	1716
125	280	120	330	486	694	959	1290	1692	2164
125	280	140	379	566	820	1148	1557	2056	2643
150	335	40	150	202	266	338	423	521	633
150	335	60	207	283	379	493	629	789	975
150	335	80	260	363	495	657	851	1083	1356
150	335	100	312	445	616	829	1091	1403	1773
150	335	120	365	527	741	1012	1346	1747	2225
150	335	140	417	612	872	1204	1617	2118	2708
175	391	40	164	221	286	364	453	554	669
175	391	60	226	308	409	527	667	831	1020
175	391	80	284	394	531	698	896	1131	1407
175	391	100	341	480	657	876	1140	1457	1830
175	391	120	398	568	788	1064	1402	1806	2286
175	391	140	454	657	923	1260	1677	2178	2774
200	447	40	178	239	308	389	482	587	705
200	447	60	245	331	437	559	704	872	1064
200	447	80	308	423	566	736	940	1180	1459
200	447	100	369	514	698	922	1190	1511	1887
200	447	120	429	606	833	1115	1458	1865	2348
200	447	140	489	700	973	1316	1737	2241	2840
225	503	40	192	256	328	413	509	618	739
225	503	60	264	354	465	591	741	912	1108
225	503	80	330	451	600	775	984	1227	1510
225	503	100	395	547	737	968	1240	1564	1944
225	503	120	460	644	878	1165	1510	1924	2410
225	503	140	526	742	1022	1371	1797	2304	2906
250	559	40	205	272	348	437	536	648	773
250	559	60	281	377	492	623	776	952	1152
250	559	80	352	478	633	813	1026	1274	1561
250	559	100	421	579	776	1009	1289	1618	2001
250	559	120	489	681	921	1215	1564	1982	2472
250	559	140	559	783	1070	1425	1853	2367	2972
275	615	40	218	289	367	459	563	678	806
275	615	60	298	398	515	653	811	991	1194
275	615	80	373	505	665	850	1068	1321	1611
275	615	100	446	611	813	1052	1337	1671	2058
275	615	120	518	716	964	1264	1618	2040	2534
275	615	140	591	823	1118	1479	1912	2430	3039
300	671	40	230	304	386	482	588	707	839
300	671	60	315	419	541	683	845	1029	1237
300	671	80	394	531	697	886	1110	1367	1661
300	671	100	471	641	850	1094	1385	1723	2114
300	671	120	549	752	1006	1309	1671	2098	2596
300	671	140	622	862	1164	1532	1970	2493	3106
325	727	40	242	320	405	503	614	736	871
325	727	60	331	440	565	712	879	1067	1278
325	727	80	414	557	728	922	1150	1412	1711
325	727	100	495	671	886	1136	1432	1775	2170
325	727	120	576	786	1047	1356	1724	2156	2658
325	727	140	652	900	1210	1585	2028	2556	3173
350	783	40	257	332	423	525	638	764	902
350	783	60	347	460	589	740	911	1104	1319
350	783	80	434	581	754	957	1190	1457	1760
350	783	100	518	701	922	1177	1478	1826	2226
350	783	120	602	819	1087	1402	1776	2213	2719
350	783	140	682	937	1254	1632	2085	2618	3239
375	839	40	268	346	440	546	662	791	933
375	839	60	363	480	613	768	944	1140	1359
375	839	80	453	606	783	991	1230	1501	1808
375	839	100	545	730	957	1217	1524	1877	2281
375	839	120	628	852	1127	1447	1828	2270	2781
375	839	140	711	974	1299	1683	2142	2680	3306
400	894	40	280	361	458	566	686	818	963
400	894	60	378	499	636	796	975	1176	1399
400	894	80	472	630	812	1025	1268	1544	1856
400	894	100	567	758	991	1257	1569	1927	2336
400	894	120	654	884	1166	1492	1878	2326	2842
400	894	140	740	1010	1342	1733	2198	2742	3372

NOTE: Detector time constant at a reference velocity of 5 ft/sec.
For SI Units: 1 ft = 0.305 m
1000 BTU/sec = 1055 kW

Table B-4.1(k)
Installed Spacing of Heat Detector: 12 feet
t_g: 50 Seconds to 1000 Btu/sec
α: 0.400 Btu/sec^3

τ	RTI	ΔT	CEILING HEIGHT IN FEET 4.0	8.0	12.0	16.0	20.0	24.0	28.0
			FIRE SIZE AT DETECTOR RESPONSE (BTU / SEC)						
25	56	40	482	585	730	897	1085	1291	1518
25	56	60	593	751	952	1184	1446	1740	2069
25	56	80	722	913	1168	1467	1810	2200	2640
25	56	100	821	1090	1384	1753	2182	2675	3238
25	56	120	927	1243	1598	2043	2565	3169	3864
25	56	140	1007	1389	1836	2339	2959	3683	4518
50	112	40	668	831	1026	1244	1482	1740	2017
50	112	60	878	1078	1338	1633	1958	2314	2702
50	112	80	993	1328	1635	2006	2422	2880	3385
50	112	100	1162	1552	1923	2374	2882	3450	4079
50	112	120	1316	1766	2206	2739	3345	4026	4788
50	112	140	1469	1977	2486	3105	3812	4613	5516
75	168	40	867	1043	1273	1533	1815	2117	2438
75	168	60	1021	1370	1663	2011	2392	2804	3248
75	168	80	1255	1668	2030	2466	2947	3472	4042
75	168	100	1461	1946	2382	2907	3491	4132	4834
75	168	120	1665	2216	2726	3342	4031	4793	5632
75	168	140	1867	2480	3065	3774	4570	5458	6441
100	224	40	957	1257	1497	1790	2111	2452	2814
100	224	60	1226	1625	1954	2349	2781	3245	3741
100	224	80	1486	1971	2383	2878	3420	4006	4638
100	224	100	1742	2303	2795	3388	4042	4753	5525
100	224	120	1993	2624	3195	3888	4654	5494	6410
100	224	140	2242	2937	3587	4380	5263	6234	7300
125	280	40	1047	1409	1695	2026	2382	2761	3160
125	280	60	1399	1852	2220	2661	3139	3651	4195
125	280	80	1708	2253	2709	3258	3857	4501	5190
125	280	100	2011	2636	3176	3833	4552	5330	6168
125	280	120	2309	2933	3625	4393	5233	6147	7137
125	280	140	2605	3283	4067	4943	5907	6960	8106
150	335	40	1199	1584	1886	2246	2636	3049	3483
150	335	60	1566	2067	2470	2953	3475	4032	4622
150	335	80	1923	2520	3015	3615	4267	4965	5710
150	335	100	2272	2874	3530	4250	5031	5872	6774
150	335	120	2618	3277	4032	4868	5778	6763	7824
150	335	140	2961	3668	4522	5473	6514	7646	8870
175	391	40	1313	1736	2064	2455	2876	3321	3789
175	391	60	1729	2273	2707	3229	3793	4392	5026
175	391	80	2133	2699	3300	3953	4656	5406	6204
175	391	100	2529	3161	3869	4647	5487	6388	7350
175	391	120	2922	3605	4419	5319	6297	7350	8479
175	391	140	3317	4035	4954	5977	7092	8299	9599
200	447	40	1425	1882	2234	2654	3105	3581	4081
200	447	60	1889	2471	2934	3493	4097	4737	5412
200	447	80	2339	2933	3577	4277	5028	5828	6676
200	447	100	2783	3436	4194	5026	5923	6882	7903
200	447	120	3226	3919	4789	5752	6793	7911	9107
200	447	140	3538	4378	5367	6460	7646	8925	10298

τ	RTI	ΔT	CEILING HEIGHT IN FEET 4.0	8.0	12.0	16.0	20.0	24.0	28.0
			FIRE SIZE AT DETECTOR RESPONSE (BTU / SEC)						
225	503	40	1535	2023	2398	2845	3325	3831	4360
225	503	60	2046	2586	3145	3747	4389	5068	5783
225	503	80	2543	3159	3843	4588	5386	6234	7130
225	503	100	3036	3702	4507	5391	6342	7357	8435
225	503	120	3416	4215	5145	6168	7271	8452	9712
225	503	140	3834	4714	5765	6925	8180	9529	10973
250	559	40	1643	2161	2556	3029	3537	4071	4630
250	559	60	2021	2763	3355	3992	4671	5388	6142
250	559	80	2746	3378	4101	4889	5732	6626	7569
250	559	100	3289	3959	4809	5744	6748	7816	8949
250	559	120	3671	4505	5490	6570	7733	8976	10298
250	559	140	4123	5039	6151	7375	8697	10114	11627
275	615	40	1750	2294	2709	3208	3742	4304	4892
275	615	60	2354	2936	3558	4230	4944	5698	6489
275	615	80	2947	3590	4351	5181	6067	7006	7995
275	615	100	3423	4200	5102	6087	7141	8262	9448
275	615	120	3921	4788	5824	6961	8182	9484	10866
275	615	140	4408	5355	6525	7811	9198	10681	12261
300	671	40	1856	2425	2858	3381	3942	4531	5145
300	671	60	2507	3104	3756	4461	5210	5999	6826
300	671	80	3149	3797	4594	5465	6393	7375	8409
300	671	100	3635	4441	5387	6420	7524	8696	9933
300	671	120	4168	5063	6150	7341	8618	9978	11419
300	671	140	4690	5663	6889	8236	9686	11233	12879
325	727	40	1960	2475	2995	3550	4136	4751	5392
325	727	60	2658	3268	3949	4686	5469	6292	7155
325	727	80	3259	3992	4831	5741	6711	7736	8813
325	727	100	3844	4676	5666	6745	7897	9118	10407
325	727	120	4412	5331	6467	7711	9044	10460	11959
325	727	140	4840	5956	7244	8651	10162	11772	13482
350	783	40	2064	2594	3136	3715	4326	4966	5634
350	783	60	2809	3428	4138	4906	5721	6579	7476
350	783	80	3430	4188	5062	6012	7022	8087	9207
350	783	100	4050	4906	5938	7062	8262	9531	10869
350	783	120	4653	5594	6778	8074	9460	10931	12486
350	783	140	5089	6249	7591	9056	10627	12299	14071
375	839	40	2166	2712	3275	3876	4511	5176	5869
375	839	60	3599	4379	5289	6276	7326	8432	9593
375	839	80	3599	4379	5289	6276	7326	8432	9593
375	839	100	4254	5132	6204	7373	8619	9936	11322
375	839	120	4765	5844	7081	8428	9867	11392	13003
375	839	140	5334	6535	7931	9453	11082	12815	14649
400	894	40	2268	2827	3410	4034	4693	5382	6100
400	894	60	3112	3740	4503	5332	6211	7134	8098
400	894	80	3766	4567	5511	6535	7623	8769	9970
400	894	100	4456	5353	6465	7677	8968	10332	11766
400	894	120	4979	6095	7379	8776	10266	11845	13509
400	894	140	5575	6817	8264	9842	11529	13321	15215

NOTE: Detector time constant at a reference velocity of 5 ft/sec.
For SI Units: 1 ft = 0.305 m
1000 BTU/sec = 1055 kW

Table B-4.1(l)
Installed Spacing of Heat Detector: 12 feet
t_g: 150 Seconds to 1000 Btu/sec
α: 0.044 Btu/sec^3

			CEILING HEIGHT IN FEET						
τ	RTI	ΔT	4.0	8.0	12.0	16.0	20.0	24.0	28.0
			FIRE SIZE AT DETECTOR RESPONSE (BTU / SEC)						
25	56	40	190	254	327	418	525	648	790
25	56	60	256	345	461	602	766	964	1194
25	56	80	316	437	596	794	1030	1313	1644
25	56	100	375	531	738	999	1318	1693	2136
25	56	120	435	628	888	1217	1623	2100	2665
25	56	140	501	729	1045	1448	1946	2542	3230
50	112	40	275	359	447	556	679	818	972
50	112	60	368	483	613	774	959	1173	1415
50	112	80	452	602	779	997	1253	1550	1893
50	112	100	534	722	954	1228	1561	1953	2407
50	112	120	621	842	1127	1475	1886	2380	2957
50	112	140	700	963	1303	1725	2227	2832	3540
75	168	40	353	439	549	675	814	969	1139
75	168	60	462	590	747	929	1134	1366	1625
75	168	80	567	745	943	1184	1461	1778	2137
75	168	100	675	889	1138	1443	1798	2209	2679
75	168	120	772	1030	1334	1708	2148	2660	3251
75	168	140	878	1173	1543	1980	2510	3132	3854
100	224	40	415	516	641	782	937	1107	1292
100	224	60	545	692	869	1070	1295	1545	1822
100	224	80	678	862	1091	1355	1655	1993	2371
100	224	100	794	1039	1311	1642	2021	2454	2943
100	224	120	914	1202	1531	1932	2397	2932	3542
100	224	140	1017	1361	1752	2227	2783	3427	4168
125	280	40	472	587	726	881	1050	1235	1435
125	280	60	634	788	982	1202	1445	1714	2009
125	280	80	771	978	1230	1516	1837	2196	2594
125	280	100	910	1164	1473	1829	2233	2688	3199
125	280	120	1029	1359	1715	2144	2635	3194	3826
125	280	140	1168	1540	1957	2462	3045	3714	4476
150	335	40	526	654	806	974	1157	1356	1570
150	335	60	704	877	1088	1326	1587	1873	2186
150	335	80	871	1089	1360	1668	2010	2390	2809
150	335	100	1004	1293	1626	2006	2434	2913	3446
150	335	120	1159	1493	1889	2345	2863	3446	4101
150	335	140	1306	1708	2152	2686	3297	3992	4778
175	391	40	578	717	881	1062	1259	1471	1698
175	391	60	771	962	1190	1443	1722	2026	2356
175	391	80	944	1193	1484	1812	2176	2576	3014
175	391	100	1111	1416	1772	2176	2627	3129	3684
175	391	120	1276	1633	2056	2538	3081	3690	4369
175	391	140	1438	1847	2337	2900	3450	4262	5072
200	447	40	640	779	954	1147	1356	1581	1821
200	447	60	836	1043	1286	1556	1852	2172	2519
200	447	80	1017	1293	1604	1951	2334	2754	3213
200	447	100	1209	1534	1912	2339	2813	3338	3915
200	447	120	1389	1768	2215	2723	3292	3926	4629
200	447	140	1566	1998	2515	3107	3775	4523	5359
225	503	40	685	837	1023	1228	1450	1687	1940
225	503	60	905	1122	1380	1665	1976	2313	2676
225	503	80	1104	1390	1718	2085	2488	2927	3405
225	503	100	1304	1647	2047	2496	2993	3540	4139
225	503	120	1499	1898	2369	2902	3497	4155	4882
225	503	140	1691	2143	2688	3307	4002	4778	5639
250	559	40	729	894	1091	1307	1540	1789	2054
250	559	60	958	1197	1470	1771	2097	2450	2829
250	559	80	1182	1483	1829	2214	2636	3095	3592
250	559	100	1396	1757	2178	2648	3167	3736	4357
250	559	120	1606	2024	2519	3076	3695	4378	5129
250	559	140	1813	2284	2855	3501	4223	5025	5913
275	615	40	772	949	1156	1383	1628	1889	2166
275	615	60	1012	1271	1557	1873	2215	2583	2977
275	615	80	1257	1574	1937	2340	2780	3258	3774
275	615	100	1487	1864	2305	2796	3336	3927	4569
275	615	120	1712	2146	2664	3245	3888	4595	5370
275	615	140	1934	2421	3017	3690	4439	5267	6180
300	671	40	814	1002	1220	1458	1713	1985	2274
300	671	60	1079	1343	1643	1972	2329	2712	3121
300	671	80	1332	1662	2042	2463	2921	3417	3951
300	671	100	1576	1968	2428	2940	3501	4113	4776
300	671	120	1816	2265	2805	3409	4076	4807	5605
300	671	140	2027	2554	3175	3874	4649	5503	6442
325	727	40	870	1055	1282	1530	1796	2080	2379
325	727	60	1137	1413	1726	2069	2440	2838	3262
325	727	80	1404	1749	2145	2582	3058	3572	4124
325	727	100	1664	2070	2549	3081	3663	4295	4979
325	727	120	1919	2381	2943	3570	4260	5014	5836
325	727	140	2136	2684	3330	4054	4855	5735	6699
350	783	40	904	1105	1342	1601	1878	2172	2483
350	783	60	1193	1481	1807	2164	2549	2961	3400
350	783	80	1476	1833	2245	2699	3192	3723	4293
350	783	100	1750	2169	2667	3218	3820	4473	5178
350	783	120	2021	2495	3078	3727	4440	5218	6062
350	783	140	2243	2812	3481	4230	5056	5961	6951
375	839	40	938	1155	1401	1670	1957	2262	2583
375	839	60	1249	1548	1887	2257	2656	3082	3535
375	839	80	1547	1916	2343	2814	3324	3872	4459
375	839	100	1836	2267	2783	3353	3975	4648	5373
375	839	120	2088	2606	3210	3881	4617	5417	6284
375	839	140	2348	2937	3629	4402	5253	6184	7198
400	894	40	973	1203	1460	1738	2035	2350	2682
400	894	60	1304	1614	1965	2348	2760	3200	3668
400	894	80	1617	1997	2440	2926	3453	4018	4622
400	894	100	1921	2362	2896	3486	4127	4819	5564
400	894	120	2180	2715	3340	4033	4790	5612	6502
400	894	140	2451	3059	3775	4572	5447	6403	7441

NOTE: Detector time constant at a reference velocity of 5 ft/sec.
For SI Units: 1 ft = 0.305 m
1000 BTU/sec = 1055 kW

Table B-4.1(m)
Installed Spacing of Heat Detector: 12 feet
t_g: 300 Seconds to 1000 Btu/sec
α: 0.011 Btu/sec^3

τ	RTI	ΔT	CEILING HEIGHT IN FEET 4.0	8.0	12.0	16.0	20.0	24.0	28.0
			FIRE SIZE AT DETECTOR RESPONSE (BTU / SEC)						
25	56	40	115	160	218	290	375	479	599
25	56	60	159	228	322	442	588	761	964
25	56	80	203	302	437	611	825	1082	1380
25	56	100	247	380	562	797	1087	1435	1840
25	56	120	294	463	697	998	1370	1818	2339
25	56	140	341	551	840	1212	1673	2228	2875
50	112	40	164	219	283	363	456	564	688
50	112	60	224	305	408	534	682	861	1069
50	112	80	282	392	536	716	932	1192	1496
50	112	100	339	482	672	911	1206	1554	1967
50	112	120	396	575	815	1121	1498	1946	2476
50	112	140	458	672	966	1343	1809	2369	3022
75	168	40	205	270	342	429	530	645	775
75	168	60	280	372	482	617	776	961	1174
75	168	80	349	473	629	814	1040	1305	1615
75	168	100	418	576	777	1025	1322	1679	2096
75	168	120	487	680	931	1245	1628	2080	2616
75	168	140	558	787	1092	1476	1948	2508	3170
100	224	40	243	312	395	491	600	722	859
100	224	60	330	433	552	697	865	1058	1278
100	224	80	411	548	711	910	1145	1418	1734
100	224	100	490	662	877	1132	1440	1804	2227
100	224	120	573	778	1042	1367	1753	2216	2757
100	224	140	649	895	1213	1608	2083	2653	3321
125	280	40	281	354	445	548	665	795	939
125	280	60	376	485	618	773	950	1151	1379
125	280	80	468	617	791	1001	1246	1528	1852
125	280	100	562	744	966	1237	1556	1928	2359
125	280	120	648	871	1149	1480	1880	2352	2899
125	280	140	734	998	1331	1732	2220	2798	3473
150	335	40	313	393	491	602	727	864	1015
150	335	60	419	537	680	845	1031	1241	1477
150	335	80	521	683	867	1089	1344	1636	1967
150	335	100	624	821	1055	1338	1668	2050	2489
150	335	120	720	958	1245	1594	2005	2486	3042
150	335	140	814	1095	1444	1857	2356	2943	3626
175	391	40	344	430	536	654	786	930	1089
175	391	60	461	587	739	913	1109	1328	1573
175	391	80	579	739	940	1172	1438	1740	2081
175	391	100	684	895	1140	1435	1777	2170	2617
175	391	120	788	1042	1342	1704	2127	2618	3183
175	391	140	895	1189	1546	1979	2490	3087	3778
200	447	40	373	466	578	704	842	994	1160
200	447	60	500	635	796	979	1184	1413	1666
200	447	80	626	798	1010	1253	1530	1842	2192
200	447	100	741	958	1222	1530	1883	2287	2744
200	447	120	861	1115	1435	1811	2247	2749	3323
200	447	140	964	1279	1649	2097	2621	3230	3930
225	503	40	401	500	619	751	897	1056	1229
225	503	60	538	682	851	1043	1257	1494	1756
225	503	80	672	855	1077	1332	1619	1941	2301
225	503	100	796	1025	1301	1621	1987	2401	2869
225	503	120	919	1201	1525	1914	2363	2877	3462
225	503	140	1034	1366	1750	2212	2750	3370	4081
250	559	40	428	534	659	798	950	1116	1295
250	559	60	575	726	904	1105	1328	1574	1844
250	559	80	717	911	1143	1408	1705	2037	2407
250	559	100	849	1090	1378	1710	2087	2513	2991
250	559	120	977	1266	1613	2015	2477	3003	3598
250	559	140	1106	1451	1848	2324	2875	3508	4230
275	615	40	455	566	697	843	1002	1174	1360
275	615	60	617	770	956	1165	1397	1651	1930
275	615	80	761	964	1207	1482	1789	2132	2511
275	615	100	905	1153	1453	1797	2186	2623	3111
275	615	120	1035	1339	1699	2114	2588	3126	3733
275	615	140	1174	1522	1944	2434	2999	3644	4377
300	671	40	481	598	735	886	1052	1231	1423
300	671	60	651	812	1006	1224	1464	1726	2013
300	671	80	804	1017	1269	1554	1872	2224	2613
300	671	100	952	1215	1526	1882	2282	2730	3229
300	671	120	1097	1409	1782	2211	2698	3248	3865
300	671	140	1240	1601	2037	2542	3120	3778	4523
325	727	40	506	628	771	929	1101	1286	1485
325	727	60	685	854	1056	1281	1529	1800	2096
325	727	80	846	1068	1329	1624	1952	2315	2713
325	727	100	999	1275	1598	1965	2376	2836	3346
325	727	120	1155	1478	1864	2305	2805	3367	3996
325	727	140	1305	1679	2128	2647	3239	3910	4667
350	783	40	531	658	807	971	1148	1340	1546
350	783	60	717	894	1104	1337	1593	1873	2176
350	783	80	892	1118	1389	1693	2031	2403	2812
350	783	100	1047	1334	1668	2046	2469	2939	3460
350	783	120	1211	1546	1943	2398	2910	3484	4125
350	783	140	1368	1754	2218	2751	3356	4040	4809
375	839	40	555	688	842	1011	1195	1393	1605
375	839	60	749	934	1151	1392	1656	1944	2255
375	839	80	929	1167	1447	1761	2109	2490	2908
375	839	100	1099	1392	1736	2125	2560	3041	3573
375	839	120	1267	1612	2022	2488	3013	3600	4252
375	839	140	1431	1828	2305	2852	3472	4169	4950
400	894	40	579	717	876	1052	1241	1445	1663
400	894	60	781	972	1197	1446	1718	2013	2333
400	894	80	966	1215	1504	1827	2185	2576	3003
400	894	100	1146	1448	1803	2204	2649	3141	3684
400	894	120	1321	1677	2099	2578	3115	3714	4378
400	894	140	1493	1901	2391	2952	3585	4295	5089

NOTE: Detector time constant at a reference velocity of 5 ft/sec.
For SI Units: 1 ft = 0.305 m
1000 BTU/sec = 1055 kW

Table B-4.1(n)
Installed Spacing of Heat Detector: 12 feet
t_g: 500 Seconds to 1000 Btu/sec
α: 0.004 Btu/sec^3

τ	RTI	ΔT	CEILING HEIGHT IN FEET 4.0	8.0	12.0	16.0	20.0	24.0	28.0
			FIRE SIZE AT DETECTOR RESPONSE (BTU / SEC)						
25	56	40	82	120	170	235	314	408	519
25	56	60	117	180	266	376	512	676	866
25	56	80	154	246	373	536	738	982	1265
25	56	100	192	318	491	713	989	1321	1710
25	56	120	233	395	618	906	1262	1692	2195
25	56	140	275	478	755	1113	1556	2090	2717
50	112	40	115	158	213	280	361	457	570
50	112	60	160	227	317	430	568	732	926
50	112	80	205	301	431	596	801	1046	1332
50	112	100	251	379	554	779	1057	1392	1783
50	112	120	298	462	687	976	1336	1768	2274
50	112	140	347	549	828	1188	1634	2173	2803
75	168	40	143	191	252	322	407	506	621
75	168	60	198	271	366	483	623	790	987
75	168	80	251	353	488	657	864	1110	1400
75	168	100	304	439	618	846	1127	1462	1858
75	168	120	358	528	756	1048	1411	1846	2355
75	168	140	413	620	902	1265	1714	2256	2889
100	224	40	168	222	286	362	451	555	673
100	224	60	232	312	413	533	678	849	1048
100	224	80	292	402	543	717	926	1176	1469
100	224	100	353	495	680	913	1197	1535	1933
100	224	120	414	591	825	1121	1487	1922	2437
100	224	140	477	690	976	1342	1795	2336	2976
125	280	40	191	251	319	400	494	601	723
125	280	60	263	350	455	582	732	907	1109
125	280	80	331	449	596	774	989	1243	1539
125	280	100	398	549	741	979	1265	1608	2010
125	280	120	466	651	892	1194	1563	2001	2519
125	280	140	535	756	1050	1421	1877	2421	3064
150	335	40	213	275	350	436	535	646	772
150	335	60	293	386	496	629	784	964	1170
150	335	80	368	493	647	830	1051	1309	1609
150	335	100	441	600	800	1042	1335	1682	2087
150	335	120	518	709	958	1266	1637	2081	2602
150	335	140	589	820	1122	1498	1959	2506	3153
175	391	40	237	301	380	471	574	690	819
175	391	60	321	420	536	675	835	1020	1230
175	391	80	402	535	693	885	1111	1374	1678
175	391	100	482	650	857	1105	1403	1755	2164
175	391	120	564	765	1022	1337	1712	2161	2686
175	391	140	641	883	1192	1576	2038	2592	3242
200	447	40	257	325	409	504	612	732	866
200	447	60	348	450	574	719	885	1074	1289
200	447	80	436	575	740	939	1171	1439	1747
200	447	100	522	697	913	1167	1471	1828	2241
200	447	120	609	819	1085	1403	1787	2241	2770
200	447	140	691	943	1261	1652	2119	2678	3332
225	503	40	276	348	436	536	648	773	911
225	503	60	374	481	611	762	933	1128	1348
225	503	80	468	615	786	991	1229	1503	1816
225	503	100	563	743	962	1227	1538	1900	2318
225	503	120	652	872	1146	1471	1861	2320	2854
225	503	140	740	1001	1328	1723	2200	2764	3422
250	559	40	295	371	463	567	684	813	955
250	559	60	399	512	647	803	980	1180	1405
250	559	80	499	653	830	1042	1286	1565	1884
250	559	100	599	788	1014	1286	1604	1972	2394
275	615	40	313	393	489	598	719	852	998
275	615	60	424	541	682	844	1026	1231	1461
275	615	80	530	685	873	1091	1342	1627	1951
275	615	100	635	832	1064	1344	1668	2042	2470
275	615	120	734	972	1258	1601	2007	2478	3021
275	615	140	833	1113	1459	1868	2359	2934	3602
300	671	40	330	414	515	627	752	890	1041
300	671	60	447	570	716	883	1071	1282	1516
300	671	80	563	721	915	1140	1396	1688	2017
300	671	100	669	874	1114	1400	1732	2112	2546
300	671	120	774	1021	1314	1666	2078	2555	3104
300	671	140	881	1168	1517	1939	2437	3019	3692
325	727	40	348	435	539	656	785	927	1082
325	727	60	471	598	750	922	1115	1331	1570
325	727	80	592	755	956	1187	1450	1747	2082
325	727	100	703	910	1162	1456	1794	2181	2620
325	727	120	813	1068	1369	1729	2148	2632	3187
325	727	140	922	1221	1578	2009	2514	3103	3782
350	783	40	364	455	564	685	818	964	1122
350	783	60	493	626	782	960	1158	1379	1624
350	783	80	619	789	996	1234	1503	1806	2146
350	783	100	736	950	1209	1510	1855	2249	2694
350	783	120	851	1115	1423	1791	2218	2708	3269
350	783	140	963	1272	1638	2077	2591	3186	3871
375	839	40	381	475	587	712	849	999	1162
375	839	60	516	653	814	997	1201	1427	1676
375	839	80	646	823	1036	1280	1555	1864	2210
375	839	100	768	989	1256	1564	1916	2316	2767
375	839	120	891	1154	1476	1852	2286	2784	3350
375	839	140	1005	1323	1697	2145	2667	3269	3960
400	894	40	397	495	611	739	881	1034	1201
400	894	60	538	679	846	1034	1243	1474	1728
400	894	80	673	856	1075	1325	1606	1921	2273
400	894	100	800	1028	1301	1617	1976	2382	2840
400	894	120	926	1198	1528	1912	2354	2858	3431
400	894	140	1047	1373	1756	2212	2741	3351	4048

NOTE: Detector time constant at a reference velocity of 5 ft/sec.
For SI Units: 1 ft = 0.305 m
1000 BTU/sec = 1055 kW

Table B-4.1(o)
Installed Spacing of Heat Detector: 12 feet
t_g: 600 Seconds to 1000 Btu/sec
α: 0.003 Btu/sec³

τ	RTI	ΔT	CEILING HEIGHT IN FEET 4.0	8.0	12.0	16.0	20.0	24.0	28.0
			FIRE SIZE AT DETECTOR RESPONSE (BTU / SEC)						
25	56	40	74	110	159	221	299	391	498
25	56	60	106	167	251	359	493	654	841
25	56	80	141	232	356	517	716	955	1235
25	56	100	178	302	472	692	964	1291	1675
25	56	120	217	378	598	882	1234	1658	2156
25	56	140	258	459	734	1087	1525	2054	2675
50	112	40	102	142	194	259	337	430	540
50	112	60	143	207	293	403	538	699	889
50	112	80	185	278	404	566	767	1008	1290
50	112	100	228	353	524	745	1020	1350	1736
50	112	120	273	433	654	940	1294	1721	2222
50	112	140	319	518	793	1149	1590	2121	2745
75	168	40	126	171	227	294	375	471	582
75	168	60	176	245	335	447	585	747	939
75	168	80	224	322	451	616	819	1061	1346
75	168	100	274	403	577	800	1077	1409	1797
75	168	120	324	488	711	999	1356	1786	2288
75	168	140	375	577	854	1212	1655	2190	2816
100	224	40	148	197	258	328	413	511	625
100	224	60	205	280	374	491	630	796	990
100	224	80	261	364	498	666	872	1115	1403
100	224	100	316	451	630	856	1134	1467	1859
100	224	120	372	542	769	1059	1418	1848	2355
100	224	140	429	636	916	1276	1722	2259	2888
125	280	40	168	222	285	361	449	550	667
125	280	60	233	312	412	531	675	844	1040
125	280	80	294	404	543	716	922	1170	1460
125	280	100	355	497	681	911	1193	1527	1922
125	280	120	417	593	825	1119	1481	1913	2423
125	280	140	481	692	977	1340	1789	2326	2961
150	335	40	187	246	312	392	484	589	708
150	335	60	259	344	447	572	719	892	1091
150	335	80	326	442	587	762	974	1225	1517
150	335	100	393	541	731	966	1249	1588	1985
150	335	120	460	643	881	1180	1545	1979	2491
150	335	140	528	747	1038	1405	1857	2396	3033
175	391	40	206	266	338	422	517	626	749
175	391	60	283	373	481	611	73	939	1141
175	391	80	356	478	629	809	1026	1280	1575
175	391	100	429	584	780	1020	1306	1649	2049
175	391	120	503	691	936	1239	1605	2045	2560
175	391	140	573	801	1097	1469	1925	2467	3107
200	447	40	225	287	363	451	550	662	788
200	447	60	307	402	514	649	805	985	1191
200	447	80	385	513	668	855	1076	1334	1633
200	447	100	463	625	827	1070	1364	1710	2113
200	447	120	542	738	989	1298	1668	2111	2629
200	447	140	617	853	1156	1534	1990	2538	3181

τ	RTI	ΔT	CEILING HEIGHT IN FEET 4.0	8.0	12.0	16.0	20.0	24.0	28.0
			FIRE SIZE AT DETECTOR RESPONSE (BTU / SEC)						
225	503	40	242	307	387	478	582	698	827
225	503	60	329	427	547	686	847	1031	1240
225	503	80	414	547	707	900	1126	1388	1690
225	503	100	496	665	874	1122	1420	1770	2177
225	503	120	580	783	1041	1353	1731	2177	2699
225	503	140	659	903	1214	1597	2057	2609	3255
250	559	40	259	327	410	506	613	732	865
250	559	60	351	454	578	722	887	1076	1289
250	559	80	441	581	746	944	1174	1441	1747
250	559	100	532	704	916	1173	1476	1830	2241
250	559	120	616	828	1093	1410	1792	2243	2769
250	559	140	700	952	1270	1660	2125	2680	3330
275	615	40	274	346	433	532	643	766	902
275	615	60	373	479	608	757	927	1120	1337
275	615	80	467	613	783	986	1222	1494	1804
275	615	100	562	742	960	1222	1531	1890	2304
275	615	120	651	871	1143	1466	1854	2309	2838
275	615	140	740	1000	1326	1718	2191	2751	3404
300	671	40	290	365	455	558	672	798	938
300	671	60	393	504	638	791	966	1163	1384
300	671	80	493	644	819	1028	1269	1545	1860
300	671	100	592	779	1002	1271	1585	1949	2368
300	671	120	686	913	1188	1521	1914	2375	2908
300	671	140	779	1047	1380	1779	2258	2822	3479
325	727	40	305	383	477	583	701	831	974
325	727	60	414	529	667	825	1004	1205	1431
325	727	80	518	671	855	1069	1316	1597	1915
325	727	100	622	815	1044	1319	1639	2008	2430
325	727	120	720	954	1235	1575	1974	2440	2977
325	727	140	817	1093	1434	1838	2323	2893	3554
350	783	40	319	401	498	607	729	862	1009
350	783	60	434	553	695	858	1041	1247	1476
350	783	80	543	700	890	1110	1361	1647	1970
350	783	100	650	850	1085	1366	1692	2066	2493
350	783	120	753	994	1282	1628	2034	2504	3046
350	783	140	854	1138	1482	1897	2389	2963	3629
375	839	40	334	418	519	631	756	893	1043
375	839	60	453	576	723	890	1078	1288	1522
375	839	80	571	729	924	1150	1406	1697	2024
375	839	100	679	880	1126	1413	1744	2123	2555
375	839	120	785	1034	1328	1681	2092	2568	3115
375	839	140	894	1183	1533	1956	2453	3033	3703
400	894	40	348	435	539	655	783	924	1077
400	894	60	472	599	750	922	1114	1329	1566
400	894	80	594	758	958	1189	1450	1746	2078
400	894	100	706	914	1165	1458	1795	2180	2617
400	894	120	817	1073	1373	1733	2150	2632	3183
400	894	140	928	1226	1584	2013	2517	3103	3777

NOTE: Detector time constant at a reference velocity of 5 ft/sec.
For SI Units: 1 ft = 0.305 m
1000 BTU/sec = 1055 kW

Table B-4.1(p)
Installed Spacing of Heat Detector: 15 ft.
t_g: 50 Seconds to 1000 Btu/sec
α: 0.400 Btu/sec^3

τ	RTI	ΔT	CEILING HEIGHT IN FEET 4.0	8.0	12.0	16.0	20.0	24.0	28.0
			FIRE SIZE AT DETECTOR RESPONSE (BTU / SEC)						
25	56	40	618	745	903	1085	1287	1509	1753
25	56	60	790	962	1181	1434	1720	2040	2395
25	56	80	935	1169	1452	1781	2157	2583	3061
25	56	100	1046	1393	1722	2131	2605	3146	3759
25	56	120	1215	1600	1992	2488	3066	3731	4490
25	56	140	1357	1799	2266	2852	3541	4340	5255
50	112	40	894	1063	1269	1503	1758	2034	2331
50	112	60	1098	1370	1656	1976	2327	2711	3128
50	112	80	1321	1664	2025	2431	2883	3380	3925
50	112	100	1541	1949	2385	2880	3435	4052	4735
50	112	120	1758	2226	2739	3327	3991	4734	5563
50	112	140	1974	2499	3091	3775	4552	5429	6412
75	168	40	1035	1356	1577	1852	2153	2476	2819
75	168	60	1370	1712	2055	2432	2843	3286	3763
75	168	80	1668	2083	2511	2986	3507	4074	4687
75	168	100	1960	2439	2951	3525	4159	4853	5611
75	168	120	2248	2783	3380	4055	4806	5634	6543
75	168	140	2533	3119	3804	4582	5453	6420	7487
100	224	40	1245	1547	1843	2162	2505	2870	3256
100	224	60	1625	2019	2412	2841	3305	3803	4334
100	224	80	1994	2460	2947	3484	4069	4701	5379
100	224	100	2356	2880	3459	4105	4813	5582	6413
100	224	120	2714	3285	3958	4714	5547	6457	7446
100	224	140	3071	3680	4447	5315	6276	7332	8485
125	280	40	1417	1760	2091	2447	2827	3231	3657
125	280	60	1870	2304	2741	3218	3731	4280	4862
125	280	80	2309	2809	3348	3944	4589	5281	6021
125	280	100	2741	3289	3930	4643	5420	6259	7160
125	280	120	3172	3752	4493	5325	6236	7224	8291
125	280	140	3485	4195	5044	5996	7043	8184	9422
150	335	40	1584	1960	2323	2713	3129	3569	4032
150	335	60	2107	2571	3049	3570	4130	4726	5357
150	335	80	2616	3137	3726	4375	5076	5827	6625
150	335	100	3121	3674	4371	5148	5990	6896	7865
150	335	120	3501	4183	4995	5900	6884	7947	9090
150	335	140	3927	4681	5605	6637	7766	8989	10309
175	391	40	1746	2151	2543	2965	3414	3889	4387
175	391	60	2339	2825	3341	3905	4509	5150	5827
175	391	80	2920	3449	4083	4784	5539	6345	7199
175	391	100	3390	4034	4790	5627	6532	7502	8535
175	391	120	3879	4598	5473	6446	7501	8636	9851
175	391	140	4356	5145	6138	7247	8454	9757	11157
200	447	40	1906	2333	2753	3205	3687	4194	4726
200	447	60	2569	3068	3620	4224	4870	5554	6276
200	447	80	3224	3749	4426	5176	5982	6840	7748
200	447	100	3707	4382	5192	6086	7051	8082	9177
200	447	120	4247	4995	5930	6969	8092	9296	10581
200	447	140	4670	5583	6649	7831	9113	10493	11970

τ	RTI	ΔT	CEILING HEIGHT IN FEET 4.0	8.0	12.0	16.0	20.0	24.0	28.0
			FIRE SIZE AT DETECTOR RESPONSE (BTU / SEC)						
225	503	40	2062	2508	2955	3436	3948	4487	5051
225	503	60	2796	3303	3889	4531	5218	5943	6707
225	503	80	3407	4029	4755	5553	6408	7317	8276
225	503	100	4017	4717	5578	6528	7551	8640	9796
225	503	120	4609	5378	6371	7472	8661	9932	11285
225	503	140	5045	6009	7141	8393	9749	11203	12755
250	559	40	2217	2678	3150	3659	4200	4769	5364
250	559	60	3023	3530	4148	4828	5553	6319	7123
250	559	80	3660	4305	5073	5917	6820	7777	8787
250	559	100	4321	5042	5951	6955	8033	9180	10394
250	559	120	4835	5740	6796	7959	9211	10547	11966
250	559	140	5409	6421	7617	8938	10363	11889	13515
275	615	40	2370	2843	3339	3875	4445	5043	5668
275	615	60	3251	3751	4440	5115	5878	6683	7527
275	615	80	3909	4573	5381	6269	7219	8224	9282
275	615	100	4622	5357	6313	7369	8502	9704	10974
275	615	120	5151	6098	7209	8432	9745	11144	12627
275	615	140	5765	6821	8079	9466	10960	12556	14254
300	671	40	2522	3003	3522	4085	4682	5309	5963
300	671	60	3362	3956	4644	5395	6194	7037	7919
300	671	80	4153	4834	5682	6613	7607	8658	9763
300	671	100	4785	5655	6666	7772	8957	10214	11539
300	671	120	5461	6446	7612	8891	10265	11725	13271
300	671	140	6114	7211	8529	9980	11541	13206	14973
325	727	40	2673	3160	3701	4289	4913	5567	6250
325	727	60	3552	4163	4882	5667	6502	7381	8302
325	727	80	4396	5089	5974	6947	7985	9081	10232
325	727	100	5049	5655	6666	7772	8957	10214	11539
325	727	120	5764	6787	8004	9340	10772	12292	13898
325	727	140	6456	7591	8968	10482	12108	13839	15674
350	783	40	2824	3313	3876	4489	5139	5820	6530
350	783	60	3739	4366	5115	5933	6803	7718	8675
350	783	80	4522	5330	6260	7274	8355	9495	10691
350	783	100	5308	6244	7345	8550	9836	11196	12628
350	783	120	6062	7119	8387	9778	11267	12846	14512
350	783	140	6793	7963	9397	10972	12662	14459	16360
375	839	40	2975	3463	4047	4684	5359	6067	6804
375	839	60	3925	4564	5342	6193	7097	8047	9040
375	839	80	4736	5573	6540	7594	8717	9899	11139
375	839	100	5563	6530	7674	8926	10261	11671	13154
375	839	120	6356	7445	8763	10207	11752	13388	15113
375	839	140	7126	8328	9817	11452	13204	15065	17032
400	894	40	3126	3611	4214	4875	5575	6309	7072
400	894	60	4108	4759	5566	6449	7386	8370	9398
400	894	80	4948	5811	6814	7908	9071	10296	11579
400	894	100	5814	6809	7997	9294	10677	12137	13670
400	894	120	6647	7764	9131	10628	12227	13920	15702
400	894	140	7455	8685	10229	11923	13736	15660	17690

NOTE: Detector time constant at a reference velocity of 5 ft/sec.
For SI Units: 1 ft = 0.305 m
1000 BTU/sec = 1055 kW

Table B-4.1(q)
Installed Spacing of Heat Detector: 15 feet
t_g: 150 Seconds to 1000 Btu/sec
α: 0.044 Btu/sec³

τ	RTI	ΔT	CEILING HEIGHT IN FEET 4.0	8.0	12.0	16.0	20.0	24.0	28.0
			FIRE SIZE AT DETECTOR RESPONSE (BTU / SEC)						
25	56	40	259	322	407	509	627	762	917
25	56	60	341	447	572	731	918	1137	1390
25	56	80	423	567	749	968	1237	1552	1916
25	56	100	511	691	930	1228	1581	2003	2492
25	56	120	592	819	1120	1498	1950	2488	3112
25	56	140	674	951	1321	1785	2348	3004	3774
50	112	40	371	451	555	675	810	961	1129
50	112	60	488	610	763	942	1147	1381	1645
50	112	80	610	767	972	1216	1500	1829	2204
50	112	100	718	923	1186	1501	1873	2307	2806
50	112	120	826	1089	1404	1798	2266	2815	3449
50	112	140	936	1247	1637	2107	2679	3352	4132
75	168	40	463	560	681	818	970	1138	1322
75	168	60	622	755	929	1129	1354	1607	1889
75	168	80	758	943	1173	1441	1747	2095	2487
75	168	100	900	1129	1419	1759	2154	2606	3121
75	168	120	1021	1314	1667	2086	2575	3142	3791
75	168	140	1161	1499	1918	2421	3014	3703	4497
100	224	40	546	658	794	947	1116	1300	1500
100	224	60	729	886	1079	1300	1545	1818	2118
100	224	80	900	1103	1357	1648	1978	2347	2759
100	224	100	1044	1316	1633	2000	2419	2894	3428
100	224	120	1212	1527	1909	2356	2872	3461	4129
100	224	140	1368	1736	2187	2719	3337	4049	4861
125	280	40	635	750	899	1067	1251	1450	1666
125	280	60	829	1006	1219	1458	1724	2016	2335
125	280	80	1011	1251	1528	1842	2195	2586	3019
125	280	100	1203	1490	1832	2226	2670	3169	3726
125	280	120	1384	1725	2136	2612	3154	3768	4458
125	280	140	1563	1957	2440	3002	3649	4385	5219
150	335	40	703	834	998	1180	1378	1592	1822
150	335	60	927	1120	1350	1608	1893	2203	2541
150	335	80	1138	1391	1689	2026	2400	2814	3268
150	335	100	1345	1654	2021	2440	2910	3433	4012
150	335	120	1549	1912	2351	2855	3425	4064	4779
150	335	140	1750	2166	2679	3272	3948	4712	5570
175	391	40	768	915	1091	1287	1499	1727	1972
175	391	60	1008	1228	1475	1751	2053	2382	2738
175	391	80	1252	1524	1842	2201	2597	3032	3507
175	391	100	1482	1810	2201	2645	3139	3687	4289
175	391	120	1708	2090	2556	3088	3685	4351	5090
175	391	140	1931	2366	2908	3532	4237	5028	5912
200	447	40	832	992	1181	1389	1615	1857	2115
200	447	60	1103	1331	1594	1888	2208	2554	2928
200	447	80	1363	1651	1990	2369	2786	3242	3738
200	447	100	1615	1960	2374	2842	3360	3932	4558
200	447	120	1863	2261	2753	3312	3936	4628	5392
200	447	140	2081	2557	3129	3782	4516	5335	6246
225	503	40	902	1067	1267	1488	1726	1981	2253
225	503	60	1189	1431	1710	2019	2356	2720	3111
225	503	80	1471	1774	2131	2531	2968	3445	3962
225	503	100	1745	2105	2541	3032	3574	4169	4818
225	503	120	2015	2426	2944	3529	4179	4897	5687
225	503	140	2242	2742	3342	4023	4786	5634	6571
250	559	40	953	1138	1350	1583	1834	2101	2386
250	559	60	1273	1527	1821	2147	2500	2881	3288
250	559	80	1576	1893	2269	2687	3145	3642	4179
250	559	100	1873	2244	2703	3216	3782	4399	5072
250	559	120	2131	2586	3128	3739	4415	5159	5974
250	559	140	2398	2920	3548	4258	5050	5925	6890
275	615	40	1006	1208	1431	1675	1938	2218	2515
275	615	60	1354	1621	1929	2270	2640	3037	3461
275	615	80	1680	2008	2402	2840	3317	3834	4390
275	615	100	1999	2380	2859	3395	3983	4624	5319
275	615	120	2266	2741	3307	3943	4645	5414	6254
275	615	140	2550	3094	3748	4487	5306	6209	7201
300	671	40	1071	1276	1509	1765	2040	2332	2641
300	671	60	1434	1712	2034	2391	2776	3188	3629
300	671	80	1782	2121	2532	2988	3484	4020	4597
300	671	100	2089	2512	3012	3570	4180	4843	5560
300	671	120	2398	2892	3482	4142	4869	5664	6528
300	671	140	2699	3264	3944	4709	5556	6487	7506
325	727	40	1128	1342	1586	1853	2139	2443	2764
325	727	60	1513	1801	2137	2508	2908	3337	3793
325	727	80	1883	2230	2658	3133	3648	4203	4798
325	727	100	2202	2641	3161	3740	4372	5057	5796
325	727	120	2528	3040	3652	4337	5088	5907	6797
325	727	140	2846	3429	4135	4927	5801	6759	7804
350	783	40	1184	1407	1661	1938	2235	2551	2884
350	783	60	1591	1888	2238	2623	3038	3482	3953
350	783	80	1983	2338	2782	3274	3808	4381	4995
350	783	100	2312	2767	3307	3906	4560	5266	6027
350	783	120	2655	3184	3819	4527	5303	6146	7060
350	783	140	2989	3591	4322	5140	6041	7026	8098
375	839	40	1239	1470	1734	2022	2330	2657	3001
375	839	60	1667	1973	2336	2735	3165	3623	4111
375	839	80	2049	2442	2903	3413	3964	4556	5188
375	839	100	2421	2891	3450	4070	4744	5472	6254
375	839	120	2780	3325	3982	4713	5513	6380	7318
375	839	140	3131	3749	4505	5349	6276	7287	8385
400	894	40	1293	1532	1806	2104	2423	2761	3116
400	894	60	1743	2056	2432	2845	3289	3763	4265
400	894	80	2139	2545	3022	3549	4118	4727	5378
400	894	100	2528	3012	3590	4230	4925	5673	6477
400	894	120	2904	3464	4143	4896	5719	6610	7572
400	894	140	3271	3905	4684	5554	6507	7544	8669

NOTE: Detector time constant at a reference velocity of 5 ft/sec.
For SI Units: 1 ft = 0.305 m
1000 BTU/sec = 1055 kW

Table B-4.1(r)
Installed Spacing of Heat Detector: 15 feet
t_g: 300 Seconds to 1000 Btu/sec
α: 0.011 Btu/sec^3

τ	RTI	ΔT	CEILING HEIGHT IN FEET						
			4.0	8.0	12.0	16.0	20.0	24.0	28.0
			FIRE SIZE AT DETECTOR RESPONSE (BTU / SEC)						
25	56	40	156	207	273	353	451	565	697
25	56	60	215	297	407	543	706	900	1125
25	56	80	275	394	553	754	997	1280	1612
25	56	100	337	498	713	984	1314	1700	2151
25	56	120	403	608	885	1234	1657	2155	2736
25	56	140	469	725	1069	1501	2026	2648	3365
50	112	40	221	279	353	442	545	664	801
50	112	60	300	394	508	650	819	1017	1246
50	112	80	378	508	674	876	1121	1411	1747
50	112	100	456	626	847	1121	1450	1843	2298
50	112	120	538	749	1029	1381	1808	2309	2895
50	112	140	617	877	1222	1657	2186	2808	3535
75	168	40	276	342	426	523	634	760	902
75	168	60	373	475	602	753	930	1134	1368
75	168	80	467	611	784	996	1249	1544	1885
75	168	100	564	745	976	1254	1591	1988	2449
75	168	120	656	882	1172	1526	1957	2466	3057
75	168	140	748	1022	1376	1816	2345	2975	3707
100	224	40	326	399	491	597	716	850	999
100	224	60	439	551	688	850	1036	1248	1489
100	224	80	554	700	888	1112	1373	1676	2023
100	224	100	658	850	1093	1385	1731	2135	2601
100	224	120	763	1006	1303	1671	2109	2624	3221
100	224	140	874	1160	1525	1969	2508	3144	3882
125	280	40	371	452	552	666	794	935	1092
125	280	60	500	621	769	941	1137	1358	1606
125	280	80	627	787	987	1222	1493	1805	2159
125	280	100	746	951	1207	1512	1868	2280	2753
125	280	120	870	1117	1432	1812	2260	2783	3386
125	280	140	980	1289	1663	2123	2671	3314	4059
150	335	40	414	502	610	732	867	1017	1181
150	335	60	557	688	846	1028	1233	1464	1721
150	335	80	697	869	1081	1327	1610	1931	2294
150	335	100	829	1047	1317	1633	2001	2423	2904
150	335	120	958	1226	1556	1949	2408	2941	3552
150	335	140	1088	1405	1800	2273	2832	3484	4236
175	391	40	454	549	665	794	938	1095	1267
175	391	60	617	752	919	1111	1326	1566	1832
175	391	80	764	947	1170	1428	1722	2054	2426
175	391	100	911	1139	1422	1751	2130	2563	3054
175	391	120	1047	1331	1675	2081	2553	3096	3716
175	391	140	1191	1522	1932	2420	2991	3653	4413
200	447	40	493	595	717	854	1005	1170	1349
200	447	60	668	812	990	1191	1415	1665	1940
200	447	80	828	1022	1257	1526	1831	2173	2555
200	447	100	982	1228	1523	1865	2256	2700	3201
200	447	120	1137	1431	1790	2210	2695	3249	3879
200	447	140	1289	1635	2060	2562	3146	3820	4589

τ	RTI	ΔT	CEILING HEIGHT IN FEET						
			4.0	8.0	12.0	16.0	20.0	24.0	28.0
			FIRE SIZE AT DETECTOR RESPONSE (BTU / SEC)						
225	503	40	530	639	768	912	1070	1242	1429
225	503	60	718	871	1057	1268	1502	1760	2044
225	503	80	894	1095	1340	1621	1937	2289	2681
225	503	100	1058	1313	1621	1976	2379	2835	3346
225	503	120	1222	1529	1902	2335	2833	3399	4040
225	503	140	1385	1744	2184	2701	3299	3984	4764
250	559	40	567	681	817	968	1133	1313	1506
250	559	60	766	928	1123	1343	1586	1854	2147
250	559	80	950	1165	1421	1713	2039	2403	2805
250	559	100	1129	1396	1716	2083	2499	2966	3488
250	559	120	1305	1623	2010	2458	2968	3547	4198
250	559	140	1478	1849	2305	2837	3449	4147	4938
275	615	40	609	722	864	1022	1194	1381	1582
275	615	60	813	983	1187	1416	1668	1945	2247
275	615	80	1006	1233	1500	1802	2140	2514	2926
275	615	100	1199	1476	1808	2188	2616	3095	3628
275	615	120	1385	1715	2116	2577	3101	3692	4355
275	615	140	1569	1952	2423	2970	3596	4306	5109
300	671	40	642	762	910	1075	1254	1448	1655
300	671	60	867	1037	1249	1486	1748	2033	2344
300	671	80	1066	1299	1576	1890	2238	2622	3045
300	671	100	1267	1554	1899	2291	2731	3221	3765
300	671	120	1464	1805	2219	2694	3231	3834	4509
300	671	140	1658	2053	2538	3100	3740	4464	5279
325	727	40	674	801	956	1127	1312	1513	1727
325	727	60	907	1090	1310	1556	1826	2120	2440
325	727	80	1122	1364	1651	1975	2334	2728	3161
325	727	100	1334	1631	1987	2391	2843	3345	3901
325	727	120	1541	1892	2319	2808	3358	3975	4661
325	727	140	1746	2151	2651	3227	3881	4619	5446
350	783	40	706	839	1000	1177	1369	1576	1798
350	783	60	947	1141	1369	1624	1902	2205	2534
350	783	80	1177	1428	1725	2058	2427	2833	3276
350	783	100	1399	1706	2073	2489	2953	3467	4034
350	783	120	1617	1978	2418	2920	3483	4113	4812
350	783	140	1819	2247	2761	3352	4021	4772	5612
375	839	40	738	877	1043	1226	1425	1638	1866
375	839	60	988	1191	1427	1690	1977	2289	2626
375	839	80	1231	1490	1796	2140	2520	2935	3388
375	839	100	1464	1779	2158	2586	3061	3587	4165
375	839	120	1693	2062	2515	3030	3606	4248	4960
375	839	140	1900	2341	2870	3475	4158	4923	5775
400	894	40	769	913	1085	1275	1480	1700	1934
400	894	60	1030	1241	1484	1755	2051	2371	2716
400	894	80	1284	1551	1867	2221	2610	3036	3499
400	894	100	1528	1851	2241	2680	3168	3705	4294
400	894	120	1767	2144	2610	3138	3727	4382	5106
400	894	140	1980	2433	2976	3596	4293	5071	5937

NOTE: Detector time constant at a reference velocity of 5 ft/sec.
For SI Units: 1 ft = 0.305 m
1000 BTU/sec = 1055 kW

Table B-4.1(s)
Installed Spacing of Heat Detector: 15 feet
t_g: 500 Seconds to 1000 Btu/sec
α: 0.004 Btu/sec³

τ	RTI	ΔT	CEILING HEIGHT IN FEET 4.0	8.0	12.0	16.0	20.0	24.0	28.0
			FIRE SIZE AT DETECTOR RESPONSE (BTU / SEC)						
25	56	40	112	156	215	289	379	484	606
25	56	60	160	235	337	464	619	801	1013
25	56	80	210	323	474	664	894	1164	1480
25	56	100	264	419	625	884	1198	1571	2001
25	56	120	321	523	789	1124	1530	2013	2570
25	56	140	381	633	965	1381	1887	2488	3183
50	112	40	155	204	267	342	433	541	665
50	112	60	216	295	399	528	683	868	1082
50	112	80	278	392	544	735	967	1239	1558
50	112	100	341	496	702	962	1279	1651	2087
50	112	120	408	606	872	1208	1617	2099	2663
50	112	140	474	722	1053	1471	1980	2580	3282
75	168	40	192	245	313	393	488	598	724
75	168	60	265	351	460	590	749	936	1152
75	168	80	337	458	614	808	1040	1316	1637
75	168	100	411	571	780	1042	1358	1735	2173
75	168	120	486	688	956	1294	1705	2190	2756
75	168	140	561	811	1143	1563	2074	2677	3382
100	224	40	226	283	356	442	541	654	784
100	224	60	309	400	514	652	814	1004	1223
100	224	80	392	521	682	878	1115	1393	1717
100	224	100	477	642	857	1123	1441	1820	2261
100	224	120	559	768	1041	1381	1792	2281	2851
100	224	140	642	898	1234	1656	2170	2775	3484
125	280	40	257	319	397	487	591	709	842
125	280	60	351	448	568	711	878	1072	1294
125	280	80	443	579	745	948	1189	1471	1798
125	280	100	537	710	931	1199	1524	1906	2350
125	280	120	627	844	1123	1469	1882	2374	2947
125	280	140	718	982	1324	1750	2262	2874	3586
150	335	40	286	353	436	531	640	762	899
150	335	60	390	492	619	768	941	1139	1365
150	335	80	491	632	807	1016	1262	1549	1879
150	335	100	593	776	1000	1277	1606	1992	2439
150	335	120	691	918	1204	1551	1972	2467	3043
150	335	140	790	1063	1412	1840	2359	2973	3689
175	391	40	313	385	472	573	686	813	954
175	391	60	427	535	668	823	1001	1204	1435
175	391	80	541	684	866	1082	1334	1626	1960
175	391	100	647	834	1070	1353	1687	2078	2529
175	391	120	753	989	1279	1636	2061	2561	3140
175	391	140	863	1142	1499	1931	2455	3074	3792
200	447	40	340	416	508	613	731	863	1008
200	447	60	463	577	715	876	1060	1269	1504
200	447	80	584	735	924	1147	1405	1701	2040
200	447	100	698	894	1137	1427	1768	2163	2618
200	447	120	812	1053	1355	1719	2150	2654	3238
200	447	140	926	1218	1579	2022	2552	3174	3896

τ	RTI	ΔT	CEILING HEIGHT IN FEET 4.0	8.0	12.0	16.0	20.0	24.0	28.0
			FIRE SIZE AT DETECTOR RESPONSE (BTU / SEC)						
225	503	40	365	445	542	652	775	911	1061
225	503	60	497	617	761	928	1117	1331	1571
225	503	80	626	784	980	1210	1474	1776	2119
225	503	100	748	951	1202	1500	1847	2248	2707
225	503	120	873	1119	1429	1800	2238	2748	3335
225	503	140	988	1292	1661	2112	2647	3275	4001
250	559	40	390	474	575	690	817	958	1112
250	559	60	530	655	806	978	1173	1393	1638
250	559	80	667	832	1035	1271	1542	1850	2198
250	559	100	796	1007	1266	1571	1925	2332	2796
250	559	120	925	1182	1501	1880	2325	2840	3432
250	559	140	1052	1359	1741	2200	2742	3375	4106
275	615	40	414	502	607	726	858	1004	1162
275	615	60	567	693	849	1027	1228	1453	1703
275	615	80	706	878	1088	1331	1608	1922	2276
275	615	100	843	1062	1328	1641	2001	2415	2885
275	615	120	978	1245	1572	1959	2411	2932	3529
275	615	140	1112	1428	1820	2287	2836	3475	4210
300	671	40	437	529	639	762	899	1048	1212
300	671	60	598	729	891	1075	1282	1512	1767
300	671	80	745	923	1140	1389	1673	1993	2353
300	671	100	893	1115	1389	1709	2077	2496	2972
300	671	120	1030	1305	1641	2036	2495	3023	3626
300	671	140	1172	1496	1897	2372	2929	3574	4315
325	727	40	460	555	669	797	938	1092	1260
325	727	60	628	765	932	1122	1334	1570	1830
325	727	80	783	968	1191	1447	1737	2063	2429
325	727	100	935	1167	1449	1776	2151	2577	3059
325	727	120	1083	1365	1709	2112	2579	3113	3722
325	727	140	1230	1563	1972	2456	3021	3673	4419
350	783	40	482	581	699	831	976	1135	1307
350	783	60	658	800	972	1168	1386	1627	1893
350	783	80	820	1011	1240	1503	1800	2132	2504
350	783	100	977	1218	1507	1842	2224	2657	3145
350	783	120	1134	1423	1776	2187	2661	3203	3818
350	783	140	1287	1628	2046	2539	3112	3770	4523
375	839	40	504	607	729	865	1014	1177	1353
375	839	60	687	834	1012	1213	1436	1683	1954
375	839	80	863	1053	1289	1558	1862	2201	2578
375	839	100	1020	1268	1565	1907	2296	2736	3230
375	839	120	1183	1480	1841	2261	2742	3291	3912
375	839	140	1343	1692	2119	2621	3201	3867	4626
400	894	40	525	632	758	898	1051	1218	1399
400	894	60	715	868	1051	1257	1486	1738	2014
400	894	80	895	1095	1337	1613	1922	2268	2651
400	894	100	1064	1317	1621	1971	2367	2814	3314
400	894	120	1232	1536	1905	2333	2823	3379	4006
400	894	140	1398	1754	2191	2702	3290	3964	4729

NOTE: Detector time constant at a reference velocity of 5 ft/sec.
For SI Units: 1 ft = 0.305 m
1000 BTU/sec = 1055 kW

Table B-4.1(t)
Installed Spacing of Heat Detector: 15 feet
t_g: 600 Seconds to 1000 Btu/sec
α: 0.003 Btu/sec³

τ	RTI	ΔT	CEILING HEIGHT IN FEET 4.0	8.0	12.0	16.0	20.0	24.0	28.0
			FIRE SIZE AT DETECTOR RESPONSE (BTU / SEC)						
25	56	40	100	143	201	273	360	462	582
25	56	60	145	220	319	444	596	775	983
25	56	80	193	305	454	640	867	1135	1445
25	56	100	245	399	603	858	1168	1536	1961
25	56	120	300	501	765	1095	1496	1973	2525
25	56	140	358	610	938	1350	1850	2445	3134
50	112	40	137	184	244	316	405	509	630
50	112	60	193	270	371	497	650	830	1040
50	112	80	251	363	512	699	927	1195	1509
50	112	100	310	462	666	922	1234	1602	2032
50	112	120	372	569	832	1164	1568	2045	2602
50	112	140	437	683	1011	1424	1927	2525	3216
75	168	40	170	219	283	360	450	557	679
75	168	60	236	317	421	548	703	885	1097
75	168	80	303	418	570	759	987	1258	1574
75	168	100	370	525	730	988	1301	1671	2103
75	168	120	441	638	902	1235	1641	2119	2679
75	168	140	511	756	1085	1499	2004	2601	3299
100	224	40	199	252	320	401	495	604	728
100	224	60	275	361	468	600	757	942	1156
100	224	80	350	472	627	819	1049	1322	1640
100	224	100	426	586	794	1054	1367	1741	2175
100	224	120	504	705	972	1307	1714	2195	2757
100	224	140	581	829	1160	1576	2083	2682	3382
125	280	40	226	283	355	440	538	650	777
125	280	60	311	401	514	650	811	998	1215
125	280	80	394	522	683	876	1110	1386	1706
125	280	100	480	644	857	1121	1436	1811	2248
125	280	120	563	770	1041	1379	1786	2271	2836
125	280	140	646	901	1234	1653	2163	2763	3466
150	335	40	251	313	389	478	579	695	825
150	335	60	345	440	558	699	864	1055	1273
150	335	80	436	570	734	934	1172	1451	1773
150	335	100	529	701	919	1184	1504	1882	2322
150	335	120	618	834	1110	1451	1860	2348	2915
150	335	140	709	970	1309	1731	2239	2845	3551
175	391	40	275	340	421	514	619	738	872
175	391	60	377	477	601	746	915	1110	1332
175	391	80	476	614	785	990	1233	1515	1840
175	391	100	576	755	976	1248	1573	1954	2395
175	391	120	672	895	1177	1520	1935	2425	2995
175	391	140	769	1038	1382	1808	2319	2928	3636
200	447	40	298	367	452	549	658	781	918
200	447	60	408	513	642	792	966	1164	1390
200	447	80	515	658	835	1046	1293	1579	1907
200	447	100	621	803	1034	1311	1640	2025	2470
200	447	120	723	954	1239	1590	2009	2503	3075
200	447	140	826	1104	1454	1881	2399	3011	3722
225	503	40	321	393	481	582	696	822	963
225	503	60	438	548	681	837	1015	1218	1447
225	503	80	555	700	883	1100	1351	1642	1974
225	503	100	664	853	1090	1373	1707	2096	2544
225	503	120	773	1012	1303	1659	2083	2580	3156
225	503	140	885	1168	1521	1957	2479	3094	3808
250	559	40	342	418	510	615	732	863	1007
250	559	60	467	581	720	880	1063	1270	1504
250	559	80	590	742	931	1152	1409	1704	2040
250	559	100	706	902	1145	1434	1773	2166	2618
250	559	120	822	1063	1365	1727	2156	2658	3237
250	559	140	937	1230	1590	2032	2559	3177	3895
275	615	40	363	442	538	647	768	902	1051
275	615	60	495	614	757	923	1110	1322	1559
275	615	80	625	782	977	1204	1466	1766	2106
275	615	100	747	949	1199	1494	1839	2236	2692
275	615	120	873	1117	1426	1795	2229	2735	3318
275	615	140	989	1286	1658	2106	2638	3261	3982
300	671	40	383	466	565	678	803	941	1093
300	671	60	523	646	794	964	1157	1373	1614
300	671	80	658	821	1022	1255	1522	1827	2171
300	671	100	787	996	1252	1553	1903	2306	2766
300	671	120	916	1170	1486	1861	2301	2812	3398
300	671	140	1041	1345	1724	2179	2716	3344	4068
325	727	40	403	489	592	708	837	979	1134
325	727	60	554	677	830	1005	1202	1423	1668
325	727	80	691	860	1066	1305	1577	1887	2235
325	727	100	826	1041	1303	1611	1967	2375	2839
325	727	120	959	1222	1544	1926	2372	2888	3479
325	727	140	1092	1403	1789	2251	2794	3427	4155
350	783	40	423	512	618	738	871	1016	1175
350	783	60	580	707	865	1045	1246	1472	1722
350	783	80	723	898	1109	1353	1631	1946	2299
350	783	100	869	1085	1354	1668	2030	2443	2911
350	783	120	1003	1272	1602	1991	2443	2964	3559
350	783	140	1141	1460	1854	2322	2871	3509	4242
375	839	40	442	534	644	767	903	1053	1215
375	839	60	605	737	899	1084	1290	1520	1774
375	839	80	755	934	1151	1401	1685	2004	2362
375	839	100	904	1129	1404	1724	2092	2510	2984
375	839	120	1047	1322	1659	2054	2512	3039	3639
375	839	140	1190	1515	1917	2392	2948	3591	4329
400	894	40	460	555	669	796	936	1088	1255
400	894	60	630	767	933	1122	1333	1567	1826
400	894	80	786	971	1193	1448	1737	2062	2425
400	894	100	939	1171	1453	1779	2153	2577	3055
400	894	120	1089	1371	1715	2117	2581	3113	3718
400	894	140	1237	1570	1979	2462	3024	3673	4415

NOTE: Detector time constant at a reference velocity of 5 ft/sec.
For SI Units: 1 ft = 0.305 m
1000 BTU/sec = 1055 kW

Table B-4.1(u)
Installed Spacing of Heat Detector: 20 feet
t_g: 50 Seconds to 1000 Btu/sec
α: 0.400 Btu/sec^3

			CEILING HEIGHT IN FEET						
τ	RTI	ΔT	4.0	8.0	12.0	16.0	20.0	24.0	28.0
			FIRE SIZE AT DETECTOR RESPONSE (BTU / SEC)						
25	56	40	906	1047	1221	1424	1650	1898	2169
25	56	60	1122	1352	1602	1890	2214	2575	2974
25	56	80	1351	1649	1975	2354	2786	3271	3813
25	56	100	1578	1940	2347	2825	3373	3994	4693
25	56	120	1804	2229	2722	3305	3979	4747	5616
25	56	140	2029	2519	3103	3797	4605	5532	6583
50	112	40	1236	1478	1711	1969	2251	2556	2883
50	112	60	1603	1922	2239	2596	2989	3417	3881
50	112	80	1960	2340	2744	3202	3710	4270	4881
50	112	100	2311	2744	3236	3800	4431	5129	5898
50	112	120	2657	3139	3723	4397	5156	6002	6940
50	112	140	3002	3527	4207	4996	5891	6893	8010
75	168	40	1543	1841	2119	2425	2756	3110	3487
75	168	60	2035	2402	2775	3192	3648	4139	4666
75	168	80	2514	2926	3396	3925	4508	5141	5824
75	168	100	2986	3429	3995	4641	5355	6135	6983
75	168	120	3362	3912	4582	5347	6197	7131	8153
75	168	140	3768	4387	5162	6050	7041	8136	9340
100	224	40	1831	2165	2483	2830	3205	3605	4028
100	224	60	2445	2833	3255	3726	4239	4789	5374
100	224	80	3048	3454	3980	4576	5227	5929	6682
100	224	100	3518	4039	4678	5400	6192	7051	7977
100	224	120	4022	4608	5358	6208	7145	8166	9273
100	224	140	4514	5164	6026	7007	8094	9282	10577
125	280	40	2109	2465	2816	3202	3618	4059	4525
125	280	60	2845	3231	3696	4219	4784	5388	6029
125	280	80	3451	3934	4520	5177	5892	6660	7478
125	280	100	4060	4606	5309	6103	6989	7903	8904
125	280	120	4651	5254	6076	7007	8027	9131	10321
125	280	140	5095	5877	6826	7897	9074	10354	11739
150	335	40	2379	2746	3129	3550	4004	4484	4990
150	335	60	3243	3607	4110	4680	5295	5950	6643
150	335	80	3886	4389	5026	5742	6517	7346	8228
150	335	100	4583	5139	5902	6763	7700	8705	9778
150	335	120	5111	5853	6751	7758	8857	10042	11312
150	335	140	5716	6553	7580	8736	10000	11368	12841
175	391	40	2646	3014	3424	3880	4369	4887	5430
175	391	60	3469	3952	4502	5117	5780	6483	7226
175	391	80	4309	4821	5507	6277	7110	7999	8940
175	391	100	4948	5637	6465	7391	8394	9468	10610
175	391	120	5642	6428	7392	8473	9648	10910	12257
175	391	140	6313	7194	8296	9533	10882	12335	13893
200	447	40	2910	3270	3706	4194	4718	5271	5850
200	447	60	3821	4289	4877	5535	6243	6993	7783
200	447	80	4603	5227	5966	6790	7678	8622	9621
200	447	100	5395	6120	7004	7991	9059	10198	11408
200	447	120	6155	6978	8006	9157	10405	11741	13164
200	447	140	6891	7809	8983	10298	11727	13263	14903

			CEILING HEIGHT IN FEET						
τ	RTI	ΔT	4.0	8.0	12.0	16.0	20.0	24.0	28.0
			FIRE SIZE AT DETECTOR RESPONSE (BTU / SEC)						
225	503	40	3174	3517	3978	4496	5052	5639	6254
225	503	60	4140	4613	5237	5937	6688	7483	8318
225	503	80	4969	5623	6408	7282	8223	9223	10277
225	503	100	5828	6585	7523	8569	9699	10902	12176
225	503	120	6654	7508	8598	9816	11134	12542	14038
225	503	140	7454	8402	9644	11034	12541	14157	15879
250	559	40	3323	3744	4239	4788	5375	5995	6643
250	559	60	4454	4927	5586	6325	7118	7956	8836
250	559	80	5325	6006	6835	7759	8751	9803	10911
250	559	100	6251	7034	8024	9128	10317	11582	12919
250	559	120	7142	8021	9170	10453	11839	13317	14885
250	559	140	8006	8976	10283	11746	13329	15023	16823
275	615	40	3543	3973	4492	5070	5688	6339	7019
275	615	60	4628	5221	5923	6701	7534	8414	9337
275	615	80	5672	6377	7250	8221	9262	10366	11526
275	615	100	6665	7471	8511	9670	10918	12242	13640
275	615	120	7621	8519	9725	11072	12524	14070	15706
275	615	140	8373	9525	10904	12438	14095	15863	17740
300	671	40	3759	4195	4738	5344	5992	6674	7385
300	671	60	4901	5516	6251	7066	7939	8860	9824
300	671	80	6013	6739	7653	8670	9760	10913	12124
300	671	100	7071	7896	8984	10198	11502	12885	14342
300	671	120	7931	8996	10265	11674	13190	14802	16506
300	671	140	8867	10066	11508	13111	14839	16682	18634
325	727	40	3972	4411	4978	5612	6288	7000	7742
325	727	60	5169	5803	6571	7423	8334	9294	10299
325	727	80	6348	7092	8046	9108	10245	11446	12707
325	727	100	7472	8311	9446	10712	12071	13511	15026
325	727	120	8362	9468	10792	12261	13840	15517	17286
325	727	140	9350	10593	12097	13767	15566	17481	19506
350	783	40	4182	4623	5213	5873	6577	7318	8089
350	783	60	5431	6083	6883	7771	8719	9718	10763
350	783	80	6678	7437	8431	9536	10719	11967	13277
350	783	100	7706	8707	9897	11215	12628	14123	15695
350	783	120	8784	9929	11307	12835	14475	16215	18049
350	783	140	9824	11109	12674	14409	16277	18261	20359
375	839	40	4392	4830	5442	6128	6860	7629	8430
375	839	60	5690	6358	7189	8112	9097	10133	11216
375	839	80	7003	7775	8807	9955	11182	12477	13834
375	839	100	8067	9103	10339	11707	13173	14722	16349
375	839	120	9199	10381	11811	13396	15097	16899	18796
375	839	140	10289	11615	13238	15038	16972	19026	21194
400	894	40	4470	5021	5666	6378	7137	7933	8763
400	894	60	5945	6627	7489	8445	9466	10540	11661
400	894	80	7326	8107	9175	10365	11637	12977	14380
400	894	100	8423	9491	10772	12190	13707	15309	16991
400	894	120	9606	10824	12306	13947	15707	17569	19528
400	894	140	10747	12111	13791	15654	17654	19776	22013

NOTE: Detector time constant at a reference velocity of 5 ft/sec.
For SI Units: 1 ft = 0.305 m
1000 BTU/sec = 1055 kW

Table B-4.1(v)
Installed Spacing of Heat Detector: 20 feet
t_g: 150 Seconds to 1000 Btu/sec
α: 0.044 Btu/sec^3

τ	RTI	ΔT	CEILING HEIGHT IN FEET 4.0	8.0	12.0	16.0	20.0	24.0	28.0
			FIRE SIZE AT DETECTOR RESPONSE (BTU / SEC)						
25	56	40	379	456	556	675	812	969	1145
25	56	60	506	629	786	975	1197	1452	1743
25	56	80	635	805	1028	1299	1618	1988	2410
25	56	100	759	994	1285	1646	2074	2571	3139
25	56	120	889	1182	1561	2017	2564	3199	3926
25	56	140	1009	1378	1845	2417	3085	3869	4766
50	112	40	540	635	754	891	1045	1217	1406
50	112	60	723	863	1041	1249	1487	1756	2058
50	112	80	898	1087	1331	1619	1952	2333	2764
50	112	100	1059	1312	1628	2004	2444	2950	3526
50	112	120	1226	1540	1934	2407	2963	3606	4341
50	112	140	1393	1771	2250	2828	3510	4301	5207
75	168	40	684	787	923	1078	1250	1439	1645
75	168	60	906	1063	1263	1493	1751	2040	2359
75	168	80	1111	1331	1600	1911	2266	2666	3114
75	168	100	1319	1597	1939	2339	2800	3324	3914
75	168	120	1525	1862	2283	2780	3355	4014	4762
75	168	140	1729	2128	2634	3234	3933	4739	5656
100	224	40	801	923	1075	1247	1436	1642	1866
100	224	60	1061	1244	1465	1716	1996	2304	2643
100	224	80	1312	1553	1846	2182	2560	2982	3450
100	224	100	1558	1856	2225	2653	3138	3684	4294
100	224	120	1801	2157	2607	3132	3732	4413	5179
100	224	140	2043	2457	2992	3621	4345	5171	6105
125	280	40	915	1049	1216	1404	1609	1832	2072
125	280	60	1211	1412	1652	1923	2224	2553	2911
125	280	80	1501	1759	2075	2435	2837	3282	3772
125	280	100	1784	2098	2493	2947	3459	4029	4662
125	280	120	2064	2432	2911	3465	4093	4798	5587
125	280	140	2304	2763	3330	3989	4742	5592	6548
150	335	40	1007	1167	1348	1551	1772	2011	2266
150	335	60	1355	1570	1828	2119	2440	2789	3167
150	335	80	1681	1953	2291	2675	3101	3569	4080
150	335	100	2002	2326	2747	3227	3765	4361	5017
150	335	120	2278	2691	3199	3782	4438	5171	5984
150	335	140	2570	3053	3651	4342	5124	6002	6982
175	391	40	1114	1280	1474	1691	1927	2181	2451
175	391	60	1492	1720	1996	2306	2646	3014	3412
175	391	80	1856	2138	2497	2904	3352	3843	4377
175	391	100	2178	2542	2988	3495	4059	4680	5361
175	391	120	2504	2939	3475	4086	4771	5531	6369
175	391	140	2824	3330	3959	4680	5493	6399	7406
200	447	40	1211	1387	1594	1825	2075	2343	2629
200	447	60	1626	1864	2156	2485	2843	3231	3647
200	447	80	2028	2315	2695	3123	3594	4108	4664
200	447	100	2367	2750	3220	3753	4342	4988	5694
200	447	120	2722	3176	3739	4379	5092	5880	6744
200	447	140	3070	3596	4254	5007	5850	6785	7819

τ	RTI	ΔT	CEILING HEIGHT IN FEET 4.0	8.0	12.0	16.0	20.0	24.0	28.0
			FIRE SIZE AT DETECTOR RESPONSE (BTU / SEC)						
225	503	40	1305	1490	1710	1954	2218	2500	2800
225	503	60	1757	2002	2311	2657	3034	3440	3875
225	503	80	2157	2485	2885	3335	3828	4364	4942
225	503	100	2551	2951	3444	4001	4616	5287	6017
225	503	120	2934	3405	3995	4663	5404	6218	7110
225	503	140	3309	3852	4540	5323	6196	7161	8224
250	559	40	1396	1590	1821	2078	2356	2652	2966
250	559	60	1886	2136	2461	2824	3218	3642	4095
250	559	80	2308	2650	3070	3540	4055	4612	5212
250	559	100	2730	3145	3661	4242	4881	5578	6332
250	559	120	3140	3627	4242	4937	5706	6548	7466
250	559	140	3542	4100	4817	5630	6533	7528	8619
275	615	40	1486	1687	1930	2199	2490	2799	3126
275	615	60	2013	2267	2606	2985	3397	3839	4310
275	615	80	2454	2810	3249	3740	4275	4853	5474
275	615	100	2905	3334	3872	4477	5140	5860	6639
275	615	120	3342	3843	4483	5205	6000	6869	7814
275	615	140	3729	4341	5086	5929	6861	7886	9005
300	671	40	1574	1782	2035	2317	2620	2942	3283
300	671	60	2100	2392	2747	3143	3571	4030	4518
300	671	80	2598	2966	3423	3934	4489	5088	5730
300	671	100	3076	3517	4077	4705	5392	6136	6939
300	671	120	3541	4053	4717	5465	6288	7184	8155
300	671	140	3942	4577	5349	6220	7182	8236	9383
325	727	40	1661	1874	2138	2431	2747	3082	3435
325	727	60	2213	2516	2885	3297	3741	4217	4722
325	727	80	2739	3119	3593	4123	4699	5318	5981
325	727	100	3244	3697	4277	4928	5638	6406	7232
325	727	120	3690	4257	4946	5720	6568	7491	8488
325	727	140	4150	4806	5605	6505	7496	8578	9755
350	783	40	1746	1964	2239	2543	2871	3218	3584
350	783	60	2324	2637	3020	3447	3908	4400	4922
350	783	80	2877	3268	3760	4308	4904	5543	6226
350	783	100	3411	3872	4473	5146	5879	6670	7520
350	783	120	3871	4458	5170	5969	6843	7792	8815
350	783	140	4354	5031	5856	6784	7803	8914	10119
375	839	40	1831	2052	2337	2653	2992	3352	3730
375	839	60	2432	2755	3152	3594	4071	4578	5117
375	839	80	3014	3413	3923	4490	5105	5763	6466
375	839	100	3530	4043	4665	5360	6115	6929	7802
375	839	120	4050	4654	5390	6213	7113	8087	9136
375	839	140	4554	5251	6102	7057	8105	9244	10477
400	894	40	1916	2139	2433	2761	3111	3483	3873
400	894	60	2539	2871	3282	3738	4230	4754	5308
400	894	80	3149	3557	4082	4668	5301	5980	6702
400	894	100	3683	4212	4854	5569	6347	7183	8079
400	894	120	4225	4847	5605	6453	7378	8377	9452
400	894	140	4751	5467	6343	7325	8401	9568	10829

NOTE: Detector time constant at a reference velocity of 5 ft/sec.
For SI Units: 1 ft = 0.305 m
1000 BTU/sec = 1055 kW

Table B-4.1(w)
Installed Spacing of Heat Detector: 20 feet
t_g: 300 Seconds to 1000 Btu/sec
α: 0.011 Btu/sec^3

τ	RTI	ΔT	CEILING HEIGHT IN FEET 4.0	8.0	12.0	16.0	20.0	24.0	28.0
			FIRE SIZE AT DETECTOR RESPONSE (BTU / SEC)						
25	56	40	232	294	375	473	589	723	876
25	56	60	322	429	566	731	928	1157	1419
25	56	80	415	572	774	1022	1311	1649	2037
25	56	100	513	726	1002	1338	1733	2193	2720
25	56	120	613	890	1247	1681	2190	2784	3464
25	56	140	717	1065	1508	2047	2685	3418	4264
50	112	40	326	395	484	588	709	847	1003
50	112	60	445	557	700	870	1071	1303	1567
50	112	80	567	725	929	1177	1471	1812	2203
50	112	100	685	902	1174	1509	1908	2371	2902
50	112	120	805	1082	1436	1865	2378	2976	3660
50	112	140	928	1270	1709	2248	2881	3623	4473
75	168	40	405	483	580	693	821	966	1128
75	168	60	556	673	824	1004	1211	1448	1718
75	168	80	695	864	1077	1333	1632	1977	2372
75	168	100	835	1059	1342	1683	2085	2552	3087
75	168	120	975	1259	1618	2054	2570	3171	3860
75	168	140	1118	1469	1907	2445	3085	3831	4685
100	224	40	477	562	668	790	927	1079	1249
100	224	60	650	778	940	1129	1346	1591	1866
100	224	80	812	992	1217	1482	1790	2142	2542
100	224	100	971	1208	1502	1852	2262	2735	3275
100	224	120	1133	1427	1797	2240	2763	3369	4062
100	224	140	1294	1650	2102	2647	3292	4041	4901
125	280	40	543	636	750	880	1026	1187	1364
125	280	60	737	876	1049	1248	1474	1728	2012
125	280	80	922	1112	1349	1625	1943	2304	2711
125	280	100	1101	1348	1655	2017	2436	2916	3462
125	280	120	1280	1586	1968	2423	2954	3567	4265
125	280	140	1459	1827	2291	2846	3498	4254	5118
150	335	40	611	705	827	966	1120	1289	1474
150	335	60	820	968	1151	1361	1598	1861	2154
150	335	80	1020	1226	1474	1763	2091	2462	2877
150	335	100	1223	1481	1801	2175	2605	3095	3649
150	335	120	1420	1738	2133	2601	3142	3763	4469
150	335	140	1616	1995	2473	3040	3702	4466	5337
175	391	40	668	771	901	1048	1210	1387	1580
175	391	60	903	1057	1250	1470	1716	1989	2291
175	391	80	1122	1334	1595	1895	2235	2616	3041
175	391	100	1339	1609	1942	2328	2770	3271	3834
175	391	120	1554	1883	2293	2773	3326	3958	4672
175	391	140	1768	2157	2650	3230	3904	4677	5555
200	447	40	724	834	971	1126	1296	1482	1682
200	447	60	973	1141	1344	1574	1831	2114	2425
200	447	80	1216	1439	1711	2022	2374	2766	3201
200	447	100	1452	1731	2077	2477	2931	3443	4016
200	447	120	1685	2022	2447	2941	3507	4149	4873
200	447	140	1902	2313	2821	3416	4102	4886	5773
225	503	40	777	895	1039	1202	1380	1573	1782
225	503	60	1045	1223	1435	1675	1942	2235	2555
225	503	80	1308	1539	1822	2146	2509	2912	3357
225	503	100	1561	1850	2208	2621	3088	3612	4195
225	503	120	1812	2157	2596	3104	3684	4338	5072
225	503	140	2040	2464	2987	3597	4296	5092	5989
250	559	40	830	954	1105	1275	1460	1661	1878
250	559	60	1120	1302	1523	1773	2049	2352	2682
250	559	80	1397	1637	1931	2266	2640	3055	3511
250	559	100	1668	1964	2336	2762	3242	3777	4372
250	559	120	1919	2288	2741	3264	3857	4523	5269
250	559	140	2173	2611	3149	3774	4487	5295	6204
275	615	40	887	1011	1169	1346	1539	1748	1972
275	615	60	1189	1379	1609	1868	2154	2467	2806
275	615	80	1484	1731	2037	2383	2769	3194	3661
275	615	100	1773	2076	2460	2899	3391	3939	4545
275	615	120	2034	2416	2883	3419	4026	4706	5463
275	615	140	2303	2753	3307	3947	4675	5496	6416
300	671	40	932	1066	1231	1415	1615	1831	2063
300	671	60	1257	1453	1692	1961	2256	2578	2927
300	671	80	1570	1824	2140	2497	2894	3331	3808
300	671	100	1859	2185	2581	3033	3538	4098	4716
300	671	120	2147	2540	3021	3572	4192	4885	5654
300	671	140	2430	2892	3461	4117	4859	5694	6626
325	727	40	977	1120	1292	1483	1690	1913	2152
325	727	60	1324	1526	1774	2052	2357	2688	3046
325	727	80	1654	1914	2240	2609	3017	3465	3953
325	727	100	1956	2291	2700	3164	3682	4254	4884
325	727	120	2258	2662	3156	3721	4355	5061	5843
325	727	140	2554	3029	3612	4283	5040	5889	6834
350	783	40	1023	1173	1351	1549	1763	1994	2240
350	783	60	1389	1598	1854	2140	2454	2795	3163
350	783	80	1737	2002	2339	2718	3138	3596	4095
350	783	100	2050	2395	2815	3292	3823	4407	5049
350	783	120	2366	2780	3288	3867	4515	5235	6029
350	783	140	2676	3162	3760	4446	5218	6081	7039
375	839	40	1073	1225	1409	1613	1835	2072	2325
375	839	60	1453	1668	1932	2227	2550	2900	3277
375	839	80	1803	2088	2435	2826	3256	3725	4235
375	839	100	2142	2497	2929	3419	3961	4558	5212
375	839	120	2472	2897	3418	4011	4673	5406	6213
375	839	140	2795	3292	3906	4607	5394	6270	7242
400	894	40	1119	1276	1466	1677	1905	2149	2409
400	894	60	1517	1736	2008	2313	2645	3003	3389
400	894	80	1880	2173	2530	2931	3372	3852	4373
400	894	100	2233	2597	3041	3542	4097	4707	5372
400	894	120	2576	3011	3546	4152	4828	5574	6394
400	894	140	2913	3421	4048	4764	5566	6457	7442

NOTE: Detector time constant at a reference velocity of 5 ft/sec.
For SI Units: 1 ft = 0.305 m
1000 BTU/sec = 1055 kW

Table B-4.1(x)
Installed Spacing of Heat Detector: 20 feet
t_g: 500 Seconds to 1000 Btu/sec
α: 0.004 Btu/sec^3

τ	RTI	ΔT	CEILING HEIGHT IN FEET 4.0	8.0	12.0	16.0	20.0	24.0	28.0
			FIRE SIZE AT DETECTOR RESPONSE (BTU / SEC)						
25	56	40	168	266	300	390	497	622	764
25	56	60	242	343	473	631	816	1033	1280
25	56	80	322	474	668	904	1184	1505	1875
25	56	100	407	617	884	1207	1589	2030	2537
25	56	120	497	772	1118	1537	2032	2603	3260
25	56	140	592	938	1370	1891	2508	3220	4040
50	112	40	230	290	366	458	567	693	836
50	112	60	323	425	553	711	898	1116	1365
50	112	80	418	568	760	996	1273	1598	1970
50	112	100	517	721	985	1308	1688	2132	2642
50	112	120	618	884	1227	1645	2138	2714	3374
50	112	140	723	1057	1485	2006	2625	3339	4162
75	168	40	284	348	429	525	636	764	910
75	168	60	394	499	632	792	981	1201	1452
75	168	80	506	656	850	1087	1367	1693	2067
75	168	100	617	823	1087	1407	1790	2237	2749
75	168	120	730	996	1337	1755	2249	2827	3489
75	168	140	846	1177	1603	2124	2739	3459	4285
100	224	40	332	401	487	587	703	835	983
100	224	60	458	569	707	872	1064	1286	1540
100	224	805	585	741	939	1179	1462	1790	2166
100	224	100	709	918	1185	1510	1894	2343	2857
100	224	120	834	1105	1448	1864	2361	2941	3606
100	224	140	962	1296	1722	2240	2859	3581	4410
125	280	40	377	450	541	647	767	903	1055
125	280	60	522	634	778	948	1145	1371	1627
125	280	80	658	820	1025	1269	1556	1887	2266
125	280	100	795	1011	1283	1611	1999	2450	2966
125	280	120	933	1206	1553	1975	2474	3056	3724
125	280	140	1072	1412	1837	2359	2980	3704	4536
150	335	40	419	497	593	704	829	969	1126
150	335	60	578	697	847	1022	1225	1455	1715
150	335	80	728	896	1107	1357	1649	1984	2365
150	335	100	880	1099	1378	1711	2103	2557	3076
150	335	120	1025	1307	1659	2085	2588	3173	3843
150	335	140	1176	1519	1952	2478	3102	3829	4663
175	391	40	459	541	643	759	889	1034	1194
175	391	60	631	756	912	1094	1302	1537	1801
175	391	80	794	969	1187	1444	1740	2080	2465
175	391	100	955	1185	1470	1810	2206	2664	3186
175	391	120	1116	1403	1763	2194	2701	3289	3962
175	391	140	1277	1626	2066	2597	3224	3954	4790
200	447	40	498	584	690	811	946	1096	1261
200	447	60	683	813	976	1164	1377	1617	1886
200	447	80	863	1040	1265	1527	1830	2175	2564
200	447	100	1030	1267	1560	1906	2309	2771	3297
200	447	120	1202	1497	1864	2302	2814	3406	4083
200	447	140	1374	1730	2177	2714	3346	4079	4919
225	503	40	535	625	736	862	1002	1157	1326
225	503	60	732	869	1037	1231	1450	1696	1970
225	503	80	921	1108	1340	1609	1918	2268	2663
225	503	100	1103	1347	1647	2001	2409	2877	3407
225	503	120	1286	1587	1963	2407	2925	3522	4203
225	503	140	1468	1831	2286	2830	3467	4204	5048
250	559	40	575	665	781	911	1056	1216	1390
250	559	60	780	922	1097	1297	1522	1773	2052
250	559	80	978	1174	1413	1689	2004	2361	2760
250	559	100	1174	1424	1733	2093	2509	2982	3517
250	559	120	1367	1676	2059	2511	3036	3638	4323
250	559	140	1559	1929	2393	2944	3587	4330	5177
275	615	40	609	704	824	959	1109	1273	1452
275	615	60	827	974	1155	1361	1592	1849	2133
275	615	80	1036	1238	1484	1767	2089	2451	2857
275	615	100	1243	1500	1816	2184	2606	3086	3626
275	615	120	1446	1762	2154	2614	3145	3753	4443
275	615	140	1649	2026	2498	3057	3707	4454	5306
300	671	40	643	742	866	1006	1161	1330	1513
300	671	60	877	1025	1211	1423	1660	1923	2213
300	671	80	1094	1301	1553	1844	2172	2541	2952
300	671	100	1310	1574	1898	2273	2703	3188	3735
300	671	120	1524	1846	2246	2714	3253	3867	4562
300	671	140	1737	2120	2601	3168	3825	4579	5435
325	727	40	675	779	907	1052	1211	1385	1573
325	727	60	919	1075	1266	1484	1727	1996	2291
325	727	80	1150	1362	1621	1919	2254	2629	3046
325	727	100	1376	1646	1977	2361	2797	3290	3842
325	727	120	1601	1928	2337	2813	3359	3980	4681
325	727	140	1814	2212	2702	3277	3942	4702	5564
350	783	40	707	815	947	1097	1260	1439	1632
350	783	60	960	1123	1320	1544	1793	2068	2368
350	783	80	1204	1422	1688	1993	2335	2716	3139
350	783	100	1441	1716	2056	2447	2891	3390	3948
350	783	120	1676	2009	2426	2911	3465	4092	4799
350	783	140	1896	2302	2801	3385	4058	4824	5692
375	839	40	738	850	987	1140	1309	1492	1689
375	839	60	1002	1171	1374	1603	1858	2138	2444
375	839	80	1257	1481	1754	2065	2414	2802	3230
375	839	100	1505	1786	2133	2532	2983	3489	4054
375	839	120	1750	2088	2514	3007	3568	4203	4917
375	839	140	1977	2390	2899	3492	4172	4946	5820
400	894	40	769	884	1025	1183	1356	1544	1746
400	894	60	1045	1217	1426	1661	1921	2207	2519
400	894	80	1310	1538	1818	2136	2492	2886	3321
400	894	100	1568	1854	2208	2615	3074	3587	4158
400	894	120	1811	2166	2600	3101	3671	4313	5033
400	894	140	2056	2478	2995	3597	4286	5067	5947

NOTE: Detector time constant at a reference velocity of 5 ft/sec.
For SI Units: 1 ft = 0.305 m
1000 BTU/sec = 1055 kW

Table B-4.1(y)
Installed Spacing of Heat Detector: 20 feet
t_g: 600 Seconds to 1000 Btu/sec
α: 0.003 Btu/sec^3

τ	RTI	ΔT	CEILING HEIGHT IN FEET 4.0	8.0	12.0	16.0	20.0	24.0	28.0
			FIRE SIZE AT DETECTOR RESPONSE (BTU / SEC)						
25	56	40	151	208	280	369	474	595	735
25	56	60	222	321	449	605	787	1000	1244
25	56	80	298	449	641	874	1149	1466	1831
25	56	100	380	590	854	1173	1551	1986	2487
25	56	120	467	743	1085	1499	1989	2554	3205
25	56	140	560	906	1334	1850	2461	3167	3979
50	112	40	205	262	336	425	531	654	794
50	112	60	290	390	517	671	855	1069	1314
50	112	80	379	527	717	949	1223	1543	1910
50	112	100	472	675	936	1255	1632	2071	2574
50	112	120	569	834	1174	1588	2079	2646	3299
50	112	140	669	1003	1428	1945	2558	3265	4080
75	168	40	251	312	389	481	588	713	854
75	168	60	352	453	582	738	923	1138	1385
75	168	80	455	603	793	1024	1300	1622	1990
75	168	100	558	760	1021	1340	1716	2157	2662
75	168	120	664	927	1265	1679	2167	2739	3394
75	168	140	774	1103	1525	2042	2652	3365	4182
100	224	40	293	358	439	534	645	771	915
100	224	60	408	513	645	804	992	1209	1457
100	224	80	524	674	866	1101	1378	1701	2071
100	224	100	638	844	1105	1422	1802	2244	2751
100	224	120	754	1019	1357	1768	2260	2833	3491
100	224	140	876	1202	1623	2140	2750	3465	4285
125	280	40	332	400	486	585	699	829	975
125	280	60	460	569	706	869	1060	1279	1529
125	280	80	587	742	939	1176	1456	1781	2153
125	280	100	713	921	1185	1507	1888	2332	2841
125	280	120	839	1108	1448	1860	2353	2928	3587
125	280	140	968	1300	1722	2235	2850	3566	4389
150	335	40	369	441	530	634	752	885	1035
150	335	60	509	623	765	933	1127	1349	1602
150	335	80	648	808	1010	1251	1534	1861	2235
150	335	100	784	997	1266	1591	1974	2420	2931
150	335	120	921	1192	1535	1952	2447	3024	3685
150	335	140	1059	1395	1817	2334	2950	3668	4493
175	391	40	404	480	573	681	803	940	1093
175	391	60	559	675	822	994	1192	1418	1674
175	391	80	705	871	1078	1324	1611	1941	2318
175	391	100	852	1071	1345	1674	2061	2509	3022
175	391	120	998	1275	1623	2044	2541	3120	3784
175	391	140	1145	1484	1913	2433	3051	3771	4598
200	447	40	437	517	615	727	853	994	1150
200	447	60	604	725	877	1054	1257	1486	1746
200	447	80	761	932	1145	1396	1687	2021	2401
200	447	100	918	1142	1422	1756	2146	2598	3114
200	447	120	1073	1355	1709	2134	2635	3217	3883
200	447	140	1229	1573	2007	2531	3152	3875	4704

τ	RTI	ΔT	CEILING HEIGHT IN FEET 4.0	8.0	12.0	16.0	20.0	24.0	28.0
			FIRE SIZE AT DETECTOR RESPONSE (BTU / SEC)						
225	503	40	470	553	654	771	901	1046	1206
225	503	60	647	773	930	1112	1319	1554	1816
225	503	80	815	991	1210	1466	1762	2100	2483
225	503	100	980	1211	1497	1836	2232	2687	3206
225	503	120	1146	1434	1794	2224	2729	3313	3982
225	503	140	1311	1661	2100	2629	3253	3979	4810
250	559	40	501	587	693	814	948	1097	1260
250	559	60	688	819	982	1169	1381	1620	1886
250	559	80	871	1049	1273	1535	1836	2178	2565
250	559	100	1042	1278	1571	1916	2316	2775	3297
250	559	120	1216	1510	1877	2312	2822	3410	4082
250	559	140	1390	1746	2192	2726	3354	4083	4917
275	615	40	531	621	731	855	994	1146	1314
275	615	60	729	865	1032	1224	1441	1684	1955
275	615	80	918	1105	1335	1602	1908	2255	2646
275	615	100	1102	1344	1643	1994	2399	2863	3389
275	615	120	1285	1585	1958	2400	2914	3506	4182
275	615	140	1467	1829	2282	2822	3455	4187	5024
300	671	40	565	654	767	896	1038	1195	1366
300	671	60	769	909	1081	1278	1500	1748	2023
300	671	80	966	1159	1395	1668	1980	2332	2727
300	671	100	1160	1408	1713	2070	2481	2949	3479
300	671	120	1352	1658	2038	2486	3006	3602	4281
300	671	140	1543	1911	2370	2916	3554	4291	5131
325	727	40	594	686	803	936	1082	1243	1418
325	727	60	808	952	1129	1331	1558	1811	2091
325	727	80	1014	1212	1454	1733	2050	2407	2807
325	727	100	1217	1471	1782	2146	2562	3036	3570
325	727	120	1418	1730	2116	2571	3096	3698	4381
325	727	140	1617	1990	2457	3010	3653	4394	5239
350	783	40	621	717	838	975	1125	1289	1469
350	783	60	846	994	1176	1383	1615	1873	2157
350	783	80	1062	1265	1512	1797	2119	2482	2886
350	783	100	1274	1532	1850	2220	2642	3121	3660
350	783	120	1482	1800	2194	2655	3186	3793	4480
350	783	140	1691	2069	2543	3103	3752	4497	5346
375	839	40	648	748	873	1013	1167	1335	1518
375	839	60	886	1036	1222	1434	1671	1933	2222
375	839	80	1108	1316	1569	1860	2188	2555	2964
375	839	100	1329	1593	1917	2293	2721	3205	3749
375	839	120	1546	1869	2270	2737	3275	3887	4579
375	839	140	1763	2146	2628	3194	3849	4600	5453
400	894	40	675	778	906	1050	1208	1381	1567
400	894	60	921	1077	1268	1485	1726	1993	2287
400	894	80	1154	1366	1625	1921	2255	2628	3042
400	894	100	1383	1652	1983	2365	2799	3289	3838
400	894	120	1609	1937	2344	2819	3363	3980	4677
400	894	140	1824	2222	2711	3284	3946	4702	5559

NOTE: Detector time constant at a reference velocity of 5 ft/sec.
For SI Units: 1 ft = 0.305 m
1000 BTU/sec = 1055 kW

Table B-4.1(z)
Installed Spacing of Heat Detector: 25 ft.
t_g: 50 Seconds to 1000 Btu/sec
α: 0.400 Btu/sec^3

τ	RTI	ΔT	CEILING HEIGHT IN FEET 4.0	8.0	12.0	16.0	20.0	24.0	28.0
			FIRE SIZE AT DETECTOR RESPONSE (BTU / SEC)						
25	56	40	1187	1381	1575	1797	2046	2319	2617
25	56	60	1529	1795	2072	2393	2756	3158	3601
25	56	80	1864	2194	2560	2990	3477	4023	4630
25	56	100	2194	2586	3050	3596	4220	4924	5711
25	56	120	2520	2977	3545	4217	4989	5865	6847
25	56	140	2846	3368	4048	4855	5786	6846	8038
50	112	40	1687	1953	2201	2479	2786	3117	3472
50	112	60	2226	2545	2885	3276	3708	4179	4688
50	112	80	2752	3103	3541	4048	4613	5233	5908
50	112	100	3272	3642	4183	4813	5518	6298	7152
50	112	120	3655	4164	4818	5578	6432	7382	8429
50	112	140	4098	4682	5452	6348	7360	8490	9742
75	168	40	2138	2432	2722	3049	3407	3791	4199
75	168	60	2869	3178	3570	4023	4520	5056	5631
75	168	80	3467	3868	4373	4954	5595	6291	7041
75	168	100	4071	4532	5151	5866	6656	7519	8455
75	168	120	4657	5177	5915	6767	7713	8752	9884
75	168	140	5114	5806	6670	7665	8774	9997	11336
100	224	40	2567	2861	3187	3557	3961	4392	4849
100	224	60	3380	3738	4183	4692	5249	5846	6483
100	224	80	4147	4555	5120	5770	6482	7250	8073
100	224	100	4770	5330	6024	6817	7688	8633	9650
100	224	120	5433	6084	6906	7845	8882	10010	11230
100	224	140	6076	6820	7773	8864	10071	11390	12823
125	280	40	2988	3258	3614	4024	4470	4945	5447
125	280	60	3894	4257	4747	5309	5921	6576	7270
125	280	80	4675	5183	5810	6523	7302	8139	9031
125	280	100	5471	6070	6830	7697	8646	9670	10765
125	280	120	6236	6926	7823	8846	9969	11185	12491
125	280	140	6978	7760	8796	9979	11280	12694	14220
150	335	40	3296	3620	4012	4460	4946	5462	6006
150	335	60	4390	4745	5276	5887	6551	7260	8010
150	335	80	5239	5777	6457	7231	8073	8975	9933
150	335	100	6139	6765	7588	8525	9548	10646	11818
150	335	120	7003	7718	8686	9788	10994	12293	13685
150	335	140	7841	8645	9759	11029	12422	13928	15546
175	391	40	3641	3968	4390	4873	5397	5952	6536
175	391	60	4728	5197	5776	6435	7149	7909	8711
175	391	80	5781	6340	7071	7902	8805	9769	10791
175	391	100	6781	7426	8308	9312	10405	11575	12820
175	391	120	7744	8471	9506	10684	11969	13350	14823
175	391	140	8515	9479	10675	12030	13510	15106	16813
200	447	40	3977	4301	4750	5267	5827	6420	7042
200	447	60	5149	5637	6256	6959	7721	8530	9382
200	447	80	6305	6880	7659	8545	9506	10529	11612
200	447	100	7405	8059	8997	10065	11225	12465	13780
200	447	120	8293	9185	10291	11542	12903	14363	15915
200	447	140	9269	10283	11552	12988	14553	16235	18031

τ	RTI	ΔT	CEILING HEIGHT IN FEET 4.0	8.0	12.0	16.0	20.0	24.0	28.0
			FIRE SIZE AT DETECTOR RESPONSE (BTU / SEC)						
225	503	40	4308	4621	5097	5646	6240	6868	7527
225	503	60	5557	6060	6716	7463	8270	9127	10027
225	503	80	6816	7399	8224	9163	10179	11261	12402
225	503	100	7852	8660	9660	10790	12016	13323	14706
225	503	120	8944	9877	11047	12368	13804	15339	16968
225	503	140	9998	11057	12397	13911	15559	17325	19205
250	559	40	4498	4918	5430	6011	6638	7301	7995
250	559	60	5955	6469	7161	7949	8801	9703	10650
250	559	80	7316	7902	8770	9760	10830	11968	13165
250	559	100	8404	9247	10301	11491	12779	14151	15601
250	559	120	9576	10547	11778	13168	14675	16283	17988
250	559	140	10706	11807	13215	14805	16532	18380	20343
275	615	40	4783	5216	5754	6365	7025	7721	8449
275	615	60	6345	6866	7593	8421	9315	10261	11254
275	615	80	7635	8379	9300	10339	11462	12653	13906
275	615	100	8942	9818	10923	12171	13521	14956	16470
275	615	120	10192	11198	12487	13943	15520	17200	18978
275	615	140	11397	12534	14008	15672	17477	19404	21449
300	671	40	5061	5505	6069	6709	7400	8128	8890
300	671	60	6728	7252	8012	8880	9815	10804	11841
300	671	80	8080	8852	9815	10903	12076	13320	14627
300	671	100	9468	10373	11528	12833	14242	15738	17316
300	671	120	10794	11831	13178	14698	16343	18093	19942
300	671	140	12074	13242	14780	16516	18397	20402	22526
325	727	40	5335	5787	6375	7044	7765	8525	9319
325	727	60	7107	7628	8421	9327	10302	11333	12413
325	727	80	8516	9312	10317	11452	12675	13970	15330
325	727	100	9982	10914	12119	13478	14945	16502	18140
325	727	120	11385	12449	13852	15435	17145	18963	20882
325	727	140	12737	13933	15534	17340	19294	21376	23577
350	783	40	5604	6063	6675	7372	8122	8913	9738
350	783	60	7308	7985	8820	9763	10778	11850	12972
350	783	80	8943	9763	10809	11989	13260	14605	16016
350	783	100	10488	11443	12696	14109	15633	17248	18946
350	783	120	11965	13053	14510	16155	17930	19815	21801
350	783	140	13391	14609	16271	18146	20171	22327	24605
375	839	40	5869	6333	6968	7692	8471	9292	10148
375	839	60	7647	8344	9211	10190	11244	12356	13518
375	839	80	9363	10204	11289	12514	13833	15227	16688
375	839	100	10985	11961	13260	14726	16305	17978	19735
375	839	120	12537	13645	15155	16859	18698	20648	22702
375	839	140	14034	15271	16992	18934	21031	23260	25611
400	894	40	6130	6597	7255	8005	8813	9663	10549
400	894	60	7979	8695	9594	10609	11700	12851	14054
400	894	80	9776	10636	11760	13029	14394	15836	17346
400	894	100	11475	12470	13814	15331	16965	18694	20509
400	894	120	13101	14225	15787	17551	19451	21465	23584
400	894	140	14670	15921	17700	19707	21873	24174	26598

NOTE: Detector time constant at a reference velocity of 5 ft/sec.
For SI Units: 1 ft = 0.305 m
1000 BTU/sec = 1055 kW

Table B-4.1(aa)
Installed Spacing of Heat Detector: 25 feet
t_g: 150 Seconds to 1000 Btu/sec
α: 0.044 Btu/sec³

τ	RTI	ΔT	CEILING HEIGHT IN FEET 4.0	8.0	12.0	16.0	20.0	24.0	28.0
			FIRE SIZE AT DETECTOR RESPONSE (BTU / SEC)						
25	56	40	520	609	724	861	1018	1195	1394
25	56	60	701	843	1029	1250	1507	1801	2131
25	56	80	881	1084	1352	1672	2045	2472	2954
25	56	100	1045	1335	1695	2126	2629	3205	3855
25	56	120	1231	1596	2058	2611	3256	3994	4828
25	56	140	1414	1875	2449	3126	3924	4836	5867
50	112	40	742	843	976	1130	1303	1495	1707
50	112	60	981	1148	1352	1590	1861	2166	2507
50	112	80	1223	1450	1734	2068	2452	2887	3376
50	112	100	1460	1755	2127	2568	3078	3659	4316
50	112	120	1696	2065	2534	3092	3740	4483	5322
50	112	140	1933	2380	2955	3640	4439	5355	6392
75	168	40	925	1042	1192	1364	1555	1765	1993
75	168	60	1228	1410	1635	1895	2186	2510	2867
75	168	80	1526	1770	2076	2433	2837	3290	3794
75	168	100	1820	2127	2522	2985	3513	4110	4779
75	168	120	2092	2484	2976	3554	4219	4974	5824
75	168	140	2371	2845	3440	4143	4955	5881	6927
100	224	40	1084	1220	1386	1576	1785	2012	2258
100	224	60	1451	1647	1893	2174	2487	2831	3208
100	224	80	1806	2060	2390	2771	3198	3673	4197
100	224	100	2129	2466	2887	3375	3928	4546	5234
100	224	120	2456	2869	3388	3993	4681	5456	6322
100	224	140	2778	3273	3896	4624	5458	6403	7463
125	280	40	1237	1385	1566	1772	1998	2243	2506
125	280	60	1661	1867	2132	2434	2768	3134	3531
125	280	80	2047	2329	2683	3088	3539	4037	4583
125	280	100	2426	2781	3229	3744	4322	4965	5675
125	280	120	2796	3228	3776	4409	5123	5923	6811
125	280	140	3160	3673	4326	5084	5945	6913	7993
150	335	40	1382	1540	1735	1957	2199	2460	2740
150	335	60	1863	2074	2357	2679	3034	3421	3838
150	335	80	2285	2583	2959	3388	3864	4385	4954
150	335	100	2707	3079	3552	4094	4699	5368	6101
150	335	120	3119	3568	4143	4805	5549	6374	7287
150	335	140	3524	4052	4735	5524	6414	7409	8513
175	391	40	1522	1687	1896	2132	2390	2667	2963
175	391	60	2031	2270	2571	2913	3288	3695	4133
175	391	80	2513	2825	3222	3674	4174	4719	5311
175	391	100	2978	3363	3861	4430	5062	5756	6514
175	391	120	3431	3891	4495	5186	5958	6812	7750
175	391	140	3839	4413	5128	5948	6868	7891	9021
200	447	40	1658	1828	2049	2300	2573	2866	3177
200	447	60	2207	2458	2776	3137	3532	3959	4416
200	447	80	2733	3056	3475	3950	4473	5041	5656
200	447	100	3239	3635	4158	4752	5411	6131	6915
200	447	120	3695	4202	4833	5553	6354	7236	8201
200	447	140	4164	4761	5505	6356	7308	8360	9518
225	503	40	1791	1963	2197	2462	2749	3057	3383
225	503	60	2378	2639	2974	3353	3767	4213	4690
225	503	80	2946	3279	3718	4215	4761	5353	5991
225	503	100	3494	3898	4444	5064	5748	6495	7304
225	503	120	3975	4501	5159	5908	6738	7648	8640
225	503	140	4477	5096	5870	6752	7734	8817	10004
250	559	40	1922	2095	2340	2618	2919	3241	3583
250	559	60	2544	2815	3166	3562	3995	4459	4956
250	559	80	3154	3495	3954	4473	5041	5655	6316
250	559	100	3697	4151	4721	5366	6076	6848	7683
250	559	120	4246	4792	5476	6252	7111	8049	9069
250	559	140	4781	5421	6223	7136	8150	9263	10479
275	615	40	2018	2221	2478	2770	3085	3421	3776
275	615	60	2706	2985	3351	3765	4216	4699	5214
275	615	80	3359	3705	4183	4722	5312	5949	6632
275	615	100	3927	4398	4990	5660	6395	7193	8053
275	615	120	4510	5074	5783	6587	7474	8440	9488
275	615	140	5077	5737	6567	7511	8555	9698	10944
300	671	40	2134	2344	2613	2917	3245	3595	3965
300	671	60	2865	3151	3532	3963	4431	4932	5466
300	671	80	3514	3909	4405	4966	5577	6236	6941
300	671	100	4152	4638	5252	5946	6706	7529	8414
300	671	120	4767	5348	6083	6914	7828	8823	9898
300	671	140	5366	6044	6903	7876	8951	10124	11399
325	727	40	2248	2465	2745	3061	3402	3765	4148
325	727	60	3022	3312	3709	4156	4641	5160	5711
325	727	80	3700	4108	4623	5204	5836	6516	7242
325	727	100	4371	4873	5508	6226	7010	7857	8767
325	727	120	5019	5617	6375	7233	8175	9197	10299
325	727	140	5650	6345	7230	8233	9338	10541	11846
350	783	40	2359	2583	2873	3201	3555	3932	4328
350	783	60	3176	3470	3881	4344	4846	5383	5952
350	783	80	3882	4303	4836	5436	6089	6790	7538
350	783	100	4586	5102	5759	6499	7308	8179	9114
350	783	120	5266	5879	6662	7546	8514	9563	10693
350	783	140	5928	6639	7551	8583	9717	10951	12285
375	839	40	2469	2698	2999	3339	3705	4094	4504
375	839	60	3288	3624	4050	4529	5048	5601	6187
375	839	80	4061	4494	5044	5664	6337	7059	7827
375	839	100	4798	5327	6004	6767	7599	8495	9453
375	839	120	5509	6136	6942	7852	8847	9923	11080
375	839	140	6201	6927	7865	8925	10089	11352	12716
400	894	40	2577	2811	3123	3474	3852	4254	4676
400	894	60	3429	3776	4215	4710	5245	5815	6418
400	894	80	4236	4681	5248	5887	6580	7322	8111
400	894	100	5006	5548	6245	7030	7885	8805	9787
400	894	120	5748	6388	7218	8153	9174	10277	11460
400	894	140	6471	7209	8174	9262	10455	11747	13140

NOTE: Detector time constant at a reference velocity of 5 ft/sec.
For SI Units: 1 ft = 0.305 m
1000 BTU/sec = 1055 kW

Table B-4.1(bb)
Installed Spacing of Heat Detector: 25 feet
t_g: 300 Seconds to 1000 Btu/sec
α: 0.011 Btu/sec^3

τ	RTI	ΔT	CEILING HEIGHT IN FEET 4.0	8.0	12.0	16.0	20.0	24.0	28.0
			FIRE SIZE AT DETECTOR RESPONSE (BTU / SEC)						
25	56	40	321	396	493	609	744	899	1074
25	56	60	451	580	746	946	1178	1444	1744
25	56	80	582	781	1030	1324	1669	2063	2508
25	56	100	719	994	1337	1740	2210	2747	3354
25	56	120	866	1223	1667	2194	2797	3491	4275
25	56	140	1013	1467	2021	2675	3426	4289	5265
50	112	40	447	527	630	751	890	1048	1225
50	112	60	616	747	916	1118	1351	1619	1921
50	112	80	781	976	1223	1518	1863	2258	2706
50	112	100	948	1214	1550	1952	2422	2961	3571
50	112	120	1119	1468	1898	2418	3025	3721	4509
50	112	140	1294	1729	2271	2914	3670	4535	5514
75	168	40	560	642	753	882	1028	1192	1374
75	168	60	757	897	1075	1283	1522	1794	2100
75	168	80	954	1156	1410	1710	2059	2457	2907
75	168	100	1151	1422	1761	2166	2638	3178	3791
75	168	120	1350	1695	2130	2650	3258	3956	4746
75	168	140	1550	1978	2517	3163	3918	4785	5767
100	224	40	654	746	865	1003	1157	1329	1518
100	224	60	890	1035	1222	1439	1687	1966	2278
100	224	80	1113	1323	1587	1896	2251	2655	3110
100	224	100	1338	1616	1964	2376	2853	3398	4014
100	224	120	1563	1914	2356	2881	3492	4193	4987
100	224	140	1789	2218	2762	3411	4169	5038	6024
125	280	40	742	842	969	1116	1279	1459	1656
125	280	60	1002	1163	1360	1588	1845	2133	2452
125	280	80	1260	1480	1755	2074	2439	2851	3312
125	280	100	1513	1799	2158	2580	3065	3617	4238
125	280	120	1765	2120	2573	3107	3725	4431	5230
125	280	140	2004	2447	3001	3657	4420	5294	6283
150	335	40	825	932	1068	1223	1395	1584	1789
150	335	60	1118	1284	1491	1729	1997	2294	2622
150	335	80	1401	1629	1914	2245	2621	3042	3511
150	335	100	1680	1972	2344	2777	3273	3833	4462
150	335	120	1944	2318	2783	3328	3955	4669	5473
150	335	140	2213	2667	3232	3898	4669	5549	6544
175	391	40	908	1019	1162	1325	1506	1703	1917
175	391	60	1226	1399	1616	1865	2143	2450	2787
175	391	80	1536	1771	2068	2411	2797	3228	3707
175	391	100	1842	2139	2523	2969	3475	4045	4683
175	391	120	2122	2507	2985	3543	4181	4904	5715
175	391	140	2412	2877	3456	4135	4915	5803	6805
200	447	40	979	1101	1252	1424	1613	1818	2040
200	447	60	1330	1510	1737	1996	2284	2601	2948
200	447	80	1667	1907	2216	2570	2968	3410	3899
200	447	100	1979	2299	2696	3154	3673	4254	4901
200	447	120	2294	2689	3181	3752	4402	5135	5956
200	447	140	2605	3081	3674	4365	5158	6056	7065
225	503	40	1054	1181	1339	1519	1715	1929	2159
225	503	60	1430	1617	1853	2122	2420	2748	3104
225	503	80	1794	2039	2359	2725	3134	3588	4087
225	503	100	2124	2453	2863	3335	3866	4459	5116
225	503	120	2460	2866	3371	3956	4619	5364	6195
225	503	140	2791	3278	3885	4591	5396	6305	7324
250	559	40	1126	1258	1423	1610	1815	2037	2275
250	559	60	1529	1720	1966	2245	2553	2890	3257
250	559	80	1900	2166	2497	2875	3297	3761	4271
250	559	100	2265	2603	3026	3511	4055	4659	5328
250	559	120	2621	3037	3557	4155	4832	5589	6430
250	559	140	2972	3469	4092	4812	5631	6552	7581
275	615	40	1196	1333	1505	1699	1912	2142	2388
275	615	60	1625	1821	2075	2364	2683	3030	3406
275	615	80	2016	2290	2632	3022	3455	3931	4452
275	615	100	2401	2749	3184	3682	4239	4856	5536
275	615	120	2778	3204	3737	4350	5040	5810	6663
275	615	140	3149	3656	4293	5028	5861	6795	7835
300	671	40	1264	1405	1584	1786	2007	2244	2498
300	671	60	1720	1919	2182	2481	2809	3166	3552
300	671	80	2129	2411	2764	3165	3610	4097	4629
300	671	100	2535	2891	3339	3850	4420	5049	5741
300	671	120	2932	3366	3913	4541	5245	6027	6893
300	671	140	3323	3837	4490	5241	6088	7035	8087
325	727	40	1331	1476	1662	1871	2099	2344	2606
325	727	60	1797	2014	2286	2594	2932	3299	3695
325	727	80	2239	2528	2892	3305	3761	4260	4803
325	727	100	2666	3030	3490	4014	4597	5239	5943
325	727	120	3083	3525	4086	4727	5446	6242	7120
325	727	140	3493	4015	4682	5449	6310	7271	8336
350	783	40	1397	1546	1738	1954	2189	2442	2711
350	783	60	1884	2107	2388	2706	3053	3430	3835
350	783	80	2347	2644	3018	3442	3910	4420	4975
350	783	100	2794	3166	3638	4175	4771	5426	6142
350	783	120	3231	3680	4255	4911	5643	6453	7343
350	783	140	3638	4189	4871	5653	6530	7505	8583
375	839	40	1461	1614	1812	2035	2277	2537	2814
375	839	60	1970	2199	2488	2815	3172	3558	3973
375	839	80	2453	2757	3141	3576	4055	4577	5143
375	839	100	2920	3299	3783	4333	4942	5609	6337
375	839	120	3377	3833	4421	5091	5837	6660	7564
375	839	140	3797	4360	5057	5854	6746	7735	8827
400	894	40	1525	1680	1885	2115	2364	2631	2915
400	894	60	2053	2288	2586	2922	3288	3684	4108
400	894	80	2558	2868	3262	3708	4199	4732	5308
400	894	100	3045	3430	3926	4488	5110	5790	6531
400	894	120	3497	3982	4584	5268	6028	6865	7782
400	894	140	3953	4528	5239	6051	6958	7962	9067

NOTE: Detector time constant at a reference velocity of 5 ft/sec.
For SI Units: 1 ft = 0.305 m
1000 BTU/sec = 1055 kW

Table B-4.1(cc)
Installed Spacing of Heat Detector: 25 feet
t_g: 300 Seconds to 1000 Btu/sec
α: 0.011 Btu/sec^3

τ	RTI	ΔT	CEILING HEIGHT IN FEET 4.0	8.0	12.0	16.0	20.0	24.0	28.0
			FIRE SIZE AT DETECTOR RESPONSE (BTU / SEC)						
25	56	40	234	307	397	505	632	776	939
25	56	60	341	470	631	820	1041	1293	1578
25	56	80	456	652	895	1181	1510	1887	2314
25	56	100	578	853	1186	1579	2030	2548	3134
25	56	120	708	1069	1503	2013	2599	3270	4030
25	56	140	847	1301	1843	2479	3210	4048	4996
50	112	40	317	389	481	589	716	861	1026
50	112	60	450	573	730	919	1140	1393	1680
50	112	80	583	772	1009	1291	1621	2000	2428
50	112	100	722	984	1312	1699	2153	2672	3259
50	112	120	869	1211	1638	2146	2731	3404	4166
50	112	140	1017	1452	1987	2621	3352	4191	5142
75	168	40	389	465	559	671	801	948	1113
75	168	60	545	670	829	1020	1241	1495	1783
75	168	80	698	885	1121	1404	1735	2114	2544
75	168	100	855	1113	1436	1824	2277	2797	3386
75	168	120	1016	1354	1776	2277	2865	3540	4304
75	168	140	1182	1606	2134	2761	3495	4336	5289
100	224	40	455	534	633	750	882	1032	1201
100	224	60	631	761	924	1118	1342	1598	1887
100	224	80	804	994	1233	1518	1849	2230	2661
100	224	100	978	1237	1562	1950	2403	2925	3515
100	224	120	1156	1491	1910	2413	3001	3677	4443
100	224	140	1337	1758	2278	2906	3640	4483	5438
125	280	40	515	598	703	824	961	1115	1287
125	280	60	712	846	1015	1213	1441	1700	1992
125	280	80	905	1098	1341	1630	1964	2347	2780
125	280	100	1095	1357	1685	2075	2530	3053	3645
125	280	120	1289	1625	2046	2550	3139	3816	4583
125	280	140	1484	1902	2425	3053	3787	4631	5588
150	335	40	576	659	769	895	1037	1196	1371
150	335	60	788	927	1102	1305	1538	1801	2096
150	335	80	996	1197	1446	1739	2077	2463	2899
150	335	100	1206	1472	1805	2199	2657	3182	3777
150	335	120	1415	1755	2180	2686	3277	3955	4725
150	335	140	1626	2044	2571	3200	3935	4780	5739
175	391	40	629	718	832	963	1110	1274	1454
175	391	60	865	1005	1186	1395	1633	1900	2199
175	391	80	1087	1292	1548	1846	2189	2579	3018
175	391	100	1312	1583	1922	2321	2783	3311	3908
175	391	120	1536	1880	2310	2821	3415	4096	4867
175	391	140	1763	2183	2714	3346	4083	4930	5891
200	447	40	680	773	893	1029	1181	1349	1534
200	447	60	931	1080	1266	1482	1725	1998	2301
200	447	80	1173	1384	1646	1951	2299	2694	3136
200	447	100	1414	1691	2036	2441	2908	3440	4040
200	447	120	1654	2002	2438	2954	3552	4236	5011
200	447	140	1887	2318	2855	3491	4231	5081	6044
225	503	40	729	827	951	1093	1250	1423	1612
225	503	60	996	1152	1344	1566	1815	2093	2402
225	503	80	1257	1473	1741	2053	2407	2807	3254
225	503	100	1513	1795	2147	2559	3031	3568	4172
225	503	120	1769	2120	2564	3086	3689	4377	5154
225	503	140	2012	2450	2993	3634	4379	5232	6198
250	559	40	778	879	1008	1155	1317	1495	1689
250	559	60	1063	1222	1420	1648	1903	2187	2501
250	559	80	1338	1559	1835	2153	2514	2919	3371
250	559	100	1610	1896	2256	2674	3153	3695	4303
250	559	120	1871	2235	2686	3215	3824	4516	5298
250	559	140	2134	2578	3128	3776	4526	5383	6352
275	615	40	824	930	1063	1215	1382	1565	1764
275	615	60	1126	1290	1494	1728	1989	2279	2598
275	615	80	1418	1643	1925	2250	2618	3029	3486
275	615	100	1705	1995	2362	2788	3273	3821	4434
275	615	120	1976	2347	2807	3343	3957	4655	5441
275	615	140	2253	2703	3261	3916	4672	5534	6507
300	671	40	875	980	1117	1273	1446	1633	1837
300	671	60	1188	1357	1567	1806	2074	2369	2694
300	671	80	1495	1725	2014	2346	2720	3138	3601
300	671	100	1788	2091	2466	2899	3391	3945	4564
300	671	120	2080	2457	2924	3468	4090	4793	5584
300	671	140	2369	2826	3392	4055	4817	5684	6661
325	727	40	916	1028	1170	1331	1508	1701	1909
325	727	60	1249	1422	1637	1883	2156	2458	2788
325	727	80	1571	1805	2101	2440	2821	3245	3714
325	727	100	1876	2185	2567	3008	3508	4068	4692
325	727	120	2181	2565	3040	3591	4220	4930	5726
325	727	140	2482	2946	3521	4191	4960	5833	6815
350	783	40	958	1075	1221	1387	1569	1766	1980
350	783	60	1308	1485	1706	1958	2238	2545	2881
350	783	80	1647	1884	2186	2532	2920	3350	3825
350	783	100	1962	2277	2667	3116	3623	4189	4820
350	783	120	2279	2670	3153	3713	4349	5066	5868
350	783	140	2593	3064	3647	4326	5102	5981	6968
375	839	40	1000	1121	1272	1442	1628	1831	2049
375	839	60	1367	1547	1774	2032	2317	2630	2972
375	839	80	1721	1960	2269	2623	3017	3454	3935
375	839	100	2047	2368	2765	3222	3736	4310	4946
375	839	120	2376	2774	3265	3833	4477	5200	6008
375	839	140	2702	3179	3771	4459	5243	6128	7121
400	894	40	1042	1166	1321	1496	1687	1894	2117
400	894	60	1424	1608	1841	2104	2396	2715	3062
400	894	80	1781	2036	2352	2712	3113	3557	4044
400	894	100	2130	2457	2862	3326	3848	4428	5072
400	894	120	2472	2875	3375	3951	4603	5334	6148
400	894	140	2809	3293	3894	4590	5382	6274	7273

NOTE: Detector time constant at a reference velocity of 5 ft/sec.
For SI Units: 1 ft = 0.305 m
1000 BTU/sec = 1055 kW

Table B-4.1(dd)
Installed Spacing of Heat Detector: 25 feet
t_g: 600 Seconds to 1000 Btu/sec
α: 0.003 Btu/sec^3

τ	RTI	ΔT	4.0	8.0	12.0	16.0	20.0	24.0	28.0
			CEILING HEIGHT IN FEET						
			FIRE SIZE AT DETECTOR RESPONSE (BTU / SEC)						
25	56	40	211	283	373	479	603	744	904
25	56	60	313	441	601	789	1005	1254	1534
25	56	80	423	620	860	1143	1468	1841	2262
25	56	100	542	817	1148	1536	1983	2495	3074
25	56	120	669	1030	1460	1965	2546	3211	3964
25	56	140	804	1259	1797	2427	3153	3983	4923
50	112	40	283	353	442	548	672	814	975
50	112	60	404	529	683	869	1087	1336	1618
50	112	80	531	719	954	1233	1559	1933	2356
50	112	100	663	925	1250	1638	2084	2597	3178
50	112	120	801	1146	1571	2075	2655	3322	4076
50	112	140	946	1383	1915	2544	3269	4102	5044
75	168	40	345	417	509	617	742	885	1047
75	168	60	488	610	766	952	1170	1419	1702
75	168	80	630	814	1047	1326	1653	2027	2451
75	168	100	776	1034	1356	1738	2186	2701	3283
75	168	120	928	1265	1685	2183	2766	3434	4190
75	168	140	1085	1509	2036	2663	3387	4221	5166
100	224	40	402	477	572	683	811	956	1119
100	224	60	563	688	846	1034	1253	1504	1788
100	224	80	721	907	1141	1421	1747	2122	2548
100	224	100	885	1138	1458	1841	2290	2805	3389
100	224	120	1048	1383	1796	2295	2878	3546	4304
100	224	140	1218	1636	2158	2779	3507	4342	5288
125	280	40	454	533	632	747	878	1026	1191
125	280	60	633	761	923	1115	1336	1589	1874
125	280	80	807	996	1233	1514	1842	2219	2645
125	280	100	983	1240	1561	1946	2395	2911	3496
125	280	120	1162	1494	1910	2408	2991	3661	4420
125	280	140	1344	1762	2278	2900	3628	4464	5412
150	335	40	504	586	689	808	942	1094	1262
150	335	60	699	832	998	1193	1418	1673	1961
150	335	80	891	1082	1322	1607	1937	2315	2743
150	335	100	1079	1339	1663	2049	2500	3017	3604
150	335	120	1271	1605	2022	2521	3105	3776	4537
150	335	140	1466	1880	2399	3021	3750	4587	5536
175	391	40	555	637	743	866	1005	1160	1332
175	391	60	762	899	1070	1270	1498	1757	2047
175	391	80	966	1164	1409	1698	2031	2412	2842
175	391	100	1171	1435	1763	2152	2605	3124	3712
175	391	120	1376	1713	2133	2634	3219	3891	4654
175	391	140	1583	1999	2520	3143	3872	4710	5662
200	447	40	599	685	796	923	1066	1225	1400
200	447	60	822	964	1140	1344	1577	1839	2133
200	447	80	1042	1243	1494	1787	2124	2508	2941
200	447	100	1260	1527	1860	2254	2710	3231	3822
200	447	120	1478	1817	2242	2746	3334	4008	4772
200	447	140	1697	2114	2639	3265	3995	4835	5788

τ	RTI	ΔT	4.0	8.0	12.0	16.0	20.0	24.0	28.0
			CEILING HEIGHT IN FEET						
			FIRE SIZE AT DETECTOR RESPONSE (BTU / SEC)						
225	503	40	642	732	847	978	1126	1288	1467
225	503	60	884	1027	1208	1417	1654	1921	2218
225	503	80	1114	1320	1576	1874	2216	2603	3039
225	503	100	1345	1617	1956	2354	2814	3338	3931
225	503	120	1576	1919	2349	2857	3448	4124	4891
225	503	140	1809	2228	2757	3385	4118	4960	5915
250	559	40	684	777	896	1032	1183	1350	1533
250	559	60	938	1088	1273	1488	1730	2001	2302
250	559	80	1185	1395	1656	1960	2306	2698	3137
250	559	100	1429	1705	2049	2452	2916	3445	4040
250	559	120	1673	2019	2454	2967	3561	4241	5010
250	559	140	1908	2338	2872	3505	4241	5085	6042
275	615	40	724	822	944	1084	1240	1411	1597
275	615	60	992	1147	1338	1557	1804	2079	2384
275	615	80	1253	1468	1735	2044	2395	2791	3234
275	615	100	1510	1791	2141	2549	3018	3550	4150
275	615	120	1767	2116	2557	3076	3674	4357	5129
275	615	140	2011	2447	2986	3624	4363	5210	6170
300	671	40	764	865	991	1135	1295	1470	1661
300	671	60	1047	1205	1400	1625	1877	2157	2466
300	671	80	1320	1540	1812	2126	2483	2884	3331
300	671	100	1590	1874	2230	2645	3119	3656	4258
300	671	120	1850	2212	2659	3183	3786	4473	5248
300	671	140	2112	2553	3099	3742	4485	5336	6298
325	727	40	803	907	1037	1185	1349	1528	1723
325	727	60	1100	1261	1462	1691	1948	2233	2547
325	727	80	1386	1609	1887	2207	2570	2975	3427
325	727	100	1669	1956	2318	2739	3219	3760	4367
325	727	120	1938	2305	2759	3289	3897	4588	5367
325	727	140	2210	2657	3209	3858	4606	5461	6426
350	783	40	841	948	1082	1234	1402	1585	1783
350	783	60	1151	1316	1522	1756	2018	2308	2626
350	783	80	1451	1677	1961	2287	2655	3065	3522
350	783	100	1746	2036	2405	2832	3317	3863	4474
350	783	120	2024	2396	2857	3393	4007	4703	5485
350	783	140	2307	2759	3318	3973	4727	5585	6554
375	839	40	882	988	1126	1282	1453	1641	1843
375	839	60	1202	1371	1581	1820	2087	2382	2705
375	839	80	1514	1744	2034	2365	2739	3155	3616
375	839	100	1812	2115	2490	2923	3414	3966	4581
375	839	120	2108	2486	2953	3496	4116	4817	5603
375	839	140	2402	2859	3425	4087	4846	5709	6682
400	894	40	916	1027	1169	1329	1504	1696	1902
400	894	60	1251	1424	1639	1883	2155	2455	2782
400	894	80	1577	1810	2105	2443	2822	3243	3709
400	894	100	1884	2193	2574	3013	3510	4067	4688
400	894	120	2191	2575	3049	3598	4224	4930	5721
400	894	140	2495	2958	3531	4199	4965	5833	6809

NOTE: Detector time constant at a reference velocity of 5 ft/sec.
For SI Units: 1 ft = 0.305 m
1000 BTU/sec = 1055 kW

Table B-4.1(ee)
Installed Spacing of Heat Detector: 30 ft.
t_g: 50 Seconds to 1000 Btu/sec
α: 0.400 Btu/sec^3

τ	RTI	ΔT	CEILING HEIGHT IN FEET 4.0	8.0	12.0	16.0	20.0	24.0	28.0	τ	RTI	ΔT	CEILING HEIGHT IN FEET 4.0	8.0	12.0	16.0	20.0	24.0	28.0
			FIRE SIZE AT DETECTOR RESPONSE (BTU / SEC)										FIRE SIZE AT DETECTOR RESPONSE (BTU / SEC)						
25	56	40	1541	1757	1963	2204	2475	2773	3096	225	503	40	5480	5821	6309	6882	7509	8174	8873
25	56	60	2013	2288	2589	2944	3344	3788	4276	225	503	60	7117	7642	8320	9106	9963	10875	11835
25	56	80	2472	2801	3207	3687	4231	4839	5512	225	503	80	8688	9332	10193	11189	12273	13430	14652
25	56	100	2925	3307	3828	4445	5148	5936	6813	225	503	100	10171	10936	11980	13185	14498	15902	17388
25	56	120	3311	3811	4458	5223	6098	7084	8183	225	503	120	11590	12477	13707	15122	16667	18321	20077
25	56	140	3718	4318	5100	6024	7084	8283	9621	225	503	140	12958	13973	15390	17018	18797	20707	22739
50	112	40	2231	2480	2735	3032	3361	3718	4101	250	559	40	5868	6207	6721	7327	7988	8689	9425
50	112	60	2986	3235	3592	4014	4484	4997	5550	250	559	60	7610	8154	8869	9698	10600	11560	12569
50	112	80	3587	3941	4414	4970	5590	6270	7009	250	559	80	9298	9962	10868	11915	13056	14271	15552
50	112	100	4208	4627	5222	5918	6698	7558	8499	250	559	100	10891	11674	12772	14038	15416	16888	18443
50	112	120	4810	5300	6023	6868	7819	8873	10031	250	559	120	12415	13320	14610	16095	17713	19444	21279
50	112	140	5293	5963	6823	7827	8959	10219	11610	250	559	140	13884	14914	16399	18105	19967	21961	24080
75	168	40	2867	3087	3379	3725	4106	4517	4955	275	615	40	6248	6582	7121	7758	8452	9188	9959
75	168	60	3727	4024	4437	4922	5458	6038	6659	275	615	60	8091	8651	9402	10272	11218	12224	13280
75	168	80	4572	4905	5441	6070	6768	7525	8340	275	615	80	9892	10572	11522	12620	13815	15086	16425
75	168	100	5231	5745	6416	7196	8061	9006	10029	275	615	100	11594	12391	13540	14865	16307	17844	19467
75	168	120	5958	6567	7375	8311	9354	10496	11739	275	615	120	13221	14137	15486	17039	18729	20535	22446
75	168	140	6664	7375	8324	9424	10652	12003	13479	275	615	140	14789	15828	17379	19161	21102	23180	25383
100	224	40	3365	3621	3952	4342	4771	5232	5719	300	671	40	6623	6947	7510	8176	8902	9672	10478
100	224	60	4462	4734	5193	5736	6333	6976	7661	300	671	60	8560	9135	9919	10830	11819	12870	13972
100	224	80	5310	5761	6363	7062	7832	8664	9554	300	671	80	10474	11166	12158	13306	14553	15879	17274
100	224	100	6213	6751	7492	8352	9300	10329	11434	300	671	100	12283	13089	14287	15670	17174	18775	20464
100	224	120	7081	7711	8596	9621	10755	11989	13321	300	671	120	14013	14933	16339	17957	19718	21596	23582
100	224	140	7923	8650	9684	10880	12207	13655	15225	300	671	140	15680	16719	18333	20188	22208	24366	26652
125	280	40	3870	4115	4479	4909	5383	5888	6423	325	727	40	6827	7290	7888	8584	9342	10144	10984
125	280	60	4990	5377	5889	6486	7141	7843	8588	325	727	60	9019	9606	10424	11373	12405	13499	14646
125	280	80	6091	6557	7214	7978	8817	9720	10682	325	727	80	11045	11746	12779	13974	15273	16652	18102
125	280	100	7137	7682	8488	9423	10450	11560	12747	325	727	100	12961	13769	15016	16455	18019	19683	21436
125	280	120	8143	8770	9728	10838	12060	13383	14805	325	727	120	14793	15710	17170	18853	20683	22632	24690
125	280	140	8954	9826	10946	12235	13658	15203	16869	325	727	140	16294	17578	19263	21190	23287	25524	27891
150	335	40	4248	4569	4970	5440	5954	6503	7082	350	783	40	7161	7635	8257	8982	9770	10605	11478
150	335	60	5589	5987	6541	7189	7898	8856	9459	350	783	60	9470	10067	10917	11905	12977	14114	15305
150	335	80	6837	7304	8013	8838	9743	10713	11744	350	783	80	11607	12312	13385	14627	15976	17408	18912
150	335	100	7873	8550	9423	10430	11533	12720	13986	350	783	100	13629	14435	15728	17223	18845	20570	22386
150	335	120	8963	9758	10793	11984	13291	14701	16210	350	783	120	15303	16459	17983	19729	21626	23645	25774
150	335	140	10016	10935	12134	13513	15029	16669	18430	350	783	140	17103	18426	20172	22170	24341	26656	29103
175	391	40	4673	5004	5436	5942	6496	7085	7706	375	839	40	7488	7973	8619	9371	10190	11055	11961
175	391	60	6166	6565	7160	7856	8616	9428	10285	375	839	60	9914	10518	11400	12424	13537	14715	15949
175	391	80	7411	8005	8771	9655	10622	11657	12754	375	839	80	12161	12867	13978	15266	16664	18147	19703
175	391	100	8667	9379	10311	11387	12563	13825	15166	375	839	100	14054	15076	16425	17974	19654	21439	23316
175	391	120	9870	10702	11805	13073	14462	15956	17550	375	839	120	16012	17201	18779	20587	22549	24636	26835
175	391	140	11031	11989	13264	14729	16336	18068	19921	375	839	140	17897	19256	21063	23129	25374	27765	30289
200	447	40	5082	5421	5881	6422	7012	7641	8301	400	894	40	7810	8304	8973	9753	10600	11497	12433
200	447	60	6726	7119	7752	8493	9303	10165	11075	400	894	60	10351	10960	11873	12934	14085	15304	16580
200	447	80	8060	8681	9496	10437	11464	12561	13721	400	894	80	12709	13411	14560	15893	17339	18872	20480
200	447	100	9432	10172	11162	12303	13549	14883	16298	400	894	100	14664	15714	17108	18710	20447	22291	24228
200	447	120	10744	11607	12774	14117	15585	17160	18837	400	894	120	16709	17929	19559	21427	23454	25608	27876
200	447	140	12010	12999	14347	15895	17589	19411	21355	400	894	140	18677	20070	21936	24070	26387	28853	31453

NOTE: Detector time constant at a reference velocity of 5 ft/sec.
For SI Units: 1 ft = 0.305 m
1000 BTU/sec = 1055 kW

Table B-4.1(ff)
Installed Spacing of Heat Detector: 30 feet
t_g: 150 Seconds to 1000 Btu/sec
α: 0.044 Btu/sec^3

τ	RTI	ΔT	CEILING HEIGHT IN FEET 4.0	8.0	12.0	16.0	20.0	24.0	28.0
			FIRE SIZE AT DETECTOR RESPONSE (BTU / SEC)						
25	56	40	684	780	911	1066	1243	1443	1665
25	56	60	919	1084	1300	1556	1850	2183	2555
25	56	80	1150	1399	1715	2088	2518	3005	3550
25	56	100	1387	1728	2157	2663	3245	3904	4641
25	56	120	1629	2072	2626	3278	4026	4872	5819
25	56	140	1877	2432	3122	3931	4858	5906	7077
50	112	40	958	1073	1220	1391	1583	1796	2030
50	112	60	1284	1465	1696	1965	2270	2613	2992
50	112	80	1603	1856	2182	2563	3000	3492	4042
50	112	100	1919	2251	2683	3192	3775	4436	5177
50	112	120	2217	2654	3203	3852	4598	5445	6394
50	112	140	2526	3066	3743	4544	5467	6514	7688
75	168	40	1194	1323	1486	1675	1885	2116	2366
75	168	60	1604	1795	2044	2334	2659	3019	3414
75	168	80	2004	2257	2602	3004	3459	3967	4529
75	168	100	2361	2716	3168	3694	4294	4967	5717
75	168	120	2732	3178	3745	4408	5166	6022	6978
75	168	140	3100	3645	4337	5148	6078	7131	8311
100	224	40	1409	1547	1726	1932	2161	2409	2678
100	224	60	1901	2093	2362	2672	3019	3399	3814
100	224	80	2335	2620	2988	3414	3891	4420	5001
100	224	100	2773	3141	3616	4167	4789	5481	6248
100	224	120	3203	3660	4251	4938	5716	6589	7560
100	224	140	3628	4180	4895	5728	6677	7745	8937
125	280	40	1611	1755	1948	2171	2417	2683	2969
125	280	60	2148	2368	2657	2988	3356	3758	4193
125	280	80	2662	2958	3349	3798	4300	4851	5454
125	280	100	3159	3537	4037	4614	5261	5977	6765
125	280	120	3647	4110	4728	5441	6245	7141	8131
125	280	140	4092	4682	5424	6284	7257	8346	9556
150	335	40	1806	1950	2157	2396	2658	2941	3244
150	335	60	2398	2628	2934	3287	3676	4098	4555
150	335	80	2972	3277	3689	4163	4689	5264	5890
150	335	100	3528	3911	4436	5039	5712	6454	7266
150	335	120	4029	4536	5181	5923	6754	7675	8689
150	335	140	4548	5157	5928	6818	7819	8933	10164
175	391	40	1996	2135	2355	2609	2888	3187	3507
175	391	60	2637	2875	3199	3571	3981	4424	4901
175	391	80	3271	3581	4014	4511	5061	5661	6310
175	391	100	3839	4267	4816	5447	6146	6914	7751
175	391	120	4417	4942	5614	6385	7245	8193	9233
175	391	140	4982	5611	6411	7331	8362	9504	10761
200	447	40	2137	2311	2544	2813	3108	3423	3759
200	447	60	2867	3111	3452	3844	4273	4738	5235
200	447	80	3521	3871	4326	4846	5420	6043	6716
200	447	100	4165	4609	5182	5839	6565	7359	8222
200	447	120	4790	5332	6030	6830	7720	8696	9762
200	447	140	5400	6047	6876	7827	8888	10060	11344

τ	RTI	ΔT	CEILING HEIGHT IN FEET 4.0	8.0	12.0	16.0	20.0	24.0	28.0
			FIRE SIZE AT DETECTOR RESPONSE (BTU / SEC)						
225	503	40	2301	2481	2727	3010	3319	3650	4002
225	503	60	3092	3339	3697	4107	4556	5040	5558
225	503	80	3788	4151	4626	5169	5766	6413	7110
225	503	100	4480	4938	5535	6217	6971	7791	8680
225	503	120	5150	5709	6433	7262	8180	9185	10279
225	503	140	5805	6468	7326	8308	9400	10601	11914
250	559	40	2461	2645	2903	3200	3524	3870	4237
250	559	60	3312	3559	3933	4361	4829	5333	5871
250	559	80	4047	4423	4917	5482	6102	6772	7492
250	559	100	4786	5257	5877	6585	7364	8211	9126
250	559	120	5501	6073	6823	7680	8627	9662	10783
250	559	140	6198	6876	7762	8775	9898	11130	12472
275	615	40	2616	2805	3075	3385	3722	4083	4465
275	615	60	3479	3772	4162	4608	5095	5618	6175
275	615	80	4299	4686	5200	5786	6428	7122	7865
275	615	100	5083	5567	6209	6942	7747	8620	956
275	615	120	5842	6427	7203	8087	9063	10126	11276
275	615	140	6582	7272	8186	9230	10385	11647	13019
300	671	40	2769	2960	3241	3564	3916	4291	4687
300	671	60	3677	3980	4385	4848	5354	5895	6472
300	671	80	4545	4942	5475	6082	6747	7463	8228
300	671	100	5374	5869	6533	7290	8121	9020	9986
300	671	120	6177	6772	7572	8485	9489	10581	11759
300	671	140	6959	7659	8600	9674	10859	12153	13555
325	727	40	2919	3112	3403	3739	4104	4493	4904
325	727	60	3871	4183	4603	5083	5606	6166	6761
325	727	80	4786	5193	5743	6371	7058	7796	8584
325	727	100	5659	6164	6849	7630	8486	9411	10402
325	727	120	6505	7109	7933	8873	9905	11025	12232
325	727	140	7329	8036	9004	10108	11324	12649	14081
350	783	40	3066	3260	3562	3910	4288	4691	5116
350	783	60	4061	4382	4816	5312	5853	6431	7044
350	783	80	5022	5437	6006	6654	7362	8122	8932
350	783	100	5940	6452	7158	7963	8843	9793	10810
350	783	120	6828	7439	8287	9253	10313	11461	12696
350	783	140	7693	8405	9400	10533	11780	13135	14597
375	839	40	3213	3405	3717	4077	4468	4884	5323
375	839	60	4248	4576	5024	5537	6095	6691	7322
375	839	80	5254	5677	6263	6931	7660	8441	9273
375	839	100	6215	6734	7461	8289	9194	10168	11211
375	839	120	7147	7762	8633	9625	10713	11889	13151
375	839	140	7974	8766	9788	10950	12227	13612	15105
400	894	40	3308	3546	3870	4242	4645	5074	5526
400	894	60	4431	4766	5229	5757	6332	6945	7594
400	894	80	5482	5912	6515	7203	7952	8755	9608
400	894	100	6488	7011	7758	8609	9538	10537	11604
400	894	120	7389	8077	8973	9991	11106	12309	13599
400	894	140	8311	9121	10168	11359	12666	14081	15604

NOTE: Detector time constant at a reference velocity of 5 ft/sec.
For SI Units: 1 ft = 0.305 m
1000 BTU/sec = 1055 kW

Table B-4.1(gg)
Installed Spacing of Heat Detector: 30 feet
t_g: 300 Seconds to 1000 Btu/sec
α: 0.011 Btu/sec^3

τ	RTI	ΔT	CEILING HEIGHT IN FEET 4.0	8.0	12.0	16.0	20.0	24.0	28.0
			FIRE SIZE AT DETECTOR RESPONSE (BTU / SEC)						
25	56	40	422	511	625	761	916	1093	1290
25	56	60	594	753	952	1187	1456	1761	2101
25	56	80	772	1018	1316	1666	2068	2520	3026
25	56	100	958	1302	1717	2194	2743	3361	4052
25	56	120	1154	1606	2147	2766	3476	4275	5169
25	56	140	1359	1930	2605	3378	4262	5257	6369
50	112	40	587	675	793	931	1089	1267	1466
50	112	60	805	961	1159	1392	1661	1965	2307
50	112	80	1023	1259	1552	1898	2297	2749	3256
50	112	100	1249	1572	1974	2447	2993	3611	4304
50	112	120	1478	1901	2424	3038	3745	4545	5441
50	112	140	1714	2251	2901	3668	4549	5545	6660
75	168	40	723	818	943	1089	1253	1437	1640
75	168	60	985	1148	1352	1591	1864	2171	2515
75	168	80	1248	1484	1780	2128	2528	2982	3491
75	168	100	1510	1830	2230	2703	3248	3867	4561
75	168	120	1775	2187	2705	3315	4020	4820	5717
75	168	140	2036	2558	3203	3964	4842	5838	6955
100	224	40	846	949	1081	1235	1408	1599	1809
100	224	60	1152	1320	1533	1780	2060	2374	2723
100	224	80	1453	1693	1997	2352	2757	3215	3728
100	224	100	1753	2072	2478	2955	3503	4124	4821
100	224	120	2041	2459	2979	3592	4297	5098	5998
100	224	140	2337	2856	3501	4261	5138	6135	7253
125	280	40	959	1069	1210	1373	1554	1753	1971
125	280	60	1307	1481	1703	1960	2249	2571	2927
125	280	80	1646	1889	2203	2567	2981	3446	3963
125	280	100	1968	2300	2716	3201	3755	4381	5082
125	280	120	2294	2717	3245	3864	4574	5378	6280
125	280	140	2619	3142	3792	4556	5436	6434	7555
150	335	40	1068	1183	1332	1503	1693	1901	2126
150	335	60	1454	1633	1864	2131	2430	2761	3126
150	335	80	1831	2075	2399	2774	3198	3671	4196
150	335	100	2178	2518	2944	3439	4003	4636	5342
150	335	120	2534	2964	3502	4130	4847	5657	6564
150	335	140	2888	3416	4075	4847	5732	6734	7859
175	391	40	1171	1292	1448	1627	1826	2042	2276
175	391	60	1595	1778	2019	2296	2605	2946	3319
175	391	80	1989	2253	2588	2974	3409	3892	4425
175	391	100	2379	2726	3164	3671	4245	4887	5601
175	391	120	2763	3201	3751	4389	5116	5934	6847
175	391	140	3145	3679	4350	5131	6025	7034	8163
200	447	40	1270	1395	1559	1747	1954	2179	2421
200	447	60	1733	1917	2167	2455	2774	3125	3508
200	447	80	2152	2424	2770	3168	3614	4107	4650
200	447	100	2572	2927	3377	3896	4481	5133	5856
200	447	120	2985	3429	3991	4642	5380	6207	7129
200	447	140	3394	3934	4617	5410	6313	7331	8467
225	503	40	1367	1495	1666	1862	2077	2311	2562
225	503	60	1849	2051	2311	2608	2938	3299	3692
225	503	80	2310	2589	2946	3356	3813	4318	4871
225	503	100	2759	3121	3583	4115	4712	5375	6108
225	503	120	3200	3651	4226	4889	5639	6477	7407
225	503	140	3636	4181	4877	5683	6598	7625	8770
250	559	40	1460	1592	1770	1974	2197	2439	2698
250	559	60	1973	2181	2450	2758	3098	3469	3872
250	559	80	2464	2749	3117	3539	4007	4523	5088
250	559	100	2941	3309	3783	4328	4939	5613	6357
250	559	120	3409	3865	4453	5131	5893	6743	7684
250	559	140	3872	4421	5131	5951	6878	7916	9070
275	615	40	1552	1686	1871	2082	2314	2564	2831
275	615	60	2093	2307	2585	2903	3253	3635	4048
275	615	80	2613	2905	3284	3717	4197	4725	5300
275	615	100	3118	3492	3979	4536	5159	5846	6601
275	615	120	3614	4074	4676	5367	6143	7005	7956
275	615	140	4074	4654	5378	6213	7153	8204	9368
300	671	40	1642	1778	1969	2188	2427	2685	2961
300	671	60	2211	2430	2717	3044	3405	3796	4219
300	671	80	2760	3057	3446	3890	4383	4922	5509
300	671	100	3293	3671	4169	4740	5375	6075	6842
300	671	120	3789	4278	4893	5598	6388	7263	8226
300	671	140	4292	4882	5621	6470	7424	8487	9663
325	727	40	1732	1867	2065	2291	2538	2804	3088
325	727	60	2325	2550	2845	3182	3553	3955	4388
325	727	80	2903	3205	3604	4061	4565	5116	5713
325	727	100	3464	3845	4356	4939	5588	6300	7079
325	727	120	3979	4477	5105	5825	6628	7516	8492
325	727	140	4505	5105	5858	6722	7691	8767	9955
350	783	40	1801	1954	2158	2392	2646	2920	3212
350	783	60	2438	2667	2971	3318	3698	4110	4553
350	783	80	3044	3350	3760	4227	4743	5305	5915
350	783	100	3605	4016	4538	5135	5796	6522	7313
350	783	120	4165	4672	5314	6047	6865	7767	8755
350	783	140	4714	5324	6091	6970	7954	9044	10245
375	839	40	1882	2039	2250	2490	2753	3034	3333
375	839	60	2549	2782	3094	3450	3840	4262	4715
375	839	80	3183	3492	3912	4390	4918	5492	6113
375	839	100	3764	4183	4717	5326	6001	6740	7543
375	839	120	4347	4864	5518	6266	7098	8013	9014
375	839	140	4918	5538	6319	7213	8212	9317	10531
400	894	40	1962	2123	2340	2587	2857	3146	3453
400	894	60	2657	2894	3215	3580	3980	4412	4875
400	894	80	3320	3631	4061	4551	5090	5676	6308
400	894	100	3920	4347	4893	5515	6203	6954	7770
400	894	120	4526	5051	5719	6481	7327	8256	9271
400	894	140	5119	5748	6544	7453	8467	9586	10814

NOTE: Detector time constant at a reference velocity of 5 ft/sec.
For SI Units: 1 ft = 0.305 m
1000 BTU/sec = 1055 kW

Table B-4.1(hh)
Installed Spacing of Heat Detector: 30 feet
t_g: 500 Seconds to 1000 Btu/sec
α: 0.004 Btu/sec^3

τ	RTI	ΔT	CEILING HEIGHT IN FEET 4.0	8.0	12.0	16.0	20.0	24.0	28.0
			FIRE SIZE AT DETECTOR RESPONSE (BTU / SEC)						
25	56	40	310	397	506	634	781	947	1132
25	56	60	455	615	810	1034	1292	1582	1906
25	56	80	609	858	1153	1490	1877	2312	2798
25	56	100	777	1124	1531	1997	2527	3125	3793
25	56	120	955	1413	1943	2552	3237	4013	4880
25	56	140	1145	1722	2385	3145	4001	4970	6052
50	112	40	416	501	608	735	881	1047	1232
50	112	60	591	742	930	1153	1409	1699	2024
50	112	80	770	1002	1288	1623	2008	2444	2931
50	112	100	958	1285	1683	2142	2672	3270	3939
50	112	120	1154	1586	2106	2705	3393	4170	5039
50	112	140	1359	1906	2559	3309	4169	5138	6222
75	168	40	512	595	705	834	981	1148	1334
75	168	60	712	862	1050	1272	1528	1818	2144
75	168	80	918	1144	1426	1759	2142	2578	3066
75	168	100	1127	1443	1832	2291	2819	3417	4087
75	168	120	1344	1762	2268	2866	3552	4329	5199
75	168	140	1567	2095	2736	3480	4338	5308	6394
100	224	40	594	682	795	928	1078	1248	1436
100	224	60	823	975	1166	1390	1647	1939	2266
100	224	805	1053	1280	1562	1894	2278	2714	3202
100	224	100	1285	1598	1984	2441	2968	3566	4237
100	224	120	1522	1930	2434	3028	3713	4490	5361
100	224	140	1765	2277	2910	3653	4509	5480	6567
125	280	40	671	763	881	1018	1173	1345	1537
125	280	60	927	1082	1277	1505	1765	2059	2388
125	280	80	1180	1409	1694	2029	2414	2850	3340
125	280	100	1435	1747	2134	2591	3118	3716	4389
125	280	120	1693	2096	2599	3191	3875	4652	5524
125	280	140	1956	2459	3087	3828	4683	5653	6742
150	335	40	744	839	962	1104	1263	1441	1636
150	335	60	1023	1184	1384	1616	1881	2178	2509
150	335	80	1301	1533	1822	2161	2549	2987	3479
150	335	100	1578	1890	2281	2740	3268	3868	4541
150	335	120	1857	2258	2761	3354	4038	4816	5689
150	335	140	2128	2637	3264	4004	4858	5828	6918
175	391	40	813	912	1040	1187	1351	1533	1733
175	391	60	1118	1281	1487	1725	1994	2295	2630
175	391	80	1417	1652	1947	2290	2682	3124	3618
175	391	100	1715	2029	2424	2887	3418	4020	4695
175	391	120	2004	2414	2921	3516	4202	4981	5855
175	391	140	2300	2809	3438	4179	5033	6004	7095
200	447	40	883	982	1115	1267	1436	1623	1827
200	447	60	1208	1375	1586	1830	2104	2410	2749
200	447	80	1529	1767	2067	2416	2813	3259	3757
200	447	100	1840	2163	2564	3031	3566	4171	4849
200	447	120	2153	2566	3077	3677	4365	5146	6022
200	447	140	2466	2977	3610	4353	5209	6181	7274
225	503	40	943	1050	1187	1344	1518	1710	1919
225	503	60	1295	1466	1682	1932	2212	2523	2867
225	503	80	1638	1878	2185	2540	2942	3393	3894
225	503	100	1966	2293	2700	3173	3713	4322	5003
225	503	120	2296	2714	3231	3835	4527	5311	6190
225	503	140	2626	3142	3779	4525	5384	6359	7453
250	559	40	1004	1116	1257	1419	1599	1795	2009
250	559	60	1379	1554	1776	2031	2317	2634	2983
250	559	80	1745	1986	2299	2661	3069	3525	4031
250	559	100	2088	2420	2833	3313	3858	4471	5156
250	559	120	2436	2858	3381	3991	4688	5475	6357
250	559	140	2783	3302	3945	4696	5559	6536	7633
275	615	40	1066	1179	1325	1492	1677	1878	2097
275	615	60	1462	1639	1867	2129	2421	2743	3097
275	615	80	1837	2092	2411	2779	3193	3655	4166
275	615	100	2206	2543	2964	3450	4001	4620	5309
275	615	120	2572	2998	3529	4145	4847	5639	6525
275	615	140	2935	3458	4108	4865	5732	6713	7813
300	671	40	1125	1241	1392	1564	1753	1960	2183
300	671	60	1543	1723	1956	2224	2522	2850	3210
300	671	80	1935	2194	2520	2895	3316	3784	4300
300	671	100	2322	2664	3091	3585	4142	4767	5460
300	671	120	2704	3136	3673	4296	5005	5802	6691
300	671	140	3084	3612	4268	5032	5904	6890	7993
325	727	40	1183	1302	1457	1633	1828	2039	2268
325	727	60	1623	1804	2043	2317	2621	2955	3320
325	727	80	2031	2295	2627	3009	3436	3910	4433
325	727	100	2435	2782	3217	3717	4282	4912	5611
325	727	120	2834	3271	3815	4446	5161	5963	6858
325	727	140	3230	3762	4426	5197	6075	7065	8172
350	783	40	1239	1361	1520	1701	1901	2117	2351
350	783	60	1701	1884	2128	2408	2718	3059	3430
350	783	80	2125	2393	2732	3121	3555	4035	4564
350	783	100	2546	2898	3340	3848	4419	5056	5761
350	783	120	2962	3403	3955	4593	5315	6124	7023
350	783	140	3374	3910	4581	5360	6244	7240	8352
375	839	40	1295	1419	1582	1768	1973	2194	2433
375	839	60	1766	1962	2212	2498	2814	3160	3527
375	839	80	2217	2490	2835	3230	3672	4159	4693
375	839	100	2655	3011	3460	3976	4555	5198	5909
375	839	120	3087	3532	4092	4738	5467	6283	7188
375	839	140	3515	4054	4734	5520	6412	7414	8531
400	894	40	1349	1476	1643	1834	2043	2270	2513
400	894	60	1839	2038	2294	2586	2908	3260	3643
400	894	80	2307	2584	2936	3339	3787	4280	4821
400	894	100	2762	3123	3579	4102	4688	5339	6056
400	894	120	3210	3660	4228	4881	5618	6440	7351
400	894	140	3654	4197	4885	5679	6578	7586	8709

NOTE: Detector time constant at a reference velocity of 5 ft/sec.
For SI Units: 1 ft = 0.305 m
1000 BTU/sec = 1055 kW

Table B-4.1(ii)
Installed Spacing of Heat Detector: 30 feet
t_g: 600 Seconds to 1000 Btu/sec
α: 0.003 Btu/sec^3

τ	RTI	ΔT	CEILING HEIGHT IN FEET 4.0	8.0	12.0	16.0	20.0	24.0	28.0
			FIRE SIZE AT DETECTOR RESPONSE (BTU / SEC)						
25	56	40	281	369	476	602	747	909	1091
25	56	60	419	579	773	995	1249	1535	1855
25	56	80	568	817	1110	1445	1826	2257	2737
25	56	100	730	1079	1484	1948	2470	3062	3723
25	56	120	906	1364	1890	2494	3174	3943	4802
25	56	140	1091	1669	2328	3082	3932	4893	5967
50	112	40	372	455	561	685	828	991	1173
50	112	60	534	685	872	1092	1345	1631	1952
50	112	80	703	938	1221	1554	1935	2365	2847
50	112	100	883	1211	1608	2065	2589	3181	3844
50	112	120	1070	1506	2024	2620	3303	4072	4933
50	112	140	1268	1820	2471	3217	4070	5032	6107
75	168	40	451	536	642	767	911	1074	1257
75	168	60	639	787	972	1191	1443	1729	2050
75	168	80	829	1056	1335	1665	2045	2475	2957
75	168	100	1026	1345	1731	2187	2710	3302	3966
75	168	120	1230	1651	2161	2752	3433	4203	5066
75	168	140	1443	1975	2616	3358	4210	5172	6249
100	224	40	527	610	719	847	993	1157	1341
100	224	60	735	884	1070	1289	1542	1828	2150
100	224	80	946	1171	1449	1777	2156	2587	3070
100	224	100	1162	1473	1857	2310	2833	3425	4089
100	224	120	1383	1792	2295	2886	3565	4336	5199
100	224	140	1611	2131	2760	3500	4351	5314	6392
125	280	40	594	680	793	924	1072	1239	1425
125	280	60	825	976	1165	1386	1640	1928	2250
125	280	80	1056	1281	1561	1890	2269	2700	3183
125	280	100	1290	1600	1983	2435	2956	3549	4214
125	280	120	1529	1933	2432	3020	3699	4469	5334
125	280	140	1773	2281	2907	3644	4494	5456	6536
150	335	40	657	747	863	998	1150	1320	1508
150	335	60	911	1064	1256	1481	1737	2027	2351
150	335	80	1161	1388	1670	2001	2381	2813	3298
150	335	100	1413	1723	2107	2559	3081	3674	4339
150	335	120	1669	2070	2568	3156	3834	4604	5469
150	335	140	1930	2431	3054	3789	4637	5600	6681
175	391	40	717	810	930	1069	1225	1398	1590
175	391	60	990	1148	1345	1573	1833	2126	2452
175	391	80	1261	1491	1776	2110	2493	2926	3413
175	391	100	1532	1842	2229	2683	3205	3799	4466
175	391	120	1805	2204	2703	3291	3969	4740	5606
175	391	140	2073	2578	3201	3935	4782	5745	6827
200	447	40	774	871	995	1138	1298	1475	1670
200	447	60	1069	1229	1430	1663	1927	2223	2552
200	447	80	1358	1590	1880	2217	2603	3039	3528
200	447	100	1646	1958	2348	2805	3330	3925	4593
200	447	120	1929	2335	2836	3426	4105	4877	5744
200	447	140	2217	2723	3346	4080	4928	5891	6974

τ	RTI	ΔT	CEILING HEIGHT IN FEET 4.0	8.0	12.0	16.0	20.0	24.0	28.0
			FIRE SIZE AT DETECTOR RESPONSE (BTU / SEC)						
225	503	40	830	930	1058	1205	1369	1550	1749
225	503	60	1144	1308	1514	1751	2019	2319	2651
225	503	80	1452	1686	1981	2323	2713	3152	3643
225	503	100	1758	2070	2465	2925	3453	4051	4721
225	503	120	2053	2462	2967	3559	4240	5013	5882
225	503	140	2356	2863	3489	4225	5073	6038	7122
250	559	40	887	987	1119	1270	1438	1623	1826
250	559	60	1217	1384	1595	1837	2110	2413	2750
250	559	80	1543	1780	2080	2427	2821	3263	3757
250	559	100	1858	2180	2579	3044	3575	4176	4848
250	559	120	2175	2587	3096	3691	4375	5150	6020
250	559	140	2492	3001	3631	4369	5219	6185	7270
275	615	40	937	1042	1178	1333	1506	1695	1901
275	615	60	1289	1459	1674	1921	2198	2507	2847
275	615	80	1632	1872	2176	2528	2927	3374	3871
275	615	100	1961	2287	2691	3161	3697	4301	4976
275	615	120	2293	2708	3222	3822	4509	5287	6159
275	615	140	2624	3137	3770	4512	5364	6332	7419
300	671	40	987	1096	1236	1395	1572	1765	1976
300	671	60	1358	1531	1751	2003	2285	2598	2943
300	671	80	1720	1961	2271	2628	3032	3483	3984
300	671	100	2062	2392	2802	3277	3817	4424	5103
300	671	120	2408	2827	3347	3951	4642	5423	6298
300	671	140	2753	3269	3907	4653	5509	6479	7568
325	727	40	1037	1149	1292	1456	1637	1834	2049
325	727	60	1427	1602	1827	2084	2371	2688	3037
325	727	80	1796	2048	2364	2726	3135	3591	4096
325	727	100	2160	2495	2910	3391	3936	4548	5229
325	727	120	2521	2944	3469	4079	4775	5559	6437
325	727	140	2879	3399	4043	4794	5653	6626	7717
350	783	40	1087	1201	1348	1515	1700	1902	2120
350	783	60	1494	1671	1901	2163	2455	2777	3131
350	783	80	1878	2134	2454	2823	3237	3698	4207
350	783	100	2257	2595	3016	3503	4053	4670	5355
350	783	120	2631	3059	3590	4205	4906	5694	6576
350	783	140	3003	3527	4177	4932	5796	6773	7867
375	839	40	1135	1251	1402	1573	1762	1968	2191
375	839	60	1560	1740	1973	2241	2538	2865	3223
375	839	80	1958	2218	2544	2918	3338	3804	4318
375	839	100	2351	2694	3121	3613	4169	4791	5481
375	839	120	2740	3171	3708	4330	5036	5829	6714
375	839	140	3125	3653	4308	5070	5939	6919	8016
400	894	40	1182	1301	1455	1630	1824	2034	2260
400	894	60	1625	1806	2045	2317	2619	2951	3314
400	894	80	2037	2300	2632	3012	3437	3908	4427
400	894	100	2444	2791	3224	3722	4284	4911	5605
400	894	120	2846	3282	3825	4453	5164	5962	6851
400	894	140	3245	3777	4438	5206	6080	7065	8165

NOTE: Detector time constant at a reference velocity of 5 ft/sec.
For SI Units: 1 ft = 0.305 m
1000 BTU/sec = 1055 kW

Table B-4.1(jj)
Installed Spacing of Heat Detector: 50 ft.
t_g: 50 Seconds to 1000 Btu/sec
α: 0.400 Btu/sec³

τ	RTI	ΔT	CEILING HEIGHT IN FEET 4.0	8.0	12.0	16.0	20.0	24.0	28.0
			FIRE SIZE AT DETECTOR RESPONSE (BTU / SEC)						
25	56	40	3499	3611	3846	4155	4512	4907	5336
25	56	60	4555	4723	5115	5604	6162	6780	7454
25	56	80	5425	5806	6382	7078	7867	8740	9695
25	56	100	6348	6890	7670	8597	9645	10804	12073
25	56	120	7255	7981	8987	10169	11502	12976	14589
25	56	140	8154	9087	10339	11799	13441	15255	17239
50	112	40	4909	5030	5295	5650	6060	6511	6996
50	112	60	6378	6566	6990	7530	8145	8819	9549
50	112	80	7744	8031	8633	9376	10217	11141	12143
50	112	100	9044	9459	10257	11224	12313	13511	14814
50	112	120	10300	10869	11881	13089	14449	15946	17578
50	112	140	11383	12270	13513	14982	16634	18454	20442
75	168	40	6159	6216	6507	6906	7368	7874	8417
75	168	60	7858	8112	8577	9173	9851	10593	11390
75	168	80	9536	9909	10558	11365	12277	13273	14347
75	168	100	11130	11646	12493	13527	14690	15963	17337
75	168	120	12669	13346	14407	15683	17116	18685	20385
75	168	140	14167	15023	16312	17847	19567	21454	23502
100	224	40	7107	7258	7585	8027	8537	9096	9692
100	224	60	9264	9497	9999	10649	11389	12196	13060
100	224	80	11254	11597	12290	13161	14144	15216	16366
100	224	100	13136	13616	14514	15619	16861	18215	19671
100	224	120	14944	15582	16698	18051	19567	21222	23005
100	224	140	16700	17513	18859	20474	22281	24255	26387
125	280	40	8093	8224	8576	9057	9613	10220	10868
125	280	60	10578	10773	11309	12011	12809	13679	14607
125	280	80	12863	13156	13891	14823	15876	17021	18247
125	280	100	15016	15438	16384	17559	18880	20317	21856
125	280	120	17078	17654	18823	20254	21856	23600	25472
125	280	140	19076	19822	21227	22925	24823	26891	29115
150	335	40	9028	9128	9503	10022	10620	11273	11969
150	335	60	11831	11970	12538	13288	14142	15072	16063
150	335	80	14401	14620	15394	16385	17505	18722	20021
150	335	100	16567	17143	18143	19387	20784	22302	23924
150	335	120	18854	19594	20824	22331	24018	25851	27814
150	335	140	21069	21988	23459	25240	27230	29393	31714
175	391	40	9927	9984	10381	10935	11574	12271	13013
175	391	60	12795	13093	13702	14500	15407	16394	17445
175	391	80	15570	15997	16820	17869	19053	20339	21709
175	391	100	18190	18766	19814	21124	22596	24192	25896
175	391	120	20701	21442	22727	24308	26078	27999	30052
175	391	140	23131	24052	25583	27445	29526	31784	34201
200	447	40	10597	10789	11218	11806	12484	13223	14009
200	447	60	13882	14175	14815	15658	16617	17659	18767
200	447	80	16902	17322	18185	19288	20535	21888	23327
200	447	100	19748	20319	21414	22788	24332	26005	27789
200	447	120	22474	23212	24549	26202	28054	30060	32202
200	447	140	25110	26028	27618	29560	31730	34082	36596

τ	RTI	ΔT	CEILING HEIGHT IN FEET 4.0	8.0	12.0	16.0	20.0	24.0	28.0
			FIRE SIZE AT DETECTOR RESPONSE (BTU / SEC)						
225	503	40	11385	11571	12023	12643	13359	14138	14966
225	503	60	14931	15215	15886	16771	17780	18875	20039
225	503	80	18187	18598	19498	20654	21962	23379	24886
225	503	100	21253	21815	22954	24389	26004	27752	29613
225	503	120	24186	24916	26304	28028	29959	32049	34277
225	503	140	27020	27932	29579	31599	33857	36301	38909
250	559	40	12148	12327	12799	13451	14203	15021	15890
250	559	60	15948	16220	16919	17847	18904	20050	21268
250	559	80	19433	19830	20766	21974	23341	24820	26393
250	559	100	27713	23260	24443	25938	27621	29442	31379
250	559	120	25848	26564	28002	29794	31802	33974	36287
250	559	140	28875	29774	31477	33573	35915	38450	41151
275	615	40	12890	13059	13552	14234	15020	15876	16785
275	615	60	16939	17194	17922	18890	19993	21189	22460
275	615	80	20648	21026	21997	23255	24678	26219	27855
275	615	100	24135	24663	25887	27442	29191	31083	33094
275	615	120	27466	28163	29649	31508	33591	35844	38240
275	615	140	30681	31562	33318	35489	37915	40539	43332
300	671	40	13614	13770	14283	14994	15815	16707	17655
300	671	60	17906	18141	18896	19903	21052	22297	23618
300	671	80	21835	22189	23194	24501	25979	27579	29278
300	671	100	25525	26028	27293	28904	30719	32680	34763
300	671	120	29048	29720	31253	33176	35334	37665	40143
300	671	140	32446	33302	35111	37354	39863	42573	45456
325	727	40	14322	14463	14995	15735	16589	17517	18502
325	727	60	18854	19065	19846	20892	22084	23377	24748
325	727	80	22998	23323	24361	25715	27248	28906	30665
325	727	100	26887	27359	28663	30331	32208	34238	36392
325	727	120	30598	31238	32817	34804	37034	39442	42000
325	727	140	34176	35000	36861	39175	41763	44559	47531
350	783	40	15017	15141	15691	16459	17344	18307	19329
350	783	60	19786	19968	20774	21857	23093	24432	25851
350	783	80	24142	24431	25501	26902	28487	30203	32021
350	783	100	28226	28660	30003	31725	33665	35761	37984
350	783	120	32121	32723	34346	36395	38695	41179	43815
350	783	140	35876	36660	38571	40954	43622	46502	49561
375	839	40	15700	15803	16371	17166	18083	19080	20137
375	839	60	20703	20851	21681	22801	24079	25463	26930
375	839	80	25267	25516	26617	28063	29701	31471	33348
375	839	100	29544	29934	31314	33089	35090	37251	39543
375	839	120	33621	34176	35842	37953	40322	42880	45594
375	839	140	37550	38285	40245	42697	45442	48404	51549
400	894	40	16373	16452	17038	17859	18807	19837	20929
400	894	60	21607	21717	22571	23727	25046	26475	27988
400	894	80	26378	26580	27711	29201	30890	32715	34649
400	894	100	30845	31184	32600	34427	36488	38713	41071
400	894	120	35101	35602	37310	39480	41918	44549	47338
400	894	140	39201	39880	41887	44406	47227	50270	53499

NOTE: Detector time constant at a reference velocity of 5 ft/sec.
For SI Units: 1 ft = 0.305 m
1000 BTU/sec = 1055 kW

Table B-4.1(kk)
Installed Spacing of Heat Detector: 50 feet
t_g: 150 Seconds to 1000 Btu/sec
α: 0.044 Btu/sec^3

τ	RTI	ΔT	4.0	8.0	12.0	16.0	20.0	24.0	28.0
			CEILING HEIGHT IN FEET						
			FIRE SIZE AT DETECTOR RESPONSE (BTU / SEC)						
25	56	40	1494	1637	1837	2075	2342	2639	2963
25	56	60	2041	2305	2663	3076	3539	4049	4605
25	56	80	2568	3009	3555	4177	4868	5625	6449
25	56	100	3120	3754	4516	5373	6319	7353	8475
25	56	120	3687	4541	5542	6658	7883	9219	10667
25	56	140	4272	5369	6630	8025	9552	11213	13012
50	112	40	2075	2207	2409	2651	2924	3225	3553
50	112	60	2794	3039	3386	3792	4248	4753	5304
50	112	80	3496	3880	4398	4998	5672	6417	7232
50	112	100	4193	4741	5456	6279	7200	8217	9328
50	112	120	4893	5628	6564	7635	8831	10147	11583
50	112	140	5571	6544	7724	9066	10559	12199	13986
75	168	40	2572	2696	2907	3163	3450	3765	4105
75	168	60	3460	3681	4034	4450	4917	5431	5990
75	168	80	4274	4656	5174	5778	6455	7202	8018
75	168	100	5097	5637	6343	7160	8076	9087	10194
75	168	120	5914	6633	7549	8603	9784	11089	12517
75	168	140	6730	7647	8794	10109	11580	13204	14980
100	224	40	3026	3136	3358	3628	3932	4263	4621
100	224	60	4020	4262	4627	5059	5543	6072	6647
100	224	80	4991	5364	5892	6510	7201	7960	8787
100	224	100	5937	6462	7174	8000	8924	9942	11054
100	224	120	6869	7564	8480	9538	10721	12026	13453
100	224	140	7793	8678	9817	11127	12593	14211	15983
125	280	40	3409	3542	3775	4060	4381	4730	5105
125	280	60	4563	4802	5179	5629	6132	6681	7274
125	280	80	5658	6024	6566	7201	7911	8688	9531
125	280	100	6721	7233	7957	8800	9740	10773	11898
125	280	120	7762	8439	9364	10434	11630	12945	14381
125	280	140	8790	9650	10794	12112	13585	15208	16983
150	335	40	3791	3924	4167	4468	4805	5172	5564
150	335	60	5076	5310	5701	6169	6692	7261	7874
150	335	80	6292	6648	7204	7859	8590	9388	10251
150	335	100	7466	7962	8701	9564	10525	11577	12720
150	335	120	8612	9268	10207	11296	12510	13842	15293
150	335	140	9741	10574	11729	13063	14551	16188	17973
175	391	40	4156	4286	4540	4855	5209	5593	6003
175	391	60	5567	5794	6198	6684	7227	7817	8451
175	391	80	6900	7241	7812	8489	9241	10062	10947
175	391	100	8183	8658	9414	10298	11282	12357	13520
175	391	120	9367	10060	11016	12126	13362	14716	16185
175	391	140	10583	11457	12628	13983	15491	17146	18948
200	447	40	4507	4633	4897	5226	5596	5996	6424
200	447	60	6041	6257	6674	7179	7741	8352	9007
200	447	80	7427	7810	8397	9094	9870	10713	11621
200	447	100	8795	9326	10099	11005	12014	13113	14300
200	447	120	10128	10821	11795	12929	14189	15567	17059
200	447	140	11435	12307	13496	14874	16406	18084	19906

τ	RTI	ΔT	4.0	8.0	12.0	16.0	20.0	24.0	28.0
			CEILING HEIGHT IN FEET						
			FIRE SIZE AT DETECTOR RESPONSE (BTU / SEC)						
225	503	40	4846	4967	5241	5584	5969	6386	6830
225	503	60	6504	6703	7133	7655	8238	8869	9545
225	503	80	7974	8358	8961	9679	10478	11345	12276
225	503	100	9439	9970	10761	11690	12723	13848	15060
225	503	120	10862	11556	12549	13707	14993	16396	17913
225	503	140	12256	13128	14337	15739	17297	19000	20846
250	559	40	5177	5289	5573	5929	6329	6762	7224
250	559	60	6877	7133	7577	8117	8719	9371	10068
250	559	80	8503	8889	9508	10246	11068	11958	12914
250	559	100	10062	10594	11402	12355	13413	14563	15801
250	559	120	11574	12268	13280	14463	15776	17206	18749
250	559	140	13053	13924	15153	16582	18167	19897	21768
275	615	40	5500	5602	5895	6264	6679	7128	7606
275	615	60	7295	7552	8009	8565	9187	9859	10577
275	615	80	9018	9404	10039	10798	11642	12556	13535
275	615	100	10668	11200	12026	13002	14086	15262	16525
275	615	120	12266	12960	13992	15200	16540	17997	19567
275	615	140	13828	14698	15948	17403	19017	20775	22674
300	671	40	5818	5907	6209	6590	7020	7484	7977
300	671	60	7702	7959	8428	9002	9642	10334	11072
300	671	80	9521	9906	10556	11335	12201	13139	14143
300	671	100	11259	11790	12634	13633	14742	15944	17234
300	671	120	12942	13635	14685	15919	17286	18772	20370
300	671	140	14584	15453	16724	18205	19848	21635	23563
325	727	40	6055	6202	6514	6908	7352	7831	8340
325	727	60	8100	8356	8838	9428	10087	10799	11557
325	727	80	10011	10396	11061	11860	12748	13710	14737
325	727	100	11837	12367	13228	14250	15384	16612	17928
325	727	120	13602	14293	15363	16622	18017	19531	21157
325	727	140	15323	16190	17482	18991	20663	22480	24437
350	783	40	6344	6491	6813	7219	7676	8170	8695
350	783	60	8489	8745	9238	9845	10522	11253	12031
350	783	80	10492	10875	11554	12373	13284	14268	15319
350	783	100	12403	12930	13808	14853	16012	17267	18610
350	783	120	14250	14937	16027	17310	18733	20276	21930
350	783	140	16048	16911	18224	19760	21462	23309	25296
375	839	40	6628	6775	7105	7523	7994	8503	9042
375	839	60	8871	9125	9631	10253	10948	11698	12496
375	839	80	10964	11344	12038	12876	13808	14815	15890
375	839	100	12960	13482	14377	15445	16629	17909	19278
375	839	120	14886	15568	16677	17986	19436	21007	22690
375	839	140	16760	17618	18951	20515	22246	24124	26141
400	894	40	6907	7053	7391	7822	8306	8828	9383
400	894	60	9246	9498	10015	10653	11365	12134	12952
400	894	80	11429	11804	12512	13369	14323	15353	16450
400	894	100	13507	14024	14936	16025	17234	18540	19936
400	894	120	15512	16187	17315	18649	20126	21725	23438
400	894	140	17461	18311	19666	21256	23017	24926	26973

NOTE: Detector time constant at a reference velocity of 5 ft/sec.
For SI Units: 1 ft = 0.305 m
1000 BTU/sec = 1055 kW

Table B-4.1(ll)
Installed Spacing of Heat Detector: 50 feet
t_g: 300 Seconds to 1000 Btu/sec
α: 0.011 Btu/sec³

τ	RTI	ΔT	CEILING HEIGHT IN FEET 4.0	8.0	12.0	16.0	20.0	24.0	28.0
			FIRE SIZE AT DETECTOR RESPONSE (BTU / SEC)						
25	56	40	942	1100	1296	1520	1769	2043	2340
25	56	60	1344	1649	2008	2409	2849	3328	3848
25	56	80	1772	2256	2807	3414	4075	4794	5572
25	56	100	2227	2923	3686	4523	5433	6420	7487
25	56	120	2703	3634	4636	5726	6908	8189	9573
25	56	140	3209	4392	5653	7016	8493	10091	11818
50	112	40	1272	1412	1598	1815	2058	2326	2620
50	112	60	1775	2039	2374	2758	3187	3660	4175
50	112	80	2275	2704	3221	3806	4454	5165	5939
50	112	100	2795	3413	4138	4951	5847	6826	7889
50	112	120	3333	4165	5123	6187	7355	8628	10008
50	112	140	3890	4959	6171	7508	8970	10560	12283
75	168	40	1559	1690	1876	2094	2333	2607	2901
75	168	60	2143	2398	2726	3104	3528	3996	4508
75	168	80	2728	3131	3630	4201	4840	5544	6313
75	168	100	3320	3895	4593	5386	6269	7240	8298
75	168	120	3922	4695	5617	6657	7810	9074	10449
75	168	140	4537	5531	6699	8008	9454	11036	12754
100	224	40	1811	1944	2133	2356	2605	2878	3176
100	224	60	2484	2731	3058	3438	3862	4330	4842
100	224	80	3145	3532	4025	4591	5225	5925	6691
100	224	100	3807	4356	5040	5822	6695	7659	8713
100	224	120	4474	5208	6107	7130	8271	9526	10896
100	224	140	5150	6091	7228	8515	9946	11518	13231
125	280	40	2048	2180	2374	2603	2858	3138	3442
125	280	60	2802	3043	3374	3758	4186	4658	5173
125	280	80	3538	3911	4404	4971	5605	6305	7070
125	280	100	4269	4795	5474	6251	7120	8080	9131
125	280	120	4977	5701	6589	7602	8733	9982	11348
125	280	140	5706	6632	7750	9023	10441	12005	13712
150	335	40	2272	2403	2602	2638	3101	3388	3699
150	335	60	3104	3339	3675	4065	4500	4978	5498
150	335	80	3892	4272	4768	5339	5977	6680	7447
150	335	100	4680	5215	5893	6671	7541	8500	9550
150	335	120	5464	6175	7058	8067	9194	10439	11802
150	335	140	6249	7156	8264	9527	10938	12495	14198
175	391	40	2486	2615	2820	3063	3334	3629	3948
175	391	60	3395	3622	3963	4361	4804	5289	5816
175	391	80	4241	4618	5118	5696	6340	7048	7821
175	391	100	5089	5619	6300	7082	7954	8916	9968
175	391	120	5930	6632	7514	8524	9651	10896	12258
175	391	140	6770	7663	8765	10025	11432	12985	14686
200	447	40	2692	2818	3028	3279	3558	3861	4188
200	447	60	3648	3893	4241	4647	5099	5593	6128
200	447	80	4675	4951	5457	6043	6695	7410	8189
200	447	100	5482	6009	6694	7482	8361	9327	10383
200	447	120	6379	7075	7959	8972	10102	11349	12712
200	447	140	7271	8154	9256	10516	11923	13475	15175
225	503	40	2892	3014	3230	3488	3775	4087	4422
225	503	60	3910	4155	4510	4924	5385	5888	6432
225	503	80	4898	5273	5786	6380	7041	7765	8551
225	503	100	5862	6386	7077	7873	8759	9733	10794
225	503	120	6813	7503	8392	9411	10547	11798	13165
225	503	140	7757	8631	9736	10999	12408	13963	15663
250	559	40	3087	3203	3425	3690	3985	4306	4649
250	559	60	4164	4409	4770	5194	5664	6177	6730
250	559	80	5211	5585	6106	6709	7380	8113	8908
250	559	100	6231	6752	7451	8255	9150	10132	11201
250	559	120	7235	7920	8815	9842	10985	12242	13614
250	559	140	8229	9096	10205	11474	12888	14446	16150
275	615	40	3251	3387	3614	3887	4190	4519	4871
275	615	60	4410	4655	5024	5456	5936	6459	7021
275	615	80	5516	5889	6417	7030	7711	8454	9259
275	615	100	6591	7109	7815	8629	9534	10525	11602
275	615	120	7646	8327	9229	10264	11416	12681	14060
275	615	140	8690	9549	10664	11940	13362	14926	16634
300	671	40	3429	3566	3799	4078	4390	4727	5088
300	671	60	4651	4896	5271	5712	6202	6734	7307
300	671	80	5814	6185	6721	7344	8035	8789	9604
300	671	100	6942	7457	8171	8996	9911	10912	11999
300	671	120	8049	8724	9633	10679	11841	13115	14502
300	671	140	9141	9993	11114	12399	13829	15401	17115
325	727	40	3603	3741	3979	4265	4585	4930	5300
325	727	60	4886	5130	5512	5963	6462	7005	7587
325	727	80	6105	6474	7018	7651	8353	9118	9943
325	727	100	7287	7797	8520	9355	10282	11294	12390
325	727	120	8443	9112	10030	11086	12259	13543	14939
325	727	140	9583	10426	11556	12851	14291	15871	17593
350	783	40	3774	3911	4154	4448	4775	5129	5507
350	783	60	5116	5359	5748	6208	6717	7270	7863
350	783	80	6391	6757	7309	7952	8665	9441	10277
350	783	100	7625	8130	8861	9707	10646	11669	12776
350	783	120	8831	9492	10419	11486	12670	13965	15371
350	783	140	10018	10851	11990	13295	14746	16336	18067
375	839	40	3941	4079	4327	4628	4962	5324	5710
375	839	60	5342	5584	5980	6448	6967	7530	8133
375	839	80	6672	7034	7594	8248	8972	9759	10607
375	839	100	7958	8456	9196	10054	11004	12039	13158
375	839	120	9214	9865	10801	11880	13076	14382	15799
375	839	140	10397	11268	12416	13733	15195	16796	18537
400	894	40	4105	4242	4496	4803	5146	5516	5910
400	894	60	5564	5805	6207	6684	7213	7786	8399
400	894	80	6949	7306	7874	8538	9274	10072	10931
400	894	100	8287	8777	9526	10395	11357	12404	13534
400	894	120	9536	10231	11177	12267	13475	14794	16222
400	894	140	10806	11678	12835	14164	15638	17251	19002

NOTE: Detector time constant at a reference velocity of 5 ft/sec.
For SI Units: 1 ft = 0.305 m
1000 BTU/sec = 1055 kW

Table B-4.1(mm)
Installed Spacing of Heat Detector: 50 feet
t_g: 500 Seconds to 1000 Btu/sec
α: 0.004 Btu/sec^3

			CEILING HEIGHT IN FEET						
τ	RTI	ΔT	4.0	8.0	12.0	16.0	20.0	24.0	28.0
			FIRE SIZE AT DETECTOR RESPONSE (BTU / SEC)						
25	56	40	706	875	1073	1292	1532	1793	2076
25	56	60	1053	1381	1738	2130	2557	3020	3520
25	56	80	1435	1948	2496	3091	3735	4432	5186
25	56	100	1851	2574	3337	4159	5047	6008	7047
25	56	120	2299	3253	4258	5323	6481	7732	9083
25	56	140	2777	3981	5241	6577	8025	9590	11280
50	112	40	920	1068	1252	1462	1697	1955	2236
50	112	60	1322	1610	1950	2331	2751	3210	3708
50	112	80	1748	2208	2734	3316	3953	4647	5399
50	112	100	2200	2859	3597	4406	5287	6245	7281
50	112	120	2672	3564	4532	5590	6740	7988	9337
50	112	140	3173	4311	5535	6863	8303	9864	11552
75	168	40	1107	1247	1427	1633	1864	2119	2398
75	168	60	1568	1836	2163	2534	2948	3403	3899
75	168	80	2039	2469	2975	3545	4175	4864	5614
75	168	100	2529	3148	3862	4657	5531	6484	7518
75	168	120	3040	3874	4818	5862	7003	8246	9594
75	168	140	3572	4644	5840	7152	8584	10141	11827
100	224	40	1278	1415	1593	1799	2029	2284	2562
100	224	60	1798	2051	2372	2738	3147	3599	4093
100	224	80	2312	2724	3217	3777	4400	5085	5832
100	224	100	2845	3435	4130	4912	5777	6726	7757
100	224	120	3393	4188	5108	6136	7270	8508	9853
100	224	140	3959	4981	6149	7446	8869	10420	12104
125	280	40	1439	1572	1751	1958	2190	2446	2725
125	280	60	2004	2257	2574	2939	3346	3796	4288
125	280	80	2571	2969	3455	4009	4626	5308	6052
125	280	100	3146	3715	4396	5168	6026	6970	7999
125	280	120	3732	4498	5399	6414	7539	8772	10114
125	280	140	4333	5317	6461	7742	9156	10702	12383
150	335	40	1592	1721	1902	2112	2347	2605	2886
150	335	60	2204	2453	2771	3135	3542	3992	4484
150	335	80	2817	3206	3688	4238	4853	5532	6274
150	335	100	3433	3988	4660	5425	6277	7216	8243
150	335	120	4058	4801	5689	6693	7810	9038	10377
150	335	140	4694	5648	6773	8041	9445	10986	12664
175	391	40	1740	1863	2047	2260	2499	2760	3044
175	391	60	2396	2642	2960	3327	3736	4186	4679
175	391	80	3053	3436	3916	4465	5078	5755	6497
175	391	100	3710	4253	4920	5680	6528	7464	8488
175	391	120	4373	5098	5976	6972	8082	9306	10642
175	391	140	5045	5973	7084	8340	9737	11273	12948
200	447	40	1867	2000	2187	2404	2646	2911	3199
200	447	60	2580	2824	3145	3514	3925	4378	4873
200	447	80	3280	3658	4138	4687	5301	5979	6720
200	447	100	3978	4511	5175	5932	6778	7712	8735
200	447	120	4679	5388	6259	7250	8356	9575	10909
200	447	140	5369	6292	7392	8640	10030	11561	13232
225	503	40	2000	2132	2322	2544	2790	3059	3351
225	503	60	2759	3000	3324	3696	4112	4568	5065
225	503	80	3501	3873	4355	4906	5522	6200	6943
225	503	100	4240	4762	5425	6182	7027	7960	8982
225	503	120	4958	5671	6538	7526	8628	9845	11177
225	503	140	5695	6605	7697	8939	10323	11850	13519
250	559	40	2128	2260	2453	2679	2930	3204	3500
250	559	60	2932	3172	3498	3875	4294	4754	5255
250	559	80	3717	4083	4567	5121	5740	6420	7164
250	559	100	4474	5006	5670	6428	7274	8208	9229
250	559	120	5241	5948	6813	7799	8900	10115	11445
250	559	140	6011	6911	7999	9236	10617	12140	13806
275	615	40	2253	2385	2581	2811	3067	3345	3646
275	615	60	3101	3338	3668	4050	4474	4938	5442
275	615	80	3910	4287	4774	5332	5954	6638	7384
275	615	100	4716	5245	5911	6671	7519	8453	9476
275	615	120	5517	6219	7084	8070	9170	10385	11715
275	615	140	6319	7212	8297	9531	10909	12430	14095
300	671	40	2374	2506	2706	2940	3200	3484	3789
300	671	60	3267	3501	3835	4221	4650	5119	5627
300	671	80	4111	4487	4977	5540	6166	6853	7603
300	671	100	4952	5479	6147	6910	7761	8698	9722
300	671	120	5787	6485	7350	8337	9439	10654	11984
300	671	140	6621	7507	8590	9824	11201	12720	14384
325	727	40	2493	2624	2828	3066	3331	3619	3929
325	727	60	3430	3660	3997	4388	4822	5296	5810
325	727	80	4307	4683	5176	5744	6375	7066	7820
325	727	100	5182	5709	6379	7146	8001	8940	9967
325	727	120	6050	6745	7612	8602	9705	10922	12252
325	727	140	6916	7797	8880	10114	11491	13010	14673
350	783	40	2610	2740	2947	3190	3460	3753	4068
350	783	60	3570	3815	4157	4553	4992	5472	5990
350	783	80	4498	4874	5372	5944	6580	7277	8035
350	783	100	5408	5933	6607	7379	8237	9181	10211
350	783	120	6309	7001	7871	8864	9970	11188	12521
350	783	140	7205	8082	9166	10402	11779	13299	14963
375	839	40	2724	2854	3063	3311	3586	3884	4204
375	839	60	3722	3968	4313	4715	5160	5644	6168
375	839	80	4686	5062	5564	6142	6783	7485	8247
375	839	100	5630	6154	6832	7609	8472	9420	10453
375	839	120	6562	7252	8125	9122	10232	11453	12788
375	839	140	7489	8362	9448	10686	12066	13587	15252
400	894	40	2837	2965	3178	3430	3710	4012	4337
400	894	60	3871	4117	4467	4874	5324	5815	6344
400	894	80	4871	5247	5753	6336	6983	7691	8458
400	894	100	5848	6371	7053	7835	8703	9656	10694
400	894	120	6812	7500	8376	9377	10491	11716	13054
400	894	140	7768	8638	9727	10968	12351	13874	15540

NOTE: Detector time constant at a reference velocity of 5 ft/sec.
For SI Units: 1 ft = 0.305 m
1000 BTU/sec = 1055 kW

Table B-4.1(nn)
Installed Spacing of Heat Detector: 50 feet
t_g: 600 Seconds to 1000 Btu/sec
α: 0.003 Btu/sec^3

τ	RTI	ΔT	CEILING HEIGHT IN FEET 4.0	8.0	12.0	16.0	20.0	24.0	28.0
			FIRE SIZE AT DETECTOR RESPONSE (BTU / SEC)						
25	56	40	645	818	1016	1233	1470	1728	2007
25	56	60	979	1311	1669	2058	2480	2938	3432
25	56	80	1350	1868	2416	3006	3645	4336	5082
25	56	100	1757	2484	3250	4063	4945	5898	6928
25	56	120	2195	3154	4156	5217	6366	7608	8950
25	56	140	2665	3874	5130	6460	7899	9454	11133
50	112	40	826	978	1163	1373	1605	1860	2137
50	112	60	1204	1500	1842	2222	2639	3094	3587
50	112	80	1610	2081	2611	3191	3824	4513	5258
50	112	100	2044	2721	3460	4266	5142	6093	7122
50	112	120	2503	3409	4382	5437	6581	7820	9160
50	112	140	2991	4145	5372	6696	8129	9681	11359
75	168	40	987	1131	1309	1514	1743	1995	2271
75	168	60	1414	1689	2018	2390	2801	3253	3744
75	168	80	1860	2298	2809	3379	4007	4692	5435
75	168	100	2322	2958	3677	4473	5343	6290	7317
75	168	120	2811	3665	4617	5660	6798	8034	9372
75	168	140	3323	4423	5623	6935	8362	9910	11587
100	224	40	1136	1274	1450	1653	1880	2131	2406
100	224	60	1610	1872	2193	2558	2966	3414	3903
100	224	80	2092	2512	3010	3570	4192	4873	5614
100	224	100	2591	3197	3898	4682	5546	6489	7514
100	224	120	3110	3926	4856	5886	7017	8249	9586
100	224	140	3649	4698	5878	7176	8596	10141	11815
125	280	40	1274	1410	1586	1789	2016	2266	2541
125	280	60	1797	2048	2364	2726	3130	3576	4064
125	280	80	2314	2721	3209	3762	4378	5056	5795
125	280	100	2849	3433	4120	4894	5751	6690	7713
125	280	120	3399	4185	5096	6115	7238	8466	9801
125	280	140	3967	4978	6135	7420	8832	10373	12046
150	335	40	1406	1538	1715	1920	2148	2400	2675
150	335	60	1965	2217	2531	2892	3294	3739	4226
150	335	80	2526	2924	3405	3954	4566	5240	5978
150	335	100	3096	3664	4340	5106	5957	6893	7914
150	335	120	3678	4441	5337	6345	7461	8685	10018
150	335	140	4275	5256	6393	7666	9071	10607	12277
175	391	40	1532	1662	1840	2047	2278	2532	2808
175	391	60	2131	2380	2694	3054	3457	3901	4388
175	391	80	2730	3120	3598	4144	4753	5426	6162
175	391	100	3335	3890	4559	5319	6165	7097	8116
175	391	120	3948	4693	5577	6576	7686	8906	10236
175	391	140	4574	5530	6652	7914	9311	10843	12510
200	447	40	1654	1781	1961	2171	2404	2660	2939
200	447	60	2291	2537	2852	3214	3618	4063	4549
200	447	80	2927	3311	3788	4332	4940	5611	6346
200	447	100	3565	4111	4775	5530	6373	7302	8319
200	447	120	4211	4941	5816	6807	7912	9128	10456
200	447	140	4866	5801	6910	8162	9552	11080	12745

τ	RTI	ΔT	CEILING HEIGHT IN FEET 4.0	8.0	12.0	16.0	20.0	24.0	28.0
			FIRE SIZE AT DETECTOR RESPONSE (BTU / SEC)						
225	503	40	1762	1895	2078	2291	2528	2787	3068
225	503	60	2445	2690	3007	3370	3776	4222	4710
225	503	80	3117	3497	3974	4518	5126	5797	6531
225	503	100	3790	4327	4988	5740	6581	7508	8523
225	503	120	4467	5183	6052	7038	8138	9351	10676
225	503	140	5152	6068	7167	8411	9795	11318	12981
250	559	40	1874	2006	2192	2408	2648	2911	3195
250	559	60	2595	2838	3157	3523	3932	4380	4870
250	559	80	3303	3679	4156	4701	5310	5981	6717
250	559	100	4009	4538	5197	5949	6788	7714	8728
250	559	120	4718	5421	6285	7268	8365	9574	10898
250	559	140	5414	6330	7421	8659	10038	11557	13218
275	615	40	1982	2115	2303	2522	2766	3032	3320
275	615	60	2741	2983	3304	3674	4085	4536	5029
275	615	80	3484	3856	4334	4882	5492	6164	6900
275	615	100	4223	4745	5403	6155	6994	7919	8933
275	615	120	4944	5654	6516	7496	8591	9798	11120
275	615	140	5681	6588	7674	8907	10281	11798	13456
300	671	40	2087	2220	2411	2634	2882	3151	3443
300	671	60	2884	3124	3448	3821	4236	4691	5186
300	671	80	3662	4029	4509	5059	5672	6346	7083
300	671	100	4415	4947	5606	6359	7198	8124	9138
300	671	120	5178	5883	6743	7723	8816	10023	11343
300	671	140	5943	6842	7924	9153	10525	12038	13694
325	727	40	2190	2323	2517	2744	2995	3269	3564
325	727	60	3024	3262	3589	3966	4384	4843	5341
325	727	80	3837	4199	4682	5234	5850	6527	7266
325	727	100	4616	5145	5806	6560	7401	8328	9342
325	727	120	5407	6108	6968	7947	9040	10246	11567
325	727	140	6199	7091	8171	9398	10768	12279	13934
350	783	40	2291	2424	2621	2851	3106	3384	3683
350	783	60	3161	3397	3728	4108	4531	4993	5495
350	783	80	3989	4365	4851	5407	6026	6706	7448
350	783	100	4812	5340	6003	6759	7602	8531	9546
350	783	120	5631	6330	7190	8170	9263	10470	11790
350	783	140	6450	7337	8415	9641	11010	12520	14174
375	839	40	2390	2523	2722	2956	3215	3497	3800
375	839	60	3296	3530	3863	4248	4675	5141	5647
375	839	80	4152	4528	5017	5577	6200	6883	7628
375	839	100	5005	5532	6197	6956	7802	8733	9750
375	839	120	5852	6547	7409	8391	9485	10692	12013
375	839	140	6697	7579	8657	9883	11251	12761	14414
400	894	40	2487	2620	2822	3059	3323	3608	3916
400	894	60	3429	3660	3997	4386	4817	5288	5797
400	894	80	4314	4689	5181	5745	6372	7059	7807
400	894	100	5195	5720	6388	7151	8000	8933	9953
400	894	120	6068	6762	7625	8609	9706	10914	12236
400	894	140	6939	7818	8896	10123	11491	13001	14654

NOTE: Detector time constant at a reference velocity of 5 ft/sec.
For SI Units: 1 ft = 0.305 m
1000 BTU/sec = 1055 kW

B-4.1.1 Example.

Input:

Ceiling height: 8 ft (2.4 m)

Detector type: Fixed temperature 135°F (57°C)

UL listed spacing: 30 ft (9.1 m)

Installed spacing: 15 ft (4.6 m)

Fire:

Fire growth rate: Slow

t_g: 600 sec

α: 0.003 Btu/sec^3

Environmental conditions:

T_o: 55°F (12.8°C)

Threshold fire size (Q_d) at detector response:

From Table B-3.2.2 the detector time constant (τ_o) is 80 seconds.

$\Delta T = T_s - T_o = 135 - 55 = 80°F$

From Table B-4.1(t)

For $\tau_o = 75$ sec; $Q_d = 418$ Btu/sec

For $\tau_o = 100$ sec; $Q_d = 472$ Btu/sec

By interpolation:

$Q_d = 418 - [(75 - 80)(418 - 472)/(75 - 100)]$

$Q_d = 429$ Btu/sec

B-5 Smoke Detector Spacing for Flaming Fires.

B-5.1 Ideally, the placement of smoke detectors should be based on a knowledge of fire plume and ceiling jet flows, smoke production rates, particulate changes due to aging, and the unique operating characteristics of the detector being used. Knowledge of plume and jet flows enabled the heat detector spacing information presented in Section B-3 to be developed. Unfortunately, that knowledge does not apply to smoke originating from smoldering fires. Understanding of smoke production and aging lags considerably behind that of heat production. The operating characteristics of smoke detectors in specific fire environments are not often measured or made generally available for other than a very few combustible materials. Hence, the existing data base precludes the development of complete engineering design information for smoke detector location and spacing.

B-5.2 In a flaming fire, smoke detector response is affected by ceiling height, and size and rate of growth of the fire in much the same way as heat detector response. The thermal energy of the flaming fire transports smoke particles to the smoke sensor just as it does heat to a heat sensor. While the relationship between the amount of smoke and the amount of heat produced by a fire is highly dependent upon the fuel and the way it is burning, research has shown that the relationship between temperature and optical density of smoke remains essentially constant within the fire plume and on the ceiling in the proximity of the plume.

[From NFPA 72E - 1990, Appendix C modified]

B-5.3 In smoldering fires, thermal energy also provides a force for transporting smoke particles to the smoke sensor. However, because the rate of energy release is usually small and the rate of growth of the fire is slow, other factors such as airflow may have a stronger influence on the transport of smoke particles to the smoke sensor. Additionally, for smoldering fires, the relationship between temperature and the optical density of smoke is not constant and, therefore, not useful.

B-5.4 Smoke detectors, regardless of whether they detect by sensing scattered light, loss of light transmission (light extinction), or reduction of ion current, are particle detectors. Particle concentration, size, color, and size distribution affect each sensing technology differently. It is generally accepted that the concentration of sub-micron-diameter particles produced by a flaming fire is greater than that produced by a smoldering fire. Conversely, the concentration of larger particles is greater from a smoldering fire. It is also known that the smaller particles agglomerate and form larger ones as they age and are carried away from the fire source. More research is required to provide sufficient data to first predict particle concentration and behavior and, secondly, to predict the response of a particular detector.

B-5.5 Unlike heat detectors, listed smoke detectors are not given a listed spacing. It has become general practice to install smoke detectors on 30-ft (9.1-m) centers on smooth ceilings with reductions made empirically to that spacing for beamed or joisted ceilings and for areas having high rates of air movement. Spacing adjustments for ceiling height are also necessary as discussed herein.

B-5.5.1 Figures B-5.5.1(a), (b), and (c) are based on the assumption that smoke transport to the detector is entirely from fire plume dynamics. It assumes that the ratio of the gas temperature rise to the optical density of the smoke is a constant and that the detector will actuate at a constant value of temperature rise equal to 20°F (-6.7C), which is considered indicative of concentrations of smoke from a number of common fuels that would cause detection by a relatively sensitive detector. It is cautioned that many fuel/detector combinations may cause operation at a higher temperature rise. In addition, it is assumed that the detector design does not significantly impair smoke entry. The data presented in Figures B-5.5.1(a), (b), and (c) clearly indicate that spacings considerably greater than 30 ft (9.1 m) are acceptable for detecting geometrically growing flaming fires when Q_d is 1000 Btu/sec or more.

B-5.5.2 In the early stages of development of a growing fire, where the heat release rate is approximately 250 Btu/sec or less, the environmental effects in spaces having high ceilings may dominate the transportation of smoke. Examples of such environmental effects are heating, cooling, humidity, and ventilation. Greater thermal energy release from the fire may be required to overcome such environmental effects. Until the growing fire reaches a sufficiently high level of heat release, closer spacing of smoke detectors on the ceiling may not significantly improve the response of the detectors to the fire. Therefore, where considering ceiling height alone, smoke detector spacing closer than 30 ft (9.1 m) may not be warranted except in instances where an engineering analysis indicates additional benefit will result. Other construction characteristics must also be con-

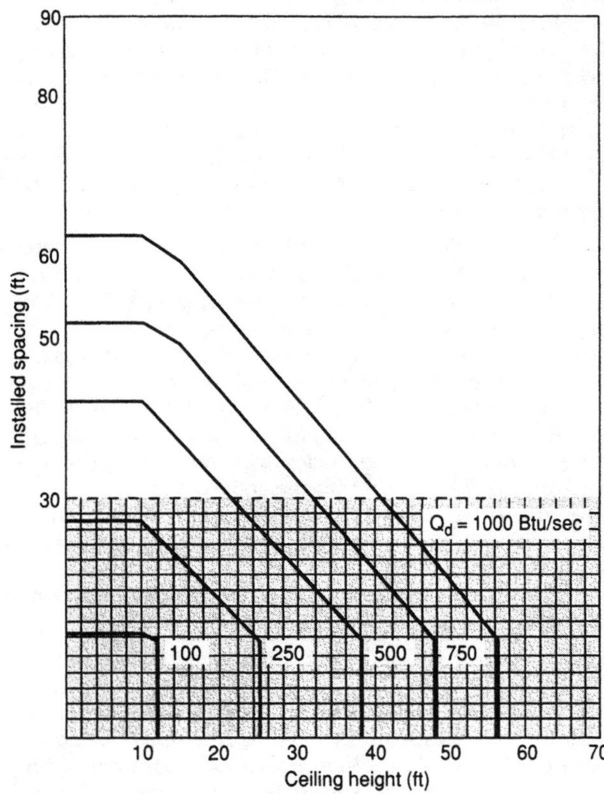

Figure B-5.5.1(a) Smoke detector — fast fire.

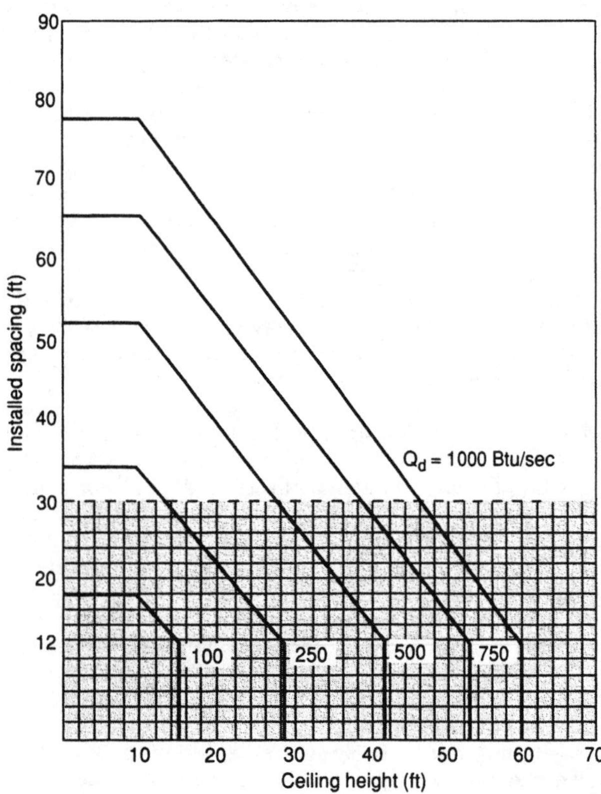

Figure B-5.5.1(b) Smoke detector — medium fire.

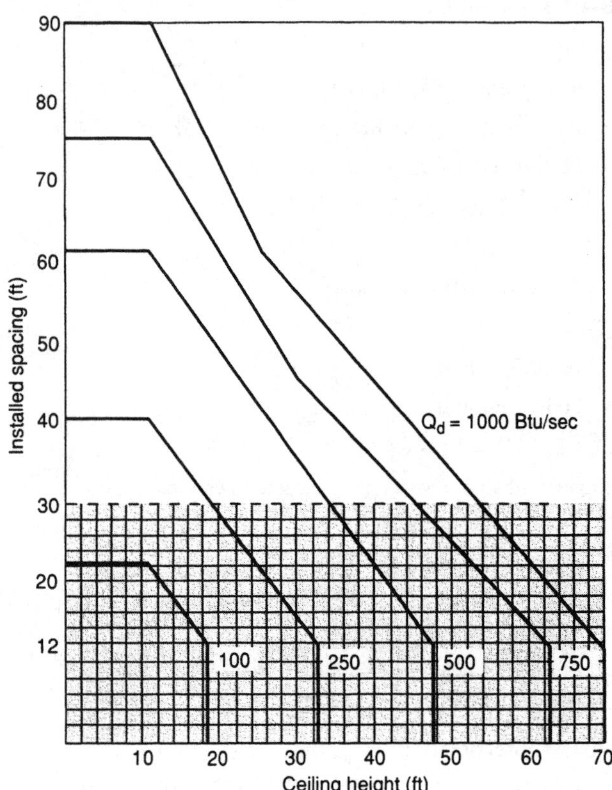

Figure B-5.5.1(c) Smoke detector — slow fire.

sidered; see the appropriate sections of Chapter 5 dealing with smoke detectors and smoke detectors for the control of smoke spread.

B-5.6 The method used to determine the spacing of smoke detectors is similar to that used for heat detectors and is based on fire size, fire growth rate, and ceiling height.

B-5.6.1 In order to use Figures B-5.5.1(a), (b), or (c) to determine the installed spacing of a smoke detector, the designer must first select Q_d, the threshold flaming fire size at which detection is desired.

B-5.6.2 In addition to threshold flaming fire size, Q_d, the designer must consider the expected fire growth rate. Figures B-5.5.1(a), (b), and (c) are used for fast-, medium-, and slow-growing flaming fires, respectively. See section B-2.2.2 for heat release rate and fire growth rate information.

[From NFPA 72E - 1990, Appendix C modified]

B-5.6.2.1 Figures B-5.5.1(a), (b), and (c) use the following values for t_g:

Fast fire growth rate, t_g = 150 seconds

Medium fire growth rate, t_g = 300 seconds

Slow fire growth rate, t_g = 600 seconds.

[From NFPA 72E - 1990, Appendix C]

B-5.6.3 Example 1. Determine the installed spacing of a smoke detector on a 30-ft (9.1-m) ceiling required to detect a 750 Btu/sec fire that is growing at a medium rate, use Figure B-5.5.1(b).

Input:

Ceiling height: 30 ft (9.1 m)

Q_d: 750 Btu/sec (791 kW)

Fire growth rate: Medium, t_g = 300 seconds

Required installed spacing:

From Figure B-5.5.1(b), using the 750 Btu/sec (791 kW) curve, installed spacing is 41 ft (12.8 m).

B-5.6.4 Example 2. Consider a 20-ft (6.1-m) ceiling with a threshold fire size of 250 Btu/sec growing at a medium rate.

Input:

Ceiling height: 20 ft (6.1 m)

Q_d: 250 Btu/Sec (264 kW)

Fire growth rate: Medium, t_g = 300 seconds

Required installed spacing:

From Figure B-5.5.1(b), using the 250 Btu/sec (264 kW) curve, installed spacing for the smoke detector is 30 ft (9.1 m), since the intersection of a vertical line at 20 ft (6.1 m) and the Q_d = 250 curve falls within the shaded area below 30 ft (9.1 m) spacing. (*See B-5.2.1.2.*)

NOTE: Both a slow and fast rate-of-growth fire would result in the same 30-ft (9.1-m) spacing using Figures B-5.5.1(a) and (c). Engineering judgment and consideration of all factors affecting smoke movement and transport should be exercised in deciding whether a reduced spacing is warranted.

B-5.6.5 Smoke detector spacings of less than 30 ft (9.1 m) may be used for detection of flaming fires where no other detector type is suitable and where environmental conditions allow the use of a smoke detector.

B-6 Theoretical Considerations.

B-6.1 Introduction. The design methods of this appendix are the joint result of extensive experimental work and of mathematical modeling of the heat and mass transfer processes involved. This section outlines models and data correlations used to generate the design data presented in this appendix. Only the general principles are described. More detailed information may be obtained from references 4, 9, 10, and 14 in Appendix C.

B-6.2 Temperature and Velocity Correlations. In order to predict the operation of any detector, it is necessary to characterize the local environment created by the fire at the detector location. For a heat detector, the important variables are temperature and velocity of the gases at the detector. Through a program of full-scale tests and using mathematical modeling techniques, general expressions for temperature and velocity at a detector location have been developed. (*See references 4, 9, 10, and 14 in Appendix C.*) The expressions are valid for fires that grow according to:

$$Q = \alpha t^2$$

Where:

Q = the theoretical fire heat release rate

α = the fire intensity coefficient characteristic of a particular fuel and configuration

t = time.

The calculations used to produce the spacing curves assume that the ratio of the actual convective heat release to the theoretical heat release for all fuels is equal to that ratio for wood crib fires.

B-6.3 Heat Detector Model. The heating of a heat detector is given by the equation:

$$\Delta T_s/dt = (T_g - T_d)/\tau$$

Where:

T_s = the temperature rating or set point of the detector

T_g = the gas temperature at the detector

τ = detector time constant.

The time constant is a measure of the detector's sensitivity and is given by:

$$\tau = (mc)/(hA)$$

Where:

m = the detector element's mass

c = the detector element's specific heat

h = the convection heat transfer coefficient for the detector

A = the surface area of the detector's element.

h varies approximately as the square root of the gas velocity, u.

It is customary to speak of the time constant at a reference velocity of u_o = 5 ft/sec.

$$\tau = \tau_0(u_o/u)^{1/2}$$

t_o can be measured most easily by a plunge test. It can also be related to the listed spacing of a detector through a calculation; Table B-3.2.2 results from these calculations. This model uses the temperature and velocity of the gases at the detector to predict the temperature rise of the detector element. Detector operation occurs when the preset conditions are reached.

The detector's sensitivity can also be expressed in units that are independent of the air velocity used in the test to determine the time constant. This is known as the response time index (RTI).

$$RTI = \tau\sqrt{u}$$

The RTI value can therefore be obtained by multiplying t_o values by $\sqrt{u_o}$; for example, where u_o = 5 ft/sec, a τ_o of 30 sec corresponds to an RTI of 67 $sec^{1/2}$ $ft^{1/2}$ or 36 $sec^{1/2}$ $m^{1/2}$

A detector having a RTI of 67 $sec^{1/2}$ $ft^{1/2}$ would have a τ_o of 23.7 sec, if measured in an air velocity of 8 ft/sec.

B-6.4 Ambient Temperature Considerations. (*See also B-3.2.3.*) The maximum ambient temperature expected to occur at the ceiling dictates the choice of temperature rating for a fixed temperature heat detector application. But the minimum ambient temperature likely at the ceiling constitutes the worst-case condition for response by that detector to a fire.

The mass, specific heat, heat transfer coefficient, and surface area of a detector's sensing element characterize that detector's time constant. The response time of a given detector to a given fire depends only on the detector's time constant and the difference between the detector's temperature rating and the ambient temperature at the detector where the fire starts. When ambient temperature at the ceiling decreases, more heat from a fire will be needed to bring the air surrounding the detector's sensing element up to its rated (operating) temperature; this translates into slower response and, in the case of a growing fire, a larger fire size at the time of detection. In a room or work area that has central heating, the minimum ambient temperature would usually be about 68°F (20°C). Certain warehouse occupancies may only be heated enough to prevent water pipe freeze-up; in this case, the minimum ambient should be considered 35°F (2°C) even though during many months of the year the actual ambient is much higher. An unheated building in northern states and in Canada should be presumed to have a minimum ambient of −40°F (−40°C) or lower.

B-6.5 Heat and Smoke Analogy — Smoke Detector Model. For smoke detectors, the temperature of the gases at the detector is not directly relevant to detection, but the mass concentration and size distribution of particulates is relevant. For many types of smoke, the mass concentration of particles is directly proportional to the optical density of the smoke, D_0. A general correlation for flaming fires has been shown to exist between the temperature rise of the fire gases at a given location and the optical density.

If the optical density at which a detector responds, D_0, was known and was independent of particle size distribution, the response of the detector could be approximated as a function of heat release rate of the burning fuel, rate of fire growth, and ceiling height, assuming that the above correlation held.

However, the more popular ionization and light-scattering detectors exhibit widely different D_0 when particle size distribution is changed; hence, where D_0 for these detectors is measured in order to predict response, the test aerosol used must be very carefully controlled so that particle size distribution is constant.

[From NFPA 72E - 1990, Appendix C modified]

Appendix C Referenced Publications

C-1 The following documents or portions thereof are referenced within this code for informational purposes only and thus are not considered part of the requirements of this document. The edition indicated for each reference is the current edition as of the date of the NFPA issuance of this document.

C-1.1 NFPA Publications. National Fire Protection Association, 1 Batterymarch Park, P.O. Box 9101, Quincy, MA 02269-9101.

NFPA 11, *Standard for Low Expansion Foam and Combined Agent Systems*, 1988 edition.

NFPA 11A, *Standard for Medium- and High-Expansion Foam Systems*, 1988 edition.

NFPA 12, *Standard on Carbon Dioxide Extinguishing Systems*, 1993 edition.

NFPA 12B, *Standard on Halon 1211 Fire Extinguishing Systems*, 1990 edition.

NFPA 13, *Standard for the Installation of Sprinkler Systems*, 1991 edition.

NFPA 14, *Standard for the Installation of Standpipe and Hose Systems*, 1993 edition.

NFPA 15, *Standard for Water Spray Fixed Systems for Fire Protection*, 1990 edition.

NFPA 17, *Standard for Dry Chemical Extinguishing Systems*, 1990 edition.

NFPA 70, *National Electrical Code*, 1993 edition.

NFPA 80, *Standard for Fire Doors and Fire Windows*, 1992 edition.

NFPA 90A, *Standard for the Installation of Air Conditioning and Ventilating Systems*, 1993 edition.

NFPA 90B, *Standard for the Installation of Warm Air Heating and Air Conditioning Systems*, 1993 edition.

NFPA 92A, *Recommended Practice for Smoke-Control Systems*, 1993 edition.

NFPA 92B, *Guide for Smoke Management Systems in Malls, Atria, and Large Areas*, 1991 edition.

NFPA *101*, *Life Safety Code*, 1991 edition.

NFPA 170, *Standard for Firesafety Symbols*, 1991 edition.

NFPA 231C, *Standard for Rack Storage of Materials*, 1991 edition.

NFPA 1221, *Standard on the Installation, Maintenance, and Use of Public Fire Service Communication Systems*, 1991 edition.

C-2 Bibliography. This part of the appendix lists other publications pertinent to the subject of this NFPA document and which may or may not be referenced.

1. Alpert, R. "Ceiling Jets." *Fire Technology*, August 1972.

2. Alpert and Ward, "Hazard Analysis of Unsprinklered Risk." *SFPE Technology Report*, 1984.

3. Babrauskas, V.; Lawson, J. R.; Walton, W. D.; and Twilley, W. H. "Upholstered Furniture Heat Release Rates Measured with a Furniture Calorimeter," (NBSIR 82-2604) (Dec. 1982). National Institute of Standards and Technology (formerly National Bureau of Standards), Center for Fire Research, Gaithersburg, MD 20889.

4. Beyler, C. "A Design Method for Flaming Fire Detection." *Fire Technology*, Volume 20, Number 4, November 1984.

5. DiNenno, P., ed. Chapter 3-1 of "SFPE Handbook of Fire Protection Engineering," by R. Schifiliti, September 1988.

6. Evans, D. D., and Stroup, D. W. "Methods to Calculate Response Time of Heat and Smoke Detectors Installed Below Large Unobstructed Ceilings," (NBSIR 85-3167) (February 1985, Issued July 1986). National Institute of Standards and Technology (formerly National Bureau of Standards), Center for Fire Research, Gaithersburg, MD 20889.

7. Heskestad, G. "Characterization of Smoke Entry and Response for Products-of-Combustion Detectors." Proceedings, 7th International Conference on Problems of Automatic Fire Detection, Rheinish-Westfalischen Technischen Hochschule Aachen (March 1975).

8. Heskestad, G. "Investigation of a New Sprinkler Sensitivity Approval Test: The Plunge Test." FMCR Tech. Report 22485, Factory Mutual Research Corporation, 1151 Providence Turnpike, Norwood, MA 02062.

9. Heskestad, G. "The Initial Convective Flow in Fire: Seventeenth Symposium on Combustion." The Combustion Institute, Pittsburgh, PA (1979).

10. Heskestad, G., and Delichatsios, M. A. "Environments of Fire Detectors — Phase 1: Effect of Fire Size, Ceiling Height and Material." Measurements vol. I (NBS-GCR-77-86), Analysis vol. II (NBS-GCR-77-95). National Technical Information Service (NTIS), Springfield, VA 22151.

11. Heskestad, G., and Delichatsios, M. A. "Update: The Initial Convective Flow in Fire." *Fire Safety Journal*, Volume 15, Number 5, 1989.

12. International Organization for Standardization, *Audible Emergency Evacuation Signal*, ISO 8201:1987.

13. Lawson, J. R.; Walton, W. D.; and Twilley, W. H. "Fire Performance of Furnishings as Measured in the NBS Furniture Calorimeter, Part 1," (NBSIR 83-2787) (August 1983). National Institute of Standards and Technology (formerly National Bureau of Standards), Center for Fire Research, Gaithersburg, MD 20889.

14. Schifiliti, R. "Use of Fire Plume Theory in the Design and Analysis of Fire Detector and Sprinkler Response." Master's thesis, Worcester Polytechnic Institute, Center for Firesafety Studies, Worcester, MA, 1986.

15. Title 47, Code of Federal Regulations, Communications Act of 1934 Amended.

Cross Reference List

Former Reference	New Reference
NFPA 71	3-8.7.7
NFPA 71	3-8.7.8
NFPA 71, Title	4-3
NFPA 71, 1-1.1	4-3.1
NFPA 71, 1-1.2	4-3.2.1
NFPA 71, 1-1.3	1-3, 1-3.1, and 1-3.2
NFPA 71, 1-2.2	4-3.2.2
NFPA 71, 1-2.3	1-7.2.3
NFPA 71, 1-2.3.1	1-7.2.3.1 and 1-7.2.3.1.2
NFPA 71, 1-2.3.1.1	1-7.2.3.1.1
NFPA 71, 1-2.3.2	1-7.2.3.2, 4-3.2.3, 4-3.2.3.1, 4-3.2.3.1.1, 4-3.2.3.1.2, 4-3.2.3.2, 4-3.2.3.2.1, and 4-3.2.3.2.2
NFPA 71, 1-2.3.2.1	1-7.2.3.2.1
NFPA 71, 1-2.3.2.2	1-7.2.3.2.2
NFPA 71, 1-2.4	4-3.2.4
NFPA 71, 1-2.5	4-3 Note
NFPA 71, 1-3	1-4
NFPA 71, 1-4.1	1-7.1.1 and 4-3.2.5
NFPA 71, 1-4.1(b)	7-1.5, 7-1.5.1, 7-1.5.2, 7-1.5.3, 7-1.6, 7-2, and 7-7.1
NFPA 71, 1-4.2	1-5.3, 1-5.3.1, and 7-2.1.1
NFPA 71, 1-4.3	1-7.2.1 and Figure 1-7.2.1
NFPA 71, 1-4.5	1-7.3, 4-3.6.2.1, and 7-5.3
NFPA 71, 1-5	1-5.5.2
NFPA 71, 1-5.1	1-5.5.2.1
NFPA 71, 1-5.2	1-5.5.2.2
NFPA 71, 1-5.3	1-5.5.5
NFPA 71, 1-5.4	1-5.5.2.3 and 7-4.3
NFPA 71, 1-5.5	1-5.5.3
NFPA 71, 1-6.2	4-3.3.1
NFPA 71, 1-7	4-3.3
NFPA 71, 1-7.1	4-3.4.1
NFPA 71, 1-7.2	4-3.4.4
NFPA 71, 1-7.2.1	4-3.4.4.1
NFPA 71, 1-7.2.2	4-3.4.4.2
NFPA 71, 1-7.2.3	4-3.4.4.3
NFPA 71, 1-7.2.4	4-3.4.4.4 and 7-4.4
NFPA 71, 1-9.1	4-3.5.1
NFPA 71, 1-9.1.2	4-3.5.1.1
NFPA 71, 1-9.5	A-7-2.1
NFPA 71, 1-9.5(a), (h), (i)	7-1.3
NFPA 71, 1-10	7-5
NFPA 71, 1-10.1	4-3.6.2.2
NFPA 71, 1-10.2	4-3.6.1
NFPA 71, 1-10.2.1	4-3.6.1.1
NFPA 71, 1-10.2.2	4-3.6.1.2
NFPA 71, 1-10.2.2.1	4-3.6.1.2.1
NFPA 71, 1-10.2.3	4-3.6.1.3
NFPA 71, 1-10.2.4	4-3.6.1.4
NFPA 71, 1-10.2.5	4-3.6.1.5
NFPA 71, 2-1	1-5.5.4
NFPA 71, 2-2.1.1	1-5.2.1
NFPA 71, 2-2.1.1 3rd paragraph	1-5.2.3 2nd paragraph
NFPA 71, 2-2.1.1 2nd paragraph	1-5.2.3 Exception No. 1, Exception No. 2, and Note
NFPA 71, 2-2.1.3	1-5.2.2
NFPA 71, 2-2.1.4	1-5.2.4
NFPA 71, 2-2.1.5	1-5.2.5
NFPA 71, 2-2.1.6	1-5.2.6
NFPA 71, 2-2.1.8	1-5.2.6.1
NFPA 71, 2-2.2	1-5.2.5
NFPA 71, 2-2.3.1	1-5.2.9.1
NFPA 71, 2-2.3.2	1-5.2.9.1
NFPA 71, 2-2.3.3	1-5.2.9.1
NFPA 71, 2-2.3.4	1-5.2.9.2
NFPA 71, 2-2.3.5	1-5.2.9.3
NFPA 71, 2-2.3.6	1-5.2.9.4 and 1-5.2.9.5
NFPA 71, 2-2.4	1-5.2.8
NFPA 71, 2-2.4.1	1-5.2.8.2
NFPA 71, 2-2.4.2	1-5.2.8.3

Former Reference	New Reference
NFPA 71, 2-2.5.1	1-5.2.11 and 1-5.2.11.1
NFPA 71, 2-2.5.2	1-5.2.11.2
NFPA 71, 2-2.5.4	1-5.2.11.3
NFPA 71, 2-2.6	1-5.2.10
NFPA 71, 2-2.6.1 without Exception	1-5.2.10.1
NFPA 71, 2-2.6.2	1-5.2.10.2
NFPA 71, 2-2.6.3	1-5.2.10.4
NFPA 71, 2-2.6.4	1-5.2.10.3
NFPA 71, 2-2.6.5	1-5.2.10.6
NFPA 71, 2-4	1-5.8
NFPA 71, 2-4.1	1-5.8.1
NFPA 71, 2-4.1 Exception No. 5	1-5.8.6.1 Exception No. 2
NFPA 71, 2-4.1 Exception No. 8	1-5.8.4 Exception No. 3
NFPA 71, 2-4.1 Exception No. 9	1-5.8.6.1 Exception No. 3
NFPA 71, 2-4.1 Exception No. 11	1-5.8.4 Exception No. 1
NFPA 71, 2-4.1 Exception No. 12	1-5.8.1 Exception No. 11
NFPA 71, 2-4.1 Exception No. 13	1-5.8.1 Exception No. 7 and Note
NFPA 71, 2-4.2	1-5.4.6
NFPA 71, 2-4.2.1	1-5.4.6.1 and 1-5.4.6.2
NFPA 71, 3-1.1.1	5-9 and 5-9.1
NFPA 71, 3-2.2	3-8.1.1
NFPA 71, 3-2.2.1	3-8.13.1
NFPA 71, 3-2.2.2	3-8.13.2
NFPA 71, 3-2.2.3	3-8.13.3
NFPA 71, 3-2.2.4	3-8.13.4
NFPA 71, 3-2.2.6	3-8.13.5
NFPA 71, 3-2.2.7	3-8.13.6
NFPA 71, 3-3.2.1	3-8.1.2
NFPA 71, 3-4.1.1	5-9.1.1
NFPA 71, 3-4.2.1	5-7.3
NFPA 71, 3-4.3	3-8.9
NFPA 71, 3-4.3.1	3-8.9.1 and 5-8.1
NFPA 71, 3-4.4	5-10
NFPA 71, 3-4.4.1	3-8.9.2
NFPA 71, 3-4.4.2	5-10.1
NFPA 71, 3-4.4.3	5-10.2
NFPA 71, 3-4.4.4	5-10.3
NFPA 71, 3-4.4.5	5-10.4
NFPA 71, 3-4.4.6	3-8.10.1
NFPA 71, 3-4.4.7	5-10.5
NFPA 71, 4-1	4-2.2
NFPA 71, 4-1.1	4-2.2.1
NFPA 71, 4-1.2	4-2.2.2
NFPA 71, 4-1.2.1	4-2.2.2.1
NFPA 71, 4-1.2.2	4-2.2.2.2
NFPA 71, 4-1.2.3	4-3.4.5
NFPA 71, 4-2.1.1	4-2.4.1
NFPA 71, 4-2.1.2	4-2.4.2
NFPA 71, 4-2.1.3	4-2.3.1.2.3
NFPA 71, 4-3.1	4-2.3.1.1
NFPA 71, 4-3.1.1	4-2.3.1.2
NFPA 71, 4-3.1.1.1	4-2.3.1.2.1
NFPA 71, 4-3.1.1.2	4-2.3.1.2.2
NFPA 71, 4-3.1.2	4-2.2.3, 4-2.2.3.1, and 4-2.2.3.3
NFPA 71, 4-3.1.3	4-2.2.4, 4-2.2.4.1, and 4-2.2.4.2
NFPA 71, 4-3.1.4	4-2.3.1.3
NFPA 71, 4-4.1	4-2.3.1.4
NFPA 71, Table 4-4.1	Table 4-2.3.1.4
NFPA 71, 4-4.2	4-2.3.1.5
NFPA 71, Chap. 5	4-2.3.2
NFPA 71, 5-1	7-4.4.1(a)
NFPA 71, 5-1.1	4-2.2.1
NFPA 71, 5-1.3	4-2.2.2.3
NFPA 71, 5-2	4-2.3.2.1
NFPA 71, 5-2.1	4-2.3.2.1.1
NFPA 71, 5-2.2	4-2.3.2.1.2
NFPA 71, 5-2.3	4-2.3.2.1.3

Former Reference	New Reference
NFPA 71, 5-2.4	4-2.3.2.1.4
NFPA 71, 5-2.5	4-2.3.2.1.5
NFPA 71, 5-2.6	4-2.3.2.1.6 and 4-2.3.2.1.6.1
NFPA 71, 5-2.7	4-2.3.2.1.7
NFPA 71, 5-2.8	4-2.3.2.1.8
NFPA 71, 5-2.8.1	4-2.3.2.1.9
NFPA 71, 5-2.9	4-2.3.2.1.10
NFPA 71, 5-3.1	4-2.3.2.2.1
NFPA 71, 5-3.1.1	4-2.3.2.2.1.1
NFPA 71, 5-3.1.2	4-2.3.2.2.1.2
NFPA 71, 5-3.2.1	4-2.4.1
NFPA 71, 5-3.2.2	4-2.4.2
NFPA 71, 5-3.3	4-2.3.2.2.2
NFPA 71, 5-3.3.1	4-2.3.2.2.2.1
NFPA 71, 5-3.3.2	4-2.3.2.2.2.2
NFPA 71, 5-3.3.3	4-2.3.2.2.2.3
NFPA 71, Table 5-3.3.3	4-2.3.2.2.2.3 (a) and (b)
NFPA 71, 5-3.3.4	4-2.3.2.2.2.4
NFPA 71, 5-3.3.5	4-2.3.2.2.2.5
NFPA 71, 5-4.1	1-5.8.6.2
NFPA 71, 5-4.2	1-5.8.6.3
NFPA 71, 5-5	4-2.3.2.3, 7-4.4.2, and 7-4.4.3
NFPA 71, 5-5.1	4-2.3.2.3.1
NFPA 71, 5-5.2	4-2.3.2.3.2
NFPA 71, 5-5.3	4-2.3.2.3.3
NFPA 71, 5-5.4	4-2.3.2.3.4
NFPA 71, 5-5.5	4-2.3.2.3.5
NFPA 71, 5-6	4-2.3.2.4
NFPA 71, 5-7	4-2.3.2.5 and 7-4.4.3.1
NFPA 71, 5-7.1	4-2.3.2.5.1
NFPA 71, 5-7.1.1	4-2.3.2.5.1.1
NFPA 71, 5-7.1.2	4-2.3.2.5.1.2
NFPA 71, 5-7.2.1	4-2.4.1
NFPA 71, 5-7.2.2	4-2.4.2
NFPA 71, Chap. 6	4-2.3.3
NFPA 71, 6-1	7-4.4.3.2
NFPA 71, 6-1.1	4-2.2.1
NFPA 71, 6-2.1	4-2.3.3.1
NFPA 71, 6-2.1.1	1-5.4.2.1 and 4-2.3.3.1.1
NFPA 71, 6-2.1.2	1-5.4.2 and 4-2.3.3.1.2
NFPA 71, 6-2.2	4-2.3.3.1.3
NFPA 71, 6-2.3	4-2.3.3.1.4
NFPA 71, 6-3	4-2.3.3.2
NFPA 71, 6-3.1	4-2.3.3.2.1
NFPA 71, 6-3.2	4-2.3.3.2.2
NFPA 71, 6-3.3	4-2.3.3.2.3
NFPA 71, 6-3.4	4-2.3.3.2.4
NFPA 71, 6-3.4.1	4-2.3.3.2.5
NFPA 71, 6-3.4.2	4-2.3.3.2.6
NFPA 71, 6-4	4-2.3.3.3
NFPA 71, 6-4.1.1	4-2.3.3.3.1
NFPA 71, 6-4.1.2	3-8.6.3 and 4-2.3.3.3.2
NFPA 71, 6-4.1.3	4-2.3.3.3.3
NFPA 71, 6-4.2	3-8.7.1.2 and 4-2.3.3.3.4
NFPA 71, 6-4.3	4-2.3.3.3.5
NFPA 71, 6-4.4	4-2.3.3.3.6
NFPA 71, 6-4.5	4-2.3.3.3.7
NFPA 71, 6-4.6	4-2.3.3.3.8
NFPA 71, Chap. 7	4-2.3.4
NFPA 71, 7-1.1	4-2.2.1
NFPA 71, 7-1.2.1	4-2.2.2.1
NFPA 71, 7-1.2.2	4-2.2.2.4 and 4-2.2.2.5
NFPA 71, 7-1.2.3	4-3.4.5
NFPA 71, 7-2.1.1	4-2.4.1
NFPA 71, 7-2.1.2	4-2.4.2
NFPA 71, 7-2.1.3	4-2.3.4.1
NFPA 71, 7-2.1.4	4-2.3.4.2

Former Reference	New Reference
NFPA 71, 7-3	4-2.3.4.3
NFPA 71, 7-3.1	4-2.3.4.3.1
NFPA 71, 7-3.1.1	4-2.3.4.3.2
NFPA 71, 7-3.1.2	4-2.2.3, 4-2.2.3.1, and 4-2.2.3.3
NFPA 71, 7-3.1.3	4-2.2.4, 4-2.2.4.1, and 4-2.2.4.2
NFPA 71, 7-3.1.4	4-2.3.4.4
NFPA 71, 7-4	4-2.3.4.5
NFPA 71, 7-4.1	4-2.3.4.5.1
NFPA 71, Chap. 8, title	4-2.3.5
NFPA 71, 8-1.1	4-2.2.1 and 4-2.2.2.3
NFPA 71, 8-1.2.1	4-2.2.2.1
NFPA 71, 8-1.2.2	4-2.2.2.4 and 4-2.2.2.5
NFPA 71, 8-1.2.3	4-2.3.5.1 and 4-3.4.5
NFPA 71, 8-2.1.1	4-2.4.1
NFPA 71, 8-2.1.2	4-2.4.2
NFPA 71, 8-2.1.3	4-2.3.5.2
NFPA 71, 8-2.1.4	4-2.3.5.3 and 4-2.3.5.3.1
NFPA 71, 8-3	4-2.3.5.4
NFPA 71, 8-3.1	4-2.3.5.4.1
NFPA 71, 8-3.1.1	4-2.3.5.4.2
NFPA 71, 8-3.1.2	4-2.2.3, 4-2.2.3.1, 4-2.2.3.2, and 4-2.2.3.3
NFPA 71, 8-3.1.3	4-2.3.5.5
NFPA 71, 8-4.1	4-2.3.5.6
NFPA 71, Table 8-4.1	Table 4-2.3.5.6
NFPA 71, 8-4.2	4-2.3.5.7
NFPA 71, A-1-2.2	A-4-3.2.2
NFPA 71, A-1-2.4	A-4-3.2.4
NFPA 71, A-1-4.1	A-4-3.2.5
NFPA 71, A-1-7.1	A-4-2.4.2
NFPA 71, A-1-7.2.2	A-4-3.4.4.2
NFPA 71, A-1-10.2.3	A-4-3.6.1.3
NFPA 71, A-1-10.2.5(b)	A-4-3.6.1.5(b)
NFPA 71, A-2-2.1.6(c)	A-1-5.2.6(c)
NFPA 71, A-2-2.1.8	A-1-5.2.6.1
NFPA 71, A-2-2.3	A-1-5.2.9
NFPA 71, A-2-2.3.4(d)	A-1-5.2.9.2(d)
NFPA 71, A-2-2.5	A-1-5.2.11
NFPA 71, A-3-4.2.1	A-5-7.2
NFPA 71, A-3-4.3	A-5-8.1
NFPA 71, A-4-1.2.3	A-4-3.4.5
NFPA 71, A-4-2.1.3(b)	A-4-2.3.1.2.3(b)
NFPA 71, A-4-3.1	A-4-2.3.1.2
NFPA 71, A-5-2.3	A-4-2.3.2.1.3
NFPA 71, A-5-2.5	A-4-2.3.2.1.5
NFPA 71, A-5-2.7	A-4-2.3.2.1.7
NFPA 71, A-5-3.2.1	A-4-2.4.1
NFPA 71, A-5-3.3.1	A-4-2.3.2.2.2.1
NFPA 71, A-5-3.3.3	A-4-2.3.2.2.2.3
NFPA 71, A-5-3.3.4	A-4-2.3.2.2.2.4
NFPA 71, A-6-2.1.2	A-4-2.3.3.1.2
NFPA 71, A-6-3.4.1(c)	A-4-2.3.3.2.5(c)
NFPA 71, A-6-3.4.2(d)(3)	A-4-2.3.3.2.6(d)(3)
NFPA 71, A-6-4.3.1	A-4-2.3.3.3.5
NFPA 71, A-7-1.2.3	A-4-3.4.5
NFPA 71, A-7-3.1.4	A-4-2.3.4.4
NFPA 71, A-8-1.2.3	A-4-2.3.5.2
NFPA 72, 1-1	1-1
NFPA 72, 1-2.1	1-2 and 1-2.1
NFPA 72, 1-2.2	1-2.2
NFPA 72, 1-3.2	1-3, 1-3.1, 1-3.2, and 7-1.1.2
NFPA 72, 1-3.3	1-3.3
NFPA 72, 1-4	1-4
NFPA 72, 2-1	1-5.5.2
NFPA 72, 2-1.1	1-5.5.2.1
NFPA 72, 2-1.2	1-5.3 and 1-5.3.1
NFPA 72, 2-1.3	1-5.5.2.2
NFPA 72, 2-1.4	1-5.5.4

Former Reference	New Reference
NFPA 72, 2-1.5	1-5.5.5
NFPA 72, 2-1.6	1-5.6
NFPA 72, 2-2	1-7
NFPA 72, 2-2.1	1-7.1.1 and 7-1.4
NFPA 72, 2-2.2	1-7.2.1, Figure 1-7.2.1, and 7-1.4
NFPA 72, 2-3	1-5.5
NFPA 72, 2-3.1	1-5.5.1
NFPA 72, 2-3.2	1-5.5.6
NFPA 72, 2-3.2.1	1-5.5.6.1
NFPA 72, 2-3.2.2	1-5.5.6.2
NFPA 72, 2-4.1	1-5.4.10
NFPA 72, 2-4.2	1-5.7.1.2
NFPA 72, 2-4.3	1-5.4.2, 1-5.4.2.1, and 5-9.1.3
NFPA 72, 2-4.4	1-5.4.3 and 1-5.4.3.1
NFPA 72, 2-4.5	1-5.4.3.2
NFPA 72, 2-4.6	1-5.7.1
NFPA 72, 2-4.6.1	1-5.7.1.1
NFPA 72, 2-4.6.2	1-5.4.4
NFPA 72, 2-4.6.3	1-5.4.5
NFPA 72, 2-4.7	1-5.4.6
NFPA 72, 2-4.7.1	1-5.4.6.1 and 1-5.4.6.2
NFPA 72, 2-4.7.2	1-5.4.6.4
NFPA 72, 2-4.7.2.1	1-5.4.6.4.1
NFPA 72, 2-4.7.2.2	1-5.4.6.4.2
NFPA 72, 2-4.8.3	6-2.2.2 and 6-2.3
NFPA 72, 2-4.10	1-5.4.7 Distinctive Signals (a) - (c)
NFPA 72, 2-4.11	1-5.4.8
NFPA 72, 2-4.12	1-5.4.9
NFPA 72, 2-5.4	7-1.2 and 7-1.2.1
NFPA 72, 2-5.6	1-5.5.2.3
NFPA 72, 2-5.7	1-7.3
NFPA 72, 2-6	3-4.2 Exceptions No. 2 and No. 3, and 3-5
NFPA 72, 2-6.2	Table 3-5.1
NFPA 72, 2-6.3	3-5.3
NFPA 72, 2-7	3-6
NFPA 72, 2-7.2	Table 3-6.1
NFPA 72, 3-1	3-3
NFPA 72, 3-2.1	5-9 and 5-9.1
NFPA 72, 3-2.2	3-8.1.1 and 5-9.1.1
NFPA 72, 3-2.3	5-9.1.2
NFPA 72, 3-2.4	3-8.1.2 and 5-9.1.2
NFPA 72, 3-2.5	3-8.1.3
NFPA 72, 3-3	3-8.2
NFPA 72, 3-3.1	3-8.2.1
NFPA 72, 3-3.2	3-8.2.2
NFPA 72, 3-3.3	3-8.2.3
NFPA 72, 3-3.4	3-8.2.4
NFPA 72, 3-3.5	3-8.2.5
NFPA 72, 3-3.6	3-8.3 and 3-8.3.1
NFPA 72, 3-3.6.1	3-8.3.1.1
NFPA 72, 3-3.6.2	3-8.3.1.2
NFPA 72, 3-3.6.3	3-8.3.2
NFPA 72, 3-3.6.4	3-8.3.3
NFPA 72, 3-3.6.5	3-8.3.4
NFPA 72, 3-3.7	3-8.4
NFPA 72, 3-4	5-10
NFPA 72, 3-4.1	3-8.6
NFPA 72, 3-4.1.1	3-8.6.1, 5-7, and 5-7.1
NFPA 72, 3-4.1.2	5-7.2
NFPA 72, 3-4.1.4	3-8.6.2
NFPA 72, 3-4.2	3-8.7
NFPA 72, 3-4.2.1	3-8.7.1
NFPA 72, 3-4.2.2	3-8.7.2
NFPA 72, 3-4.2.3	3-8.7.3
NFPA 72, 3-4.2.4	3-8.7.4
NFPA 72, 3-4.2.5	3-8.7.3 Note, 3-8.7.5, and 5-10.1
NFPA 72, 3-4.2.6	5-10.2

Former Reference	New Reference
NFPA 72, 3-4.2.7	5-10.3
NFPA 72, 3-4.2.8	5-10.4
NFPA 72, 3-4.2.9	3-8.10 and 3-8.10.2
NFPA 72, 3-4.3	3-8.11
NFPA 72, 3-4.3.1	3-8.11.1
NFPA 72, 3-4.3.2	3-8.11.2
NFPA 72, 3-5	3-8.12
NFPA 72, 3-5.1.1	3-8.12.2
NFPA 72, 3-5.1.3	3-8.12.3
NFPA 72, 3-5.2	3-8.13
NFPA 72, 3-5.2.1	3-8.13.1
NFPA 72, 3-5.2.2	3-8.13.2
NFPA 72, 3-5.2.3	3-8.13.3
NFPA 72, 3-5.2.4	3-8.13.4
NFPA 72, 3-5.2.5	3-8.13.5
NFPA 72, 3-5.2.6	3-8.13.6
NFPA 72, 3-5.2.7	3-8.12.3
NFPA 72, 3-6	3-8.14
NFPA 72, 3-6.1	3-8.14.1
NFPA 72, 3-6.2	3-8.14.2
NFPA 72, 3-6.3	3-8.14.3
NFPA 72, 3-6.4	3-8.14.4 Exception
NFPA 72, 3-6.5	3-8.14.5
NFPA 72, 3-7.1	1-5.4.1
NFPA 72, 3-7.2.1	3-8.9.3
NFPA 72, 3-7.3	3-8.15
NFPA 72, 3-7.3.1	3-8.15.1
NFPA 72, 3-7.3.2	3-8.15.2
NFPA 72, 3-7.3.3	3-8.15.3
NFPA 72, 3-7.3.5	3-8.15.4 and (a)
NFPA 72, 4-2	1-5.8
NFPA 72, 4-2.1	1-5.8.1
NFPA 72, 4-2.1 Exception No. 1	1-5.8.1 Exception No. 1
NFPA 72, 4-2.1 Exception No. 2	1-5.8.1 Exception No. 2
NFPA 72, 4-2.1 Exception No. 5	1-5.8.1 Exception No. 4
NFPA 72, 4-2.1 Exception No. 6	1-5.8.6.1 Exception No. 2
NFPA 72, 4-2.1 Exception No. 7	1-5.8.1 Exception No. 3
NFPA 72, 4-2.1 Exception No. 8	1-5.8.1 Exception No. 5 and 1-5.8.4 Exception No. 2
NFPA 72, 4-2.1 Exception No. 9	1-5.8.1 Exception No. 6
NFPA 72, 4-2.1 Exception No. 10	1-5.8.1 Exception No. 7 and Note
NFPA 72, 4-2.1 Exception No. 11	1-5.8.1 Exception No. 8
NFPA 72, 4-2.1 Exception No. 12	1-5.8.1 Exception No. 9
NFPA 72, 4-2.2	1-5.8.2 and 4-2.3.6.3
NFPA 72, 4-2.3	1-5.8.3
NFPA 72, 4-3	1-5.8.1
NFPA 72, 4-4	1-5.8.5.1
NFPA 72, 4-5	1-5.8.6
NFPA 72, 4-5.1	1-5.8.6.1
NFPA 72, 4-5.2	1-5.8.6.1
NFPA 72, 5-1	1-5.2.1
NFPA 72, 5-2	1-5.2.2
NFPA 72, 5-3	1-5.2.3 Exception No. 1, Exception No. 2, and Note
NFPA 72, 5-3.1	1-5.2.3 Exception No. 1, Exception No. 2, and Note
NFPA 72, 5-3.2	1-5.2.4
NFPA 72, 5-3.3	1-5.2.5
NFPA 72, 5-3.5	1-5.2.7
NFPA 72, 5-4	1-5.2.8
NFPA 72, 5-4.1	1-5.2.8.1
NFPA 72, 5-4.2	1-5.2.8.2
NFPA 72, 5-4.3	1-5.2.8.4
NFPA 72, 5-5	1-5.2.9
NFPA 72, 5-5.1	1-5.2.9.2
NFPA 72, 5-5.2	1-5.2.9.1
NFPA 72, 5-5.3	1-5.2.9.4 and 1-5.2.9.5
NFPA 72, 5-5.4	1-5.2.9.3
NFPA 72, 5-6	1-5.2.10
NFPA 72, 5-6.1	1-5.2.10.1

Former Reference	New Reference
NFPA 72, 5-6.2	1-5.2.10.2
NFPA 72, 5-6.3	1-5.2.10.4
NFPA 72, 5-6.4	1-5.2.10.5
NFPA 72, 5-6.5	1-5.2.10.6
NFPA 72, 6-1	3-2 Exception
NFPA 72, 6-2.2	3-8.6.3
NFPA 72, 6-2.3	3-8.7.1.2
NFPA 72, 6-3	1-5.8.1
NFPA 72, 6-4	Table 3-7.1
NFPA 72, 6-5	3-13
NFPA 72, 6-5.1	3-13.1
NFPA 72, 6-5.2	2-3.1.2 Exception No. 2 and 3-13.2
NFPA 72, 6-5.3	3-13.3
NFPA 72, 6-5.3.1	3-13.3.1
NFPA 72, 6-5.3.2	3-13.3.2
NFPA 72, 6-5.3.3	3-13.3.3
NFPA 72, 6-5.3.4	3-13.3.4
NFPA 72, 6-5.3.5	3-13.3.5
NFPA 72, 6-5.4	3-13.4
NFPA 72, 6-5.4.1	3-13.4.1
NFPA 72, 6-5.4.2	3-13.4.2
NFPA 72, 6-5.4.3	3-13.4.3
NFPA 72, 6-5.4.4	3-13.4.4
NFPA 72, 6-5.4.5	3-13.4.5
NFPA 72, 6-5.4.6	3-13.4.6
NFPA 72, Chap. 7	4-7
NFPA 72, 7-1	4-7.1
NFPA 72, 7-2	4-7.2
NFPA 72, 7-2.3	4-7.2.1
NFPA 72, 7-2.4	4-7.2.2
NFPA 72, 7-2.5	4-7.2.3
NFPA 72, 7-2.6	4-7.2.4
NFPA 72, 7-3	4-7.4.1
NFPA 72, 7-3(a)	4-7.4.1(a)
NFPA 72, 7-3(b)	4-7.4.1(b)
NFPA 72, 7-3(c)	4-7.4.1(c) and Note
NFPA 72, 7-4.2	4-7.4.4
NFPA 72, 7-4.2.1	4-7.4.4.1
NFPA 72, 7-4.2.2	4-7.4.4.2
NFPA 72, 7-4.2.3	4-7.4.4.3
NFPA 72, 7-4.2.4	4-7.4.4.4
NFPA 72, 7-4.7	4-7.4.4.5
NFPA 72, 7-6.1.1	4-7.4.1(b)1.
NFPA 72, 7-6.1.2	4-7.4.1(b)2.
NFPA 72, 7-6.1.3	4-7.4.1(b)3.
NFPA 72, 7-6.1.4	4-7.4.1(b)4.
NFPA 72, 7-6.1.5	4-7.4.1(b)5.
NFPA 72, 7-6.1.6	4-7.4.1(b)6.
NFPA 72, 7-6.1.7	4-7.4.1(b)7.
NFPA 72, 7-6.1.8	4-7.4.1(b)8.
NFPA 72, 7-6.2.1	4-7.4.1(a)1.
NFPA 72, 7-6.2.2	4-7.4.1(a)2.
NFPA 72, 7-6.3.1	4-7.4.1(c)1.
NFPA 72, 7-6.3.2	4-7.4.1(c)2.
NFPA 72, 7-6.3.3	4-7.4.1(c)3.
NFPA 72, Chap. 8	4-5
NFPA 72, 8-1.1	4-5.1
NFPA 72, 8-2	4-5.2
NFPA 72, 8-2.1	4-5.2.1
NFPA 72, 8-2.2	4-5.3.1
NFPA 72, 8-2.3	4-5.3.2
NFPA 72, 8-2.4	4-5.3.3
NFPA 72, 8-2.5	4-5.5
NFPA 72, 8-2.6	4-5.2.2
NFPA 72, 8-3.1	4-5.6.1
NFPA 72, 8-3.2	4-5.4.4
NFPA 72, 8-3.3	4-5.6.2

Former Reference	New Reference
NFPA 72, 8-3.4	4-5.4.1.2 and 4-5.4.1.5
NFPA 72, 8-3.5	4-5.4.1.2
NFPA 72, 8-3.6	4-5.4.1.5
NFPA 72, 8-4	4-5.6.4
NFPA 72, 8-5	4-2.3.6.5
NFPA 72, 8-5.1	4-2.3.6.5.1
NFPA 72, 8-5.4	4-2.3.6.5.2
NFPA 72, 8-5.9	4-2.3.6.5.2 Note
NFPA 72, 8-6.1	4-2.3.6.1
NFPA 72, 8-6.2	4-2.3.6.2
NFPA 72, 8-6.3	4-2.3.6.4
NFPA 72, 8-7	4-2.3.2
NFPA 72, 8-7.1.3	4-2.2.2.3
NFPA 72, 8-7.2	4-2.3.2.1
NFPA 72, 8-7.2.1	4-2.3.2.1.1
NFPA 72, 8-7.2.2	4-2.3.2.1.2
NFPA 72, 8-7.2.3	4-2.3.2.1.3
NFPA 72, 8-7.2.4	4-2.3.2.1.4
NFPA 72, 8-7.2.5	4-2.3.2.1.5
NFPA 72, 8-7.2.6	4-2.3.2.1.6 and 4-2.3.2.1.6.1
NFPA 72, 8-7.2.7	4-2.3.2.1.7
NFPA 72, 8-7.2.8	4-2.3.2.1.8
NFPA 72, 8-7.2.9	4-2.3.2.1.10
NFPA 72, 8-7.3.1	4-2.3.2.2.1
NFPA 72, 8-7.3.1.1	4-2.3.2.2.1.1
NFPA 72, 8-7.3.1.2	4-2.3.2.2.1.2
NFPA 72, 8-7.3.2.1	4-2.4.1
NFPA 72, 8-7.3.2.2	4-2.4.2
NFPA 72, 8-7.3.3	4-2.3.2.2.2
NFPA 72, 8-7.3.3.1	4-2.3.2.2.2.1
NFPA 72, 8-7.3.3.2	4-2.3.2.2.2.2
NFPA 72, 8-7.3.3.3	4-2.3.2.2.2.3
NFPA 72, 8-7.3.3.4	4-2.3.2.2.2.4
NFPA 72, 8-7.3.3.5	4-2.3.2.2.2.5
NFPA 72, Chap 9	4-4
NFPA 72, 9-1	4-4.2.3
NFPA 72, 9-2	4-4.2
NFPA 72, 9-2.1	4-4.3.1
NFPA 72, 9-2.2	4-4.3.2
NFPA 72, 9-2.3	4-4.5.1 and 4-4.5.2
NFPA 72, 9-2.4	4-4.5.3
NFPA 72, 9-3.1	4-4.6.4
NFPA 72, 9-3.2	4-4.6.5
NFPA 72, 9-3.3	4-4.6.6
NFPA 72, 9-3.4	4-4.6.7.4
NFPA 72, 9-4	4-4.6.2
NFPA 72, 9-5	4-2.3.7
NFPA 72, 9-5.1	4-2.3.7.1
NFPA 72, 9-5.2	4-2.3.7.2
NFPA 72, 9-5.3	4-2.3.7.3
NFPA 72, 9-6	4-4.3.5
NFPA 72, 9-7.1	4-4.4 and 4-4.4.1
NFPA 72, 9-7.3	4-4.4.2
NFPA 72, 9-8.1.1	4-4.4.3
NFPA 72, 9-8.1.2	4-4.4.4
NFPA 72, 9-8.1.3	4-4.4.5
NFPA 72, 9-8.2	4-4.4.6
NFPA 72, 9-8.3.1	4-4.4.7
NFPA 72, 9-8.3.2	4-4.4.8
NFPA 72, 9-8.3.3	1-5.4.6.3 and 4-4.4.9
NFPA 72, 9-9	4-4.4.10
NFPA 72, 9-10	4-4.6.7
NFPA 72, 9-10.1	4-4.6.8.1 and 4-4.6.8.2
NFPA 72, 9-10.2	4-4.6.7.1
NFPA 72, 9-10.3	4-4.6.7.2
NFPA 72, 9-10.4	4-4.6.7.3
NFPA 72, 9-10.5	4-4.6.7.4

Former Reference	New Reference
NFPA 72, Chap. 10	3-12
NFPA 72, 10-2.2	1-5.8.5.2
NFPA 72, 10-2.4	7-5.2
NFPA 72, 10-3.1	3-2.4
NFPA 72, 10-3.2	3-12.1, 3-12.2, 3-12.3, and 3-12.3.1
NFPA 72, 10-3.3	3-12.3.2
NFPA 72, 10-3.4	3-12.3.3
NFPA 72, 10-3.5	3-12.3.4
NFPA 72, 10-4	3-12.4
NFPA 72, 10-4.1	3-12.4.1
NFPA 72, 10-4.2	3-12.4.2
NFPA 72, 10-4.3	3-12.4.3
NFPA 72, 10-4.3.1	3-12.4.3.1
NFPA 72, 10-4.3.2	3-12.4.3.2
NFPA 72, 10-4.3.3	3-12.4.3.3
NFPA 72, 10-4.4.1	3-12.4.4
NFPA 72, 10-4.5	3-12.4.5
NFPA 72, 10-4.5.1	3-12.4.5.1
NFPA 72, 10-4.5.2	3-12.4.5.2
NFPA 72, 10-4.6	3-12.4.6
NFPA 72, 10-4.6.1	3-12.4.6.1
NFPA 72, 10-4.6.2	3-12.4.6.2
NFPA 72, 10-4.6.3	3-12.4.6.3
NFPA 72, 10-5	3-12.6
NFPA 72, 10-5.1	3-12.6.1
NFPA 72, 10-5.2	3-12.6.2
NFPA 72, 10-5.3	3-12.6.3
NFPA 72, 10-5.5	3-12.6.4
NFPA 72, 10-5.6	3-12.6.5
NFPA 72, 10-5.7	3-12.6.6
NFPA 72, A-1-2.1	A-1-2.1
NFPA 72, A-2-1.4	A-1-5.5.4
NFPA 72, A-2-2.2	A-1-5.8.5.1 and A-1-7.2.1
NFPA 72, A-2-2.3(a)	1-7.2.2, 1-7.2.2.1, 1-7.2.2.2, and 1-7.2.2.2.1
NFPA 72, A-2-3.1(a)	A-1-5.5.1(a)
NFPA 72, Figure A-2-4.10(a)(1)	Figure A-2-2.2.2(a) and Figure A-3-7.2(a)(1)
NFPA 72, Figure A-2-4.10(a)(2)	Figure A-2-2.2.2(b) and Figure A-3-7.2(a)(2)
NFPA 72, Figure A-2-4.10(a)(3)	Figure A-2-2.2.2(c) and Figure A-3-7.2(a)(3)
NFPA 72, A-2-4.10(b)	A-1-5.4.7(b)
NFPA 72, A-2-4.3	A-1-5.4.2.1 and A-4-2.3.3.1.2
NFPA 72, A-2-6.2	A-3-4.1, A-3-4.2, A-3-5.1, and A-3-6.1
NFPA 72, A-2-7.2	A-3-4.1, A-3-4.2, A-3-5.1, and A-3-6.1
NFPA 72, A-3-3.6.5	A-3-8.2.3 and A-3-8.3.4
NFPA 72, A-3-3.7	A-3-8.4
NFPA 72, A-3-4.1.2	A-5-7.2
NFPA 72, A-3-4.3.2	A-3-8.11.2 and A-3-8.14.1
NFPA 72, A-3-7.3.5(a) and (b)	A-3-8.15.4
NFPA 72, Figure A-3-7.3.5(a)	Figure A-3-8.15.4(a)
NFPA 72, Figure A-3-7.3.5(b)	Figure A-3-8.15.4(b)
NFPA 72, Figure A-7-3(a)(1)	Figure A-4-7.4.1(a)(1)
NFPA 72, Figure A-7-3(a)(2)	Figure A-4-7.4.1(a)(2)
NFPA 72, Figure A-7-3(b)(1)	Figure A-4-7.4.1(b)(1)
NFPA 72, Figure A-7-3(b)(2)	Figure A-4-7.4.1(b)(2)
NFPA 72, Figure A-7-3(c)	Figure A-4-7.4.1(c)
NFPA 72, A-8-7.2.3	A-4-2.3.2.1.3
NFPA 72, A-8-7.2.5	A-4-2.3.2.1.5
NFPA 72, A-8-7.2.7	A-4-2.3.2.1.7
NFPA 72, A-8-7.3.2.1	A-4-2.4.1
NFPA 72, A-8-7.3.3.1	A-4-2.3.2.2.2.1
NFPA 72, A-8-7.3.3.3	A-4-2.3.2.2.2.3
NFPA 72, A-8-7.3.3.4	A-4-2.3.2.2.2.4
NFPA 72, A-9-1	A-4-4.2.3
NFPA 72, A-9-3.2	A-4-4.6.5
NFPA 72, A-9-3.3	A-4-4.6.6
NFPA 72, A-9-5.2(b)	A-4-2.3.7.2(b)
NFPA 72, A-10-4.1	A-3-12.4.1
NFPA 72, A-10-4.6.2	6-3.1.3, 6-3.1.4, and 6-3.1.5

Former Reference	New Reference
NFPA 72E, 1-1	5-1.1
NFPA 72E, 1-1.2	5-1.2.1
NFPA 72E, 1-2.1	5-1.1
NFPA 72E, 1-2.2	5-1.2.2
NFPA 72E, 1-2.3	5-1.2.2
NFPA 72E, 2-1	1-4
NFPA 72E, 2-1.1	1-4
NFPA 72E, 2-2.1	1-4
NFPA 72E, 2-2.1.1	5-2.3.1.1
NFPA 72E, 2-2.1.3	1-4
NFPA 72E, 2-2.1.3.1	5-1.2.3
NFPA 72E, 2-2.1.3.2	5-1.2.4
NFPA 72E, 2-2.1.4	1-4
NFPA 72E, 2-2.1.5	1-4
NFPA 72E, 2-2.2.1	1-4
NFPA 72E, 2-2.2.2	1-4
NFPA 72E, 2-2.2.3	1-4
NFPA 72E, 2-2.3.1	1-4
NFPA 72E, 2-2.3.2	1-4
NFPA 72E, 2-3	1-4
NFPA 72E, 2-3.1	1-4
NFPA 72E, 2-3.1.1	1-4
NFPA 72E, 2-3.1.2	1-4
NFPA 72E, 2-4	1-4
NFPA 72E, 2-4.1	1-4
NFPA 72E, 2-4.1.1	1-4
NFPA 72E, 2-4.1.2	1-4
NFPA 72E, 2-4.1.3	1-4
NFPA 72E, 2-4.1.4	1-4
NFPA 72E, 2-5.1	1-5.3 and 1-5.3.1
NFPA 72E, 2-5.1.1	1-5.3.2
NFPA 72E, 2-5.1.2	1-7.1.1
NFPA 72E, 2-5.1.3	1-7.1.2
NFPA 72E, 2-7	5-1.3
NFPA 72E, 2-7.1	5-1.3.1
NFPA 72E, 2-7.2	5-1.3.2
NFPA 72E, 2-7.3	5-1.3.3
NFPA 72E, 2-7.4	5-1.3.4
NFPA 72E, 2-7.5	5-1.3.5 and A-5-1.3.5
NFPA 72E, 2-7.6	5-1.3.6
NFPA 72E, 2-7.7	5-1.4.1
NFPA 72E, Chap. 3	5-2
NFPA 72E, 3-1	5-2.1
NFPA 72E, 3-1.1.1	5-2.1
NFPA 72E, 3-1.1.2	5-2.2
NFPA 72E, 3-2	5-2.3
NFPA 72E, 3-2.1	5-2.3.1
NFPA 72E, 3-2.1.2	5-2.3.1.2
NFPA 72E, 3-2.1.3	5-2.3.1.3
NFPA 72E, 3-2.2	5-2.3.2
NFPA 72E, 3-2.2.1	5-2.3.2.1
NFPA 72E, 3-2.2.2	5-2.3.2.2
NFPA 72E, 3-2.3	5-2.3.3
NFPA 72E, 3-2.3.1	5-2.3.3.1
NFPA 72E, 3-2.3.2	5-2.3.3.2
NFPA 72E, 3-3	5-2.4
NFPA 72E, 3-3.1	5-2.4.1 and Table 5-2.4.1
NFPA 72E, 3-3.1.1	5-2.4.1.1
NFPA 72E, 3-4	5-2.5
NFPA 72E, 3-4.1	5-2.5.1
NFPA 72E, 3-4.2	5-2.5.2
NFPA 72E, 3-4.3	5-2.6
NFPA 72E, 3-5	5-2.7
NFPA 72E, 3-5.1	5-2.7.1
NFPA 72E, 3-5.1.1	5-2.7.1.1
NFPA 72E, 3-5.1.2	5-2.7.1.2
NFPA 72E, Table 3-5.1.2	Table 5-2.7.1.2

Former Reference	New Reference
NFPA 72E, 3-5.2	5-2.7.2
NFPA 72E, 3-5.3	5-2.7.3
NFPA 72E, 3-5.4	5-2.7.4
NFPA 72E, 3-5.4.1	5-2.7.4.1
NFPA 72E, 3-5.4.2	5-2.7.4.2
NFPA 72E, 3-5.4.3	5-2.7.4.3
NFPA 72E, Chap. 4	5-3
NFPA 72E, 4-1	5-3.1
NFPA 72E, 4-1.1	5-3.1.1
NFPA 72E, 4-1.2	5-3.1.2
NFPA 72E, 4-1.2.1	5-3.1.3
NFPA 72E, 4-1.2.2	5-3.1.4
NFPA 72E, 4-1.3	5-3.2
NFPA 72E, 4-2	5-3.3 and 5-3.4
NFPA 72E, 4-2.1	5-3.3.1
NFPA 72E, 4-2.1.1	5-3.3.1.1
NFPA 72E, 4-2.1.2	5-3.3.1.2
NFPA 72E, 4-2.2	5-3.3.2
NFPA 72E, 4-2.2.1	5-3.3.2.1
NFPA 72E, 4-2.2.2	5-3.3.2.2
NFPA 72E, 4-2.3	5-3.3.3
NFPA 72E, 4-2.3.1	5-3.3.3.1
NFPA 72E, 4-2.3.2	5-3.3.3.2
NFPA 72E, 4-2.4	5-3.3.4
NFPA 72E, 4-3.1	5-3.4.1
NFPA 72E, 4-3.1.1	5-3.4.2
NFPA 72E, 4-4	5-3.5
NFPA 72E, 4-4.1	5-3.5.1
NFPA 72E, 4-4.1.1	5-3.5.1.1
NFPA 72E, 4-4.1.2	5-3.5.1.2
NFPA 72E, 4-4.2	5-3.5.2
NFPA 72E, 4-4.2.1	5-3.5.2.1
NFPA 72E, 4-4.3.1	5-3.5.3.1
NFPA 72E, 4-4.3.1.1	5-3.5.3.1.1
NFPA 72E, 4-4.4	5-3.5.4
NFPA 72E, 4-4.5	5-3.5.5
NFPA 72E, 4-4.5.1	5-3.5.5.1
NFPA 72E, 4-4.5.1.1	5-3.5.5.1.1
NFPA 72E, 4-4.5.2	5-3.5.5.2
NFPA 72E, 4-4.6	5-3.5.6
NFPA 72E, 4-4.6.1	5-3.5.6.1
NFPA 72E, 4-4.6.2	5-3.5.6.2
NFPA 72E, 4-4.7	5-3.5.7
NFPA 72E, 4-4.7.1	5-3.5.7.1
NFPA 72E, 4-4.7.2	5-3.5.7.2
NFPA 72E, 4-4.7.3	5-3.5.7.3
NFPA 72E, 4-4.7.4	5-3.5.7.4
NFPA 72E, 4-4.8	5-3.5.8
NFPA 72E, 4-4.8.1	5-3.5.8.1
NFPA 72E, 4-4.8.2	5-3.5.8.2
NFPA 72E, 4-4.9	5-3.5.9
NFPA 72E, 4-4.10	5-3.5.10
NFPA 72E, 4-5	5-3.6
NFPA 72E, 4-5.1	5-3.6.1
NFPA 72E, 4-5.2	5-3.6.2
NFPA 72E, 4-5.2.1	5-3.6.2.1
NFPA 72E, 4-6	5-3.7
NFPA 72E, 4-6.1	5-3.7.1
NFPA 72E, 4-6.1.1	5-3.7.1.1
NFPA 72E, 4-6.1.2	5-3.7.1.2
NFPA 72E, 4-6.1.3	5-3.7.1.3
NFPA 72E, 4-6.2.1	5-3.7.2.1
NFPA 72E, 4-6.2.2	5-3.7.2.2
NFPA 72E, 4-6.3	5-3.7.3
NFPA 72E, 4-6.3.1	5-3.7.3.1
NFPA 72E, 4-6.3.2	5-3.7.3.2
NFPA 72E, 4-6.4	5-3.7.5

Former Reference	New Reference
NFPA 72E, 4-6.5	5-3.7.6
NFPA 72E, 4-6.5.1	5-3.7.6.1
NFPA 72E, 4-6.5.3	5-3.7.6.2
NFPA 72E, 4-6.5.4	5-3.7.6.3
NFPA 72E, 4-6.5.4(a)	Figure 5-3.7.6.3
NFPA 72E, 4-6.5.4(b)	Table 5-3.7.6.3
NFPA 72E, 5-1.1	5-4.1.2
NFPA 72E, 5-1.2	5-4, 5-4.1, and 5-4.1.1
NFPA 72E, 5-2	5-4.2
NFPA 72E, 5-2.1	5-4.2.1
NFPA 72E, 5-2.1.1	5-4.2.1
NFPA 72E, 5-2.1.2	5-4.2.1
NFPA 72E, 5-2.1.3	5-4.2.1
NFPA 72E, 5-2.1.4	5-4.2.1
NFPA 72E, 5-2.1.5	5-4.2.1
NFPA 72E, 5-2.1.6	5-4.2.1
NFPA 72E, 5-2.1.7	5-4.2.1
NFPA 72E, 5-2.1.8	5-4.2.1
NFPA 72E, 5-2.1.9	5-4.2.1
NFPA 72E, 5-2.2	5-4.2.2
NFPA 72E, 5-2.2.1	5-4.2.2.1
NFPA 72E, 5-2.2.2	5-4.2.2.2
NFPA 72E, 5-2.2.3	5-4.2.2.3
NFPA 72E, 5-2.2.4	5-4.2.2.4
NFPA 72E, 5-2.3	5-4.2.3
NFPA 72E, 5-2.3.1	5-4.2.3
NFPA 72E, 5-3	5-4.3
NFPA 72E, 5-3.1	5-4.3.1
NFPA 72E, 5-4	5-4.4
NFPA 72E, 5-4.1	5-4.4.1
NFPA 72E, 5-4.1.1	5-4.4.1.1
NFPA 72E, 5-4.1.2	5-4.4.1.2
NFPA 72E, 5-4.2	5-4.4.2
NFPA 72E, 5-4.2.1	5-4.4.2.1
NFPA 72E, 5-4.2.2	5-4.4.2.2
NFPA 72E, 5-4.2.3	5-4.4.2.3
NFPA 72E, 5-4.2.4	5-4.4.2.4
NFPA 72E, 5-4.2.5	5-4.4.2.5
NFPA 72E, 5-4.2.6	5-4.4.2.6
NFPA 72E, 5-4.3	5-4.5
NFPA 72E, 5-4.3.1	5-4.5.1
NFPA 72E, 5-4.3.2	5-4.5.2
NFPA 72E, 5-4.3.3	5-4.5.3
NFPA 72E, 5-4.3.4	5-4.5.4
NFPA 72E, 5-4.3.5	5-4.5.5
NFPA 72E, 5-4.3.6	5-4.5.6
NFPA 72E, 5-5.1	5-4.4.2.5
NFPA 72E, 5-6	5-4.6
NFPA 72E, 5-6.1	5-4.3.2
NFPA 72E, 5-6.2	5-4.6.1
NFPA 72E, 5-6.3	5-4.6.2
NFPA 72E, 5-6.4	5-4.6.3
NFPA 72E, Chap. 6	5-5
NFPA 72E, 6-1.1.3	5-5.2
NFPA 72E, 6-1.1.4	5-5.3
NFPA 72E, 6-2	5-5.5
NFPA 72E, 6-2.1	5-5.5.1
NFPA 72E, 6-2.2	5-5.5.2
NFPA 72E, 6-3	5-5.6
NFPA 72E, 6-3.1	5-5.6.1
NFPA 72E, 6-3.1.1	5-5.6.1.1
NFPA 72E, 6-3.1.2	5-5.6.1.2
NFPA 72E, 6-3.2	5-5.6.2
NFPA 72E, 6-3.3	5-5.6.3
NFPA 72E, 6-3.4	5-5.6.4
NFPA 72E, 6-3.4.1	5-5.6.4.1
NFPA 72E, 6-3.5	5-5.6.5

Former Reference	New Reference
NFPA 72E, 6-3.5.1	5-5.6.5.1
NFPA 72E, 6-3.5.2	5-5.6.5.2
NFPA 72E, 6-3.6	5-5.6.6
NFPA 72E, 6-3.6.1	5-5.6.6.1
NFPA 72E, 6-3.6.2	5-5.6.6.2
NFPA 72E, 6-3.6.3	5-5.6.6.3
NFPA 72E, 6-3.7	5-5.6.7
NFPA 72E, 6-3.7.1	5-5.6.7.1
NFPA 72E, 6-3.7.2	5-5.6.7.2
NFPA 72E, 6-3.8	5-5.6.8
NFPA 72E, 6-3.9	5-5.6.9
NFPA 72E, 6-4	5-5.7
NFPA 72E, 6-4.1	5-5.7.1
NFPA 72E, 6-4.2	5-5.7.2
NFPA 72E, 6-4.2.1	5-5.7.2.1
NFPA 72E, 6-5	5-5.8
NFPA 72E, 6-5.1	5-5.8.1
NFPA 72E, 6-5.1.1	5-5.8.1.1
NFPA 72E, 6-5.1.2	5-5.8.1.2
NFPA 72E, 6-5.1.3	5-5.8.1.3
NFPA 72E, Chap. 7	5-6
NFPA 72E, 7-1	5-6.1
NFPA 72E, 7-1.1.2	5-6.2
NFPA 72E, 7-2.1	5-6.3
NFPA 72E, 7-2.2	5-6.4
NFPA 72E, 7-3	5-6.5
NFPA 72E, 7-3.1	5-6.5.1
NFPA 72E, 7-3.2	5-6.5.2
NFPA 72E, 7-3.3	5-6.5.3
NFPA 72E, 7-3.4	5-6.5.4
NFPA 72E, 8-1.2	7-1.1.1
NFPA 72E, 8-1.3	7-1.2
NFPA 72E, 8-1.3.1	7-1.2
NFPA 72E, 8-1.3.2	7-1.2.2
NFPA 72E, 8-1.4	7-1.3
NFPA 72E, 8-3.2	7-3, 7-3.1, 7-3.1.1, and 7-3.1.2
NFPA 72E, 8-4.1	7-4.1 and 7-4.2
NFPA 72E, Chap. 9	5-11
NFPA 72E, 9-1	5-11 Note
NFPA 72E, 9-1.1	5-11.1
NFPA 72E, 9-1.2	5-11.2
NFPA 72E, 9-1.3	5-11.3
NFPA 72E, 9-2	5-11.4
NFPA 72E, 9-2.1	5-11.4.1
NFPA 72E, 9-2.2	5-11.4.2
NFPA 72E, 9-2.3	5-11.4.3
NFPA 72E, 9-2.4	5-11.4.4
NFPA 72E, 9-3	5-11.5
NFPA 72E, 9-3.1	5-11.5.1
NFPA 72E, 9-3.2	5-11.5.2
NFPA 72E, 9-3.2.1	5-11.5.2.1
NFPA 72E, 9-3.2.2	5-11.5.2.2
NFPA 72E, 9-4	5-11.6
NFPA 72E, 9-4.1	5-11.6.1
NFPA 72E, 9-4.2	5-11.6.2
NFPA 72E, 9-4.3	5-11.6.3
NFPA 72E, 9-4.4	5-11.6.4
NFPA 72E, 9-4.5	5-11.6.5
NFPA 72E, 9-4.6	5-11.6.6
NFPA 72E, 9-4.7	5-11.6.7
NFPA 72E, 9-5	5-11.7
NFPA 72E, 9-5.1	5-11.7.1
NFPA 72E, 9-5.2	5-11.7.2
NFPA 72E, 9-5.3	5-11.7.3
NFPA 72E, 9-5.4	5-11.7.4
NFPA 72E, 9-5.4.1	5-11.7.4.1
NFPA 72E, 9-5.4.1.1	5-11.7.4.1.1 and Figure 5-11.7.4.1.1

Former Reference	New Reference
NFPA 72E, 9-5.4.1.2	5-11.7.4.1.2
NFPA 72E, 9-5.4.1.3	5-11.7.4.1.3
NFPA 72E, 9-5.4.1.4	5-11.7.4.1.4
NFPA 72E, 9-5.4.2	5-11.7.4.2
NFPA 72E, 9-5.4.3	5-11.7.4.3
NFPA 72E, 9-5.4.3.1	5-11.7.4.3.1 and Figure 5-11.7.4.3.1
NFPA 72E, 9-5.4.3.2	5-11.7.4.3.2
NFPA 72E, 9-5.4.3.3	5-11.7.4.3.3
NFPA 72E, 9-5.4.4	5-11.7.4.4
NFPA 72E, 9-5.4.4.1	5-11.7.4.4.1
NFPA 72E, 9-5.5	5-11.7.5
NFPA 72E, 9-5.5.1	5-11.7.5.1 and 5-11.7.5.2
NFPA 72E, A-2-7.7	A-5-1.4
NFPA 72E, Figure A-2-7.7(a)	Figure A-5-1.4(a)
NFPA 72E, Figure A-2-7.7(b)	Figure A-5-1.4(b)
NFPA 72E, Figure A-3-4.1	Figure A-5-2.5.1
NFPA 72E, Figure A-3-5.1	Figure A-5-2.7.1
NFPA 72E, A-3-5.1(a)	Figure A-5-2.7.1(a)
NFPA 72E, A-3-5.1(b)	Figure A-5-2.7.1(b)
NFPA 72E, Figure A-3-5.1(c)	Figure A-5-2.7.1(c)
NFPA 72E, Figure A-3-5.1(d)	Figure A-5-2.7.1(d)
NFPA 72E, Figure A-3-5.1.1	Figure A-5-2.7.1.1
NFPA 72E, A-3-5.1.2	A-5-2.7.1.2
NFPA 72E, A-3-5.2	Figure A-5-2.7.2
NFPA 72E, A-3-5.3	A-5-2.7.3 (a) and (b)
NFPA 72E, A-3-5.4.1	Figure A-5-2.7.4.1
NFPA 72E, A-3-5.4.2	Figure A-5-2.7.4.2
NFPA 72E, A-4-1.1	A-5-3.1.1
NFPA 72E, A-4-1.3	A-5-3.2
NFPA 72E, A-4-2.2	A-5-3.3.2
NFPA 72E, A-4-2.3	A-5-3.3.3
NFPA 72E, A-4-4.1	A-5-3.5.1
NFPA 72E, A-4-4.1.2	A-5-3.5.1.2
NFPA 72E, Figure A-4-4.1.2	Figure A-5-3.5.1.2
NFPA 72E, A-4-4.2	A-5-3.5.2
NFPA 72E, Figure A-4-4.3.1.1	Figure A-5-3.5.2.1
NFPA 72E, A-4-4.5.2	A-5-3.5.5.2
NFPA 72E, Figure A-4-4.5.2	Figure A-5-3.5.5.2
NFPA 72E, A-4-4.6	A-5-3.5.6
NFPA 72E, A-4-4.7.4	A-5-3.5.7.4
NFPA 72E, A-4-5.1	A-5-3.6.1
NFPA 72E, A-4-6.1.1	A-5-3.7.1.1
NFPA 72E, A-4-6.1.2	A-5-3.7.1.2
NFPA 72E, Table A-4-6.1.4	Table A-5-3.7.1.1
NFPA 72E, Table A-4-6.1.5(a)	Table A-5-3.7.1.2(a)
NFPA 72E, Table A-4-6.1.5(b)	Table A-5-3.7.1.2(b)
NFPA 72E, Figure A-4-6.1.8(a)	Figure A-5-3.7.5(a)
NFPA 72E, Figure A-4-6.1.8(b)	Figure A-5-3.7.5(b)
NFPA 72E, A-4-6.2.2	A-5-3.7.2.2
NFPA 72E, A-4-6.4	A-5-3.7.5
NFPA 72E, A-5-2.1.1	A-5-4.2.1
NFPA 72E, A-5-2.1.6	A-5-4.2.1
NFPA 72E, A-5-2.1.9	A-5-4.2.1
NFPA 72E, A-5-3.1	A-5-4.3.1
NFPA 72E, A-5-4.1.1	A-5-4.4.1.1 and Figure A-5-4.4.1.1
NFPA 72E, A-5-4.2.1	A-5-4.4.2.1
NFPA 72E, A-5-4.2.3	A-5-4.4.2.3 and Figure A-5-4.4.2.3
NFPA 72E, A-5-4.2.4	A-5-4.4.2.4
NFPA 72E, A-5-4.2.6	A-5-4.4.2.6
NFPA 72E, A-5-4.3.1	A-5-4.5.1
NFPA 72E, A-5-4.3.2	A-5-4.5.2
NFPA 72E, A-5-4.3.5	A-5-4.5.5
NFPA 72E, A-5-4.3.6	A-5-4.5.6
NFPA 72E, A-6-1.1.1	A-5-5.1
NFPA 72E, A-6-3.1	A-5-5.6.1
NFPA 72E, A-6-3.3	A-5-5.6.3
NFPA 72E, A-6-3.6.3	A-5-5.6.6.3

Former Reference	New Reference
NFPA 72E, A-6-4.1	A-5-5.7.1
NFPA 72E, A-6-5.1.3	A-5-5.8.1.3
NFPA 72E, A-8-1.3.2	7-1.2.2
NFPA 72E, A-9-1.1	A-5-11.1
NFPA 72E, A-9-1.2(a) and (b)	A-5-11.2
NFPA 72E, A-9-3.2.2	A-5-11.5.2.2 and Figure A-5-11.5.2.2(b)
NFPA 72E, A-9-3.2.2(a)	Figure A-5-11.5.2.2(a)
NFPA 72E, A-9-3.2.2(b)	Figure A-5-11.5.2.2(b)
NFPA 72E, A-9-3.2.2(c)	Figure A-5-11.5.2.2(c)
NFPA 72E, A-9-4.8(a)	Figure A-5-11.6.2(a)
NFPA 72E, A-9-4.8(b)	Figure A-5-11.6.2(b)
NFPA 72E, A-9-4.8(c)	Figure A-5-11.6.2(c)
NFPA 72E, A-9-5.4.3.2	Figure A-5-11.7.4.3.2
NFPA 72E, A-9-5.4.3.3	Figure A-5-11.7.4.3.3
NFPA 72E, B-1-1	B-2.1.1
NFPA 72E, B-1-2	B-2.1.2
NFPA 72E, B-1-3	B-2.1.3
NFPA 72E, B-1-4	B-2.1.4
NFPA 72E, B-1-5	B-2.1.5
NFPA 72E, B-1-6	B-2.1.6
NFPA 72E, B-1-7	B-2.1.7
NFPA 72E, Appendix C	Appendix B
NFPA 72E, C-2-2.2.3	B-2.2.2.4
NFPA 72E, C-3-4.1.3	B-3.4.1.2 and B-3.4.2
NFPA 72E, C-5-2	B-1.2.2
NFPA 72E, C-5-2.2.1	Table B-3.2.2
NFPA 72E, Table C-5-2.2.2	Table B-2.2.2.3
NFPA 72E, C-5-2.3	B-1.2.4
NFPA 72E, C-5-3.4	B-3.3, B-3.3.1, B-3.3.2, and Table B-3.3.2
NFPA 72G, 1-2.1	6-1.1
NFPA 72G, 1-2.2	6-1.2
NFPA 72G, 1-2.3	6-1.5
NFPA 72G, Chap. 2	6-1.4
NFPA 72G, 2-1.1	1-4
NFPA 72G, 2-1.1.1	1-4
NFPA 72G, 2-1.1.1.1	1-4
NFPA 72G, 2-1.1.1.2	1-4
NFPA 72G, 2-1.1.1.3	1-4
NFPA 72G, 2-1.1.2	1-4
NFPA 72G, 2-1.1.3	1-4
NFPA 72G, 2-2	1-4
NFPA 72G, 2-2.1	1-4
NFPA 72G, 2-2.2	1-4
NFPA 72G, 2-2.3	1-4
NFPA 72G, 2-3.1	1-4
NFPA 72G, 2-3.2	1-4
NFPA 72G, 2-4	6-2.2
NFPA 72G, 2-4.1	6-2.2.1
NFPA 72G, 3-1	6-3
NFPA 72G, 3-1.1.1	6-3.1.1
NFPA 72G, 3-1.1.2	6-3.1.5 Note and 6-3.2
NFPA 72G, 3-1.1.3	6-3.3
NFPA 72G, 3-1.1.4	6-3.4 and A-6-3.1
NFPA 72G, 3-2.1.1	6-4 and 6-4.1
NFPA 72G, 3-2.1.2	6-4 and 6-4.1
NFPA 72G, 3-2.2.1	6-6
NFPA 72G, 3-2.2.2	6-6.1
NFPA 72G, 3-2.3.1	6-4.2
NFPA 72G, 3-2.3.2	6-4.2.1
NFPA 72G, 3-2.3.3	6-4.2.2
NFPA 72G, 3-2.4.1	6-4.3
NFPA 72G, 3-3.1	6-5
NFPA 72G, 3-4.2	6-1.3
NFPA 72G, 3-5.1	6-2.4
NFPA 72G, 3-5.2	6-2.5
NFPA 72G, 4-1.1	6-3.5, 6-3.5.1, 6-3.5.2, and 6-3.6
NFPA 72G, 4-2.1	6-3.1.2

Former Reference	New Reference
NFPA 72G, 4-3.1	6-2.2.2 and 6-2.3
NFPA 72G, 4-4.1	6-3.7
NFPA 72G, 5-2.1.1	6-4.4
NFPA 72G, 5-2.1.4	6-4.4.1, Figure 6-4.4.1, Tables 6-4.4.1(a) and (b), 6-4.4.1.1, 6-4.4.1.2, 6-4.4.2, Table 6-4.4.2, 6-4.4.2.1, 6-4.4.2.2, 6-4.4.3, Table 6-4.4.3, 6-4.4.3.1, 6-4.4.3.2, and 6-4.4.4
NFPA 72G, 5-2.1.5	6-6.2
NFPA 72G, 5-3.1	6-2.2.2 and 6-2.3
NFPA 72G, 6-1.1	6-7
NFPA 72G, 7-2.1.1	6-8, 6-8.1, and 6-8.2
NFPA 72G, 7-3.1	6-2.2.2 and 6-2.3
NFPA 72G, 7-4.1	6-8.3
NFPA 72G, 7-4.2	6-8.4 and 6-8.5
NFPA 72G, 8-2.1	6-9.1
NFPA 72G, 8-2.1.1	6-9.1.1
NFPA 72G, 8-2.1.2	6-9.1.2
NFPA 72G, 8-2.2	6-9.1.3
NFPA 72G, 8-4.1	6-9.2
NFPA 72G, 8-4.1 Exception	6-9.2 Exception
NFPA 72G, 9-4.1	7-4.1 and 7-4.2
NFPA 72H, 1-1.3	7-1.1.2
NFPA 72H, 2-1	7-5.2
NFPA 72H, 2-2.1	7-1.3
NFPA 72H, 4-1	7-1.3, 7-2.2, Table 7-2.2, Table 7-3.1, 7-3.2, Table 7-3.2, 7-3.4
NFPA 72H, Figure 7-2	Figure A-7-2.2(a)
NFPA 72H, Figure 7-3	Figure A-7-2.2(b)
NFPA 72H, Figure 7-4	Figure A-7-2.2(c)
NFPA 72H, Figure 7-5	Figure A-7-2.2(d)
NFPA 72H, Figure 7-6	Figure A-7-2.2(e)
NFPA 72H, Figure 7-7	Figure A-7-2.2(f)
NFPA 72H, Figure 7-8	Figure A-7-2.2(g)
NFPA 72H, Figure 7-9	Figure A-7-2.2(h)
NFPA 72H, Figure 7-10.2	Figure A-7-2.2(j)
NFPA 72H, Figure 7-11	Figure A-7-2.2(k)
NFPA 72H, Figure 7-12	Figure A-7-2.2(l)
NFPA 72H, Figure 7-13	Figure A-7-2.2(i) and Figure A-7-2.2(m)
NFPA 72H, Figure 7-14	Figure A-7-2.2(n)
NFPA 72H, Figure 7-15	Figure A-7-2.2(o)
NFPA 72H, Figure 7-17	Figure A-7-2.2(p)
NFPA 74, 1-1	2-1.1
NFPA 74, 1-2	2-1.2
NFPA 74, 1-2.1	2-1.2.1
NFPA 74, 1-2.2	2-1.2.2
NFPA 74, 1-2.3	2-1.2.3
NFPA 74, 1-2.4	2-1.2.4
NFPA 74, 1-2.5	2-1.2.5
NFPA 74, 1-3	2-1.3
NFPA 74, 1-3.1.1	2-1.3.1
NFPA 74, 1-3.1.2	2-1.3.2
NFPA 74, 1-4	1-4
NFPA 74, Chap. 2	2-2
NFPA 74, 2-1	2-2.1
NFPA 74, 2-1.1	2-2.1.1
NFPA 74, 2-1.1.1	2-2.1.1.1
NFPA 74, 2-1.1.2	2-2.1.1.2
NFPA 74, 2-2	2-2.2
NFPA 74, 2-2.1	2-2.2.1
NFPA 74, Chap. 3	2-3 and 2-3.1
NFPA 74, 3-1.1	2-3.1.1
NFPA 74, 3-1.1.1	2-3.1.2 Exception No. 3
NFPA 74, 3-2	2-3.2
NFPA 74, 3-2.1	2-3.2.1
NFPA 74, 3-2.2	2-3.2.2
NFPA 74, 3-2.3	2-3.2.3
NFPA 74, 3-2.4	2-3.2.4
NFPA 74, 3-2.5	2-3.2.5
NFPA 74, 3-2.7	2-3.2.6

Former Reference	New Reference
NFPA 74, 3-3	2-3.3
NFPA 74, 3-3.1	2-3.3.1
NFPA 74, 3-3.1(a)	2-3.3.1(a)
NFPA 74, 3-3.1(b)	2-3.3.1(b)
NFPA 74, 3-3.1(c)	2-3.3.1(c)
NFPA 74, 3-3.1(d)	2-3.3.1(d)
NFPA 74, 3-3.1(e)	2-3.3.1(e)
NFPA 74, 3-3.1(f)	2-3.3.1(f)
NFPA 74, 3-3.1(g)	2-3.3.1(g)
NFPA 74, 3-4	2-3.5
NFPA 74, Chap. 4	2-4
NFPA 74, 4-1	2-4.1
NFPA 74, 4-2	2-4.2
NFPA 74, 4-2.1	2-4.2.1
NFPA 74, 4-3	2-4.3 and 5-2.4.2
NFPA 74, 4-3.1	2-4.3.1
NFPA 74, 4-4	2-4.4
NFPA 74, 4-4.1	2-4.4.1
NFPA 74, 4-5	2-4.5
NFPA 74, 4-5.1	2-4.5.1
NFPA 74, 4-5.2	2-4.5.2
NFPA 74, 4-5.3	2-4.5.3
NFPA 74, 4-5.4	2-4.5.4
NFPA 74, 4-5.5	2-4.5.5
NFPA 74, 4-7	2-4.7
NFPA 74, 4-7.1	2-4.7.1
NFPA 74, 4-7.2	2-4.7.2
NFPA 74, Chap. 5	2-5
NFPA 74, 5-1	2-5.1
NFPA 74, 5-1.1	2-5.1.1
NFPA 74, 5-1.1.1	2-5.1.1.1
NFPA 74, 5-1.1.2	2-5.1.1.2
NFPA 74, 5-1.1.3	2-5.1.1.3
NFPA 74, 5-1.1.4	2-5.1.1.4
NFPA 74, 5-1.1.5	2-5.1.1.5
NFPA 74, 5-1.2	2-5.1.2
NFPA 74, 5-1.2.1	2-5.1.2.1
NFPA 74, 5-2	2-5.2
NFPA 74, 5-2.1	2-5.2.1
NFPA 74, 5-2.1.1	2-5.2.1.1
NFPA 74, 5-2.1.2	2-5.2.1.2
NFPA 74, 5-2.1.3	2-5.2.1.3
NFPA 74, 5-2.1.4	2-5.2.1.4
NFPA 74, 5-2.1.5	2-5.2.1.5
NFPA 74, 5-2.2	2-5.2.2
NFPA 74, 5-2.2.1	2-5.2.2.1
NFPA 74, 5-2.2.2	2-5.2.2.2
NFPA 74, 5-2.2.4	2-5.2.2.4
NFPA 74, 5-2.2.5	2-5.2.2.5
NFPA 74, 5-3	2-5.3
NFPA 74, Chap. 6	2-6
NFPA 74, 6-1	2-6.1
NFPA 74, 6-2	2-6.2.1
NFPA 74, 7-1.1.1	2-7
NFPA 74, 7-1.2.1	2-7(a)
NFPA 74, 7-1.2.2	2-7(b)
NFPA 74, 7-1.2.3	2-7(c)
NFPA 74, 7-1.2.4	2-7(d)
NFPA 74, 7-1.2.5	2-7(e)
NFPA 74, 7-1.2.6	2-7(f)
NFPA 74, 7-1.2.7	2-7(g)
NFPA 74, 7-1.2.8	2-7(h)
NFPA 74, 7-1.2.9	2-7(i) and Exception
NFPA 74, A-1-1	A-2-1.1
NFPA 74, A-2-1.1	A-2-2.1.1 and Figure A-2-2.1.1.2
NFPA 74, A-2-2	A-2-2.2
NFPA 74, A-4-3	A-2-4.3 and A-5-2.4.2

Former Reference	New Reference
NFPA 74, A-4-3.1	A-2-4.3.1 and A-5-2.6
NFPA 74, A-5-1.2.1	A-2-5.1.2.1
NFPA 74, A-5-2.1.6	A-2-5.2.1.6 2nd, 3rd, 4th paragraphs
NFPA 74, A-5-2.2.3	A-2-5.2.2.3
NFPA 74, A-5-2.2.5	A-2-5.2.2.5 and A-5-2.7
NFPA 74, A-6-1	A-2-6.1
NFPA 74, A-6-2	A-2-6.2
NFPA 74, B-1.1	A-2-5.2
NFPA 74, B-2	A-2-5.2.1 and A-2-5.2.1.6 1st paragraph
NFPA 74, Figure B-2.1.1	Figure A-2-5.2.1(a)
NFPA 74, Figure B-2.1.2	Figure A-2-5.2.1(b)
NFPA 74, Figure B-2.1.3	Figure A-2-5.2.1(c)
NFPA 74, B-3	A-2-5.2.2
NFPA 74, Figure B-3.2.1	Figure A-2-5.2.2(b)
NFPA 74, Figure B-3.4.2	Figure A-2-5.2.2(d)
NFPA 74, Appendix C	A-2
NFPA 1221, 1-3	1-4
NFPA 1221, 2-1.10.2.2	A-7-2.2 and Note; A-7-3.2, Note, and (a) - (e)
NFPA 1221, 2-1.11.2	7-1.2.1
NFPA 1221, 3-1.5.3.2	A-7-2.2 and Note; A-7-3.2, Note, and (a) - (e)
NFPA 1221, Chap. 4	4-6
NFPA 1221, 4-1.1	4-6.2
NFPA 1221, 4-1.1.1	4-6.2.1
NFPA 1221, 4-1.1.2	1-5.3 Compatibility and 1-5.3.1
NFPA 1221, 4-1.1.3	4-6.2.2
NFPA 1221, 4-1.1.4	4-6.2.3
NFPA 1221, 4-1.1.5	4-6.2.4
NFPA 1221, 4-1.2	4-6.3
NFPA 1221, 4-1.3	4-6.4
NFPA 1221, 4-1.3.1	1-5.3 Compatibility and 1-5.3.1
NFPA 1221, 4-1.3.3	1-5.5.1
NFPA 1221, 4-1.3.4	4-6.4.1
NFPA 1221, 4-1.3.6	1-5.5.2.3
NFPA 1221, 4-1.3.9	1-5.5.1
NFPA 1221, 4-1.3.10	1-5.5.5
NFPA 1221, 4-1.3.11	1-5.5.4
NFPA 1221, 4-1.4	5-9.2
NFPA 1221, 4-1.4.1.1	4-6.4.2, 4-6.4.3, and 5-9.2.6
NFPA 1221, 4-1.4.1.2	4-6.4.4
NFPA 1221, 4-1.4.1.3	4-6.4.5 and 5-9.2.8
NFPA 1221, 4-1.4.1.4	4-6.4.6 and 5-9.2.8
NFPA 1221, 4-1.4.1.5	4-6.4.7 and 5-9.2.9
NFPA 1221, 4-1.4.1.6	5-9.2.10
NFPA 1221, 4-1.4.1.7	1-5.5.4 and 5-9.2.10
NFPA 1221, 4-1.4.1.8	4-6.4.8 and 5-9.2.7
NFPA 1221, 4-1.3.10	1-5.5.5
NFPA 1221, 4-1.3.11	1-5.5.4
NFPA 1221, 4-1.4.2	4-6.5
NFPA 1221, 4-1.4.2.1	5-9.2.1
NFPA 1221, 4-1.4.2.2	5-9.2.2
NFPA 1221, 4-1.4.2.3	5-9.2.3
NFPA 1221, 4-1.4.2.4	4-6.4.9
NFPA 1221, 4-1.4.2.5	5-9.2.4
NFPA 1221, 4-1.4.2.6	5-9.2.5
NFPA 1221, 4-1.4.3	4-6.6
NFPA 1221, 4-1.4.3.1	4-6.6
NFPA 1221, 4-1.4.3.2	4-6.6 and A-4-6.6
NFPA 1221, 4-1.4.3.3	4-6.6
NFPA 1221, 4-1.5.1.1	1-5.2.2
NFPA 1221, 4-1.5.1.2	1-5.2.8.2
NFPA 1221, 4-1.5.1.4	1-5.2.8.2
NFPA 1221, 4-1.5.2	1-5.2.3 Exception No. 1, Exception No. 2, and Note
NFPA 1221, 4-1.5.2(a)	1-5.2.4
NFPA 1221, 4-1.5.2(c)	1-5.2.5
NFPA 1221, 4-1.5.3	4-6.7
NFPA 1221, 4-1.5.3.1	4-6.7.1.6
NFPA 1221, 4-1.5.3.1.1	4-6.7.1.7
NFPA 1221, 4-1.5.3.1.1.1	4-6.7.1.1

Former Reference	New Reference
NFPA 1221, 4-1.5.3.1.1.2	4-6.7.1.2
NFPA 1221, 4-1.5.3.1.1.3	4-6.7.1.3
NFPA 1221, 4-1.5.3.1.2	4-6.7.1.8
NFPA 1221, 4-1.5.3.1.3	4-6.7.1.9
NFPA 1221, 4-1.5.3.2	4-6.7.1.4
NFPA 1221, 4-1.5.3.3	4-6.7.1.5
NFPA 1221, 4-1.5.4	4-6.7.2
NFPA 1221, 4-1.5.4.1	4-6.7.2.1
NFPA 1221, 4-1.5.4.2	4-6.7.2.2
NFPA 1221, 4-1.5.4.3	4-6.7.2.3
NFPA 1221, 4-1.5.4.4	4-6.7.2.4
NFPA 1221, 4-1.5.5	1-5.2.10 and 4-6.7.3
NFPA 1221, 4-1.5.5.1	4-6.7.3.1
NFPA 1221, 4-1.5.5.2	1-5.2.10.2 and 4-6.7.3.2
NFPA 1221, 4-1.5.5.3	4-6.7.3.3
NFPA 1221, 4-1.5.5.4	1-5.2.10.4 ,1-5.2.10.5, and 4-6.7.3.4
NFPA 1221, 4-1.5.5.5	1-5.2.10.5 and 4-6.7.3.5
NFPA 1221, 4-1.5.5.6	1-5.2.10.3 and 4-6.7.3.6
NFPA 1221, 4-1.5.5.7	1-5.2.10.6 and 4-6.7.3.7
NFPA 1221, 4-1.5.5.8	4-6.7.3.8
NFPA 1221, 4-1.5.6	4-6.7.4
NFPA 1221, 4-1.5.6.1	1-5.2.9.1 and 4-6.7.4.1
NFPA 1221, 4-1.5.6.2	1-5.2.9.1 and 4-6.7.4.2
NFPA 1221, 4-1.5.6.3	1-5.2.9.1 and 4-6.7.4.3
NFPA 1221, 4-1.6.2.3	A-7-2.2 and Note; A-7-3.2, Note, and (a) - (e)
NFPA 1221, 4-1.8	4-6.8
NFPA 1221, 4-1.8.1	4-6.8.1
NFPA 1221, 4-1.8.1.1	4-6.8.1.1
NFPA 1221, 4-1.8.1.2	4-6.8.1.2
NFPA 1221, 4-1.8.1.3	4-6.8.1.3
NFPA 1221, 4-1.8.1.4	4-6.8.1.4
NFPA 1221, 4-1.8.2	4-6.8.2
NFPA 1221, 4-1.8.2.1	4-6.8.2.1
NFPA 1221, 4-1.8.2.1(a)	4-6.8.2.1.1
NFPA 1221, 4-1.8.2.1(b)	4-6.8.2.1.2
NFPA 1221, 4-1.8.2.1(c)	4-6.8.2.1.3
NFPA 1221, 4-1.8.2.1(d)	4-6.8.2.1.4
NFPA 1221, 4-1.8.2.1(e)	4-6.8.2.1.5
NFPA 1221, 4-1.8.2.1(f)	4-6.8.2.1.6
NFPA 1221, 4-1.8.2.2	4-6.8.2.2
NFPA 1221, 4-1.8.2.2(a)	4-6.8.2.2.1
NFPA 1221, 4-1.8.2.2(b)	4-6.8.2.2.2
NFPA 1221, 4-1.8.2.2(c)	4-6.8.2.2.3
NFPA 1221, 4-1.8.2.2(d)	4-6.8.2.2.4
NFPA 1221, 4-1.8.2.2(e)	4-6.8.2.2.5
NFPA 1221, 4-1.8.2.2(f)	4-6.8.2.2.6
NFPA 1221, 4-1.8.3	4-6.8.2.3
NFPA 1221, 4-1.8.3.1	4-6.8.2.3.1
NFPA 1221, 4-1.8.3.2	4-6.8.2.3.2
NFPA 1221, 4-1.8.3.3	4-6.8.2.3.3
NFPA 1221, 4-1.8.3.4	4-6.8.2.3.4
NFPA 1221, 4-1.8.3.5	4-6.8.2.3.5
NFPA 1221, 4-1.8.4	4-6.8.2.4
NFPA 1221, 4-1.8.4.1	4-6.8.2.4.1
NFPA 1221, 4-1.8.4.2	4-6.8.2.4.2
NFPA 1221, 4-1.8.5	4-6.8.2.5
NFPA 1221, 4-1.8.5.1	4-6.8.2.5.1
NFPA 1221, 4-1.8.5.2	4-6.8.2.5.2
NFPA 1221, 4-1.8.5.3	4-6.8.2.5.3
NFPA 1221, 4-1.8.5.4	4-6.8.2.5.4
NFPA 1221, 4-1.8.5.5	4-6.8.2.5.5
NFPA 1221, 4-1.8.5.6	4-6.8.2.5.6
NFPA 1221, 4-1.8.5.7	4-6.8.2.5.7
NFPA 1221, 4-1.8.5.8	4-6.8.2.5.8
NFPA 1221, 4-2.1	4-6.9.1
NFPA 1221, 4-2.1.1	4-6.9.1.1
NFPA 1221, 4-2.1.1.1	4-6.9.1.1.1
NFPA 1221, 4-2.1.1.2	4-6.9.1.1.2

Former Reference	New Reference
NFPA 1221, 4-2.1.1.3	4-6.9.1.1.3
NFPA 1221, 4-2.1.1.4	4-6.9.1.1.4
NFPA 1221, 4-2.1.1.5	4-6.9.1.1.5
NFPA 1221, 4-2.1.2	4-6.9.1.2
NFPA 1221, 4-2.1.2.1	4-6.9.1.2.1 and 5-9.2.11
NFPA 1221, 4-2.1.2.2	4-6.9.1.2.2
NFPA 1221, 4-2.1.2.3	4-6.13 and 4-6.13.1
NFPA 1221, 4-2.1.2.4	4-6.13.2
NFPA 1221, 4-2.1.2.5	4-6.13.3
NFPA 1221, 4-2.1.2.6	4-6.13.4
NFPA 1221, 4-2.1.3	4-6.9.1.3
NFPA 1221, 4-2.1.3.1	4-6.9.1.3.1
NFPA 1221, 4-2.1.3.2	4-6.9.1.3.3
NFPA 1221, 4-2.2	4-6.9.1.4
NFPA 1221, 4-2.2.1	4-6.9.1.4.1
NFPA 1221, 4-2.2.1.1	4-6.9.1.4.1.1
NFPA 1221, 4-2.2.1.2	4-6.9.1.4.1.2
NFPA 1221, 4-2.2.1.3	4-6.9.1.4.1.3
NFPA 1221, 4-2.2.1.4	4-6.9.1.4.1.4
NFPA 1221, 4-2.2.1.5	4-6.9.1.4.1.5
NFPA 1221, 4-2.2.1.6	4-6.9.1.4.1.6
NFPA 1221, 4-2.2.2	4-6.9.1.4.2
NFPA 1221, 4-2.2.2.1	4-6.9.1.4.2.1
NFPA 1221, 4-2.2.2.2	4-6.9.1.4.2.2
NFPA 1221, 4-2.2.2.3	4-6.9.1.4.3
NFPA 1221, 4-2.2.3.1	4-6.9.1.4.3.1
NFPA 1221, 4-2.2.3.2	4-6.9.1.4.3.2
NFPA 1221, 4-2.2.3.3	4-6.9.1.4.3.3
NFPA 1221, 4-2.2.3.4	4-6.9.1.4.3.4
NFPA 1221, 4-2.3	4-6.10
NFPA 1221, 4-2.3.1	4-6.10.1
NFPA 1221, 4-2.3.1.1	4-6.10.1.1
NFPA 1221, 4-2.3.1.2	4-6.10.1.2
NFPA 1221, 4-2.3.1.3	4-6.10.1.3
NFPA 1221, 4-2.3.1.4	4-6.10.1.4
NFPA 1221, 4-2.4	4-6.11
NFPA 1221, 4-2.4.1	4-6.11.2
NFPA 1221, 4-2.4.1.1	4-6.11.2.1
NFPA 1221, 4-2.4.1.2	4-6.11.2.2
NFPA 1221, 4-2.4.2.1	4-6.13.5
NFPA 1221, 4-2.4.3	4-6.11.1
NFPA 1221, 4-2.4.3.1	4-6.11.1.1
NFPA 1221, 4-2.4.3.2	4-6.11.1.2
NFPA 1221, 4-2.4.3.3	4-6.11.1.3
NFPA 1221, 4-2.5	4-6.12
NFPA 1221, 4-2.5.1	4-6.12.1
NFPA 1221, 4-2.5.2	4-6.12.2
NFPA 1221, 4-2.5.3	4-6.12.3
NFPA 1221, 4-2.5.4	4-6.12.4
NFPA 1221, 4-2.5.5	4-6.12.5
NFPA 1221, 4-3	4-6.14
NFPA 1221, 4-3.1	4-6.14.1
NFPA 1221, 4-3.1.1	4-6.14.1.1
NFPA 1221, 4-3.1.2	4-6.14.1.2
NFPA 1221, 4-3.1.3	4-6.14.1.3
NFPA 1221, 4-3.2.1	4-6.9.1.1.1 and 4-6.9.1.1.2
NFPA 1221, 4-3.2.2	4-6.14.2
NFPA 1221, 4-3.3	5-9.2.12
NFPA 1221, 4-3.3.1	5-9.2.12.1
NFPA 1221, 4-3.3.2.1	5-9.2.12.2
NFPA 1221, 4-3.3.2.2	5-9.2.12.3
NFPA 1221, 4-3.3.2.3	5-9.2.12.4
NFPA 1221, 4-3.3.2.4	5-9.2.12.5
NFPA 1221, 4-3.3.2.5	5-9.2.12.6
NFPA 1221, 4-3.3.3	5-9.2.13
NFPA 1221, 4-3.3.3.1	5-9.2.13.1
NFPA 1221, 4-3.3.3.2	5-9.2.13.2

Former Reference	New Reference
NFPA 1221, 4-3.3.3.3	5-9.2.13.3
NFPA 1221, 4-3.3.3.4	5-9.2.13.4
NFPA 1221, 4-3.3.3.5	5-9.2.13.5
NFPA 1221, 4-3.4	4-6.14.3
NFPA 1221, 4-3.4.2	4-6.14.3.1
NFPA 1221, 4-3.4.2.1	4-6.14.3.1.1
NFPA 1221, 4-3.4.2.2	4-6.14.3.1.2
NFPA 1221, 4-3.4.2.3	4-6.14.3.1.3
NFPA 1221, 4-3.4.3	4-6.14.3.2
NFPA 1221, 4-3.4.3.1	4-6.14.3.2.1
NFPA 1221, 4-3.4.3.2	4-6.14.3.2.2
NFPA 1221, 4-3.5	4-6.14.4
NFPA 1221, 4-3.6.1	4-6.14.1.4
NFPA 1221, 4-3.7	4-6.12
NFPA 1221, 4-3.7.1	4-6.14.6
NFPA 1221, 4-3.7.2	4-6.12.2
NFPA 1221, 4-3.7.3	4-6.12.3
NFPA 1221, 4-3.7.4	4-6.12.4
NFPA 1221, 4-3.7.5	4-6.12.5
NFPA 1221, 4-4	4-6.15
NFPA 1221, 4-4.1.1.1	4-6.9.1.1.1
NFPA 1221, 4-4.1.1.2	4-6.9.1.1.2
NFPA 1221, 4-4.1.1.3	4-6.9.1.1.3
NFPA 1221, 4-4.1.1.4	4-6.9.1.1.4
NFPA 1221, 4-4.1.1.5	4-6.9.1.1.5
NFPA 1221, 4-4.1.2.1	4-6.15.6
NFPA 1221, 4-4.1.2.2	4-6.15.7
NFPA 1221, 4-4.1.2.3	4-6.15.8
NFPA 1221, 4-4.1.3	4-6.9.1.3
NFPA 1221, 4-4.1.3.1	4-6.9.1.3.1
NFPA 1221, 4-4.1.3.2	4-6.9.1.3.2
NFPA 1221, 4-4.2	4-6.9.1.4
NFPA 1221, 4-4.2.1	4-6.9.1.4.1
NFPA 1221, 4-4.2.1.1	4-6.9.1.4.1.1
NFPA 1221, 4-4.2.1.2	4-6.9.1.4.1.2
NFPA 1221, 4-4.2.1.3	4-6.9.1.4.1.3
NFPA 1221, 4-4.2.1.4	4-6.9.1.4.1.4
NFPA 1221, 4-4.2.1.5	4-6.9.1.4.1.5
NFPA 1221, 4-4.2.1.6	4-6.9.1.4.1.6
NFPA 1221, 4-4.2.2	4-6.9.1.4.2
NFPA 1221, 4-4.2.2.1	4-6.9.1.4.2.1
NFPA 1221, 4-4.2.2.2	4-6.9.1.4.2.2
NFPA 1221, 4-4.2.2.3	4-6.9.1.4.3
NFPA 1221, 4-4.2.3.1	4-6.9.1.4.3.1
NFPA 1221, 4-4.2.3.2	4-6.9.1.4.3.2
NFPA 1221, 4-4.2.3.3	4-6.9.1.4.3.3
NFPA 1221, 4-4.2.3.4	4-6.9.1.4.3.4
NFPA 1221, 4-4.3	4-6.10
NFPA 1221, 4-4.3.1	4-6.10.1
NFPA 1221, 4-4.3.1.1	4-6.10.1.1
NFPA 1221, 4-4.3.1.2	4-6.10.1.2
NFPA 1221, 4-4.3.1.3	4-6.10.1.3
NFPA 1221, 4-4.3.1.4	4-6.10.1.4
NFPA 1221, 4-4.4	5-9.2.14
NFPA 1221, 4-4.4.1	5-9.2.14.1
NFPA 1221, 4-4.4.2	5-9.2.14.2
NFPA 1221, 4-4.5.1	4-6.15.1
NFPA 1221, 4-4.5.2	4-6.15.2
NFPA 1221, 4-4.5.3	4-6.15.3
NFPA 1221, 4-4.5.4	4-6.11.1.1
NFPA 1221, 4-4.5.5	4-6.11.1.2
NFPA 1221, 4-4.5.6	4-6.15.4
NFPA 1221, 4-4.5.7	4-6.15.5
NFPA 1221, 4-4.5.8	4-6.11.1.3
NFPA 1221, 4-4.7	4-6.12
NFPA 1221, 4-4.7.1	4-6.12.1
NFPA 1221, 4-4.7.2	4-6.12.2

Former Reference	New Reference
NFPA 1221, 4-4.7.3	4-6.12.3
NFPA 1221, 4-4.7.4	4-6.12.4
NFPA 1221, 4-4.7.5	4-6.12.5
NFPA 1221, 4-5	4-6.16
NFPA 1221, 4-5.1.1.2	4-6.9.1.1.2
NFPA 1221, 4-5.1.1.3	4-6.9.1.1.3
NFPA 1221, 4-5.1.1.4	4-6.9.1.1.4
NFPA 1221, 4-5.1.1.5	4-6.9.1.1.5
NFPA 1221, 4-5.1.2	4-6.16.1
NFPA 1221, 4-5.1.2.1	4-6.16.1.1
NFPA 1221, 4-5.1.2.2	4-6.16.1.2
NFPA 1221, 4-5.1.2.3	4-6.16.1.3
NFPA 1221, 4-5.1.3	4-6.16.1.4
NFPA 1221, 4-5.2	4-6.9.1.4
NFPA 1221, 4-5.2.1	4-6.9.1.4.1
NFPA 1221, 4-5.2.1.1	4-6.9.1.4.1.1
NFPA 1221, 4-5.2.1.2	4-6.9.1.4.1.2
NFPA 1221, 4-5.2.1.3	4-6.9.1.4.1.3
NFPA 1221, 4-5.2.1.4	4-6.9.1.4.1.4
NFPA 1221, 4-5.2.1.5	4-6.9.1.4.1.5
NFPA 1221, 4-5.2.1.6	4-6.9.1.4.1.6
NFPA 1221, 4-5.2.2	4-6.9.1.4.2.1
NFPA 1221, 4-5.2.2.3	4-6.9.1.4.3
NFPA 1221, 4-5.2.3.1	4-6.9.1.4.3.1
NFPA 1221, 4-5.2.3.2	4-6.9.1.4.3.2
NFPA 1221, 4-5.2.3.3	4-6.9.1.4.3.3
NFPA 1221, 4-5.2.3.4	4-6.9.1.4.3.4
NFPA 1221, 4-5.3	4-6.16.1.5
NFPA 1221, 4-5.4	5-9.2.14
NFPA 1221, 4-5.4.1	5-9.2.14.2
NFPA 1221, 4-5.4.2	5-9.2.14.1
NFPA 1221, 4-5.5	4-6.16.2
NFPA 1221, 4-5.5.1	4-6.16.2.1
NFPA 1221, 4-5.5.6	4-6.16.2.2
NFPA 1221, 4-5.5.7	4-6.16.2.3
NFPA 1221, 4-5.5.8	4-6.11.1.3
NFPA 1221, 4-5.7	4-6.12
NFPA 1221, 4-5.7.1	4-6.12.2
NFPA 1221, 4-5.7.2	4-6.12.3
NFPA 1221, 4-5.7.3	4-6.12.4
NFPA 1221, 4-5.7.4	4-6.12.5
NFPA 1221, 4-5.7.5	4-6.16.2.4
NFPA 1221, A-2-1.10.2.2(b)	A-7-2.2 Note
NFPA 1221, A-4-1.4.1.5	A-4-6.4.7 and A-5-9.2.9
NFPA 1221, A-4-3.3.2.2	A-5-9.2.12.3
NFPA 1221, Figure B-4.1.5.3.1.1(a)	Figure A-4-6.7.1.7(a)
NFPA 1221, Figure B-4.1.5.3.1.1(b)(1)	Figure A-4-6.7.1.7(b)(1)
NFPA 1221, Figure B-4.1.5.3.1.1(b)(2)	Figure A-4-6.7.1.7(b)(2)
NFPA 1221, Figure B-4.1.5.3.1.1(c)	Figure A-4-6.7.1.7(c)
NFPA 1221, Figure B-4.1.5.3.1.2(a)	Figure A-4-6.7.1.8(a)
NFPA 1221, Figure B-4.1.5.3.1.2(b)(1)	Figure A-4-6.7.1.8(b)(1)
NFPA 1221, Figure B-4.1.5.3.1.2(b)(2)	Figure A-4-6.7.1.8(b)(2)
NFPA 1221, Figure B-4.1.5.3.1.3(a)	Figure A-4-6.7.1.9(a)
NFPA 1221, Figure B-4.1.5.3.1.3(b)(1)	Figure A-4-6.7.1.9(b)(1)
NFPA 1221, Figure B-4.1.5.3.1.3(b)(2)	Figure A-4-6.7.1.9(b)(2)
NFPA 1221, Figure B-4.1.5.3.1.3(c)	Figure A-4-6.7.1.9(c)
NFPA 1221, Figure B-4.3.4.2.1	Figure A-4-6.14.3.1.1

Index

UNIFORM FIRE CODE STANDARD 24-1
AIRCRAFT FUELING
See Sections 2401.15 and 2402.2.1, *Uniform Fire Code*

The National Fire Protection Association Standard for Aircraft Fuel Servicing, NFPA 407—1990, is hereby adopted by reference as UFC Standard 24-1.

The provisions of this standard shall apply to the fuel servicing of aircraft with liquid petroleum fuel except when a provision of *Uniform Fire Code,* Volume 1 or an amendment specified in Section 24.101 is applicable, in which case *Uniform Fire Code,* Volume 1 provisions or the amendment shall take precedence.

Supplemental standards referenced by NFPA 407—1990 shall only be considered as guidelines subject to approval by the chief.

NFPA 407—1990 is available from the National Fire Protection Association, 1 Batterymarch Park, Box 9101, Quincy, Massachusetts 02269-9101.

SECTION 24.101 — AMENDMENTS

The Standard for Aircraft Fuel Servicing, NFPA 407—1990, applies to the fueling of aircraft on airport grounds, except as follows:

1. Sec. 1-1 is revised by adding a new subsection (d) as follows:

(d) **Conditions Regulated by *Uniform Fire Code,* Volume 1.** When the provisions of *Uniform Fire Code,* Volume 1 apply, they shall take precedence over the provisions of this standard.

2. Sec. 1-3 is revised by amending the definition of "authority having jurisdiction" as follows:

AUTHORITY HAVING JURISDICTION is the official responsible for the administration and enforcement of this standard.

The definitions of "approved," "labeled" and "listed" shall be as set forth in *Uniform Fire Code,* Volume 1.

The definition of "should" is deleted.

3. Sec. 2-1.2.4 is revised as follows:

2-1.2.4. Type C hose constructed in accordance with nationally recognized standards shall be used to prevent electrostatic discharges but shall not be used to accomplish required bonding. See *Uniform Fire Code* Article 90. Type A hose constructed in accordance with nationally recognized standards and hose having a static wire in the hose wall shall not be used.

4. Sec. 2-1.6.2 is revised as follows:

2-1.6.2. Portable fire extinguishers shall be provided and maintained in accordance with UFC Standard 10-1.

5. Sec. 2-2.1 is revised as follows:

2-2.1 Performance Requirements. Hose and couplings shall be designed for aviation fuel service and shall be in accordance with nationally recognized standards. See *Uniform Fire Code* Article 90.

6. Sec. 2-2.3 is revised by substituting the phrase "nationally recognized standard, see *Uniform Fire Code* Article 90" for the phrase "API 1529."

7. Sec. 2-3.1 is revised as follows:

2-3.1. Use on Public Roadways. Aircraft fuel servicing tank vehicles which are used on public roadways shall also comply with the requirements of UFC Standard 79-4.

8. Sec. 2-3.3 is revised as follows:

2-3.3. Cargo tanks shall be supported by and attached to, or be a part of, the tank vehicle upon which it is carried in accordance with UFC Standard 79-4.

9. Secs. 2-3.7.3, 2-3.7.4 and 2-3.7.5 are revised by substituting the phrase "(See the Electrical Code.)" for the phrase "(See NFPA 70, *National Electrical Code.*)."

10. Sec. 2-3.12.1 is revised by substituting the phrase "UFC Standard 79-4" for the phrase "Article 22 of NFPA 385, *Recommended Regulatory Standard for Tank Vehicles for Flammable and Combustible Liquids.*"

11. Sec. 2-3.12.2 is revised by changing the last sentence as follows:

2-3.12.2. Aluminum alloys for high-strength welded construction shall be joined by an inert gas arc-welding process using filler metals (commercial designation) R-GR40A, E-GR40A (5154 alloy) and R-GM50A, E-GM50A (5356 alloy).

12. Sec. 2-3.12.5 is revised as follows:

2-3.12.5. Venting shall be in accordance with UFC Standard 79-4.

13. Sec. 2-4.4.1 is revised as follows:

2-4.4.1 General. The construction and spacing of fuel storage tanks shall conform to the applicable requirements of *Uniform Fire Code* Article 79.

14. Sec. 2-4.6.4 is revised as follows:

2-4.6.4 Basic Design Criteria. Piping, valves and fittings shall be metal, suitable for aviation service, and designed for working pressures and the mechanical, thermal and structural stresses to which they could be subjected. The minimum requirements of nationally recognized standards and *Uniform Fire Code* Article 79 shall be used as the basic design criteria. See *Uniform Fire Code* Article 90.

15. Sec. 2-4.6.10 is revised as follows:

2-4.6.10 Welded joints shall be made by qualified welders using materials and methods in accordance with nationally recognized standards. See *Uniform Fire Code* Article 90.

16. Sec. 2-4.9 (e) is revised as follows:

(e) Portable electrical equipment used during the repair of the vehicle shall conform to the requirements of the Electrical Code.

17. Sec. 2-4.11 is revised as follows:

2-4.11. Ramps used for aircraft fueling shall slope away from buildings and loading walkways at a grade of not less than 1 percent for the first 50 feet (15 240 mm). The balance of such ramps shall slope to a drainage system at a grade not less than $^1/_2$ percent. When drainage inlets are provided, they shall be at least 50 feet (15 240 mm) from buildings and loading walkways.

18. Sec. 2-5.2.1 is revised as follows:

2-5.2.1 Basic Construction and Protection Requirements. In addition to the special requirements of this chapter, heliports shall comply with *Uniform Fire Code* Article 24 and the Building Code.

19. Sec. 2-5.11 is revised as follows:

2-5.11 Fire Protection. Fixed fire-protection systems shall be in accordance with *Uniform Fire Code* Article 10.

20. Sec. 2-6.1 is revised as follows:

2-6.1 General. In addition to the special requirements of this chapter, the fuel storage, dispensing and piping system shall comply with *Uniform Fire Code* Article 79 and with the applicable portions of Chapters 3, 4 and 5 of this standard.

21. Sec. 3-2.5 is revised as follows:

3-2.5 Unauthorized Discharge. Unauthorized discharges of hazardous materials shall be reported and documented in accordance with *Uniform Fire Code* Article 80.

22. Chapter 4 is deleted.

UNIFORM FIRE CODE STANDARD 52-1
COMPRESSED NATURAL GAS (CNG) VEHICULAR FUEL SYSTEMS

See Sections 5201.1, 5204.2 and 5204.10.2.3.5, *Uniform Fire Code*

This standard, with certain exceptions, is based on the National Fire Protection Association Standard for Compressed Natural Gas (CNG) Vehicular Fuel Systems, NFPA 52—1992.[1]

Part I of this standard contains the exceptions to NFPA 52—1992.[1]

Part II of this standard contains NFPA 52—1992[1] reproduced in its entirety with permission of the publisher.

[revision marker] vertically in the margin of Part II indicates there is a revision to the provisions within Part I.

Supplemental standards referenced by NFPA 52—1992[1] shall be considered as guidelines subject to approval by the chief.

[1]The current edition is NFPA 52—1995.

Part I

SECTION 52.101 — AMENDMENTS

The Standard for Compressed Natural Gas (CNG) Vehicular Fuel Systems applies to the design, construction, installation, maintenance and operation of containers, compression and dispensing equipment, and associated equipment used for the storage and dispensing of compressed natural gas, except as otherwise provided in *Uniform Fire Code,* Volume 1 and the Mechanical Code and except as follows:

1. Sec. 1-1 is deleted.

2. Sec. 1-2 is deleted.

3. Sec. 1-3 is revised to read as follows:

1-3 Retroactivity. The provisions of this standard shall be applied in accordance with UFC Section 102.

4. Sec. 1-5 is revised by changing the definitions as follows:

AUTHORITY HAVING JURISDICTION is the official responsible for the administration and enforcement of this standard.

The definitions of "approved," "labeled" and "listed" shall be as set forth in *Uniform Fire Code,* Volume 1.

The definition of "code" is revised by changing the first sentence as follows:

CODE. For new construction, "Code" shall mean the applicable edition of the ASME Code referenced in this UFC standard.

(Remainder of definition to remain as printed.)

Add the following definition:

HAZARDOUS MATERIALS are those chemicals or substances which are physical hazards or health hazards as defined and classified in *Uniform Fire Code,* Volume 1.

Delete the definitions of "limited-combustible material" and "noncombustible material."

5. Sec. 4-3.8 is revised to read as follows:

4-3.8 Engine driven compressor installations shall conform, where applicable, to nationally recognized standards.

6. Sec. 4-4.2.4 is revised to read as follows:

4-4.2.4 Compression, storage and dispensing equipment outdoors shall be located not less than 10 feet (3048 mm) from the nearest public street or sidewalk line, at least 25 feet (7620 mm) from the nearest rail of any railroad track, and at least 50 feet (15 240 mm) from the nearest rail or any railroad main track or any railroad or transit line where power from train propulsion is provided by an outside electrical source such as third rail or overhead catenary.

7. Sec. 4-4.3 is revised to read as follows:

4-4.3 Indoors.

4-4.3.1 General. Compression, dispensing equipment and storage containers connected for use are allowed to be located inside of buildings. The buildings shall be constructed in accordance with the Building Code and the requirements of *Uniform Fire Code* Article 80 for flammable gases.

4-4.3.1.1 Quantity Limit. Storage shall be limited to not more than 10,000 cubic feet (283 168 L) of natural gas in each building.

EXCEPTION: Compressed natural gas stored in vehicle-mounted fuel-supply containers.

4-4.3.2 Explosion Control. Explosion control shall be provided in accordance with *Uniform Fire Code* Article 80.

4-4.3.3 Automatic Fire-extinguishing System. Rooms or buildings used for the storage, compression or dispensing of CNG shall be protected throughout by an automatic sprinkler system. The automatic sprinkler system shall be designed in accordance with *Uniform Fire Code* Article 80 and the Building Code (see UBC Standard 9-1).

4-4.3.4 Mechanical Ventilation. Ventilation shall be provided throughout for buildings or rooms used for the storage, compression or dispensing of CNG. Ventilation shall be by a continuous mechanical ventilation system or by a mechanical ventilation system activated by a supervised methane gas-detection system when a gas concentration of not more than 20 percent of the lower flammability limit is present. Failure of the mechanical ventilation system shall shut down the fuel compression and dispensing system.

The mechanical ventilation system shall be in accordance with *Uniform Fire* Code Article 80 and the Mechanical Code. In addition, the mechanical ventilation system shall be designed for both lighter than air and heavier than air vapors.

EXCEPTION: When approved, the mechanical ventilation system can be designed for methane when the building or room is used exclusively for the dispensing of CNG.

4-4.3.5 Supervised Methane Gas-detection System. A supervised methane gas-detection system shall be provided throughout buildings or rooms used for the storage, compression or dispensing of CNG. The gas-detection system shall sound a distinct alarm signal when a gas concentration of not more than 20 percent of the lower flammability limit is present. Activation of the gas-detection system shall shut down the fuel compression and dispensing system.

4-4.3.6 Electrical Service. Buildings and rooms used for the storage, compression or dispensing of CNG shall be classified in accordance with Table 4-12 for installations of electrical equipment. Electrical equipment shall be installed in accordance with the Electrical Code.

4-4.3.7 Emergency Shutdown Devices. Emergency shutdown devices shall be provided in rooms or buildings used for the storage, compression or dispensing of CNG. Such devices shall be provided at each dispenser, at each exit, and at the room or building used for the storage or compression of CNG. Activation of the emergency shutdown devices shall shut down the compression and dispensing equipment.

4-4.3.8 Discharge of Relief Devices. Pressure-relief devices on storage and compression systems shall be provided with an approved means of discharging CNG outside of the building. The point of discharge shall be a minimum of 10 feet (3048 mm) from building and ventilation openings, property lines, public ways and paths of egress. The point of discharge shall not impinge on the building.

4-4.3.9 Signs. Rooms or buildings used for the storage, compression or dispensing of CNG shall be provided with warning signs with the words WARNING—NO SMOKING—FLAMMABLE GAS. The wording shall be in plainly legible red letters on a white, retroreflective background, with letters no less than 1 inch (25.4 mm) high.

8. Sec. 4-6.1 is revised by deleting "(See 4-4.3.9.)" at the end of the paragraph.

9. Sec. 4-6.4 is added as follows:

4-6.4 Sufficient pressure safety-relief devices shall be installed on CNG pressure vessels to allow each relief device to be individually isolated for testing or maintenance while maintaining the required pressure-relieving capacity. When only one relief device is required, a full-opening three-way shutoff valve shall be installed.

EXCEPTION: DOT-approved cylinders used for the storage of CNG.

10. Sec. 4-11.6 is deleted.

11. Sec. 4-12 is revised by substituting "the Electrical Code" for "NFPA 70, *National Electrical Code*" in the main paragraph.

12. Sec. 4-14.2 is revised by deleting "(See 4-6.3.)" at the end of the paragraph.

13. Sec. 4-14.8 is revised by deleting "(See 4-4.3.)" at the end of the paragraph.

14. Sec. 4-15 is revised to read:

4-15 Portable fire extinguishers shall be provided at the dispensing area as set forth in the *Uniform Fire Code.*

15. Chapters 5 and 6 are deleted and substitute Chapter 5 as follows:

5-1 Vehicle Fueling Appliances.

5-1.1 Applicability. Vehicle fueling appliances shall be installed, operated and maintained in accordance with this chapter, *Uniform Fire Code* Article 52, the Mechanical Code and the Plumbing Code.

5-1.2 Permits. For vehicle fueling permits, see Section 105.8, Permit m.3.

5-1.3 Maximum Flow and Pressure. Vehicle fueling appliances shall not exceed a flow rate of 10 standard cubic feet per minute (4.7 L/s) at a discharge pressure of 4,000 psi (27 579 kPa) at NTP. Vehicle fueling appliances used for residential service shall not exceed a flow rate of 5 standard cubic feet per minute (2.35 L/s) at a discharge pressure of 4,000 psi (27 579 kPa) at NTP.

5-2 Location and Installation.

5-2.1 Vehicle fueling appliances shall be installed outside of buildings. The appliance shall be a minimum of 3 feet (914 mm) from property lines and building openings. When approved, vehicle fueling appliances may be installed indoors when installed in accordance with Section 5-2.1.3 and *Uniform Fire Code* Article 52.

5-2.1.1 Foundation. Vehicle fueling appliances shall be fastened to a foundation to resist loads in accordance with the Building Code.

5-2.1.2 Physical and Impact Protection. Equipment related to the vehicle fueling appliance shall be protected to minimize the possibility of physical damage. When subject to vehicle impact, vehicle fueling appliances shall be provided with vehicular impact protection. See *Uniform Fire Code* Section 8001.11.3.

5-2.1.3 Safe Functioning of the Appliance. The vehicle fueling appliance shall be located to prevent damage resulting from flooding, ice buildup or blockage of ventilation.

5-2.2 Appliance Vent Lines.

5-2.2.1 General. Vehicle fueling appliances shall be provided with an approved method to discharge methane outdoors as the result of the operation of a relief valve or device.

5-2.2.2 Arrangement. Relief valves or devices shall be provided with an approved means of safely discharging natural gas outside of buildings. The method employed shall be designed such that the design flow capacity of the relief valve or device is not restricted.

5-2.2.3 Location. Relief valves or devices shall be terminated in accordance with the following minimum requirements:

1. **Sources of ignition.** Relief valves or devices shall terminate a minimum of 36 inches (914 mm) from sources of ignition.

2. **Building openings.** Relief valves or devices shall terminate a minimum of 36 inches (914 mm) horizontally and 12 inches (304.8 mm) vertically above openings or vents into buildings or a space where flammable vapors are likely to accumulate.

3. **Paths of egress.** Relief valves or devices shall not terminate within 5 feet (1524 mm) of sidewalks or paths of egress.

5-2.2.4 Termination. Relief valves or devices shall be terminated so as to prevent the entry of water, insects, ice or other materials.

5-2.3 Hoses.

5-2.3.1 General. Hoses used for the supply of natural gas to the vehicle fueling appliances or the dispensing of natural gas into motor vehicles shall be in accordance with Section 5-2.1.3.

5-2.3.2 Supply Hoses. A single hose having a maximum length of 3 feet (914 mm) is allowed to be used to terminate the natural gas supply into the intake of the vehicle fueling appliances. The hose shall be installed when it is necessary to prevent abrasion damage resulting from vibration at the compressor intake or discharge.

5-2.3.3 Dispensing Hoses. The use of hoses for dispensing of natural gas from vehicle fueling appliances into a motor vehicle shall be in accordance with the following minimum requirements:

1. **Length.** The maximum length of hose shall not exceed 25 feet (7620 mm).

2. **Protection.** Hoses shall be protected from abrasion, mechanical damage and being driven over.

3. **Number of hoses.** The number of hoses that may be used for the dispensing of natural gas into motor vehicles shall be in accordance with the appliance's listing.

4. **Breakaway protection.** The vehicle dispensing hose shall be equipped with a breakaway connection. Operation of the breakaway connection shall stop the flow of natural gas from the vehicle

fueling appliance. The maximum force necessary to effect breakaway shall be 40 pounds (177.9 N) in any horizontal direction.

5-2.4 Signs.

5-2.4.1 General. Signs concerning the safe operation of vehicle fueling appliances shall be provided in accordance with Section 5-2.4.

5-2.4.2 No Smoking. NO SMOKING WITHIN 3 FEET signs shall be provided at the vehicle fueling appliance.

5-2.4.3 Automobile Ignition. TURN OFF IGNITION BEFORE FUELING signs shall be provided at the vehicle fueling appliance.

5-2.4.4 Electrical Disconnect. Approved CNG COMPRESSOR EMERGENCY ELECTRICAL DISCONNECT signs shall be provided at the electrical disconnect switch.

5-2.5 Electrical Disconnect.

5-2.5.1 An emergency electrical disconnect switch shall be provided in an approved location not less than 5 feet (1524 mm) or more than 25 feet (7620 mm) away from the vehicle fueling appliance. The disconnect switch shall be in view of the vehicle fueling appliance.

5-2.6 Gas Supply.

5-2.6.1 Vehicle fueling appliances shall be provided with an approved method of shutting off the supply of natural gas.

5-3 Dispensing of CNG.

5-3.1 General. The exterior and interior dispensing of natural gas into motor vehicles shall be in accordance with this section.

5-3.2 Exterior dispensing. The exterior dispensing of natural gas into motor vehicles shall be in accordance with Chapter 5 of this standard and *Uniform Fire Code* Article 52.

5-3.3 Interior Dispensing. When approved, the fueling of vehicles inside of buildings shall be in accordance with Section 5-3.1 and the following requirements:

1. **Mechanical ventilation.** The room or area where natural gas is dispensed shall be provided with mechanical ventilation that is designed to not recirculate air. The ventilation system shall terminate outside of the building. The ventilation system shall be designed to provide a minimum ventilation rate of at least 10 times the maximum flow rate of the vehicle refueling appliance.

2. **Gas detection.** The room or area where natural gas is dispensed shall be provided with an approved listed gas-detection system. The detector shall be designed to activate an audible and visual alarm and shut off the gas flow when the amount of natural gas exceeds 25 percent of the lower flammability limit for methane.

3. **System failure.** Failure of the mechanical ventilation system or the gas-detection system shall shut off power to the vehicle fueling appliance.

5-4 Maintenance and Inspection.

5-4.1 General. Installation and maintenance of vehicle fueling appliances shall be in accordance with the manufacturer's instructions and listing.

5-4.2 Identification. A water-resistant tag, label or other approved means shall be affixed to the vehicle fueling appliance which identifies that the appliance has been serviced in accordance with the manufacturer's instructions.

Part II

Contents

NFPA 52

Standard for

Compressed Natural Gas (CNG) Vehicular Fuel Systems

1992 Edition

NOTICE: An asterisk (*) following the number or letter designating a paragraph indicates explanatory material on that paragraph in Appendix A.

Information on referenced publications can be found in Chapter 6 and Appendix B.

Chapter 1 Introduction

1-1* Scope. This standard applies to the design and installation of compressed natural gas (CNG) engine fuel systems on vehicles of all types including aftermarket and OEMs and to their associated fueling (dispensing) systems.

Exception: Vehicles complying with Federal Motor Vehicle Safety standards covering the installation of CNG fuel systems on vehicles and certified by the manufacturer as meeting these standards shall not be required to comply with 2-8.4 and Chapter 3, Engine Fuel Systems (except 3-11, Labeling).

1-2 Alternate Provisions. It is recognized that advancement in technology and improvements in system design and equipment may result in equipment fabrication methods, component design requirements, and installation and operating practices that differ from those specifically called for in this standard. Such deviations or improvements may provide desirable safety and compatible operation meeting the intent of this standard. Such deviations may be accepted when the authority having jurisdiction has seen evidence that a special investigation of all factors has been made and, based on sound experience and engineering judgment, has concluded that the proposed deviations meet the intent of this standard.

1-3 Retroactivity. The provisions of this document are considered necessary to provide a reasonable level of protection from loss of life and property from fire and explosion. They reflect situations and the state of the art at the time the standard was issued.

Unless otherwise noted, it is not intended that the provisions of this document be applied to facilities, equipment, structures, or installations that were existing or approved for construction or installation prior to the effective date of the document, except in those cases where it is determined by the authority having jurisdiction that the existing situation involves a distinct hazard to life or adjacent property.

1-4 Metric Practice. Metric units in this standard are based on ASTM-380, *Standard for Metric Practice.*

1-5 Definitions.

ANSI. American National Standards Institute.

Approved. Acceptable to the "authority having jurisdiction."

NOTE: The National Fire Protection Association does not approve, inspect or certify any installations, procedures, equipment, or materials nor does it approve or evaluate testing laboratories. In determining the acceptability of installations or procedures, equipment or materials, the authority having jurisdiction may base acceptance on compliance with NFPA or other appropriate standards. In the absence of such standards, said authority may require evidence of proper installation, procedure or use. The authority having jurisdiction may also refer to the listings or labeling practices of an organization concerned with product evaluations which is in a position to determine compliance with appropriate standards for the current production of listed items.

ASME Code. The American Society of Mechanical Engineers' *Boiler and Pressure Vessel Code.*

Authority Having Jurisdiction. The "authority having jurisdiction" is the organization, office or individual responsible for "approving" equipment, an installation or a procedure.

NOTE: The phrase "authority having jurisdiction" is used in NFPA documents in a broad manner since jurisdictions and "approval" agencies vary as do their responsibilities. Where public safety is primary, the "authority having jurisdiction" may be a federal, state, local or other regional department or individual such as a fire chief, fire marshal, chief of a fire prevention bureau, labor department, health department, building official, electrical inspector, or others having statutory authority. For insurance purposes, an insurance inspection department, rating bureau, or other insurance company representative may be the "authority having jurisdiction." In many circumstances the property owner or his designated agent assumes the role of the "authority having jurisdiction"; at government installations, the commanding officer or departmental official may be the "authority having jurisdiction."

Bulk Storage. Storage in pressure vessels other than cylinders.

Capacity. The water volume of a container in standard cu ft (m^3) per gallons.

Cascade Storage System. Storage in multiple pressure vessels, cylinders, or containers.

Code. For new construction, "Code" shall mean the applicable edition of the ASME Code referenced in this edition of NFPA 52. For secondhand pressure vessels and existing installations, the term "Code" shall include those editions of the ASME Code that were current at the time that a pressure vessel was built.

Composite Container. A container fabricated of two or more materials that interact to facilitate the container design criteria.

Compressed Natural Gas (CNG). Mixtures of hydrocarbon gases and vapors, consisting principally of methane in gaseous form that has been compressed for use as a vehicular fuel.

Container. A pressure vessel or cylinder used to store CNG.

Container Appurtenances. Devices connected to container openings for safety, control, or operating purposes.

Container Valve. A valve connected directly to a container outlet.

Cylinder. A container constructed, inspected, and maintained according to DOT or TC regulations, ANSI/AGA NGV2, or CSA B51 standards.

Dew Point (at Container Pressure). The dew point value of the gas at the maximum anticipated container pressure of the CNG vehicular fuel system (usually measured in the container prior to pressure reduction). When presenting or referencing dew point, the value shall be given in terms of the container pressure, e.g., -4°F dew point at 3600 psig.

Dew Point Temperature. The temperature, referred to a specific pressure, at which water vapor begins to condense.

Dispensing Station. A natural gas installation that dispenses CNG from storage containers or a distribution pipeline by means of a compressor or pressure booster into fuel supply containers or into portable cylinders.

Enclosure. A structure whose purpose is to protect equipment from the environment or to provide noise attenuation.

Flexible Metal and Wire Braid Hose. A metal hose made from continuous tubing that is corrugated for flexibility and that, for pressurized applications, shall have an external wire braid.

Fuel Line. The pipe, tubing, or hose, including all related fittings, on a vehicle through which natural gas passes.

Fuel Supply Container. A container mounted on a vehicle to store CNG as the fuel supply to the internal combustion engine of this vehicle.

Installation. A system that includes natural gas containers, pressure booster, compressors, and all attached valves, piping, and appurtenances. When filling containers or transferring natural gas directly from distribution lines by means of a compressor, an installation includes the compressor and all piping and piping components beyond the shutoff valve between the distribution system and the compressor.

Labeled. Equipment or materials to which has been attached a label, symbol or other identifying mark of an organization acceptable to the "authority having jurisdiction" and concerned with product evaluation, that maintains periodic inspection of production of labeled equipment or materials and by whose labeling the manufacturer indicates compliance with appropriate standards or performance in a specified manner.

Limited-Combustible Material. A material (as defined in NFPA 220, *Standard on Types of Building Construction*) not complying with the definition of noncombustible material that, in the form in which it is used, has a potential heat value not exceeding 3500 Btu per lb (8141 kJ/kg) and complies with one of the following paragraphs (a) or (b). Materials subject to increase in combustibility or flame spread rating beyond the limits herein established through the effects of age, moisture, or other atmospheric condition shall be considered combustible. (*See NFPA 259, Standard Test Method for Potential Heat of Building Materials.*)

(a) Materials having a structural base of noncombustible material, with a surfacing not exceeding a thickness of $^{1}/_{8}$ in. (3.2 mm) that has a flame spread rating not greater than 50.

(b) Materials, in the form and thickness used, other than as described in (a), having neither a flame spread rating greater than 25 nor evidence of continued progressive combustion and of such composition that surfaces that would be exposed by cutting through the material on any plane would have neither a flame spread rating greater than 25 nor evidence of continued progressive combustion.

Listed. Equipment or materials included in a list published by an organization acceptable to the "authority having jurisdiction" and concerned with product evaluation, that maintains periodic inspection of production of listed equipment or materials and whose listing states either that the equipment or material meets appropriate standards or has been tested and found suitable for use in a specified manner.

NOTE: The means for identifying listed equipment may vary for each organization concerned with product evaluation, some of which do not recognize equipment as listed unless it is also labeled. The "authority having jurisdiction" should utilize the system employed by the listing organization to identify a listed product.

Metallic Hose. A hose in which the strength of the hose depends primarily on the strength of metallic parts; it may have metallic liners and/or covers.

Natural Gas. Mixtures of hydrocarbon gases and vapors consisting principally of methane in gaseous form.

Noncombustible Material. A material (as defined in NFPA 220, *Standard on Types of Building Construction*) that, in the form in which it is used and under the conditions anticipated, will not ignite, burn, support combustion, or release flammable vapors when subjected to fire or heat. Materials reported as noncombustible, when tested in accordance with ASTM E-136, *Standard Method of Test for Behavior of Materials in a Vertical Tube Furnace at 750°C*, shall be considered noncombustible materials.

Point of Transfer. The point where the fueling connection is made.

Pressure Relief Device. A pressure and/or temperature activated device used to prevent the pressure from rising above a predetermined maximum and thereby prevent the rupture of a normally charged cylinder when subjected to a standard fire test as required by 49 CFR 173.34(d) or 73.34(d) of the TC Regulations. Pressure relief devices for DOT/TC cylinders shall also include devices capable of protecting partially charged cylinders when subjected to these fire tests.

Pressure Relief Device Channels. The passage or passages beyond the operating parts of the pressure relief device through which fluid must pass to reach the atmosphere.

Pressure Vessel. A container or other component designed in accordance with the ASME Code.

SCF. Cu ft of gas determined at 14.7 psia and 60°F (101 kPa and 16°C).

Service Pressure. The settled pressure at a uniform gas temperature of 70°F (21°C) and full gas content. It is the pressure for which the equipment has been constructed, under normal conditions.

Service Valve. A valve operated by hand connected directly to the outlet of a container other than a cylinder not larger than $^{3}/_{4}$-in. pipe size and having an inlet diameter not exceeding the internal diameter of $^{1}/_{2}$-in., Schedule 80 pipe.

Settled Pressure. The pressure in a container at 70°F (21°C) that cannot exceed the marked service or design pressure on the container.

Shall. Indicates a mandatory requirement.

Should. Indicates a recommendation or that which is advised but not required.

Sources of Ignition. Devices or equipment that, because of their modes of use or operation, are capable of providing sufficient thermal energy to ignite flammable compressed natural gas-air mixtures when introduced into such a mixture or when such a mixture comes into contact with them and that will permit propagation of flame away from them.

Chapter 2 General CNG and Equipment Qualifications

2-1* General. The provisions of this chapter apply only to pressurized system components handling CNG.

2-2* Gas Quality. Gas quality in the container shall comply with the following:

H_2S and soluble sulfides partial pressure .....0.05 psi, max
water vapor.....................................7.0 lb/MMCF, max
CO_2 partial pressure ....7 psi, max
O_2..0.5 volume %, max

Exception: When the dew point of the gas entering the cylinder is below the lowest anticipated container temperature at the maximum anticipated container pressure, the above shall not apply.

NOTE: For additional information on gas quality see SAE J1616, *Surface Vehicle Recommended Practice for Natural Gas Vehicle Fuel Composition.*

Natural gas introduced into any system covered by this standard shall have a distinctive odor potent enough for its presence to be detected down to a concentration in air of not over $^{1}/_{5}$ of the lower limit of flammability.

2-3 Approval.

2-3.1 Systems and/or system components, as follows, shall be listed or approved:

(a) Containers

(b) Pressure relief devices, including pressure relief valves

(c) Pressure gauges

(d) Pressure regulators

(e) Valves

(f) Hose and hose connections

(g) Vehicle fueling connections

(h) Engine fuel systems

(i) Electrical equipment related to CNG systems.

2-3.2 Devices not otherwise specifically provided for shall be constructed to provide safety equivalent to that required for other parts of a system.

2-4* Design and Construction of Containers.

2-4.1 Containers shall comply with 2-4.2 through 2-4.6 or shall be designed, fabricated, tested, and marked using criteria that incorporate an investigation to determine that they are safe and suitable for the proposed service, are recommended for that service by the manufacturer, and are acceptable to the authority having jurisdiction.

2-4.1.1 Containers shall be fabricated of steel, aluminum, or composite materials.

The container shall be designed to be suitable for CNG service and permanently marked CNG by the manufacturer.

Containers manufactured prior to the effective date of this standard may be used in CNG service if recommended for CNG service by the container manufacturer or acceptable to the authority having jurisdiction.

2-4.2 Cylinders shall be manufactured, inspected, marked, tested, retested, equipped, and used in accordance with U.S. Department of Transportation (DOT) or Canada Transport (TC) regulations, exemptions, or special permits, or ANSI/AGA NGV2, *Basic Requirements of Type 3NG Fuel Containers*, specifically for CNG service and shall have a rated service pressure of not less than 2400 psig at 70°F (16.5 MPa at 21.1°C).

NOTE 1: Current DOT and TC specifications, exemptions, and specific permits do not address the use of cylinders as vehicle fuel containers. The intent of the reference in this standard is to permit only those cylinders that are approved for the transportation of natural gas to be used in CNG service.

NOTE 2: Four relevant cylinder inspection standards that are useful are Compressed Gas Association, Inc. pamphlets:

(a) C-6, *Standards for Visual Inspection of Compressed Gas Cylinders.*

(b) C-6.1, *Standards for Visual Inspection of High Pressure Aluminum Compressed Gas Cylinders.*

(c) C-6.2, *Guidelines for Visual Inspection and Requalification of Fiber Reinforced High Pressure Cylinders.*

(d) C-10, *Recommendations for Changes of Service for Compressed Gas Cylinders Including Procedures for Inspection and Contaminant Removal.*

2-4.3 Pressure vessels shall be manufactured, inspected, marked, and tested in accordance with the Rules for the Construction of Unfired Pressure Vessels, Section VIII (Division 1) or Section X, ASME *Boiler and Pressure Vessel Code.*

2-4.3.1 Adherence to applicable ASME Code case interpretations and addenda shall be considered as compliance with the ASME Code.

2-4.4 The "+" (plus) and "*" (star) markings on DOT and TC cylinders shall not apply in accordance with DOT and TC regulations for cylinders for flammable compressed gases. The star marking shall be removed/obliterated. The removal of the marking shall be done by peening and otherwise in accordance with DOT or TC regulations. Grinding is prohibited.

2-4.5 In addition to the marking required by documents cited in 2-4.2 and 2-4.3, such containers and any used under the provisions of 2-4.1 shall be labeled with the words "CNG ONLY" in letters at least 1 in. (25 mm) high in contrasting color and in a location that will be visible after installation. Decals or stencils are acceptable. (*See 3-11.1.*)

2-4.6 Welding or brazing for the repair or alteration of an ASME pressure vessel shall comply with the documents under which the pressure vessel was fabricated. Other welding or brazing is permitted only on saddle plates, lugs, or brackets attached to the pressure vessel by the pressure vessel manufacturer.

The exchange or interchange of pressure vessel appurtenances (*see definition*) intended for the same purpose is not considered a repair or alteration.

2-5 Pressure Relief Devices.

2-5.1 Each fuel supply cylinder complying with 2-4.2 shall be fitted with one or more pressure relief devices in accordance with 2-5.1.1 and 2-5.1.2.

2-5.1.1 Pressure relief devices for cylinders shall be in accordance with Compressed Gas Association (CGA) Pamphlet S-1.1, *Pressure Relief Device Standards – Part 1, Cylinders for Compressed Gases.*

Cylinders produced under DOT and TC exemptions or special permits that require fire tests for design qualification shall be equipped with pressure relief devices in accordance with CGA S-1.1 and of the type, temperature rating, pressure rating, number, and location used in the fire tests.

2-5.1.2 The pressure relief device shall be in direct communication with the fuel and be vented to the atmosphere by a method that will withstand the maximum pressure that will result.

The discharge flow rate of the pressure relief device shall not be reduced below that required for the capacity of the container upon which the device is installed.

Pressure relief devices shall be located so that the temperature to which they are subjected shall be representative of the temperature to which the cylinder is subjected.

2-5.2 Pressure vessels complying with 2-4.3 shall be provided with one or more springloaded pressure relief valves set to open in accordance with the ASME Code.

2-5.2.1 The minimum rate of discharge of pressure relief devices on containers shall be in accordance with CGA Pamphlet S-1.1, *Pressure Relief Device Standards – Part 1, Cylinders for Compressed Gases* or the ASME *Boiler and Pressure Vessel Code,* whichever is applicable.

2-5.2.2 Pressure relief valves for CNG service shall not be fitted with lifting devices. The adjustment, if external, shall be provided with means for sealing the adjustment to prevent tampering by unauthorized persons. If at any time it is necessary to break such seal, the valve shall be removed from service until it has been reset and sealed. Any adjustments necessary shall be made by the manufacturer or other companies having competent personnel and adequate facilities for the repair, adjustment, and testing of such valves. The organization making such adjustment shall attach a permanent tag with the setting, capacity, and date.

2-5.3 Containers and pressure vessels complying otherwise with 2-4.1 shall be provided with pressure relief devices approved by the authority having jurisdiction.

2-6 Pressure Gauges.

2-6.1 A pressure gauge, if provided, shall be capable of reading at least 1.2 times the system design pressure.

2-6.2 A gauge shall have an opening not to exceed 0.055 in. (1.4 mm) (No. 54 drill size) at the inlet connection.

2-7 Pressure Regulators.

2-7.1 A pressure regulator inlet and each chamber shall be designed for its maximum service pressure with a pressure safety factor of at least 4.

2-7.2 Low pressure chambers shall provide for overpressure relief or shall be able to withstand the service pressure of the upstream pressure chamber.

2-8 Piping.

2-8.1 Pipe, tubing, fittings, gaskets, and packing material shall be compatible with the fuel under the service conditions.

2-8.2 Pipe, tubing, fittings, and other piping components between a container and the first shutoff valve shall be capable of withstanding a hydrostatic test of at least four times the rated service pressure without structural failure.

2-8.3 Natural gas piping shall be fabricated and tested in accordance with ANSI/ASME B31.3, *American National Standard Code for Chemical Plant and Petroleum Refinery Piping.*

2-8.4 The following components shall not be used:

(a) Fittings, street ells, and other piping components of cast irons other than those complying with ASTM A-536 (Grade 60-40-18), A-395, and A-47 (Grade 35018),

(b) Plastic pipe, tubing, and fittings for high pressure service,

(c) Galvanized pipe and fittings,

(d) Aluminum pipe, tubing, and fittings,

Exception No. 1: Refueling connection may be made of nonsparking wrought aluminum alloy suitable for the pressure employed.

Exception No. 2: Aluminum pipe, tubing, and fittings may be used downstream of the first stage pressure regulator in an engine fuel system.

(e) Pipe nipples for the initial connection to a container, and

(f) Copper alloy with copper content exceeding 70 percent.

2-8.5 Piping components such as strainers, snubbers, and expansion joints shall be permanently marked by the manufacturer to indicate the service ratings.

2-9 Valves.

2-9.1 Valves, valve packing, and gaskets shall be suitable for the fuel over the full range of pressures and temperatures to which they may be subjected under normal operating conditions.

2-9.1.1 Shutoff valves shall have a rated service pressure not less than the rated service pressure of the entire system and shall be capable of withstanding a hydrostatic test of at least four times the rated service pressure without rupture. Leakage shall not occur at less than $1^1/_2$ times the rated service pressure using dry air as the test medium.

2-9.2 Valves of cast irons other than those complying with ASTM A-536 (Grade 60-40-18), A-395, and A-47 (Grade 35018) shall not be used as primary stop valves.

2-9.3 Valves of a design that will allow the valve stem to be removed without removal of the complete valve bonnet or disassembly of the valve body shall not be used.

2-9.4 The manufacturer shall stamp or otherwise permanently mark the valve body to indicate the service ratings.

Exception: Container valves incorporating integral pressure relief devices marked in accordance with CGA S-1.1 need no additional marking.

2-10 Hoses and Hose Connections.

2-10.1 Hose and metallic hose shall be of or lined with materials that are resistant to corrosion and the actions of natural gas.

2-10.2 Hose, metallic hose, flexible metal hose, tubing, and their connections shall be suitable for the most severe pressure and temperature conditions expected under normal operating conditions with a burst pressure of at least four times the service pressure.

2-10.3 Hose assemblies shall be tested by the manufacturer or its designated representative prior to use to at least twice the service pressure.

2-10.4 Hose and metallic hose shall be distinctly marked by the manufacturer, either by the manufacturer's permanently attached tag or by distinct markings, indicating the manufacturer's name or trademark, applicable service identifier, and design pressure.

2-11 Vehicle Fueling Connection.

2-11.1 A vehicle fueling connection shall provide for the reliable and secure connection of the fuel system containers to a source of high pressure natural gas.

2-11.2 The fueling connection shall be suitable for the pressure expected under normal conditions and corrosive conditions that might be encountered.

2-11.3 The fueling connection shall prevent escape of gas when the connector is not properly engaged or becomes separated.

2-11.4 The refueling receptacle on an engine fuel system shall be firmly supported and shall:

(a) Receive the fueling connector and accommodate the service pressure of the vehicle fuel system,

(b) Incorporate a means to prevent the entry of dust, water, and other foreign material. If the means used is capable of sealing system pressure it shall be capable of being depressurized before removal, and

(c) Have a different fueling connection for each pressure base vehicle fuel system.

2-11.5 Where refueling is available for use by the general public, a vehicle fueling connection complying with ANSI/AGA NGV1, *Standard for Compressed Natural Gas Vehicle (NGV) Fueling Connection Devices,* Requirement 1-90, shall be provided.

Chapter 3 Engine Fuel Systems

3-1* Application.

3-1.1 This chapter applies to the design, installation, inspection, and testing of CNG fuel supply systems for vehicular internal combustion engines.

3-1.2 Components shall be installed in accordance with their manufacturers' instructions.

3-2 System Component Qualifications.

3-2.1 System components shall comply with the appropriate provisions in Chapter 2 and with 3-2.2 through 3-2.4.

3-2.2 Components in the engine compartment shall be suitable for service over a range of temperatures from -40°F to 250°F (-40 to 121°C). All other components shall be suitable for service over a range of -40°F to 180°F (-40 to 82.2°C).

3-2.3 Aluminum or copper pipe, tubing, or fittings shall not be used between the fuel container and the first stage pressure regulator.

3-2.4 Fuel carrying components shall be labeled or stamped with the following:

(a) The manufacturer's name or symbol,

(b) The model designation,

(c) The design service pressure,

(d) Direction of fuel flow when necessary for correct installation, and

(e) Capacity or electrical rating as applicable.

Exception: Not applicable to container valves, tubing, and fittings.

3-3 Installation of Fuel Supply Containers.

3-3.1 Fuel supply containers on vehicles may be located within, below, or above the driver or passenger compartment provided all connections to the container(s) are external to, or sealed and vented from, these compartments.

3-3.2 Each fuel supply container shall be mounted in a location to minimize damage from collision. No part of a container or its appurtenances shall protrude beyond the sides or top of the vehicle at the point where it is installed.

3-3.2.1 The fuel system shall be installed with as much road clearance as practical but not less than the minimum road clearance of the vehicle when loaded to its gross vehicle weight rating. This minimum clearance shall be measured from the lowest part of the fuel system.

3-3.2.2 No portion of a fuel supply container or container appurtenance shall be located ahead of the front axle or behind the rear bumper mounting face of a vehicle. Container valves shall be protected from physical damage using the vehicle structure, valve protectors, or a suitable metal shield.

3-3.3 Each container rack shall be secured to the vehicle body, bed, or frame to prevent damage from road hazards, slippage, loosening, or rotation using a method capable of withstanding a static force in the six principal directions (*see Figure 3-3.3*) of eight times the weight of a fully pressurized container(s).

3-3.3.1 Each fuel supply container in the rack shall be secured to its cradle in such a manner that it is capable of withstanding a static force applied in the six principal directions (*see Figure 3-3.3*) of eight times the weight of the fully pressurized container with a maximum displacement of 1/2 in. (13 mm).

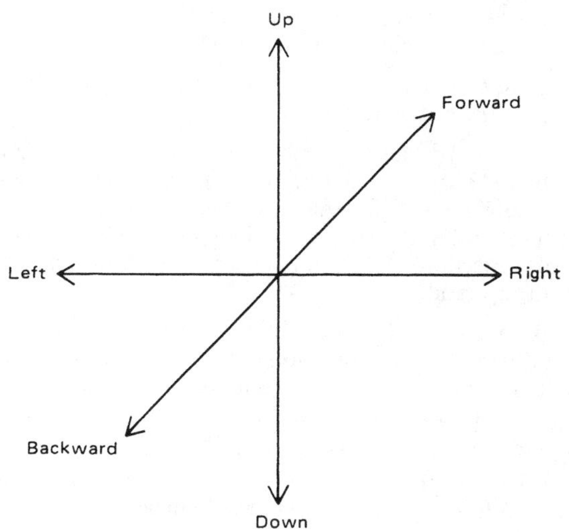

Figure 3-3.3 The six principal directions.

3-3.4 The container weight shall not be supported by outlet valves, manifolds, or other fuel connections.

3-3.5 Fuel supply containers located less than 8 in. (200 mm) from the exhaust system shall be shielded against direct heat.

3-3.6 The mounting system shall minimize fretting corrosion between the container and the mounting system.

3-3.7 Fuel supply containers shall not be installed so as to adversely affect the driving characteristics of the vehicle.

3-3.8 Metal clamping bands and their supports shall not be in direct contact with a container. A resilient non-water-retaining gasket shall be installed between the clamping bands and their supports and a container.

3-3.9 A container, when located in a vehicle compartment capable of accumulating natural gas, shall be installed such that:

(a) The pressure relief device for the protection of the container is installed in the same vehicle compartment as the container;

(b) The discharge from a pressure relief device referred to in (a) above is:

(i) Vented to the outside thorough a smooth walled metallic tube no smaller than the outlet diameter of the relief device , secured at 12-in. (300-mm) intervals when the tube exceeds 24 in. (610 mm) in length, and

(ii) Located so that the vent opening will not be blocked by debris thrown up from the road, such as snow, ice, mud, etc., or otherwise affected by the elements.

3-3.10 Where a container is installed above the operator or passenger compartment of a vehicle:

(a) The container, its piping, fittings, and valve shall be protected from damage by,

(i) A guard rail or similar device that is designed to absorb the impact of a collision with a stationary object when the vehicle is moving either forward or backward at 5 mph (8 kph), and the guard rail or similar device shall be free of projections that could damage a container, its valves and fittings, and

(ii) A shield designed to absorb impacts that may occur during loading, unloading, or use of the vehicle and the shield shall be free of projections that could damage a container, its valve, and fittings,

(b) The top of the container and any CNG piping, fitting, valve, housing, guard rail, or shield shall not be more than 13.5 ft (4.12 m) above the road surface.

(c) The cylinder shall be protected by metallic or nonmetallic covers from accidental contact with overhead electrical wiring,

3-3.11 The minimum clearance from the road to a container, its housing and fittings, whichever is lowest when the container is installed below the frame and between the axles of a CNG vehicle, shall not, with the vehicle loaded to its gross weight rating, be less than:

(a) 7 in. (175 mm) for a vehicle having a wheel base less than or equal to 127 in. (3230 mm), or

(b) 9 in. (225 mm) for a vehicle having a wheel base greater than 127 in. (3230 mm).

3-3.12 Containers that are installed behind a rear axle of a CNG vehicle shall be installed transversely.

Exception: Containers shall be permitted to be installed in other orientations when the container valve and fittings are located at the end of the container most protected from a source of impact.

3-4 Installation of Venting Systems.

3-4.1 All pressure relief devices and connections between pressure carrying components installed within a closed compartment (*see 3-3.1*) shall be vented to the outside of the vehicle in a suitable location.

NOTE: It is not permitted to terminate the vent outlet in the engine compartment.

3-4.2 The venting system for the discharge of pressure relief devices (pressure relief device channels) shall be constructed of metallic tubing with threaded, compression, or flare fittings and shall be secured at the outer end.

3-4.3 The vent or vents for the venting system shall not exit into a wheel well.

3-4.4 A vent shall not restrict the operation of a container pressure relief device or pressure relief device channel.

3-4.5 Vent outlets shall be protected by caps, covers, or other means to keep water, dirt, and insects from collecting in the lines. Protective devices shall not restrict the flow of gas.

3-4.6 The neck of the container and all CNG fittings within the compartment shall be enclosed in a gastight enclosure made of linear low density polyethylene having a minimum thickness of 8 mils (200 μm) or an equally gastight alternative enclosure that is vented directly outside of the vehicle.

3-5 Installation of Piping.

3-5.1 Manifolds connecting fuel containers shall be fabricated to minimize vibration and shall be installed in a protected location or shielded to prevent damage from unsecured objects.

3-5.2 A pipe thread jointing material impervious to the action of the natural gas used in the system shall be applied to all male pipe threads prior to assembly.

3-5.3 Piping and fittings shall be clear and free from cutting or threading burrs and scales, and the ends of all piping shall be reamed.

3-5.4 Where necessary to prevent abrasion, fuel lines passing through a panel shall be protected by grommets or similar devices.

3-5.5 Fuel lines shall have the maximum practical clearance from the engine exhaust system.

3-5.6 Fuel lines shall be mounted, braced, and supported to minimize vibration and protected against damage, corrosion, or breakage due to strain or wear. A fuel line shall be supported at least every 24 in. (610 mm).

3-5.7 A bend in piping or tubing is prohibited where such a bend weakens the pipe or tubing.

3-5.8 A joint or connection shall be located in an accessible location.

3-6 Installation of Valves.

3-6.1 Every container shall be equipped with a manual or normally closed remotely actuated shutoff valve connected directly to the container. Remotely actuated valves shall be equipped with a provision to manually bleed the container.

3-6.2 In addition to the valve required by 3-6.1, a manual shutoff valve shall be installed in an accessible location that will permit isolation of the container(s) from the remainder of the fuel system. The manual shutoff valve shall have no more than a 90-degree rotation from open to closed positions.

3-6.2.1 The valve shall be securely mounted and shielded or installed in a protected location to minimize damage from vibration and unsecured objects.

3-6.2.2 The valve location shall be marked with the words "MANUAL SHUTOFF VALVE." Decals or stencils are acceptable.

3-6.3 A valve shall be provided in the system that automatically prevents the flow of gaseous fuel to the engine when the engine is not running even if the ignition is switched on.

3-6.4 Where multiple fuel systems are installed on the vehicle, automatic valves shall be provided, as necessary, to shut off the fuel not being used.

3-6.5 The fueling system shall be equipped with a backflow check valve that will prevent the return flow of gas from the container(s) to the filling connection.

NOTE: Electronic fuel injectors are considered to be automatic valves.

3-7 Installation of Pressure Gauges.

3-7.1 A pressure gauge located within a driver or passenger compartment shall be installed in such a manner that no gas will flow through the gauge in the event of failure.

3-7.2 A pressure gauge installed outside a driver or passenger compartment shall be equipped with a limiting orifice, a shatterproof dial lens, and a body relief.

3-7.3 Gauges shall be securely mounted, shielded, and installed in a protected location to prevent damage from vibration and unsecured objects.

3-8 Installation of Pressure Regulators.

3-8.1 An automatic pressure reducing regulator(s) shall be installed to reduce the fuel container pressure to a level consistent with the service pressure required by the gas-air mixer.

3-8.2 Means shall be provided to prevent regulator malfunctions due to refrigeration effects.

3-8.3 Regulators shall be installed so that their weight is not placed on, or supported by, the attached gas lines.

3-9 Installation of Fueling Connection.

3-9.1 A fueling connection receptacle complying with Section 2-11 shall be installed in each vehicle.

3-9.2 The fueling connection receptacle shall be mounted to withstand the breakaway force specified in 4-11.8. The receptacle shall be installed in accordance with the manufacturer's instructions.

3-10 Wiring Installation.

3-10.1 All wiring shall be secured and protected from abrasion and corrosion to the same standard as the original wiring on the vehicle.

3-10.2 All wiring shall be sized and fuse-protected with the fuse rating adequate to the current draw.

3-11 Labeling.

3-11.1 A vehicle equipped with a CNG fuel system shall bear the following durable labels.

3-11.1.1 A label readily visible and located in the engine compartment shall include the following:

(a) CNG fueled vehicle,

(b) System service pressure,

(c) Installer's name or company,

(d) Container retest date(s) or expiration date,

(e) Total container water volume in gallons (liters).

3-11.1.2 A label located at the fueling connection receptacle shall include the following:

(a) CNG fueled vehicle,

(b) System working pressure,

(c) Container retest date or expiration date.

Exception: If both labels are located in one of the above areas, the labels can be combined into a single label.

3-11.2 Each vehicle shall be identified with a weather-resistant, diamond-shaped label located on an exterior vertical or near vertical surface on the lower right rear of the vehicle (on the trunk lid of a vehicle so equipped, but not on the bumper of any vehicle) inboard from any other markings. The label shall be a minimum of $4^3/_4$ in. (120 mm) long by $3^1/_4$ in. (83 mm) high. The marking shall consist of a border and the letters "CNG" [1 in. (25 mm) minimum height centered in the diamond] of silver or white reflective luminous material on a blue background.

3-12 System Testing.

3-12.1 The complete assembly shall be leak tested using natural gas or inert gas (carbon dioxide or nitrogen or a mixture of these).

3-12.2 Before use, every connection shall be checked with a nonammonia soap solution or a leak detector instrument after the equipment is connected and pressurized to its service pressure.

3-12.3 If the completed assembly is leak tested with natural gas, the testing shall be done under adequately ventilated conditions.

3-12.4* When a vehicle is involved in an accident or fire causing damage to the CNG container, the CNG container shall be replaced or removed, inspected, and retested in accordance with the document under which it was originally manufactured before being returned to service.

3-12.5 When a vehicle is involved in an accident or fire causing damage to any part of the CNG fuel system, the system shall be repaired and retested (*see Section 3-13*) before being returned to service.

3-13 Maintenance and Repair.

3-13.1 Damaged fuel lines shall be replaced, not repaired.

3-13.2 The owner or user or both shall maintain all containers, container appurtenances, piping systems, venting systems, and other components in a safe condition. The above individual(s) shall be responsible for verifying working pressure and container retest date or expiration date currentness.

3-13.3 Pressure relief devices on cylinder shall be maintained in accordance with CGA pamphlet S-1.1

Pressure relief devices on all other containers shall be maintained in accordance with the following:

(a) Pressure relief device channels or other parts that could interfere with the functioning of the device shall not be plugged by paint or accumulation of dirt.

(b) Compressed natural gas containers shall be stored so as to avoid damage.

(c) Only qualified personnel shall be allowed to service pressure relief devices.

(d) Only assemblies or original manufacturer's parts shall be used in the repair of pressure relief devices unless the interchange of parts has been proved by suitable tests.

Chapter 4 CNG Compression, Storage, and Dispensing Systems

4-1* Application. This chapter applies to the design, construction, installation, and operation of containers, pressure vessels, compression equipment, buildings and structures, and associated equipment used for storage and dispensing of CNG as an engine fuel in fleet and public dispensing operations.

4-2 System Component Qualification. System components shall comply with the appropriate provisions in Chapter 2 and with Sections 4-5 through 4-13.

4-3 General.

4-3.1 Where systems are served by a gas utility, the utility shall be notified of all CNG installations.

4-3.2 Equipment related to a compression, storage, or dispensing installation shall be protected to minimize the possibilities of physical damage and vandalism.

4-3.3 Control devices shall be installed so that internal or external icing or hydrate formation will not cause malfunction.

4-3.4 Vehicles shall not be considered a source of ignition with respect to the provisions of this chapter.

Exception: Vehicles containing fuel-fired equipment, e.g., recreational vehicles and catering trucks, shall be considered a source of ignition unless this equipment is shut off completely before entering an area in which ignition sources are prohibited.

4-3.5 The fueling connection shall prevent escape of gas where the connector is not properly engaged or becomes separated.

4-3.6 Compression equipment shall be designed for use with CNG and for the pressure and temperatures to which it may be subjected under normal operating conditions. It shall have pressure relief devices that shall limit each stage pressure to the maximum allowable service pressure for the compression cylinder and piping associated with that stage of compression.

4-3.7 When CNG compression equipment is operated unattended, it shall be equipped with a high discharge and low suction pressure automatic shutdown control.

4-3.8 Engine driven compressor installations shall conform, where applicable, to NFPA 37, *Standard for the Installation and Use of Stationary Combustion Engines and Gas Turbines.*

4-3.9 Compression equipment shall incorporate an automatic condensate system to eliminate liquid carryover to the storage system.

4-4 Siting.

4-4.1 CNG compression, storage, and dispensing shall be located and conducted outdoors or indoors in compliance with 4-4.2 and 4-4.3.

4-4.2 Outdoors.

4-4.2.1 CNG storage containers charged with CNG not connected for use shall be located outdoors.

4-4.2.2 A facility in which CNG compression, storage, and dispensing equipment is sheltered by an enclosure constructed of noncombustible or limited-combustible materials that has at least one side predominantly open and a roof designed for ventilation and dispersal of escaped gas shall be regarded as outdoors.

4-4.2.3 Compression, storage, and dispensing equipment outdoors shall be located aboveground, not beneath electric power lines or where exposed by their failure, and a minimum of 10 ft (3.0 m) from the nearest important building or line of adjoining property that may be built upon or source of ignition.

4-4.2.4 Compression, storage, and dispensing equipment outdoors shall be located not less than 10 ft (3.0 m) from the nearest public street or sidewalk line and at least 50 ft (15 m) from the nearest rail of any railroad main track.

4-4.2.5 A clear space of at least 3 ft (1 m) shall be provided for access to all valves and fittings of multiple groups of containers.

4-4.2.6 Readily ignitable material shall not be permitted within 10 ft (3.0 m) of any stationary container.

4-4.2.7 The minimum separation between containers and aboveground tanks containing flammable or combustible liquids shall be 20 ft (6.1 m).

4-4.2.8 During outdoor fueling operations, the point of transfer (*see definition*) shall be located at least 10 ft (3.0 m) from any important building, mobile home, public sidewalk, highway, street, or road and at least 3 ft (1 m) from storage containers.

Exception: At the discretion of the authority having jurisdiction, the point of transfer may be located at a lesser distance from buildings or walls constructed of concrete or masonry materials, but at least 10 ft (3.0 m) from any building openings.

4-4.3 Indoors.

4-4.3.1 General. Compression, dispensing equipment, and storage containers connected for use may be located inside of buildings reserved exclusively for these purposes or in rooms within or attached to buildings used for other purposes in accordance with 4-4.3.

4-4.3.1.1 Storage shall be limited to not more than 10,000 cu ft (283 m^3) of natural gas in each building or room.

Exception: CNG stored in vehicle mounted fuel supply containers.

4-4.3.2 Deflagration Venting. Deflagration (explosion) venting shall be provided in exterior walls or roof only. Vents shall be permitted to consist of any one or any combination of the following:

(a) Walls of light material;

(b) Lightly fastened hatch covers;

(c) Lightly fastened, outward opening doors in exterior walls;

(d) Lightly fastened walls or roof.

NOTE: For information on venting of explosions see NFPA 68, *Guide for the Venting of Deflagrations*.

Where applicable, snow loads shall be considered.

4-4.3.3 Rooms within Buildings. Rooms within or attached to other buildings shall be constructed of noncombustible or limited-combustible materials. Interior walls or partitions shall be continuous from floor to ceiling, shall be securely anchored, and shall have a fire resistance rating of at least 2 hours. At least one wall shall be an exterior wall. Windows and doors shall be located so as to be readily accessible in case of emergency.

Exception: Window glazing shall be permitted to be plastic.

4-4.3.3.1 Explosion venting shall be provided in accordance with 4-4.3.2.

4-4.3.3.2 Access to the room shall be from outside the primary structure.

Exception: If such access is not possible, access from within the primary structure is permitted provided such access is made through a barrier space having two vapor-sealing, self-closing fire doors suitable for installation in a wall having the fire resistance rating selected.

4-4.3.4 Indoor locations shall be ventilated utilizing air supply inlets and exhaust outlets arranged to provide air movement as uniformly as practical. Inlets shall be uniformly arranged on exterior walls near floor level. Outlets shall be located at the high point of the room in exterior walls or the roof.

4-4.3.4.1 Ventilation shall be by a continuous mechanical ventilation system or by a mechanical ventilation system activated by a continuous monitoring natural gas detection system when a gas concentration of not more than one-fifth of the lower flammable limit is present. In either case, the system shall shut down the fueling system in the event of failure of the ventilation system.

4-4.3.4.2 The ventilation rate shall be at least 1 cu ft/min per 12 cu ft (1 m^3/min per 12 m^3) of room volume.

NOTE: This corresponds to 5 air changes per hour.

4-4.3.4.3 A ventilation system for a room within or attached to another building shall be separate from any ventilation system for the other building.

4-4.3.5 A gas detection system shall be equipped to sound an alarm when a maximum of one-fifth of the lower flammable limit is reached.

4-4.3.6 Reactivation of the fueling system shall be by manual restart conducted by trained personnel.

4-4.3.7 Buildings and rooms used for compression, storage, and dispensing shall be classified in accordance with Table 4-12 for installations of electrical equipment.

4-4.3.8 Sources of ignition, other than electrical as permitted by 4-4.3.7, shall be prohibited.

4-4.3.9 Pressure relief devices on storage systems shall have pressure relief device channels to convey escaping gas to the outdoors and then upward to a safe area so as not to impinge upon buildings, other equipment, or areas that could be occupied by the public, e.g., sidewalks.

4-4.3.10 Access doors shall have warning signs with the words "WARNING—NO SMOKING—FLAMMABLE GAS." Such wording shall be in plainly legible, bright red letters on a white background with letters not less than 1 in. high.

4-5 Installation of Containers and Container Appurtenances (Other than Pressure Relief Devices).

4-5.1* Storage containers shall be installed aboveground on stable, noncombustible foundations or in vaults with ventilation and drainage. Horizontal containers shall have no more than two points of support longitudinally. Where flooding can occur, they shall be securely anchored to prevent floating.

4-5.2 Containers shall be protected by painting or other equivalent means where necessary to inhibit corrosion. Horizontally installed containers shall not be in direct contact with each other.

Exception: Composite containers shall not be painted without prior permission from the container manufacturer.

4-5.3 Adequate means shall be provided to prevent the flow or accumulation of flammable or combustible liquids under containers, such as by grading, pads, or diversion curbs.

4-6 Installation of Pressure Relief Devices.

4-6.1 Pressure relief valves shall be so arranged that they will discharge to a safe area and so that escaping gas will not impinge upon buildings, other equipment, or areas that could be occupied by the public. (*See 4-4.3.9.*)

4-6.2 Pressure relief valves on pressure vessels shall be installed so that any discharge will be in a vertical position and shall be fitted with suitable raincaps.

4-6.3 A pressure relief device shall be provided in the transfer system to prevent overpressure in the vehicle.

4-7 Installation of Pressure Regulators. Regulators shall be designed, installed, or protected so their operation will not be affected by the elements (freezing rain, sleet, snow) or ice, mud, or debris. This protection may be integral with the regulator.

4-8 Installation of Pressure Gauges. Gauges shall be installed to indicate compression discharge pressure, storage pressure, and fuel supply container fill pressure.

4-9 Installation of Piping and Hoses.

4-9.1 Piping and hoses shall be run as directly as practical with adequate provisions for expansion, contraction, jarring, vibration, and settling. Exterior piping shall be either buried or installed aboveground and shall be well supported and protected against mechanical damage. Underground piping shall be buried not less than 18 in. (460 mm) below the surface of the ground unless otherwise protected. Underground and aboveground piping shall be protected from corrosion in compliance with present recognized practices. Threaded pipe and fittings shall not be used underground.

4-9.1.1 Manifolds connecting fuel containers shall be fabricated to minimize vibration and shall be installed in a protected location or shielded to prevent damage from unsecured objects.

4-9.1.2 A pipe thread jointing material impervious to the action of the natural gas used in the system shall be applied to all male pipe threads prior to assembly.

4-9.1.3 Piping and fittings shall be clear and free from cutting or threading burrs and scales, and the ends of all piping shall be reamed.

4-9.1.4 A bend in piping or tubing is prohibited where such a bend weakens the pipe or tubing.

4-9.1.5 A joint or connection shall be located in an accessible location.

4-9.2 Natural gas shall only be vented to a safe point of discharge. A vent pipe or stack shall have the open end suitably protected to prevent entrance of rain, snow, and solid material. Vertical vent pipes and stacks shall have provision for drainage.

4-9.3 The use of hose in an installation shall be limited to:

(a) A vehicle fueling hose;

(b) An inlet connection to compression equipment;

(c) A section of metallic hose not exceeding 36 in. (910 mm) in length in a pipeline to provide flexibility where necessary. Each section shall be so installed that it will be protected against mechanical damage and be readily visible for inspection. The manufacturer's identification shall be retained in each section.

4-10 Testing.

4-10.1 Piping, tubing and hoses, and hose assemblies shall be leak tested after assembly to prove them free from leaks at a pressure equal to at least the normal service pressure of that portion of the system.

4-10.2 Pressure relief valves shall be tested at least every five years.

4-11 Installation of Emergency Shutdown Equipment.

4-11.1 Manually operated container valves shall be provided for each container.

4-11.2 The fill line on a storage container shall be equipped with a back-flow check valve to prevent discharge of natural gas from the container in case of line, hose, or fittings rupture.

4-11.3 A manually operated shutoff valve shall be installed in a manifold as close to a container or group of containers as practical. This valve shall be downstream of the back-flow check valve referred to in 4-11.2.

4-11.4 Where excess-flow check valves are used, the closing flow shall be less than the flow rating of the piping system that would result from a pipeline rupture between the excess-flow valve and the equipment downstream of the excess-flow check valve.

4-11.5 Gas piping from an outdoor compressor or storage system into a building shall be provided with shutoff valves located outside the building.

4-11.6 An emergency manual shutdown device shall be provided at the dispensing area and also at a location remote from the dispensing area. This device, when activated, shall shut off the power supply and gas supply to the compressor and the dispenser.

4-11.6.1 Emergency shutdown devices shall be distinctly marked for easy recognition with a permanently affixed legible sign.

4-11.7 Breakaway protection shall be provided in a manner such that, in the event of a pullaway, natural gas will cease to flow at any separation.

4-11.8 A breakaway device shall be installed at every dispensing point. Such a device shall be arranged to separate by a force not greater than 44 lb (20 kg) when applied in any horizontal direction.

4-11.9 Control circuits shall be arranged such that when an emergency shutdown device is activated or electric power is cut off, systems that shut down shall remain down until manually activated or reset after a safe situation is restored.

4-11.10 Each line between a gas storage facility and a dispenser at a fast-fill station shall have a valve that will close when:

(a) The power supply to the dispenser is cut off, or

(b) Any emergency shutdown device at the refueling station is activated.

4-11.11 A fast closing, "quarter turn" manual shutoff valve shall be provided at a fast fill station upstream of the breakaway device referred to in 4-11.8, where it is readily accessible to a person dispensing natural gas unless:

(a) The self-closing valve referred to in 4-11.10 is located immediately upstream of the dispenser, or

(b) The dispenser is equipped with a self-closing valve that closes each time the control arm is turned to the "OFF" position or an emergency device is activated.

4-11.12 A self-closing valve shall be provided on the inlet of the compressor that will shut off the gas supply to the compressor when:

(a) An emergency shutdown device is activated;

(b) A power failure occurs; or

(c) The power to the compressor is switched off.

4-12* Installation of Electrical Equipment. Electrical equipment shall be installed in accordance with NFPA 70, *National Electrical Code,®* for Class I, Group D, Division 1 or 2 locations in accordance with Table 4-12.

Exception: Electrical equipment on internal combustion engines installed in accordance with NFPA 37, Standard for the Installation and Use of Stationary Combustion Engines and Gas Turbines.

Table 4-12 Electrical Installations

Location	Division	Extent of Classified Area*
Containers (other than mounted fuel supply containers)	2	Within 10 ft of container
Area containing compression and ancillary equipment		
Outdoors	2	Up to 15 ft from equipment
Indoors	2	Up to 15 ft from equipment
Dispensing equipment		
Outdoors**	1	Inside dispenser enclosure
Outdoors**	2	From 0 to 20 ft from the dispenser
Indoors	1	Inside the dispenser enclosure
Indoors	2	Entire room, with adequate ventilation (See 4-4.3)

*The classified area shall not extend beyond an unpierced wall, roof, or vaportight partition.

**Refer to Figure A-4-12 for an illustration of classified areas in and around dispensers.

NOTE: The electrical classification under Table 4-12 may be permitted to be reduced, or hazardous areas limited or eliminated, by adequate positive pressure ventilation from a source of clean air or inert gas in conjunction with effective safeguards against ventilator failure by purging methods recognized in NFPA 496, *Standard for Purged and Pressurized Enclosures for Electrical Equipment.* Such changes should be subject to approval by the authority having jurisdiction.

4-13 Stray or Impressed Currents and Bonding.

4-13.1 When stray or impressed currents are used or may be present on dispensing systems (such as cathodic protection), protective measures to prevent ignition shall be taken in accordance with API RP 2003, *Protection Against Ignitions Arising Out of Static, Lightning, and Stray Currents.*

4-13.2 Static protection is not required when CNG is loaded or unloaded by conductive or nonconductive hose, flexible metallic tubing, or pipe connections where both halves of the metallic couplings are in contact.

4-14 Operation.

4-14.1 A cylinder shall not be charged in excess of the design pressure at normal temperature for that cylinder. DOT and TC cylinders shall be charged in accordance with DOT and TC regulations.

DOT and TC cylinders shall not be subjected to pressure in excess of 125 percent of the marked service pressure even if on cooling it settles to the marked service pressure. Pressure vessels shall be charged in accordance with the requirements of ASME Code, Section VIII, Division 1.

4-14.1.1 A fuel supply container shall not have a settled pressure above the service pressure stamped on the container and displayed on a label near the filling connection, corrected for the ambient temperature at time of filling.

4-14.2 CNG dispensing systems shall be equipped to automatically stop fuel flow when a fuel supply container reaches the temperature-corrected fill pressure. (*See 4-6.3.*)

4-14.3 The transfer of CNG into a fuel supply container shall be performed in accordance with instructions posted at the dispensing station.

4-14.4 When CNG is being transferred to or from a motor vehicle, the engine shall be stopped.

4-14.5 During the transfer of CNG to or from cargo vehicles, the hand or emergency brake of the vehicle shall be set and chock blocks used to prevent rolling of the vehicle.

4-14.6 Transfer systems shall be capable of depressurizing to facilitate disconnection. Bleed connections shall lead to a safe point of discharge.

4-14.7 CNG shall not be used to operate any device or equipment that has not been designed or properly modified for CNG service.

4-14.8 Sources of ignition shall not be permitted within 10 ft (3 m) of any filling connection during a transfer operation. (*See 4-4.3.*)

4-14.9 Warning signs with the words "STOP MOTOR," "NO SMOKING," "FLAMMABLE GAS" shall be posted at dispensing station and compressor areas. The location of signs shall be determined by local conditions, but the lettering shall be large enough to be visible and legible from each point of transfer.

4-15 Fire Protection. A portable fire extinguisher having a rating of not less than 20-B:C shall be provided at the dispensing area.

4-16 Maintenance.

4-16.1 Containers and their appurtenances, piping systems, compression equipment, controls, and devices shall be maintained in proper operating condition.

4-16.2 After the original installation, vehicle fueling hoses shall be examined visually at such intervals as are necessary to assure that they are safe for use. Hose shall be tested for leaks at least annually, and any unsafe leakage shall be reason for rejection.

4-16.3 While in transit, fueling hose and flexible metal hose on a cargo vehicle to be used in a transfer operation, including their connections, shall be depressurized and protected from wear and injury.

4-16.4 Pressure relief valves shall be maintained in proper operating condition.

4-16.4.1 As a precaution to keep pressure relief devices in reliable operating condition, care shall be taken in the handling or storing of compressed natural gas containers to avoid damage. Care shall also be exercised to avoid plugging by paint or other dirt accumulation of pressure relief device channels or other parts that could interfere with the functioning of the device. Only qualified personnel shall be allowed to service pressure relief devices. Only assemblies or original manufacturer's parts shall be used in the repair of pressure relief devices unless the interchange of parts has been proved by suitable tests.

4-17 Vehicle Fueling Appliances in Commercial Applications.

4-17.1 Vehicle fueling appliances (VFAs) shall not exceed a gas flow of 10 scfm. VFAs shall be listed.

4-17.2 The installation of VFAs shall be exempt from the requirements of Sections 4-2, 4-3, 4-4, 4-6, and 4-8 through 4-16. The VFA shall be exempt from Sections 2-5 through 2-10.

4-17.3 A VFA installed with storage containers shall comply with the provisions of Chapters 2 and 4.

4-17.4 The installation of VFAs shall comply with the requirements of Chapter 5, other than those for gas flow.

4-17.5 Where more than one VFA are located in a common area, spacing between the VFAs shall not be less than 3 ft (1 m) unless permitted in the installation instructions.

4-17.6 Unless specifically permitted in the installation instructions, multiple VFAs shall not be manifolded together on the discharge side.

4-17.7 VFAs shall not be installed within 10 ft (3 m) of any storage.

Exception: Storage in the vehicle fuel supply container.

Chapter 5 Residential Fueling Facility

5-1 Scope.

5-1.1 A residential fueling facility (RFF) is an assembly used for the compression and delivery of natural gas into vehicles with its associated equipment and piping. The capacity of an RFF shall not exceed 5 SCFM of natural gas. Storage of CNG, except in the vehicle fuel supply container, is prohibited.

5-1.2 This chapter applies to the design, construction, installation, and operation of an RFF as defined in 5-1.1.

5-1.3 The provisions of this chapter shall apply to all residential refueling installations except where prohibited by local laws.

5-2 System Component Qualifications.

5-2.1 System components not part of a listed fueling appliance shall comply with the appropriate provisions in Chapter 2.

5-2.2* Fueling appliances shall be listed.

5-2.3 VFAs shall be exempt from the requirements for Sections 4-2, 4-3, 4-4, 4-6, 4-8 through 4-16, and 2-5 through 2-9.

5-3 General.

5-3.1 All equipment related to RFF installation shall be protected to minimize the possibilities of physical damage and vandalism. This requirement may be met by enclosing the compressor package in an enclosure, similar to that of a central air conditioner.

5-3.2 All equipment related to RFF installation shall be designed for the pressure, temperature, and service expected.

5-3.3 Vehicles shall be considered as unclassified electrically with respect to Article 500 of NFPA 70, *National Electrical Code.*

Exception: Vehicles containing fuel-fired equipment, e.g., recreational vehicles, shall be considered a source of ignition unless this equipment is shut off completely before entering an area in which ignition sources are prohibited.

5-3.4 Natural gas shall not be vented to the atmosphere under normal operation.

Exception: Leakage of 1.0 standard cu in. of gas shall be permitted to be released to the atmosphere per filling during disconnection of the fueling hose.

5-3.5 Unless specifically permitted in the installation instructions of a listed VFA, multiple VFAs shall not be manifolded together on the discharge side.

5-3.6 Where more than one VFA are installed in a common area, spacing between the VFAs shall not be less than 3 ft (1 m) unless the installation instructions of a listed VFA permit spacing less than 3 ft (1 m).

5-4 Installation.

5-4.1 General.

5-4.1.1 Approval of residential refueling installations shall be obtained from the authority having jurisdiction and the natural gas distribution company.

5-4.1.2 The primary concern for the location of the refueling system shall be based solely upon its safety, whether it be indoors or outdoors. CNG compression and dispensing shall be located and conducted outdoors wherever practicable. However, where not practicable, e.g., where inclement weather is common, compression and dispensing can be located indoors.

5-4.1.3 All RFF equipment shall be installed in accordance with the equipment manufacturer's instructions.

5-4.1.4 The RFF shall have a nameplate marked with minimum and maximum gas inlet pressure and flow rate, gas outlet maximum pressure, and electrical requirements.

5-4.2 Indoor Installations.

5-4.2.1 Where it is necessary to install the compression equipment and refueling connection indoors, the compression unit shall be mounted to or otherwise located adjacent to an outside wall to facilitate the rapid venting of released gases. The room or garage shall be considered for an acceptable site when the compressor enclosure is vented to the outside.

5-4.2.2 When the RFF or the vehicle being fueled is located indoors, a gas detector set to operate at one-fifth the lower limit of flammability of natural gas shall be installed in the room. The detector shall be located within 6 in. (150 mm) of the ceiling or highest point in the room. The detector shall stop the compressor and operate an audible or visual alarm.

5-4.3 Outdoor Installations. The RFF shall be installed on a firm, noncombustible support to prevent undue stress on piping and conduit.

5-5 Installation of Pressure Relief Valves. Pressure relief valves shall have pressure relief device vents or vent lines to convey escaping gas to outdoors and then upwards to a safe area so as not to impinge on buildings, other equipment, or areas that could be occupied by the public, e.g., sidewalks.

5-6 Installation of Pressure Gauges. For measurement and test purposes, pressure gauges may be installed but are not required.

5-7 Pressure Regulation. An RFF shall be equipped to automatically stop fuel flow when container(s) reach temperature corrected fill pressure.

5-8 Piping and Hose.

5-8.1 All piping and hose from the outlet of the compressor shall be supplied as part of the RFF.

5-8.2 All gas piping to the RFF shall be installed in accordance with NFPA 54, *National Fuel Gas Code.*

5-8.3 The use of hose in an installation is restricted to:

(a) A fueling hose that shall be limited to a maximum length of 25 ft (7.6 m) and shall be supported above the floor/ground level or otherwise protected from mechanical damage from abrasion and being driven over.

(b) A maximum of 3 ft (1 m) in length when used to prevent abrasion damage, resulting from vibration on the inlet and/or outlet.

5-8.4 Transfer systems shall be capable of depressurizing to facilitate disconnection. Bleed connections shall lead to a safe point of discharge.

5-9 Testing. All piping and tubing shall be tested after assembly to prove free from leaks at a pressure equal to the maximum service pressure of that portion of the system.

5-10 Installation of Emergency Shutdown Equipment.

5-10.1 An RFF shall be equipped with emergency manual shutdown of the gas supply and electric power. The emergency electrical switch shall be at least 5 ft (1.5 m) from the RFF and in view of the RFF.

5-10.2 Break-away protection shall be provided in a manner such that, in the event of a pull-away, natural gas will cease to flow.

5-10.2.1 A breakaway device shall be installed at every dispensing point. Such a device shall be arranged to separate by a force not greater than 44 lb (20 kg) when applied in any horizontal direction.

5-11 Operation.

5-11.1 An RFF shall be operated in accordance with the manufacturer's instructions.

5-11.2 A fuel supply container shall not be charged in excess of its maximum allowable service pressure at normal temperature. DOT and TC containers shall be charged in accordance with DOT and TC regulations.

5-11.3 When CNG is being transferred to a motor vehicle, the engine shall be stopped.

5-12 Maintenance and Inspection.

5-12.1 All RFF equipment shall be inspected and maintained in accordance with the manufacturer's instructions.

5-12.2 After installation, all hoses shall be examined visually as part of this inspection. Hoses that are kinked or worn shall be replaced.

5-12.3 All safety relief valves shall be maintained in proper operating condition, in accordance with manufacturer's/supplier's recommendation.

Chapter 6 Referenced Publications

6-1 The following documents or portions thereof are referenced within this standard and shall be considered part of the requirements of this document. The edition indicated for each reference is the current edition as of the date of the NFPA issuance of this document.

6-1.1 NFPA Publications. National Fire Protection Association, 1 Batterymarch Park, P.O. Box 9101, Quincy, MA 02269-9101.

NFPA 37, *Standard for the Installation and Use of Stationary Combustion Engines and Gas Turbines*, 1990 edition

NFPA 54, *National Fuel Gas Code*, 1992 edition

NFPA 70, *National Electrical Code*, 1993 edition

NFPA 220, *Standard on Types of Building Construction*, 1992 edition

NFPA 259, *Standard Test Method for Potential Heat of Building Materials*, 1987 edition

NFPA 496, *Standard for Purged and Pressurized Enclosures for Electrical Equipment*, 1989 edition.

6-1.2 Other Publications.

6-1.2.1 ASME Publications. American Society of Mechanical Engineers, 345 East 47th St., New York, NY 10017.

ANSI/ASME B31.3 (1980), *American National Standard Code for Chemical Plant and Petroleum Refinery Piping*

Boiler and Pressure Vessel Code (1986).

6-1.2.2 ASTM Publications. American Society for Testing and Materials, 1916 Race St., Philadelphia, PA 19103.

ASTM A-47-1984, *Specification for Malleable Iron Castings*

ASTM A-395-1986, *Specification for Ferritic Ductile Iron Pressure-Retaining Castings for Use at Elevated Temperatures*

ASTM A-536-1984, *Specification for Ductile Iron Castings*

ASTM E-136-1982, *Standard Method of Test for Behavior of Materials in a Vertical Tube Furnace at 750°C*

ASTM 380, *Standard for Metric Practice.*

6-1.2.3 CGA Publication. Compressed Gas Association, Inc., 1235 Jefferson Davis Highway, Arlington, VA 22202.

CGA S-1.1, *Cylinders for Compressed Gases* (1979).

6-1.2.4 U.S. DOT and TC container data is available from the U.S. Department of Transportation, 400 7th St., SW, Washington, DC 20590 and the Canadian Transport Commission, Transport Canada Building, Place de Ville, Ottawa, Ontario, K1A ON5.

6-1.2.5 API Publication. American Petroleum Institute, 2101 L St., NW, Washington, DC 20037.

API RP 2003, *Protection Against Ignitions Arising Out of Static, Lightning and Stray Currents*, Fourth Edition, 1982.

6-1.2.6 AGA Publications. American Gas Association, 1515 Wilson Blvd., Arlington, VA 22209.

ANSI/AGA NGV1, 1994, *Standard for Compressed Natural Gas Vehicle (NGV) Fueling Connection Devices*

ANSI/AGA NGV2, 1992, *Basic Requirements for Compressed Natural Gas Vehicle (NGV) Fuel Containers*

6-1.2.7 CSA Publication. Canadian Standards Association, 55 Scarsdale Rd., Don Mills, Ontario, Canada M3B 2R3.

CSA B51-1991, *Boiler, Pressure Vessel and Pressure Piping Code.*

Appendix A Explanatory Material

This Appendix is not a part of the requirements of this NFPA document, but is included for information purposes only.

A-1-1 Properties of CNG. Natural gas is a flammable gas. It is colorless, tasteless, and nontoxic. It is a light gas, weighing about two-thirds as much as air. As used in the systems covered by this standard, it tends to rise and diffuses rapidly in air when it escapes from the system.

Natural gas burns in air with a luminous flame. At atmospheric pressure, the ignition temperature of natural gas-air mixtures has been reported to be as low as 900°F (482°C). The flammable limits of natural gas-air mixtures at atmospheric pressure are about 5 percent to 15 percent by volume natural gas.

Natural gas is nontoxic but can cause anoxia (asphyxiation) when it displaces the normal 21 percent oxygen in air in a confined area without adequate ventilation.

A-2-1 Vehicle Fuel Systems. A typical vehicle fuel system consists of one or more (if more than one, the containers are manifolded together) fuel supply containers holding CNG at high pressure and fitted with pressure relief devices and manual shutoff valves, a filling connection with a check valve to prevent flow back out of the connection, a manual valve downstream from the container valve or valves, a valve that will automatically close if the engine stops for any reason, a pressure regulator to reduce fuel supply container pressure to a low engine service pressure, a gas-air mixer to produce a flammable mixture, and a pressure gauge to show fuel supply container pressure.

Systems are designed to operate at fuel supply container pressures of 2400, 3000, or 3600 psi (16.5, 20.6, or 25 MPa). Fueling connections are designed to accommodate compatible filling nozzles suitable only for the proper pressure.

Fuel supply containers are installed on either the outside of the vehicle or inside the vehicle. If inside, all connections to the containers are either external to a driver or passenger compartment or inside a compartment that is gastight with respect to a driver or passenger compartment. The compartment is vented to outside the vehicle.

See Figure A-2-1.

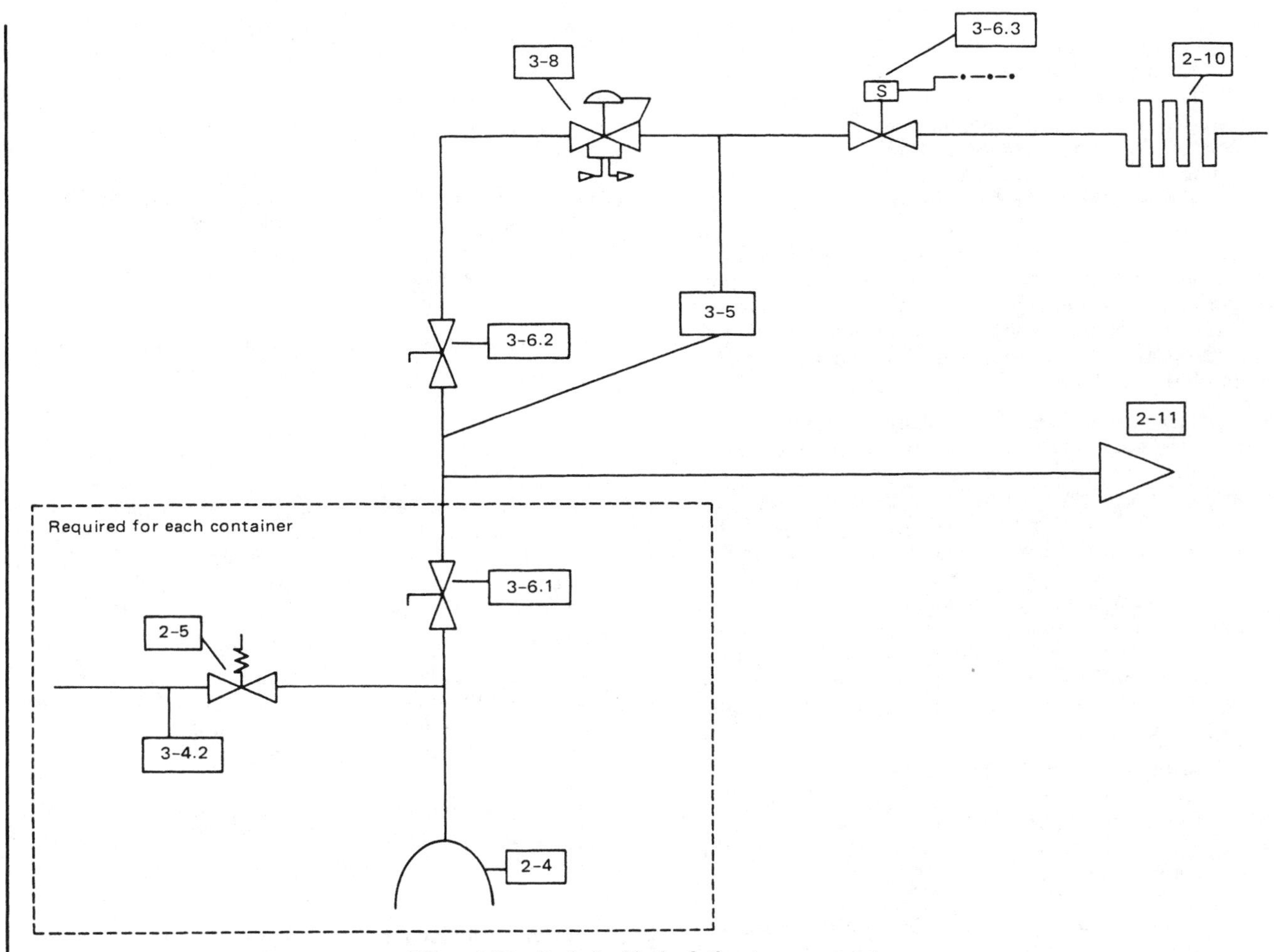

Figure A-2-1 Typical vehicular fuel system components.

A-2-2 Natural gas is not a unique, specific substance with a common composition at all times and in all places. While, as noted in the definition of Compressed Natural Gas in Section 1-5, natural gas consists principally of methane, it also contains ethane, small amounts of propane, butane, and higher hydrocarbons and may contain small amounts of nitrogen, carbon dioxide, hydrogen sulfide, and helium. The quantity of nitrogen, carbon dioxide, hydrogen sulfide, and helium will vary from zero to a few percent depending upon the source, seasonal effects, etc.

As distributed in the extensive gas transmission and distribution piping network in the United States and Canada, natural gas also contains water vapor. This "pipeline quality" gas can contain up to 7 lb or more of water per million cu ft of gas.

Some constituents of natural gas, especially carbon dioxide and hydrogen sulfide in the presence of liquid water, can be corrosive to carbon steel, and the corrosive effect is increased by pressure. The pressures used in CNG systems covered by NFPA 52 are substantial and well above those used in transmission and distribution piping and in other natural gas consuming equipment. As excessive corrosion can lead to sudden explosive rupture of a container, this hazard must be controlled.

As a result of such a failure in a cylinder comprising one of several such in a tube trailer in 1978, the U.S. Department of Transportation has specified CNG composition for CNG being transported in interstate commerce. The limits for carbon dioxide, hydrogen sulfide, and water are very low, e.g., the limit for water is 0.5 lb per million cu ft.

There is a substantial body of opinion on the Committee that the DOT-stipulated composition is intentionally conservative and would require expensive, sophisticated gas conditioning equipment to be used. This view is supported by experience of up to 15 years' duration with no failure of either storage or fuel supply containers in CNG vehicle applications. This experience has largely been with carbon steel cylinders fabricated to DOT 3A or 3AA specification and, therefore, relatively subject to internal corrosion if the conditions are present.

Corrosion protection can also be addressed by the use of materials that are corrosion resistant. A number of exemptions and special permits have been issued by DOT and TC for cylinders made of materials other than carbon steel. However, the impetus for these materials has come from other considerations, principally lighter weight.

The Committee encouraged the conducting of a research program to explore this gas quality/material matter and the research work was performed by Southwest Research Institute in San Antonio, Texas. Funding was provided by the New York State Energy Research and Development Authority (NYSERDA), the New York Gas Group (NYGAS), and the U.S. Department of Energy (DOE). The Committee gratefully acknowledges both the financial support of NYSERDA, NYGAS, and DOE and the cooperation and contributions of management, engineering, and operating personnel of the gas transmission companies, gas distribution companies, and CNG container manufacturers who supplied technical data, used gas cylinders, test materials, and test gases for this research program.

The principal objective of the research program was to define natural gas contaminant concentration limits necessary to insure that internal corrosion of CNG containers does not constitute a hazard over the lifetimes of the containers. A secondary objective included definition of the effects of materials variables, container fabrication procedures, and other CNG system parameters on internal corrosion of CNG containers and container materials. Accomplishment of the research program objectives permitted the Committee to define the limiting concentrations of corrosive contaminants in CNG necessary to prevent corrosion or corrosion-related damage to vehicle fuel and storage containers.

As a control of the amount of hydrogen sulfide and sulfides, water, carbon dioxide, and oxygen, Section 2-2 reflects a Committee consensus that if the water content is limited the other potentially corrosive constituents should not be a major concern.

A-2-4 Container Capacity. Containers are described by their liquid capacity and the design and allowable service pressures. The liquid capacity (cu ft of water) is the volume of liquid that would be required to fill the container. The allowable service pressure is the maximum pressure at which the container should be operating. From the liquid capacity and allowable service pressure, the gas storage capacity can be calculated.

The amount of gas being stored in a cylinder can be calculated by applying the "ideal gas law" taking account of the "compressibility factor" (or "supercompressibility") of the specific gas being stored.

The ideal gas law states that, if the absolute pressure of a certain volume of gas is doubled, the volume will decrease to half (at a constant temperature). However, natural gas does not follow the ideal gas law exactly. The term "supercompressibility," as it relates to natural gas, simply indicates that more natural gas can be stored in a given volume [below about 5,000 psig (35 MPa)] than would be indicated by the ideal gas law.

A-3-1 Fueling Systems. A typical fueling system consists of one or more compressors taking suction from a natural gas transmission or distribution pipeline or a building piping system connected to a transmission or distribution pipeline with the compressor discharging into either one or more storage containers or to a dispensing system, and a dispensing system consisting of a hose and nozzle and sometimes a meter. Where a storage container is present, it discharges to a dispensing system.

Where storage containers are used, the system is known as a "fast-fill" system with a vehicle filling time of about 3-5 minutes. Where storage containers are not used, the system is known as a "slow-fill" system, and filling times can be several hours.

The suction pressure for compressors ranges from about 2-500 psig (13.7 kPa-3.4 MPa) with most being under 60 psig (40 kPa). The delivery pressure is more than the vehicle system pressure but less than 5000 psi (35 MPa), with most around 3600 psi (25 MPa).

CNG is stored in two types of storage systems — bulk storage and cascade storage. They differ in the manner in which the CNG is withdrawn from them.

A-3-12.4

1. Before a CNG vehicle is returned into service following an accident that caused damage or dislocation to the CNG fuel system, or following the repair or replacement of any part of a CNG fuel system that is subject to container pressure, the system should be tested in compliance with Section 3-12.

2. Prior to maintenance or repair of a CNG fuel system:

(a) The supply of CNG should be shut off before commencing the work by closing the shutoff valves and operating the engine until the engine stops running and ensure that the valves remain shut off throughout the entire inoperative period.

(b) CNG should not be vented indoors.

(c) Upon completion of the work, leak test the CNG fuel system in accordance with the requirements of Section 3-12.

3. Prior to making repairs to gasoline related equipment on a CNG vehicle, to other than the CNG fuel system, the following should be done:

(a) Prior to removal of the natural gas mixer, shut off the supply of CNG by closing the shut off valves and operating the engine until the engine stops running and ensure that the valves remain off throughout the entire inoperative period; and

(b) Upon completion of the work, replace the natural gas mixer in its original location without any change or adjustment before the CNG shutoff valves are reopened.

4. Prior to making collision repairs on a CNG vehicle to other than the CNG fuel system shall the following should be done:

(a) Close the shutoff valve at the outlet of the CNG container before commencing the work and ensure that the valve remains off throughout the entire inoperative period; and

(b) The CNG vehicle owner or operator should be instructed to take the vehicle to a vehicle conversion center for inspection of the CNG fuel system before the shut off valve referenced in (a) above is reopened.

A-4-1 Bulk storage of CNG can be accomplished with one large container or a number of smaller containers manifolded together. As vehicles draw CNG from bulk storage, all containers draw down (reduce in pressure) at the same rate.

Bulk storage provides less "available" CNG storage than the cascade system.

Storage containers arranged in a cascade can provide more "available" CNG storage than a bulk system for the same size containers. A brief description of the operation of a typical cascade system is as follows:

A cascade is usually arranged in at least three banks of containers with the containers in any one bank manifolded together so that each bank acts as one large container. The banks are separated by automatic switching valves. The valve sequencing is controlled automatically by a sequencing control panel.

The cascade banks are initially filled with CNG in sequence by the compressor to the normal service pressure of the system. The highest pressure bank is refilled first ("Bank 1"), followed by successively lower pressure banks ("Bank 2," "Bank 3," etc.). This sequence is called "priority fill."

Vehicles can then be fueled from the cascade, beginning with Bank 3 (for a three-bank cascade).

If there is insufficient CNG in Bank 3 to pressurize the vehicle fuel supply container(s), Bank 3 will be valved off and Bank 2 will "top up" the vehicle container(s). Successive vehicles will draw from Banks 3 and 2 as above, until Bank 1 is required to "top up" the vehicle container(s). When Bank 1 pressure is reduced to a preset value, the compressor will bypass the cascade and fill the vehicle directly. At the completion of the last vehicle fill, the compressor will continue running, and refill the cascade by priority fill.

Cascade valving can be arranged to provide more available storage than the system described.

A-4-5.1 Where space is at a premium or not available, consideration should be given to installation of storage containers on a roof made of noncombustible material at fueling stations.

A-4-12 See Figure A-4-12.

A-5-2.2 For information on standards for listing fueling appliances see AGA *Requirements for Natural Gas Vehicle (NGV) Fueling Appliances*, No. 2-90 (November 1, 1990).

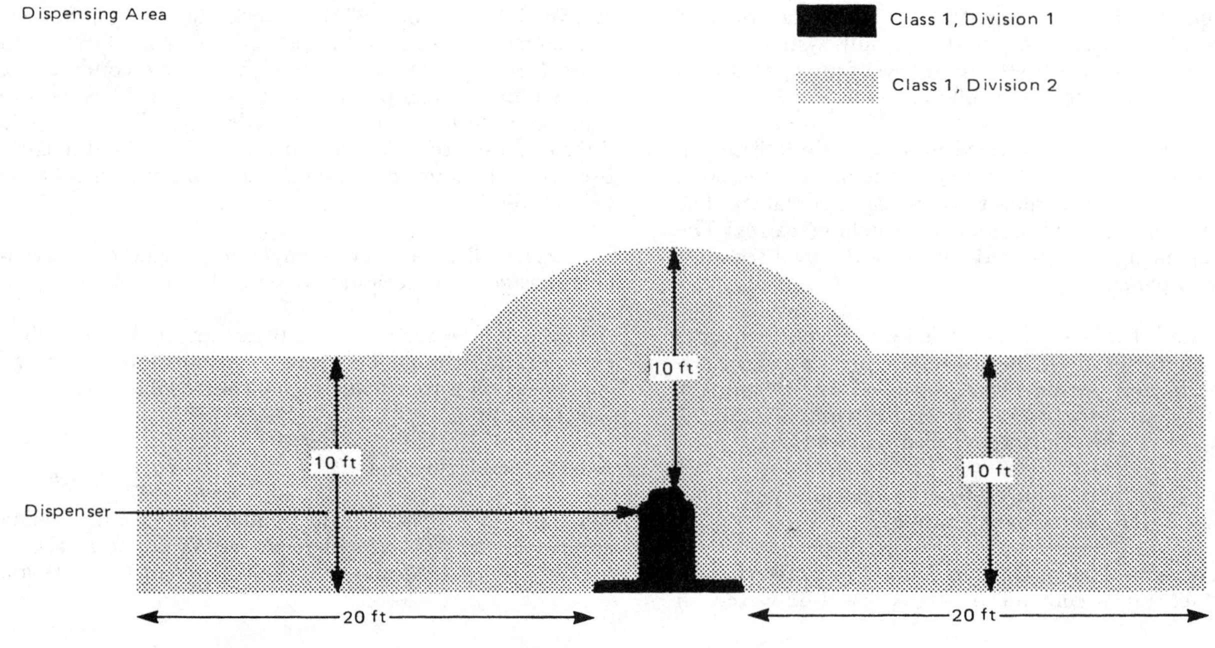

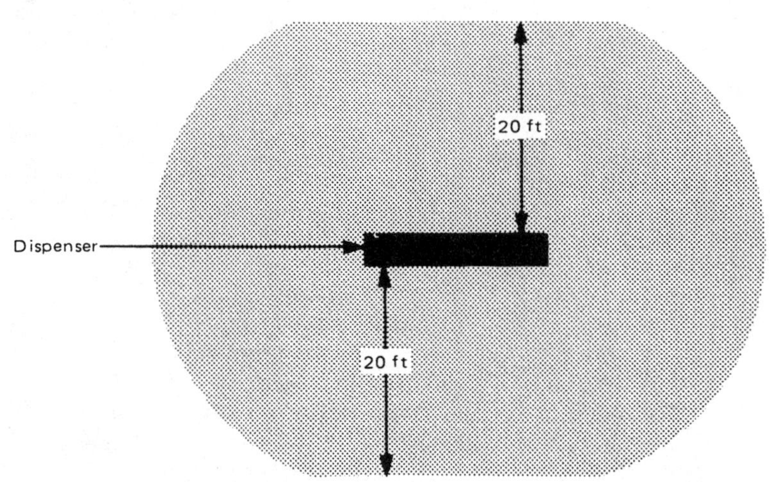

Figure A-4-12 Classified areas in and around dispensers as detailed in Table 4-12.

Appendix B Referenced Publications

B-1 The following documents or portions thereof are referenced within this standard for informational purposes only and thus are not considered part of the requirements of this document. The edition indicated for each reference is the current edition as of the date of the NFPA issuance of this document.

B-1.1 CGA Publications. Compressed Gas Association, 1235 Jefferson Davis Highway, Arlington, VA 22202.

C-6 *Standards for Visual Inspection of Compressed Gas Cylinders* (1984)

C-6.1 *Standards for Visual Inspection of High Pressure Aluminum Compressed Gas Cylinders* (1984)

C-6.2 *Guidelines for Visual Inspection and Requalification of Fiber Reinforced High Pressure Cylinders* (1982)

C-10 *Recommendations for Changes of Service for Compressed Gas Cylinders Including Procedures for Inspection and Contaminant Removal* (1985).

B-1.2 SAE Publication. Society of Automotive Engineers, 400 Commonwealth Drive, Warrendale, PA 15096.

SAE J1616, *Surface Vehicle Recommended Practice for Natural Gas Vehicle Fuel Composition.*

Index

UNIFORM FIRE CODE STANDARD 62-1
OVENS AND FURNACES
See Sections 6201 and 6205.1, *Uniform Fire Code*

The National Fire Protection Association Standard for Ovens and Furnaces, NFPA 86—1990, is hereby adopted by reference as UFC Standard 62-1.

The provisions of this standard shall apply to Classes A and B ovens except when a provision of *Uniform Fire Code,* Volume 1 or an amendment specified in Section 62.101 is applicable, in which case *Uniform Fire Code,* Volume 1 provisions or the amendment shall take precedence.

Supplemental standards referenced by NFPA 86—1990 shall only be considered as guidelines subject to approval by the chief.

NFPA 86—1990 is available from the National Fire Protection Association, 1 Batterymarch Park, Box 9101, Quincy, Massachusetts 02269-9101.

SECTION 62.101 — AMENDMENTS

The Standard for Ovens and Furnaces, NFPA 86—1990 applies to ovens and furnaces operating at approximately atmospheric pressures and vacuum furnaces operating at below atmospheric pressures for the processing of materials and also to bakery ovens, except where the provisions of *Uniform Fire Code,* Volume 1 and the Mechanical Code apply, and except as follows:

1. Sec. 1-1 is revised by amending the fourth subparagraph as follows:

This standard also applies to listed bakery ovens and hereby requires all bakery ovens to be listed.

2. Sec. 1-4 is revised by changing definitions as follows:

AUTHORITY HAVING JURISDICTION is the official responsible for the administration and enforcement of this standard.

FUEL OIL is an approved liquid hydrocarbon fuel for an oven or a furnace.

HEATER, INDUCTION, is a heating system by means of which a current-carrying conductor induces the transfer of electrical energy to the work by eddy currents.

The definitions of "approved," "Electrical Code," "hazardous material," "labeled" and "listed" shall be as set forth in *Uniform Fire Code,* Volume 1.

The definition of "should" is deleted.

3. Sec. 1-5.3 is revised as follows:

1-5.3 Wiring shall be in accordance with the Electrical Code.

4. Sec. 2-1.4.5 is revised by deleting the note.

5. Sec. 2-1.5.3, Item (d), is revised by substituting the phrase "Electrical Code" for the phrase "Article 356 . . . of NFPA 70, *National Electrical Code.*"

6. Sec. 2-2.3.3.1, Note 4, is revised as follows:

4. Explosion control shall be in accordance with the Building Code.

7. Sec. 2-2.4.13 is revised by changing the note as follows:

NOTE: For additional information, see the Uniform Building and Uniform Mechanical codes.

8. Sec. 3-2 is revised by substituting the phrase "Electrical Code" for the phrase "NFPA 70, *National Electrical Code.*"

9. Sec. 3-3.3.1 is revised by changing Notes 1 and 2 as follows:

1. Installation of LPG storage and handling systems shall comply with UFC Standard 82-1.

2. Piping from the point of delivery to the equipment isolation valve shall comply with the Plumbing Code and the Mechanical Code as appropriate.

10. Sec. 3-3.4.2.1 is revised as follows:

3-3.4.2.1 Material for piping and fittings shall comply with the Plumbing and Mechanical codes as appropriate.

11. Sec. 3-3.9.2, subparagraphs (c) and (d), is revised by substituting the phrase "Electrical Code" for the phrase "NFPA 70, *National Electrical Code.*"

12. Sec. 3-4.4.1 is revised by adding the phrase "as referenced in the Mechanical Code" at the end of the sentence.

13. Sec. 3-5.3.1 is revised as follows:

3-5.3.1 Design, materials of construction, installation and tests of piping shall comply with the applicable sections of nationally recognized standards. See *Uniform Fire Code* Article 90.

14. Sec. 3-5.3.2 is revised as follows:

3-5.3.2 Oxygen piping and controls shall be in accordance with nationally recognized standards.

15. Sec. 3-5.3.8 is revised as follows:

3-5.3.8 Oxygen piping and controls shall be inspected and maintained in accordance with nationally recognized standards.

16. Sec. 3-6.1.3 is revised by substituting the phrase "Electrical Code" for the phrase "NFPA 70, *National Electrical Code.*"

17. Sec. 3-6.2.3.2 is revised by substituting the phrase "Electrical Code" for the phrase "in Article 725 of NFPA 70, *National Electrical Code.*"

18. Sec. 3-6.3.1 is revised by substituting the phrase "Electrical Code" for the phrase "NFPA 70, *National Electrical Code* with special reference to Article 665, entitled *Induction and Dielectric Heating Equipment.*"

19. Sec. 3-6.3.3.2 is revised by amending the second sentence of the note as follows:

Dry transformers shall have 150°C rise insulation.

20. Sec. 3-6.3.3.3 is revised by substituting the phrase "Electrical Code" for the phrase "NFPA 70, *National Electrical Code.*"

21. Sec. 3-7.1 is revised by changing the note as follows:

NOTE: The construction and controls for steam boilers shall be in accordance with the Mechanical Code.

22. Sec. 3-7.2.1 is revised by adding the following after the first sentence:

Piping and fittings associated with steam heat exchangers shall be in accordance with nationally recognized standards. See *Uniform Fire Code* Article 90.

23. Sec. 4-8 is revised by substituting the phrase "the Plumbing Code or Mechanical Code, as appropriate" for the phrase "NFPA 54, *National Fuel Gas Code.*"

24. Sec. 4-12.2.1 is revised by substituting the phrase "See the Electrical Code" for the phrase "See NFPA 70, *National Electrical Code.*"

25. Sec. 4-16 is revised by substituting the phrase "Electrical Code" for the phrase "NFPA 70, *National Electrical Code.*"

26. Sec. 6-5.1.1 is revised by deleting the last sentence and substituting "Approved standards shall be followed."

27. Sec. 6-5.1.3 is revised as follows:

6-5.1.3 ASME tank-relief devices shall be provided, sized, constructed and tested in accordance with nationally recognized standards. See *Uniform Fire Code* Article 90.

28. Sec. 6-5.1.4 is revised by deleting the last sentence and substituting "Approved standards shall be followed."

29. Sec. 10-1.2 is revised as follows:

10-1.2 Dip tanks and drain boards within the oven enclosure shall be protected with an automatic fire-extinguishing system in accordance with *Uniform Fire Code* Article 45.

30. Sec. 10-1.3.1 is revised as follows:

10-1.3.1 Automatic sprinkler systems shall be in accordance with the Building Code (see UBC Standard 9-1).

31. Sec. 10-1.4.1 is revised as follows:

10-1.4.1 Automatic water-spray fire-extinguishing systems shall be in accordance with UFC Standard 79-2.

32. Sec. 10-2.2.1 is revised as follows:

10-2.2.1 Carbon dioxide systems shall be in accordance with approved nationally recognized standards and shall be designed to be activated either automatically or manually.

33. Sec. 10-2.3.1 is revised as follows:

10-2.3.1 Foam automatic fire-extinguishing systems shall be designed and installed in accordance with UFC Standard 79-1.

34. Sec. 10-2.4.1 is revised as follows:

10-2.4.1 Dry chemical automatic fire-extinguishing systems shall be of an approved design. Such systems shall be designed in accordance with nationally recognized standards or shall be listed as a pre-engineered assembly.

35. Sec. 10-3.1 is revised by changing the last sentence as follows:

Such installations shall be in accordance with UFC Standard 10-1.

36. Sec. 10-3.2 is revised as follows:

10-3.2 Hose connections shall be in accordance with the Building Code.

37. Sec. 10-4.1 is revised as follows:

10-4.1 Inspection. All fire-protection equipment shall be inspected and maintained in accordance with *Uniform Fire Code* Article 10.

38. Chapter 11 is deleted.

UNIFORM FIRE CODE STANDARD 74-1
MEDICAL GAS AND VACUUM SYSTEMS

See Section 7404.2.3, *Uniform Fire Code*

This standard, with certain exceptions, is the National Fire Protection Association Standard for Health Care Facilities, NFPA 99—1993, Chapter 2, Definitions, and Chapter 4, Gas and Vacuum Systems, adopted by reference.

The National Fire Protection Association Standard for Health Care Facilities, NFPA 99—1993, Chapter 2, Definitions, and Chapter 4, Gas and Vacuum Systems, are hereby adopted by reference as UFC Standard 74-1.

The provisions of this standard shall apply to medical gas and vacuum systems except when a provision of *Uniform Fire Code,* Volume 1 or an amendment specified in Section 74.101 is applicable, in which case *Uniform Fire Code,* Volume 1 provisions or the amendment shall take precedence.

Supplemental standards referenced by NFPA 99—1993, Chapter 2 or 4, shall only be considered as guideline standards subject to approval by the chief.

NFPA 99—1993 is available from the National Fire Protection Association, 1 Batterymarch Park, Box 9101, Quincy, Massachusetts 02269-9101.

SECTION 74.101 — AMENDMENTS

The Standard for Health Care Facilities, NFPA 99—1993, Chapter 2, Definitions, and Chapter 4, Gas and Vacuum Systems, applies to medical gas and vacuum systems, except as follows:

1. Sec. 4-3.1 is revised by substituting the phrase "UFC Standard 74-1" for the phrase "NFPA 50, *Standard for Bulk Oxygen Systems on Consumer Sites.*"

2. Sec. 4-3.1.1.2 is revised by deleting the last sentence and substituting as follows:

Labels and stencils shall be lettered in accordance with nationally recognized standards.

3. Sec. 4-3.1.2.1 (d) is revised by substituting the phrase "the Electrical Code" for the phrase "NFPA 70, *National Electrical Code.*"

4. Sec. 4-3.1.2.2 (a) is revised by substituting the phrase "UFC Standard 74-1" for the phrase "NFPA 50, *Standard for Bulk Oxygen Systems at Consumer Sites.*"

5. Sec. 4-3.1.2.4 (b) is revised by substituting the phrase "the Electrical Code" for the phrase "NFPA 70, *National Electrical Code.*"

Also:

Sec. 4-3.1.2.4 (c) is revised by substituting the phrase "the Mechanical Code" for the phrase "NFPA 90A, *Standard for the Installation of Air Conditioning and Ventilating Systems.*"

Also:

Sec. 4-3.1.2.4 (f) is revised by substituting the phrase "the Electrical Code" for the phrase "NFPA 70, *National Electrical Code.*"

8. Sec. 4-3.4 is revised by changing the note to read as follows:

NOTE: Refer to *Uniform Fire Code,* Volume 1 and the Mechanical Code.

9. Sec. 4-4.2.11.1 is revised by deleting the exception.

10. Sec. 4-4.2.11.2 is revised by deleting the exception.

11. Sec. 4-4.3.5 is revised by substituting the phrase "the Mechanical Code and UFC Standard 82-1" for the phrase "NFPA 54, *National Fuel Gas Code,* and NFPA 58, *Standard for the Storage and Handling of Liquefied Petroleum Gases.*"

12. Sec. 4-4.3.6 is revised by substituting the phrase "nationally recognized standards and *Uniform Fire Code,* Volume 1" for the phrase "NFPA 50A, *Standard for Gaseous Hydrogen Systems at Consumer Sites.*"

13. Sec. 4-8.1.1 (d) is revised by substituting the phrase "the Electrical Code" for the phrase "NFPA 70, *National Electrical Code.*"

14. Sec. 4-8.1.2.1 is revised by deleting Note 1 in its entirety.

UNIFORM FIRE CODE STANDARD 79-1
FOAM FIRE-PROTECTION SYSTEMS
See Sections 7902.2.4.2 and 7902.2.8.2, *Uniform Fire Code*

The National Fire Protection Association Standard for Low-Expansion Foam and Combined Agent Systems, NFPA 11—1988, is hereby adopted by reference as UFC Standard 79-1.

The provisions of this standard shall apply to low-expansion foam and combined agent systems except when a provision of *Uniform Fire Code,* Volume 1 or an amendment specified in Section 79.101 is applicable, in which case *Uniform Fire Code,* Volume 1 provisions or the amendment shall take precedence.

Supplemental standards referenced by NFPA 11—1988 shall only be considered as guidelines subject to approval by the chief.

NFPA 11—1988 is available from the National Fire Protection Association, 1 Batterymarch Park, Box 9101, Quincy, Massachusetts 02269-9101.

SECTION 79.101 — AMENDMENTS

The Standard for Low-Expansion Foam and Combined Agent Systems, NFPA 11—1988, applies to the characteristics of foam-producing materials and the requirements for design, installation, testing, operation and maintenance of equipment and systems used for protecting stationary tanks used for the storage of Class I or II liquids aboveground and outside of buildings except as follows:

1. Secs. 1-1 and 1-2 are deleted.

2. Sec. 1-4 is revised by changing the definition of "authority having jurisdiction" as follows:

AUTHORITY HAVING JURISDICTION is the official responsible for the administration and enforcement of this standard.

The definitions of "approved," "combustible liquid," "flammable liquid," "labeled" and "listed" shall be as set forth in *Uniform Fire Code,* Volume 1.

The definition of "flammable and combustible liquids" is deleted.

3. Sec. 3-2.11.2 is revised by changing the second sentence as follows:

When a covered floating roof tank is not designed according to *Uniform Fire Code* Article 79, it shall be treated as a fixed roof tank.

4. Sec. 5-2.2 is revised as follows:

5-2.2 Pressure Tests. Piping shall be subjected to a two-hour hydrostatic pressure test at 200 psig (1379 kPa) or 50 psi (344.7 kPa) in excess of the maximum pressure anticipated, whichever is greater, in accordance with the Building Code.

EXCEPTION: Piping handling expanded foam for other than subsurface application.

Normally dry horizontal piping shall be inspected for drainage pitch.

5. Chapter 7 is deleted.

UNIFORM FIRE CODE STANDARD 79-2
FIXED WATER-SPRAY AUTOMATIC FIRE-PROTECTION SYSTEMS

See Sections 7902.1.14.4 and 7902.2.6.3.4, *Uniform Fire Code*

The National Fire Protection Association Standard for Water Spray Fixed Systems for Fire Protection, NFPA 15—1990, is hereby adopted by reference as UFC Standard 79-2.

The provisions of this standard shall apply to fixed systems except when a provision of *Uniform Fire Code,* Volume 1 or an amendment specified in Section 79.201 is applicable, in which case *Uniform Fire Code,* Volume 1 provisions or the amendment shall take precedence.

Supplemental standards referenced by NFPA 15—1990 shall only be considered as guidelines subject to approval by the chief.

NFPA 15—1990 is available from the National Fire Protection Association, 1 Batterymarch Park, Box 9101, Quincy, Massachusetts 02269-9101.

SECTION 79.201 — AMENDMENTS

The Standard for Water Spray Fixed Systems for Fire Protection, NFPA 15—1990, applies to the design, installation, maintenance and testing of automatic water-spray fixed systems where required by *Uniform Fire Code,* Volume 1 for fire-protection service, except as follows:

1. Sec. 1-3 is revised by changing definitions to read as follows:

AUTHORITY HAVING JURISDICTION is the official responsible for the administration and enforcement of this standard.

FLAMMABLE (EXPLOSIVE) LIMITS is the minimum and maximum percentages of air mixtures with vapors or gases below or above which propagation of flame will not occur when the mixture is exposed to an ignition source.

The definitions of "approved," "combustible liquid," "flammable liquid," "labeled" and "listed" shall be as set forth in *Uniform Fire Code,* Volume 1.

The definitions of "flammable and combustible liquids" and "should" are deleted.

2. Sec. 1-6 is revised by deleting the second paragraph.

3. Sec. 1-11 is revised as follows:

1-11 Certification of Water-spray Systems. The contractor shall prepare and submit plans and specifications of the system and its boundaries of protection, maintenance and instruction bulletins and certify that the work has been completed and is tested in accordance with the plans and specifications before requesting final approval of the fixed water-spray automatic fire-protection system.

4. Sec. 2-1.3 is revised by substituting the phrase "the Building Code" for the phrase "NFPA 13."

5. Sec 2-4.1 is revised as follows:

2-4.1 Pipe and tube used in water-spray systems shall be of welded or seamless ferrous piping, electric resistance-welded steel pipe or wrought steel pipe in accordance with the Building Code. Pipe and tube used in water-spray systems shall be designed to withstand a working pressure of not less than 175 psi (1206.6 kPa). Materials which are allowed are listed in Table 2-4.1.

6. Sec. 2-11.3 is revised as follows:

2-11.3 Electrical equipment for use in hazardous locations shall be in accordance with the Electrical Code.

7. Sec. 4-6.2 (d) is revised as follows:

(d) For the methods of drainage and diking, see *Uniform Fire Code* Article 79.

8. Sec. 4-7.1.1.1 (d) is revised by deleting the second sentence.

9. Sec. 4-9.2.2.9 is revised as follows:

4-9.2.2.9 The welding procedures, welders and welding machine shall be approved.

10. Sec. 5-2 is revised as follows:

5-2 Hydrostatic Pressure Tests. New system piping shall be hydrostatically tested in accordance with the Building Code.

11. Sec. 8-1 is revised by substituting the phrase "UFC Standard 10-2" for the phrase "NFPA 72E, *Standard on Automatic Fire Detectors.*"

12. Sec. 8-4.1 is revised by substituting the phrase "UFC Standard 10-2" for the phrase "NFPA 72E, *Standard on Automatic Fire Detectors.*"

13. Chapter 9 is deleted.

UNIFORM FIRE CODE STANDARD 79-3

IDENTIFICATION OF THE HEALTH, FLAMMABILITY AND REACTIVITY OF HAZARDOUS MATERIALS

See Section 209, Table 4703-A and Sections 6307.4, 6319, 7401.5.2, 7902.1.3.2, 8001.4.3.3, 8004.1.15, 8004.2.2.2 and 8004.4.3, *Uniform Fire Code*

This standard, with certain exceptions, is based on the National Fire Protection Association Standard System for the Identification of the Fire Hazards of Materials, NFPA 704—1990.[1]

Part I of this standard contains the exceptions to NFPA 704—1990.[1]

Part II of this standard contains NFPA 704—1990[1] reproduced in its entirety with the permission of the publisher.

▨▨▨ vertically in the margin of Part II indicates there is a revision to the provision within Part I.

Supplemental standards referenced by NFPA 704—1990[1] shall be considered as guidelines subject to approval by the chief.

[1]The current edition is NFPA 704—1996.

Part I

SECTION 79.301 — AMENDMENTS

The Standard System for the Identification of the Fire Hazards of Materials, NFPA 704—1990, applies to facilities for the manufacture, storage or use of hazardous materials, except as follows:

1. Sec. 1-2.1 is revised as follows:

1-2.1 Facilities for the manufacturing, storage or use of hazardous materials shall be identified by markings complying with this standard when required by *Uniform Fire Code,* Volume 1.

2. Sec. 1-5.1 is revised by deleting the last sentence in the paragraph.

3. Sec. 1-5.3 is revised as follows:

1-5.3 The hazard evaluation shall be performed by experienced, technically competent persons based on the inherent hazards of the material, including the extent of change in behavior to be anticipated under exposure to fire or to fire-control procedures. See *Uniform Fire Code* Article 47 for fumigant hazard signals.

Part II

Reproduced with permission from the Standard System for the Identification of the Fire Hazards of Materials, NFPA 704, copyright 1990, National Fire Protection Association, 1 Batterymarch Park, Box 9101, Quincy, Massachusetts 02269-9101. Persons desiring to reprint in whole or part any portion of the Standard System for the Identification of the Fire Hazards of Materials, NFPA 704—1990, must secure permission from the National Fire Protection Association. The following standard is not necessarily the latest revision used by NFPA. If the reader desires to compare with that version, the same is available from NFPA.

Contents

NFPA 704

Standard System for the

Identification of the Fire Hazards of Materials

1990 Edition

Information on referenced publications can be found in Appendix E.

Foreword

The Committee on Fire Hazards of Materials has been working on the material in this standard since early 1957. A great deal of preliminary work was developed as a manual by the Sectional Committee on Classification, Labeling and Properties of Flammable Liquids of the NFPA Committee on Flammable Liquids starting in 1952. Progress reports were given on this activity at NFPA Annual Meetings and reported in the NFPA *Quarterly* in July issues of 1954, 1956, and 1958. The material was tentatively adopted as a guide in 1960, adopted in 1961, and further amended in 1964, 1966, 1969, 1975, and 1980.

As originally conceived, the purpose of the standard is to safeguard the lives of those individuals who may be concerned with fires occurring in an industrial plant or storage location where the fire hazards of materials may not be readily apparent.

Chapter 1 General

1-1 Scope.

1-1.1 This standard shall address the health, flammability, reactivity, and related hazards that may be presented by short-term, acute exposure to a material during handling under conditions of fire, spill, or similar emergencies.

1-1.2 This standard provides a simple, readily recognized, easily understood system of markings that provides a general idea of the hazards of a material and the severity of these hazards as they relate to handling, fire prevention, exposure, and control. The objectives of the system are:

(a) to provide an appropriate signal or alert and on-the-spot information to safeguard the lives of both public and private emergency response personnel;

(b) to assist in planning for effective fire and emergency control operations, including clean-up;

(c) to assist all designated personnel, engineers, plant and safety personnel in evaluating hazards;

1-1.3 It is recognized that local conditions will have a bearing on evaluation of hazards; therefore, discussion must be kept in general terms.

1-2 Applicability.

1-2.1 This standard is applicable to industrial, commercial, and institutional facilities that manufacture, process, use, or store hazardous materials.

1-2.2 This standard is not applicable to transportation or to use by the general public.

1-2.3 This standard is not applicable to chronic exposure or to nonemergency occupational exposure.

1-3 Purpose. This system is intended to provide basic information to fire fighting, emergency, and other personnel, enabling them to more easily decide whether to evacuate the area or to commence emergency control procedures. It is also intended to provide them with information to assist in selecting fire fighting tactics and emergency procedures.

1-4 Description.

1-4.1 This system identifies the hazards of a material in terms of three principal categories: "health," "flammability," and "reactivity." It indicates the degree of severity by a numerical rating that ranges from four (4), indicating severe hazard, to zero (0), indicating no hazard.

1-4.2 The information is presented by a spatial arrangement of numerical ratings with the health rating always at the nine o'clock position; the flammability rating always at the twelve o'clock position; and the reactivity rating always at the three o'clock position. Each rating is located in a square-on-point field, each of which is assigned a color: blue for health hazard; red for flammability hazard; yellow for reactivity hazard. Alternately, the square-on-point field may be any convenient contrasting color and the numbers themselves may be colored. See pages 9-10 for examples of the spatial arrangements.

1-4.3 The fourth space, at the six o'clock position, is reserved for indicating any unusual reactivity with water. The standard symbol for indicating unusual reactivity with water is the letter "W" with a line through the center: W̶. No special color is associated with this symbol.

1-4.3.1 This space may also be used to indicate other unusual hazards, but only if not needed to indicate reactivity with water. Approved symbols will be designated in Chapter 5 of this standard.

1-5 Assignment of Ratings.

1-5.1 While the system is basically simple in application, the hazard evaluation required to determine the correct numerical ratings for a specific material shall be performed by persons who are technically competent and experienced in the interpretation of the hazard criteria set forth in this Standard. Assignment of ratings shall be based on factors that encompass a knowledge of the inherent hazards of the material, including the extent of change in behavior to be anticipated under conditions of exposure to fire or fire control procedures. (For additional information, see NFPA 49, *Hazardous Chemicals Data*, and NFPA 325M, *Fire Hazard Properties of Flammable Liquids, Gases, and Volatile Solids*.)

1-5.2 The system is based on relative rather than absolute values. Therefore, it is anticipated that conditions of storage and use may result in different ratings being assigned to the same material by different persons. Furthermore, the guidance presented in the following chapters is necessarily limited. For example, flash point is the primary criterion for assigning the flammability rating, but other criteria may be of equal importance. For example, autoignition temperature, flammability limits, and susceptibility of a container to failure due to fire exposure also must be considered. For reactivity, emphasis has been placed on the ease by which an energy-releasing reaction is triggered. For health, consideration is given not only to inherent hazard but also to protective measures that must be taken to minimize effects of short-term exposure.

1-5.3 In some situations, such as warehouses, storage rooms or buildings, laboratory facilities, etc., a variety of materials may be present in one localized area. In such cases considerable judgement may be needed to properly assign ratings to the area.

Chapter 2 Health Hazards

2-1 General.

2-1.1 This chapter shall address the capability of a material to cause personal injury due to contact with or entry into the body via inhalation, ingestion, skin contact, or eye contact. Only the hazards that arise from an inherent toxic property of the material or its products of decomposition or combustion shall be considered. Injury resulting from the heat of a fire or from the force of an explosion shall not be considered.

2-1.2 In general, the health hazard that results from a fire or other emergency condition is one of acute (single) short-term exposure to a concentration of a hazardous material. This exposure may vary from a few seconds to as long as one hour. The physical exertion demanded by fire-fighting or other emergency activity may be expected to intensify the effects of any exposure. In addition, the hazard under ambient conditions will likely be exaggerated at elevated temperatures. Health hazards that may result from chronic or repeated long-term exposure to low concentrations of a hazardous material shall not be considered.

2-1.3 The oral route of exposure, i.e. ingestion, is highly unlikely under the conditions anticipated by this standard. If situations are encountered, however, where the oral toxicity values indicate a significantly different health hazard rating than from other, more likely routes of exposure or where the oral toxicity values would tend to either exaggerate or minimize the hazards likely to be encountered, then professional judgement shall be exercised in assigning the health hazard rating. In such cases, other routes of entry may be considered to be more appropriate to assessing the hazard. Also, based on professional judgement, it may be appropriate to either increase or decrease the health hazard rating to more accurately assess the likely degree of hazard that will be encountered under the conditions anticipated by this standard. Similarly, inhalation of dusts and mists is unlikely under the conditions anticipated by this standard. In such cases, the health hazard ratings should also be based on data for the more likely routes of exposure.

2-1.4 This chapter shall consider two major categories of health hazards in emergencies. One originates with the inherent physical and toxic properties of the material; the other arises from the generation of toxic products during decomposition or combustion of the material. For purposes of assigning the health hazard rating, only the inherent physical and toxic properties of the material shall be considered unless the combustion or decomposition products present a significantly greater degree of risk.

2-1.5 The degree of hazard shall indicate to fire fighting and emergency response personnel one of the following: that they can work safely only with specialized protective equipment; that they can work safely with suitable respiratory protective equipment; or that they can work safely in the area with ordinary clothing.

2-2 Definitions.

Health Hazard. The likelihood of a material to cause, either directly or indirectly, temporary or permanent injury or incapacitation due to an acute exposure by contact, inhalation, or ingestion.

2-3 Degrees of Hazard.

2-3.1 The degrees of health hazard shall be ranked according to the probable severity of the effects of exposure to personnel as follows:

4 Materials that, on very short exposure, could cause death or major residual injury, including those that are too dangerous to be approached without specialized protective equipment. This degree usually includes:

Materials that, under normal conditions or under fire conditions, are extremely hazardous (i.e., toxic or corrosive) through inhalation or through contact with or absorption by the skin;

Materials whose LD_{50} for acute oral toxicity is less than or equal to 5 milligrams per kilogram (mg/kg);

Materials whose LD_{50} for acute dermal toxicity is less than or equal to 40 milligrams per kilogram (mg/kg);

Dusts and mists whose LC_{50} for acute inhalation toxicity is less than or equal to 0.5 milligrams per liter (mg/L);

Any liquid whose saturated vapor concentration at 20 °C is equal to or greater than ten times its LC_{50} for acute inhalation toxicity, if its LC_{50} is less than or equal to 1000 parts per million (ppm);

Gases whose LC_{50} for acute inhalation toxicity is less than or equal to 1000 parts per million (ppm).

3 Materials that, on short exposure, could cause serious temporary or residual injury, including those requiring protection from all bodily contact. This degree usually includes:

Materials that give off highly toxic combustion products;

Materials whose LD_{50} for acute oral toxicity is greater than 5 milligrams per kilogram (mg/kg), but less than or equal to 50 milligrams per kilogram (mg/kg);

Materials whose LD_{50} for acute dermal toxicity is greater than 40 milligrams per kilogram (mg/kg), but less than or equal to 200 milligrams per kilogram (mg/kg);

Dusts and mist whose LC_{50} for acute inhalation toxicity is greater than 0.5 milligrams per liter (mg/L), but less than or equal to 2 milligrams per liter (mg/L);

Any liquid whose saturated vapor concentration at 20 °C is equal to or greater than its LC_{50} for acute inhalation toxicity, if its LC_{50} is less than or equal to 3000 parts per million (ppm) and that does not meet the criteria for degree of hazard 4;

Gases whose LC_{50} for acute inhalation toxicity is greater than 1000 parts per million (ppm), but less than or equal to 3000 parts per million (ppm);

Materials that either are severely corrosive to skin on single, short exposure or cause irreversible eye damage.

2 Materials that, on intense or short exposure, could cause temporary incapacitation or possible residual injury, including those requiring the use of respiratory protective equipment that has an independent air supply. This degree usually includes:

Materials that give off toxic or highly irritating combustion products;

Materials that, under normal conditions or fire conditions, give off toxic vapors that lack warning properties;

Materials whose LD_{50} for acute oral toxicity is greater than 50 milligrams per kilogram, but less than or equal to 500 milligrams per kilogram (mg/kg);

Materials whose LD_{50} for acute dermal toxicity is greater than 200 milligrams per kilogram (mg/kg), but less than or equal to 1000 milligrams per kilogram (mg/kg);

Dusts and mists whose LC_{50} for acute inhalation toxicity is greater than 2 milligrams per liter (mg/L), but less than or equal to 10 milligrams per liter (mg/L);

Any liquid whose saturated vapor concentration at 20 °C is equal to or greater than one-fifth ($^1/_5$) its LC_{50} for acute inhalation toxicity, if its LC_{50} is less than or equal to 5000 parts per million (ppm) and that does not meet the criteria for either degree of hazard 3 or degree of hazard 4;

Gases whose LC_{50} for acute inhalation toxicity is greater than 3000 parts per million (ppm), but less than or equal to 5000 parts per million (ppm);

Materials that cause severe but reversible respiratory, skin, or eye irritation.

1 Materials that, on short exposure, could cause irritation, but only minor residual injury, including those requiring the use of an approved air-purifying respirator. This degree usually includes:

Materials that, under fire conditions, give off irritating combustion products;

Materials that, under fire conditions, cause skin irritation, but not destruction of tissue;

Materials whose LD_{50} for acute oral toxicity is greater than 500 milligrams per kilogram (mg/kg), but less than or equal to 2000 milligrams per kilogram (mg/kg);

Materials whose LD_{50} for acute dermal toxicity is greater than 1000 milligrams per kilogram (mg/kg), but less than or equal to 2000 milligrams per kilogram (mg/kg);

Dusts and mists whose LC_{50} for acute inhalation toxicity is greater than 10 milligrams per liter (mg/L), but less than or equal to 200 milligrams per liter (mg/L);

Gases and vapors whose LC_{50} for acute inhalation toxicity is greater than 5000 parts per million (ppm), but less than or equal to 10,000 parts per million (ppm);

Materials that are moderate respiratory irritants or that cause slight to moderate eye irritation.

0 Materials that on short exposure under fire conditions, would offer no hazard beyond that of ordinary combustible materials. This degree usually includes:

Materials whose LD_{50} for acute oral toxicity is greater than 2000 milligrams per kilogram (mg/kg);

Materials whose LD_{50} for acute dermal toxicity is greater than 2000 milligrams per kilogram (mg/kg);

Dusts and mists whose LC_{50} for acute inhalation toxicity is greater than 200 milligrams per liter (mg/L);

Gases and vapors whose LC_{50} for acute inhalation toxicity is greater than 10,000 parts per million (ppm).

Chapter 3 Flammability Hazards

3-1 General.

3-1.1 This chapter shall address the degree of susceptibility of materials to burning. Since many materials will burn under one set of conditions but will not burn under others, the form or condition of the material shall be considered, along with its inherent properties.

3-2 Degrees of Hazard.

3-2.1 The degrees of hazard shall be ranked according to the susceptibility of materials to burning as follows:

4 Materials that will rapidly or completely vaporize at atmospheric pressure and normal ambient temperature or that are readily dispersed in air, and which will burn readily. This degree usually includes:

Flammable gases;

Flammable cryogenic materials;

Any liquid or gaseous material that is liquid while under pressure and has a flash point below 73 °F (22.8 °C) and a boiling point below 100 °F (37.8 °C) (i.e. Class IA flammable liquids);

Materials that ignite spontaneously when exposed to air.

3 Liquids and solids that can be ignited under almost all ambient temperature conditions. Materials in this degree produce hazardous atmospheres with air under almost all ambient temperatures or, though unaffected by ambient temperatures, are readily ignited under almost all conditions. This degree usually includes:

Liquids having a flash point below 73 °F (22.8 °C) and having a boiling point at or above 100 °F (37.8 °C) and those liquids having a flash point at or above 73 °F (22.8 °C) and below 100 °F (37.8 °C) (i.e. Class IB and Class IC flammable liquids);

Materials that on account of their physical form or environmental conditions can form explosive mixtures with air and that are readily dispersed in air, such as dusts of combustible solids and mists of flammable or combustible liquid droplets;

Materials that burn with extreme rapidity, usually by reason of self-contained oxygen (e.g., dry nitrocellulose *and many organic peroxides*).

2 Materials that must be moderately heated or exposed to relatively high ambient temperatures before ignition can occur. Materials in this degree would not under normal conditions form hazardous atmospheres with air, but under high ambient temperatures or under moderate heating may release vapor in sufficient quantities to produce hazardous atmospheres with air. This degree usually includes:

Liquids having a flash point above 100 °F (37.8 °C), but not exceeding 200 °F (93.4 °C) (i.e. Class II and Class IIIA combustible liquids);

Solid materials in the form of coarse dusts that may burn rapidly but that generally do not form explosive atmospheres with air;

Solid materials in a fibrous or shredded form that may burn rapidly and create flash fire hazards, such as cotton, sisal, and hemp;

Solids and semisolids that readily give off flammable vapors.

1 Materials that must be preheated before ignition can occur. Materials in this degree require considerable preheating, under all ambient temperature conditions, before ignition and combustion can occur. This degree usually includes:

Materials that will burn in air when exposed to a temperature of 1500 °F (815.5 °C) for a period of 5 minutes or less;

Liquids, solids, and semisolids having a flash point above 200 °F (93.4 °C) (i.e. Class IIIB combustible liquids);

Most ordinary combustible materials.

0 Materials that will not burn. This degree usually includes any material that will not burn in air when exposed to a temperature of 1500 °F (815.5 °C) for a period of 5 minutes.

Chapter 4 Reactivity (Instability) Hazards

4-1 General.

4-1.1 This chapter shall address the degree of susceptibility of materials to release energy. Some materials are capable of rapid release of energy by themselves, as by self-reaction or polymerization, or can undergo violent explosive reaction if contacted with water or other extinguishing agents or with certain other materials.

4-1.2 The violence of reaction or decomposition of materials may be increased by heat or pressure, by mixture with certain other materials to form fuel-oxidizer combinations, or by contact with incompatible substances, sensitizing contaminants, or catalysts.

4-1.3 Because of the wide variations of accidental combinations possible in fire or other emergencies, these extraneous hazard factors (except for the effect of water) cannot be applied in a general numerical scaling of hazards. Such extraneous factors must be considered individually in order to establish appropriate safety factors, such as separation or segregation. Such individual consideration is particularly important where significant amounts of materials are to be stored or handled. Guidance for this consideration is provided in NFPA 49, *Hazardous Chemicals Data*.

4-1.4 The degree of reactivity hazard shall indicate to fire fighting and emergency personnel that the area should be evacuated, that a fire must be fought from a protected location, that caution must be used in approaching a spill or fire to apply extinguishing agents, or that a fire may be fought using normal procedures.

4-2 Definitions.

4-2.1 For the purposes of this standard, a reactive material is one that can enter into a violent chemical reaction with water. Reactions with other materials may also result in violent release of energy but are beyond the scope of this standard.

4-2.2 For the purposes of this standard, an unstable material is one that, in the pure state or as commerially produced, will vigorously polymerize, decompose or condense, become self-reactive, or otherwise undergo a violent chemical change under conditions of shock, pressure, or temperature.

4-2.3 Stable materials are those that normally have the capacity to resist changes in their chemical composition, despite exposure to air, water, and heat as encountered in fire emergencies.

4-3 Degrees of Hazard.

4-3.1 The degrees of hazard shall be ranked according to ease, rate, and quantity of energy release as follows:

4 Materials that in themselves are readily capable of detonation or explosive decomposition or explosive reaction at normal temperatures and pressures. This degree usually includes materials that are sensitive to localized thermal or mechanical shock at normal temperatures and pressures.

3 Materials that in themselves are capable of detonation or explosive decomposition or explosive reaction, but that require a strong initiating source or that must be heated under confinement before initiation. This degree usually includes:

Materials that are sensitive to thermal or mechanical shock at elevated temperatures and pressures;

Materials that react explosively with water without requiring heat or confinement.

2 Materials that readily undergo violent chemical change at elevated temperatures and pressures. This degree usually includes:

Materials that exhibit an exotherm at temperatures less than or equal to 150 °C when tested by differential scanning calorimetry;

Materials that may react violently with water or form potentially explosive mixtures with water.

1 Materials that in themselves are normally stable, but that can become unstable at elevated temperatures and pressure. This degree usually includes:

Materials that change or decompose on exposure to air, light, or moisture;

Materials that exhibit an exotherm at temperatures greater than 150 °C, but less than or equal to 300 °C, when tested by differential scanning calorimetry.

0 Materials that in themselves are normally stable, even under fire conditions. This degree usually includes:

Materials that do not react with water;

Materials that exhibit an exotherm at temperatures greater than 300 °C but less than or equal to 500 °C when tested by differential scanning calorimetry;

Materials that do not exhibit an exotherm at temperature less than or equal to 500 °C when tested by differential scanning calorimetry.

Chapter 5 Special Hazards

5-1 General.

5-1.1 This chapter shall address the other properties of the material that may cause special problems or require special fire fighting techniques.

5-1.2 Special hazards symbols shall be shown in the fourth space of the diagram or immediately above or below the entire symbol.

5-2 Symbols.

5-2.1 Materials that demonstrate unusual reactivity with water shall be identified with the letter W with a horizontal line through the center (~~W~~).

5-2.2 Materials that possess oxidizing properties shall be identified by the letters OX.

Chapter 6 Identification of Materials by Hazard Signal System

6-1 One of the systems delineated in the following illustrations shall be used for the implementation of this standard.

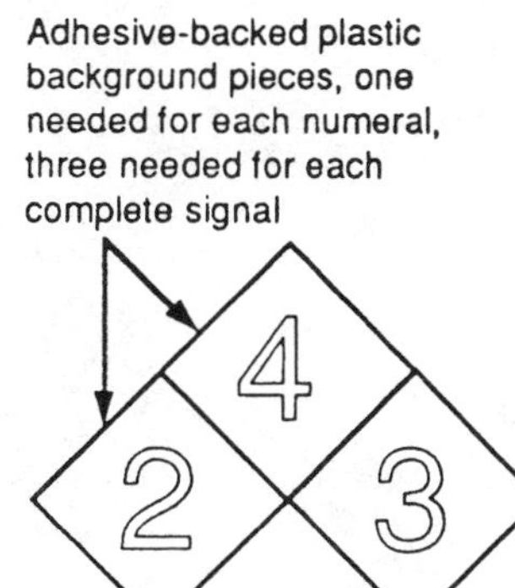

Figure 1 For use where specified color background is used with numerals of contrasting colors.

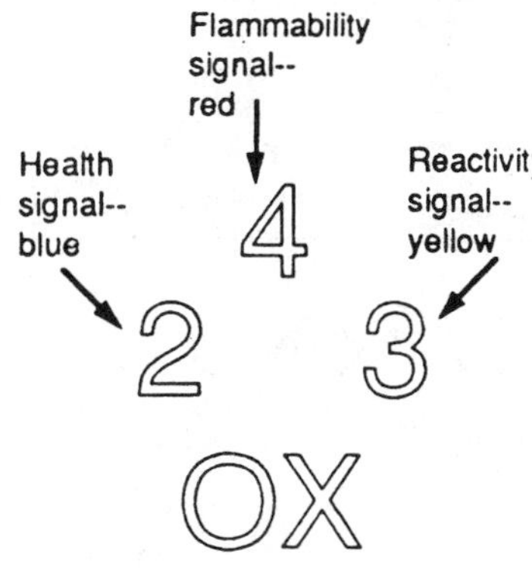

Figure 2 For use where white background is necessary.

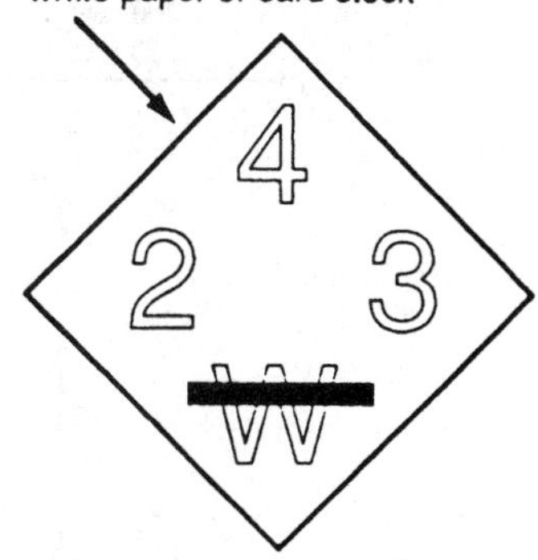

Figure 3 For use where white background is used with painted numerals, or for use when signal is in the form of sign or placard.

Figure 6-1 Alternate arrangements for display of NFPA 704 Hazard Identification System.

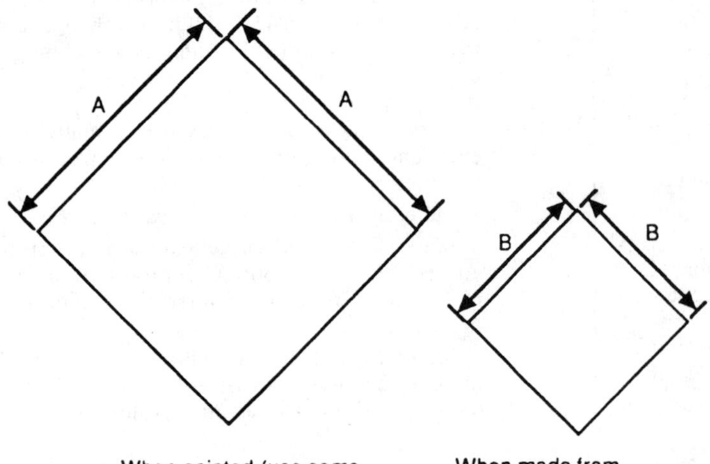

Minimum Dimensions of White Background for Signals (White Background is Optional)

Size of Signals H	W	T	A	B
1	0.7	5/32	2 1/2	1 1/4
2	1.4	5/16	5	2 1/2
3	2.1	15/32	7 1/2	3 3/4
4	2.8	5/8	10	5
6	4.2	15/16	15	7 1/2

All dimensions given in inches

Exception: For containers with a capacity of one gallon or less, symbols may be reduced in size, provided:

1. This reduction is proportionate.

2. The color coding is retained.

3. The vertical and horizontal dimensions of the diamond are not less than 1 in. (2.5 cm).

4. The individual numbers are no smaller than 1/8 in. tall.

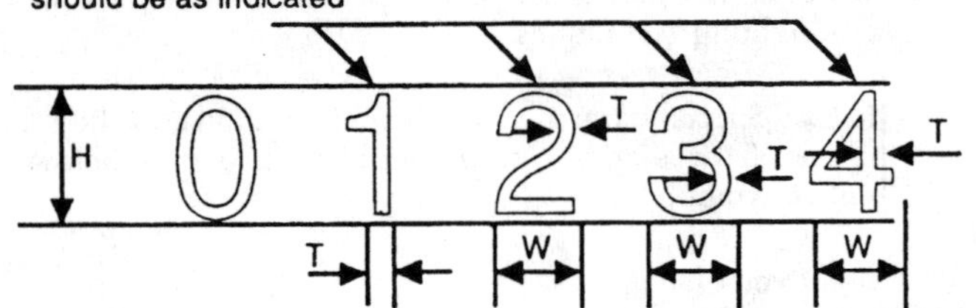

Note: Style of numerals shown is optional.

Figure 6-2 Dimensions of NFPA 704 placard and numerals.

Arrangement and Order of Signals – Optional Form of Application

Distance at which signals must be legible	Minimum size of signals required
50 feet	1"
75 feet	2"
100 feet	3"
200 feet	4"
300 feet	6"

Note: This shows the correct spatial arrangement and order of signals used for identification of materials by hazard.

Figure 6-3 Minimum size of numerals for legibility at distance.

Appendix A

This Appendix is not a part of the requirements of this NFPA document, but is included for information purposes only.

A-1 This is a system for the identification of hazards to life and health of people in the prevention and control of fires and explosions in the manufacture and storage of materials. The bases for identification are the physical properties and characteristics of materials that are known or can be determined by standard methods. Technical terms, expressions, trade names, etc., are purposely avoided as this system is concerned only with the identification of the involved hazard from a standpoint of safety.

The explanatory material in this Appendix is to assist users of this standard, particularly the person who assigns the degree of hazard in each category.

Identification of Health Hazard Color Code: BLUE		Identification of Flammability Color Code: RED		Identification of Reactivity (Stability) Color Code: YELLOW	
	Type of Possible Injury	Susceptibility of Materials to Burning		Susceptibility to Release of Energy	
Signal		Signal		Signal	
4	Materials that on very short exposure could cause death or major residual injury.	4	Materials that will rapidly or completely vaporize at atmosphereic pressure and normal ambient temperature, or that are readily dispersed in air and that will burn readily.	4	Materials that in themselves are readily capable of detonation or of explosive decomposition or reaction at normal temperatures and pressures.
3	Materials that on short exposure could cause serious temporary or residual injury.	3	Liquids and solids that can be ignited under almost all ambient temperature conditions.	3	Materials that in themselves are capable of detonation or explosive decomposition or reaction but require a strong initiating source or which must be heated under confinement before initiation or which react explosively with water.
2	Materials that on intense or continued but not chronic exposure could cause temporary incapacitation or possible residual injury.	2	Materials that must be moderately heated or exposed to relatively high ambient temperatures before ignition can occur.	2	Materials that readily undergo violent chemical change at elevated temperatures and pressures or which react violently with water or which may form explosive mixtures with water.
1	Materials that on exposure would cause irritation but only minor residual injury.	1	Materials that must be preheated before ignition can occur.	1	Materials that in themselves are normally stable, but which can become unstable at elevated temperatures and pressures.
0	Materials that on exposure under fire conditions would offer no hazard beyond that of ordinary combustible material.	0	Materials that will not burn.	0	Materials that in themselves are normally stable, even under fire exposure conditions, and which are not reactive with water.

A-2 In developing this edition of NFPA 704, the Committee on Fire Hazards of Materials determined that the standard should provide quantitative guidelines for determining the numerical health hazard rating of a material. In addition, the Committee agreed that a "4" or a "3" health hazard rating should be assigned to any material classified as a "Poison - Inhalation Hazard" by the U.S. Department of Transportation (DOT). This classification, "Poison-Inhalation Hazard", was adopted by DOT from the United Nations (UN) criteria detailed in the UN publication, *Recommendations on the Transport of Dangerous Goods*, 4th Edition - Revised, 1986. (See also Notice of Proposed Rulemaking, *Federal Register*, Vol. 50, p 5270 et seq., February 7, 1985, and Notice of Final Rule, *Federal Register*, Vol. 50, p. 41092 et seq., October 8, 1985.)

The UN criteria for inhalation toxicity is based upon the LC_{50} and saturated vapor concentration of the material. Furthermore, in addition to inhalation toxicity, the UN has established criteria for oral and dermal toxicity, as well as corrosivity. Based upon these criteria, the UN assigns a given material to categories called Packing Groups I, II, or III.Packing Group I materials represent a severe hazard in transport, Group II materials a serious hazard, and Group III materials a low hazard.

The Committee decided to adopt the UN criteria for toxicity and corrosivity, and correlate Packing Groups I, II, and III with the health hazard ratings "4," "3," and "2," respectively. Adoption of the UN system has several advantages. First, it addresses hazards in transportation, which are similar to the type of emergencies likely to be encountered by fire fighting personnel and emergency responders. Most other hazard ranking systems have been developed for occupational exposures. Secondly, the UN system is well established, and it is presumed that a large number of chemical manufacturers have already classified (or can easily clasify) materials into the appropriate Packing Groups. Finally, users of chemicals can assign "4," "3," or "2" health hazard ratings by establishing if chemicals have been assigned to UN Packing Groups due to toxicity or corrosivity.

In order to establish "1" and "0" health hazard rankings, the Committee utilized criteria for the "1" and "0" ratings contained in the Hazardous Materials Identification System (HMIS™) developed by the National Paint & Coatings Association (NPCA) (Hazardous Materials Identification System Revised, Implementation Manual, 1981). Although the NPCA criteria were developed for occupational exposure, the "1" and "0" criteria are on the low end of the hazard spectrum and are fairly consistent with, and complementary to, the "4," "3," and "2" ratings based upon the UN criteria. No UN criteria was established for eye irritation, and the Committee adopted NPCA "3," "2," and "1," and "0" criteria as health hazard ratings for eye irritation.

The Committee made a number of revisions to the proposed hazard rating system to provide conformity with existing industrial practice and to recognize limitations and availability of corrosivity and eye irritation into a single "skin/eye contact" category and utilize descriptive terms for the health hazard ratings. Minor changes were made to the "2," "1," and "0" criteria for oral toxicity and to the "1" and "0" criteria for dermal toxicity. Specifically, the distinction between solids and liquids in the oral toxicity criteria was eliminated, and the cutoff between "1" and "0" rankings for oral and dermal toxicity was lowered from 5000 to 2000 mg/kg.

In summary, the "4," "3," and "2" health hazard rankings for oral, dermal, and inhalation toxicity are based primarily on UN criteria. The "1" and "0" health hazard rankings for oral, dermal, and inhalation toxicity, and all of the "skin/eye contact" rankings are based primarily on NPCA criteria.

For the assistance of the user of this standard, the following definitions are quoted from Section 6.5 of Recommendations on the Transport of Dangerous Goods, Fourth Revised Edition, 1986, published by the United Nations, New York, NY.

"LD_{50} for acute oral toxicity:

"That dose of the substance administered which is most likely to cause death within 14 days in one half of both male and female young adult albino rats. The number of animals tested shall be sufficient to give a statistically significant result and be in conformity with good pharmacological practice. The result is expressed in milligrams per kilogram of body weight.

"LD_{50} for acute dermal toxicity:

"That dose of the substance which, administered by continuous contact for 24 hours with the bare skin of albino rabbits, is most likely to cause death within 14 days in one half of the animals tested. The number of animals tested shall be sufficient to give a statistically significant result and be in conformity with good pharmacological practice. The result is expressed in milligrams per kilogram of body weight.

"LC_{50} for acute toxicity on inhalation:

"That concentration of vapour, mist or dust which, administered by continuous inhalation to both male and female young adult albino rats for one hour, is most likely to cause death within 14 days in one half of the animals tested. If the substance is administered to the animals as dust or mist, more than 90 percent of the particles available for inhalation in the test must have a diameter of 10 microns or less, provided that it is reasonably forseeable that such concentrations could be encountered by man during transport. The result is expressed in milligrams per liter of air for dusts and mists or in millilitres per cubic meter of air (parts per million) for vapors."

The following information quoted from Section 6.4 of the above-cited Recommendations also applies:

"The criteria for inhalation toxicity of dusts and mists are based on LC_{50} data relating to 1 hour exposures and where such information is available it should be used. However, where only LC_{50} data relating to 4 hour exposures to dusts and mists are available, such figures can be multipled by four and the product substituted in the above criteria, i.e. LC_{50} (4 hour) × 4 is considered equivalent of LC_{50} (1 hour).

"The criteria for inhalation toxicity of vapors are based on LC_{50} data relating to 1 hour exposures, and where such information is available it should be used. However, where only LC_{50} data relating to 4 hour exposures to dusts and mists are available, such figures can be multiplied by two and the product substituted in the above criteria, i.e. LC_{50} (4 hour) × 2 is considered equivalent of LC_{50} (1 hour)."

Appendix B

This Appendix is not a part of the requirements of this NFPA document, but is included for information purposes only.

The information contained within Appendix B is derived from introductory explanatory material on the 704 system contained within NFPA 49, *Hazardous Chemicals Data*; and NFPA 325M, *Fire Hazard Properties of Flammable Liquids, Gases, and Volatile Solids*. The following paragraphs summarize the meanings of the numbers in each hazard category and explain what a number should tell fire fighting personnel about protecting themselves and how to fight fires where the hazard exists.

Health.

In general, health hazard in fire fighting is that of a single exposure that may vary from a few seconds up to an hour. The physical exertion demanded in fire fighting or other emergency conditions may be expected to intensify the effects of any exposure. Only hazards arising out of an inherent property of the material are considered. The following explanation is based upon protective equipment normally used by fire fighters.

4 Materials too dangerous to health to expose fire fighters. A few whiffs of the vapor could cause death, or the vapor or liquid could be fatal on penetrating the fire fighter's normal full protective clothing. The normal full protective clothing and breathing apparatus available to the average fire department will not provide adequate protection against inhalation or skin contact with these materials.

3 Materials extremely hazardous to health but areas may be entered with extreme care. Full protective clothing, including self-contained breathing apparatus, coat, pants, gloves, boots, and bands around legs, arms, and waist should be provided. No skin surface should be exposed.

2 Materials hazardous to health, but areas may be entered freely with full-faced mask self-contained breathing apparatus that provides eye protection.

1 Materials only slightly hazardous to health. It may be desirable to wear self-contained breathing apparatus.

0 Materials that on exposure under fire conditions would offer no hazard beyond that of ordinary combustible material.

Flammability.

Susceptibility to burning is the basis for assigning degrees within this category. The method of attacking the fire is influenced by this susceptibility factor.

4 Very flammable gases or very volatile flammable liquids. Shut off flow and keep cooling water streams on exposed tanks or containers.

3 Materials that can be ignited under almost all normal temperature conditions. Water may be ineffective because of the low flash point.

2 Materials that must be moderately heated before ignition will occur. Water spray may be used to extinguish the fire because the material can be cooled below its flash point.

1 Materials that must be preheated before ignition can occur. Water may cause frothing if it gets below the surface of the liquid and turns to steam. However, water fog gently applied to the surface will cause a frothing that will extinguish the fire.

0 Materials that will not burn.

Reactivity (Stability).

The assignment of degrees in the reactivity category is based upon the susceptibility of materials to release energy either by themselves or in combination with water. Fire exposure is one of the factors considered along with conditions of shock and pressure.

4 Materials that (in themselves) are readily capable of detonation or of explosive decomposition or explosive reaction at normal temperatures and pressures. Includes materials that are sensitive to mechanical or localized thermal shock. If a chemical with this hazard rating is in an advanced or massive fire, the area should be evacuated.

3 Materials that (in themselves) are capable of detonation or of explosive decomposition or of explosive reaction but which require a strong initiating source or which must be heated under confinement before initiation. Includes materials that are sensitive to thermal or mechanical shock at elevated temperatures and pressures or that react explosively with water without requiring heat or confinement. Fire fighting should be done from a location protected from the effects of an explosion.

2 Materials that (in themselves) are normally unstable and readily undergo violent chemical change but do not detonate. Includes materials that can undergo chemical change with rapid release of energy at normal temperatures and pressures or that can undergo violent chemical change at elevated temperatures and pressures. Also includes those materials that may react violently with water or that may form potentially explosive mixtures with water. In advanced or massive fires, fire fighting should be done from a safe distance or from a protected location.

1 Materials that (in themselves) are normally stable but which may become unstable at elevated temperatures and pressures or which may react with water with some release of energy but not violently. Caution must be used in approaching the fire and applying water.

0 Materials that (in themselves) are normally stable even under fire exposure conditions and that are not reactive with water. Normal fire fighting procedures may be used.

Appendix C Flammability

This Appendix is not a part of the requirements (recommendations) of this NFPA document, but is included for information purposes only.

The selection of the flash point breaks for the assigning of degrees within the Flammability category has been based upon the recommendations of the Technical Committee on Classification and Properties of Flammable Liquids of the NFPA Committee on Flammable Liquids. This Technical Committee initiated the study that led to the development of this standard. Close cooperation between the Technical Committee and the Committee on Fire Hazards of Materials has continued.

Flash point tells several things. One, if the liquid has no flash point, it is not a flammable liquid. Two, if it has a flash point, it must be considered flammable or combustible. Three, the flash point is normally an indication of susceptibility to ignition.

The flash point test may give results that would indicate that the liquid is nonflammable or that it comes under degree 1 or 2 when it is a mixture containing, for example, carbon tetrachloride. As a specific example, sufficient carbon tetrachloride can be added to gasoline so that the mixture has no flash point. However, on standing in an open container, the carbon tetrachloride will evaporate more rapidly than the gasoline. Over a period of time, therefore, the residual liquid will first show a high flash point, then a progressively lower one until the flash point of the final 10 percent of the original sample will approximate that of the heavier fractions of the gasoline. In order to evaluate the fire hazard of such liquid mixtures, fractional evaporation tests can be conducted at room temperature in open vessels. After evaporation of appropriate fractions, such as 10, 20, 40, 60, and 90 percent of the original sample, flash point tests can be conducted on the residue. The results of such tests indicate the grouping into which the liquid should be placed if the conditions of use are such as to make it likely that appreciable evaporation will take place. For open system conditions, such as in open dip tanks, the open-cup test method may give a more reliable indication of the flammability hazard.

In the interest of reproducibility of results, it is recommended that:

The flash point of liquids having a viscosity less than 45 SUS (Saybolt Universal Seconds) at 100 °F (37.8 °C) and a flash point below 200 °F (93.4 °C) may be determined in accordance with ASTM D-56-79, *Standard Method of Test for Flash Point by the Tag Closed Tester*. (In those countries that use the Abel or Abel-Pensky closed cup tests as an official standard, these tests will be equally acceptable to the Tag Closed Cup Method.)

The flash point of aviation turbine fuels may be determined in accordance with ASTM D3828-81, *Test Method for Flash Point by Setaflash Closed Tester*.

For liquids having flash points in the range of 32 °F (0 °C) to 230 °F (110 °C) the determination may be made in accordance with ASTM D3278-82, *Flash Point of Liquids by Setaflash Closed Tester*.

For viscous and solid chemicals the determination may be made in accordance with ASTM E502-74, *Flash Point of Chemicals by Closed Cup Methods*.

The flash point of liquids having a viscosity of 45 SUS (Saybolt Universal Seconds) or more at 100 °F (37.8 °C) or a flash point of 200 °F (93.4 °C) or higher may be determined in accordance with ASTM D-93-79, *Standard Method of Test for Flash Point by the Pensky-Martens Closed Tester*.

Appendix D Reactivity, Differential Scanning Calorimetry (DSC)

This Appendix is not a part of the requirements (recommendations) of this NFPA document, but is included for information purposes only.

Differential Scanning Calorimetry (DSC) is the primary screening test for assessing reactivity hazard. It indicates whether a material undergoes an exothermic or endothermic reaction, and a general temperature range in which the reaction occurs.

This test is routinely run before other more sophisticated tests are run, such as an Accelerating Rate Calorimetry (ARC) test or drop weight testing. Heats of reaction, heats of decomposition, and heats of fusion, as well as kinetic information, can be determined by DSC for homogenous solids and liquids, as well as heterogenous systems.

DSC data should be used with caution, avoiding any inference that the test conditions duplicate those that the material will experience in a foreign environment.

A DSC test consists of heating a small quanity of material (typically 1-10 milligrams) held in a sample container from room temperature to approximately 500 °C. Exotherms are usually detected by the DSC test at temperatures higher than that expected in systems that are more adiabatic (insulated tanks, large masses of material, etc.)

Small changes in the composition of a material can have a significant effect on its thermal behavior. For example, a material may not decompose in the container in which DSC is done, but it may be catalytically decomposed by the material of construction of the container used in service.

The DSC is a screening test that is used primarily to determine if further testing is required.

Appendix E Referenced Publications

E-1 The following documents or portions thereof are referenced within this standard for informational purposes only and thus are not considered part of the requirements of this document. The edition indicated for each reference is the current edition as of the date of the NFPA issuance of this document.

E-1.1 NFPA Publications. National Fire Protection Association, 1 Batterymarch Park, P.O. Box 9101, Quincy, MA 02269-9101.

NFPA 49-1975, *Hazardous Chemicals Data*

NFPA 325M-1984, *Fire Hazard Properties of Flammable Liquids, Gases, and Volatile Solids.*

E-1.2 ASTM Publications. American Society for Testing and Materials, 1916 Race Street, Philadelphia, PA 19103.

ASTM D-56-87, *Standard Method for Test for Flash Point by the Tag Closed Tester*

ASTM D-3828-87, *Test Method for Flash Point by Setaflash Closed Tester*

ASTM D-3278-82, *Flash Point of Liquids by Setaflash Closed Tester*

ASTM D-93-85, *Test Methods for Flash Point by the Pensky-Martens Closed Tester*

ASTM E-502-84, *Flash Point of Chemicals by Closed Cup Methods.*

E-1.3 Other Publications.

Tou, J.C. and Whiting, L.F.; "A Cradle-Glass Ampoule Sample Container for Differential Scanning Calorimetric Analysis"; Thermochimica Acta; Vol. 42; Elsevier Scientific Publishing Co.; Amsterdam; 1980.

Whiting, L.F., LaBean, M.S., and Eadie, S.S.; "Evaluation of a Capillary Tube Sample Container for Differential Scanning Calorimetry"; Thermochimica Acta; Vol. 136; Elsevier Scientific Publishing Co.; Amsterdam; 1988.

UNIFORM FIRE CODE STANDARD 79-4
VEHICLES FOR TRANSPORTING FLAMMABLE OR COMBUSTIBLE LIQUIDS
See Sections 2402.2.1 and 7904.6.1, *Uniform Fire Code*

The National Fire Protection Association Standard for Tank Vehicles for Flammable and Combustible Liquids, NFPA 385—1990, is hereby adopted by reference as UFC Standard 79-4.

The provisions of this standard shall apply to the design and construction of tank vehicles used for transporting combustible and flammable liquids except when a provision of *Uniform Fire Code,* Volume 1 or an amendment specified in Section 79.401 is applicable, in which case *Uniform Fire Code,* Volume 1 provisions or the amendment shall take precedence.

Supplemental standards referenced by NFPA 385—1990 shall only be considered as guidelines subject to approval by the chief.

NFPA 385—1990 is available from the National Fire Protection Association, 1 Batterymarch Park, Box 9101, Quincy, Massachusetts 02269-9101.

SECTION 79.401 — AMENDMENTS

The Standard for Tank Vehicles for Flammable and Combustible Liquids, NFPA 385—1990, applies to tank vehicles used for the transportation of asphalt or normally stable flammable and combustible liquids with a flash point below 200°F (182.2°C), except as follows:

1. Sec. 1-1.4 is revised as follows:

1-1.4 The requirements for aircraft fuel servicing tank vehicles are contained in UFC Standard 24-1.

2. Sec. 1-2 is revised by changing the definitions of "approved," "combustible liquid," "flammable liquid," "flash point," "liquid," "listed" and "vapor pressure" to be as set forth in *Uniform Fire Code,* Volume 1.

3. Sec. 2-2 is revised by substituting the phrase "UFC Standard 82-1" for the phrase "Chapter 6 of the *Standard for the Storage and Handling of Liquefied Petroleum Gases,* NFPA 58."

4. Sec. 2-3.1 is revised as follows:

2-3.1 General. Cargo tanks constructed after the effective date of this standard shall be constructed in accordance with Section 2-3. Continued use of existing cargo tanks is allowed only when authorized by the chief.

5. Sec. 2-3.2 is deleted and substitute as follows:

2-3.2 Material. Sheet and plate material for shells, heads, bulkheads and baffles for cargo tanks shall provide reasonable safety to personnel and property, such as the safety provided by aluminum alloys (commercial designation) 5052, 5086, 5154, 5254 or 5652, in accordance with nationally recognized standards such as the specification for Aluminum and Aluminum-Alloy Sheet and Plate, ASTM B 209.

6. Sec. 2-3.4.1 is revised as follows:

2-3.4.1 Maximum Stress Values. The maximum calculated stress value shall not exceed 20 percent of the minimum ultimate strength of the material as authorized, except when the pressure vessel satisfies the design requirements of nationally recognized standards. See *Uniform Fire Code* Article 90.

7. Sec. 2-4.1 is revised by substituting the phrase "5.82 centistokes" for the phrase "45 Saybolt Universal Seconds."

8. Sec. 2-4.1.1 is revised by substituting the phrase "5.82 centistokes" for the phrase "45 Saybolt Universal Seconds."

9. Sec. 2-5 is revised by substituting the phrase "5.82 centistokes" for the phrase "45 Saybolt Universal Seconds."

10. Sec. 6-2.8 is revised as follows:

6-2.8 The secondary shutoff control system shall be labeled as to the manufacturer and type. Electrical systems shall be labeled as to the manufacturer and type. Electrical systems used for secondary shutoff shall be in accordance with the Electrical Code.

11. Sec. 6-3.1 is revised as follows:

6-3.1 Each tank vehicle manufactured shall be equipped with at least one portable fire extinguisher having at least a 2-A:20-B:C rating.

12. Sec. 6-3.2 is revised as follows:

6-3.2 Fire extinguishers shall be kept in good operating condition at all times, and they shall be located in an accessible place on each tank vehicle. Extinguishers shall be maintained in accordance with UFC Standard 10-1.

13. Chapter 7 is deleted.

UNIFORM FIRE CODE STANDARD 79-5
PORTABLE FLAMMABLE OR COMBUSTIBLE LIQUID TANKS
See Sections 7902.1.8.1.1 and 7902.5.11.2.4, *Uniform Fire Code*

The National Fire Protection Association Standard for Portable Shipping Tanks for Flammable and Combustible Liquids, NFPA 386—1990, is hereby adopted by reference as UFC Standard 79-5.

The provisions of this standard shall apply to portable shipping tanks used for the transportation of flammable and combustible liquids except when a provision of *Uniform Fire Code,* Volume 1 or an amendment specified in Section 79.501 is applicable, in which case *Uniform Fire Code,* Volume 1 provisions or the amendment shall take precedence.

Supplemental standards referenced by NFPA 386—1990 shall only be considered as guideline standards subject to approval by the chief.

NFPA 386—1990 is available from the National Fire Protection Association, 1 Batterymarch Park, Box 9101, Quincy, Massachusetts 02269-9101.

SECTION 79.501 — AMENDMENTS

The Standard for Portable Shipping Tanks for Flammable and Combustible Liquids, NFPA 386—1990, applies to the design and construction of portable tanks used for Class I, II or III-A liquids, except as follows:

1. Sec. 1-1.4.1 is revised by deleting the second sentence.

2. Sec. 1-2 is revised by adding the following definition:

AUTHORITY HAVING JURISDICTION is the official responsible for the administration and enforcement of this standard.

The definitions of "approved," "combustible liquid," "flammable liquid," "flash point," "liquid," "listed" and "vapor pressure" shall be as set forth in *Uniform Fire Code,* Volume 1.

The definition of "should" is deleted.

3. Sec. 2-1.3 is revised by changing the second sentence as follows:

In case of doubt, the supplier or producer of the liquid, or other competent authority, as deemed appropriate by the chief, shall be consulted as to the suitability of the material to be used in construction.

4. Sec. 2-2.4 is revised by changing the first sentence of the second paragraph as follows:

Sheet for shells, including tops, bottoms, baffles and bulkheads of portable shipping tanks shall provide reasonable safety to persons and property such as the safety provided by aluminum alloys (commercial designation) 5052, 5454, 5154, 5086, 5254 or 5652, in accordance with nationally recognized standards, such as the Specification for Aluminum and Aluminum-Alloy Sheet and Plate, ASTM B 209.

5. Sec. 2-4.1 is revised by adding a second sentence as follows:

The chief is authorized to require retesting when there is indication that the portable shipping tank has suffered physical damage, shows signs of deterioration or when information satisfactory to the chief is not available to show that the portable shipping tank has been properly tested.

6. Chapters 4 and 5 are deleted.

UNIFORM FIRE CODE STANDARD 79-6
INTERIOR LINING OF UNDERGROUND STORAGE TANKS

Supplemental standards referenced in UFC Standard 79-6 shall only be considered as guideline standards subject to approval by the chief.

See Section 7902.6.10, *Uniform Fire Code*

SECTION 79.601 — GENERAL

79.601.1 Scope. Interior lining of steel underground tanks used for the storage of flammable and combustible liquids shall be in accordance with this standard. Included under the scope of this standard is the protection of tanks from internal corrosion and the lining of steel tanks for product compatibility. All applicable safety and health laws, regulations and ordinances shall be complied with. The contractor shall be knowledgeable of the contents of this standard as well as the referenced material listed herein.

79.601.2 Application. This standard applies to the opening, lining and testing of steel tanks.

79.601.3 Definitions. For the purposes of this standard, certain terms are defined as follows:

APPROVED. See UFC Article 2.

CLASS I, DIVISION 1, GROUP D. See Electrical Code.

COMBUSTIBLE LIQUID. See UFC Article 2.

FLAMMABLE LIQUID. See UFC Article 2.

LOWER FLAMMABLE LIMIT (LFL) is the minimum concentration of vapor in air or oxygen below which propagation of a flame does not occur on contact with a source of ignition.

PURGING is the method by which gases, vapors or other airborne impurities are displaced from a confined space.

QUALIFIED PERSON is a person designated by the employer, in writing, as capable, by education or specialized training, of anticipating, recognizing and evaluating employee exposure to hazardous substances or other unsafe conditions in a confined space; capable of specifying necessary control or protective action to ensure worker safety; and knowledgeable of the procedures described in this standard.

SELF-CONTAINED BREATHING APPARATUS is a portable respiratory protective device designed to protect the wearer from an oxygen-deficient or other hazardous atmosphere. It supplies a respirable atmosphere that is either carried in or generated by the apparatus and is independent of the ambient environment. It is normally equipped with a full-face piece and is approved by the National Institute of Occupational Safety and Health.

STANDBY PERSON is a person trained in emergency rescue procedures and assigned to remain on the outside of the confined space and to be in communication with those working inside.

STATIC ELECTRICITY is the electrification of materials through physical contact and separation and the various effects that result from the positive and negative charges so formed, particularly where they constitute a fire or explosion hazard.

VAPOR AREA. See UFC Article 2.

WHITE-METAL FINISH is a surface with a gray-white uniform metallic color roughened to form a minimum $1^1/_2$-mil (0.04 mm) anchor profile pattern for linings. The surface, when viewed without magnification, shall be free of all oil, grease, dirt, visible mill-scale, rust, corrosion products, oxides, paint or other foreign matter.

79.601.4 Permits and Plans.

79.601.4.1 Permit application. Prior to engaging in any activities relating to the alteration or repair of tanks or equipment in connection with the storage, handling, use or sale of flammable or combustible liquids regulated by the *Uniform Fire Code,* a permit shall be obtained from the chief. On-site work shall not be initiated until a permit has been issued. See *Uniform Fire Code* Article 1.

79.601.4.2 Documents. At the time a permit is applied for, the applicant shall submit all certificates, specifications, licenses, certificates of insurance, and other documents required by this standard and the chief.

79.601.5 Materials.

79.601.5.1 General. Materials used for the interior lining of underground tanks shall be approved. Materials shall satisfy the requirements of Section 79.601.5 and be in accordance with nationally recognized and accepted standards, principles and tests.

79.601.5.2 Immersion conditioning. Representative coating samples shall be tested to determine compatibility. Samples shall be immersed in the liquids listed below at either 100°F (37.8°C) for periods of one, three and six months, or 74°F (23.3°C) for periods of one, three, six and 12 months:

Intended Service Liquids:

Unleaded gasoline

Leaded gasoline

No. 2 fuel oil or diesel fuel

Gasohol (10 percent ethanol)

Gasoline and five percent methanol with appropriate co-solvent

Gasoline

Additional Liquids:

(These liquids are not intended for service; however, the liner materials are to be tested in these liquids to further demonstrate the liner's immersion resistance.)

ASTM Reference Fuel C

Toluene

Xylene

Distilled water

79.601.5.3 Post-immersion tests. Upon completion of each immersion period, samples shall be tested in accordance with approved procedures. See the following:

TEST	PURPOSE
ASTM D 4541-85, Pull-off Strength of Coating Using Portable Adhesion Testers	Bonding Strength
ASTM D 790-86, Flexural Properties of Unreinforced and Reinforced Plastics and Electrical Insulating Materials	Flexural Strength

TEST	PURPOSE
ASTM D 2794-84, Resistance of Organic Coating to the Effects of Rapid Deformation (Impact)	Impact Resistance
ASTM D 2583-81, (Using Model 935) Indentation Hardness of Rigid Plastics by Means of a Barcol Impressor	Hardness
ASTM D 543-87, Procedure 1, Resistance of Plastics to Chemical Reagents	Film Integrity

79.601.5.4 Conditions of acceptance. Each test sample shall be visually examined after each immersion period and shall exhibit no evidence of peeling, blistering, surface wrinkling or roughness.

Physical properties after the final immersion period shall be a minimum of 30 percent of the original physical properties before immersion with a stable trend indicating little or no further long-term deterioration for toluene, xylene and distilled water and 50 percent for all other listed materials.

Before storage of liquids other than those listed is allowed, test results demonstrating the liner will meet the above requirements in such liquids shall be submitted by the manufacturer.

SECTION 79.602 — SAFETY REQUIREMENTS

79.602.1 Site Conditions.

79.602.1.1 Ignition controls. Prior to excavation, the site shall be safeguarded from all sources of ignition for an area of 25 feet (7620 mm) in all directions until the area is vapor free. All open flame and spark-producing equipment within the area shall be shut down. Barricades and warning signs reading FLAMMABLE—NO SMOKING shall be provided as required by the chief.

79.602.1.2 Fire extinguishers. Two portable fire extinguishers, each having a rating not less than 80B:C, shall be provided on the site in accordance with UFC Standard 10-1 for extra (high) hazard.

79.602.1.3 Emergency communications. A dependable method, acceptable to the chief, shall be available for notifying the fire department in the event of a fire or other emergency.

79.602.1.4 Static electricity control. Precautions shall be taken to prevent the accumulation and discharge of static electricity. See API 2003—March 1982.

79.602.1.5 Electrical equipment. Electrical equipment used in the area shall be explosion proof, meeting the requirements of Class I, Group D, Division 1, or approved for the service.

79.602.2 Preparation for Opening the Tank.

79.602.2.1 Tank isolation. Before work on the exterior surface of the tank begins, tanks shall be inspected to determine how the tank is to be isolated. If a tank is equipped with a manifold vent, fill line or syphon assembly, necessary measures shall be taken to isolate the tank to be worked on from other tanks. Product and vapor-recovery piping shall be disconnected and blanked off. The vent for the tank being lined shall be isolated from vents for other tanks which could still be in service. When necessary, a temporary, separate vent for the tank being lined shall be installed.

79.602.2.2 Electrical disconnect. Electrical switches supplying electrical current to submerged pumps and other equipment connected to the tank shall be disconnected and locked.

79.602.3 Removal of Liquid Product. Product, water and sediment shall be removed as thoroughly as is possible using explosion-proof or air-driven pumps. Pump motors and suction hoses shall be bonded to the tank to prevent electrostatic ignition hazards. See API 2003—March 1982. A small quantity of water is allowed to be pumped into the tank to float the product from a low spot where it can be pumped from the tank. Also, where possible, fill or drop tubes shall be removed to allow for maximum removal of all liquids and to provide for adequate air ventilation.

EXCEPTION: When purging using an eductor-type air mover, the fill or drop tube shall remain in place. See Appendix I, Figure 79-6-1.

79.602.4 Purging.

79.602.4.1 Removal of flammable vapors (gas freeing). The tank shall be thoroughly purged with air to remove flammable vapors. The concentration of flammable vapors in a tank could go through the flammable range before a safe atmosphere is obtained. Precautions shall be taken to eliminate the possibility of static electricity discharge during gas-freeing procedures. See API 2003—March 1982.

79.602.4.2 Pressure limit. Air pressure in the tank must not exceed 5-pounds-per-square-inch (34.5 kPa) gage. To prevent excess air pressure, the vent line shall be checked to make certain it is free from obstruction and traps.

79.602.4.3 Methods. Ventilation of the tank shall be accomplished by one of three methods as listed below:

1. An eductor-type air mover, usually driven by compressed air, shall be properly bonded to prevent the possibility of static electricity generation and discharge. When using this method, the fill or drop tube shall remain in place to ensure the vapors are drawn from the bottom of the tank. An extension shall be used to discharge vapors to a minimum of 12 feet (3657.6 mm) above the grade. See Appendix I, Figure 79-6-1.

2. A diffused air blower shall have the air-diffusing pipe properly bonded to prevent the possibility of static electricity generation and discharge. Fill or drop tubes are allowed to be removed to enhance diffusion of the air in the tank. Air supply shall be from a compressor which has been checked to ensure a clean air supply, free from volatile vapors. Air pressure in the tank shall not exceed 5-pounds-per-square-inch (34.5 kPa) gage. See Appendix I, Figure 79-6-2.

3. A fan-type air mover shall be used to blow air into the tank through the fill opening of the tank. The fan shall be driven by compressed air or a Class I, Group D, Division 1 approved electric motor. The fan shall be properly bonded to the tank to prevent the possibility of static electricity generation and discharge. Fill or drop tubes are allowed to be removed to enhance diffusion of air in the tank. The tank vent shall be inspected to make sure it is free of all obstructions. Air pressure in the tank shall not exceed 5-pounds-per-square-inch (34.5 kPa) gage. See Appendix I, Figure 79-6-3.

79.602.5 Testing Flammable Vapor Concentrations. Tests shall be conducted to determine flammability of the vapor in the excavated area and in the tank. Such tests shall be made with a combustible gas indicator, which is properly calibrated on hexane in air and thoroughly checked and maintained in accordance with manufacturer's instructions. Persons responsible for testing shall be trained and thoroughly familiar with the use of the instrument and interpretation of the instrument's readings.

When purging is being performed by a diffused air blower or fan air blower, the tank shall be tested by placing the combustible gas indicator probe into the fill opening with the fill or drop tube removed. Readings shall be taken at the bottom, middle and upper portions of the tank, and the instrument shall be purged with fresh air after each reading. When purging is being performed by an eductor-type air mover, readings shall be conducted through a probe hole provided at the base of the eductor. See Appendix I, Figure 79-6-1. Readings of 10 percent or less of the lower flammable limit, as indicated in the tank and at the vent riser or eductor, shall be obtained before the tank is considered safe for opening.

79.602.6 Opening the Tank.

79.602.6.1 Steel tank. If no access opening exists in a tank, an opening with the minimum dimension of 24 inches by 30 inches (609.6 mm by 762.0 mm) shall be cut in the top. The tank section to be removed shall be marked square with chalk, and a hole drilled with a nonsparking drill, such as an air-driven drill, at one corner of the section using lubricating oil to reduce friction, heat and possible sparks. After the hole is drilled, the tank vapors shall again be tested by inserting the meter probe into the hole to verify that the vapor concentration does not exceed 10 percent of the lower flammable limit.

The tank shall be cut using a nonsparking tool, such as an air-driven saber saw or a snipper, using lubricating oil to reduce friction, heat and possible sparks. Prior to the final cut, the plate shall be supported to prevent it from falling into the tank.

79.602.6.2 Purging safety. Purging, air ventilation and testing shall continue throughout the entire operation. During the tank-cutting operation, minimal air pressure shall be maintained to prevent a blow out.

79.602.7 Tank Entry.

79.602.7.1 Pre-entry procedures. When entering tanks, safe entry procedures shall be followed. See API Publications 2015—September 1985 and 2015A—June 1982. Procedures shall include checking the oxygen content inside the tank with a properly calibrated oxygen monitor. At all times, personnel entering the tank shall be equipped with positive-pressure air-supplied equipment with full-face enclosure and safety harness connected to a safety line held by a standby person outside the tank. A self-contained breathing apparatus shall be immediately available to the standby person for rescue operations or other emergencies.

Oil- and water-resistant rubber or neoprene boots and gloves shall be worn. Clothing shall cover the arms, legs, torso and head of the tank entry personnel. Disposable clothing, impervious to product, shall be used. Clothing saturated with product shall be removed immediately. Personnel working inside the tank shall be knowledgeable of safety requirements for working in tanks and confined spaces. See ANSI Z117.1—1977.

79.602.7.2 Post-entry procedures. Tests with the combustible gas indicator shall be performed periodically in the tank to ascertain that the tank vapors are 10 percent or less of lower flammable limit. During sludge removal, monitoring shall be continuous. The vent line shall remain clear and unobstructed to allow continuous ventilation. All other lines and openings shall be plugged or capped off to ensure no liquids or vapors can enter the tank during the lining operation.

79.602.8 Sludge Removal. Sludge accumulation on the bottom of the tank shall be removed and placed in approved containers. Disposal and documentation shall be in accordance with appropriate local, state and federal regulations.

SECTION 79.603 — TANK INSPECTION, PREPARATION AND QUALIFICATION

79.603.1 Abrasive Blasting.

79.603.1.1 Precautions. Abrasive blasting personnel shall be familiar with ignition hazards and necessary precautions. See API Publication 2027—December 1982.

Before abrasive blasting, the tank shall be checked with the combustible gas indicator to ensure that flammable vapors have not entered the tank.

Abrasive blast cleaning operations shall not be conducted on surfaces that will be wet after blasting and before application of the lining material, when the surface is less than 5°F (2.8°C) above the dewpoint or when the relative humidity of the air is greater than 85 percent.

Abrasive blast operators shall wear approved helmets connected to sources of clean air. Bonding shall be provided between the blasting nozzle and the work surface, or the blasting nozzle shall be grounded to provide equivalent protection from static charges.

Separators and traps shall be used to remove oil and water from compressed air utilized to operate blasting equipment.

79.603.1.2 Preliminary inspection. A visual inspection and assessment of the tank's condition shall be conducted prior to sandblasting to determine if the tank will satisfy the criteria for acceptance.

79.603.1.3 Steel tanks. The entire internal tank surface shall be abrasive blasted to a white-metal finish, completely free of scale, rust and foreign matter. See SSPC SP 5, White Metal Blast Cleaning—1985.

Following completion of the abrasive blasting operation, the surface shall be brushed with a clean brush constructed of hair bristle or fiber, blown with compressed air and vacuum cleaned.

79.603.2 Tank Inspection and Testing.

79.603.2.1 Qualifications. Openings are allowed to be cut in tanks for entry for inspection purposes.

79.603.2.2 Equipment. During tank inspection, the entire internal surface of the tank shall be visually inspected using a light fixture and cords, if required, approved for Class I, Group D, Division 1 hazardous locations.

79.603.2.3 Steel tanks. The visual inspection of steel tanks shall determine the existence and extent of defects such as pitting, perforations, split seams, internal corrosion and evidence of shell metal thickness. Shell metal thickness shall be determined by one of the following test methods:

1. Ultrasonic technique, nondestructive test method.
2. Other approved test methods.

79.603.2.4 Ultrasonic thickness gaging. Ultrasonic thickness gaging procedures, when used, shall establish that the average shell metal thickness is greater than 75 percent of the original shell thickness. In no case shall the shell thickness be less than $^1/_8$ inch (3.2 mm).

Ultrasonic thickness gaging qualifications, procedures, reports and acceptance standards shall be approved. See Appendix II.

SECTION 79.604 — APPLICATION OF LINING AND TANK CLOSING

79.604.1 Application of Lining.

79.604.1.1 General. Personnel safety and clothing shall comply with the requirements of Sections 79.602.1 and 79.602.7.

79.604.1.2 Steel tanks. Prior to application of lining material, a minimum $^{1}/_{4}$-inch-thick (6.4 mm) steel reinforcing plate, rolled to the contour of the tank, and with minimum dimensions of 8 inches by 8 inches (203.2 mm by 203.2 mm) shall be installed under the fill or drop tube and the gaging tube. The plate shall be covered with fiberglass cloth embedded in resin.

The blast-cleaned surface shall be lined or primed within eight hours after blasting and before any visible rusting occurs. Only those lining materials meeting the specifications in Section 79.601.5 shall be used. Manufacturer's instructions shall be followed on handling and mixing of resin compounds, and the compounds shall be applied to the entire interior surface of the tank by the manufacturer or authorized distributor following the specified method of application. The lining shall be applied to a minimum thickness of 100 mils (2.54 mm) and a nominal thickness of 125 mils (3.2 mm) at the recommended application temperature. If a heater is used to accelerate the curing process, other work that might release flammable vapors in the work area shall be discontinued. The heating unit shall be attended whenever it is in operation.

79.604.2 Post-lining Testing.

79.604.2.1 Steel tanks. Upon completion of lining application, the following tests shall be performed:

1. A high-voltage electrical inspection, Holiday Tightness Test, shall be performed using a Tinker Rasor Holiday Detector Model AP/W output power voltage pac 6,000 volt/1,600 volt 15-inch (381.0 mm) silicon brush electrode, or other acceptable instrument to ensure the absence of air pockets or pin holes in the lining material. The test shall be conducted at a rate of 100 volts per mil (0.025 mm) of nominal lining thickness, but in no case less than 10,000 volts. See NACE Standard RP-02-74.

2. A lining thickness test shall be performed using an Elcometer thickness gage or other acceptable instrument to determine that the lining thickness meets the above requirements.

3. A lining hardness test shall be performed using a Barcol Hardness Tester GYZJ 935 or other acceptable instrument to determine that the lining hardness meets the manufacturer's specifications.

79.604.2.2 Pipe testing. Prior to closing a tank, pressure tightness tests of the piping are allowed to be conducted from the interior of the tank in accordance with *Uniform Fire Code* Section 7901 in lieu of conducting pipe line tests from the exterior after the tank has been closed. Piping shall be free of flammable and combustible liquids or vapors prior to conducting pressure tightness tests of pipes.

79.604.2.3 Remedial action. Test failures shall require correction and retesting until test specifications are met.

79.604.3 Tank Closure. If an opening has been cut, the tank shall be sealed as follows:

1. A $^{1}/_{4}$-inch-thick-minimum (6.4 mm) steel cover plate, but not less in thickness than the original size plate, rolled to the contour of the tank, shall be made to overlap the hole at least 2 inches (50.8 mm) on each side. The cover shall be welded to the tank or sealed in accordance with this section.

2. The cover shall be used as a template to locate $^{3}/_{4}$-inch-diameter (19.0 mm) holes not exceeding 5-inch (127.0 mm) centers, 1 inch (25.4 mm) from the edge of the cover and tank opening.

3. The cover plate and the tank shell exterior which will be under the cover plate shall be abrasive blasted to white metal on both sides, and the entire inside cover surface shall be coated with a gasket of interior lining material.

4. Before the gasket material on the cover cures, the cover shall be fastened to the tank using minimum $^{3}/_{8}$-inch-diameter (9.5 mm) by minimum $1^{1}/_{2}$-inch-long (38.1 mm) bolts, with washers sized to span the $^{3}/_{4}$-inch (19.0 mm) holes in the cover plate.

When not using self-tapping bolts, the bolt shafts shall be placed through the holes from inside of the tank and held in place by spring clips, then fastened with washers and nuts. See Appendix I, Figure 79-6-4.

5. After being bolted to the tank, the cover plate and surrounding tank surface shall be lined to a minimum distance of 4 inches (101.6 mm) on all sides of the cover plate and allowed to cure.

6. A high-voltage electrical inspection Holiday Test shall be performed on the cover plate in accordance with Section 79.604.2.

7. The cover plate seal shall be tightness tested by performing an air-pressure test of the tank at no less than 3-pounds-per-square-inch (20.7 kPa) gage and applying a soap solution to the cover and inspecting for bubbles. The test shall be performed while the tank is free of petroleum product liquid and prior to covering the entry area with backfill and paving.

79.604.4 Final Test. Lined tanks shall be tested as specified in *Uniform Fire Code* Section 7902 as required for underground tanks. Certification of tank tightness shall be provided by the tank owner.

APPENDIX I
FIGURES

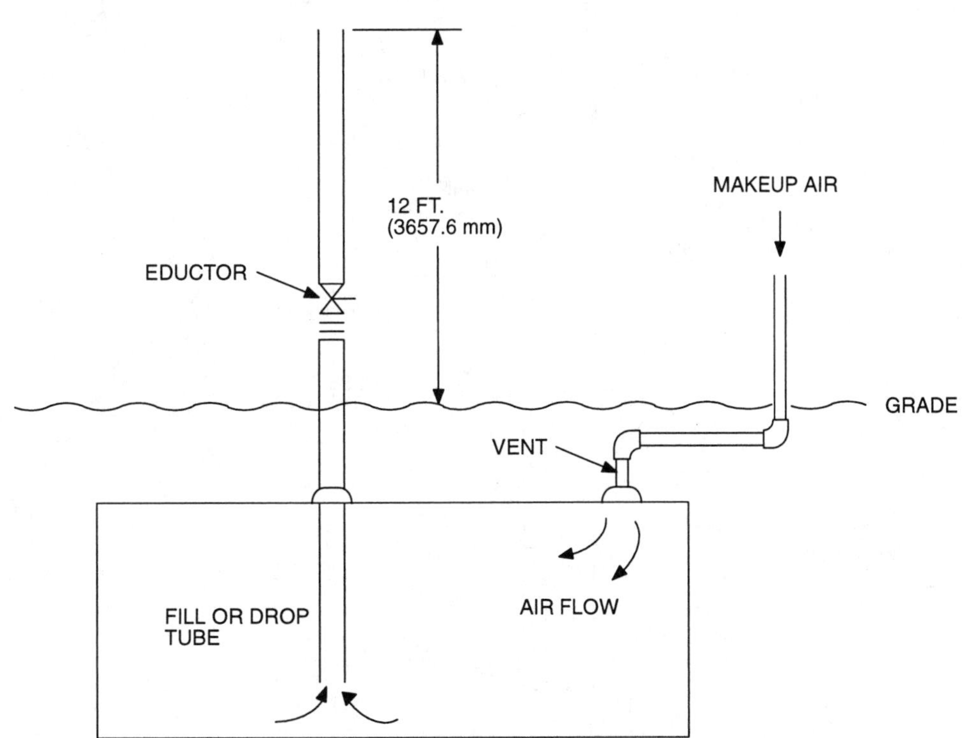

FIGURE 79-6-1—EDUCTOR-TYPE AIR MOVER

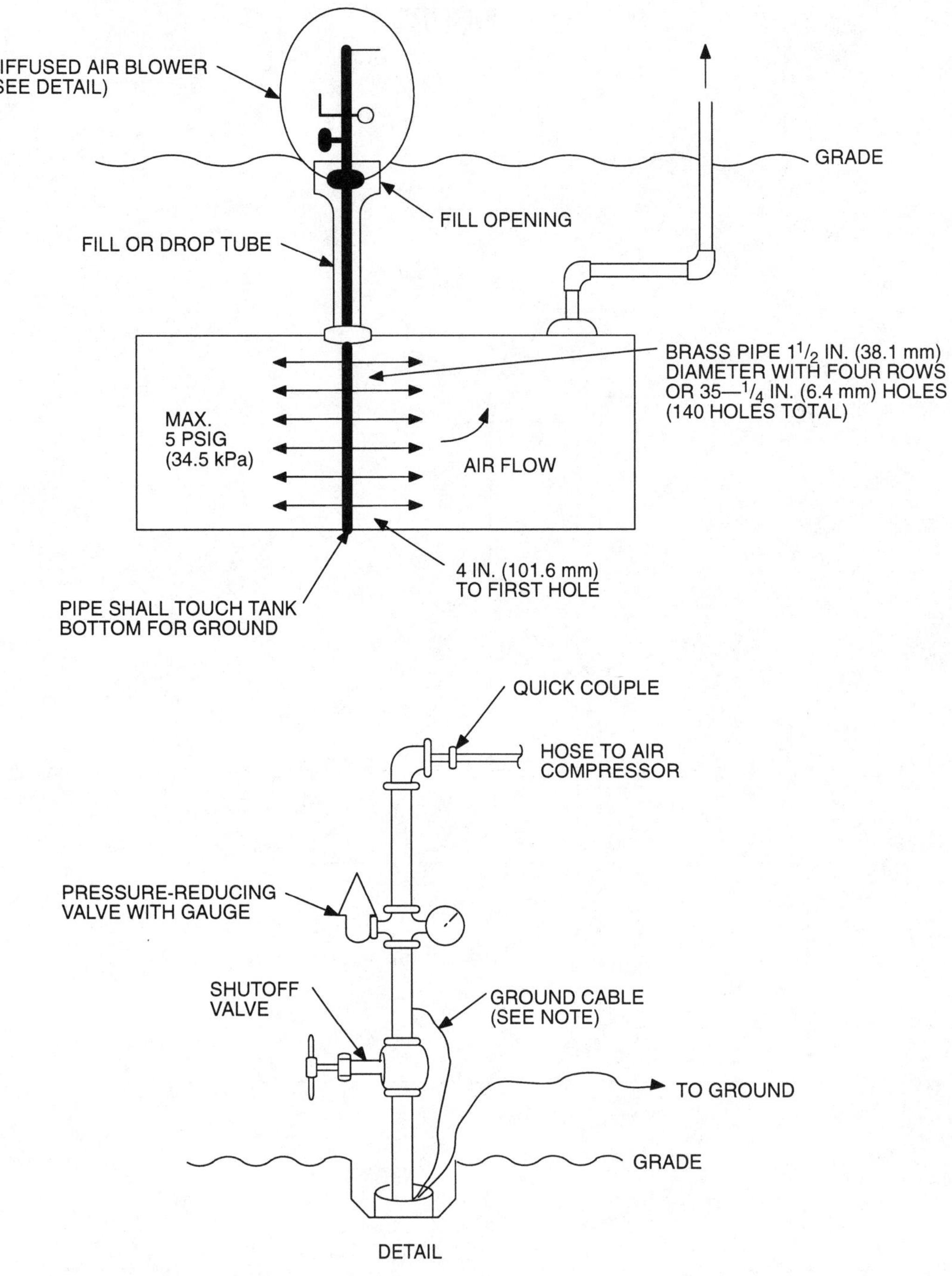

NOTE: Ground cable brazed to pipe shall be clamped to fill pipe. Use 12-gage ground wire from fill pipe to water pipe or ground rod.

FIGURE 79-6-2—DIFFUSED AIR BLOWER

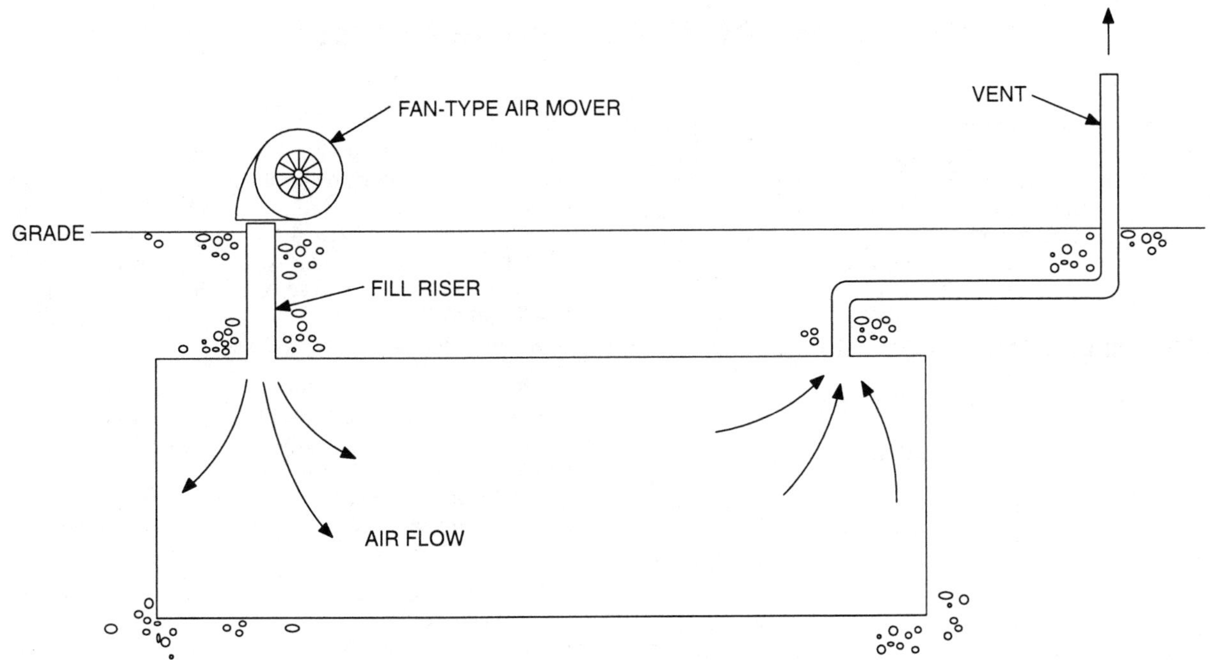

FIGURE 79-6-3—FAN-TYPE AIR MOVER

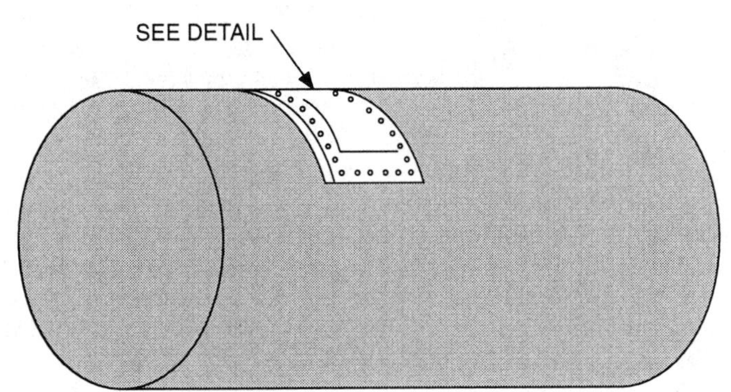

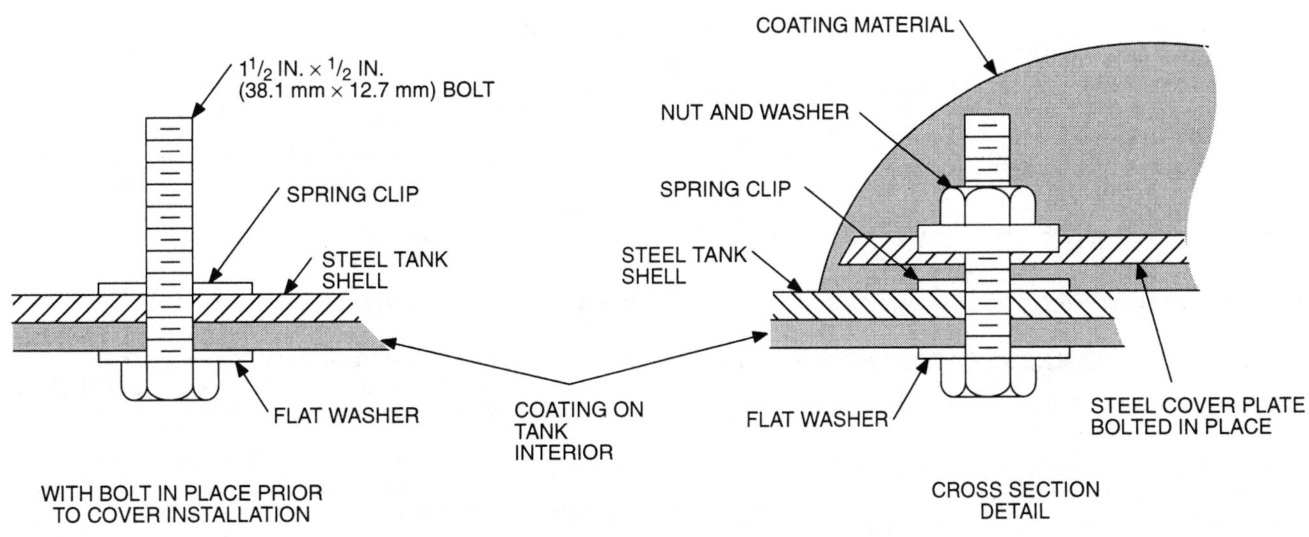

FIGURE 79-6-4— INSTALLATION OF TANK COVER PLATE

APPENDIX II
ULTRASONIC THICKNESS GAGING PROCEDURE

1. SCOPE

Internal inspection and assessment of installed underground storage tanks by ultrasonic thickness gaging shall be in accordance with this appendix. In general, this appendix prescribes personnel certification requirements, test equipment capability, tank interior surface preparation, gaging procedures, minimum acceptable grid patterns for ultrasonic thickness gaging, tank inspection report requirements, and pass and fail criteria.

2. PERSONNEL QUALIFICATION

Personnel performing ultrasonic thickness gaging of installed underground storage tanks shall be trained and certified in an approved manner. An acceptable level of training and certification is Nondestructive Testing, Level I, competence in accordance with the guidelines specified by the American Society for Nondestructive Testing, Recommended Practice SNT-TC-1A—1988. Qualification requirements shall be limited to ultrasonic thickness gaging.

Qualified personnel shall be responsible for conducting ultrasonic thickness gaging, data interpretation and evaluation.

The employer shall establish and maintain a written procedure for administration of training, examination and certification of nondestructive testing personnel.

3. EQUIPMENT CAPABILITY SPECIFICATION

Equipment used for gaging shall meet the following minimum requirements:

Measurement range	0.050 inch to 2 inches (1.27 mm to 50.8 mm)
Resolution	0.002 inch (0.05 mm) minimum

4. SURFACE PREPARATION

After the tank has been emptied, the interior tank surfaces shall be cleaned as required for the use of ultrasonic thickness gaging equipment.

5. GAGING OBJECTIVE

The objective of thickness gaging is to ensure the average tank shell thickness is greater than 75 percent of the original shell metal thickness through a series of identified, averaged measurements of 3-foot-by-3-foot (914.4 mm by 914.4 mm) quadrants; 1-foot-by-1-foot (304.8 mm by 304.8 mm) subdivisions of quadrants; perforations; and thin metal target areas.

6. ORIGINAL SHELL METAL THICKNESS

Original shell metal thickness shall be established by gage measurements taken at the tank top access way.

7. ULTRASONIC THICKNESS GAGING PROCEDURE

Control Quadrants. For gaging measurement control, tank walls shall be divided into quadrants as follows:

Walls. Measurements for tank walls shall be divided into 3-foot by 3-foot (914.4 mm by 914.4 mm) quadrants beginning at the bottom of the end of the tank nearest the fill pipe and extending outward around the tank circumference and along the tank length. Any additional area of the tank wall which is less than 3 feet by 3 feet (914.4 mm by 914.4 mm) shall be measured and treated as additional quadrants. See Figure 79-6-5.

Heads. Measurements for tank heads shall divide each head into four equal sections by establishing a horizontal and vertical diameter line as an axis. Each section shall be divided into 3-foot-by-3-foot (914.4 mm by 914.4 mm) quadrants beginning at the axis center point and extending outward on each axis line. Any additional area of the tank head which is less than 3 feet by 3 feet (914.4 mm by 914.4 mm) shall be measured and treated as additional quadrants. See Figure 79-6-6.

Quadrant Gaging. Thickness gaging measurements shall be taken in the center of each quadrant of the tank wall and heads. Thickness readings 75 percent or less than the original shell metal thickness shall require further gaging as prescribed for subdivided quadrant gaging. Thickness readings greater than 75 percent of the original shell metal thickness shall establish the average measurement reported for the quadrant. See Figure 79-6-7.

Gaging Quadrant Subdivisions. Quadrants with center gage measurements of 75 percent or less than the original shell metal thickness shall be further divided into nine equal subdivisions, except for perimeter subdivisions of head quadrants, which are allowed to be less than equal in size. See Figure 79-6-5. Thickness gaging measurements shall be taken in the center of each subdivision. The subdivision thickness readings shall be averaged, and the results shall establish the average measurement reported for the quadrant. See Figure 79-6-8. Subdivision thickness readings of less than 50 percent of the original shell metal thickness shall require further gaging as prescribed for target areas. See Figure 79-6-9.

Thin Wall Target Area Gaging. Areas where the thickness gaging measurement is less than 50 percent of the original shell metal thickness shall each receive eight additional readings made at 1.5-inch (38.1 mm) and 3-inch (76.2 mm) radiuses around such identified areas. See Figure 79-6-9. The average of the nine readings shall establish the average measurement reported for the subdivision. See Figure 79-6-8.

Tank Shell Average. Tank shell average thickness shall be established from the computations in Figure 79-6-7.

8. REPORTS

Thickness gaging readings shall be reported on an ultrasonic thickness gaging report. See Figures 79-6-7 and 79-6-8.

Reports shall be maintained for reference and shall be made available to the chief. Computer recording, file maintenance and reference retrieval are allowed to be used in lieu of the report forms in Figures 79-6-7 and 79-6-8.

9. PASS/FAIL CRITERIA

A tank shall be considered unacceptable for interior lining if the average shell thickness is 75 percent or less than the original shell metal thickness as computed in Figure 79-6-7, or

If the average of the gage readings of the subdivisions of a quadrant is 50 percent or less than the original shell metal thickness as computed in Figure 79-6-8, or

If the thickness of the shell wall is less than $^1/_8$ inch (3.2 mm) at any point.

APPENDIX III
REFERENCED STANDARDS

The following organizations publish standards referenced herein:

American National Standards Institute, Inc.
1430 Broadway
New York, NY 10018

American Petroleum Institute
1220 L. Street, N.W.
Washington, DC 20005

American Society for Nondestructive Testing
1711 Arlingate Lane
Post Office Box 28518
Columbus, OH 43228-0518

American Society for Testing and Materials
100 Barr Harbor Drive
West Conshohocken, PA 19428

National Association of Corrosion Engineers
1440 South Creek Drive
Houston, TX 77084

Steel Structures Painting Council
4400 5th Avenue
Pittsburgh, PA 15213

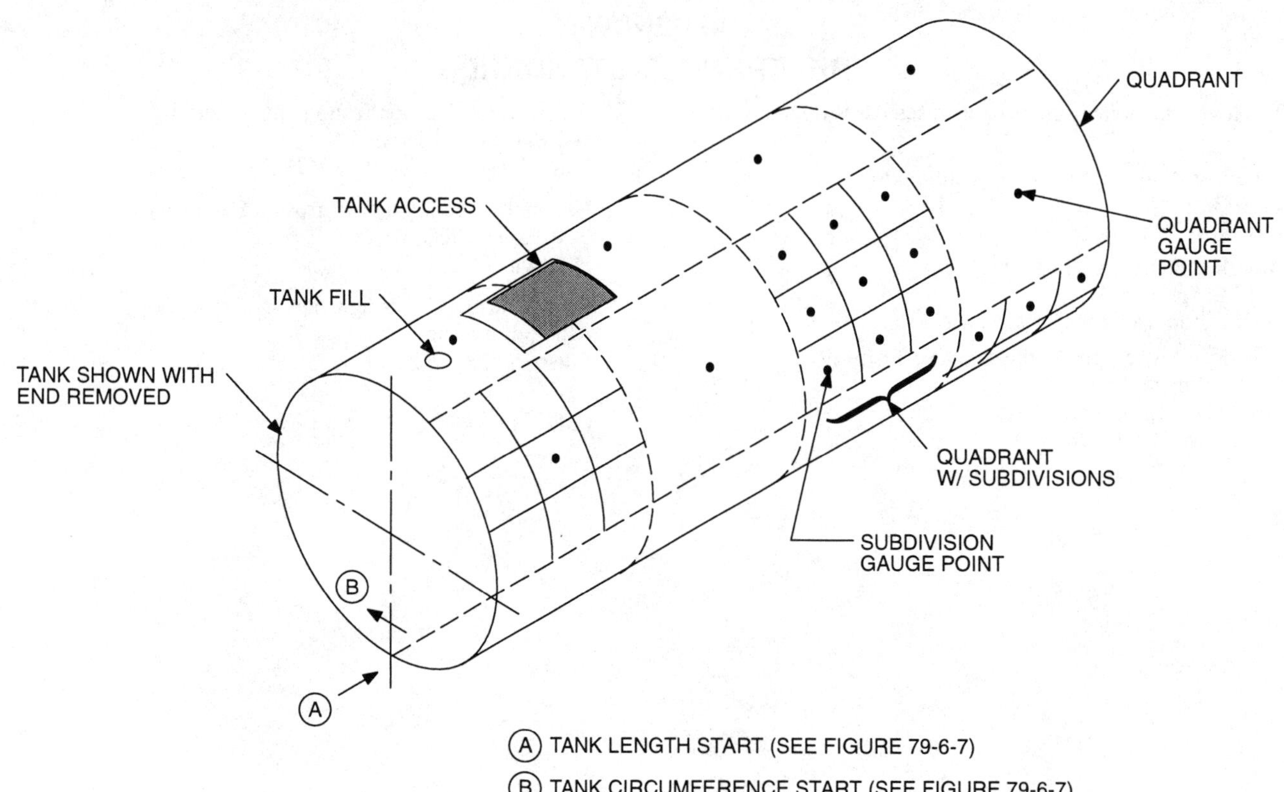

FIGURE 79-6-5—TANK WALL DIAGRAM

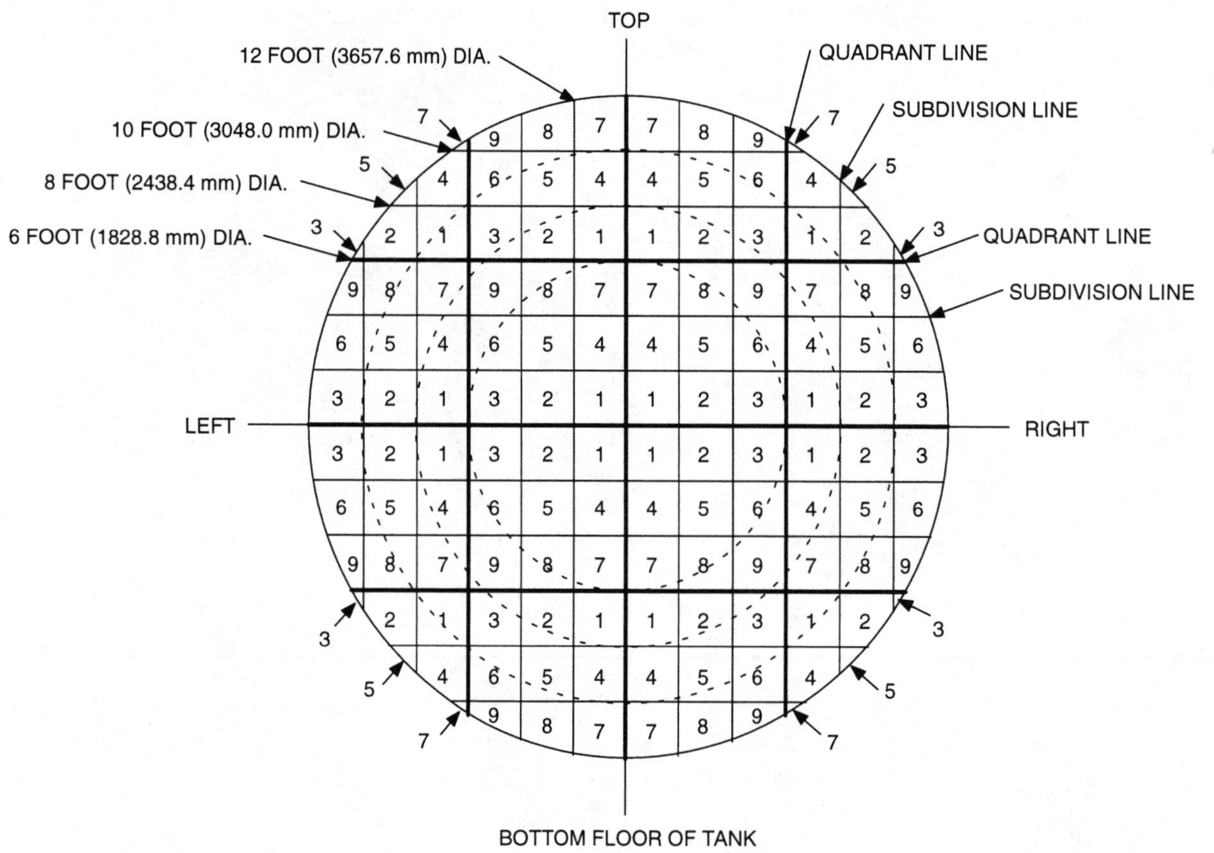

FIGURE 79-6-6—TYPICAL TANK-HEAD DIAGRAM

ULTRASONIC THICKNESS GAGING REPORT

For subdivided quadrants and targets, use Figure 79-6-8

TANK WALLS

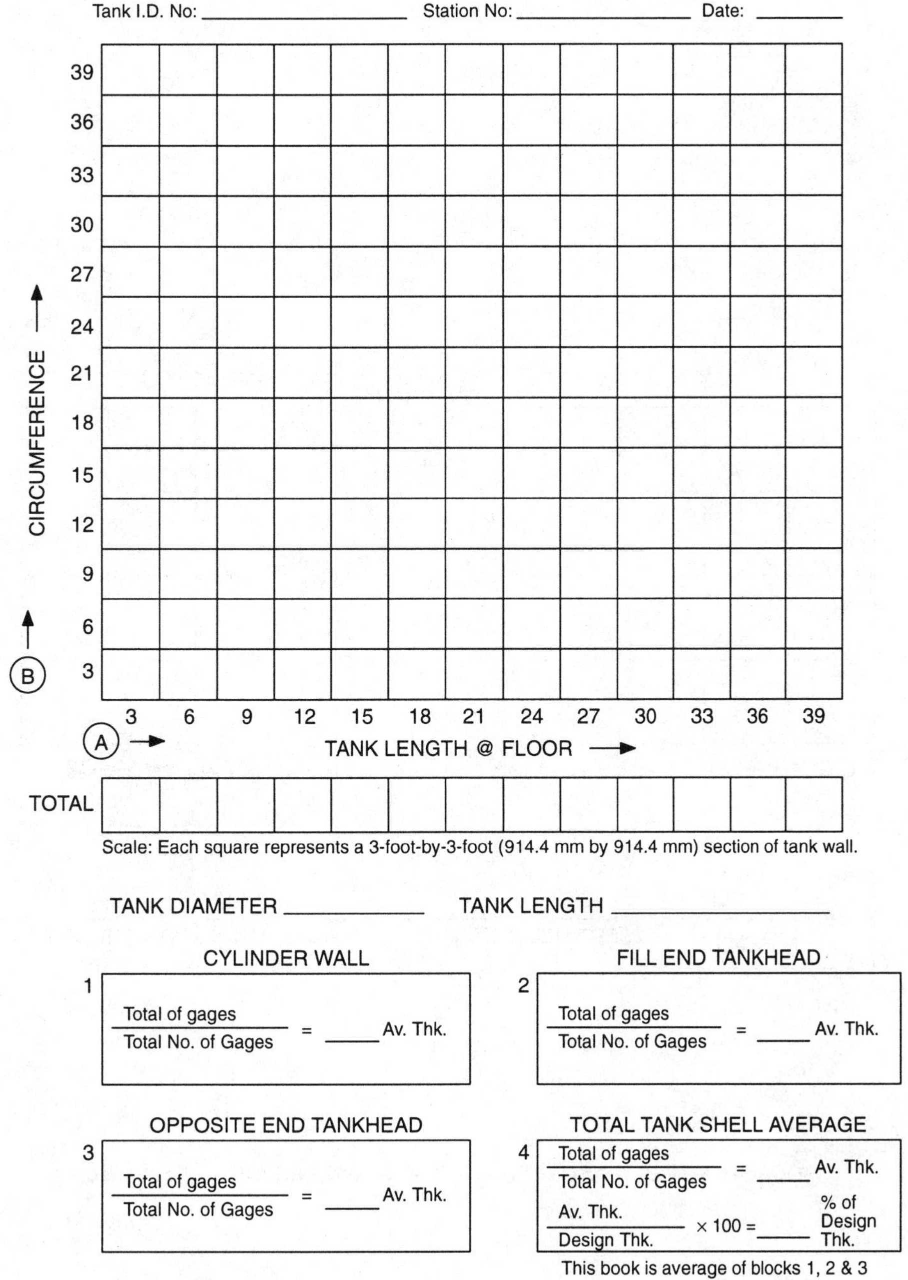

Tank I.D. No: ____________ Station No: ____________ Date: ________

CIRCUMFERENCE →

B → 3, 6, 9, 12, 15, 18, 21, 24, 27, 30, 33, 36, 39

A → 3, 6, 9, 12, 15, 18, 21, 24, 27, 30, 33, 36, 39

TANK LENGTH @ FLOOR →

TOTAL

Scale: Each square represents a 3-foot-by-3-foot (914.4 mm by 914.4 mm) section of tank wall.

TANK DIAMETER ____________ TANK LENGTH ____________

1 CYLINDER WALL

$\frac{\text{Total of gages}}{\text{Total No. of Gages}}$ = ______ Av. Thk.

2 FILL END TANKHEAD

$\frac{\text{Total of gages}}{\text{Total No. of Gages}}$ = ______ Av. Thk.

3 OPPOSITE END TANKHEAD

$\frac{\text{Total of gages}}{\text{Total No. of Gages}}$ = ______ Av. Thk.

4 TOTAL TANK SHELL AVERAGE

$\frac{\text{Total of gages}}{\text{Total No. of Gages}}$ = ______ Av. Thk.

$\frac{\text{Av. Thk.}}{\text{Design Thk.}}$ × 100 = ______ % of Design Thk.

This book is average of blocks 1, 2 & 3

FIGURE 79-6-7—ULTRASONIC THICKNESS GAGING REPORT

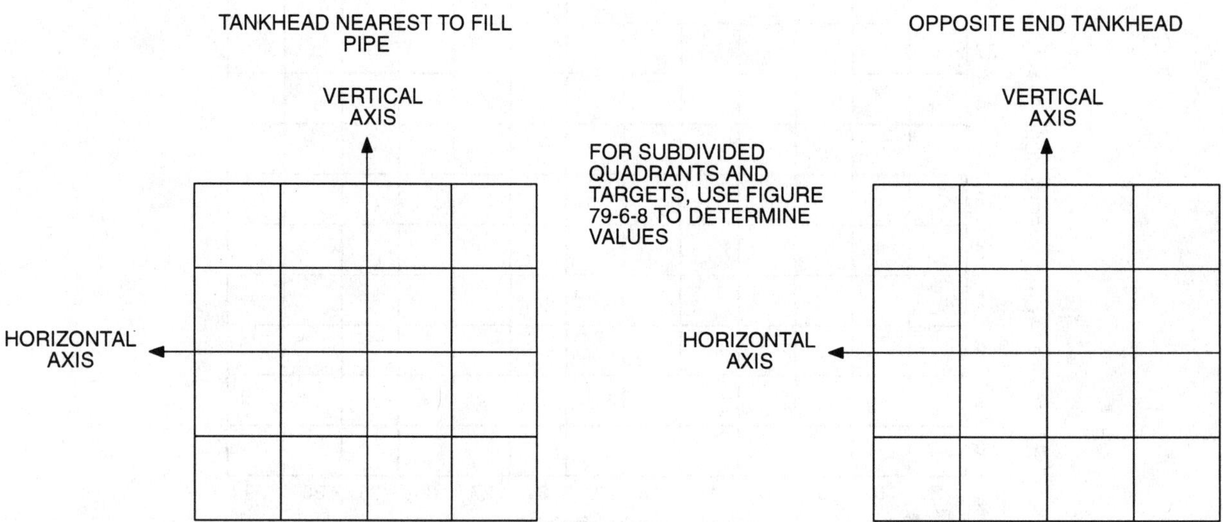

SCALE: Each square foot represents a 3-foot-by-3-foot (914.4 mm by 914.4 mm) section of tankhead

	ACCEPT
	REJECT

CERTIFIED INSTALLER CERTIFICATION LEVEL (SEE SECTION 2) DATE

FIGURE 79-6-7—ULTRASONIC THICKNESS GAGING REPORT—(Continued)

ULTRASONIC THICKNESS GAGING REPORT FOR SUBDIVIDED QUADRANTS

QUADRANT NO.
TL. AVG. THK.

Subquadrant Target No.	Average Thickness

Total of gages / Total No. of Gages = ______ Av. Thk.

Av. Thk. / Design Thk. x 100 = ______ % of Design Thk.

Each quadrant which is subdivided shall be assigned a number in the order it is identified.

Transfer the "Summary" Box to the appropriate square on Figure 79-6-7.

If average of quadrant is 50% or less than original shell metal thickness, refer to Pass and Fail Criteria.

☐ Perforation ☐ Thin Metal

SUB-QUADRANT/TARGET #1	
Location	**Thickness**
TOTAL	

Total of gages / Total No. of Gages = ______ Av. Thk.

☐ Perforation ☐ Thin Metal

SUB-QUADRANT/TARGET #2	
Location	**Thickness**
TOTAL	

Total of gages / Total No. of Gages = ______ Av. Thk.

☐ Perforation ☐ Thin Metal

SUB-QUADRANT/TARGET #3	
Location	**Thickness**
TOTAL	

Total of gages / Total No. of Gages = ______ Av. Thk.

☐ Perforation ☐ Thin Metal

SUB-QUADRANT/TARGET #4	
Location	**Thickness**
TOTAL	

Total of gages / Total No. of Gages = ______ Av. Thk.

☐ Perforation ☐ Thin Metal

SUB-QUADRANT/TARGET #5	
Location	**Thickness**
TOTAL	

Total of gages / Total No. of Gages = ______ Av. Thk.

☐ Perforation ☐ Thin Metal

SUB-QUADRANT/TARGET #6	
Location	**Thickness**
TOTAL	

Total of gages / Total No. of Gages = ______ Av. Thk.

☐ Perforation ☐ Thin Metal

SUB-QUADRANT/TARGET #7	
Location	**Thickness**
TOTAL	

Total of gages / Total No. of Gages = ______ Av. Thk.

☐ Perforation ☐ Thin Metal

SUB-QUADRANT/TARGET #8	
Location	**Thickness**
TOTAL	

Total of gages / Total No. of Gages = ______ Av. Thk.

☐ Perforation ☐ Thin Metal

SUB-QUADRANT/TARGET #9	
Location	**Thickness**
TOTAL	

Total of gages / Total No. of Gages = ______ Av. Thk.

FIGURE 79-6-8—ULTRASONIC THICKNESS GAGING REPORT FOR SUBDIVIDED QUADRANTS

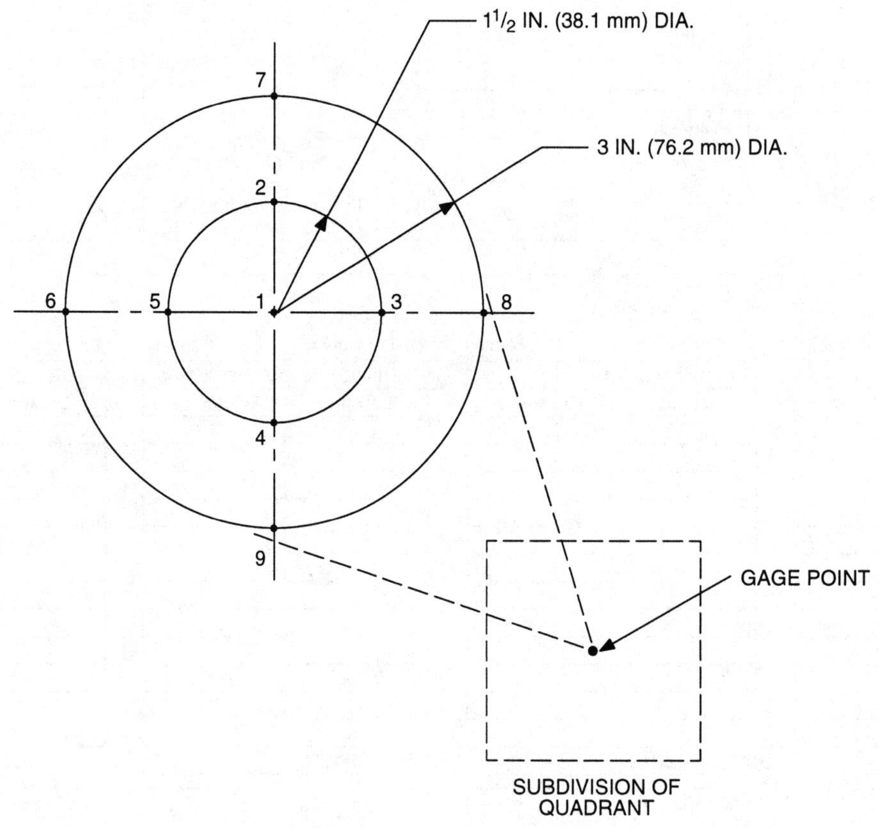

FIGURE 79-6-9—THIN-WALL TARGET

UNIFORM FIRE CODE STANDARD 79-7

TESTING REQUIREMENTS FOR PROTECTED ABOVEGROUND TANKS

Used to Store Motor Vehicle Fuels within the Scope of Appendix II-F, *Uniform Fire Code*

See Sections 7902.1.8.2.7, 7903.3.3 and Appendix II-F, *Uniform Fire Code*

NOTE: This standard was formerly Uniform Fire Code Standard A-II-F-1.

SECTION 79.701 — SCOPE

Aboveground atmospheric motor vehicle fuel storage tanks intended for use in conjunction with dispensing motor fuels into vehicles shall be in accordance with this standard. This standard includes requirements for test tanks, test tank conditioning, fire testing, postfire testing, physical testing and pass-fail criteria.

This standard also establishes performance criteria for thermal and physical testing of protected aboveground atmospheric motor vehicle fuel storage tanks and requires an evaluation of applicable environmental exposure factors.

The purpose of this test is to evaluate protected aboveground atmospheric motor vehicle fuel storage tanks which are intended to provide a level of thermal and physical protection similar to that achieved with underground tank installations.

SECTION 79.702 — TESTING PROCEDURES

79.702.1 Prefire Test Tank Condition and Configuration.

79.702.1.1 Size of test tank. When test results are to be applied to multiple tank sizes, the tank to be tested shall be that tank with the greatest ratio of fire-exposed surface to tank volume. This is not necessarily the tank with the smallest capacity. One tank size test shall satisfy the testing need for all similarly designed tanks in a product line which have an equal or smaller ratio of fire-exposed surface area to tank volume.

79.702.1.2 Dryness. When the tank protective materials contain moisture such as water, solvents, etc., the materials shall be conditioned such that the dampest portion of the material has achieved a moisture content corresponding to drying to equilibrium with air in the range of 50 percent to 75 percent relative humidity at 73°F ± 5°F (22.8°C ± 2.8°C).

If samples dried in a heated building do not comply with these requirements after a 12-month conditioning period, or if the nature of the construction is such that drying of the sample interior will be prevented by hermetic sealing, these requirements are allowed to be waived, and the sample is allowed to be tested in the condition in which it then exists.

79.702.1.3 Temperature. The ambient air temperature at the beginning of the test shall be within the range of 50°F to 90°F (10.0°C to 32.2°C).

79.702.1.4 Materials. The tank and all protective materials shall be in their normal operating condition.

79.702.1.5 Venting. Venting devices for normal and emergency operation shall be properly installed.

79.702.1.6 Appurtenances and external equipment. Nonferrous external appurtenances which are intended to be installed in the tank openings shall be installed during the test to determine the potential for such appurtenances to melt and allow an explosive condition to occur. Equipment external to the tank not installed during the test shall be represented by an uninsulated capped Schedule 40 iron pipe nipple a minimum of 6 inches (152.4 mm) in exposed length. The pipe diameter shall be consistent with the opening but shall not be less than $1^1/_2$ inches (38.1 mm).

79.702.2 Type of Fire Test.

79.702.2.1 General. The tests shall be two-hour full-scale tests. Either a pool fire or a furnace test is acceptable as long as the required heat flux is provided. The temperature of the environment that generates the heat flux shall be between 1800°F and 2200°F (982.2°C and 1204.4°C) at all times after the first five minutes of the test. The test specimen shall be exposed to heat flux and temperature conditions representative of total engulfment in the luminous flame regime of a large free-burning liquid-hydrocarbon-fueled pool fire.

79.702.2.2 Tank contents. Test specimens shall be empty during the two-hour test.

79.702.2.3 Furnace test.

79.702.2.3.1 Heat flux. The furnace shall be capable of maintaining a total heat flux of 65,000 Btu per exposed square feet per hour ± 5,000 Btu per exposed square feet per hour (738 176 kJ/m^{2}h ± 56 783 kJ/m^{2}h).

79.702.2.3.2 Furnace curve. The accuracy of the furnace control shall be such that the area under the time-temperature curve, obtained by averaging the results from the furnace probes, is within 7.5 percent of the desired temperature for a two-hour test.

79.702.2.4 Pool fire test. An average total cold wall heat flux of 50,000 Btu per exposed square feet per hour ± 2,500 Btu per exposed square feet per hour (567 828 kJ/m^{2}h ± 28 391 kJ/m^{2}h) averaged over the duration of the test on all exposed surfaces shall be maintained.

79.702.3 Thermocouples.

79.702.3.1 Placement. Thermocouples shall be placed uniformly on the interior surface of the primary tank with no more than 9 square feet (0.84 m^2) per thermocouple and no less than one thermocouple per segment and face or end. Thermocouples shall be placed no closer than 12 inches (304.8 mm) to any tank opening.

79.702.3.2 Recording. The thermocouple readings shall be recorded at intervals not to exceed five minutes during the two-hour fire test.

79.702.4 Fire Test Pass/Fail. A tank shall be considered to be acceptable under Section 79.702.2, provided that:

1. The thermocouple readings shall not exceed an average maximum temperature rise of 260°F (144.4°C), and maximum temperature of any single thermocouple of 400°F (204.4°C),

2. The structural integrity of the primary tank and its supports is maintained, and

3. The required emergency venting remains operational.

79.702.5 Postfire Testing.

79.702.5.1 Hose stream test. Immediately after the fire test, the protected tank shall be subjected to a hose stream test in accordance with the procedures established by the Building Code (see UBC Standard 7-1, Section 7.108, for testing of wall assemblies).

79.702.5.2 Leakage test. A leakage test shall be conducted on each primary tank tested using the production pressure test required in the manufacturer's listing procedure, or a 24-hour leakage test shall be conducted on each primary tank tested maintaining the tank completely full of water.

79.702.6 Postfire Testing Pass/Fail. The tank shall be considered to be acceptable under Section 79.702.5, provided that the primary tank shall remain leak tight.

79.702.7 Physical Testing.

79.702.7.1 General. This phase of testing is allowed to be conducted on either a tested tank or a tank not subjected to the tests described in Section 79.702.2.

79.702.7.2 Impact protection. When impact protection is not provided by guard posts, the tank shall be tested for resistance to heavy vehicle impact by resisting an impact of 12,000 pounds at 10 mph (53 378.6 N at 16.1 km/h) or the equivalent impact energy. The load shall be applied over a 1 square foot (0.093 m^2) area centered at a height of 18 inches (457.2 mm) above the grade. The test tank shall be anchored in accordance with the manufacturer's instructions.

79.702.7.3 Projectile protection. When a projectile test is required by the chief, the protected tank shall be tested in accordance with the requirements for bullet resistance as specified in UFC Section 7702.3.4.3.

79.702.8 Physical Testing Pass/Fail. The tank shall be considered acceptable under Section 79.702.5, provided that the primary tank shall remain leak tight.

79.702.9 Climatic/Environmental Testing. The evaluation of climatic and environmental exposures to which a protected tank could be exposed during its anticipated service life shall be made of the test tank to assess the ability of the protective characteristics of the test tank to perform as intended to meet the requirements of this standard for thermal and physical protection.

SECTION 79.703 — REPORTING OF RESULTS

79.703.1 Report of Test. The report of the test shall contain the following:

1. Description of the test tank to include: drawings showing structural design, plan, elevation, principle cross-section, and other sections as needed for clarity.

2. Location of thermocouples.

3. General ambient conditions at test time.

4. Information on the actual moisture content of the test tank protective material obtained within 72 hours prior to the test.

5. Average and individual temperature data measured in the fire environment.

6. Visual observation made during the test.

7. Photographs of the test tank prior to test, test in progress, and the test tank exterior—posttest.

8. Performance for the protected tank with respect to damage.

9. Pass/fail criteria results.

10. Results of the evaluation of the environmental exposures conducted to assess the ability of the protective characteristics of the tank to perform as intended to meet the requirements of this standard for thermal and physical protection for the service life of the tank.

11. Manufacturer's statement on the expected service life of the tank and limitations on the types of climates or environments to which the tank could be exposed during its service life.

79.703.2 Labeling. A protected tank and other tanks in the same line of tanks manufactured to the specification of the tanks that qualify as meeting the performance criterion of this standard are eligible for labeling. Each tank shall be labeled in the factory prior to installation. The label shall indicate compliance with this standard including any limitations. It shall be permanently attached to the exterior of the protected tank in a location which is readily visible after the tank is installed in the field.

UNIFORM FIRE CODE STANDARD 80-1
STORAGE, DISPENSING AND USE OF SILANE AND ITS MIXTURES

See Sections 8003.8.1, 8003.8.2 and 8004.1.16, *Uniform Fire Code*

SECTION 80.101 — GENERAL

80.101.1 Scope. The storage and use of silane gas and mixtures with a concentration of silane gas 2 percent or more by volume in excess of the exempt amounts in UFC Section 8001.15 shall be in accordance with this standard.

80.101.2 Applicability. *Uniform Fire Code* Article 80 shall apply in addition to this standard.

80.101.3 Building Construction. Indoor storage and use of silane shall be within a room or building conforming to the Building Code. (See UBC Section 307.)

80.101.4 Valves.

80.101.4.1 General. Flow control and container, cylinder and tank valves shall be in accordance with Section 80.101.4.

80.101.4.2 Flow control. Compressed gas containers, cylinders and tanks shall be equipped with reduced-flow valves equipped with restrictive-flow orifices not exceeding 0.010 inch (0.254 mm) in diameter. The presence of the restrictive-flow orifice shall be indicated on the valve and on the container, cylinder or tank by means of a label placed at a prominent location by the manufacturer.

EXCEPTIONS: 1. Manufacturing and filling facilities where silane is produced or mixed and stored prior to sale.

2. Permanently mounted cylinders connected to a manifold, provided that the outlet connection from the manifold is equipped with a restrictive flow orifice.

80.101.4.3 Valves. Container, cylinder and tank valves shall be constructed of stainless steel or other approved materials. Valves shall be equipped with outlet fittings in accordance with nationally recognized standards. See Appendix VI-A, Section 4.2.2.

SECTION 80.102 — STORAGE

80.102.1 Indoor Storage.

80.102.1.1 General. Indoor storage shall be in accordance with UFC Section 8003.8 and Section 80.102.1.

80.102.1.2 Fire protection. When automatic fire-extinguishing systems are required, automatic sprinkler systems shall be used.

80.102.1.3 Gas cabinets or exhausted enclosures. When provided, gas cabinets and exhausted enclosures shall be installed in accordance with UFC Sections 8003.3.1.3.2 and 8003.3.1.3.3. Gas cabinets and exhausted enclosures shall be internally sprinklered. The velocity of ventilation across unwelded fittings and connections on the piping system shall not be less than 200 linear feet per minute (1.02 m/s). The average velocity at the face of the access ports or windows in the gas cabinet shall not be less than 200 linear feet per minute (1.02 m/s) with a minimum velocity of 150 linear feet per minute (0.76 m/s) at any point of the access port or window.

80.102.1.4 Emergency power. Emergency power shall be provided for ventilation systems.

80.102.2 Outdoor Storage. Outdoor storage shall be in accordance with UFC Section 8003.8.2 and the following:

1. Maximum volume of 10,000 cubic feet (283.2 m^3) of gas for each nest.

2. Storage nests shall be separated by aisles a minimum of 6 feet (1828.8 mm) in width.

3. Storage shall be located 25 feet (7620.0 mm) or more from property lines, streets, alleys, public ways, exits to public ways or buildings.

4. Storage shall be separated from other hazardous materials in accordance with UFC Section 8001.11.8.

5. Security shall be provided in accordance with UFC Section 8001.11.2.

SECTION 80.103 — USE AND DISPENSING

80.103.1 Indoor Use and Dispensing.

80.103.1.1 General. Indoor use and dispensing shall be in accordance with UFC Sections 8004.1 and 8004.2 and Section 80.103.1.

80.103.1.2 Gas cabinets or exhausted enclosures. When provided, gas cabinets and exhausted enclosures shall be installed in accordance with UFC Sections 8003.3.1.3.2 and 8003.3.1.3.3. Gas cabinets and exhausted enclosures shall be internally sprinklered. The velocity of ventilation across unwelded fittings and connections on the piping system shall not be less than 200 linear feet per minute (1.02 m/s). The average velocity at the face of the access ports or windows in the gas cabinet shall not be less than 200 linear feet per minute (1.02 m/s) with a minimum velocity of 150 linear feet per minute (0.76 m/s) at any point of the access port or window.

80.103.1.3 Purge gases. Purging of piping and controls located in gas cabinets or exhausted enclosures shall only be performed using a dedicated inert gas supply that is designed to prevent silane from entering the inert gas supply. The use of nondedicated systems or portions of piping systems is allowed on portions of the venting system that are continuously vented to atmosphere. Devices which could interrupt the continuous flow of purge gas to the atmosphere are prohibited.

EXCEPTION: Manufacturing and filling facilities where silane is produced or mixed.

80.103.1.4 Purging operations. Purging operations shall be performed by means ensuring complete purging of the piping and control system before the system is opened to the atmosphere.

80.103.2 Outdoor Use and Dispensing. The outdoor use and dispensing shall be in accordance with UFC Sections 8004.1 and 8004.3 and Section 80.103.1.

UNIFORM FIRE CODE STANDARD 80-2
INDUSTRIAL AND INSTITUTIONAL BULK OXYGEN SYSTEMS

See Sections 7401.1, 7501.1 and 8004.1.14, *Uniform Fire Code*

NOTE: This standard was formerly Uniform Fire Code Standard 74-1.

The National Fire Protection Association Standard for Bulk Oxygen Systems on Consumer Sites, NFPA 50—1990, is hereby adopted by reference as UFC Standard 80-2.

The provisions of this standard shall apply to bulk oxygen systems on consumer premises except when a provision of *Uniform Fire Code,* Volume 1 or an amendment specified in Section 80.201 is applicable, in which case *Uniform Fire Code,* Volume 1 provisions or the amendment shall take precedence.

Supplemental standards referenced by NFPA 50—1990 shall only be considered as guidelines subject to approval by the chief.

NFPA 50—1990 is available from the National Fire Protection Association, 1 Batterymarch Park, Box 9101, Quincy, Massachusetts 02269-9101.

SECTION 80.201 — AMENDMENTS

The Standard for Bulk Oxygen Systems at Consumer Sites, NFPA 50—1990, applies to the installation of bulk oxygen systems located at industrial and institutional sites where the supply to consumer premises originates outside the consumer premises and is delivered by mobile equipment, except as amended by this part. This standard does not apply to bulk oxygen storage systems regulated by *Uniform Fire Code* Articles 49 and 75.

1. Sec. 1-2.1 is deleted.

2. Secs. 1-2.4 and 1-2.5 are deleted.

3. Sec. 1-3 is revised by adding and changing the definitions as follows:

AUTHORITY HAVING JURISDICTION is the official responsible for the administration and enforcement of this standard.

DOT SPECIFICATIONS are the Specifications of the United States Department of Transportation as set forth in the Code of Federal Regulations.

FIRE-RESISTIVE CONSTRUCTION is a building which complies with the requirements for Type I or Type II fire-resistive, Type II One-hour, Type III One-hour or Type V One-hour construction in the Building Code.

NONCOMBUSTIBLE MATERIAL is as defined in *Uniform Fire Code* Article 2.

NONCOMBUSTIBLE/LIMITED-COMBUSTIBLE CONSTRUCTION is a building which complies with the requirements for Type I or Type II construction in the Building Code.

WOOD FRAME CONSTRUCTION is a building which complies with the requirements for Type III-N, Type IV or Type V construction in the Building Code.

The definitions of "approved," "combustible liquid," "flammable liquid," "labeled" and "listed" shall be as set forth in *Uniform Fire Code,* Volume 1.

4. Sec. 2-1.1 is revised by changing the first sentence as follows:

2-1.1 Bulk oxygen storage systems shall be located aboveground out-of-doors, or shall be installed in Type I, Type II, Type III One-Hour or Type IV buildings which are adequately vented and used for that purpose exclusively.

5. Sec. 2-2.1.1 is revised as follows:

2-2.1.1 Not less than 1 foot (304.8 mm) from buildings of noncombustible construction, not less than 50 feet (15 240 mm) from buildings of combustible construction, and not less than 50 feet (15 240 mm) from property lines.

6. Sec. 2-2.1.2 is deleted.

7. Sec. 2-2.1.13 is deleted.

8. Sec. 3-1.2.1 is revised as follows:

3-1.2.1 Be fabricated from materials meeting the impact test reference requirements in accordance with nationally recognized standards. See *Uniform Fire Code* Article 90. Containers operating at pressures above 15 psig (103.4 kPa) shall be designed, constructed and tested in accordance with the appropriate requirements in accordance with nationally recognized standards. See *Uniform Fire Code* Article 90. Insulation surrounding the liquid oxygen container shall be noncombustible.

9. Sec. 3-1.3.1 is revised as follows:

3-1.3.1 Containers shall be designed, constructed and tested in accordance with nationally recognized standards. See *Uniform Fire Code* Article 90.

10. Revise Sec. 3-2.2 as follows:

3-2.2 Material specifications and thickness requirements for piping and tubing shall be in accordance with nationally recognized standards. See *Uniform Fire Code* Article 90.

11. Sec. 3-2.3 is revised as follows:

3-2.3 Piping or tubing for operating temperatures below –20°F (–28.9°C) shall be fabricated from materials meeting the impact requirements in accordance with nationally recognized standards. See *Uniform Fire Code* Article 90.

12. Sec. 3-3.1 is revised as follows:

3-3.1 Bulk oxygen storage containers, regardless of design pressure, shall be equipped with safety-relief devices in accordance with nationally recognized standards. See *Uniform Fire Code* Article 90.

13. Sec. 3-3.3 is revised as follows:

3-3.3 Bulk oxygen storage containers designed and constructed in accordance with Section 3-1.2.1 shall be equipped with a safety-relief valve meeting the provisions of nationally recognized standards for safety-relief devices for compressed gas storage containers which has been approved.

14. Sec. 3-5.9 is revised as follows:

3-5.9 Electrical wiring shall comply with the Electrical Code.

15. Chapter 5 is deleted.

UNIFORM FIRE CODE STANDARD 80-3

FLAMMABLE CRYOGENIC FLUID SYSTEMS AT CONSUMER SITES

See Section 7501.1, *Uniform Fire Code*

NOTE: This is a new standard.

The National Fire Protection Association Standard for Liquefied Hydrogen Systems at Consumer Sites, NFPA 50B—1994, is hereby adopted by reference as UFC Standard 80-3.

The provisions of this standard shall apply to the installation, inspection, maintenance and testing of bulk flammable cryogenic fluid containers and systems at consumer sites except when a provision of *Uniform Fire Code,* Volume 1 or an amendment specified in Section 80.301 is applicable, in which case *Uniform Fire Code,* Volume 1 provisions or the amendment shall take precedence.

Supplemental standards referenced by NFPA 50B—1994 shall only be considered as guidelines subject to approval by the chief.

NFPA 50B—1994 is available from the National Fire Protection Association, 1 Batterymarch Park, Box 9101, Quincy, Massachusetts 02269-9101.

Section 80.301 — AMENDMENTS

The Standard for Liquefied Hydrogen Systems at Consumer Sites, NFPA 50B—1994, shall apply to the installation of bulk flammable cryogenic fluid systems located at industrial sites where the supply to consumer premises originates outside the consumer premises and is delivered by mobile equipment, except as amended by this part. This standard does not apply to noncryogenic flammable fluid systems regulated by *Uniform Fire Code* Articles 49, 79 and 80 or to Liquefied Natural Gas (LNG) facilities regulated under NFPA 59-A—1994. The term "liquefied hydrogen" as used in Chapters 2 through 9 of the standard shall be replaced with the term "flammable cryogenic fluid" throughout unless otherwise indicated.

1. Sec. 1-1.1 is deleted.

2. Section 1-3 is revised by adding and changing the definitions as follows:

AUTHORITY HAVING JURISDICTION is the official responsible for the administration and enforcement of this standard.

CONTAINER is a cryogenic vessel used for transportation, handling or storage.

FLAMMABLE CRYOGENIC FLUID SYSTEM is a system into which flammable cryogenic fluid is delivered and stored and from which it is discharged in the liquid or gaseous form to user piping. The system may include stationary or portable containers, pressure regulators, pressure-relief devices, manifolds, interconnecting piping, and controls as required. The system originates at the storage container fill connection and terminates at the point where flammable cryogenic fluid at service pressure first enters the user's supply line.

The definitions of "approved," "combustible liquid," "flammable liquid," "labeled," "listed," and "noncombustible material" shall be as set forth in *Uniform Fire Code,* Volume 1.

The term "liquefied hydrogen system" is deleted from the definition and replaced with the term "flammable cryogenic fluid system." The balance of the definition remains as published.

The definition of "limited-combustible material" is deleted.

The definition of "portable containers" is deleted and replaced with the definition of "portable tank" as set forth in *Uniform Fire Code,* Volume 1.

3. Sec. 2-1 is revised as follows:

2-1 Containers. Flammable cryogenic fluid containers shall comply with the following:

1. Storage containers shall be designed, constructed and tested in accordance with nationally recognized standards. See UFC Section 9003, Standard a.5.1.

2. Portable containers shall be designed, constructed and tested in accordance with nationally recognized standards. See UFC Section 9003, Standard u.3.3.

4. Sec. 2-2 is revised as follows:

2-2 Supports. Permanently installed containers shall be provided with substantial supports of noncombustible material securely anchored on firm foundations constructed of noncombustible materials. Supports in excess of 18 inches (457.2 mm) in height supporting flammable cryogenic fluid containers shall have a minimum two-hour fire-resistive rating in accordance with nationally recognized standards. See UFC Section 9003, Standard a.4.16.

5. Sec. 2-3 is revised as follows:

2-3 Marking. Each container shall be legibly marked to indicate "Liquefied (name of gas)—Flammable Gas."

6. Sec. 2-4.1 is revised as follows:

2-4.1 Stationary flammable cryogenic fluid containers shall be equipped with pressure-relief devices sized in accordance with nationally recognized standards. See UFC Section 9003, Standard c.1.5.

7. Sec. 2-4.2 is revised as follows:

2-4.2 Portable, flammable cryogenic fluid containers shall be equipped with pressure-relief devices in accordance with nationally recognized standards. See UFC Section 9003, Standard u.3.3. Pressure-relief devices shall be sized in accordance with nationally recognized standards. See UFC Section 9003, Standards c.1.3 and c.1.4.

8. Sec. 2-5.2 is revised as follows:

2-5.2 Material specifications and thickness requirements for piping and tubing shall conform to nationally recognized standards and shall be fabricated from materials meeting the impact test requirements when tested at the minimum operating temperature to which the piping will be subjected in service. See UFC Section 9003, Standard a.2.5.

9. Sec. 2-5.5 is revised as follows:

2-5.5 Uninsulated piping and equipment operating at cryogenic fluid temperatures below –280°F (–173°C) shall be installed so as to prevent contact of liquid air with combustible materials and combustible surfaces located beneath such piping and equipment. Drip pans installed under uninsulated piping and equipment shall retain and vaporize condensed liquid air.

10. Sec. 2-7.1 is revised as follows:

2-7.1 After installation, all field-erected piping shall be tested and proved gastight at operating pressure and temperature. Testing shall be performed in accordance with nationally recognized standards. See UFC Section 9003, Standard a.2.5.

11. Sec. 2-9 is revised by changing the first sentence as follows:

Electrical wiring and equipment shall comply with this section and the Electrical Code requirements for Class I locations.

12. Sec. 3-1.1 is revised by changing the second sentence as follows:

Fire apparatus access roadways shall be provided.

13. Sec. 3-1.6 is added as follows:

3-1.6 Storage of flammable cryogens in stationary containers is prohibited within the limits established by law as the limits of districts in which such storage is prohibited. (See sample adoption ordinance, UFC Section 8.)

14. Table 3-2.2 is revised by deleting and substituting the following items under "Type of Exposure" as follows:

1(a). Wall(s) of buildings of Type I or Type II construction adjacent to the system

2(b). Wall(s) of buildings of Type III, IV or V construction adjacent to the system

5. Between stationary flammable cryogenic fluid containers

6. Flammable gas storage other than the flammable cryogenic fluid stored

15. Sec. 4-1.2 is revised as follows:

4-1.2 If walls, roofs, weather shelters or canopies are provided, they shall be constructed of Type I or Type II construction.

16. Sec. 4-2.1 is revised as follows:

4-2.1 Separate buildings containing more that 300 gal (1136 L) of flammable cryogenic fluid shall comply with the requirements for Type I or Type II construction as specified in the Building Code. Explosion control shall be provided in accordance with the Building Code. Doors shall be located in such a manner that they will be readily accessible to personnel in an emergency.

17. Sec. 4-2.2 is revised as follows:

4-2.2 Ventilation shall be provided in accordance with UFC Section 8003.1.8. Mechanical ventilation systems shall be installed in accordance with the Mechanical Code. When natural ventilation is provided it shall comply with the following:

1. Inlet openings shall be located near the floor level in exterior walls only. Outlet openings shall be located at the high point of the room in exterior walls or the roof.

2. Both the inlet and outlet vent openings shall have a minimum total area of 1 square foot per 1,000 cubic feet (1 m^2/305 m^3) of room volume.

3. Discharge from outlet openings shall be directed or conducted to a safe location in accordance with the requirements of the Mechanical Code.

18. Sec 4-3.1 is revised by changing the first sentence as follows:

Special rooms shall be located in buildings of Type I or Type II construction as indicated in the Building Code.

19. Sec. 4-3.3 is revised as follows:

4-3.3 Explosion control shall be provided in accordance with the Building Code.

20. Chapter 8 is deleted.

UNIFORM FIRE CODE STANDARD 80-4
INERT CRYOGENIC FLUID SYSTEMS AT CONSUMER SITES

See Section 7501.1, *Uniform Fire Code*

NOTE: This is a new standard.

This standard, with certain exceptions, is based on the Compressed Gas Association Standard for Bulk Inert Gas Systems at Consumer Sites, CGA P-18—1992.

Part I of this standard contains the exceptions to CGA P-18—1992.

Part II of this standard contains CGA P-18—1992 reproduced in its entirety with permission of the publisher.

▭ vertically in the margin of Part II indicates there is a revision to the provisions within Part I.

Supplemental standards referenced by CGA P-18—1992 shall only be considered as guidelines subject to approval by the chief.

Part I

SECTION 80.401 — AMENDMENTS

The Standard for Bulk Inert Gas Systems at Consumer Sites, CGA P-18—1992, applies to the installation, maintenance and use of inert cryogenic fluid systems except as follows:

1. Chapter 2 is revised as follows:

The provisions of this standard shall apply to the installation, inspection, maintenance and testing of bulk inert gas containers and systems at consumer sites, except that when a *Uniform Fire Code,* Volume 1 provision or an amendment is specified, the *Uniform Fire Code,* Volume 1 or amendment provisions specified shall be applicable. The gases might be stored as inert compressed gases or as inert cryogenic fluids in either stationary or portable containers. The bulk system terminates at the point where gas at service pressure enters the supply line.

2. Chapter 3 is revised by adding, deleting and changing definitions as follows:

AUTHORITY HAVING JURISDICTION is the official responsible for the administration and enforcement of this standard.

CONTAINER is a cryogenic vessel used for transportation, handling or storage.

NONCOMBUSTIBLE/LIMITED-COMBUSTIBLE CONSTRUCTION is a building which complies with the requirements for Type I or Type II construction in the Building Code.

The definition of "cryogenic liquid" is deleted and replaced with the term "cryogenic fluid" as set forth in *Uniform Fire Code,* Volume 1.

The definitions of "combustible liquid," "fire-resistive construction," "flammable liquid" and "inert gas" shall be as set forth in *Uniform Fire Code,* Volume 1.

The definitions of "commodity specification," "grade," "qualified representative," "quality verification level" and "should" are deleted.

3. Chapter 4 is deleted.

4. Sec. 5.1 is revised by changing the first sentence as follows:

Bulk inert gas systems not in accordance with Section 5.2 shall be located outdoors. Installation of inert cryogenic fluids shall not be diked. The location shall not expose the system to electric power lines, craneways, or utility or process piping in any manner which creates a hazard condition.

5. Sec. 5.1.1 is revised as follows:

5.1.1 Other Storage Bulk inert gas systems installed outdoors shall be installed so that liquid leakage and fire-protection water from stored flammable and combustible liquids cannot flow to the bulk inert gas system. When it is necessary to locate a bulk inert gas system at a lower ground level than adjacent flammable or combustible liquid storage, the flammable or combustible liquids shall be diked or other means provided to divert any leaking flammable or combustible liquid away from the bulk inert gas system.

6. Sec. 5.1.2 is revised as follows:

5.1.2 Distance Between Bulk Inert Gas Systems and Exposures The minimum distance between the bulk inert gas system and other exposures will be not less than required by UFC Article 75.

7. Sec. 5.1.3 is revised as follows:

5.1.3 Pressure-relief devices on containers installed out-of-doors shall be protected against accumulation of ice, snow and freezing moisture from the air.

8. Sec. 5.2.1 is revised as follows:

5.2.1 When a bulk inert cryogenic fluid container or inert gas storage system is installed in a building, room, courtyard or similar confined area, the following provisions apply:

9. Sec. 5.2.1.1 is revised as follows:

5.2.1.1 Connections used for filling and liquid level limit controls shall be installed at an approved location at the exterior of the building. In addition, they shall be in accordance with the following:

1. Filling controls shall be accessible to the delivery vehicle.

2. Liquid level limit controls and pressure gages on the storage vessel shall either be visible, readable and operable at the delivery point, or duplicate controls shall be provided.

3. Filling controls shall be protected from the elements. Provisions shall be made to prevent the accumulation of ice, snow and freezing moisture from the air.

4. Filling controls shall be secured against unauthorized access.

10. Sec. 5.2.1.2 is revised as follows:

5.2.1.2 When bulk inert gas systems are installed in a building of other than Type I or II construction, an approved, supervised smoke-detection system shall be provided in the room or area in which the system is installed. Activation of the smoke-detection system shall initiate a local alarm and transmit a signal to a constantly attended control station.

11. Sec. 5.2.1.4 is revised as follows:

5.2.1.4 When bulk inert gas systems are installed in buildings, continuous mechanical ventilation shall be provided in the room or area in which the system is located in accordance with UFC

Section 8003.1.4. Mechanical ventilation systems shall be installed in accordance with the Mechanical Code.

12. Sec. 5.2.1.5 is revised as follows:

5.2.1.5 Indoor storage areas shall be provided with a continuous gas-detection system which monitors for an oxygen-deficient atmosphere. The gas-detection system shall initiate a local alarm and transmit a signal to a constantly attended location. The alarm shall be both visual and audible and shall be designed to provide warning both inside and outside of the storage area.

13. Sec. 5.2.3 is added as follows:

5.2.3 Bulk inert cryogenic fluid systems installed indoors shall be provided with a means to control spills to prevent the flow of liquid into adjoining areas in the building.

14. Sec. 6.1.2 is revised as follows:

6.1.2 Pressure-relief Devices Inert cryogenic fluid containers and the annular space of insulating containers shall be equipped with pressure-relief devices as required by nationally recognized standards. See UFC Section 9003, Standard c.1.5.

15. Sec. 6.1.3 is revised as follows:

6.1.3 Markings Portable containers shall be marked in accordance with nationally recognized standards. See UFC Section 9003, Standard c.1.1.

16. Sec. 6.2.1.1 is revised as follows:

6.2.1.1 Fabricated and tested in accordance with nationally recognized standards. See UFC Section 9003, Standard a.5.1.

17. Sec. 6.2.1.2 is revised as follows:

6.2.1.2 Designed, constructed, tested and maintained in accordance with nationally recognized standards. See UFC Section 9003, Standard u.3.3.

18. Sec. 6.3.1.1 is revised as follows:

6.3.1.1 Designed, constructed and tested in accordance with nationally recognized standards. See UFC Section 9003, Standard a.5.1.

19. Sec. 6.3.1.2 is revised as follows:

6.3.1.2 Designed, constructed, tested and maintained in accordance with nationally recognized standards. See UFC Section 9003, Standard u.3.3.

20. Sec. 6.3.1.3 is revised as follows:

6.3.1.3 Markings Portable containers shall be marked in accordance with nationally recognized standards. See UFC Section 9003, Standard c.1.1.

21. Sec. 6.3.2 is revised by changing the second sentence as follows and deleting the third sentence.

Cylinder valve outlets and manifold or regulator inlet connections shall conform with nationally recognized standards. See UFC Section 9003, Standard c.1.6.

22. Sec. 7.1.1.1 is revised as follows:

7.1.1.1 Piping and Tubing Material specifications and thickness requirements for piping and tubing shall conform to nationally recognized standards. See UFC Section 9003, Standard a.2.5.

23. Sec. 7.1.2.2 is revised by changing the second sentence as follows:

Pressure-relief device discharge lines shall be designed in accordance with nationally recognized standards. See UFC Section 9003, Standard a.5.1.

24. Sec. 7.1.3 is revised by changing the last sentence as follows:

Vacuum-insulated pipe is allowed for inert cryogenic fluid piping installed underground.

25. Sec. 7.1.4 is revised as follows:

7.1.4 Protection Piping passing through walls shall be protected from mechanical damage.

26. Sec. 7.1.6 is revised as follows:

7.1.6 Labeling and Marking Piping systems shall be identified as required by UFC Article 75.

27. Sec. 7.2.2 is deleted.

28. Sec. 7.2.3 is deleted.

29. Sec. 7.3.1 is deleted.

30. Sec. 7.3.2 is revised by changing the first sentence as follows:

Vaporizers shall be anchored to prevent overturning and connecting piping shall be designed to allow for expansion and contraction due to temperature changes.

31. Sec. 7.3.4 is revised by changing the second sentence as follows:

When electric heat is used, installation shall be in accordance with the Electrical Code.

32. Sec. 8.1.1 is deleted.

33. Sec. 8.1.2 is revised by changing the first sentence as follows:

Joints in piping and tubing shall be made by welding or brazing, or by the use of flanged, threaded, slip or compression-type fittings.

34. Sec. 8.1.4 is deleted.

35. Sec. 8.2.2 is deleted.

36. Sec. 8.2.3 is deleted.

37. Sec. 8.3.1 is deleted.

38. Sec. 9 is deleted.

Part II

Reproduced with permission from the Standard for Bulk Inert Gas Systems at Consumer Sites, CGA P–18, copyright 1992, Compressed Gas Association, Inc., 1725 Jefferson Davis Highway, Suite 1004, Arlington, Virginia 22202–4100. Persons desiring to reprint in whole or part any portion of the Standard for Bulk Inert Gas Systems at Consumer Sites, CGA P–18—1992, must secure permission from the Compressed Gas Association. The following standard is not necessarily the latest revision used by CGA. If the reader desires to compare with that version, the same is available from CGA.

TABLE OF CONTENTS

1. INTRODUCTION

This publication is one of a series compiled by the Compressed Gas Association, Inc. to satisfy the demand for information relative to the production, transportation, handling, and storage of compressed gases, cryogenic liquids, and related products.

2. SCOPE

The purpose of this standard is to provide information on installation of industrial bulk inert gas systems at consumer sites for argon, nitrogen, and helium service. Large industrial and institutional users of argon, nitrogen, and helium need storage units on their premises with greater capacity than that provided by manifolded cylinders. These bulk supply systems are an assembly of storage containers, pressure regulators, pressure relief devices, vaporizers, manifolds, and interconnecting piping. The inert gases may be stored as gas or liquid in either stationary or portable containers. The bulk system terminates at the point where gas at service pressure enters the supply line. This standard does not apply to medical bulk inert gas systems or to carbon dioxide systems. For information on medical bulk inert gas systems, see Chapter 4 of NFPA-99, *Standard for Health Care Facilities* [1];[1)] information on bulk carbon dioxide systems is given in CGA G-6.1, *Standard for Low Pressure Carbon Dioxide Systems at Consumer Sites* [2].

3. DEFINITIONS

For the purposes of this standard, the following definitions apply:

3.1 Authority Having Jurisdiction

The organization, office, or individual responsible for approving equipment, an installation, or a procedure.

3.2 Bulk Systems

An assembly of equipment, such as storage containers, pressure regulators, pressure relief devices, vaporizers, manifolds, and interconnecting piping, which has a storage capacity of more than 20,000 scf (566 m^3) of compressed gas, including unconnected reserves, on site.

3.3 Combustible Liquid

A liquid having a closed cup flash point at or above 100 °F (37.8 °C).

3.4 Combustible material

A material made or surfaced with wood, compressed paper, plant fibers, plastics or other materials that will ignite or burn.

3.5 Commodity Specification

A specification for compressed gas or cryogenic liquid.

3.6 Cryogenic Liquid

A liquefied gas having a boiling point lower than -130 °F (-90 °C) at one atmosphere.

3.7 Fire-Resistive Construction

A type of building construction defined in NFPA 220, *Standard on Types of Building Construction* [3].

3.8 Flammable Liquid

A liquid having a closed cup flash point below 100 °F (37.8 °C) and a vapor pressure not exceeding 40 lbs/sq. in. absolute (276 kPa) at 100 °F (37.8 °C).

3.9 Grade

Letter designation for a specification, i.e., Grade A helium.

3.10 High Pressure

Pressure higher than 250 psig (1724 kPa).

3.11 Inert Gas

Argon, nitrogen and helium.

3.12 Low Pressure

Pressure not exceeding 250 psig (1724 kPa).

3.13 Noncombustible/Limited-Combustible Construction

A type of building construction as defined in NFPA 220, *Standard on Types of Building Construction* [3].

3.14 Noncombustible Material

A material which, in the form in which it is used and under the conditions anticipated, will not ignite, burn, support combustion, or release flammable vapors when subjected to fire or heat [3]. Materials reported as noncombustible, when tested in accordance with ASTM E-136, *Standard Method of Test for Behavior of Materials in a Vertical Tube Furnace at 750 °C* [4], shall be considered noncombustible materials.

3.15 Design Pressure

The maximum gauge pressure that a pressure vessel, device, component, or system is designed to withstand safely.

3.16 Operating Pressure

The pressure at which the system normally operates.

[1)] References in this document are shown by bracketed numbers and are listed in the order of appearance in Section 9, References.

3.17 Oxygen-Deficient Atmosphere

Air in which the oxygen concentration by volume is less than 19.5% or whose oxygen partial pressure is less than 148 torr (mm Hg).

3.18 Qualified Representative

One familiar with the gases as well as the construction and operation of the equipment and the hazards involved.

3.19 Quality Verification Level (QVL)

The impurity levels that have to be verified to meet a commodity specification.

3.20 Shall

Indicates a mandatory requirement.

3.21 Should

Indicates a recommendation which is advised but is not mandatory.

3.22 Standard Cubic Foot (SCF)

A cubic foot of gas measured at 70 °F (21 °C) and 14.7 psia (101 kPa absolute).

4. GENERAL

4.1 Properties of Inert Gases

4.1.1 Argon

4.1.1.1 Argon is an element which at atmospheric temperatures and pressure exists as a colorless, odorless, tasteless gas. About 1% of the atmosphere is argon (0.93% by volume).

4.1.1.2 Argon is non-toxic, non-flammable, and chemically inert. It can act as an asphyxiant by displacing the necessary amount of oxygen required to support life.

4.1.1.3 As a gas at ambient temperature, argon is about 38% heavier than air. It may be liquefied to a colorless liquid which under atmospheric pressure boils at -302.6 °F (-185.9 °C). As liquid at its normal boiling point, argon is 1.39 times as heavy as water. When heated above its critical temperature of -188 °F (-122.3 °C), argon can exist only as a gas regardless of the pressure.

4.1.1.4 Argon is classed according to type and grade (Quality Verification Level). Gaseous argon is designated as Type I and liquefied argon as Type II. The grade (QVL) indicates the maximum amount of impurities which may be present. Further details are given in CGA G-11.1, *Commodity Specification for Argon* [5].

4.1.1.5 Some of the physical constants of argon are listed in Table 1 [6].

4.1.2 Nitrogen

4.1.2.1 Nitrogen is an element which at atmospheric temperatures and pressures exists as a colorless, odorless, tasteless gas. About four-fifths of the atmosphere is nitrogen (78.09% by volume).

4.1.2.2 Nitrogen is non-toxic, non-flammable and, for all practical purposes, chemically inert. It can act as an asphyxiant by displacing the necessary amount of oxygen required to support life.

4.1.2.3 As a gas at ambient temperature, nitrogen is about 3% lighter than air. It may be liquefied to a colorless liquid which under atmospheric pressure boils at -320.4 °F (-195.8 °C). As liquid at its normal boiling point, nitrogen is about 81% as heavy as water. When heated above its critical temperature of -232.5 °F (-147.0 °C), nitrogen can exist only as a gas regardless of the pressure.

4.1.2.4 Nitrogen is classed according to type and grade (Quality Verification Level). Gaseous nitrogen is designated as Type I and liquefied nitrogen as Type II. The grade (QVL) indicates the maximum amount of impurities which may be present. Further details are given in CGA G-10.1, *Commodity Specification for Nitrogen* [7].

4.1.2.5 Some of the physical constants of nitrogen are listed in Table 1 [6].

4.1.3 Helium

4.1.3.1 Helium is an element which at atmospheric temperatures and pressures exists as a colorless, odorless, tasteless gas. The principal source of helium is helium-bearing natural gas which is found in certain gas fields in Kansas, Wyoming, Oklahoma, Texas, and New Mexico. Helium is extracted from natural gas from wells containing 0.3-1% helium, but wells with up to 8% helium have been found. The helium content of the atmosphere is 5 ppm. Helium is a depletable natural resource, and it is the only industrial gas that diffuses out of the earth's atmosphere.

4.1.3.2 Helium is non-toxic, non-flammable, and chemically inert. It can act as an asphyxiant by displacing the necessary amount of oxygen to support life.

4.1.3.3 As a gas at ambient temperature, helium is about 86% lighter than air. Helium is the only known substance that will not freeze under its own vapor pressure. It has no triple point, existing only as a liquid under its vapor pressure to a temperature

Table 1. Physical Constants of Inert Gases

	Argon	Nitrogen	Helium
Chemical Formula	Ar	N_2	He
Vol. % in air	0.93	78.03	.0005
Gas Properties			
Density lb/ft^3, 70 °F, 1 atm	0.1034	0.0725	0.0103
Density kg/m^3, 15 °C, 1 atm	1.65	1.153	0.165
Ratio gas/air density	1.38	0.97	0.138
Ratio of vapor density at normal boiling point to that of air at 70 °F and 1 atm.	4.7	3.8	1.4
Liquid Properties			
Normal boiling point, °F	– 302.6	– 320.4	– 452.1
Normal boiling point, °C	– 185.9	– 195.8	– 268.9
Volume Expansion Ratio-Liquid at normal boiling point to gas at 70 °F and 1 atm	841.2	696.5	754.2

of absolute zero. Helium can be liquefied to a colorless liquid with a boiling point of -452.1 °F (-268.9 °C). As liquid at its normal boiling point, helium is about 12% as heavy as water. When heated above its critical temperature of -450.2 °F (-267.9 °C), helium can exist only as a gas regardless of the pressure.

4.1.3.4 Helium is classed according to type and grade (Quality Verification Level). Gaseous helium is designated as Type I and liquefied helium as Type II. The grade (QVL) indicates the maximum amount of impurities which may be present. Further details are given in CGA G-9.1, *Commodity Specification for Helium* [8].

4.1.3.5 Some of the physical constants of helium are listed in Table 1 [6].

4.2 Cryogenic Inert Gases

4.2.1 Storage, Handling, and Use

4.2.1.1 Any area in which a liquefied inert gas is used or stored should be properly ventilated. Never dispose of a liquefied inert gas in an indoor work or storage area. Personnel working in an area where the air has become enriched with argon, nitrogen, or helium can become unconscious without warning. See CGA P-14, *Accident Prevention in Oxygen-Rich and Oxygen-Deficient Atmospheres* [9], and CGA SB-15, *Avoiding Hazards in Confined Work Spaces During Maintenance, Construction, and Similar Activities* [10]. Remove the victim to fresh air. When necessary, artificial respiration should be administered and a physician summoned.

4.2.1.2 Because of the extremely low temperatures of cryogenic inert gases, the physical properties of materials with which they come in contact are apt to be greatly altered. Metals used for liquefied inert gas equipment must have satisfactory physical properties at the operating temperature. Ordinary carbon steels lose ductility at cryogenic temperatures and are considered unsafe for this service. Some suitable materials are austenitic chromium-nickel steels, copper, copper-silicon alloys, aluminum, monel, and some brasses and bronzes. Material selection must be carefully considered wherever cryogenic inert gases are handled. See CGA P-12, *Safe Handling of Cryogenic Liquids* [11].

4.2.1.3 Because of their extremely low temperatures, cryogenic inert gases should never be allowed to come into contact with the skin or with clothing. Contact can cause frostbite, an effect on the skin similar to that of a burn. Skin damage can also be caused by contact with the cold surfaces of an uninsulated pipe or vessel. ***Full face shields, gloves, and aprons should be worn when handling cryogenic liquids.*** Leather gloves loose enough to permit quick removal are recommended. High-top safety shoes with cuffless trousers worn outside the shoes are desirable. Any clothing that is splashed with cryogenic liquid should be immediately removed. If liquid does contact the skin, immediately flood the skin area with large quantities of unheated water. If the skin has been blistered or the eyes have been affected, obtain medical treatment promptly.

4.2.1.4 Removal of cold gas from large vessels and deep pits can be difficult due to the relatively high density of the gas compared to air. Air introduced into the bottom of such spaces tends to diffuse up through the dense gas without displacing it, and purging is liable to take much longer that expected. It may be more effective to exhaust the gas from the bottom of the vessel or pit. ***Verify that the oxygen concentration is above 19.5% before entering and during activity in the vessel or pit. See 4.3.1.3.***

4.2.1.5 Although inert gases are used mostly in gaseous form, large amounts are shipped as liquid to minimize distribution costs. One cubic foot of liquid argon (28.32 l) is the equivalent of 841.2 scf (23.8 m^3) of gaseous argon; the corresponding figure for nitrogen is 696.5 scf (19.7 m^3), and for helium, 754.2 scf (21.4 m^3). At the point of utilization, the liquid may be transferred into a storage unit on the premises and subsequently converted to gas for use, or it may be converted into gaseous form before storage.

4.2.1.6 Cryogenic liquids are stored and shipped in specially designed, well-insulated containers which maintain the pressure of the vapor above the liquid at atmospheric or a low positive pressure. The temperature of the liquid will remain at or near its normal boiling point and any heat leak into the container will not alter the temperature if the container is vented to permit vaporized product to escape.

4.2.1.7 Never attempt to transfer liquefied inert gas into a container or vessel that was not specifically designed for cryogenic liquid service. Containers used in shipment, storage, and transfer of cryogenic liquids are fabricated from materials that are able to withstand impact shock at low temperatures as well as to sustain the thermal stresses created by extreme temperature changes during the cool-down period.

4.2.1.8 Cryogenic containers shall be provided with pressure relief devices to ensure that the maximum design pressure of the container is not exceeded. Portable containers such as small dewars or flasks shall be vented to the atmosphere, and the vents should be inspected periodically to make sure the vent port has not become obstructed by ice. Small cryogenic containers should be loosely covered to prevent condensation and freezing of atmospheric moisture by the cold liquid which could obstruct or plug the container outlet.

4.2.1.9 Cryogenic inert gas liquids in containers should be handled or used only by trained personnel.

4.2.1.10 Introduction of a substance which is at room temperature, such as a transfer tube, into a liquefied inert gas at extremely low temperature is hazardous. There is a violent generation of cold gas and there is likely to be considerable splashing of liquid. Personnel doing this work should be instructed on the hazards and should always wear a full face shield and appropriate protective clothing.

4.2.1.11 All piping systems or vessels in which liquefied inert gases may be trapped between closed valves shall be equipped with pressure relief devices. In cases where liquefied inert gas may be trapped in any valve cavity, means of venting must be provided.

4.2.1.12 All marking, labeling and placarding must be done in accordance with applicable laws, regulations, and nationally recognized standards. The product shipping name and product identification number must be stencilled on the container or appear on a label, in addition to the non-flammable gas diamond label. See CGA C-7, *Guide to the Preparation of Precautionary Labeling and Marking of Compressed Gas Containers* [12]. If a cylinder is not labeled, return it to the supplier unused. If a regulator with the correct CGA connection does not fit the cylinder valve outlet connection, return the container to the supplier. Adapters shall not be used.

4.2.2 Inert Gas Piping and Manifold Systems

4.2.2.1 Piping and manifold systems for inert gases should be designed in accordance with applicable state, provincial or municipal codes and installed under the supervision of a qualified representative. Consultation with gas suppliers is recommended.

4.2.2.2 Piping systems and accessories used in liquid transfer operations must be fabricated from materials suitable for inert gas service at the temperatures and pressures involved (i.e., copper, aluminum, brass, and stainless steel).

4.2.2.3 Design of low temperature piping must consider the contraction stresses which occur during system cool down. Another consideration is prevention of freezing of valve packing. Frozen packing can leak and can also prevent valve operation. This problem can be minimized by the use of extended-stem valves installed with the stem at an angle above the horizontal.

4.2.2.4 Pressure relief devices should be installed at every point in the system where liquid can become trapped. Piping between two shut-off valves or between a shut-off valve and a regulator or check valve are examples of locations where liquid may be trapped and will vaporize. Unless relieved, the resulting pressure increase could rupture the system. A pressure relief device shall be installed with a thermal extension if moisture from the air may condense and freeze on the device and interfere with its operation.

4.3 Health Hazards

4.3.1 Oxygen-Deficient Atmospheres

4.3.1.1 Hazards

Inert gases can displace oxygen in the air creating an oxygen-deficient atmosphere which is a serious hazard to life. Depending on the degree of oxygen deficiency, the effects on humans can vary from physiological changes to acute illness or even death by asphyxiation.

4.3.1.2 Exposure to atmospheres containing 12% or less oxygen will bring about unconsciousness without warning and so quickly that the individual cannot help or protect himself. See Table 2 for symptoms of oxygen deficiency.

4.3.1.3 Before any person enters a space where there is any possibility that the atmosphere may be oxygen deficient, the atmosphere shall be analyzed for oxygen content with a calibrated, reliable, accurate analyzer. Entrance without a supplied air breathing system is permissible only if the oxygen concentration by volume is above 19.5% upon entry and remains above this level during occupancy of the confined area [10].

4.3.2 Personnel Contact

4.3.2.1 Skin or Eye Frostbite

Always handle cryogenic liquids carefully. At their extremely low temperatures, they can produce frostbite on skin and exposed eye tissue. When spilled, they tend to cover a surface completely, cooling a large area. The vapor from these liquids is also extremely cold. Delicate tissues, such as those of the eyes, can be damaged by exposure to these cold gases, even when the contact is too brief to affect the skin of the hands or face.

4.3.2.2 Boiling and Splashing

Stand clear of boiling or splashing cryogenic liquid and its vapors. Boiling and splashing always occur when filling a warm container, or when inserting warm objects into a cryogenic liquid. Use tongs to introduce or withdraw objects immersed in a cryogenic liquid. Always perform these operations slowly to minimize boiling and splashing. If liquid or cold vapor contacts the skin or eyes, follow the first aid recommendations in 4.3.3.

4.3.2.3 Flesh Tearing

Never allow any unprotected part of the body to touch uninsulated pipes or vessels which contain cryogenic fluids. The extremely cold metal will cause the flesh to stick fast and tear when one attempts to withdraw from it. Even nonmetallic materials are dangerous to touch at low temperatures.

4.3.3 First Aid for Cold-Contact Burns

4.3.3.1 In the event of contact with a liquid or cold gas, a cold-contact "burn" may occur. Actually, the skin or eye tissue freezes. Recommended emergency treatment for a cold-contact burn is as follows:

4.3.3.1.1 Remove any clothing that may restrict circulation to the frozen area. Do not rub frozen

Table 2. Symptoms of Oxygen Deficiency

Humans vary considerably in their reactions to an oxygen-deficient atmosphere. It is, therefore, not possible to predict exactly how people will react. A general indication of what is liable to happen is given, but it should be understood that individual reactions may be different from those listed.

Oxygen Content (% by volume)	*Effects and Symptoms (at atmospheric pressure)*
15–19%	Decreased ability to work strenuously. May impair coordination and may induce early symptoms in persons with coronary, pulmonary, or circulatory problems.
12–15%	Respiration increased in exertion, pulse up, impaired coordination, perception, and judgement.
10–12%[2)]	Respiration further increases in rate and depth; poor judgement; lips blue.
8–10%	Mental failure; fainting, unconsciousness; ashen face; blueness of lips; nausea, and vomiting.
6–8%	8 minutes, 100% fatal; 6 minutes, 50% fatal; 4-5 minutes, recovery with treatment.
4–6%	Coma in 40 seconds; convulsions; respiration ceases, death.

[2)]Exposure to atmosphere containing 12% or less oxygen will bring about unconsciousness without warning, and so quickly that the individual cannot help or protect himself.

parts, as tissue damage may result. Obtain medical assistance as soon as possible.

4.3.3.1.2 As soon as practical, immerse the affected part of the body in a warm water bath which has a temperature not exceeding 105 °F (40 °C). Never use dry heat. The victim should also be in a warm room.

4.3.3.1.3 If there has been massive exposure so that the general body temperature is depressed, prompt medical attention is imperative. If immediate medical assistance is unavailable, the patient may be rewarmed by immersion in 105 °F (40 °C) water. It is likely the patient will lapse into shock and standard treatment for this condition should be administered.

4.3.3.1.4 Frozen tissues are painless and appear waxy with a possible yellow color. They become swollen, painful, and prone to infection when thawed. Do not rewarm rapidly under any circumstances. Thawing may require from 15 to 60 minutes and should be continued until the pale tint of the skin turns pink or red. Medication may be required to control the pain during thawing and should be administered under professional medical supervision.

4.3.3.1.5 If the frozen area has thawed by the time medical attention has been obtained, cover the area with a dry sterile dressing and with a large bulky protective covering.

4.3.3.1.6 Alcoholic beverages and smoking decrease blood flow to the frozen tissues and should not be used. Warm drinks and food may be given to a conscious victim.

5. LOCATION OF BULK INERT GAS SYSTEMS

5.1 Outdoors

Bulk inert gas systems should preferably be located outdoors and above-ground and not diked. The location should not expose the system to electric power lines, craneways, or utility or process piping in any manner which could create a hazard. The location shall be accessible to mobile supply equipment and be provided with adequate foundations, supports, lighting, vehicle protection and identification signs. Access shall be restricted to authorized personnel.

5.1.1 Other Storage

When locating bulk inert gas systems near above-ground flammable or combustible liquid storage which may be either indoors or outdoors, it is advisable to locate the system on ground higher than the flammable or combustible liquid storage. When it is necessary to locate a bulk inert gas system at a lower ground level than adjacent flammable or combustible liquid storage, dikes, diversion curbs, or grading should be used to divert any leaking flammable or combustible liquid away from the bulk inert gas system.

5.1.2 Distance Between Bulk Inert Gas Systems and Exposures

The minimum distance between the bulk inert gas system and other exposures will be determined by applicable federal, provincial, state and municipal regulations and good engineering practice.

5.1.3 Containers in outdoor service must have valves and pressure relief devices protected against accumulation of ice, snow and to freezing moisture from the air.

5.2 Indoors

5.2.1 When a bulk container or inert gas storage system is installed in a building, room, courtyard, or any confined area without adequate ventilation or access, the following additional provisions apply:

5.2.1.1 Fill connections and full trycock lines shall be extended to the outside and be accessible for the delivery vehicle. If the liquid level and pressure gauges are not visible at the delivery point, duplicate gauges shall be installed at the filling connection to enable the driver to fill the storage container and maintain the required pressure in the container. Outside fittings and gauges at the filling location should be protected from the elements and from access by unauthorized personnel. All pressure relief devices and vents shall be piped to discharge outside in a safe direction and configured so that rain or snow cannot enter the discharge line. Discharge lines from pressure relief devices shall be designed in accordance with Section M-8 of the ASME Code [13].

5.2.1.2 When a bulk inert gas storage system container is installed in a building constructed of combustible materials, or close to combustible materials or sources of heat that could endanger the integrity of the storage container, a heat and/or smoke detection system shall be installed in the building, room, or enclosure containing the storage container. When the temperature reaches 120 °F (48.9 °C), or when smoke is present, the system shall sound an audible alarm and/or activate warning lights at a continuously manned station.

5.2.1.3 Warning signs shall be posted at each entrance to the building, room, enclosure, or confined space where the bulk inert gas system is installed. Wording for such signs shall include, as a minimum, the following:

WARNING—(Name of Gas)
HIGH CONCENTRATION OF GAS MAY OCCUR
IN THIS AREA
AND MAY CAUSE ASPHYXIATION.
VERIFY THAT OXYGEN CONCENTRATION IS
ABOVE 19.5% BEFORE ENTERING
AND DURING ACTIVITY IN THIS AREA.

5.2.1.4 Adequate ventilation is to be provided when bulk inert gas systems are installed in courtyards and similar enclosed areas, and such areas shall be clearly posted with a warning as recommended in paragraph.

5.2.1.5 Storage areas where an accumulation of inert gas could occur should be continuously monitored with an appropriate alarm system to indicate an oxygen-deficient atmosphere.

5.2.2 Portable containers in service inside a building shall be located a minimum of 20 ft (6.1 m) from highly combustible materials and where they are not liable to be exposed to temperatures in excess of 125 °F (51.7 °C), physical damage, or access by unauthorized personnel. Empty containers shall have their valves closed to prevent contamination.

6. INERT GAS STORAGE CONTAINERS

6.1 General

6.1.1 Foundations and Supports

Permanently installed containers shall be provided with substantial supports of non-combustible material and foundations of non-combustible materials.

6.1.2 Pressure Relief Devices

Every inert gas storage container shall be equipped with the pressure relief devices required by the specifications to which the container was fabricated. The sizing of pressure relief devices for storage containers shall be in accordance with CGA S-1.3, *Pressure Relief Device Standards—Part 3 -Compressed Gas Storage Containers* [14], and the requirements of the authority having jurisdiction must be met. The annular space of liquid containers shall be equipped with suitable pressure relief devices.

6.1.3 Markings

Each portable container shall be marked in accordance with CGA C-7, *Guide to Preparation of Precautionary Labeling and Marking of Compressed Gas Containers* [12], and the requirements of the authority having jurisdiction.

6.2 Low Pressure Containers

6.2.1 Requirements

Low pressure inert gas storage containers shall be either:

6.2.1.1 Fabricated from materials meeting the impact test requirements of Paragraph UG-84 of the ASME *Boiler and Pressure Vessel Code*, Section VIII—Unfired Pressure Vessels [13]. Containers operating at pressures above 15 psig (103 kPa) shall be designed, constructed and tested in accordance with appropriate requirements of the ASME Code. The container insulation shall be of noncombustible material in accordance with ASME E-84 [15].

6.2.1.2 Designed, constructed, tested and maintained in accordance with U.S. Department of Transportation [16], Transport Canada [17], or Canadian Transport Commission [18] specifications and regulations.

6.3 High Pressure Containers

6.3.1 Requirements

High pressure inert gas containers shall be either:

6.3.1.1 Designed, constructed, and tested in accordance with appropriate requirements of the ASME *Boiler and Pressure Vessel Code*, Section VIII—Unfired Pressure Vessels, and the authority having jurisdiction, or,

6.3.1.2 Designed, constructed, tested, and maintained in accordance with the U.S. Department of Transportation specifications and regulations [16] or Transport Canada specifications and regulations which refer to CAN/CSA B 339 [17], and CAN/CSA B 340 [18].

6.3.1.3 Markings

Each portable container shall be marked in accordance with CGA C-7, *Guide to the Preparation of Precautionary Labeling and Marking of Compressed Gas Containers* [12], and the requirements of the authority having jurisdiction.

6.3.2 Manifolds

Manifolds shall be designed and constructed of materials suitable for the specific inert gas and the pressures involved. Cylinder valve outlets and manifold or regulator inlet connections shall conform with the ANSI/CSA/CGA V-1, *Standards for Compressed Gas Cylinder Valve Outlet and Inlet Connections* [19]. It is advisable to obtain manifolds from and install them under the supervision of a manufacturer or supplier familiar with proper practices for their construction and use. High pressure manifolds shall be located in a secure area.

7. INERT GAS SYSTEM COMPONENTS

7.1 General

7.1.1 Piping, Tubing and Fittings

Piping, tubing, and fittings shall be suitable for the specific gas service and the pressures and temperatures involved.

7.1.1.1 Piping and Tubing

Material specifications and thickness requirements for piping and tubing shall conform to ASME B31.3, *Code for Chemical Plant and Petroleum Refinery Piping* [20], and the requirements of the authority having jurisdiction.

7.1.2 Pressure Relief Devices

7.1.2.1 General

Pressure relief devices shall be installed in any part of the system in which liquid or cold vapor could be trapped. If liquefied inert gas may become trapped in any valve cavity, means of venting must be provided.

7.1.2.2 Venting

Pressure relief devices on bulk liquid storage containers and on piping systems located indoors shall be vented outdoors away from personnel and suitably protected from the elements. Pressure relief device discharge lines shall be designed in accordance with Section M-8 of the ASME Code [13].

7.1.2.3 Protection

All pressure relief devices shall be designed and installed so that moisture cannot collect and freeze in a manner which would interfere with proper operation of the device.

7.1.3 Location

Gas piping located inside or outside of buildings may be placed above or below ground. All piping shall be run as directly as practicable, carefully protected against physical damage, and with allowance for expansion, contraction and vibration. Underground pipe shall be below the frost line and adequately protected against corrosion and other physical damage. Underground piping shall be in ducts or casings when it passes under roads, railroad tracks or parking lots. Liquid nitrogen piping may be located underground in vacuum insulated pipe.

7.1.4 Protection

Pipes passing through walls should be protected from mechanical damage.

7.1.5 Shut-off Valves

Shut-off valves shall be provided for all buildings at outside locations where they are readily accessible for shutting off the gas supply to the building in case of emergency. A shut-off valve at the gas supply shall also be provided. Signs clearly establishing the location and identity of shut-off valves are to be provided.

7.1.6 Labeling and Marking

All piping systems should be identified by appropriate labeling with the name of the gas and any other information required by authorities having jurisdiction.

7.2 Regulators

7.2.1 General

Regulators and automatic pressure reducing valves shall be suitable for the intended service including pressure and temperature.

7.2.2 Union Nuts and Connections

Union nuts and connections on regulators should be inspected before attachment. Damaged nuts or connections should be replaced.

7.2.3 Testing, Repair, and Maintenance

Pressure gauges on regulators should be periodically tested to ensure their accuracy. Repairs to regulators shall be performed by qualified personnel. In general, it is advisable to return regulators to the supplier for repairs, calibration, or adjustments.

7.3 Vaporizers

7.3.1 General

Vaporizers are used for converting cryogenic liquid to gas.

7.3.2 Installation

The vaporizer shall be anchored and its connecting piping shall be designed to allow for expansion and contraction due to temperature changes. Adequate provisions for drainage of melting ice are required. Suitable foundations shall be provided to support the vaporizer weight as well as the maximum ice load.

7.3.3 Pressure Relief

The vaporizer and its piping shall be adequately protected on the gas side and, where necessary, on the heating medium side, with pressure relief devices.

7.3.4 Heating Medium

Heat for a vaporizer may be supplied by electricity, steam, air, water, or other heat transfer mediums. When electric heat is used, installation should be in accordance with the National Electric Code [21] and applicable federal, provincial, state or municipal codes.

8. SYSTEM ASSEMBLY, INSTALLATION, OPERATION AND MAINTENANCE

8.1 Assembly and Installation

8.1.1 General

Equipment assembled into an inert gas system shall be clean before being placed in service.

8.1.2 Joining and Sealing

Joints in piping and tubing may be made by welding or brazing, or by the use of flanged, threaded, slip, or compression fittings. Gaskets or thread sealants shall be suitable for the intended service.

8.1.3 Accessories

Valves, gauges, and other accessories shall be suitable for the intended service.

8.1.4 Supervision

Installation of inert gas systems shall be supervised by personnel familiar with proper practices for their construction and use.

8.1.5 Testing

After installation, all field-erected piping shall be proof pressure tested at 110% of the maximum operating pressure and shall be tested bubble free to soapy water or leak detecting solution at a reduced pressure. The test medium shall be oil-free dry air, or any inert gas.

8.2 Operation

8.2.1 General

Adequate operating instructions shall be provided for inert gas bulk systems. The operating instructions should be readily available on site. Personnel assigned to operate the equipment shall be adequately trained in the hazards of and safety precautions for operating inert gas systems.

8.2.2 Opening Valves

Never permit gas to enter unpressurized equipment or piping systems suddenly. Always open all valves slowly. A valve should be opened to the full open position and then closed a quarter turn. This ensures easy turning of the hand wheel if someone checks the valve position.

8.2.3 Safety Information

It is recommended that personnel handling inert gases review CGA P-1, *Safe Handling of Compressed Gases in Containers* [22], CGA P-14, *Accident Prevention in Oxygen-Rich and Oxygen-Deficient Atmospheres* [9], and CGA P-12, *Safe Handling of Cryogenic Liquids* [11].

8.3 Maintenance

8.3.1 Annual Inspection and Maintenance

Each inert gas system installed on consumer premises shall be inspected at least annually and maintained by a qualified representative of the equipment owner.

8.3.2 Fire Prevention

The area within 15 feet (4.6 meters) of any inert gas storage container shall be maintained free of paper, leaves, weeds, dry grass, or other combustible debris.

8.3.3 Leak Tests

Leak testing should be carried out on a regular basis while the system is in service.

9. REFERENCES

[1] NFPA 99, *Standard for Health Care Facilities*, National Fire Protection Association, Batterymarch Park, Quincy, MA 02269.

[2] CGA G-6.1, *Standard for Low Pressure Carbon Dioxide Systems at Consumer Sites*, Compressed Gas Association, Inc., 1725 Jefferson Davis Highway, Arlington, VA 22202-4100.

[3] NFPA 220, *Standard on Types of Building Construction*, National Fire Protection Association, Batterymarch Park, Quincy, MA 02269.

[4] ASTM E-136, *Standard Method of Test for Behavior of Materials in a Vertical Tube Furnace at 750 °C*, American Society for Testing and Materials, 1916 Race Street, Philadelphia, PA 19103-1187.

[5] CGA G-11.1, *Commodity Specification for Argon*, Compressed Gas Association, Inc., 1725 Jefferson Davis Highway, Arlington, VA 22202-4100.

[6] *Handbook of Compressed Gases*, Compressed Gas Association, Inc., 1725 Jefferson Davis Highway, Arlington, VA 22202-4100.

[7] CGA G-10.1, *Commodity Specification for Nitrogen*, Compressed Gas Association, Inc., 1725 Jefferson Davis Highway, Arlington, VA 22202-4100.

[8] CGA G-9.1, *Commodity Specification for Helium*, Compressed Gas Association, Inc., 1725 Jefferson Davis Highway, Arlington, VA 22202-4100.

[9] CGA P-14, *Accident Prevention in Oxygen-Rich and Oxygen Deficient Atmospheres*, Compressed Gas Association, Inc., 1725 Jefferson Davis Highway, Arlington, VA 22202-4100.

[10] CGA SB-15, *Avoiding Hazards in Confined Work Spaces During Maintenance, Construction, and Similar Activities*, Compressed Gas Association, Inc., 1725 Jefferson Davis Highway, Arlington, VA 22202-4100.

[11] CGA P-12, *Safe Handling of Cryogenic Liquids*, Compressed Gas Association, Inc., 1725 Jefferson Davis Highway, Arlington, VA 22202-4100.

[12] CGA C-7, *Guide to the Preparation of Precautionary Labeling and Marking of Compressed Gas Containers*, Compressed Gas Association, Inc., 1725 Jefferson Davis Highway, Arlington, VA 22202-4100.

[13] ASME Boiler and Pressure Vessel Code, Section VIII—Division I, *Unfired Pressure Vessels*,

American Society of Mechanical Engineers, 345 East 47th Street, New York, NY 10017.

[14] CGA S-1.3, *Pressure Relief Device Standards Compressed Gas Storage Containers*, Compressed Gas Association, Inc., 1725 Jefferson Davis Highway, Arlington, VA 22202-4100.

[15] ASME E-84, *Standard Test Method for Surface Burning Characteristics of Building Materials*, American Society of Mechanical Engineers, 345 East 47th Street, New York, NY 10017.

[16] Code of Federal Regulations, Title CFR 49 Parts 100 to 199 (Transportation) U.S. Department of Transportation, Superintendent of Documents, Washington, DC 20402.

[17] CAN/CSA B 339, *Cylinders, Spheres and Tubes for the Transportation of Dangerous Goods*, Canadian Standards Association, 178 Rexdale Boulevard, Rexdale, Ont, CANADA M9W 1R3.

[18] CAN/CSA B 340, *Selection and Use of Cylinders, Spheres, Tubes and Other Containers for the Transportation of Dangerous Goods—Class 2*, Canadian Standards Association, 178 Rexdale Boulevard, Rexdale, Ont. CANADA M9W 1R3.

[19] CGA V-1, *Standards for Compressed Gas Cylinder Valve Outlet and Inlet Connections*, Compressed Gas Association, Inc., 1725 Jefferson Davis Highway, Arlington, VA 22202-4100.

[20] ASME B31.3, *Code for Chemical Plant and Petroleum Refinery Piping*, American National Standards Institute, 1430 Broadway, New York, NY 10018; American Society of Mechanical Engineers, 345 East 47th Street, New York, NY 10017.

[21] NFPA 70, National Electrical Code, National Fire Protection Association, Batterymarch Park, Quincy, MA 02269.

[22] CGA P-1, *Safe Handling of Compressed Gases in Containers*, Compressed Gas Association, Inc., 1725 Jefferson Davis Highway, Arlington, VA 22202-4100.

UNIFORM FIRE CODE STANDARD 81-1
HIGH-PILED GENERAL STORAGE OF COMBUSTIBLES IN BUILDINGS

See Sections 8102.9.1, 8102.10.1, 8103.2 and 8803.2, *Uniform Fire Code*

This standard, with certain exceptions, is based on the National Fire Protection Association Standard for General Storage, NPFA 231—1990.[1]

Part I of this standard contains the exceptions to NFPA 231—1990.[1]

Part II of this standard contains NFPA 231—1990[1] reproduced in its entirety with permission of the publisher.

▨▨▨ vertically in the margin of Part II indicates there is a revision to the provisions within Part I.

Supplemental standards referenced by NFPA 231—1990[1] shall only be considered as guideline standards subject to approval by the chief.

[1]The current edition is NFPA 231—1995.

Part I

SECTION 81.101 — AMENDMENTS

The Standard for General Storage, NFPA 231—1990, applies to the classification of commodities and the installation of fire-protection equipment used in conjunction with high-piled storage in solid piles or similar configurations, except as follows:

1. Sec. 1-1 is revised as follows:

1-1 Scope.

This standard applies to storage of materials representing the broad range of combustibles, 30 feet (9144.0 mm) or less in height, including the storage of Groups B and C plastics in all configurations and free-flowing Group A plastics. This standard applies to storage of Group A plastics, except free flowing, up to 25 feet (7620.0 mm) in height.

Storage piled higher than the above stated heights are not within the scope of this standard and require special consideration.

This standard does not apply to:

1. Storage of commodities which, with their packaging and storage aids, would be classified as noncombustible.

2. Unpackaged bulk materials such as grain, coal, or similar commodities.

3. Commodities covered by other standards except where specifically mentioned herein.

4. Commodities presenting special fire hazards not covered by specific standards, e.g., roll paper, wax-coated cartons, etc.

5. Storage on racks.

2. Sec. 1-2 is revised by deleting the definitions of "shelf storage" and "should."

3. Sec. 2-1.1 is revised as follows:

2-1.1 Commodity classification shall be as set forth in UFC Article 81.

4. Secs. 2-1.2 through 2-1.5 are deleted.

5. Sec. 3-1 is deleted.

6. Sec. 4-2.1 is revised by substituting the phrase "UFC Article 11" for the phrase "NFPA 13, *Standard for the Installation of Sprinkler Systems.*"

7. Sec. 4-5 is revised as follows:

4-5 Storage of flammable and combustible liquids shall be in accordance with UFC Article 79.

8. Sec. 5-1 is revised by substituting the phrase "the Building Code. See UBC Standard 9-1" for the phrase "NFPA 13, *Standard for the Installation of Sprinkler Systems,*" wherever it appears.

9. Sec. 5-1.3 is revised by substituting the phrase "UFC Standard 81-2" for the phrase "NFPA 231C, *Standard for Rack Storage of Materials.*"

10. Sec. 5-1.5 is revised to read as follows:

5-1.5 The densities and areas provided in the tables and curves in Chapters 6, 7 and 8 are based on fire tests using standard response, standard orifice [$^1/_2$ inch (12.7 mm)] and large orifice [$^{17}/_{32}$ inch (13.5 mm)] sprinklers. The use of extra large orifice sprinklers is allowed when listed for such use. For the use of large drop and ESFR sprinklers, see Chapters 9 and 10 of this standard.

11. Sec. 5-3.1 is revised by changing the first sentence as follows:

When required by UFC Table 81-A, small hose stations shall be provided and shall be spaced such that they are accessible to reach all portions of the high-piled storage area based on the length of hose and travel paths.

12. Sec. 5-3.1 is revised by adding an exception as follows:

> **EXCEPTION:** In buildings served by a single automatic sprinkler system, the hose stations are allowed to be supplied from the ceiling sprinkler piping downstream of the sprinkler control valve.

13. Sec. 5-3.2 is revised by substituting the phrase "UFC Article 10" for the phrase "NFPA 10, *Standard for Portable Fire Extinguishers.*"

14. Sec. 5-4 is revised as follows:

5-4 The water supply requirements for protection of the building and premises shall be in accordance with UFC Article 9.

15. Sec. 5-5 is deleted.

16. Sec. 5-6 is revised by deleting all text following the first sentence.

17. Secs. 7-1.3 and 7-1.4 are revised by substituting the phrase "the Building Code. See UBC Standard 9-1" for the phrase "NFPA 13."

18. Figure 7-1.1, Note 1, is revised as follows:

1. Sprinklers rated at 286°F (141.1°C) shall be used unless specific tests verify fire control using sprinklers rated at other temperatures for the proposed storage configuration and sprinkler system design.

19. Sec. 8-1.2 is revised as follows:

8-1.2 All requirements in the Building Code shall apply. See UBC Standard 9-1.

20. Sec. 8-3.1 is deleted.

21. Sec. 9-3.1 is revised as follows:

9-3.1 All requirements in the Building Code shall apply. See UBC Standard 9-1.

22. Chapters 10 and 11 are deleted.

Part II

Reproduced with permission from the Standard for General Storage, NFPA 231, copyright 1990, National Fire Protection Association, 1 Batterymarch Park, Box 9101, Quincy, Massachusetts 02269-9101. Persons desiring to reprint in whole or part any portion of the Standard for General Storage, NFPA 231—1990, must secure permission from the National Fire Protection Association. The following is not necessarily the latest revision used by NFPA. If the reader desires to compare that version, the same is available from NFPA.

Contents

NFPA 231

Standard for

General Storage

1990 Edition

NOTICE: An asterisk (*) following the number or letter designating a paragraph indicates explanatory material on that paragraph in Appendix A.

Information on referenced publications can be found in Chapter 11 and Appendix D.

Chapter 1 Introduction

1-1 Scope.

1-1.1 This standard applies to:

1-1.1.1 Storage of materials representing the broad range of combustibles up to 30 ft (9.1 m) in height.

1-1.1.2 Storage of plastics (Groups B and C — all configurations; Group A — free-flowing only) up to 30 ft (9.1 m) in height.

1-1.1.3 Storage of Group A plastics (except free-flowing) up to 25 ft (7.6 m) in height.

1-1.1.4 New buildings and existing buildings that are converted to storage occupancy.

NOTE: It may be used as a basis for evaluating existing storage facilities.

1-1.1.5 Outdoor Storage of a Broad Range of Combustibles. *(See Appendix C.)*

1-1.2 Storage piled higher than stated in 1-1.1.1, 1-1.1.2, or 1-1.1.3 is not within the scope of this standard and requires special consideration.

1-1.3 This standard does not apply to:

1-1.3.1 Unsprinklered buildings.

1-1.3.2 Storage of commodities that, with their packaging and storage aids, would be classified as noncombustible.

1-1.3.3 Unpackaged bulk materials such as grain, coal, or similar commodities.

1-1.3.4 Inside or outside storage of commodities covered by other NFPA standards except where specifically mentioned herein, e.g., pyroxylin plastics.

1-1.3.5 Storage on racks.

1-1.4 Nothing in this standard is intended to restrict new technologies or alternate arrangements providing the level of safety prescribed by the standard is not lowered.

1-2 Definitions. Unless expressly stated elsewhere, for the purpose of this standard, the following definitions shall apply:

Array.

Closed Array. A storage arrangement where air movement through the pile is restricted because of 6 in. (152 mm) or less vertical flues.

Open Array.* A storage arrangement where air movement through the pile is enhanced because of vertical flues larger than 6 in. (152 mm).

Available Height for Storage.* The maximum height at which commodities can be stored above the floor and still maintain adequate clearance from structural members and the required clearance below sprinklers.

Bin Box Storage. Storage in 5-sided wood, metal, or cardboard boxes with open face on the aisles. Boxes are self-supporting or supported by a structure so designed that little or no horizontal or vertical space exists around boxes.

Clearance. The distance from the top of storage to the ceiling sprinkler deflectors.

Commodity. Combinations of products, packing material, and container.

Compartmented.* The rigid separation of the products in a container by dividers that form a stable unit under fire conditions.

Container (shipping, master, or outer container).* A receptacle strong enough, by reason of material, design, and construction, to be shipped safely without further packaging.

Early Suppression Fast Response (ESFR) Sprinklers. A listed ESFR sprinkler is a thermosensitive device designed to react at a predetermined temperature by automatically releasing a stream of water and distributing it in a specified pattern and quantity over a designated area so as to provide early suppression of a fire when installed on the appropriate sprinkler piping.

Encapsulated. A method of packing consisting of a plastic sheet completely enclosing the sides and top of a pallet load containing a combustible commodity or combustible packages.

NOTE: Banding, i.e., stretch wrapping, around the sides only of a pallet load is not considered to be encapsulated.

Expanded (foamed or cellular) Plastics. Those plastics, the density of which is reduced by the presence of numerous small cavities (cells), interconnecting or not, dispersed throughout their mass.

Exposed Group A Plastic Commodities. Those plastics not in packaging or coverings that will absorb water or otherwise appreciably retard the burning hazard of the commodity (paper wrapped and/or encapsulated should be considered exposed).

Free-flowing Plastic Materials. Those plastics that will fall out of their containers in a fire condition, fill flue spaces, and create a smothering effect on the fire. Example: Powder, pellets, flakes, or random packed small objects [razor blade dispensers, 1-2 oz (28-57 g) bottles, etc.].

Large Drop Sprinkler. A listed large drop sprinkler is characterized by a K factor between 11.0 and 11.5, and proven ability to meet prescribed penetration, cooling, and distribution criteria prescribed in the large drop sprinkler examination requirements. The deflector/discharge characteristics of the large drop sprinkler generate large drops of such size and velocity as to enable effective penetration of the high-velocity fire plume.

Noncombustible. Commodities, packaging, or storage aids that will not ignite, burn, or liberate flammable gases when heated to a temperature of 1,380°F (749°C) for 5 min.

Packaging. Commodity wrapping, cushioning, or container.

Palletized Storage. Storage of commodities on pallets or other storage aids that form horizontal spaces between tiers of storage.

Pile Stability.*

Stable Piles. Those arrays where collapse, spillage of content, or leaning of stacks across flue spaces is not likely to occur soon after initial fire development.

NOTE: Storage on pallets, compartmented storage, or plastic components that are held in place by materials that do not deform readily under fire conditions are examples of stable storage.

Unstable Piles. Those arrays where collapse, spillage of contents, or leaning of stacks across flue spaces will occur soon after initial fire development.

NOTE: Leaning stacks, crushed bottom cartons, or reliance on combustible bands for stability are examples of potential pile instability under a fire condition. An increase in pile height will tend to increase instability.

Shall. Indicates a mandatory requirement.

Shelf Storage. Storage on structures less than 30 in. (76.2 cm) deep with shelves usually 2 ft (0.6 m) apart vertically and separated by approximately 30-in. (76.2-cm) aisles.

Should. Indicates a recommendation or that which is advised but not required.

Solid Unit Load of a Nonexpanded Plastic (either cartoned or exposed). A load that does not have voids (air) within the load and will burn only on the exterior of the load; water from sprinklers may reach most surfaces available to burn.

Sprinkler Temperature Rating. A 165°F (74°C) rating includes temperature ratings between 135°F (57°C) and 175°F (80°C), and a 286°F (141°C) rating includes temperature ratings between 250°F (121°C) and 300°F (149°C).

Storage Aids. Commodity storage devices, such as pallets, dunnage, separators, and skids.

Unit Load. A pallet load or module held together in some manner and normally transported by material-handling equipment.

Chapter 2 Classification of Storage

2-1 Commodity Classification.

2-1.1 Class I commodity is defined as essentially noncombustible products on combustible pallets, in ordinary corrugated cartons with or without single-thickness dividers, or in ordinary paper wrappings with or without pallets.

Examples of Class I products are:

Foods. Noncombustible foodstuffs and beverages. Foods in noncombustible containers; frozen foods; meats; fresh fruits and vegetables in nonplastic trays or containers; liquid dairy products in nonwax-coated paper containers or in plastic-coated paper containers; beer and wine, up to 20 percent alcohol, in metal, glass, or ceramic containers in ordinary corrugated cartons.

Glass Products. Glass bottles, empty or filled with noncombustible liquids, and mirrors.

Metal Products. Metal desks with plastic tops and trim; electrical coils; electrical devices in their metal enclosures; pots and pans; electrical motors; dry cell batteries; metal parts; empty cans; stoves; washers; dryers; and metal cabinets.

Others. Oil-filled and other types of distribution transformers; cement in bags; electrical insulators; gypsum board; inert pigments; and dry insecticides.

2-1.2 Class II commodity is defined as Class I products in slatted wooden crates, solid wooden boxes, multiple thickness paperboard cartons or equivalent combustible packaging material with or without pallets.

Examples of Class II products are:

Thinly coated fine wire such as radio coil wire on reels or in cartons; incandescent or fluorescent light bulbs; Class I products if in small cartons or small packages placed in ordinary paperboard cartons; book signatures; and beer or wine up to 20 percent alcohol in wood containers.

2-1.3 Class III commodity is defined as wood, paper, natural fiber cloth, or Group C plastics or products thereof, with or without pallets. Products may contain a limited amount of Group A or B plastics. Metal bicycles with plastic handles, pedals, seats, and tires are an example of a commodity with a limited amount of plastic.

Examples of Class III products are:

Leather Products. Shoes; jackets; gloves; and luggage.

Paper Products. Books; magazines; stationery; plastic-coated paper food containers; newspapers; paper or cardboard games; and tissue products.

Textiles. Natural fiber upholstered nonplastic furniture; wood or metal furniture with plastic padded and covered arm rests; mattresses without expanded plastic or rubber; absorbent cotton in cartons; natural fiber and viscose yarns, thread, and products; synthetic thread and yarn; natural fiber clothing or textile products.

Wood Products. Doors; windows; door and window frames; combustible fiberboard; wood cabinets and furniture, and other wood products.

Others. Tobacco products in paperboard cartons; nonflammable liquids such as soaps, detergents, and bleaches in plastic containers; nonnegative-producing film packs in sealed tin foil wrappers in paperboard packages; combustible foods or cereal products; and nonflammable pharmaceuticals.

2-1.4 Class IV commodity is defined as Class I, II, or III products containing an appreciable amount of Group A plastics in ordinary corrugated cartons and Class I, II, and III products in corrugated cartons with Group A plastic packing, with or without pallets. Group B plastics and free-flowing Group A plastics are also included in this class. An example of packing material is a metal typewriter in a foamed plastic cocoon in an ordinary corrugated carton. (*Figure 7-1.1, Note 3.*)

Examples of Class IV products are:

Small appliances, typewriters, and cameras with plastic parts; plastic-backed tapes; nonviscose synthetic fabrics or clothing; telephones; vinyl floor tiles; wood or metal frame upholstered furniture or mattresses with plastic covering and/or padding; plastic-padded metal bumpers and dashboards; insulated conductor and power cable on wood or metal reels or in cartons; inert solids in plastic containers; and building construction insulating panels of polyurethane sandwiched between nonplastic material.

2-1.5* Classification of Plastics, Elastomers, and Rubber.

NOTE: The following categories are based on unmodified plastic materials. The use of fire or flame-retarding modifiers or the physical form of the material may change the classification.

Group A

ABS (acrylonitrile-butadiene-styrene copolymer)
Acrylic (polymethyl methacrylate)
Acetal (polyformaldehyde)
Butyl rubber
EPDM (ethylene-propylene rubber)
FRP (fiberglass reinforced polyester)
Natural rubber (if expanded)
Nitrile rubber (acrylonitrile-butadiene rubber)
PET (thermoplastic polyester)
Polybutadiene
Polycarbonate
Polyester elastomer
Polyethylene
Polypropylene
Polystyrene
Polyurethane
PVC (polyvinyl chloride — highly plasticized, e.g., coated fabric, unsupported film)
SAN (styrene acrylonitrile)
SBR (styrene-butadiene rubber)

Group B

Cellulosics (cellulose acetate, cellulose acetate butyrate, ethyl cellulose)
Chloroprene rubber
Fluoroplastics (ECTFE — ethylene-chlorotrifluoroethylene copolymer; ETFE — ethylene-tetrafluoroethylene copolymer; FEP — fluorinated ethylene-propylene copolymer)
Natural rubber (not expanded)
Nylon (nylon 6, nylon 6/6)
Silicone rubber

Group C

Fluoroplastics (PCTFE — polychlorotrifluoroethylene; PTFE — polytetrafluoroethylene)
Melamine (melamine formaldehyde)
Phenolic
PVC (polyvinyl chloride — rigid or lightly plasticized, e.g., pipe, pipe fittings)
PVDC (polyvinylidene chloride)
PVF (polyvinyl fluoride)
PVDF (polyvinylidene fluoride)
Urea (urea formaldehyde)

Chapter 3 Building Construction

3-1 Construction.

3-1.1* Buildings used for storage of materials that are stored and protected in accordance with this standard shall be of any of the types described in NFPA 220, *Standard on Types of Building Construction*.

3-1.2 Adequate access shall be provided to all portions of the premises for fire fighting purposes.

3-2* Emergency Smoke and Heat Venting. Protection outlined in this standard shall apply to buildings with or without roof vents and draft curtains.

Chapter 4 Storage Arrangement

4-1 Piling Procedures and Precautions.

4-1.1 Any commodities that may be hazardous in combination with each other shall be stored so they cannot come into contact with each other.

4-1.2* Safe floor loads shall not be exceeded. For water absorbent commodities, normal floor loads shall be reduced to take into account the added weight of water that can be absorbed during fire fighting operations.

4-2 Commodity Clearance.

4-2.1 The clearance between top of storage and sprinkler deflectors shall conform to NFPA 13, *Standard for the Installation of Sprinkler Systems*, except as modified by this standard.

4-2.2* If the commodity is stored above the lower chord of roof trusses, at least 1 ft (30.5 cm) of clear space shall be maintained to permit wetting of the truss unless the truss is protected with 1-hr fireproofing.

4-2.3 Storage clearance from ducts shall be maintained in accordance with NFPA 91, *Standard for the Installation of Blower and Exhaust Systems for Dust, Stock, and Vapor Removal or Conveying*, Section 2-8.

4-2.4 The clearance between stored materials and unit heaters, radiant space heaters, duct furnaces, and flues shall not be less than 3 ft (0.9 m) in all directions or shall be in accordance with the clearances shown on the approval agency label.

4-2.5* Clearance shall be maintained to lights or light fixtures to prevent possible ignition.

4-2.6 Sufficient clearance shall be maintained around the path of fire door travel to assure proper operation and inspection.

4-3 Aisles.

4-3.1 Wall aisles shall be at least 24 in. (61 cm) wide in warehouses used for the storage of commodities that expand with the absorption of water.

4-3.2* Aisles shall be maintained to retard transfer of fire from one pile to another and to permit convenient access for fire fighting, salvage, and removal of storage.

4-4* Storage of Idle Pallets.

4-4.1 Wood Pallets or Nonexpanded Polyethylene Solid Deck Pallets.

4-4.1.1* Pallets shall preferably be stored outside or in a detached building.

4-4.1.2 Pallets, when stored indoors, shall be protected as indicated in Table 4-4.1.2, unless the following conditions are met:

(a) Stored no higher than 6 ft (1.8 m), and

(b) Each pallet pile of no more than 4 stacks shall be separated from other pallet piles by at least 8 ft (1.4 m) of clear space or 25 ft (7.6 m) of commodity.

NOTE: No additional protection is necessary as long as items (a) and (b) above are met.

Table 4-4.1.2 Protection for Indoor Storage of Wood Idle Pallets or Nonexpanded Polyethylene Solid Deck Idle Pallets

Height of Pallet Storage ft (m)	Sprinkler Density Requirements gpm/ft² [(L/S)/m²]	Area of Sprinkler Demand ft² (m²) Temperature Rating 286°F (141°C)	165°F (74°C)
Up to 6 (1.8)	.20 [.14]	2,000 (186)	3,000 (279)
6 (1.8) to 8 (2.4)	.30 [.20]	2,500 (232)	4,000 (372)
8 (2.4) to 12 (3.7)	.60 [.41]	3,500 (325)	6,000 (557)
12 (3.7) to 20 (6.1)	.60 [.41]	4,500 (418)	—

4-4.2* Plastic Pallets (other than noted in 4-4.1).

4-4.2.1 Plastic pallets shall preferably be stored outdoors or in a detached shed (*see Table A-4.4.1.1*).

4-4.2.2 Plastic pallets where stored indoors shall be protected as follows:

(a) When stored in cutoff rooms:

(1) The cutoff rooms shall have at least one exterior wall.

(2) The plastic pallet storage shall be separated from the remainder of the building by 3-hr rated fire walls.

(3) The storage shall be protected by sprinklers designed to deliver 0.60 gpm/ft² [0.41 (L/s)/m²] for the entire room or by high expansion foam and sprinklers as indicated in Section 5-2.

(4) The storage shall be piled no higher than 12 ft (3.7 m).

(5) Any steel columns shall be protected by 1-hr fireproofing or a sidewall sprinkler directed to one side of the column at the top or at the 15-ft (4.6-m) level, whichever is lower (*see A-4-2.2*).

(b) When stored without cutoffs from other storage:

(1) Plastic pallet storage shall be piled no higher than 4 ft (1.2 m).

(2) Sprinkler protection shall employ 286°F (141°C) rated sprinklers.

(3) Each pallet pile of no more than two stacks shall be separated from other pallet piles by at least 8 ft (2.4 m) of clear space or 25 ft (7.6 m) of stored commodity.

4-5 Flammable and Combustible Liquids. Only limited quantities of flammable and combustible liquids shall be permitted in general storage warehouses. Any such storage shall be segregated from other stored combustible material. See Chapter 4 of NFPA 30, *Flammable and Combustible Liquids Code*.

Chapter 5 Fire Protection — General

5-1 Automatic Sprinkler Systems.

5-1.1 Sprinkler systems installed in buildings used for solid pile, bin box, shelf, or palletized storage shall be in accordance with NFPA 13, *Standard for the Installation of Sprinkler Systems*, except as modified by this standard.

5-1.2 The design density shall not be less than 0.15 gpm/ft^2 [0.10 (L/s)/m^2] and the design area shall not be less than 2000 ft^2 (186 m^2) for wet systems, 2600 ft^2 (242 m^2) for dry systems, for any commodity, class, or group.

5-1.2.1 The sprinkler design density for any given area of operation for a Class IV commodity, calculated in accordance with Chapter 6, *shall not be less than* the density for the corresponding area of operation for Ordinary Hazard Group 3 in NFPA 13, *Standard for the Installation of Sprinkler Systems.*

5-1.2.2 The sprinkler design density for any given area of operation for a Class III commodity, calculated in accordance with Chapter 6, *shall not be less than* the density for the corresponding area of operation for Ordinary Hazard Group 2 in NFPA 13, *Standard for the Installation of Sprinkler Systems.*

5-1.2.3 The water supply requirements for sprinklers only, shall be based on the actual calculated demand for the hazard using Chapter 6 requirements, and adjusting (if necessary) to satisfy 5-1.2, 5-1.2.1, and 5-1.2.2.

5-1.3 Where palletized or solid pile storage is placed on top of racks, the provisions of NFPA 231C, *Standard for Rack Storage of Materials,* shall apply to the entire height of storage with regard to sprinkler requirements and water supplies for ceiling and rack sprinklers.

5-1.4 In warehouses that have portions containing rack storage and other portions containing palletized, solid pile, bin box, or shelf storage, the standard applicable to the storage configuration shall apply.

5-1.5 Standard response 1/2-in. (12.7-mm) or 17/32-in. (13.5-mm) sprinklers shall be used in applying the curves in Chapters 6 and 7.

Exception: Use of these curves with quick response or other sprinklers shall be at the discretion of the authority having jurisdiction.

5-1.6 In buildings occupied in part for storage, within the scope of this standard, the required sprinkler protection shall extend 15 ft (4.6 m) beyond the perimeter of the storage area.

5-2 High Expansion Foam.

5-2.1 High expansion foam systems installed in addition to automatic sprinklers shall be installed in accordance with NFPA 11A, *Standard for Medium- and High-Expansion Foam Systems,* except as modified herein.

High expansion foam used to protect the idle pallets shall have a maximum fill time of 4 min.

5-2.2 High expansion foam systems shall be automatic in operation.

5-2.3 Detectors shall be listed and shall be installed at no more than one-half listed spacing.

5-2.4 Detection systems, concentrate pumps, generators, and other system components essential to the operation of the system shall have an approved standby power source.

5-2.5 A reduction in ceiling density to one-half that required for Class I through IV commodities, idle pallets, or plastics (using the secondary demand point) shall be permitted without revising the design area, but shall be not less than 0.15 gpm/ft^2 [0.10 (L/s)/m^2].

5-3 Manual Inside Protection.

5-3.1 Small Hose Systems. Small hose lines [1 1/2 in. (38 mm)] shall be available to reach all portions of the storage area, giving due consideration to access aisle configuration with maximum anticipated storage in place. Such small hose shall be supplied from one of the following:

(a) Outside hydrants.

(b) A separate piping system for small hose stations.

(c) Valved hose connections on sprinkler risers where such connections are made upstream of sprinkler control valves.

(d) Adjacent sprinkler systems (*see NFPA 13*).

5-3.2 Portable Fire Extinguishers. Portable fire extinguishers shall be provided in accordance with NFPA 10, *Standard for Portable Fire Extinguishers.* Up to one-half of the required complement of portable fire extinguishers for Class A fires may be omitted in storage areas where fixed, small hose lines [1 1/2 in (38 mm)] are available to reach all portions of the storage area.

5-4* Hydrants. At locations without public hydrants, or where hydrants are not within 250 ft (76.2 m), private hydrants shall be installed in accordance with NFPA 24, *Standard for the Installation of Private Fire Service Mains and Their Appurtenances.*

5-5* Fire Organization.

5-5.1 Arrangements shall be made to permit rapid entry into the premises by the municipal fire department, police department, or other authorized personnel in case of fire or other emergency.

5-5.2 Plant emergency organizations, where provided, shall be instructed and trained in the following procedures:

(a) Maintaining the security of the premises.

(b) Means of summoning outside aid immediately, in an emergency.

(c) Use of hand extinguishers and hose lines on small fires and mop-up operations.

(d) Operation of sprinkler system and water supply equipment.

(e) Use of material handling equipment while sprinklers are operating to effect final extinguishment.

(f) Supervision of sprinkler valves after system is turned off so that system can be reactivated if rekindling occurs.

(g) Need for breathing apparatus.

(h) Proper operation of emergency smoke and heat venting systems where these have been provided.

NOTE: Information on emergency organization is given in the following publications:

NFPA *Industrial Fire Brigades Training Manual.*

NFPA 27, *Recommendations for Organization, Training, and Equipment of Private Fire Brigades.*

5-5.3 A fire watch shall be maintained when the sprinkler system is not in service.

5-6 Alarm Service. Central station, auxiliary, remote station, or proprietary sprinkler waterflow alarm shall be provided. Local waterflow alarm is acceptable where recorded guard service is provided. (*See NFPA 71, Standard for the Installation, Maintenance and Use of Signaling Systems for Central Station Service; and NFPA 72, Standard for the Installation, Maintenance, and Use of Protective Signaling Systems.*)

Chapter 6* Fire Protection — Commodity Classes I through IV

6-1 General.

6-1.1 Protection specified in this chapter shall apply to nonencapsulated commodities and encapsulated commodities up to 15 ft (4.6 m) high.

6-1.2* Sprinkler design criteria for solid pile, palletized, and bin box storage over 12 ft (3.7 m), and shelf storage over 12 ft up to 15 ft (3.7 m to 4.6 m) high, and encapsulated storage up to 15 ft (4.6 m) high shall be in accordance with Figures 6-1.2(a), 6-1.2(b), and 6-2.2.

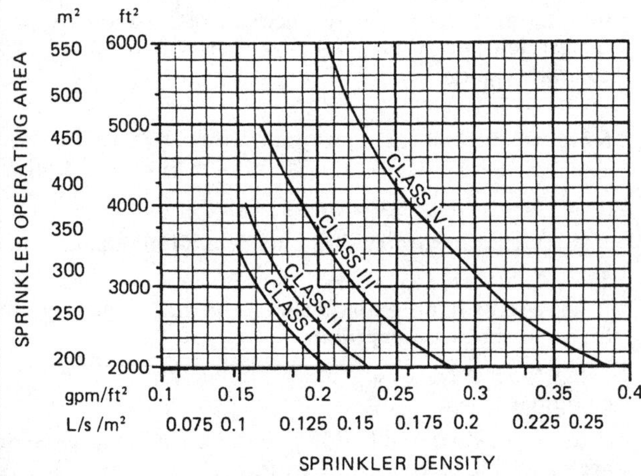

Figure 6-1.2(a) Sprinkler System Design Curves 20-ft High Storage — 165°F (74°C) Sprinklers.

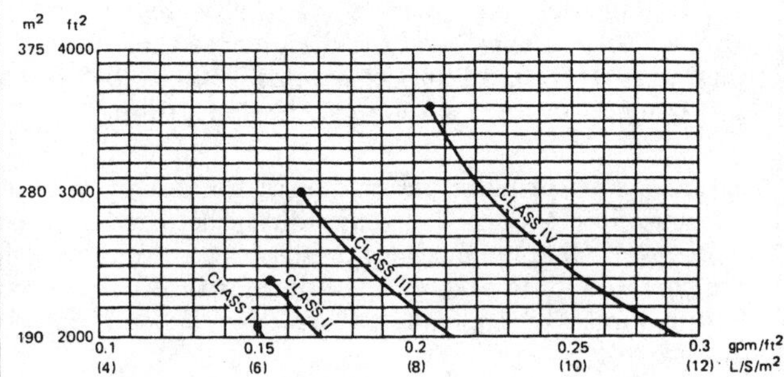

Figure 6-1.2(b) Sprinkler System Design, Curves, 20-ft High 286°F (141°C) Sprinklers.

Note: Sprinkler demand for 20 ft (6 m) high storage may be selected from any point on the appropriate class curve in Figure 6-1.2(b).
Figure 6-1.2(b) provides protection curves for sprinkler systems using only 286°F (141°C) rated sprinklers.

Exception No. 1: For bin boxes and closed shelves constructed of metal with a face area not exceeding 16 ft² (1.49 m²), the area of application is permitted to be reduced by 50 percent, but not to less than 2000 ft² (186 m²) for wet systems and 2600 ft² (242m²) for dry systems.

Exception No. 2: Chapter 8 (Large Drop Sprinklers) and Chapter 9 (ESFR Sprinklers) provide acceptable alternate methods of protection.

The density provided for the area of application shall be permitted to be selected from any point on the curve applicable to the commodity, classification, and arrangement of the stored commodities and sprinkler temperature rating. It is not necessary to meet more than one point on the selected curve.

6-1.2.1 For storage heights other than 20 ft (6.1 m) the densities shall be modified according to Figure 6-2.2.

6-1.3 Bin box and shelf storage over 12 ft (2.7 m) and provided with walkways at not over 12-ft (3.7-m) vertical intervals shall be provided with automatic sprinklers under the walkways as well as at the ceiling. The design density for ceiling and walkway sprinklers shall be permitted to be in accordance with the height adjustment of Figure 6-2.2.

6-2* Water Supplies.

6-2.1 Sprinkler water demand for 20-ft (6.1-m) high palletized storage, solid pile, and bin box storage shall be in accordance with Figure 6-1.2(b).

6-2.2 Where storage height is less than 30 ft (9.1 m) high, but more than 12 ft (3.7 m) high in solid piles, palletized, or bin box storage, ceiling densities indicated in the design curves in Figures 6-1.2(a) and 6-1.2(b), shall be modified in accordance with Figure 6-2.2 without revising the design area. (*See A-1-2, Available Height for Storage.*)

6-2.3 For shelf storage over 12 to 15 ft (3.7 to 4.6 m) high, ceiling densities indicated in the design curves in Figures 6-1.2(a) and 6-1.2(b) shall be modified in accordance with Figure 6-2.2 without revising the design area.

6-2.4 Where dry-pipe systems are used, the areas of operation indicated in the design curves shall be increased by 30 percent. Densities shall be selected so that areas of operation, after the 30 percent increase, do not exceed the upper area limits given in the design curves.

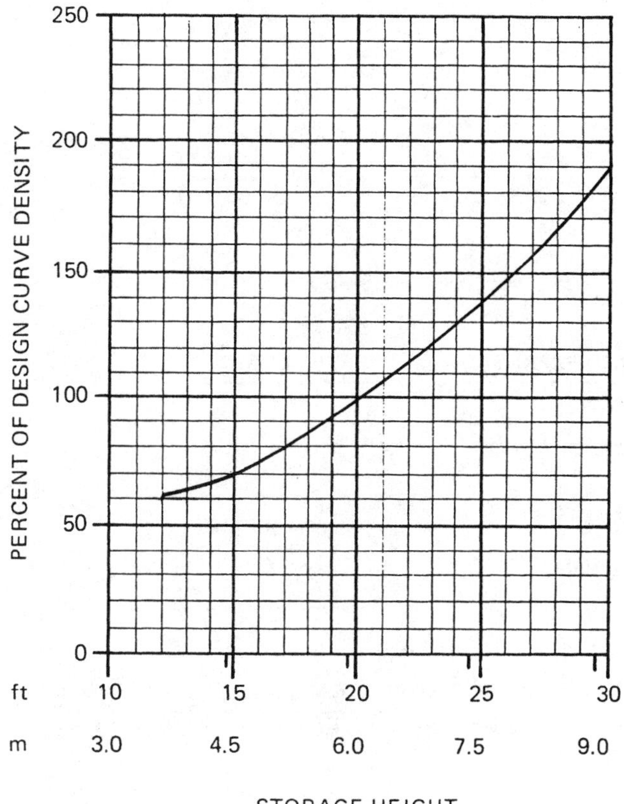

Figure 6-2.2 Ceiling Sprinkler Density Versus Storage Height.

6-2.5 A minimum of 500 gpm (32 L/s) shall be added to the sprinkler demand (*see 5-1.2.3*) for combined large and small hose stream demand.

6-2.6 Water supply duration shall be:

Duration (hours)

Storage Height ft (m)	Commodity Class	
	Classes I, II, & III	**Class IV**
over 12 (3.7) up to 20 (6.1)	$1^1/_2$	2
over 20 (6.1) up to 30 (9.1)	2	$2^1/_2$

6-3 High Expansion Foam (*see Section 5-2*).

Chapter 7 Fire Protection — Plastics and Rubber

7-1* General. (*See Appendix B.*)

7-1.1* Group A plastics shall be protected as indicated by Figure 7-1.1, Decision Tree. The decision tree shall be followed to determine the protection in each specific situation.

Exception: Chapter 8 (Large Drop Sprinklers) and Chapter 9 (ESFR sprinklers) provide acceptable alternative methods of protection.

7-1.2* Factors affecting protection requirements such as closed/open array, clearance between storage and sprinklers, stable/unstable piles, and two-point demands shall be applicable only to storage of Group A plastics. The factors contained in 7-2.1, A-7-2.1, and Appendix B shall be given serious consideration prior to giving the final protection requirements. This decision tree shall also be used to determine protection for commodities that are not wholly Group A plastics but contain such quantities and arrangements of the same that they are deemed more hazardous than Class IV commodities.

7-1.3 Group B plastics and free-flowing Group A plastics shall be protected in the same manner as a Class IV commodity. Storages 12 ft (3.7 m) or less in height shall be protected in accordance with NFPA 13 for Ordinary Hazard Group 3.

7-1.4 Group C plastics shall be protected in the same manner as a Class III commodity. Storages 12 ft (3.7 m) or less in height shall be protected in accordance with NFPA 13 for Ordinary Hazard Group 2.

7-2 Water Supplies.

7-2.1* The design of the sprinkler system shall be based on the conditions that will routinely or periodically exist in a building creating the greatest water demand. These conditions include: (a) pile height, (b) clearance, (c) pile stability, and (d) array.

7-2.2 Design areas and densities for 20-ft (6.1-m) high storage with between $1^1/_2$ ft (0.5 m) to $4^1/_2$ ft (1.4 m) clearance shall be selected for the appropriate storage configuration from Figures 7-2.2(a), 7-2.2(b), 7-2.2(c), 7-2.2(d), and 7-2.2(e).

7-2.2.1 Both an initial and a secondary density/area shall be met. The unadjusted secondary density shall be at least 0.25 gpm/ft^2 [0.17 (L/s)/m^2] less than the unadjusted initial density, and the minimum secondary design area, after all credits and penalties (height, clearance, and array), shall be 2000 ft^2 (186 m^2) for wet systems and 2600 ft^2 (242 m^2) for dry systems.

Exception: For storage 5 ft (1.5 m) to 10 ft (3.0 m) high, design areas and density for the secondary demand only shall be used.

7-2.2.2 Where clearance is in excess of $4^1/_2$ ft (1.4 m), the design areas for the initial and secondary demands shall be multiplied by the factors from Figure 7-2.2.2, without revising the density.

NOTE: There is insufficient test data available to define protection requirements for clearances in excess of 10 ft (3 m).

7-2.2.3 Where the height is other than 20 ft (6.1 m), the design densities shall be adjusted in accordance with Figure 7-2.2.3, without revising the design area.

7-2.3 Where there is a closed array (not including solid unit load or expanded exposed storage), the density/area shall be obtained as directed by 7-2.1, and corrected for height and clearance as directed in 7-2.2.2 and 7-2.2.3. A

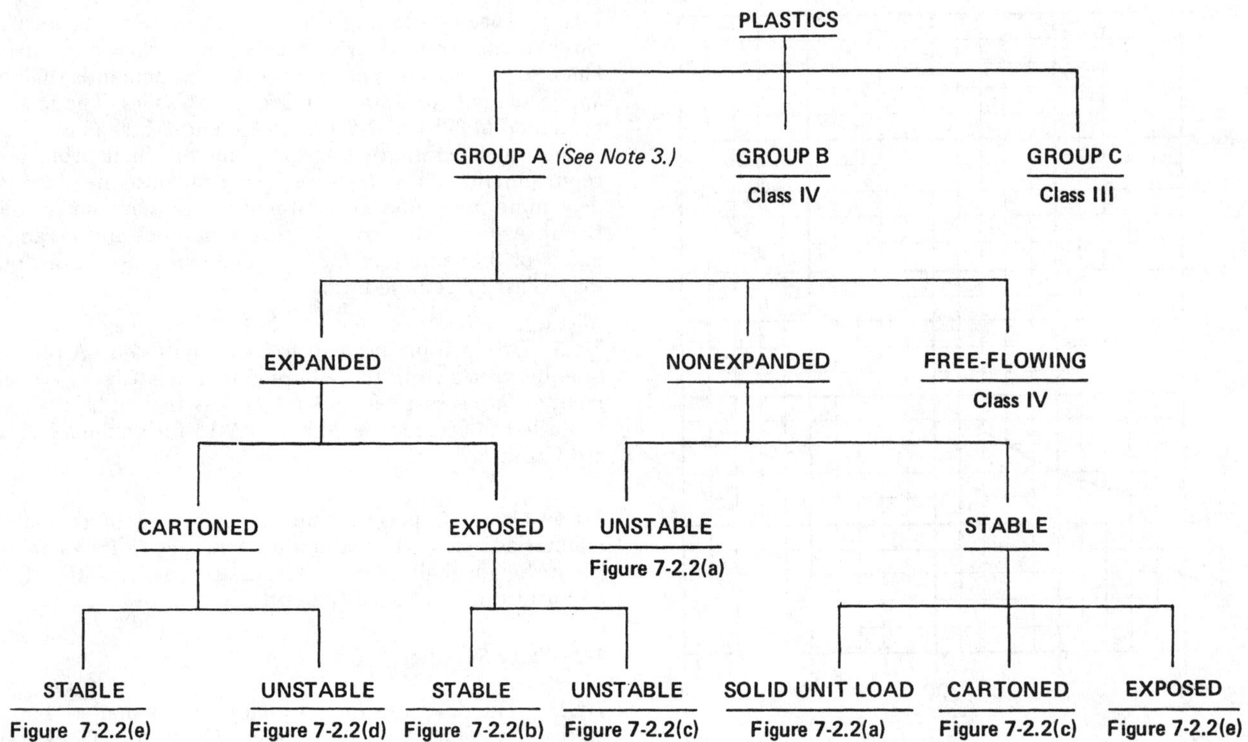

Figure 7-1.1 Decision Tree.

NOTES:

1. It is recommended that 286°F (141°C) rated sprinklers be installed, since most tests upon which this standard is based used 286°F (141°C) rated sprinklers.
2. The density/area curves are the starting points for determining proper protection in a given situation. The starting point assumes 20-ft (6.1-m) high storage and $1^1/_2$-ft (0.5-m) to $4^1/_2$-ft (1.4-m) clearance.
3. Cartons that contain Group A plastic material may be treated as Class IV commodities under the following conditions:

(a) There are multiple layers of corrugation or equivalent outer material that would significantly delay fire involvement of the Group A plastic.

(b) The amount and arrangement of the Group A plastic material within an ordinary carton would not be expected to significantly increase the fire hazard.

secondary area reduction of 50 percent for stable piles and 25 percent for unstable piles shall be applied (without revising the density) to the less hazardous closed array.

7-2.4 Where sprinkler protection has been designed for Group A plastics, at least 500 gpm (32 L/s) shall be added to the secondary density/area demand for hose streams.

7-2.5 Water supply duration (secondary sprinkler demand plus hose streams) shall be 2-hr duration for 5 ft (1.5 m) to 20 ft (6.1 m) and $2^1/_2$-hr duration for 20 ft (6.1 m) to 25 ft (7.6 m).

7-2.6* Where dry-pipe systems are used for Group A plastics, the operating area for the secondary density/area demand only, indicated in the design curves, shall be increased by 30 percent without revising the density.

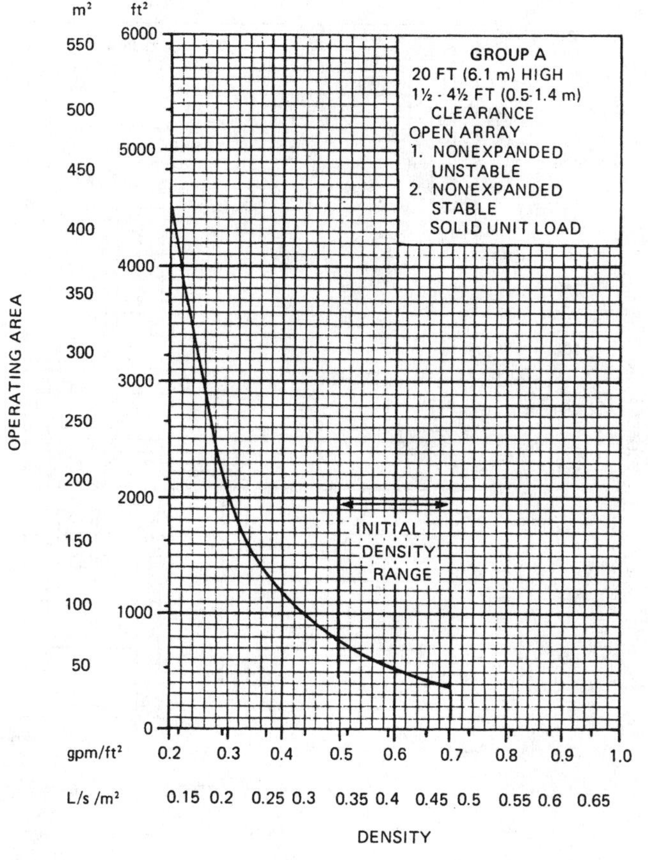

Figure 7-2.2(a).

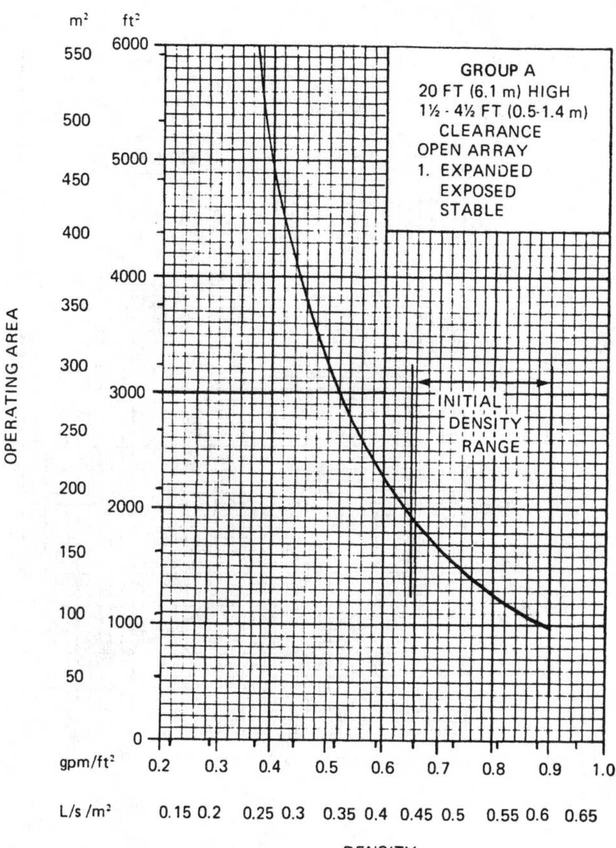

Figure 7-2.2(b).

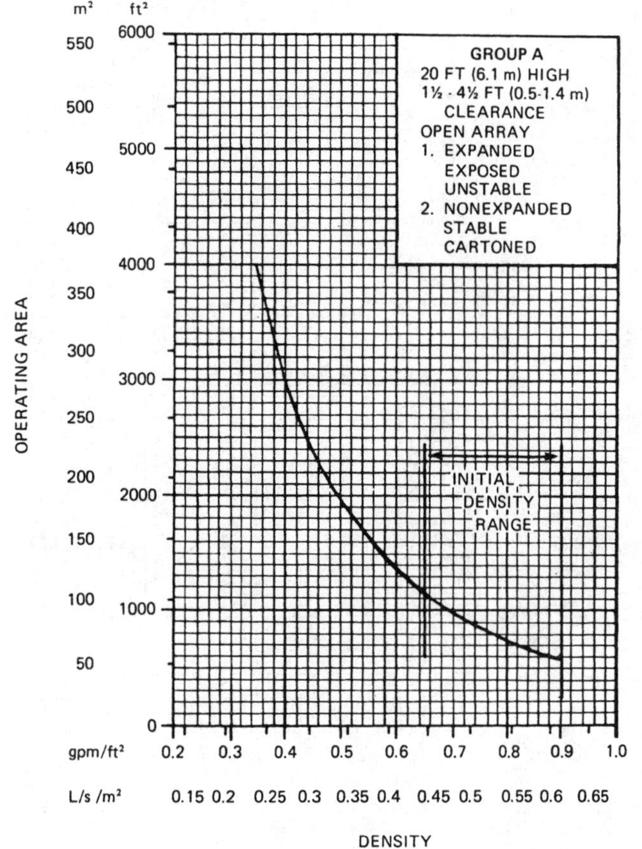

Figure 7-2.2(c).

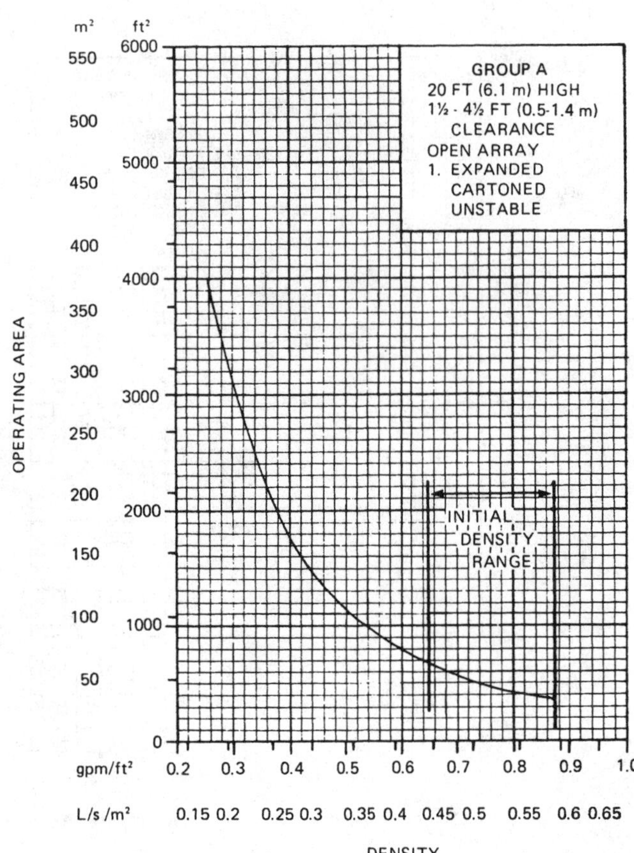

Figure 7-2.2(d).

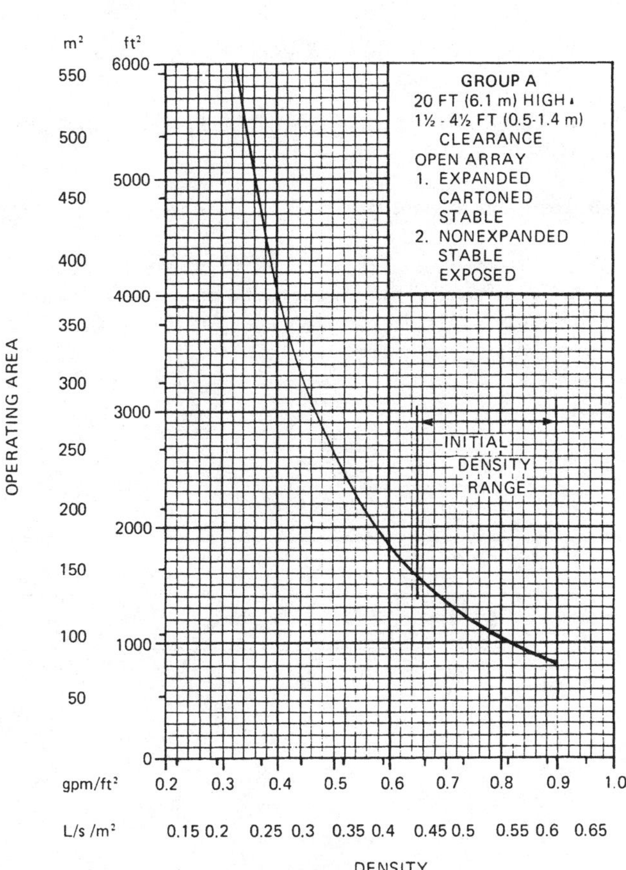

Figure 7-2.2(e).

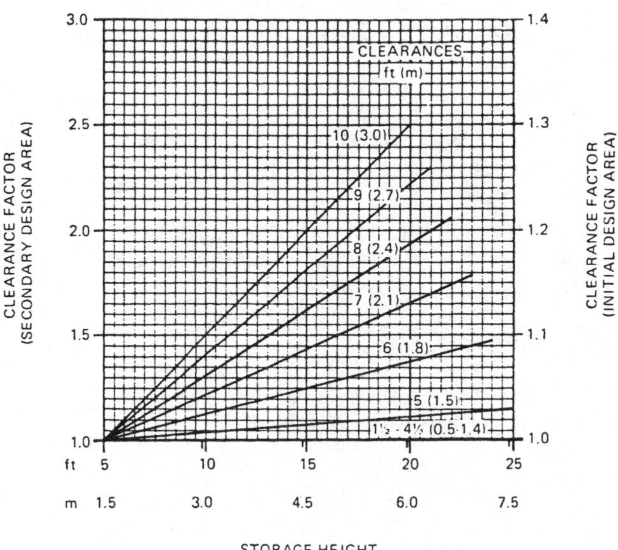

Figure 7-2.2.2.

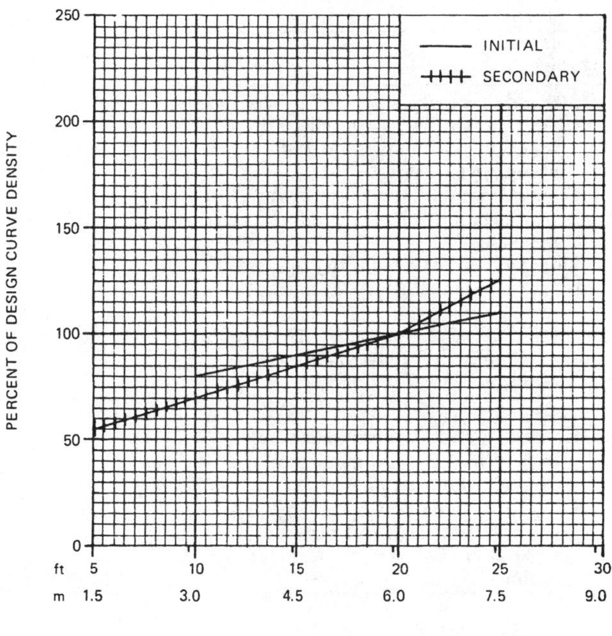

Figure 7-2.2.3.

Chapter 8 Large Drop Sprinklers

8-1 General.

8-1.1 Large drop sprinklers shall be permitted for use with the hazards listed in Table 8-1.

8-1.2 All requirements contained in NFPA 13, *Standard for the Installation of Sprinkler Systems*, particularly Chapter 9, shall apply.

8-2 Water Supplies.

8-2.1 Sprinkler water demand for large drop sprinklers shall be in accordance with Table 8-1.

8-2.2 A minimum of 500 gpm (32L/s) shall be added to the sprinkler demand for combined large and small hose stream demand.

8-2.3 Water supply duration shall be at least $1^1/_2$ hr.

8-2.4 Large drop sprinklers shall be limited to wet-pipe or preaction systems.

8-3 Sprinkler System Design.

8-3.1 All requirements contained in NFPA 13, *Standard for the Installation of Sprinkler Systems*, particularly Chapter 9, shall apply, except as modified by this standard.

Table 8-1

Minimum Operating Pressure (Note 1) psi (bar)	25 (1.7)	50 (3.4)	75 (5.2)
Hazard (Note 2)		Number Design Sprinklers	
Palletized Storage			
Class I, II, and III commodities up to 25 ft (7.6 m) with maximum 10-ft (3.0-m) clearance to ceiling	15	Note 3	Note 3
Class IV commodities up to 20 ft (6.1 m) with maximum 10-ft (3.0-m) clearance to ceiling	20	15	Note 3
Unexpanded plastics up to 20 ft (6.1 m) with maximum 10-ft (3.0-m) clearance to ceiling	25	15	Note 3
Idle wood pallets up to 20 ft (6.1 m) with maximum 10-ft (3.0-m) clearance to ceiling	15	Note 3	Note 3
Solid-Piled Storage			
Class I, II, and III commodities up to 20 ft (6.1 m) with maximum 10-ft (3.0-m) clearance to ceiling	15	Note 3	Note 3
Class IV commodities and unexpanded plastics up to 20 ft (6.1 m) with maximum 10-ft (3.0-m) clearance to ceiling	Does Not Apply	15	Note 3

Notes:

1. Open wood joist construction. Testing with open wood joist construction showed that each joist channel should be fully firestopped to its full depth at intervals not exceeding 20 ft (6.1 m). In unfirestopped open wood joist construction, or if firestops are installed at intervals exceeding 20 ft (6.1 m), the minimum operating pressures should be increased by 40 percent.
2. Building steel required no special protection for the occupancies listed.
3. The higher pressure will successfully control the fire, but the required number of design sprinklers should not be reduced from that required for the lower pressure.
4. Sprinklers used in the tests were high temperature rating.

Chapter 9 Early Suppression Fast Response (ESFR) Sprinklers

9-1* General.

9-1.1 ESFR sprinklers shall be permitted for the protection of cartoned plastics (Group A, B, or C) and Class I through IV commodities in palletized and solid pile storage up to a height of 25 ft (7.6 m).

Exception: ESFR protection as now defined does not apply to:

1. exposed plastics or expanded polystyrene plastic in cartons.

2. storage involving combustible open top cartons or containers.

9-1.2* ESFR sprinklers shall be permitted for use in buildings having a maximum roof or ceiling height of 30 ft (9.1 m) and one of the following types of roof construction:

(a) Smooth ceiling

(b) Bar joist

(c) Beam and girder

(d) Panel

9-1.3 Roof slope shall not exceed 1 in./ft.

9-2* Water Supplies.

9-2.1* ESFR sprinkler systems shall be designed to provide a minimum operating pressure of 50 psi (3.4 bars) to the 12 most hydraulically remote sprinklers, based on flowing four sprinklers in each of three branch lines.

9-2.2 A minimum of 250 gpm (16L/s) shall be added to the sprinkler demand for combined large and small hose streams.

9-2.3 Water supply duration shall be at least 1 hr.

9-2.4 ESFR sprinklers shall be limited to wet-pipe systems.

9-3 Sprinkler System Design.

9-3.1 All requirements contained in NFPA 13, *Standard for the Installation of Sprinkler Systems*, particularly Chapter 9 shall apply, except as modified by this standard.

Chapter 10 Building Equipment, Maintenance, and Operations

10-1* Mechanical Handling Equipment.

10-1.1* Industrial Trucks. Power-operated industrial trucks shall comply with NFPA 505, *Firesafety Standard for Powered Industrial Trucks Including Type Designations, Areas of Use, Maintenance and Operation.*

10-2 Building Service Equipment.

10-2.1 Electrical equipment shall be installed in accordance with the provisions of NFPA 70, *National Electrical Code®*.

10-3 Cutting and Welding Operations.

10-3.1* When welding or cutting operations are necessary, the precautions contained in NFPA 51B, *Standard for Fire Prevention in Use of Cutting and Welding Processes*, shall be followed. When possible, work shall be removed to a safe area.

10-3.2 Welding, soldering, brazing, and cutting shall be permitted to be performed on building components that cannot be removed, provided no storage is located below and within 25 ft (7.6 m) of the working area, and flameproof tarpaulins enclose this section. During any of these operations the sprinkler system shall be in service. Extinguishers suitable for Class A fires with a minimum rating of 2A and charged and manned inside hose lines, where provided, shall be located in the working area. A fire watch shall be maintained during these operations and for not less than 30 min following completion of open flame operation.

10-4 Waste Disposal. Rubbish, trash, and other waste material shall be disposed of at regular intervals.

10-5 Smoking. Smoking shall be strictly prohibited, except in locations prominently designated as smoking areas. "No Smoking" signs shall be posted in prohibited areas.

10-6 Maintenance and Inspection.

10-6.1 Fire walls, fire doors, and floors shall be maintained in good repair at all times.

10-6.2 The sprinkler system and the water supplies shall be maintained and serviced. (*For further information see NFPA 13A, Recommended Practice for the Inspection, Testing and Maintenance of Sprinkler Systems.*)

10-7 Refrigeration Systems. Refrigeration systems, if used, shall conform to the recommendations of *Safety Code for Mechanical Refrigeration*, ANSI/ASHRAE 15-70.

Chapter 11 Referenced Publications

11-1 The following documents or portions thereof are referenced within this standard and shall be considered part of the requirements of this document. The edition indicated for each reference is the current edition as of the date of the NFPA issuance of this document.

11-1.1 NFPA Publications. National Fire Protection Association, 1 Batterymarch Park, P.O. Box 9101, Quincy, MA 02269-9101.

NFPA 10-1990, *Standard for Portable Fire Extinguishers*

NFPA 11A-1988, *Standard for Medium- and High-Expansion Foam Systems*

NFPA 13-1989, *Standard for the Installation of Sprinkler Systems*

NFPA 24-1987, *Standard for the Installation of Private Fire Service Mains and Their Appurtenances*

NFPA 30-1990, *Flammable and Combustible Liquids Code*

NFPA 51B-1989, *Standard for Fire Prevention in Use of Cutting and Welding Processes*

NFPA 70-1990, *National Electrical Code*

NFPA 71-1989, *Standard for the Installation, Maintenance, and Use of Signaling Systems for Central Station Service*

NFPA 72-1990, *Standard for the Installation, Maintenance, and Use of Protective Signaling Systems*

NFPA 91-1990, *Standard for the Installation of Blower and Exhaust Systems for Dust, Stock, and Vapor Removal or Conveying*

NFPA 220-1985, *Standard on Types of Building Construction*

NFPA 231C-1986, *Standard for Rack Storage of Materials*

NFPA 505-1987, *Firesafety Standard for Powered Industrial Trucks Including Type Designations, Areas of Use, Maintenance and Operation*

11-1.2 ASHRAE Code. American Society of Heating, Refrigerating and Air Conditioning Engineers, United Engineering Center, 345 East 49th Street, New York, NY 10017.

ASHRAE 15-1989, *Safety Code for Mechanical Refrigeration*

Appendix A

This Appendix is not a part of the requirements of this NFPA document, but is included for information purposes only.

A-1-2 Definitions.

Open Array. Fire tests that were conducted to represent a closed array utilized 6-in. (152-mm) longitudinal flues and no transverse flues. Fire tests that were conducted to represent an open array utilized 12-in. (305-mm) longitudinal flues.

Available Height for Storage. For new sprinkler installations, maximum height of storage is the height at which commodities can be stored above the floor when the minimum required unobstructed space below sprinklers is maintained. For the evaluation of existing situations, maximum height of storage is the maximum existing height, if space between sprinklers and storage is equal to or greater than required.

Compartmented. Cartons used in most of the Factory Mutual-sponsored plastic tests involved ordinary 200-lb (90.7-kg) test, outside corrugated cartons with 5 layers of vertical pieces of corrugated carton used as dividers on the inside. There were also single horizontal pieces of corrugated carton between each layer. Other tests sponsored by the Society of Plastics Industry, Industrial Risk Insurers, Factory Mutual, and Kemper used two vertical pieces of carton (not corrugated) to form an "X" in the carton for separation of product. This was not considered compartmented, as the pieces of carton used for separations were flexible (not rigid), and only two pieces were in each carton.

Container. Container designates cartons, wrappings, etc. Fire retardant containers or tote boxes do not of themselves create a need for automatic sprinklers unless coated with oil or grease. Containers may lose their fire retardant properties if washed. For obvious reasons, they should not be exposed to rainfall.

Pile Stability. Pile stability has been shown to be a difficult item to judge under fire conditions, prior to the fire. In the test work completed, compartmented cartons (described above) have shown to be stable under fire conditions. Those tests on cartons that were not compartmented tended to be unstable under fire conditions.

A-2-1.5 The classes of plastics used in this standard were basically derived from a series of large-scale and laboratory-type small-scale fire tests using a variety of expanded and nonexpanded plastic materials. It is recognized that not all plastics in a class will burn with exactly the same characteristics.

A-3-1.1 With protection installed in accordance with this standard, fire protection of overhead steel and steel columns may not be necessary.

Consideration should be given to subdividing large area warehouses in order to reduce the amount of merchandise that would be affected by a single fire.

It is desirable to provide walls or partitions to separate the storage area from mercantile, manufacturing, or other occupancies to prevent the possibility of transmission of fire or smoke between the two occupancies. Door openings should be equipped with automatic closing fire doors appropriate for the fire resistance rating of the wall or partition.

A-3-2 Smoke removal is important to manual fire fighting and overhaul. Since most fire tests were conducted without smoke and heat venting, protection specified in Sections 5-1, 6-1, and 7-1 was developed without the use of such venting. However, venting through eaveline windows, doors, monitors, gravity, or mechanical exhaust systems is essential to smoke removal after control of the fire is achieved. (*See NFPA 204M, Guide for Smoke and Heat Venting.*)

A-4.1.2 Commodities that are particularly susceptible to water damage should be stored on skids, dunnage, pallets, or elevated platforms in order to maintain at least 4 in. (10.2 cm) clearance from the floor.

A-4-2.2 Protection for exposed steel structural roof members may be needed and should be provided as indicated by the authority having jurisdiction.

A-4-2.5 Incandescent light fixtures should have shades or guards to prevent ignition of commodity from hot bulbs where possibility of contact with storage exists.

A-4-3.2 Storage should be separated by aisles so that piles are not more than 50 ft (15.2 m) wide or 25 ft (7.6 m) wide if they abut a wall. Main and cross aisles should be located opposite window or door openings in exterior walls. This is of particular importance in buildings where exterior openings are few. Aisle width should be at least 8 ft (2.4 m). In judging the adequacy of existing sprinkler protection, aisle spacing and frequency should be given consideration.

A-4-4 Idle pallet storage introduces a severe fire condition. Stacking idle pallets in piles is the best arrangement of combustibles to promote rapid spread of fire, heat release, and complete combustion. After pallets are used for a short time in warehouses, they dry out and edges become frayed and splintered. In this condition they are subject to easy ignition from a small ignition source. Again, high piling increases considerably both the challenge to sprinklers and the probability of involving a large number of pallets when fire occurs.

A-4-4.1.1 *(See Table A-4-4.1.1.)*

Table A-4-4.1.1 Recommended Clearance Between Outside Idle Pallet Storage and Building.

Wall Construction		Minimum Distance, ft(m) of Wall from Storage of		
Wall Type	**Openings**	**Under 50 Pallets**	**50 to 200 Pallets**	**Over 200 Pallets**
Masonry	None	0	0	0
	Wired glass with outside sprinklers 1-hr doors	0	10 (3.0)	20 (6.1)
	Wired or plain glass with outside sprinklers $^3/_4$-hr doors	10 (3.0)	20 (6.1)	30 (9.1)
Wood or metal with outside sprinklers				
Wood, metal, or other		20 (6.1)	30 (9.1)	50 (15.2)

Notes:
1. Fire-resistive protection comparable to that of the wall should also be provided for combustible eave lines, vent openings, etc.
2. When pallets are stored close to a building, the height of storage should be restricted to prevent burning pallets from falling on the building.
3. Manual outside open sprinklers generally are not a reliable means of protection unless property is attended to at all times by plant emergency personnel.
4. Open sprinklers controlled by a deluge valve are preferred.

A-4-4.2 A fire in stacks of idle plastic and wooden pallets is one of the greatest challenges to sprinklers. The undersides of the pallets create a dry area on which a fire can grow and expand to other dry or partially wet areas. This process of jumping to other dry, closely located, parallel, combustible surfaces continues until the fire bursts through the top of the stack. Once this happens, very little water is able to reach the base of the fire. The only practical method of stopping a fire in a large concentration of pallets with ceiling sprinklers is by a great amount of prewetting. In high stacks this cannot be done without abnormally high water supplies. The storage of empty wood pallets should not be permitted in an unsprinklered warehouse containing other storage.

A-5-4 At windowless warehouses and where windows are scant, hydrants should be located at or in the vicinity of entrances.

A-5-5 Manual fire fighting operations in a storage warehouse are not a substitute for sprinkler operation. The sprinkler system should be kept in operation during manual fire fighting operations until visibility has cleared so that the fire can be clearly seen and the extent of fire reduced to a stage requiring only mopping up. It is essential that charged hose lines be available before venting is started because of a possible increase in fire intensity. When a sprinkler valve is closed, a responsible person should remain at the valve so it can be opened promptly if necessary. The water supply for the sprinkler system should be augmented where possible and care exercised that the water supply for the sprinkler system is not rendered ineffective by the use of excessive hose streams.

Where a private fire brigade is provided, sufficient large hose [$2^1/_2$ in. (64 mm)] and related equipment should be available.

A-6 The following procedure should be followed in determining the proper density and area as specified in Chapter 6.

1. Determine the commodity class.

2. Select the density and area of application from Figure 6-1.2(a) or Figure 6-1.2(b).

3. Adjust the required density for height of storage in accordance with Figure 6-2.2.

4. Increase operating area by 30 percent in accordance with 6-2.4 when a dry pipe system is used.

5. Satisfy minimum densities and areas as indicated in 5-1.2, 5-1.2.1, and 5-1.2.2.

The following is an example using these procedures:

Storage – greeting cards in boxes in cartons on pallets

Height – 22 ft (6.7 m)

Clearance – 6 ft (1.8 m)

Sprinklers – decided to use 165°F (74°C) sprinkler system – dry.

1. Classify – Class III

2. Select Density/Area – 0.225 gpm/3000 ft^2 (0.014 L/s/ 276 m^2) from Figure 6-1.2(a).

3. Adjust for height of storage 1.15 × 0.225 = 0.259
From Figure 6-2.2 Round up = 0.26 gpm/ft^2

4. Adjust area of operation for dry system – 1.3 × 3000 = 3900 ft^2 (363 m^2)

5. Satisfy minimum densities and areas

In 5-1.2 the minimum for a dry sprinkler system is 0.15/2600 (this has been satisfied) for Class III.

5-1.2.2 refers to ordinary hazard Group 2 of NFPA 13. That density at 3000 ft^2 (279 m^2) is 0.16 gpm/ft^2 (0.1 L/s/m^2) (This minimum has been satisfied) 3000 × 1.3 = 3900 ft^2 (363 m^2), 0.16 gpm/3900 ft^2 (0.1 L/s/363 m^2).

The design density and area of application is 0.26 gpm/ft^2 (0.18 L/s/m^2) over 3900 ft^2 (363 m^2).

A-6-1.2 Full-scale tests show no appreciable difference in the number of sprinkler heads that open for either nonencapsulated or encapsulated products up to 15 ft high (4.6 m). Test data is not available for encapsulated products stored higher than 15 ft (4.6 m). However in rack storage tests involving encapsulated storage 20 ft (6 m) high, increased protection was needed over that for nonencapsulated storage.

Protection specified in this chapter contemplates a maximum of 10 ft (3 m) clearances from top of storage to sprinkler deflectors for storage heights of 15 ft (4.6 m) and higher.

A-6-2 Recommended water supplies contemplate successful sprinkler operation. Because of the small, but still significant, number of uncontrolled fires in sprinklered properties for various reasons, there should be an adequate water supply available for fire department use.

A-7-1 The densities and area of application have been developed from fire test data. Most of these tests were conducted with large orifice [17/32 in (13.5 mm)] sprinklers and 80- or 100-ft^2 (7.4-9.3 m^2) sprinkler spacing. These and other tests have indicated that, with densities of 0.40 gpm/ft^2 [0.27 (L/s)/m^2] and higher, better results are obtained with large orifice and 70- to 100-ft^2 (7.4-9.3 m^2) sprinkler spacing than when using 1/2-in. (12.7-mm) orifice sprinklers at 50 ft^2 (4.6 m^2) spacing. A discharge pressure of 100 psi (689 kPa) was used as a starting point on one of the fire tests. It was successful, but has a 1 1/2-ft (0.5-m) clearance between the top of storage and ceiling sprinklers. A clearance of 10 ft (3.0 m) may have produced a different result due to the tendency of the higher pressure to atomize the water and the greater distance for the fine water droplets to travel to the burning fuel.

A-7-1.1 Two direct comparisons between 165°F (74°C) and 286°F (141°C) rated sprinklers are possible:

(a) With nonexpanded polyethylene 1-gal (3.8-L) bottles in corrugated cartons, a 3-ft (0.9-m) clearance, and the same density, approximately the same number of sprinklers operated [9 at 286°F (141°C) VS 7 at 165°F (74°C)].

(b) With exposed, expanded polystyrene meat trays, a 9.5-ft (1.9-m) clearance, and the same density, three times as many 165°F (74°C) rated sprinklers operated as did 286°F (141°C) rated sprinklers [11 at 286°F (141°C) VS, 33 at 165°F (74°C)].

The cartoned plastics requirements of this standard are based to a great extent on test work that used a specific commodity – 16 oz. (0.473 L) polystyrene plastic jars individually separated by thin carton stock within a large corrugated carton [3 1/2 ft^2 (0.32 m^2)]. (*See Figure A.*)

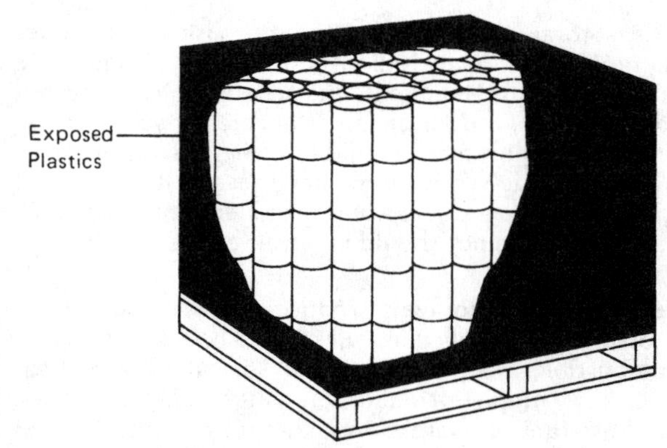

Figure A.

Other Group A plastic commodities may be so arranged in cartons that they are separated by multiple thicknesses of carton material. In such arrangements less plastic becomes involved in the fire at any one time. This could result in a less vigorous fire that could be controlled by Class IV commodity protection.

Other situations exist in which the plastics component is surrounded by several layers of less hazardous material and is therefore temporarily protected or insulated from a fire involving adjacent plastic products. Such situations also could produce a less vigorous fire and be successfully handled by Class IV protection. (*See Figure B.*)

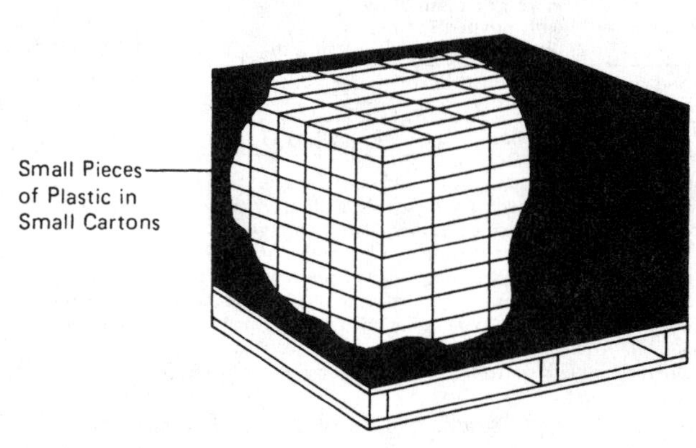

Figure B.

The decision to protect as a Class IV commodity, however, should be done only with experienced judgement and only with an understanding of the consequences of underprotecting the storage segment.

A-7-1.2 There are few storage facilities in which the commodity mix or storage arrangement remains constant, and a designer should be aware that the introduction of different materials may change protection requirements considerably. Design should be on the side of higher densities and areas of application, and the various reductions allowed should be applied cautiously. For evaluation of existing situations, however, the allowances may be quite helpful.

A-7-2.1 An evaluation for each field situation should be made to determine the worst applicable height-clearance relationship that can be expected to appear in a particular case. Fire tests have shown that considerably greater demands occur where clearance is 10 ft (3.0 m) as compared to 3 ft (0.9 m), and where a pile is stable as compared to an unstable pile. Since a system is designed for a particular clearance, the system could be inadequate when significant areas do not have piling to the design height and larger clearances exist between stock and sprinklers. This can also be true where the packaging or arrangement is changed so that stable piling is created where unstable piling existed. Recognition of these conditions is essential to avoid installation of protection that is inadequate or becomes inadequate because of changes.

No tests were conducted simulating a peaked roof configuration. However, it is expected that the principles of Chapter 7 still apply. The worst applicable height-clearance relationship that can be expected to occur should be found, and protection designed for it. If storage is all at the same height, the worst height-clearance relationship creating the greatest water demand would occur under the peak. If commodities are stored higher under the peak, the various height-clearance relationships should be tried and the one creating the greatest water demand used for designing protection.

A-7-2.6 Wet systems are recommended for storage occupancies. Dry-pipe systems are acceptable only where it is impractical to provide heat.

A-9-1 ESFR sprinklers were designed to respond quickly to growing fires and deliver heavy discharge to "suppress" fires rather than "control" them. ESFR sprinklers cannot be relied upon to provide suppression if they are used outside these design parameters.

A-9-1.2 Storage in single story or multistory buildings is permissible provided the 30 ft (10 m) maximum ceiling/roof height is satisfied for each storage area.

A-9-2 Design parameters were determined from a series of full scale fire tests conducted as a joint effort between Factory Mutual and the National Fire Protection Research Foundation. (Copies of the test reports are available from the NFPRF).

A-10-1 Locomotives should not be allowed to enter storage areas.

A-10-1.1 Industrial trucks using gas or liquid fuel should be refueled outside of the storage building at a location designated for that purpose.

A-10-3.1 The use of welding, cutting, soldering, or brazing torches in the storage areas introduces a severe fire hazard. The use of mechanical fastenings and mechanical saws or cutting wheels is recommended.

Appendix B

This Appendix is not a part of the requirements of this NFPA document, but is included for information purposes only.

Appendix B explains and gives examples of the methods and procedures to follow in using this standard to determine proper protection for Group A plastics.

Metric Conversion Factors for Examples

To convert from	to	Multiply by
feet (ft)	meter (m)	0.3048
square feet (ft^2)	meter^2 (m^2)	0.0920
gal/min (gpm)	liter/second (L/s)	0.0631
gal per min/ft^2 (gpm/ft^2)	liter per second/m^2 [(L/s)/m^2]	0.679

Example 1

Building height ________ 26 ft

Sprinkler deflector height from floor ________ 25 ft

Commodity ________ rolls of nonexpanded polyethylene film on end on pallets. One roll completely fills one pallet. Each roll with pallet is 5 ft high.

Storage height normally ________ 20 ft

Wet or dry sprinkler system ________ wet

Clearance normally ________ 5 ft

Open or closed array ________ flue spaces are 10 in.: open array.

(The conclusions arrived at for water demand are theoretical minimum. Actual water demand will be greater as a result of system sprinkler design.)

It was decided commodity is a Group A plastic (*see Commodity Classifications, Chapter 2*).

From storage description it was decided it was solid-unit load storage (it would burn only on exterior of unit load) and it was determined it was nonexpanded.

From decision tree (*see Figure 7-1.1*) — Group A, nonexpanded, stable, solid unit load, it says to go to Figure 7-2.2(a).

From Figure 7-2.2(a):

For initial demand there is a range: 0.7 gpm/ft^2 over 400 ft^2 to 0.5 gpm/ft^2 over 780 ft^2.

It is decided to choose........ 0.7 gpm/ft^2 over 400 ft^2.

For secondary demand there is a range: 0.5 gpm/ft^2 over 780 ft^2 to 0.2 gpm/ft^2 over 4,500 ft^2.

At least a 0.25 gpm/ft^2 difference between the initial density and the secondary density is needed. Also a minimum final design area of 2,000 ft^2 for the secondary point is necessary. Therefore, it is decided to pick 0.32 gpm/ft^2 over 1,800 ft^2.

The initial demand is 0.7 gpm/ft^2 over 400 ft^2 and the secondary demand is 0.32 gpm/ft^2 over 1,800 ft^2. However, these demands are for a 20-ft high, $^1/_2$- to 4$^1/_2$-ft clearance condition.

The actual condition is 20 ft high and a 5-ft clearance.

To adjust for height use Figure 7-2.2.3:

Initial demand: 100 percent × 0.7 gpm/ft^2 = 0.7 gpm/ft^2

Secondary demand: 100 percent × 0.32 gpm/ft^2 = 0.32 gpm/ft^2.

To adjust for clearance use Figure 7-2.2.2:

Initial demand: 1.02 × 400 ft^2 = 408 ft^2

Secondary demand: 1.13 × 1,800 ft^2 = 2,034 ft^2.

For 20-ft high storage and 5-ft clearance the demand is:

Initial demand: 0.7 gpm/ft^2 over 408 ft^2

Secondary demand: 0.32 gpm/ft^2 over 2,034 ft^2.

However, sometimes storage height is only 3 pallet loads high, or 15 ft high with 10-ft clearance.

The demand for 20-ft high storage and 1$^1/_2$-ft to 4$^1/_2$-ft clearance *was*:

Initial demand: 0.7 gpm/ft^2 over 400 ft^2

Secondary demand: 0.32 gpm/ft^2 over 1,800 ft^2.

To adjust for height use Figure 7-2.2.3:

Initial demand: 90 percent × 0.7 gpm/ft^2 = 0.63 gpm/ft^2

Secondary demand: 85 percent × 0.32 gpm/ft^2 = 0.27 gpm/ft^2.

To adjust for clearance use Figure 7-2.2.2:

Initial demand: 1.2 × 400 ft^2 = 480 ft^2

Secondary demand: 2.0 × 1,800 ft^2 = 3,600 ft^2.

For 15-ft high storage and 10-ft clearance the demand is:

Initial demand: 0.63 gpm/ft^2 over 480 ft^2

Secondary demand: 0.27 gpm/ft^2 over 3,600 ft^2.

Conclusion:

0.7 gpm/ft^2 over 408 ft^2 = 285 gpm **0.32 gpm/ft^2 over 2,034 ft^2 = 650 gpm**	**20-ft high storage** **5-ft clearance**
0.63 gpm/ft^2 over 480 ft^2 = 302 gpm **0.27 gpm/ft^2 over 3,600 ft^2 = 972 gpm**	**15-ft high storage** **10-ft clearance**

The gratest gpm demand would be for 15-ft high storage. Therefore, the protection sepcified would be:

Initial demand: 0.63 gpm/ft^2 over 500 ft^2

Secondary demand: 0.27 gpm/ft^2 over 3,600 ft^2.

(Areas should be rounded to nearest 100 ft^2).

Example 2

Building height ________________________ 29 ft

Sprinkler deflector height from floor __________ 28 ft

Commodity ________________ polyethylene bottles in compartmented cartons on pallets. The height of one loaded pallet 6 ft.

Normal storage height _______ 18 ft

Wet or dry sprinkler system _____ wet

Clearance normally ____________ 10 ft high

Open or closed array _________ flue spaces were 11 in.: open array.

(The conclusions arrived at for water demand are theoretical minimum. Actual water demand will be greater as a result of system sprinkler design.)

It was decided commodity is a Group A plastic (*see Commodity Classifications, Chapter 2*).

From storage description it was determined to be stable, nonexpanded, and cartoned.

From decision tree (*see Figure 7-1.1*) — Group A, nonexpanded, stable, cartoned, go to Figure 7-2.2(c).

From Figure 7-2.2(c):

For initial demand
there is a range: 0.9 gpm/ft^2 over 600 ft^2 to 0.65 gpm/ft^2 over 1,150 ft^2.

It is decided to choose...... 0.9 gpm/ft^2 over 600 ft^2.

For secondary demand
there is a range: 0.65 gpm/ft^2 over 1,150 ft^2
0.35 gpm/ft^2 over 4,000 ft^2.

At least a 0.25 gpm/ft^2 difference between the initial density and the secondary density is needed. Also a minimum final design area of 2,000 ft^2 for the secondary point is necessary. Therefore, it is decided to pick 0.65 gpm/ft^2 over 1,150 ft^2.

The initial demand is 0.9 gpm/ft^2 over 600 ft^2 and the secondary demand is 0.65 gpm/ft^2 over 1,150 ft^2. However, these demands are for a 20-ft high, $^1/_2$- to 4$^1/_2$-ft clearance condition.

Actual condition is 18 ft high with a 10-ft clearance.

To adjust for height use Figure 7-2.2.3:

Initial demand: 96 percent of 0.9 gpm/ft^2 = 0.86 gpm/ft^2

Secondary demand: 94 percent of 0.65 gpm/ft^2 = 0.61 gpm/ft^2.

To adjust for clearance use Figure 7-2.2.2:

Initial demand: 1.26 × 600 ft^2 = 756 ft^2

Secondary demand: 2.3 × 1,150 ft^2 = 2,645 ft^2.

For 18-ft high storage and 10-ft clearance the demand is:

Initial demand: 0.86 gpm/ft^2 over 756 ft^2

Secondary demand: 0.61 gpm/ft^2 over 2,645 ft^2.

Commodity: Rolls P.E. Film **Storage Height:** 20 **Clear Space:** 5
Stable/Unstable: Stable **Open/Closed Array:** Open **Wet/Dry System:** Wet

Fig. No.		Density / Area	Hgt. Fact.	Density (Adj.) / Area	Clearance Fact.	Density / Area (Adj.)	Array Fact.	Density / Area (Adj.)	Dry Penalty	Density / Area (Adj.)	Notes:
7-2.2(a)	Initial	0.7 / 400	100%	0.7 / 400	1.02	0.7 / 408	None				285 gpm
	Secondary	0.32 / 1,800	100%	0.32 / 1,800	1.13	0.32 / 2,034	None		None		650 gpm

Commodity: Rolls P.E. Film **Storage Height:** 15 **Clear Space:** 10
Stable/Unstable: Stable **Open/Closed Array:** Open **Wet/Dry System:** Wet

Fig. No.		Density / Area	Hgt. Fact.	Density (Adj.) / Area	Clearance Fact.	Density / Area (Adj.)	Array Fact.	Density / Area (Adj.)	Dry Penalty	Density / Area (Adj.)	Notes:
7-2.2(a)	Initial	0.7 / 400	90%	0.63 / 400	1.2	0.63 / 480	None				302 gpm
	Secondary	0.32 / 1,800	85%	0.27 / 1,800	2.0	0.27 / 3,600	None		None		972 gpm

Commodity: P.E. Bottles **Storage Height:** 18 ft **Clear Space:** 10 ft
Stable/Unstable: Stable **Open/Closed Array:** Open **Wet/Dry System:** Wet

Fig. No.		Density / Area	Hgt. Fact.	Density (Adj.) / Area	Clearance Fact.	Density / Area (Adj.)	Array Fact.	Density / Area (Adj.)	Dry Penalty	Density / Area (Adj.)	Notes:
7-2.2(c)	Initial	0.9 / 600	96%	0.86 / 600	1.26	0.86 / 756	None				650 gpm
	Secondary	0.65 / 1,150	94%	0.61 / 1,150	2.3	0.61 / 2,645	None		None		1,613 gpm

Commodity: P.E. Bottles **Storage Height:** 24 ft **Clear Space:** 4 ft
Stable/Unstable: Stable **Open/Closed Array:** Open **Wet/Dry System:** Wet

Fig. No.		Density / Area	Hgt. Fact.	Density (Adj.) / Area	Clearance Fact.	Density / Area (Adj.)	Array Fact.	Density / Area (Adj.)	Dry Penalty	Density / Area (Adj.)	Notes:
7-2.2(c)	Initial	0.9 / 600	108%	0.97 / 600	1.00	0.97 / 600	None				582 gpm
	Secondary	.50 / 2,000	120%	.600 / 2,000	1.00	.600 / 2,000	None		None		1,200 gpm

However, sometimes storage height is 24 ft high with 4-ft clearance.

The demand for 20-ft high storage and $1^1/_2$-ft to $4^1/_2$-ft clearance *was*:

Initial demand: 0.9 gpm/ft^2 over 600 ft^2

Secondary demand: 0.65 gpm/ft^2 over 1,150 ft^2.

However, since the clearance factor for increasing the area is going to be small and a final area of at least 2,000 ft^2 is needed, it is decided to pick a density for the secondary point that would create an area demand equal to or closer to the 2,000 ft^2 area.

From Figure 7-2.2(c), the demand for 20-ft high storage and $1^1/_2$-ft to 4-$^1/_2$-ft clearance decided on was:

Initial demand: 0.9 gpm/ft^2 over 600 ft^2

Secondary demand: 0.50 gpm/ft^2 over 2,000 ft^2.

To adjust for height use Figure 7-2.2.3:

Initial demand: 108 percent × 0.9 gpm/ft^2 = 0.97 gpm/ft^2

Secondary demand: 120 percent × 0.50 gpm/ft^2 = 0.60 gpm/ft^2.

To adjust for clearance use Figure 7-2.2.2:

Initial demand: 1.00 × 600 ft^2 = 600 ft^2

Secondary demand: 1.00 × 2,000 ft^2 = 2,000 ft^2.

Conclusion:

0.86 gpm/ft^2 over 756 ft^2 = 650 gpm
0.61 gpm/ft^2 over 2,645 ft^2 = 1,613 gpm } **18-ft high storage 10-ft clearance**

0.97 gpm/ft^2 over 600 ft^2 = 582 gpm
0.60 gpm/ft^2 over 2,000 ft^2 = 1,200 gpm } **24-ft high storage 4-ft clearance**

The gratest gpm demand would be for 18-ft high storage and 10-ft clearance. Therefore, the protection sepcified would be:

Initial demand: 0.86 gpm/ft^2 over 800 ft^2

Secondary demand: 0.61 gpm/ft^2 over 2,600 ft^2.

(Areas should be rounded to nearest 100 ft^2.)

Appendix C Protection of Outdoor Storage

C-1 General.

C-1.1 The hazards of exposure to outdoor storage from ignition sources and exposing fires and the infinite variety of conditions under which such exposures may occur render impossible the formulation of any single table, formulae, or set of rules that will adequately cover all conditions.

C-1.2 Recommendations contained in this Appendix are for the protection of outdoor storage of commodities covered by the standard. (*See 1-1, Scope.*)

C-1.3 In general, the provision of automatic fire protection is impractical for outdoor storage. As a result, emphasis must be placed upon:

(a) Control of potential ignition sources such as from exposing buildings, transformers, yard equipment, refuse burners, overhead power lines, and vandals.

(b) Elimination of adverse factors such as trash accumulations, weeds, and brush.

(c) Provision of favorable physical conditions such as limited pile sizes, low storage heights, wide aisles, and possible use of fire retardant covers (e.g., tarpaulins).

(d) The rapid and effective application of manual fire fighting efforts by the provision of fire alarms, strategically located hydrants, and adequate hose houses or hose reels.

C-1.4 Outdoor storage should be avoided in most cases, but is recognized as a necessity in many industries.

C-1.4.1 Outdoor storage is acceptable for materials that are:

(a) Of low fire hazard, not requiring protection even if located indoors.

(b) Of low value that a potential loss would not justify the utilization of building space.

(c) Of such great fire hazard that indoor protection is impractical, when balanced against potential loss.

(d) Of large volume and bulk, making it impractical to construct and protect a building to house the storage.

C-1.4.2 Where materials that normally would be stored in buildings are stored outdoors in temporary emergencies, it is recommended that special precaution be taken for their safeguard and that they be moved to a storage warehouse as soon as possible.

C-1.5 Standards referencing outdoor storage of specific commodities are also listed in Chapter 11.

C-2 Responsibility of Management.

C-2.1 It is the responsibility of management to take proper consideration of the hazards of the various materials handled. Protection requirements and storage arrangements will vary with the combustibility of the materials. Management should determine any special precautions that must be followed for the types of material stored. The care, cleanliness, and maintenance exercised by management will determine to a large extent the relative firesafety in the storage area.

C-2.2 Consideration should be given by management to proper storage of materials in order to prevent the undue concentration of quantities of such materials in a single location, subject to one catastrophe. The criterion of the amount of such material that should be stored in a single location is not only dependent upon the dollar value of the commodity but also upon the total supply and availability of the material. The impact of the loss of the storage upon the ability to continue production should be considered.

C-3 Site.

C-3.1 In selecting a site for outdoor storage, preference should be given to a location having:

(a) Adequate municipal fire and police protection.

(b) Adequate public water system with hydrants suitably located for protection of the storage.

(c) Adequate all-weather roads for fire department apparatus response.

(d) Sufficient clear space from buildings or from other combustible storage that constitute an exposure hazard.

(e) Absence of flood hazard.

(f) Adequate clearance space between storage piles and any highways, bridges, railroads, and woodlands.

(g) Topography as level as possible to provide storage stability.

C-3.2 The entire site should be surrounded by a fence or other suitable means to prevent access of unauthorized persons. An adequate number of gates should be provided in the surrounding fence or other barriers so as to permit ready access of fire apparatus.

C-4 Material Piling.

C-4.1 Materials should be stored in unit piles as low in height and small in area as is consistent with good practice for the materials stored. The maximum height should be determined by the stability of pile, effective reach of hose streams, combustibility of the commodity, and ease of pile breakdown under fire or mop-up conditions. Long narrow piles are preferred over large square piles to facilitate manual fire fighting. (The short dimension increases the effectiveness of hose streams and eases pile breakdown.)

C-4.2 Aisles should be maintained between individual piles, between piles and buildings, and between piles and the boundary line of the storage site. Sufficient driveways having the width of at least 15 ft (4.5 m) should be provided to permit the travel of fire equipment to all portions of the storage area. Aisles should be at least twice the pile height to reduce spread of fire from pile to pile and to permit ready access for fire fighting, emergency removal of material, or for salvage purposes.

C-4.3 As the commodity class increases in combustibility, or where storage could be easily ignited from radiation, wider aisles should be provided. Smaller unit piles may be an alternative to wider aisles if yard space is limited.

C-4.4 For outdoor idle pallet storage, see Section 4-4 and A-4-4.1.1 of this standard. Separation between piles of idle pallets and other yard storage should be as follows:

Pile Size	Minimum Distance (Ft)
Under 50 pallets	20 (6 m)
50-200 pallets	30 (9.1 m)
Over 200 pallets	50 (15.2 m)

C-4.5 Boundary posts with signs designating piling limits should be provided to indicate yard area, roadway and aisle limits.

C-5 Buildings and Other Structures.

C-5.1 Yard storage, particularly commodities in the higher heat release category, should have as much separation as is practical from important buildings and structures, but not less than that offered by NFPA 80A, *Recommended Practice for Protection of Buildings from Exterior Fire Exposures*.

C-5.1.1 As guidance in using NFPA 80A in establishing clear spaces, the following Classification of Severity with Commodity Classes of this standard may be used on the basis of 100 percent openings representing yard storage:

(a) *Light Severity:* Commodity Class I.

(b) *Moderate Severity:* Commodity Class II.

(c) Interpolate between Moderate and Severe Severity for Commodity Class III.

(d) *Severe Severity:* Commodity Class IV and Class A plastics.

NOTE: The above guidelines apply to the equivalent commodity classes of this standard. The severity of the exposing building or structure should also be a consideration when establishing a clear space.

C-6 Yard Maintenance and Operations.

C-6.1 The entire storage site should be kept free from accumulation of unnecessary combustible materials. Vegetation should be kept cut low. Procedures should be provided for weed control and the periodic cleanup of the yard area.

C-6.2 Adequate lighting should be provided to allow supervision of all parts of the storage area at night.

C-6.3 All electrical equipment and installations should conform to the provisions of NFPA 70, *National Electrical Code*.

C-6.4 No heating equipment should be located or used within the storage area. Salamanders, braziers, portable heaters, and other open fires should not be used.

C-6.5 Smoking should be prohibited, except in locations prominently designated as smoking areas. "No Smoking" signs should be posted in prohibited areas.

C-6.6 Welding and cutting operations should be prohibited in the storage area, unless the precautions in NFPA 51B, *Standard for Fire Prevention in Use of Cutting and Welding Processes*, are followed.

C-6.7 Tarpaulins, used for protection of storage against the weather, should be of fire retardant fabric.

C-6.8 Locomotives from which glowing particles may be emitted from exhaust stacks should not be permitted in the yard.

C-6.9 Motorized vehicles using gasoline, diesel fuel, or liquefied petroleum gas as fuel should be garaged in a separate detached building.

C-6.9.1 Storage and handling of fuel should conform with NFPA 30, *Flammable and Combustible Liquids Code*, and NFPA 58, *Standard for Storage and Handling of Liquefied Petroleum Gases*.

C-6.9.2 Repair operations should be conducted outside the yard unless a separate masonry wall building is provided. Vehicles should not be greased, repaired, painted, or otherwise serviced in the yard. Such work should be conducted in conformity with NFPA 88B, *Standard for Repair Garages*.

C-7 Fire Protection.

C-7.1 Provisions should be made for promptly notifying the public fire department and private fire brigade (if available) in case of fire or other emergency.

C-7.2 Hydrants should be spaced to provide a sufficient number of hose streams. Refer to NFPA 24, *Standard for the Installation of Private Fire Services Mains and Their Appurtenances*.

C-7.2.1 Provisions should be made to permit direction of an adequate number of hose streams on any pile or portion of the storage area that may be involved in fire. It is recommended that, unless adequate protection is provided by the municipal fire department, sufficient hose and other equipment be kept on hand at the storage property, suitably housed, and provision be made for trained personnel available to put it into operation.

C-7.2.2 Hydrants and all fire fighting equipment should be accessible for use at all times. No temporary storage should be allowed to obstruct access to fire fighting equipment, and any accumulation of snow or obstructing material should be promptly removed.

C-7.3 Monitor nozzles should be provided at strategic points where large quantities of highly combustible materials are stored or where average amounts of combustible materials are stored in inaccessible locations.

C-7.4 Fire extinguishers of an appropriate type should be placed at well marked, strategic points throughout the storage area so that one or more portable fire extinguisher units can quickly be made available for use at any point. Where the climate is such to involve the danger of freezing, suitable extinguishers for freezing temperatures should be used. For guidance in the type and use of extinguishers refer to NFPA 10, *Standard for Portable Fire Extinguishers.*

C-8 Guard Service.

C-8.1 Guard service should be provided and continuously maintained throughout the yard and storage area at all times while the yard is otherwise unoccupied. Duties and training of guards should follow that specified in NFPA 601, *Standard for Guard Service in Fire Loss Prevention.* It is recommended that there be some suitable means of supervising the guard's activities to be sure that required rounds are made at regular intervals.

C-8.2 Attention is directed to the value of strategically placed watchtowers in large yards where a guard stationed at a point of advantage can keep the entire property under observation. It is recommended that such watchtowers be connected to the alarm system so that prompt notification of fire may be given.

Appendix D Referenced Publications

D-1 The following documents or portions thereof are referenced within this standard for informational purposes only and thus are not considered part of the requirements of this document. The edition indicated for each reference is the current edition as of the date of the NFPA issuance of this document.

D-1.1 NFPA Publications. National Fire Protection Association, 1 Batterymarch Park, P.O. Box 9101, Quincy, MA 02269-9101.

NFPA 10-1990, *Standard for Portable Extinguishers*

NFPA 13A-1987, *Recommended Practice for the Inspection, Testing and Maintenance of Sprinkler Systems*

NFPA 24-1987, *Standard for the Installation of Private Fire Service Mains and Their Appurtenances*

NFPA 30-1990, *Flammable and Combustible Liquids Code*

NFPA 51B-1989, *Standard for Fire Prevention in Use of Cutting and Welding Processes*

NFPA 58-1989, *Standard for the Storage and Handling of Liquefied Petroleum Gases*

NFPA 70-1990, *National Electrical Code*

NFPA 80A-1987, *Recommended Practice for Protection of Buildings from Exterior Fire Exposures*

NFPA 88B-1985, *Standard for Repair Garages*

NFPA 204M-1985, *Guide for Smoke and Heat Venting*

NFPA 600-1986, *Recommendation for Organization, Training and Equipment of Private Fire Brigades*

NFPA 601-1986, *Standard for Guard Service in Fire Loss Prevention*

Index

UNIFORM FIRE CODE STANDARD 81-2
HIGH-PILED STORAGE OF COMBUSTIBLES ON RACKS IN BUILDINGS

See Sections 7902.5.11.5.1, 7902.5.12.5.1, 8102.9, 8102.10.1, 8104.2, 8104.4 and 8803.2, *Uniform Fire Code*

This standard, with certain exceptions, is based on the National Fire Protection Association Standard for Rack Storage of Materials, NFPA 231C—1991.[1]

Part I of this standard contains the exceptions to NFPA 231C—1991.[1]

Part II of this standard contains NFPA 231C—1991[1] reproduced in its entirety with permission of the publisher.

▨▨▨ vertically in the margin of Part II indicates there is a revision to the provisions within Part I.

Supplemental standards referenced by NFPA 231C—1991[1] shall only be considered as guideline standards subject to approval by the chief.

[1]The current edition is NFPA 231C—1995.

Part I

SECTION 81.201 — AMENDMENTS

The Standard for Rack Storage of Materials, NFPA 231C—1991, applies to the classification of commodities and the installation of fire-protection equipment used in conjunction with the rack storage of materials except as follows:

1. Sec. 1-1 is revised as follows:

1-1 Scope. This standard applies to storage of materials representing the broad range of combustibles over 12 feet (3657.6 mm) in height on racks. For storage heights of 12 feet (3657.6 mm) or less, see UBC Standard 9-1.

Storage on plastic pallets or plastic shelves is outside the scope of this standard.

Storage of high-hazard materials such as tires, plastic and flammable liquids is outside the scope of this standard.

2. Sec. 1-2 is revised by changing definitions as follows:

AUTHORITY HAVING JURISDICTION is the official responsible for the administration and enforcement of this standard.

COMMODITY is a designation of combinations of products, packaging materials and containers.

The definitions of "approved," "labeled," "listed" and "shelf storage" shall be as set forth in *Uniform Fire Code,* Volume 1.

The definitions of "should" and "solid shelving" are deleted.

Revise the definition of ESFR as follows:

EARLY SUPPRESSION FAST-RESPONSE (ESFR) SPRINKLER is a listed thermosensitive device designed to react at a predetermined temperature by automatically releasing a stream of water and distributing it in a specified pattern and quantity over a designated area so as to provide early suppression of a fire when installed on the appropriate sprinkler piping.

3. Sec. 2-1.1 is revised as follows:

2-1.1 Commodity classification shall be as set forth in UFC Article 81.

4. Secs. 2-1.2 through 2-1.5 are deleted.

5. Secs. 3-1, 3-2.1, 3-2.2 and 3-3 are deleted.

6. Sec. 3-2.3 is revised by adding a paragraph as follows:

Regardless of the requirements of this section, fire protection for the structure shall comply with the requirements set forth in the Building Code.

7. Sec. 3-2.3 (b) is revised by adding a paragraph as follows:

Each sprinkler protecting a column shall be capable of discharging 30 gpm (113.6 L/min) simultaneously with the overhead sprinkler system and other demands as required by this standard. The spray shall be directed towards the column such that as much of the column is protected as possible.

8. Sec. 4-3 is revised as follows:

4-3 Flue spaces. Flue spaces shall be as set forth in UFC Article 81.

9. Sec. 4-7 is revised by substituting the phrase "UFC Standard 81-1" for the phrase "NFPA 231, *Standard for General Storage.*"

10. Sec. 5-1.2 is revised as follows:

5-1.2 The densities and areas provided in the tables and curves in Chapters 6 and 7 are based on fire tests using standard response, standard orifice [$^1/_2$ inch (12.7 mm)] and large orifice [$^{17}/_{32}$ inch (13.5 mm)] sprinklers. The use of extra large orifice sprinklers is allowed when listed for such use. For the use of large drop sprinklers, see Chapter 9.

11. Sec. 5-2.1 is revised by substituting the phrase "the Building Code. See UBC Standard 9-1" for the phrase "Installation of Sprinkler Systems, NFPA 13."

12. Sec. 5-8 is revised by deleting the first sentence and substituting as follows:

When required by UFC Table 81-A, small hose stations shall be provided and shall be spaced such that they are accessible to reach all portions of the high-piled storage area based on the length of hose and travel paths.

Also:

Add an exception as follows:

EXCEPTION: In buildings served by a single automatic sprinkler system, the hose stations are allowed to be supplied from the ceiling sprinkler piping downstream of the sprinkler control valve.

13. Sec. 5-13.2 is revised as follows:

5-13.2 Sprinklers shall be installed at the ceiling and beneath shelves in single-, double- and multiple-row racks with solid shelves, as set forth in UFC Section 8104.2.3, in accordance with Table 5-13.2. Design curves for combined ceiling and in-rack sprinklers shall be used with this type of storage configuration.

TABLE 5-13.2—SPRINKLER REQUIREMENTS FOR SOLID SHELF STORAGE

COMMODITY CLASS	STORAGE HEIGHT (feet) × 304.8 for mm	SPRINKLERS REQUIRED IN-RACK: Shelf Area 32-50 Square Feet (2.97 to 4.65 m^2)	SPRINKLERS REQUIRED IN-RACK: Shelf Area Greater Than 50 Square Feet (4.65 m^2)
I-IV	Over 12-20	1 level[1]	Every tier of storage
	Over 20-25	2 levels[2]	Every tier of storage
	Over 25	[3]	[3]
High hazard	Over 12	Every tier of storage	Every tier of storage

[1]Locate one level of in-rack sprinklers at a height of one half to two thirds of the rack height.

[2]Locate one level of in-rack sprinklers at a height of one fourth to one third of the rack height and a second level at two thirds to three fourths of the rack height.

[3]Protect in accordance with nationally recognized standards. See UFC Article 90, Standard f.1.1.

14. Sec. 6-1 is revised by substituting the phrase "the Building Code. See UBC Standard 9-1" for the phrase "NFPA 13."

15. Sec. 7-1 is revised by substituting the phrase "the Building Code. See UBC Standard 9-1" for the phrase "NFPA 13."

16. Sec. 8-1.4, Exception No. 4, is revised by substituting the phrase "the Building Code. See UBC Standard 9-1" for the phrase "NFPA 13, *Standard for the Installation of Sprinkler Systems.*"

17. Sec. 8-1.5.1 is revised by substituting the phrase "the Building Code. See UBC Standard 9-1" for the phrase "NFPA 13, *Standard for the Installation of Sprinkler Systems.*"

18. Sec. 9-1.2 is revised by substituting the phrase "the Building Code. See UBC Standard 9-1" for the phrase "NFPA 13, *Installation of Sprinkler Systems.*"

19. Sec. 10-2.3 is revised by substituting the phrase "the Building Code. See UBC Standard 9-1" for the phrase "NFPA 13, *Standard for the Installation of Sprinkler Systems.*"

20. Chapters 11, 12 and 13 are deleted.

Part II

 The following is not necessarily the latest revision used by NFPA. If the reader desires to compare that version, the same is available from NFPA.

Contents

NFPA 231C

Standard for

Rack Storage of Materials

1991 Edition

NOTICE: An asterisk (*) following the number or letter designating a paragraph or section in the text indicates explanatory material on that paragraph or section in Appendix A.

A dagger (†) following the number or letter designating a paragraph or section in the text indicates explanatory test data and procedures in regard to that paragraph or section in Appendix B.

Information on referenced publications can be found in Chapter 13 and Appendix C.

Chapter 1 Introduction

1-1† Application and Scope. This standard applies to storage of materials representing the broad range of combustibles stored over 12 ft (3.66 m) in height on racks. For storage height of 12 ft (3.66 m) or less, see NFPA 13, *Standard for the Installation of Sprinkler Systems*.

Storage on plastic pallets or plastic shelves is outside the scope of this standard.

Storage of high hazard materials such as tires, roll paper stored on end, and flammable liquids is outside the scope of this standard. Storage of such commodities shall be protected in accordance with the provisions of NFPA 30, *Flammable and Combustible Liquids Code*; NFPA 40, *Standard for the Storage and Handling of Cellulose Nitrate Motion Picture Film*; NFPA 490, *Code for the Storage of Ammonium Nitrate*; NFPA 58, *Standard for the Storage and Handling of Liquefied Petroleum Gases*; NFPA 81, *Standard for Fur Storage, Fumigation and Cleaning*; NFPA 231, *Standard for General Storage*; NFPA 231D, *Standard for Storage of Rubber Tires*; NFPA 231E, *Recommended Practice for the Storage of Baled Cotton*; NFPA 231F, *Standard for the Storage of Roll Paper*; and NFPA 232, *Standard for the Protection of Records*, as applicable.

Bin storage and shelf storage are outside the scope of this standard.

1-2 Definitions. Unless expressly stated elsewhere, the following terms shall, for the purpose of this standard, have the meanings indicated below.

Aisle Width. The horizontal dimension between the face of the loads in racks under consideration. (*See Figure 1-2.1.*)

Approved. Acceptable to the "authority having jurisdiction."

NOTE: The National Fire Protection Association does not approve, inspect or certify any installations, procedures, equipment, or materials nor does it approve or evaluate testing laboratories. In determining the acceptability of installations or procedures, equipment or materials, the authority having jurisdiction may base acceptance on compliance with NFPA or other appropriate standards. In the absence of such standards, said authority may require evidence of proper installation, procedure or use. The authority having jurisdiction may also refer to the listings or labeling practices of an organization concerned with product evaluations which is in a position to determine compliance with appropriate standards for the current production of listed items.

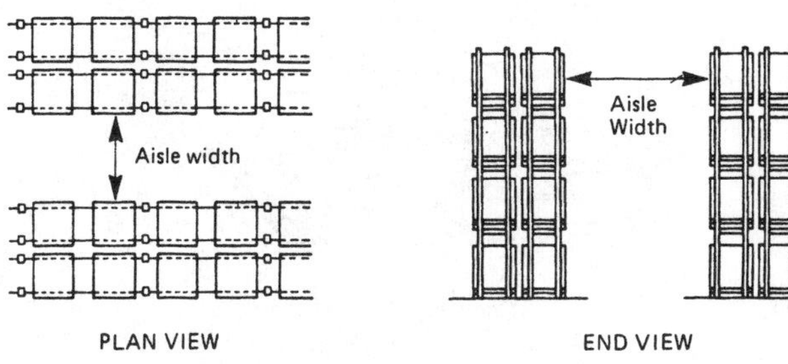

Figure 1-2.1 Illustration of Aisle Width.

Authority Having Jurisdiction. The "authority having jurisdiction" is the organization, office or individual responsible for "approving" equipment, an installation or a procedure.

NOTE: The phrase "authority having jurisdiction" is used in NFPA documents in a broad manner since jurisdictions and "approval" agencies vary as do their responsibilities. Where public safety is primary, the "authority having jurisdiction" may be a federal, state, local or other regional department or individual such as a fire chief, fire marshal, chief of a fire prevention bureau, labor department, health department, building official, electrical inspector, or others having statutory authority. For insurance purposes, an insurance inspection department, rating bureau, or other insurance company representative may be the "authority having jurisdiction." In many circumstances the property owner or his designated agent assumes the role of the "authority having jurisdiction"; at government installations, the commanding officer or departmental official may be the "authority having jurisdiction."

Bulkhead. A vertical barrier across the rack.

Clearance. Clearance is the distance from the top of storage to the ceiling sprinkler deflectors.

Commodity. Designates combinations of product, packing material, and container upon which commodity classification is based.

Conventional Pallets. A material handling aid designed to support a unit load with openings to provide access for material handling devices (*see Figure 1-2.2*).

Encapsulated. A method of packaging consisting of a plastic sheet completely enclosing the sides and top of a pallet load containing a combustible commodity or a combustible package or a group of combustible commodities or combustible packages. Totally noncombustible commodities on wood pallets enclosed only by a plastic sheet as described are not considered to fall under this definition. Banding, i.e., stretch wrapping around the sides only of a pallet load, is not considered to be encapsulated. The term encapsulated does not apply to individual plastic-enclosed items inside a large nonplastic enclosed container.

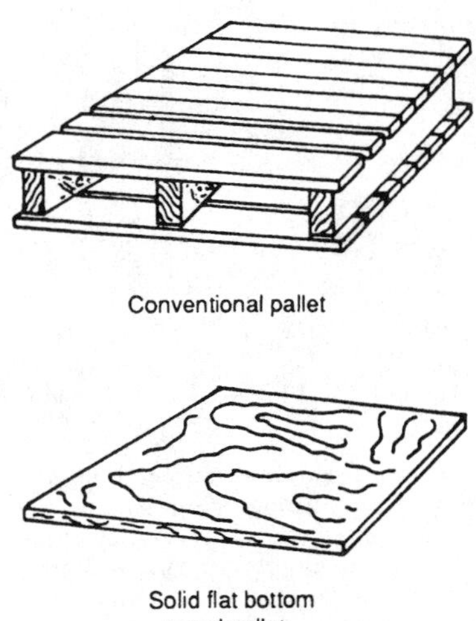

Figure 1-2.2 Typical Pallets.

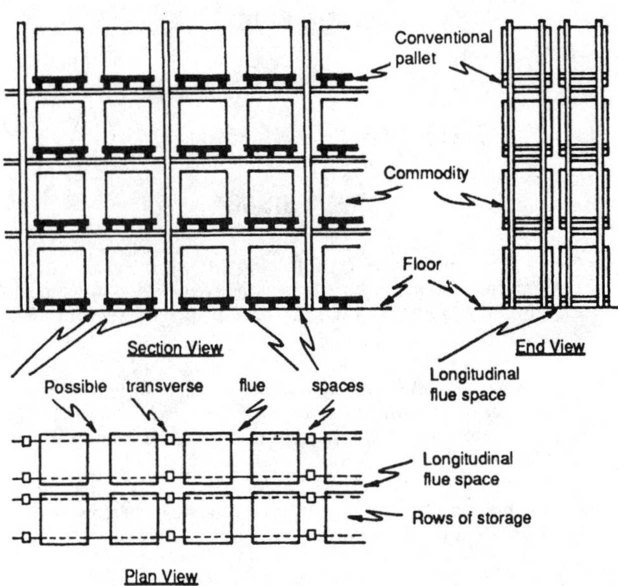

Figure 1-2.3 Typical Double Row (Back-to-Back) Rack Arrangement.

ESFR. See NFPA 13, *Standard for the Installation of Sprinkler Systems*.

Face Sprinklers. Standard sprinklers located in transverse flue spaces along the aisle or in the rack, within 18 in. (0.46 m) of the aisle face of storage to oppose vertical development of fire on the external face of storage.

Free-Flowing Plastic Materials. Those plastics which will fall out of their containers in a fire condition, fill flue spaces, and create a smothering effect on the fire. Example: powder, pellets, flakes, or random packed small objects [razor blade dispensers, 1-2 oz (30-59 ml) bottles, etc.].

Horizontal Barrier. A solid barrier in the horizontal position covering the entire rack, including all flue spaces at certain height increments, to prevent vertical fire spread.

Labeled. Equipment or materials to which has been attached a label, symbol or other identifying mark of an organization acceptable to the "authority having jurisdiction" and concerned with product evaluation, that maintains periodic inspection of production of labeled equipment or materials and by whose labeling the manufacturer indicates compliance with appropriate standards or performance in a specified manner.

Listed. Equipment or materials included in a list published by an organization acceptable to the "authority having jurisdiction" and concerned with product evaluation, that maintains periodic inspection of production of listed equipment or materials and whose listing states either that the equipment or material meets appropriate standards or has been tested and found suitable for use in a specified manner.

NOTE: The means for identifying listed equipment may vary for each organization concerned with product evaluation, some of which do not recognize equipment as listed unless it is also labeled. The "authority having jurisdiction" should utilize the system employed by the listing organization to identify a listed product.

Longitudinal Flue Space. The space between rows of storage perpendicular to the direction of loading (*see Figure 1-2.3*).

Rack. Any combination of vertical, horizontal, and diagonal members that support stored materials. Some rack structures use solid shelves. Racks may be fixed, portable, or movable [*see Figures A-4-1(a) through (k)*]. Loading may be either manual, using lift trucks, stacker cranes, or hand placement; or automatic, using machine controlled storage and retrieval systems.

Single Row Racks. Single row racks are racks with no longitudinal flue space and having a width up to 6 ft (1.8 m) with aisles at least 3.5 ft (1.1 m) from other storage.

Double Row Racks. Double row racks are two single row racks placed back to back, having a combined width up to 12 ft (3.7 m) with aisles at least 3.5 ft (1.1 m) on each side.

Multi-Row Racks. Multi-row racks are racks greater than 12 ft (3.7 m) wide or single or double row racks separated by aisles less than 3.5 ft (1.1 m) wide having an overall width greater than 12 ft (3.7 m).

Portable Racks. Portable racks are racks that are not fixed in place. They can be arranged in any number of configurations.

Movable Racks. Movable racks are racks on fixed rails or guides. They can be moved back and forth only in a horizontal two-dimensional plane. A moving aisle is created as abutting racks are either loaded or unloaded, then moved across the aisle to abut other racks. Rack arrangements generally result in the same protection needs as for multi-row racks.

Shall. Indicates a mandatory requirement.

Shelf Storage. Storage in structures usually less than 30 in. (0.76 m) deep, seldom more than 2 ft (0.61 m) between shelves and seldom higher than 12 ft (3.66 m).

Should. Indicates a recommendation or that which is advised but not required.

Slave Pallet. A special pallet captive to a material handling system (*see Figure 1-2.2*).

Solid Shelving. Solid shelving is solid, slatted, or other types of shelves located within racks that obstruct sprinkler water penetration down through the racks.

Transverse Flue Space. The space between rows of storage parallel to the direction of loading (*see Figure 1-2.3*).

Chapter 2 Classification of Storage

2-1† Commodity Classifications.

2-1.1 Class I commodity is defined as essentially noncombustible products on wood pallets, or in ordinary corrugated cartons with or without single thickness dividers, or in ordinary paper wrappings, all on wood pallets. Such products are permitted to have a negligible amount of plastic trim, such as knobs or handles.

Examples of Class I products are:

Metal Products. Metal desks with plastic tops and trim, electrical coils, electrical devices in their metal enclosures, pots and pans, electrical motors, dry cell batteries, metal parts, empty cans, stoves, washers, dryers, and metal cabinets.

Glass Products. Glass bottles, empty or filled with noncombustible liquids; mirrors.

Foods. Foods in noncombustible containers; frozen foods; meat; fresh fruits and vegetables in nonplastic trays or containers; dairy products in nonwax-coated paper containers; beer or wine, up to 20 percent alcohol, in metal, glass, or ceramic containers.

Others. Oil-filled and other types of distribution transformers, cement in bags, electrical insulators, gypsum board, inert pigments, and dry insecticides.

2-1.2 Class II commodity is defined as Class I products in slatted wooden crates, solid wooden boxes, multi-wall corrugated cartons, or equivalent combustible packaging material on wood pallets.

Examples of Class II products are: thinly coated fine wire such as radio coil wire on reels or in cartons; incandescent or fluorescent light bulbs; beer or wine, up to 20 percent alcohol, in wood containers; and Class I products, if in small cartons or small packages placed in ordinary corrugated cartons.

2-1.3 Class III commodity is defined as wood, paper, natural fiber cloth, Group C plastics, or products thereof; on wood pallets. Products are permitted to contain a limited amount of Group A or B plastics. Wood dressers with plastic drawer glides, handles, and trim are examples of a commodity with a limited amount of plastic.

Examples of Class III products are:

Paper Products. Books, magazines, newspapers; stationery; plastic-coated paper food containers; paper or cardboard games; tissue products; rolled paper on side or steel banded on end; and regenerated cellulosics (cellophane).

Leather Products. Shoes, jackets, gloves, and luggage.

Wood Products. Doors, windows, door and window frames, combustible fiberboard, wood cabinets, furniture, and other wood products.

Textiles. Natural fiber upholstered nonplastic furniture; wood or metal furniture with plastic padded and covered armrests; mattresses without expanded plastic or rubber; absorbent cotton in cartons; natural fiber and viscose yarns, thread, and products; and natural fiber clothing or textile products.

Others. Tobacco products in paperboard cartons; nonflammable liquids such as soaps, detergent and bleaches, and nonflammable pharmaceuticals in plastic containers; combustible foods or cereal products; and nonnegative-producing film packs in sealed metal foil wrappers in paperboard packages.

2-1.4 Class IV commodity is defined as Class I, II, or III products containing an appreciable amount of Group A plastics in a paperboard carton or Class I, II, or III products with Group A plastic packing in paperboard cartons on wood pallets. Group B plastics and free-flowing Group A plastics are also included in this class. (*See Section 1-1.*)

Examples of Class IV products are: small appliances, typewriters, and cameras with plastic parts; plastic-backed tapes and synthetic fabrics or clothing. An example of packing material is a metal product in a foamed plastic cocoon in a corrugated carton.

Class IV commodities also include:

Textiles. Synthetic thread and yarn except viscose, and nonviscose synthetic fabrics or clothing.

Others. Vinyl floor tile, wood or metal frame upholstered furniture or mattresses with plastic covering and/or padding, and plastic-padded metal dashboards or metal bumpers.

2-1.5 Classification of Plastics, Elastomers, and Rubber.

Note: The following categories are based on unmodified plastic materials. The use of fire or flame-retarding modifiers or the physical form of the material may change the classification.

Group A

ABS (Acrylonitrile-Butadiene-Styrene Copolymer)
Acetal (Polyformaldehyde)
Acrylic (Polymethyl Methacrylate)
Butyl Rubber
EPDM (Ethylene-Propylene Rubber)
FRP (Fiberglass Reinforced Polyester)
Natural Rubber
Nitrile Rubber (Acrylonitrile-Butadiene Rubber)
PET (Thermoplastic Polyester)
Polybutadiene
Polycarbonate
Polyester Elastomer
Polyethylene

Polypropylene
Polystyrene
Polyurethane
PVC (Polyvinyl Chloride — highly plasticized, e.g., coated fabric, unsupported film)
SAN (Styrene Acrylonitrile)
SBR (Styrene-Butadiene Rubber)

Group B

Cellulosics (Cellulose Acetate, Cellulose Acetate Butyrate, Ethyl Cellulose)
Chloroprene Rubber
Fluoroplastics (ECTFE — Ethylene-Chlorotrifluoroethylene Copolymer; ETFE — Ethylene-Tetrafluoroethylene Copolymer; FEP — Fluorinated Ethylene-Propylene Copolymer)
Nylon (Nylon 6, Nylon 6/6)
Silicon Rubber

Group C

Fluoroplastics (PCTFE — Polychlorotrifluoroethylene; PTFE — Polytetrafluoroethylene)
Melamine (Melamine Formaldehyde)
Phenolic
PVC (Polyvinyl Chloride — rigid or lightly plasticized, e.g., pipe, pipe fittings)
PVDC (Polyvinylidene Chloride)
PVDF (Polyvinylidene Fluoride)
PVF (Polyvinyl Fluoride)
Urea (Urea Formaldehyde)

Chapter 3 Building Construction

3-1 Construction. Buildings used for the rack storage of materials that are protected in accordance with this standard shall be of any of the types described in NFPA 220, *Standard on Types of Building Construction*.

3-2 Fire Protection of Steel.

3-2.1† With sprinkler systems installed in accordance with Chapters 6, 7, 8, 9, and 10, fire protection of roof steel is not required.

3-2.2† Where ceiling sprinklers and sprinklers in racks are installed in accordance with Chapters 5, 6, 7, and 8, fire protection of steel building columns is not required.

3-2.3† Where storage height exceeds 15 ft (4.57 m) and ceiling sprinklers only are installed, fire protection by one of the following methods is required for all types of steel building columns located within the racks or for vertical rack members that support the building:

(a) One-hr fire proofing.

(b) Side wall sprinklers at the 15-ft (4.57-m) elevation, pointed toward one side of the steel column.

(c) For storage heights above 15 ft (4.57 m), up to and including 20 ft (6.1 m), provision of ceiling sprinkler density for a minimum of 2000 sq ft (185.9 m^2) with 165°F (74°C) or 286°F (141°C) temperature-rated sprinklers as shown in Table 3-2.3.

(d) Provision of large drop or ESFR ceiling sprinkler protection in accordance with Chapters 9 and 10, respectively.

Table 3-2.3

Commodity Class	Aisle 4 ft (1.22 m)	Aisle 8 ft (2.44 m)
I	0.37	0.33
II	0.44	0.37
III	0.49	0.42
IV and Plastics	0.68	0.57

NOTE: For aisle widths between 4 ft and 8 ft (1.22 m - 2.44 m), a direct linear interpolation between densities may be made.

3-3† Vents and Draft Curtains. Design curves are based upon roof vents and draft curtains not being used.

Chapter 4 Storage Arrangements

4-1* Rack Structure. Rack configurations shall be of a generally accepted arrangement.

4-2* Rack Loading. Racks shall not be loaded beyond their design capacity.

4-3 Flue Space.

4-3.1*† In double row racks with height of storage up to and including 25 ft (7.62 m), and without solid shelves, a longitudinal flue space (back-to-back clearance) is not necessary. Nominal 6-in. (152.4-mm) transverse flue space between loads or at rack uprights shall be maintained. Random variations in the width of the flue spaces or in their vertical alignment shall be permitted. (*See Figure 4-3.1.*)

Exception: A longitudinal flue space is necessary when ESFR sprinkler protection is provided.

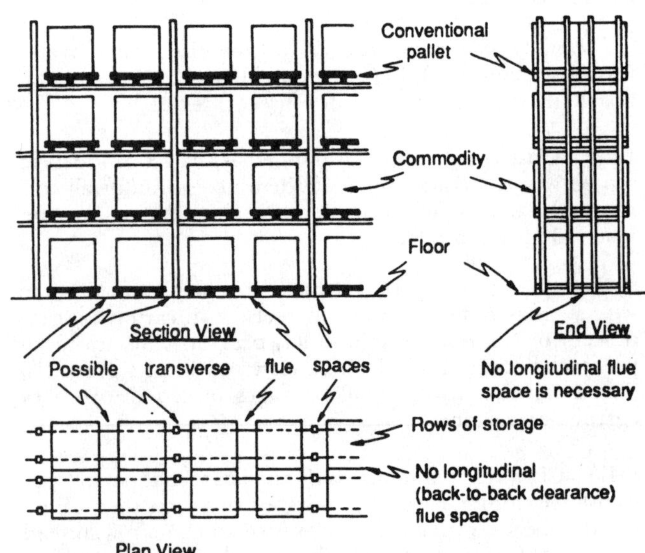

Figure 4-3.1 Typical Double Row Rack with Back-to-Back Loads.

4-3.2 In double row racks with height of storage over 25 ft (7.62 m), a minimum longitudinal flue space of (nominal) 6 in. (152.4 mm) shall be provided.

4-4* Aisle Widths.

4-4.1 Aisle widths and depth of racks are determined by material handling methods. Width of aisles shall be considered in the design of the protection system (*see Chapters 5, 6, and 7*).

4-4.2 This standard contemplates that aisle widths will be maintained either by fixed rack structures or control in placing of portable racks. Any decrease in aisle width shall require a review of the adequacy of the protective system.

4-5*† Storage Heights. The distance from the top of the pile to the ceiling sprinkler deflectors shall be not less than 18 in. (0.46 m).

Exception: When large-drop or ESFR sprinkler protection is used, the distance from top of storage to the ceiling sprinkler deflectors shall be not less then 36 in. (0.91 m).

4-6 Commodity Clearances.

4-6.1* Commodity clearances shall be maintained in accordance with NFPA 91, *Standard for the Installation of Blower and Exhaust Systems for Dust, Stock and Vapor Removal or Conveying*.

4-6.2* Incandescent Light Fixtures.

4-7*† Storage of Idle Combustible Pallets. Bulk storage of idle combustible pallets shall be in accordance with NFPA 231, *Standard for General Storage*.

Chapter 5 Fire Protection — General

5-1 Protection Systems.

5-1.1 Protection systems that are provided for rack storage facilities shall be in accordance with the provisions of this chapter.

5-1.2 The densities and areas provided in the tables and curves in Chapters 6, 7, and 8 are based on fire tests using standard response; standard orifice [1/2 in. (12.7 mm)] and large orifice [17/32 in. (13.5 mm)] sprinklers. For the use of large-drop and ESFR sprinklers, see Chapters 9 and 10, respectively.

5-2 Ceiling Sprinklers.

5-2.1* Where automatic sprinkler systems are installed, they shall be in accordance with NFPA 13, *Standard for the Installation of Sprinkler Systems*, except as modified by this standard.

5-2.2* In buildings that are occupied in part for rack storage of commodities, the ceiling sprinkler system design within 15 ft (4.57 m) of the racks shall be the same as that provided over the rack storage area.

5-3† Ceiling Sprinkler Spacing. For the purpose of selecting sprinkler spacings in hydraulically designed sprinkler systems, to obtain a stipulated density, 60 psi (413.7 kPa) shall be the maximum discharge pressure used at the calculation starting point.

5-4 In-Rack Sprinkler System Size. The area protected by a single system of sprinklers in racks (in-rack sprinklers) shall not exceed 40,000 sq ft (3716 m^2) of floor area occupied by the racks, including aisles, regardless of the number of intermediate sprinkler levels.

5-5* In-Rack Sprinkler System Control Valves.

5-5.1* When sprinklers are installed in racks, separate indicating control valves and drains shall be provided for ceiling sprinklers and sprinklers in racks.

Exception No. 1: In-rack installations of 20 or less sprinklers.

Exception No. 2: The separate indicating valves may be arranged as sectional control valves when the racks occupy only a portion of the area protected by the ceiling sprinklers. (See 5-2.2.)

5-6 In-Rack Sprinkler Water Demand. Water demand of sprinklers installed in racks shall be added to ceiling sprinkler water demand at the point of connection. The demand shall be balanced to the higher pressure.

5-7*† Sprinkler Waterflow Alarm.

5-8† Hose Connections. For first aid fire fighting and for mop-up operations, small [1 1/2 in. (38.1 mm)] hose lines shall be available to cover all areas of the rack structure. Such small hose shall be supplied from:

(a) Outside hydrants

(b) A separate piping system for small hose stations

(c) Valved hose connections on sprinkler risers where such connections are made upstream of all sprinkler control valves

(d) Adjacent sprinkler systems.

Exception: When separately controlled in-rack sprinklers are provided, the ceiling sprinkler system in the same area shall be permitted to be used.

5-9 Hose Demand.

5-9.1 For inside hose streams an allowance of at least 100 gpm (378 L/min) shall be added to sprinkler water demand for Class I, II, III, IV, or plastic commodities.

5-9.2 For combined inside and outside hose streams, an allowance of at least 500 gpm (1893 L/min) shall be added to sprinkler water demand for Class I, II, III, IV, or plastic commodities.

5-10† Duration of Water Supplies. For double row racks the water supply duration shall be at least 1 1/2 hr for Class I, II, and III commodities and at least 2 hr for Class IV and Group A plastic commodities. For multiple row racks the water supply duration shall be at least 2 hr for all classifications of commodities.

5-11 High Expansion Foam.

5-11.1* When high expansion foam systems are installed, they shall be in accordance with NFPA 11A, *Standard for Medium- and High-Expansion Foam Systems*, except as modified by this standard, and they shall be automatic in operation.

5-11.2 When high expansion foam systems are used in combination with ceiling sprinklers, in-rack sprinklers shall not be required.

5-12 Detectors for High Expansion Foam Systems.

5-12.1 Detectors shall be listed and shall be installed:

(a) At the ceiling only if installed at one-half listed linear spacing [e.g., 15 ft × 15 ft (4.57 m × 4.57 m) instead of 30 ft × 30 ft (9.15 m × 9.15 m)].

Exception: Ceiling detectors only should not be used when clearance from the top of storage exceeds 10 ft (3.05 m) or height of storage exceeds 25 ft (7.62 m).

or,

(b) At the ceiling at listed spacing and in racks at alternate levels, or

(c) When listed for rack storage installation and installed in accordance with their listing to provide response within one min after ignition using ignition source equal to that used on the rack storage testing program.

5-13 Solid and Slatted Shelves.

5-13.1* Slatted shelves shall be considered the same as solid shelves.

5-13.2† Sprinklers shall be installed at the ceiling and beneath each shelf in double or multiple row racks with solid shelves that obstruct both longitudinal and transverse flue spaces. Design curves for combined ceiling and in-rack sprinklers shall be used with this storage configuration.

5-14† Open-Top Combustible Containers.

5-15 Movable Racks.

5-15.1 Rack storage in movable racks shall be protected in the same manner as multiple row racks.

Chapter 6 Fire Protection — Storage up to and Including 25 Feet (7.62 m) in Height

Part A General

NOTE: See also Chapter 5.

6-1 In-Rack Sprinkler Type. Sprinklers in racks shall be ordinary temperature classification with nominal 1/2-in. (12.7-mm) orifice size pendent or upright. Sprinklers with 212°F (100°C) and 286°F (141°C) temperature ratings shall be used near heat sources as required by NFPA 13.

6-2 In-Rack Sprinkler Pipe Size. The number of sprinklers and the pipe sizing on a line of sprinklers in racks is restricted only by hydraulic calculations and not by any piping schedule.

6-3† In-Rack Sprinkler Water Shields. Water shields shall be provided directly above in-rack sprinklers, or listed sprinklers equipped with water shields shall be used when there is more than one level, if not shielded by horizontal barriers.

6-4 In-Rack Sprinkler Location.

6-4.1*† The elevation of in-rack sprinkler deflectors with respect to storage shall not be a consideration in single or double rack storage up to and including 20 ft (6.1 m) high.

6-4.2* In single or double row racks without solid shelves with height of storage over 20 ft (6.1 m), or in multiple row racks, or in single or double row racks with solid shelves and height of storage up to and including 25 ft (7.62 m), a minimum of 6 in. (152.4 mm) vertical clear space shall be maintained between the sprinkler deflectors and the top of a tier of storage. Sprinkler discharge shall not be obstructed by horizontal rack members.

6-4.3 In-rack sprinklers at one level only for storage up to and including 25 ft (7.62 m) high in single or double row racks shall be located at the first tier level at or above one-half of the storage height.

6-4.4 In-rack sprinklers at two levels only for storage up to and including 25 ft (7.62 m) high shall be located at the first tier level at or above one-third and two-thirds of the storage height.

6-5 In-Rack Sprinkler Spacing.

6-5.1* Maximum horizontal spacing of sprinklers in single or double row racks with nonencapsulated storage up to and including 25 ft (7.62 m) in height shall be in accordance with the following table:

	Commodity Class		
Aisle Widths	**I & II**	**III**	**IV**
8 ft	12 ft	12 ft	8 ft
4 ft	12 ft	8 ft	8 ft

For SI Units: 1 ft = 0.3048 m

For encapsulated storage, maximum horizontal spacing is 8 ft (2.44 m).

6-5.2† Sprinklers installed in racks shall be spaced without regard to rack uprights.

6-6† In-Rack Sprinkler Discharge Pressure. Sprinklers in racks shall discharge at not less than 15 psi (103.4 kPa) for all classes of commodity.

6-7† In-Rack Sprinkler Water Demand. Water demand for sprinklers installed in racks shall be based on simultaneous operation of the most hydraulically remote:

(a) Six sprinklers when only one level is installed in racks with Class I, II, or III commodity.

(b) Eight sprinklers when only one level is installed in racks with Class IV commodity.

(c) Ten sprinklers (five on each two top levels) when more than one level is installed in racks with Class I, II, or III commodity.

(d) Fourteen sprinklers (seven on each two top levels) when more than one level is installed in racks with Class IV commodity.

6-8 Ceiling Sprinkler Water Demand.

6-8.1*† Design curves in Figures 6-11.1(a) through (g) apply to nominal 20-ft (6.1-m) height of storage.

6-8.1.1 The design curves indicate water demands for nominal 165°F (74°C) and nominal 286°F (141°C) sprinklers at the ceiling. The 165°F (74°C) design curves shall be used for sprinklers with ordinary and intermediate temperature classification but not less than 160°F (71°C). The 286°F (141°C) design curve shall be used for sprinklers with high temperature classification.

6-8.2 For height of storage up to and including 25 ft (7.62 m) protected with ceiling sprinklers only, and for height of storage up to and including 20 ft (6.1 m) protected with ceiling sprinklers and minimum acceptable in-rack sprinklers, densities given in design curves shall be adjusted according to Figure 6-8.2.

6-8.3 For height of storage over 20 ft (6.1 m) up to and including 25 ft (7.62) protected with ceiling sprinklers and minimum acceptable in-rack sprinklers, densities given in design curves shall be used. Densities shall not be adjusted per Figure 6-8.2.

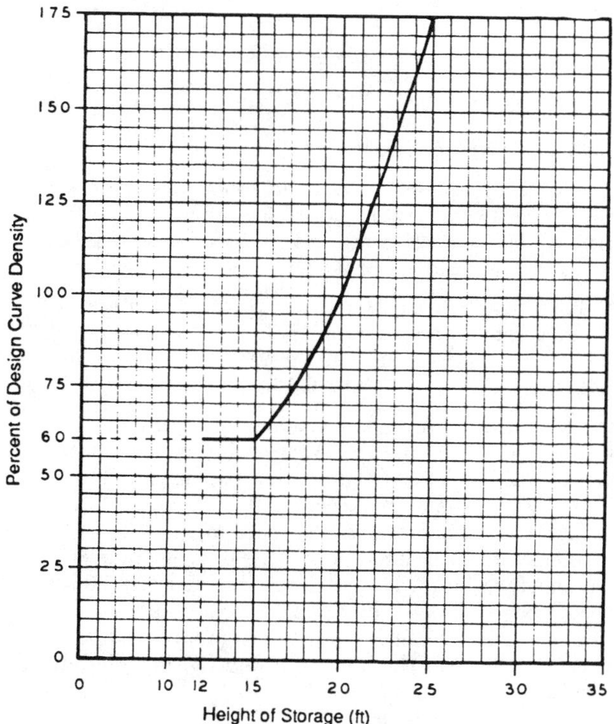

For SI Units: 1 ft = 0.3048 m

Figure 6-8.2 Ceiling Sprinkler Density versus Storage Height.

Table 6-8.2 Adjustment to Ceiling Sprinkler Density for Storage Height and In-Rack Sprinklers

Stge. Height (ft)	In-Rack Sprinklers	Apply Fig. 6-8.2	Permitted Ceiling Sprinklers Density Adjustments
Over 12 Ft Through 25 Ft	None	Yes	None
Over 12 Ft Through 20 Ft	Minimum Acceptable	Yes	None
	More than Minimum but Not In Every Tier	Yes	Reduce Density 20% from that for Minimum In-Rack Sprinklers
	In Every Tier	Yes	Reduce Density 40% from that for Minimum In-Rack Sprinklers
Over 20 Ft Through 25 Ft	Minimum Acceptable	No	None
	More than Minimum but Not In Every Tier	No	Reduce Density 20% from that for Minimum In-Rack Sprinklers
	In Every Tier	No	Reduce Density 40% from that for Minimum In-Rack Sprinklers

For SI Units: 1 ft = 0.3048 m

6-8.4 For height of storage up to and including 20 ft (6.1 m) protected with ceiling sprinklers and with more than one level of in-rack sprinklers, but not in every tier, densities given in design curves and adjusted according to Figure 6-8.2 shall be permitted to be reduced an additional 20 percent.

6-8.5 For height of storage over 20 ft (6.1 m) up to and including 25 ft (7.6 m) protected with ceiling sprinklers, and with more than the minimum acceptable level of in-rack sprinklers, but not in every tier, densities given in design curves shall be permitted to be reduced 20 percent. Densities shall not be adjusted per Figure 6-8.2.

6-8.6 For height of storage up to and including 20 ft (6.1 m) protected with ceiling sprinklers and in-rack sprinklers at each tier, densities given in design curves and adjusted according to Figure 6-8.2 shall be permitted to be reduced an additional 40 percent.

6-8.7 For height of storage over 20 ft (6.1 m) up to and including 25 ft (7.62 m) protected with ceiling sprinklers and in-rack sprinklers at each tier, densities given in design curves shall be permitted to be reduced 40 percent. Densities shall not be adjusted per Figure 6-8.2.

6-8.8† When clearance from top of storage to ceiling is less than $4^1/_2$ ft (1.37 m) (*see Section 4-5*), the sprinkler operating area indicated in curves E, F, G, and H in Figures 6-11.1(a), (b), (c), (d), and (e) shall be permitted to be reduced as indicated in Figure 6-8.8, but not less than 2,000 sq ft (185.8 m^2) (*see 6-8.9*).

6-8.9 When clearance from ceiling to top of Class I or II encapsulated storage is $1^1/_2$ to 3 ft (0.46 m to 0.91 m), sprinkler operating area indicated in curve F only of Figure 6-11.1(e) shall be permitted to be reduced by 50 percent but to not less than 2,000 sq ft (185.8 m^2).

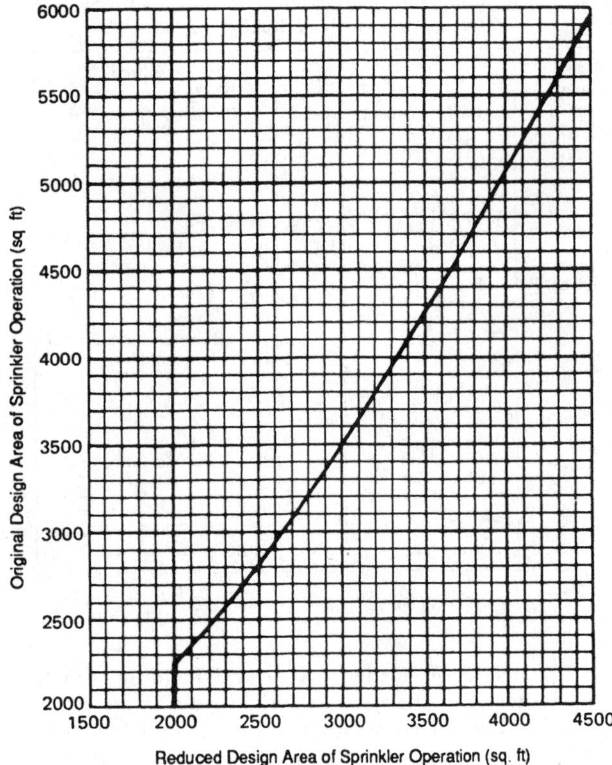

For SI Units: 1 ft = 0.0929 m^2

Figure 6-8.8 Adjustment of Design Area of Sprinkler Operation for Clearance from Top of Storage to Ceiling.

6-8.10 Where solid flat bottom wood pallets are used, with height of storage up to and including 25 ft (7.62 m), the densities indicated in the design curves, based on conventional pallets, shall be increased 20 percent for the given area. This percentage shall be applied to the density resulting from the application of Figure 6-8.2. This increase shall not apply when in-rack sprinklers are installed.

6-9 High Expansion Foam Submergence.

6-9.1* When high expansion foam systems are used without sprinklers, the maximum submergence time shall be 5 min for Class I, II, or III commodities and 4 min for Class IV commodities.

6-9.2 When high expansion foam systems are used in combination with ceiling sprinklers, the maximum submergence time shall be 7 min for Class I, II, or III commodities and 5 min for Class IV commodities.

6-10 High Expansion Foam Ceiling Sprinkler Density. When high expansion foam systems are used in combination with ceiling sprinklers, the minimum ceiling sprinkler design shall be a density of 0.2 gpm per sq ft [(8.15 L/min)/m^2] for Class I, II, or III commodities or 0.25 gpm per sq ft [(10.2 L/min)/m^2] for Class IV commodities for the most hydraulically remote 2,000-sq ft (185.8-m^2) operating area.

Part B Double and Single Row Racks

NOTE: See also Chapter 5.

6-11 Ceiling Sprinkler Water Demand.

6-11.1* For Class I, II, III, or IV commodities encapsulated or nonencapsulated in single or double row racks, ceiling sprinkler water demand in terms of density (gpm per sq ft) and area of sprinkler operation (sq ft of ceiling or roof) shall be selected from curves given in Figures 6-11.1(a) through (g). The curves in Figures 6-11.1(a) through (g) shall also apply to portable racks arranged in the same manner as single or double row racks or multiple row racks. The design shall be sufficient to satisfy a single point on the appropriate curve related to the storage configuration and commodity class. It shall not be necessary to meet all points on the selected curve. Figure 6-8.2 shall be used to adjust density for storage height unless otherwise specified.

6-11.2† Design curves for single and double row racks shall be selected corresponding to aisle width. For aisle widths between 4 ft (1.22 m) and 8 ft (2.44 m), a direct linear interpolation between curves shall be made. Density given for 8-ft (2.44-m) wide aisles shall be applied to aisles wider than 8 ft (2.44 m). Density given for 4-ft (1.22-m) wide aisles shall be applied to aisles narrower than 4 ft (1.22 m) down to 3$^1/_2$ ft (1.07 m). When aisles are narrower than 3$^1/_2$ ft (1.07 m), racks shall be considered as multiple row racks.

6-12 In-Rack Sprinkler Location. In single or double row racks without solid shelves, in-rack sprinklers shall be installed as indicated in Table 6-11.1.

Part C Multiple Row Racks

NOTE: See also Chapter 5.

6-13 In-Rack Sprinkler Location.

6-13.1† For encapsulated or nonencapsulated storage in multiple row racks no deeper than 16 ft (4.88 m) with aisles no narrower than 8 ft (2.44 m), in-rack sprinklers shall be installed as indicated in Table 6-13.1.

6-13.2 For encapsulated or nonencapsulated storage in multiple row racks deeper than 16 ft (4.88 m), or with aisles less than 8 ft (2.44 m) wide, in-rack sprinklers shall be installed as indicated in Table 6-13.2.

6-13.3* Maximum horizontal spacing of sprinklers on branch lines, in multiple row racks with encapsulated or nonencapsulated storage up to and including 25 ft (7.62 m) in height, shall not exceed 12 ft (3.66 m) for Class I, II, or III commodities and 8 ft (2.44 m) for Class IV commodities, with area limitations of 100 sq ft (9.29 m^2) per sprinkler for Class I, II, or III commodities and 80 sq ft (7.43 m^2) per sprinkler for Class IV commodities. The rack plan view shall be considered in determining area covered by each sprinkler. The aisles are not to be included in area calculations.

6-13.4 A minimum of 6 in. (152.4 mm) shall be maintained between the sprinkler deflector and top of a tier of storage.

Height	Commodity Class	Encap-sulated	Aisles (Ft) (4-4.1) (B-6-11.2)	Sprinklers Mandatory In-Rack	Ceiling Sprinkler Water Demand: With In-Rack Sprinklers			Ceiling Sprinkler Water Demand: Without In-Rack Sprinklers		
					Fig.	Curves	Apply Fig. 6-8.2	Fig.	Curves	Apply Fig. 6-8.2
Over 12 Ft, Up Thru 20 Ft	I	No	4 8	No	6-11.1(a)	C&D A&B	Yes	6-11.1(a)	G&H E&F	Yes
		Yes	4 8	No	6-11.1(e)	C&D A&B		6-11.1(e)	G&H E&F	Yes
	II	No	4 8	No	6-11.1(b)	C&D A&B		6-11.1(b)	G&H E&F	Yes
		Yes	4 8	No	6-11.1(e)	C&D A&B		6-11.1(e)	G&H E&F	Yes
	III	No	4 8	No	6-11.1(c)	C&D A&B		6-11.1(c)	G&H E&F	Yes
		Yes	4 8	1 Level	6-11.1(f)	C&D A&B				
	IV	No	4 8	No	6-11.1(d)	C&D A&B		6-11.1(d)	G&H E&F	Yes
		Yes	4 8	1 Level	6-11.1(g)	C&D A&B				
Over 20 Ft, Up Thru 22 Ft	I	No	4 8	No	6-11.1(a)	C&D A&B	No	6-11.1(a)	G&H E&F	Yes
		Yes	4 8	1 Level	6-11.1(e)	C&D A&B				
	II	No	4 8	No	6-11.1(b)	C&D A&B		6-11.1(b)	G&H E&F	Yes
		Yes	4 8	1 Level	6-11.1(e)	C&D A&B				
	III	No	4 8	No	6-11.1(c)	C&D A&B		6-11.1(c)	G&H E&F	Yes
		Yes	4 8	1 Level	6-11.1(f)	C&D A&B				
	IV	No	4 8	No	6-11.1(d)	C&D A&B		6-11.1(d)	G&H E&F	Yes
		Yes	4 8	1 Level	6-11.1(g)	C&D A&B				
Over 22 Ft, Up Thru 25 Ft	I	No	4 8	No	6-11.1(a)	C&D A&B	No	6-11.1(a)	G&H E&F	Yes
		Yes	4 8	1 Level	6-11.1(e)	C&D A&B				
	II	No	4 8	No	6-11.1(b)	C&D A&B		6-11.1(b)	G&H E&F	Yes
		Yes	4 8	1 Level	6-11.1(e)	C&D A&B				
	III	No	4 8	No	6-11.1(c)	C&D A&B		6-11.1(c)	G&H E&F	Yes
		Yes	4 8	1 Level	6-11.1(f)	C&D A&B				
	IV	No	4 8	1 Level	6-11.1(d)	C&D A&B				
		Yes	4 8		6-11.1(g)	C&D A&B				

For SI Units: 1 ft = 0.3048 m

Table 6-11.1 Single or Double Row Racks. Height of Storage up to and Including 25 Ft, Aisles Wider than 4 Ft, without Solid Shelves.

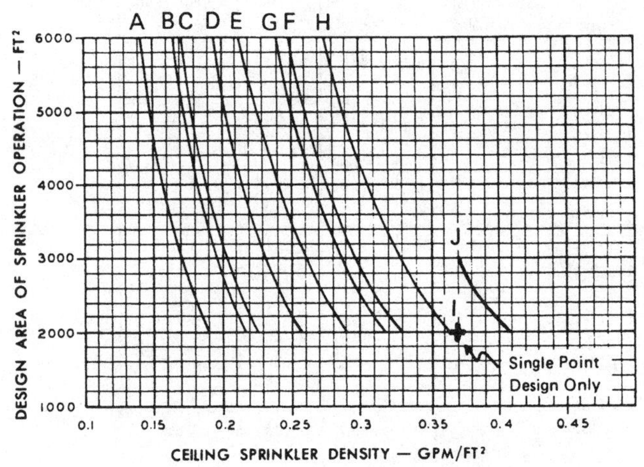

Curve	Legend
A —	*Single or double row racks with 8-ft aisles with 286°F ceiling sprinklers and 165°F in-rack sprinklers.*
B —	*Single or double row racks with 8-ft aisles with 165°F ceiling sprinklers and 165°F in-rack sprinklers.*
C —	*Single or double row racks with 4-ft aisles or multiple row racks with 286°F ceiling sprinklers and 165°F in-rack sprinklers.*
D —	*Single or double row racks with 4-ft aisles or multiple row racks with 165°F ceiling sprinklers and 165°F in-rack sprinklers.*
E —	*Single or double row racks with 8-ft aisles and 286°F ceiling sprinklers.*
F —	*Single or double row racks with 8-ft aisles and 165°F ceiling sprinklers.*
G —	*Single or double row racks with 4-ft aisles and 286°F ceiling sprinklers.*
H —	*Single or double row racks with 4-ft aisles and 165°F ceiling sprinklers.*
I —	*Multiple row racks with 8-ft or wider aisles and 286°F ceiling sprinklers.*
J —	*Multiple row racks with 8-ft or wider aisles and 165°F ceiling sprinklers.*

For SI Units: 1 ft = 0.3048 m; C = 5/9 (F-32); 1 gpm/ft² = 40.746 (L/min)/m²

Figure 6-11.1(a) Sprinkler System Design Curves — 20-Ft High Rack Storage — Class I Nonencapsulated Commodities — Conventional Pallets.

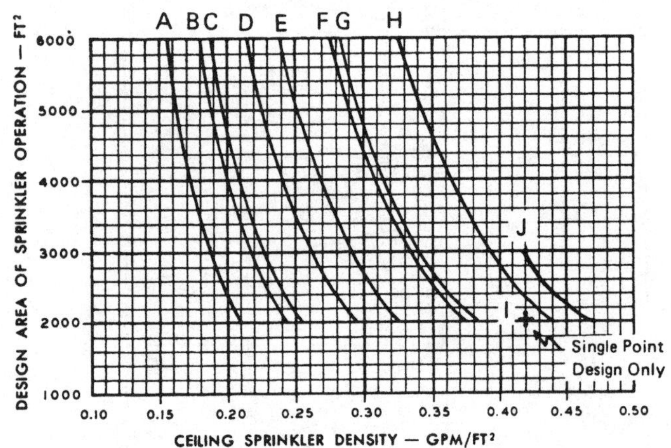

Curve	Legend
A —	*Single or double row racks with 8-ft aisles with 286°F ceiling sprinklers and 165°F in-rack sprinklers.*
B —	*Single or double row racks with 8-ft aisles with 165°F ceiling sprinklers and 165°F in-rack sprinklers.*
C —	*Single or double row racks with 4-ft aisles or multiple row racks with 286°F ceiling sprinklers and 165°F in-rack sprinklers.*
D —	*Single or double row racks with 4-ft aisles or multiple row racks with 165°F ceiling sprinklers and 165°F in-rack sprinklers.*
E —	*Single or double row racks with 8-ft aisles and 286°F ceiling sprinklers.*
F —	*Single or double row racks with 8-ft aisles and 165°F ceiling sprinklers.*
G —	*Single or double row racks with 4-ft aisles and 286°F ceiling sprinklers.*
H —	*Single or double row racks with 4-ft aisles and 165°F ceiling sprinklers.*
I —	*Multiple row racks with 8-ft or wider aisles and 286°F ceiling sprinklers.*
J —	*Multiple row racks with 8-ft or wider aisles and 165°F ceiling sprinklers.*

For SI Units: 1 ft = 0.3048 m; C = 5/9 (F-32); 1 gpm/ft² = 40.746 (L/min)/m²

Figure 6-11.1(b) Sprinkler System Design Curves — 20-Ft High Rack Storage — Class II Nonencapsulated Commodities — Conventional Pallets.

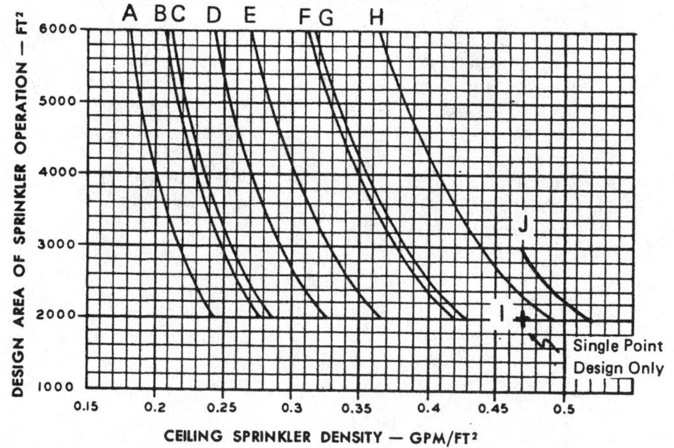

Curve	Legend
A —	*Single or double row racks with 8-ft aisles with 286°F ceiling sprinklers and 165°F in-rack sprinklers.*
B —	*Single or double row racks with 8-ft aisles with 165°F ceiling sprinklers and 165°F in-rack sprinklers.*
C —	*Single or double row racks with 4-ft aisles or multiple row racks with 286°F ceiling sprinklers and 165°F in-rack sprinklers.*
D —	*Single or double row racks with 4-ft aisles or multiple row racks with 165°F ceiling sprinklers and 165°F in-rack sprinklers.*
E —	*Single or double row racks with 8-ft aisles and 286°F ceiling sprinklers.*
F —	*Single or double row racks with 8-ft aisles and 165°F ceiling sprinklers.*
G —	*Single or double row racks with 4-ft aisles and 286°F ceiling sprinklers.*
H —	*Single or double row racks with 4-ft aisles and 165°F ceiling sprinklers.*
I —	*Multiple row racks with 8-ft or wider aisles and 286°F ceiling sprinklers.*
J —	*Multiple row racks with 8-ft or wider aisles and 165°F ceiling sprinklers.*

For SI Units: 1 ft = 0.3048 m; C = 5/9 (F-32); 1 gpm/ft² = 40.746 (L/min)/m²

Figure 6-11.1(c) Sprinkler System Design Curves — 20-Ft High Rack Storage — Class III Nonencapsulated Commodities — Conventional Pallets.

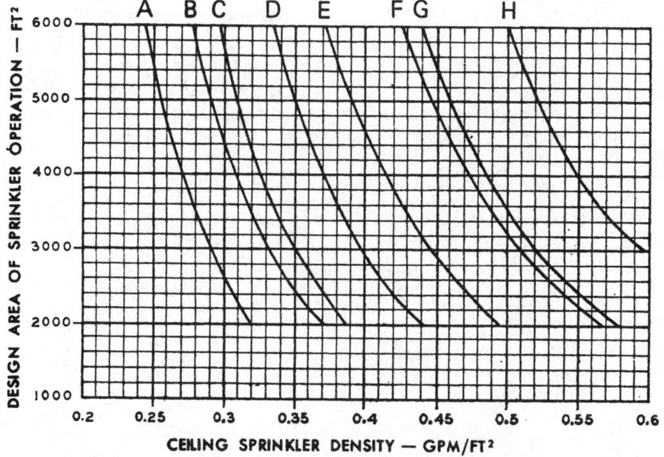

Curve	Legend
A —	*Single or double row racks with 8-ft aisles with 286°F ceiling sprinklers and 165°F in-rack sprinklers.*
B —	*Single or double row racks with 8-ft aisles with 165°F ceiling sprinklers and 165°F in-rack sprinklers.*
C —	*Single or double row racks with 4-ft aisles or multiple row racks with 286°F ceiling sprinklers and 165°F in-rack sprinklers.*
D —	*Single or double row racks with 4-ft aisles or multiple row racks with 165°F ceiling sprinklers and 165°F in-rack sprinklers.*
E —	*Single or double row racks with 8-ft aisles and 286°F ceiling sprinklers.*
F —	*Single or double row racks with 8-ft aisles and 165°F ceiling sprinklers.*
G —	*Single or double row racks with 4-ft aisles and 286°F ceiling sprinklers.*
H —	*Single or double row racks with 4-ft aisles and 165°F ceiling sprinklers.*

Note: Curves C and D also apply to ceiling sprinklers only for multiple row racks up to and including 15 ft (4.2 m) high, and Figure 6-8.2 shall not be applied.

For SI Units: 1 ft = 0.3048 m; C = 5/9 (F-32); 1 gpm/ft² = 40.746 (L/min)/m²

Figure 6-11.1(d) Sprinkler System Design Curves — 20-Ft High Rack Storage — Class IV Nonencapsulated Commodities — Conventional Pallets.

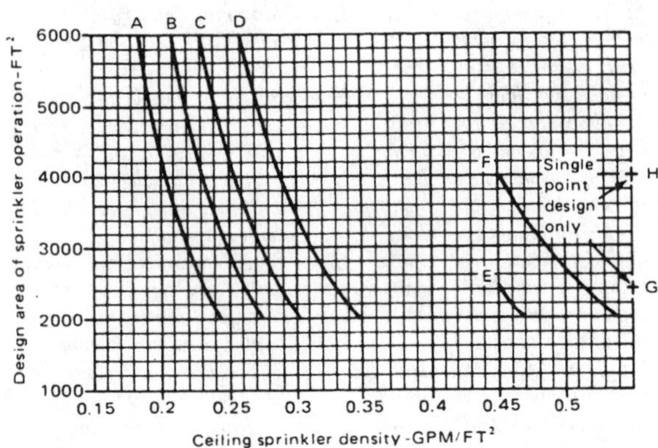

Curve	Legend	Curve	Legend
A —	*8-ft aisles with 286°F ceiling sprinklers and 165°F in-rack sprinklers.*	*E* —	*8-ft aisles with 286°F ceiling sprinklers.*
B —	*8-ft aisles with 165°F ceiling sprinklers and 165°F in-rack sprinklers.*	*F* —	*8-ft aisles with 165°F ceiling sprinklers.*
C —	*4-ft aisles with 286°F ceiling sprinklers and 165°F in-rack sprinklers.*	*G* —	*4-ft aisles with 286°F ceiling sprinklers.*
D —	*4-ft aisles with 165°F ceiling sprinklers and 165°F in-rack sprinklers.*	*H* —	*4-ft aisles with 165°F ceiling sprinklers.*

For SI Units: 1 ft = 0.3048 m; C = 5/9 (F-32); 1 gpm/ft² = 40.746 (L/min)/m²

Figure 6-11.1(e) Single or Double Row Racks — 20-Ft High Rack Storage — Sprinkler System Design Curves — Class I & II Encapsulated Commodities — Conventional Pallets.

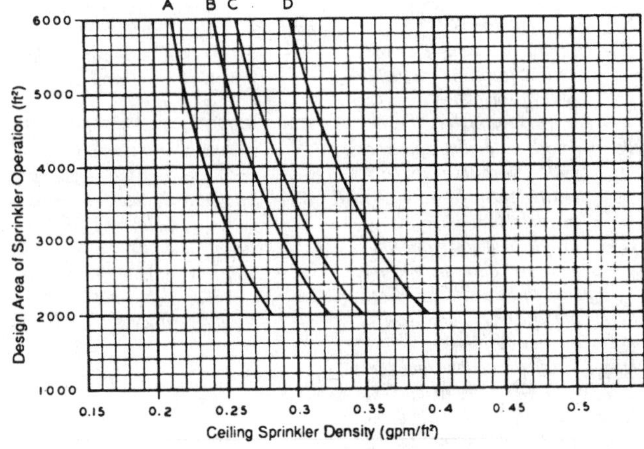

Curve	Legend	Curve	Legend
A —	*8-ft aisles with 286°F ceiling sprinklers and 165°F in-rack sprinklers.*	*C* —	*4-ft aisles with 286°F ceiling sprinklers and 165°F in-rack sprinklers.*
B —	*8-ft aisles with 165°F ceiling sprinklers and 165°F in-rack sprinklers.*	*D* —	*4-ft aisles with 165°F ceiling sprinklers and 165°F in-rack sprinklers.*

For SI Units: 1 ft = 0.3048 m; C = 5/9 (F-32); 1 gpm/ft² = 40.746 (L/min)/m²

Figure 6-11.1(f) Single or Double Row Racks — 20-Ft High Rack Storage — Sprinkler System Design Curves — Class III Encapsulated Commodities — Conventional Pallets.

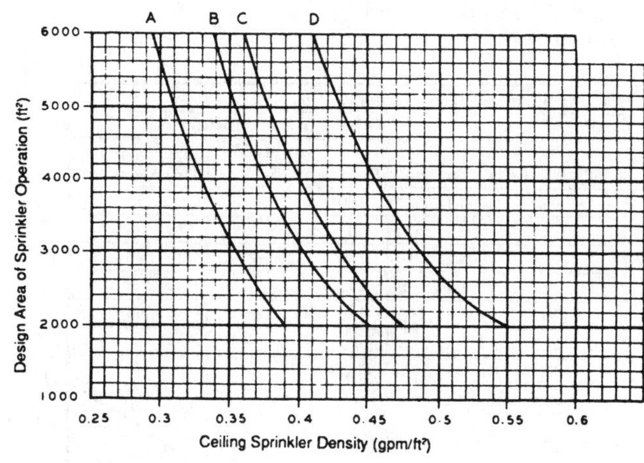

Curve	Legend
A —	*8-ft aisles with 286°F ceiling sprinklers and 165°F in-rack sprinklers.*
B —	*8-ft aisles with 165°F ceiling sprinklers and 165°F in-rack sprinklers.*
C —	*4-ft aisles with 286°F ceiling sprinklers and 165°F in-rack sprinklers.*
D —	*4-ft aisles with 165°F ceiling sprinklers and 165°F in-rack sprinklers.*

For SI Units: 1 ft = 0.3048 m; C = 5/9 (F-32); 1 gpm/ft² = 40.746 (L/min)/m²

Figure 6-11.1(g) Single or Double Row Racks — 20-Ft High Rack Storage — Sprinkler System Design Curves — Class IV Encapsulated Commodities — Conventional Pallets.

Table 6-13.1 Multiple-Row Racks. Rack Depth up to 16 Ft, Aisles Wider than 8 Ft, Storage Height up to 25 Ft.

				Ceiling Sprinkler Water Demand							
				With In-Rack Sprinklers				Without In-Rack Sprinklers			
Height	Commodity Class	Encap-sulated	Sprinklers Mandatory In-Racks	Fig. No.	Curves	Apply Fig. 6-8.2	1.25 x Density	Fig. No.	Curves	Apply Fig. 6-8.2	1.25 x Density
Over 12 Ft Up Thru 15 Ft	I	No	No	6-11.1(a)	C&D	Yes	No	6-11.1(a)	I&J	Yes	No
		Yes		6-11.1(a)			Yes	6-11.1(a)	I&J		Yes
	II	No		6-11.1(b)			No	6-11.1(b)	I&J	Yes	No
		Yes		6-11.1(b)			Yes	6-11.1(b)	I&J		Yes
	III	No	No	6-11.1(c)			No	6-11.1(c)	I&J	Yes	No
		Yes	1 Level	6-11.1(c)			Yes				
	IV	No	No	6-11.1(d)			No	6-11.1(d)	C&D	No	No
		Yes	1 Level	6-11.1(d)	A&B		1.50 x Density				
Over 15 Ft Up Thru 20 Ft	I	No	No	6-11.1(a)	C&D	Yes	No	6.11.1(a)	I&J	Yes	No
		Yes		6-11.1(a)			Yes	6-11.1(a)	I&J		Yes
	II	No		6-11.1(b)			No	6-11.1(b)	I&J	Yes	No
		Yes		6-11.1(b)			Yes	6-11.1(b)	I&J		Yes
	III	No	No	6-11.1(c)			No	6-11.1(c)	I&J	Yes	No
		Yes	1 Level	6-11.1(c)			Yes	(crossed out)			
	IV	No	1 Level	6-11.1(d)			No	(crossed out)			
		Yes		6-11.1(d)	A&B		1.50 x Density	(crossed out)			
Over 20 Ft Up Thru 25 Ft	I	No	No	6-11.1(a)	C&D	No	No	6-11.1(a)	I&J	Yes	No
		Yes	1 Level	6-11.1(a)			Yes	(crossed out)			
	II	No	1 Level	6-11.1(b)			No	(crossed out)			
		Yes		6-11.1(b)			Yes	(crossed out)			
	III	No		6-11.1(c)			No	(crossed out)			
		Yes		6-11.1(c)			Yes	(crossed out)			
	IV	No	2 Levels	6-11.1(d)			No	(crossed out)			
		Yes		6-11.1(d)	A&B		1.50 x Density	(crossed out)			

For SI Units: 1 ft = .3048 m

Table 6-13.2 Multiple-Row Racks. Rack Depth up to 16 Ft or Aisles Narrower than 8 Ft, Storage Height up to 25 Ft.

Height	Commodity Class	Encap-sulated	Sprinklers Mandatory In-Racks	Ceiling Sprinkler Water Demand							
				With In-Rack Sprinklers				Without In-Rack Sprinklers			
				Fig. No.	Curves	Apply Fig. 6-8.2	1.25 x Density	Fig. No.	Curves	Apply Fig. 6-8.2	1.25 x Density
Over 12 Ft Up Thru 15 Ft	I	No	No	6-11.1(a)	C&D	Yes	No	6-11.1(a)	I&J	Yes	No
		Yes		6-11.1(a)			Yes	6-11.1(a)	I&J		Yes
	II	No		6-11.1(b)			No	6-11.1(b)	I&J	Yes	No
		Yes		6-11.1(b)			Yes	6-11.1(b)	I&J		Yes
	III	No		6-11.1(c)			No	6-11.1(c)	I&J	Yes	No
		Yes	1 Level	6-11.1(c)			Yes				
	IV	No	No	6-11.1(d)			No	6-11.1(d)	C&D	No	No
		Yes	1 Level	6-11.1(d)			1.50 x Density				
Over 15 Ft Up Thru 20 Ft	I	No	1 Level	6-11.1(a)	C&D	Yes	No				
		Yes		6-11.1(a)			Yes				
	II	No		6-11.1(b)			No				
		Yes		6-11.1(b)			Yes				
	III	No		6-11.1(c)			No				
		Yes		6-11.1(c)			Yes				
	IV	No		6-11.1(d)			No				
		Yes		6-11.1(d)			1.50 x Density				
Over 20 Ft Up Thru 25 Ft	I	No	1 Level	6-11.1(a)	C&D	No	No				
		Yes		6-11.1(a)			Yes				
	II	No		6-11.1(b)			No				
		Yes		6-11.1(b)			Yes				
	III	No		6-11.1(c)			No				
		Yes		6-11.1(c)			Yes				
	IV	No	2 Levels	6-11.1(d)			No				
		Yes		6-11.1(d)			1.50 x Density				

For SI Units: 1 ft = .3048 m

6-14 Ceiling Sprinkler Water Demand.

6-14.1 For nonencapsulated Class I, II, III, or IV commodities, ceiling sprinkler water demand in terms of density (gpm per sq ft) and area of sprinkler operation (sq ft of ceiling or roof) shall be selected from curves given in Figures 6-11.1(a) through (d). The curves in Figures 6-11.1(a) through (d) also apply to portable racks arranged in the same manner as single, double, or multiple row racks. The design shall be sufficient to satisfy a single point on the appropriate curve related to the storage configuration and commodity class. It shall not be necessary to meet all points on the selected curve. Figure 6-8.2 shall be used to adjust density for storage height unless otherwise specified. (*See A-6-5.1 and A-6-11.1.*)

6-14.2 For encapsulated Class I, II, or III commodities with height of storage up to and including 25 ft (7.62 m) on multiple row racks, ceiling sprinkler density shall be 25 percent greater than for nonencapsulated commodities on multiple row racks.

6-14.3 For encapsulated Class IV commodities with height of storage up to and including 25 ft (7.62 m) on multiple row racks, ceiling sprinkler density shall be 50 percent greater than for nonencapsulated commodities on double row racks.

Chapter 7 Fire Protection — Storage over 25 Feet (7.62 m) in Height

Part A General

7-1 In-Rack Sprinkler Type. Sprinklers in racks shall be ordinary temperature classification with nominal 1/2-in. (12.7-mm) orifice size, pendent or upright. Sprinklers with 212°F (100°C) and 286°F (141°C) temperature ratings shall be used near heat sources as required in NFPA 13.

7-2 In-Rack Sprinkler Spacing. In-rack sprinklers shall be staggered horizontally and vertically when installed as indicated in Table 7-10.1, Figures 7-10.1(a) through (j), and Figures 7-10.3(a) through (e).

7-3 In-Rack Sprinkler Pipe Size. The number of sprinklers and the pipe sizing on a line of sprinklers in racks is restricted only by hydraulic calculations and not by any piping schedule.

7-4 In-Rack Sprinkler Water Shields. Water shields shall be provided directly above in-rack sprinklers, or listed sprinklers equipped with water shields shall be provided when there is more than one level, if not shielded by horizontal barriers (*see Appendix B-6-3*).

7-5 In-Rack Sprinkler Location. In double row or multiple row racks, a minimum 6 in. (152.4 mm) vertical clear space shall be maintained between the sprinkler deflectors and the top of a tier of storage. Face sprinklers in such racks shall be located a minimum of 3 in. (76.2 mm) from rack uprights and no more than 18 in. (0.46 m) from the aisle face of storage. Other sprinklers in racks shall be located a minimum of 2 ft (0.61 m) from rack uprights.

Exception: When the distance between uprights is less than 4 ft (1.22 m), sprinklers shall be centered between uprights.

7-6 In-Rack Sprinkler Discharge Pressure. Sprinklers in racks shall discharge at not less than 30 psi (206.8 kPa) for all classes of commodity (*see Appendix B-6-7*).

7-7 In-Rack Sprinkler Water Demand.

7-7.1 Water demand for sprinklers installed in racks shall be based on simultaneous operation of the most hydraulically remote:

(a) Six sprinklers when only one level is installed in racks with Class I, II, or III commodity.

(b) Eight sprinklers when only one level is installed in racks with Class IV commodity.

(c) Ten sprinklers (five on each two top levels) when more than one level is installed in racks with Class I, II, or III commodity.

(d) Fourteen sprinklers (seven on each two top levels) when more than one level is installed in racks with Class IV commodity.

7-8 High Expansion Foam Submergence. When high expansion foam systems are used for storage over 25 ft (7.62 m) high, up to and including 35 ft (10.67 m) high, they shall be used in combination with ceiling sprinklers. The maximum submergence time for the high expansion foam shall be 5 min for Class I, II, or III commodities and 4 min for Class IV commodities.

7-9 High Expansion Foam—Ceiling Sprinkler Water Demand. When high expansion foam is used in combination with ceiling sprinklers, the sprinkler design shall be 0.2 gpm per sq ft [(8.15 L/min)/m^2] for Class I, II, or III commodities and 0.25 gpm per sq ft [(10.19 L/min)/m^2] for Class IV commodities, over the most hydraulically remote 2,000-sq ft (185.8-m^2) area.

Part B Double and Single Row Racks

7-10 In-Rack Sprinkler Location.

7-10.1 In double row racks without solid shelves and with a maximum of 10 ft (3.05 m) between top of storage and ceiling, in-rack sprinklers shall be installed as indicated in Table 7-10.1 and Figures 7-10.1(a) through (j). The highest level of in-rack sprinklers shall be not more than 10 ft (3.05 m) below top of storage (*see Section 7-11*).

7-10.2 In-rack sprinklers for storage higher than 25 ft (7.62 m) in double row racks shall be spaced horizontally and located in horizontal space nearest the vertical intervals indicated in Table 7-10.1, Figures 7-10.1(a) through (j).

7-10.3* In single row racks without solid shelves with height of storage over 25 ft (7.62 m) and a maximum of 10 ft (3.05 m) between top of storage and ceiling, sprinklers shall be installed as indicated in Figures 7-10.3(a) through (e).

7-11* In-Rack Sprinkler Horizontal Barriers. Horizontal barriers used in conjunction with in-rack sprinklers to impede vertical fire development shall be constructed of sheet metal, wood, or similar material and shall extend the full length and width of the rack. Barriers shall be fitted within 2-in. (50.8-mm) horizontally around rack uprights [*see Table 7-10.1, Figures 7-10.1(a), (g), and (j), and Figures 7-10.3(c) and (e)*].

7-12 Ceiling Sprinkler Water Demand.

7-12.1†* Water demand for nonencapsulated storage on racks without solid shelves separated by aisles at least 4-ft (1.22-m) wide and with not more than 10 ft (3.05 m) between top of storage and sprinklers shall be based on sprinklers in a 2,000 sq ft (185.8 m^2) operating area, discharging a minimum of 0.25 gpm per sq ft [(10.18 L/min)/m^2] for Class I commodities, 0.3 gpm per sq ft [(12.2 L/min)/m^2] for Class II and III commodities, and 0.35 gpm per sq ft [(14.26 L/min)/m^2] for Class IV commodities, for 165°F (74°C) sprinklers; or a minimum of 0.35 gpm per sq ft [(14.26 L/min)/m^2]for Class I commodities, 0.40 gpm per sq ft [(16.3 L/min)/m^2] for Class II and III commodities, and 0.45 gpm per sq ft [(18.3 L/min)/m^2] for Class IV commodities, for 286°F (141°C) sprinklers (*see Table 7-10.1*).

7-12.2 Where storage as described in 7-12.1 is encapsulated, ceiling sprinkler density shall be 25 percent greater than for nonencapsulated.

Table 7-10.1 Double-Row Racks without Solid Shelves, Storage Higher than 25 Ft, Aisles Wider than 4 Ft

Commodity Class	In-rack sprinklers — approximate vertical spacing at tier nearest the vertical distance and maximum horizontal spacing [1][2]: Longitudinal Flue[3]	Face [4][8]	Fig. No.	Maximum Storage Height	Stagger	Ceiling Sprinkler Operating Area	Ceiling Sprinkler Density (gpm/sq ft)[6] Clearance[5] Up to 10 ft[7]: 165°	286°
I	Vertical 20 ft Horizontal 10 ft under horizontal Barriers	None	7-10.1(a)	30 ft	No	2000 sq ft	0.25	0.35
	Vertical 20 ft Horizontal 10 ft	Vertical 20 ft Horizontal 10 ft	7-10.1(b)	Higher than 25 ft	Yes		0.25	0.35
I, II, & III	Vertical 10 ft or at 15 ft & 25 ft Horizontal 10 ft	None	7-10.1(c)	30 ft	Yes	2000 sq ft	0.30	0.40
	Vertical 10 ft Horizontal 10 ft	Vertical 30 ft Horizontal 10 ft	7-10.1(d)	Higher than 25 ft	Yes		0.30	0.40
	Vertical 20 ft Horizontal 10 ft	Vertical 20 ft Horizontal 5 ft	7-10.1(e)		Yes		0.30	0.40
	Vertical 25 ft Horizontal 5 ft	Vertical 25 ft Horizontal 5 ft	7-10.1(f)		No		0.30	0.40
	Horizontal barriers at 20 ft. Vertical intervals-2 lines of sprinklers under barriers-maximum horizontal spacing 10 ft staggered.		7-10.1(g)		Yes		0.30	0.40
I, II, III, & IV	Vertical 15 ft Horizontal 10 ft	Vertical 20 ft Horizontal 10 ft	7-10.1(h)	Higher than 25 ft	Yes	2000 sq ft	0.35	0.45
	Vertical 20 ft Horizontal 5 ft	Vertical 20 ft Horizontal 5 ft	7-10.1(i)		No		0.35	0.45
	Horizontal barriers at 15 ft. Vertical intervals-2 lines of sprinkler under barriers-maximum horizontal spacing 10 ft staggered		7-10.1(j)		Yes		0.35	0.45

For SI Units: 1 ft = 0.3048 m

Footnotes to Table 7-10.1

[1]Minimum in-rack sprinkler pressure, 30 psi (2.1 bar) (Section 7-6).
[2]Water shields required (Section 6-3 and Section 7-4).
[3]Install sprinklers at least 2 ft (0.61 m) from uprights (A-6-4.1).
[4]Install sprinklers at least 3 in. (76.2 mm) from uprights (Section 7-5).
[5]Clearance is distance between top of storage and ceiling.
[6]For encapsulated commodity, increase density 25 percent (7-12.1).
[7]See A-7-10.3, A-7-11, and A-7-12.1 for protection suggestions when clearance is greater than 10 ft (3.05 m).
[8]Face sprinklers are not mandatory for a Class I commodity consisting of noncombustible products on wood pallets (without combustible containers) except for arrays shown in Figure 7-10.1(g) and Figure 7-10.1(j).

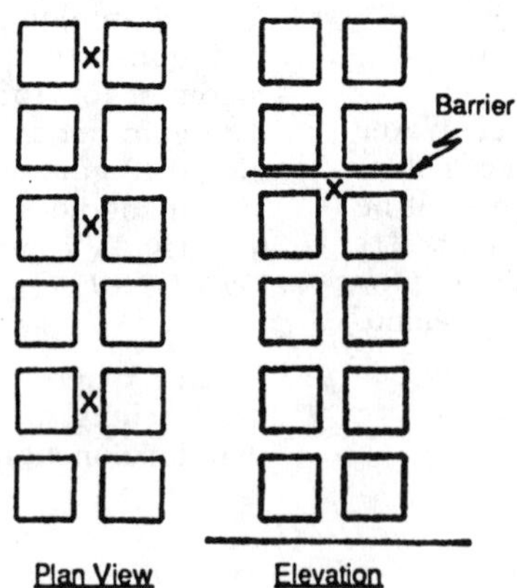

Figure 7-10.1(a) In-Rack Sprinkler Arrangement, Class I Commodity, Maximum Height of Storage 25 Ft (7.62 m) to 30 Ft (9.15 m).

NOTES:
1. Symbol X indicates in-rack sprinklers.
2. Each square in the figure represents a storage cube measuring 4 to 5 ft (1.25 to 1.56 m) on a side.

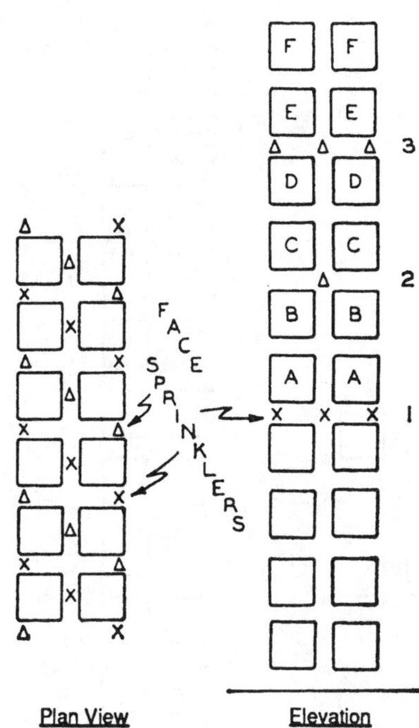

Figure 7-10.1(b) In-Rack Sprinkler Arrangement, Class I Commodity, Height of Storage over 25 Ft (7.62 m).

NOTES:
1. Sprinklers labeled 1 (the selected array from Table 7-10.1) required when loads labeled A or B represent top of storage.
2. Sprinklers labeled 1 and 2 required when loads labeled C or D represent top of storage.
3. Sprinklers labeled 1 and 3 required when loads labeled E or F represent top of storage.
4. For storage higher than represented by loads labeled F, the cycle defined by notes 2 and 3 is repeated WITH STAGGER AS INDICATED.
5. Symbols Δ or X indicate sprinklers on vertical or horizontal stagger.
6. Each square in the figure represents a storage cube measuring 4 to 5 ft (1.25 to 1.56 m) on a side.

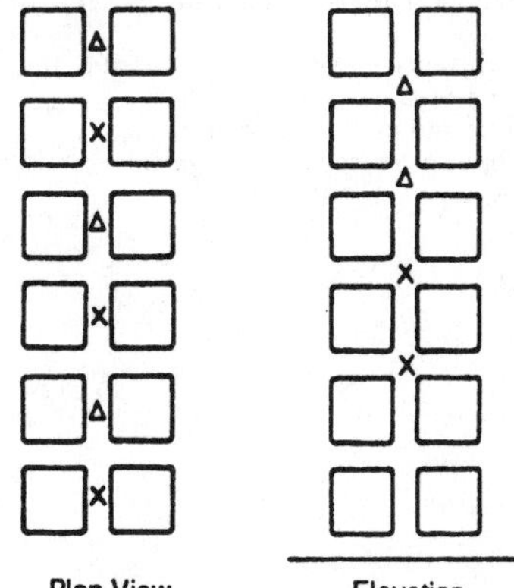

Figure 7-10.1(c) In-Rack Sprinkler Arrangement, Class I, II, or III Commodity, Maximum Height of Storage 25 Ft (7.62 m) to 30 Ft (9.15 m).

NOTES:
1. Alternate location of in-rack sprinklers. Sprinklers may be installed at the second and fourth or the third and fifth tiers.
2. Symbols Δ or X indicate sprinklers on vertical or horizontal stagger.
3. Each square in the figure represents a storage cube measuring 4 to 5 ft (1.25 to 1.56 m) on a side.

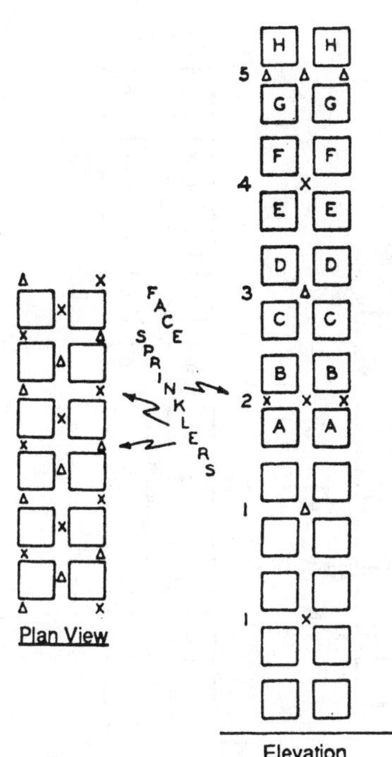

Figure 7-10.1(d) In-Rack Sprinkler Arrangement, Class I, II, or III Commodity, Height of Storage over 25 Ft (7.62 m).

NOTES:
1. Sprinklers labeled 1 required when loads labeled A represent the top of storage.
2. Sprinklers labeled 1 and 2 required when loads labeled B or C represent top of storage.
3. Sprinklers labeled 1, 2, and 3 required when loads labeled D or E represent top of storage.
4. Sprinklers labeled 1, 2, 3, and 4 required when loads labeled F or G represent top of storage.
5. Sprinklers labeled 1, 2, 3, 4, and 5 required when loads labeled H represent top of storage.
6. For storage higher than represented by loads labeled H, the cycle defined by notes 3, 4, and 5 is repeated with stagger as indicated.
7. The indicated face sprinklers may be omitted when commodity consists of unwrapped or unpackaged metal parts on wood pallets.
8. Symbols Δ or X indicate sprinklers on vertical or horizontal stagger.
9. Each square in the figure represents a storage cube measuring 4 to 5 ft (1.25 to 1.56 m) on a side.

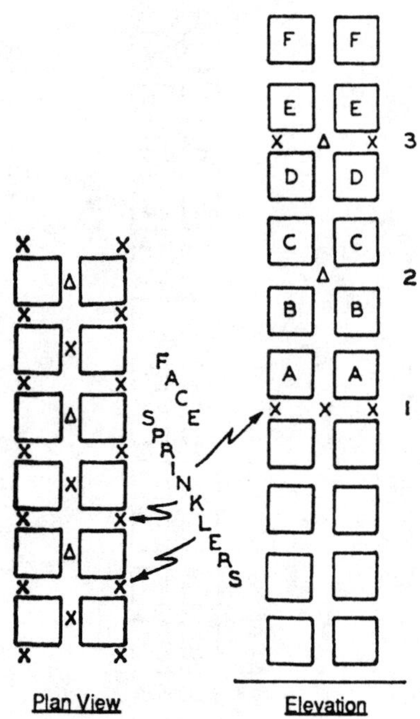

Figure 7-10.1(e) In-Rack Sprinkler Arrangement, Class I, II, or III Commodity, Height of Storage over 25 Ft (7.62 m).

NOTES:

1. Sprinklers labeled 1 (the selected array from Table 7-10.1) required when loads labeled A or B represent top of storage.
2. Sprinklers labeled 1 and 2 required when loads labeled C or D represent top of storage.
3. Sprinklers labeled 1 and 3 required when loads labeled E or F represent top of storage.
4. For storage higher than represented by loads labeled F, the cycle defined by notes 2 and 3 is repeated, with stagger as indicated.
5. Symbols Δ or X indicate sprinklers on vertical or horizontal stagger.
6. Each square in the figure represents a storage cube measuring 4 to 5 ft (1.25 to 1.56 m) on a side.

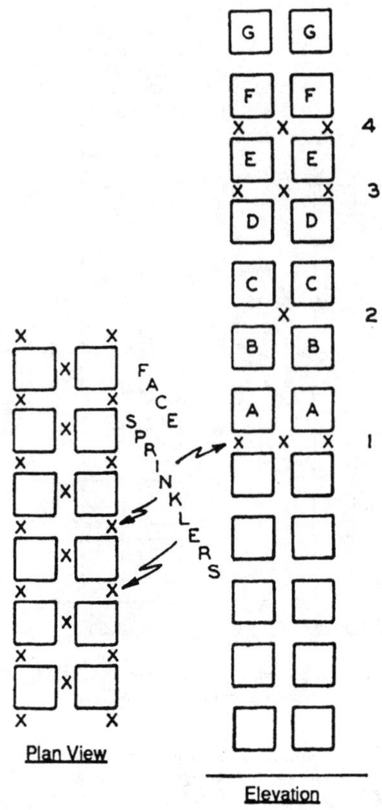

Figure 7-10.1(f) In-Rack Sprinkler Arrangement, Class I, II, or III Commodity, Height of Storage over 25 Ft (7.62 m).

NOTES:

1. Sprinklers labeled 1 (the selected array from Table 7-10.1) required when loads labeled A or B represent top of storage.
2. Sprinklers labeled 1 and 2 required when loads labeled C or D represent top of storage.
3. Sprinklers labeled 1 and 3 required when loads labeled E represent top of storage.
4. Sprinklers labeled 1 and 4 required when loads labeled F or G represent top of storage.
5. For storage higher than represented by loads labeled G, the cycle defined by notes 2, 3, and 4 is repeated.
6. Symbol X indicates face and in-rack sprinklers.
7. Each square in the figure represents a storage cube measuring 4 to 5 ft (1.25 to 1.56 m) on a side.

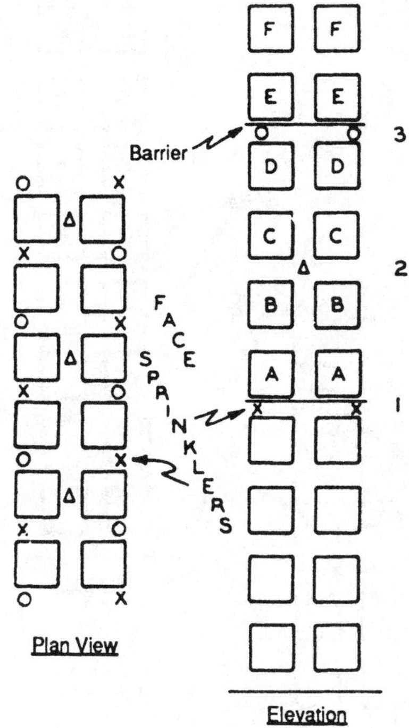

Figure 7-10.1(g) In-Rack Sprinkler Arrangement, Class I, II, or III Commodity, Height of Storage over 25 Ft (7.62 m).

NOTES:

1. Sprinklers labeled 1 (the selected array from Table 7-10.1) required when loads labeled A or B represent top of storage.
2. Sprinklers labeled 1 and 2 required when loads labeled C or D represent top of storage.
3. Sprinklers labeled 1 and 3 required when loads labeled E or F represent top of storage.
4. For storage higher than represented by loads labeled F, the cycle defined by notes 2 and 3 is repeated.
5. Symbols O, Δ, or X indicate sprinklers on vertical or horizontal stagger.
6. Each square in the figure represents a storage cube measuring 4 to 5 ft (1.25 to 1.56 m) on a side.

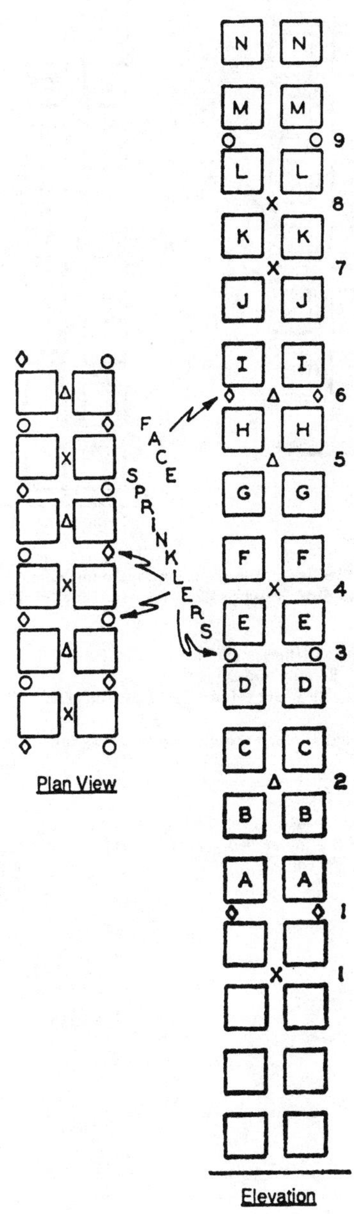

Figure 7-10.1(h) In-Rack Sprinkler Arrangement, Class I, II, III, or IV Commodity, Height of Storage over 25 Ft (7.62 m).

NOTES to Figure 7-10.1(h):

1. Sprinklers labeled 1 (the selected array from Table 7-10.1) required when loads labeled A or B represent top of storage.
2. Sprinklers labeled 1 and 2 required when loads labeled C or D represent top of storage.
3. Sprinklers labeled 1, 2, and 3 required when loads labeled E or F represent top of storage.
4. Sprinklers labeled 1, 2, 3, and 4 required when loads labeled G represent top of storage.
5. Sprinklers labeled 1, 2, 3, 4, and 5 required when loads labeled H represent top of storage.
6. Sprinklers labeled 1, 2, 3, 4, and 6 (not 5) required when loads labeled I or J represent top of storage.
7. Sprinklers labeled 1, 2, 3, 4, 6, and 7 required when loads labeled K represent top of storage.
8. Sprinklers labeled 1, 2, 3, 4, 6, and 8 required when loads labeled L represent top of storage.
9. Sprinklers labeled 1, 2, 3, 4, 6, 8, and 9 required when loads labeled M or N represent top of storage.
10. For storage higher than represented by loads labeled N, the cycle defined by notes 1 through 9 is repeated, with stagger as indicated. In the cycle, loads labeled M are equivalent to loads labeled A.
11. Symbols O, X, Δ, indicate sprinklers on vertical or horizontal stagger.
12. Each square in the figure represents a storage cube measuring 4 to 5 ft (1.25 to 1.56 m) on a side.

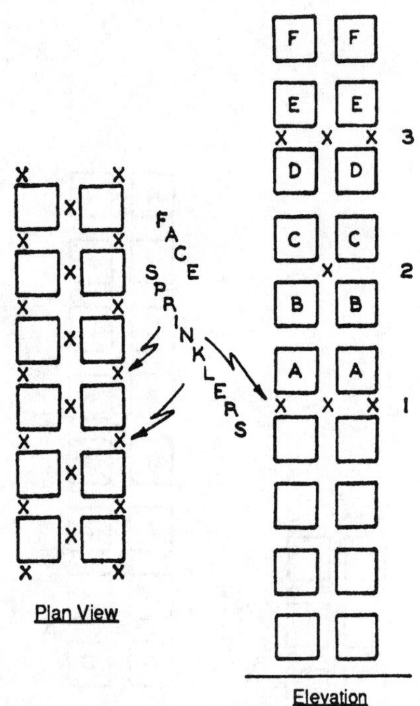

Figure 7-10.1(i) In-Rack Sprinkler Arrangement, Class I, II, III, or IV Commodity, Height of Storage over 25 Ft (7.62 m).

NOTES:

1. Sprinklers labeled 1 (the selected array from Table 7-10.1) required when loads labeled A or B represent top of storage.
2. Sprinklers labeled 1 and 2 required when loads labeled C or D represent top of storage.
3. Sprinklers labeled 1 and 3 required when loads labeled E or F represent top of storage.
4. For storage higher than represented by loads labeled F, the cycle defined by notes 2 and 3 is repeated.
5. Symbol X indicates face and in-rack sprinklers.
6. Each square in the figure represents a storage cube measuring 4 to 5 ft (1.25 to 1.56 m) on a side.

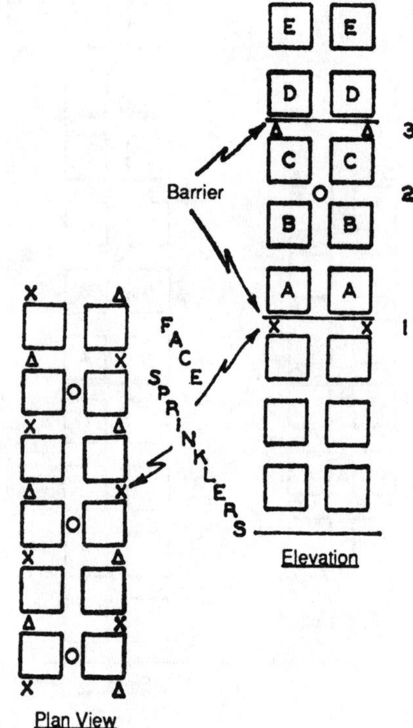

Figure 7-10.1(j) In-Rack Sprinkler Arrangement, Class I, II, III, or IV Commodity. Height of Storage over 25 Ft (7.62 m).

NOTES:

1. Sprinklers and barrier labeled 1 (the selected array from Table 7-10.1) required when loads labeled A or B represent top of storage.
2. Sprinklers labeled 1 and 2 and barrier labeled 1 required when loads labeled C represent top of storage.
3. Sprinklers and barriers labeled 1 and 3 required when loads labeled D or E represent top of storage.
4. For storage higher than represented by loads labeled E, the cycle defined by notes 2 and 3 is repeated.
5. Symbols Δ or X indicate sprinklers on vertical or horizontal stagger.
6. Symbol O indicates longitudinal flue space sprinklers.
7. Each square in the figure represents a storage cube measuring 4 to 5 ft (1.25 to 1.56 m) on a side.

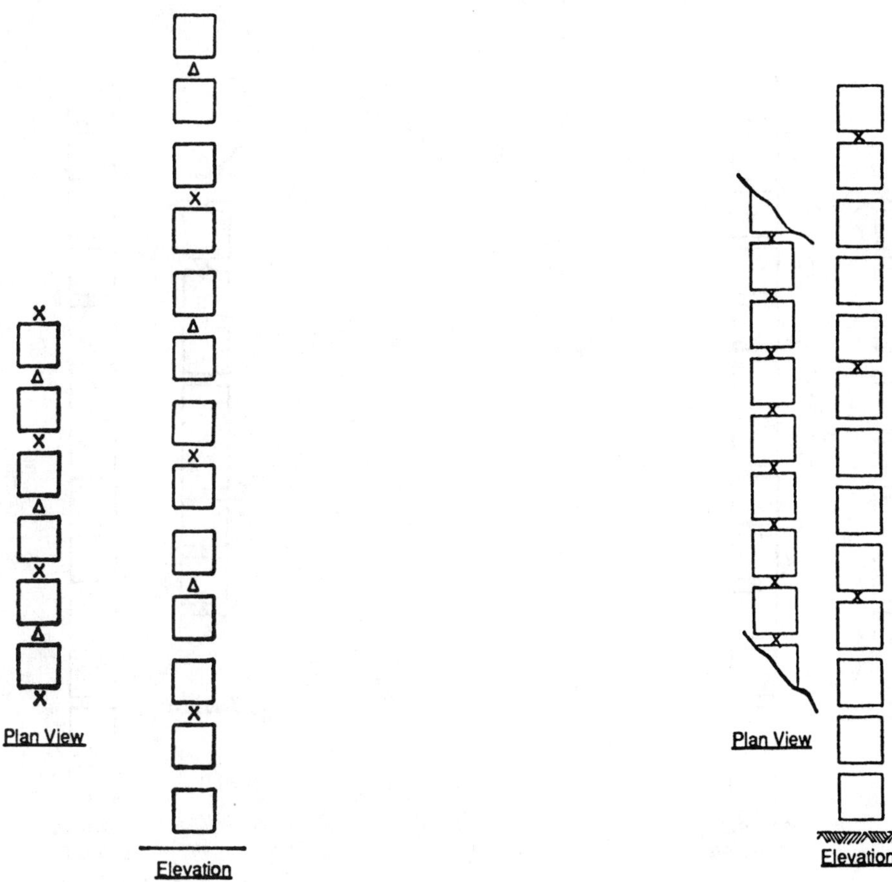

Figure 7-10.3(a) Class I, II, III, or IV. In-Rack Sprinkler Arrangement, Single Row Racks, Height of Storage over 25 Ft (7.62 m).

NOTES:

1. For all storage heights, install sprinklers in every other tier and stagger as indicated.
2. Symbols Δ or X indicate sprinklers on vertical or horizontal stagger.
3. Each square in the figure represents a storage cube measuring 4 to 5 ft (1.25 to 1.56 m) on a side.

Figure 7-10.3(b) Class I, II, or III Commodity.

NOTE:

1. Each square in the figure represents a storage cube measuring 4 to 5 ft (1.25 to 1.56 m) on a side.

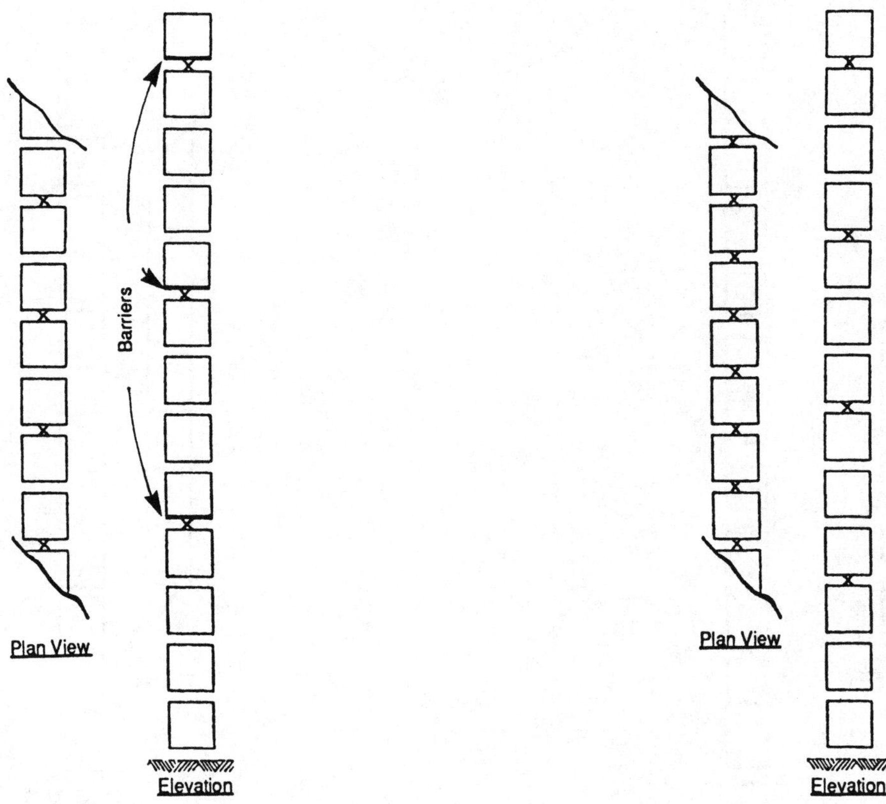

Figure 7-10.3(c) Class I, II, or III Commodity.

NOTE:
1. Each square in the figure represents a storage cube measuring 4 to 5 ft (1.25 to 1.56 m) on a side.

Figure 7-10.3(d) Class I, II, III, or IV Commodity.

NOTE:
1. Each square in the figure represents a storage cube measuring 4 to 5 ft (1.25 to 1.56 m) on a side.

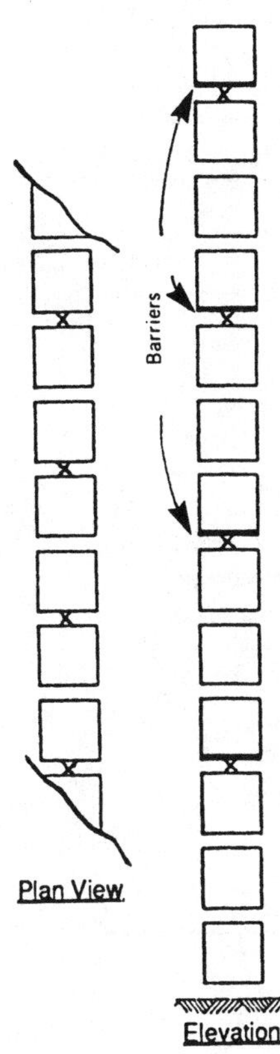

Figure 7-10.3(e) Class I, II, III, or IV Commodity.

NOTE:
1. Each square in the figure represents a storage cube measuring 4 to 5 ft (1.25 to 1.56 m) on a side.

Part C Multiple Row Racks

7-13* In-Rack Sprinkler Location. In multiple row racks with a maximum of 10 ft (3.05 m) between top of storage and ceiling, in-rack sprinklers shall be installed as indicated in Figures 7-13(a), (b), and (c). The highest level of in-rack sprinklers shall be not more than 10 ft (3.05 m) below maximum height of storage for Class I, II, or III commodities or 5 ft (1.52 m) below top of storage for Class IV commodities (*see Table 7-13*).

7-14 In-Rack Sprinkler Spacing. Maximum horizontal spacing of sprinklers in multiple row racks with storage higher than 25 ft (7.62 m) shall be in accordance with Figures 7-13(a), (b), and (c).

7-15 Ceiling Sprinkler Water Demand.

7-15.1 Water demand for nonencapsulated storage on racks without solid shelves separated by aisles at least 4 ft (1.22 m) wide and with not more than 10 ft (3.05 m) between top of storage and sprinklers shall be based on sprinklers in a 2,000-sq ft (185.8-m^2) operating area for multiple row racks, discharging a minimum of 0.25 gpm per sq ft [(10.19 L/min)/m^2] for Class I commodities, 0.3 gpm per sq ft [(12.2 L/min)/m^2] for Class II and III commodities, and 0.35 gpm per sq ft [(14.26 L/min)/m^2] for Class IV commodities, for 165°F (74°C) sprinklers; or a minimum of 0.35 gpm per sq ft [(14.26 L/min)/m^2] for Class I commodities, 0.40 gpm per sq ft [(16.8 L/min)/m^2] for Class II and III commodities, and 0.45 gpm per sq ft [(18.3 L/min)/m^2] for Class IV commodities, for 286°F (141°C) sprinklers (*see Table 7-13*).

7-15.2 Where such storage is encapsulated, ceiling sprinkler density shall be 25 percent greater than for nonencapsulated.

Table 7-13 Multiple Row Racks. Storage Heights over 25 Ft.

Commodity Class	Encap-sulated	In-Rack Sprinklers[1] Approximate Vertical Spacing (ft)	Maximum Horizontal Spacing In a Flue (ft)	Maximum Horizontal Spacing Across Flue (ft)	Height Limit (ft)	Stagger	Fig. No.	Maximum Spacing from Top of Storage to Highest In-Rack Sprinklers (ft)	Ceiling Sprinkler Operating Area (ft^2)	Ceiling Sprinklers Density (gpm/ft^2) 165° Rating	286° Rating
I	No	20	12	10	None	Between adjacent flues	7.13(a)	10	2000	.25	.35
	Yes									.31	.44
I, II, &III	No	15	10	10			7-13(b)	10		.30	.40
	Yes									.37	.50
I, II, III, &IV	No	10	10	10			7.13(c)	5		.35	.45
	Yes									.44	.56

[1]All four rack faces should be protected by sprinklers located within 18 in. of the faces, as indicated in Figs. 7-13(a), (b), and (c). It is not necessary for each sprinkler level to protect all faces (*see A-7-13*).

For SI Units: 1 ft = 0.3048 m; C = 5/9 (F-32); 1 gpm/ft^2 = 40.746 (L/min)/m^2

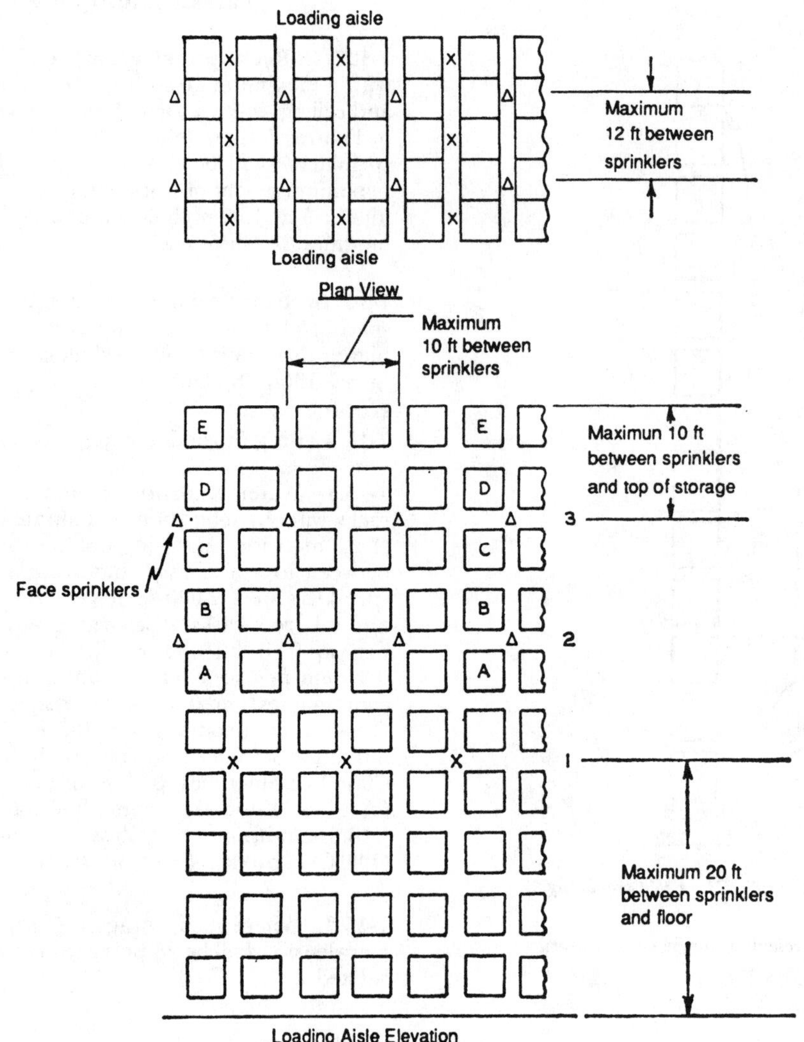

Figure 7-13(a) In-Rack Sprinkler Arrangement — Multiple Row Racks, Class I Commodity. Height of Storage over 25 Ft.

For SI Units: 1 ft = 0.3048 m

NOTES:

1. Sprinklers labeled 1 required if loads labeled A represent top of storage.
2. Sprinklers labeled 1 and 2 required if loads labeled B or C represent top of storage.
3. Sprinklers labeled 1 and 3 required if loads labeled D or E represent top of storage.
4. For storage higher than represented by loads labeled E, the cycle defined by notes 2 and 3 is repeated, with stagger as indicated.
5. Symbols Δ or X indicate sprinklers on vertical or horizontal stagger.
6. Each square in the figure represents a storage cube measuring 4 to 5 ft (1.25 to 1.56 m) on a side.

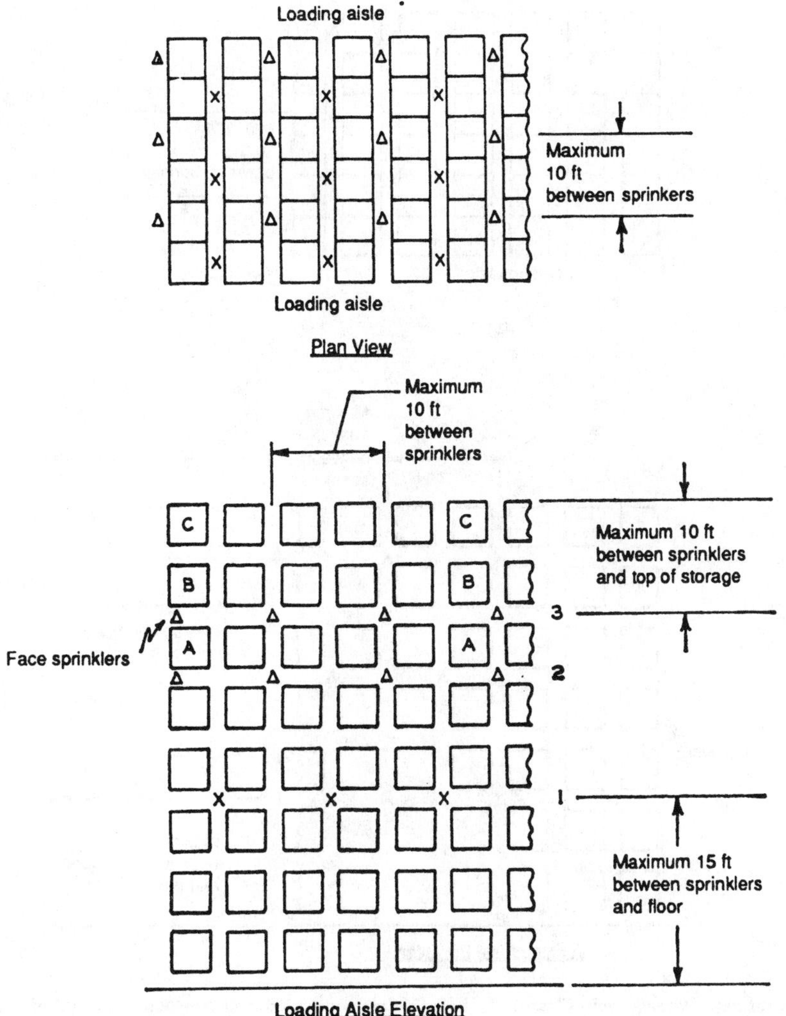

Figure 7-13(b) In-Rack Sprinkler Arrangement — Multiple Row Racks, Class I, II, or III Commodity. Height of Storage over 25 Ft.

For SI Units 1 ft = 0.3048 m

NOTES:

1. Sprinklers labeled 1 and 2 required if loads labeled A represent top of storage.
2. Sprinklers labeled 1 and 3 required if loads labeled B or C represent top of storage.
3. For storage higher than represented by loads labeled C, the cycle defined by notes 1 and 2 is repeated, with stagger as indicated.
4. Symbols Δ or X indicate sprinklers on vertical or horizontal stagger.
5. Each square in the figure represents a storage cube measuring 4 to 5 ft (1.25 to 1.56 m) on a side.

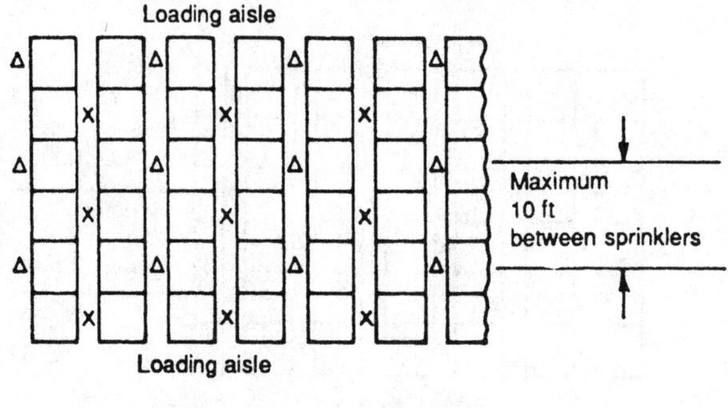

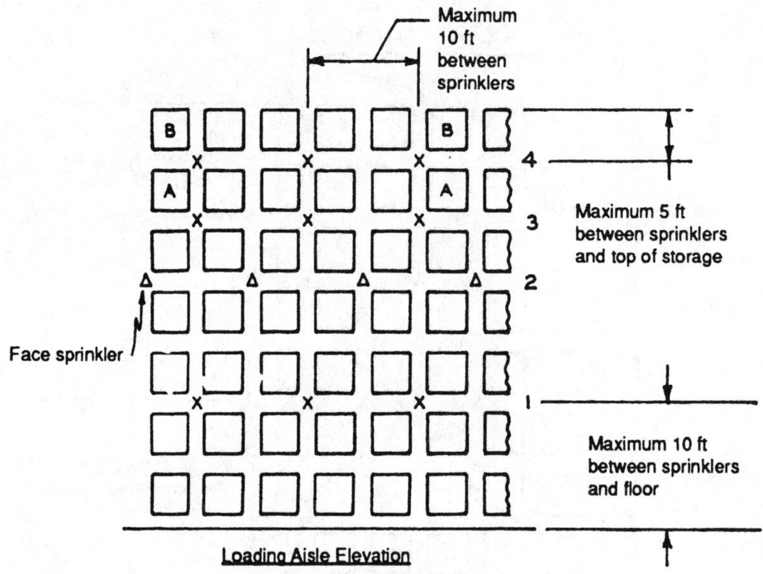

Figure 7-13(c) In-Rack Sprinkler Arrangement, Class I, II, III & IV Commodity, Multiple Row Racks. Height of Storage over 25 Ft.

For SI Units: 1 ft = 0.3048 m

NOTES:
1. Sprinklers labeled 1, 2, and 3 required if loads labeled A represent top of storage.
2. Sprinklers labeled 1, 2, and 4 required if loads labeled B represent top of storage.
3. For storage higher than represented by loads labeled B, the cycle defined by notes 1 and 2 is repeated, with stagger as indicated.
4. Symbols Δ or X indicate sprinklers on vertical or horizontal stagger.
5. Each square in the figure represents a storage cube measuring 4 to 5 ft (1.25 to 1.56 m) on a side.

Chapter 8* Plastics

8-1† General.

8-1.1 Plastics in corrugated cartons shall be protected as indicated by Figure 8-1.1. This decision tree shall also be used to determine protection for commodities that are not wholly Group A plastics but contain such quantities and arrangement of the same that they are deemed more hazardous than Class IV commodities.

8-1.2 Group B plastics and free-flowing Group A plastics shall be protected the same as Class IV commodities.

8-1.3 Group C plastics shall be protected the same as Class III commodities.

8-1.4† Ceiling sprinklers shall be large orifice [$^{17}/_{32}$ in. (13.5 mm)] and ordinary to high temperature rated.

Exception No. 1: Large-drop sprinklers as indicated in Chapter 9.

Exception No. 2: ESFR sprinklers as indicated in Chapter 10.

Exception No. 3: For densities of 0.30 gpm/sq ft [(12.2 L/min)/m²] or less, one-half-in. (12.7-mm) orifice sprinklers shall be permitted.

Exception No. 4: High temperature sprinklers shall be used where required by NFPA 13, Standard for the Installation of Sprinkler Systems.

8-1.5 In-Rack Sprinklers.

8-1.5.1 In-Rack Sprinkler Classification. Sprinklers in racks shall be ordinary temperature classification, except higher temperature sprinklers shall be used as specified in NFPA 13, *Standard for the Installation of Sprinkler Systems.*

8-1.5.2 In-Rack Sprinkler Pipe Size. The number of sprinklers and the pipe sizing on a line of sprinklers in racks are restricted only by the hydraulic calculations and not by any piping schedule.

8-1.5.3 In-Rack Storage Water Shields. If in-rack sprinklers are not shielded by horizontal barriers, water shields shall be provided above the sprinklers, or listed sprinklers equipped with water shields shall be used.

8-1.5.4 The minimum of 6 in. (152.4 mm) vertical clear space shall be maintained between the sprinkler deflectors and the top of a tier of storage.

8-1.5.5 In-Rack Sprinkler Water Demand. Water demand for sprinklers installed in racks shall be based on simultaneous operation of the most hydraulically remote:

(a) Eight sprinklers when only one level is installed in racks.

(b) Fourteen sprinklers (seven on each top two levels) when more than one level is installed in racks.

8-1.5.6 Chapters 1 through 5 apply to plastics storage.

8-2 Single, Double, and Multi-Row Racks — Storage up to and Including 25 ft (7.6 m) — Clearances up to and Including 10 ft (3 m).

8-2.1 Ceiling Sprinkler Water Demand. For Group A plastic commodities in cartons, encapsulated or nonencapsulated in single, double, and multi-row racks, ceiling sprinkler water demand in terms of density (gpm/ft²) and area of operation (ft²) shall be selected from Figures 8-2 (a) through (i). Linear interpolation of design densities and areas of application shall be permitted between storage heights with the same clearances. No interpolation between clearances shall be permitted.

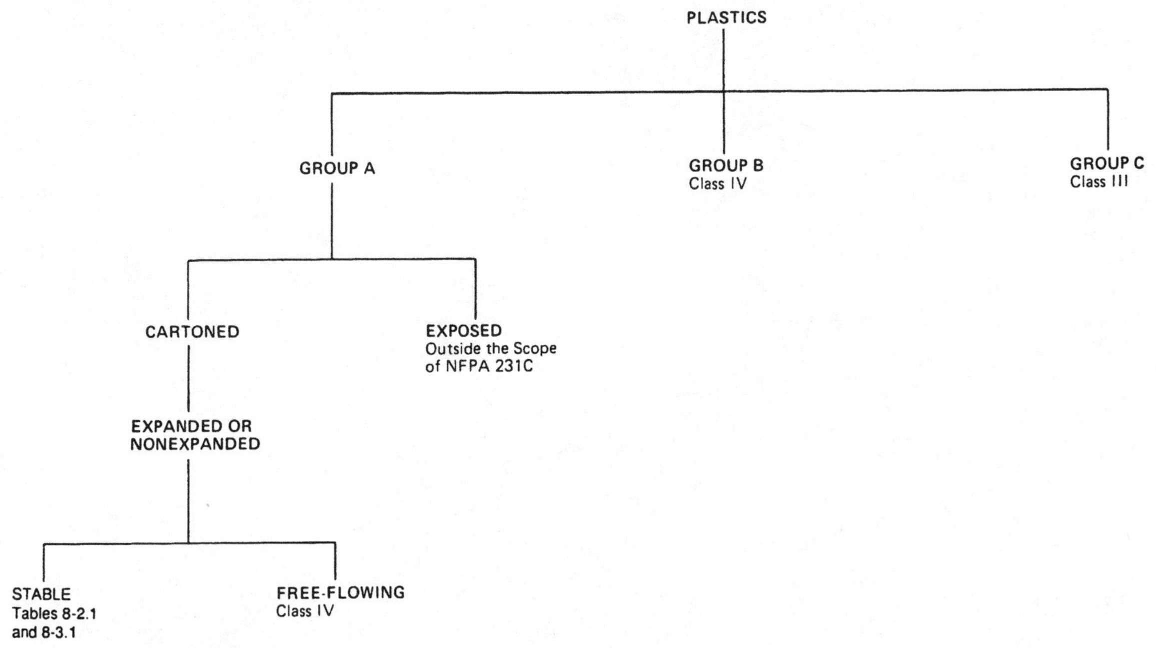

Figure 8-1.1 Decision Tree.

Strategies for Protection Rack Storage of Plastics Single Row, Double Row, & Multiple Row Rack Configurations Unexposed (Expanded and Unexpanded)

Group A Plastics

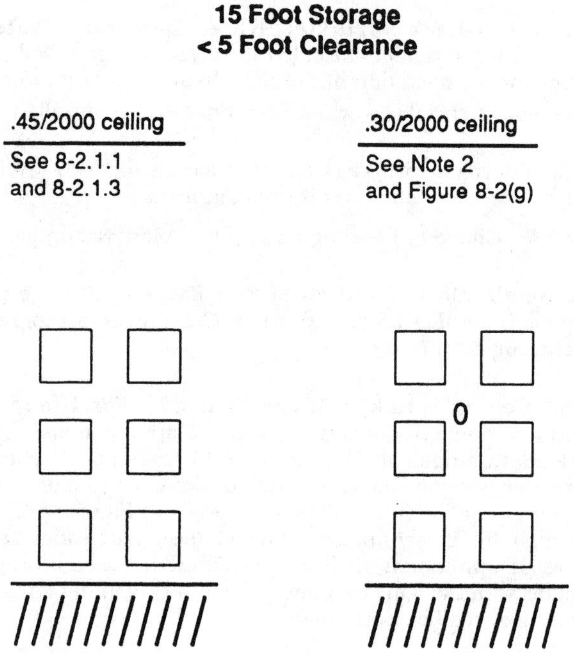

15 Foot Storage
< 5 Foot Clearance

.45/2000 ceiling

See 8-2.1.1
and 8-2.1.3

.30/2000 ceiling

See Note 2
and Figure 8-2(g)

0

Figure 8-2(a).

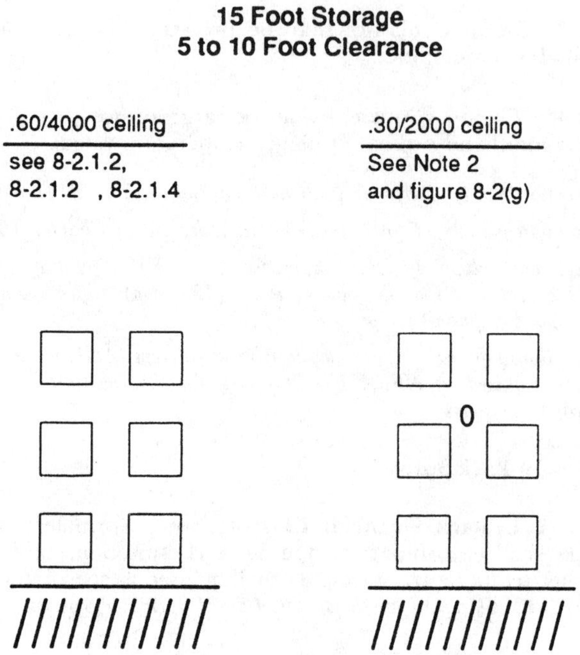

15 Foot Storage
5 to 10 Foot Clearance

.60/4000 ceiling

see 8-2.1.2,
8-2.1.2 , 8-2.1.4

.30/2000 ceiling

See Note 2
and figure 8-2(g)

0

Figure 8-2(b).

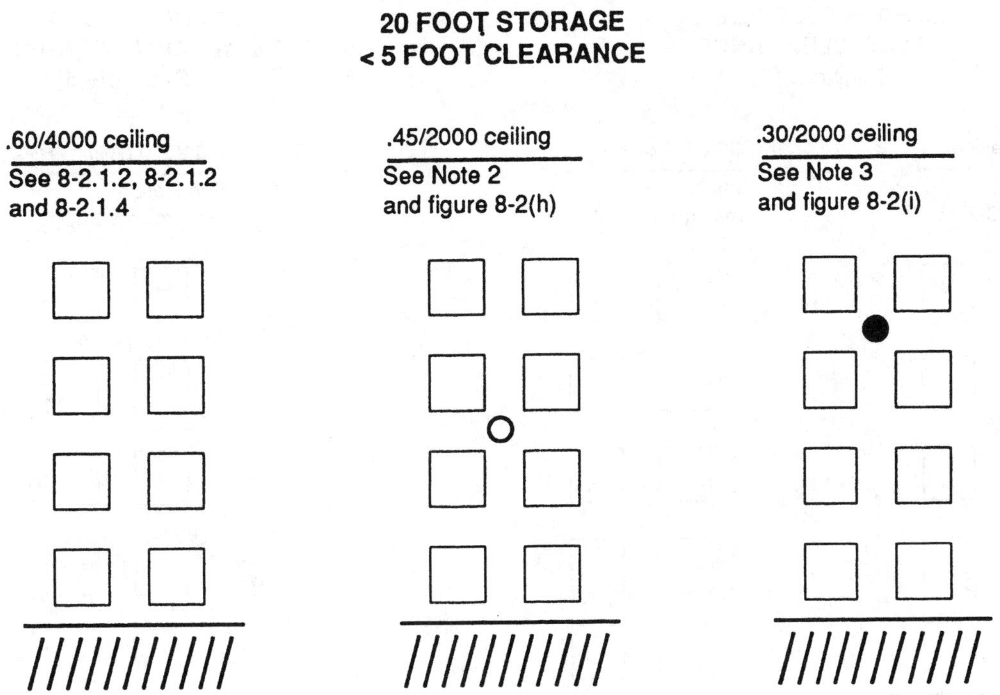

20 FOOT STORAGE
< 5 FOOT CLEARANCE

.60/4000 ceiling
See 8-2.1.2, 8-2.1.2
and 8-2.1.4

.45/2000 ceiling
See Note 2
and figure 8-2(h)

.30/2000 ceiling
See Note 3
and figure 8-2(i)

Figure 8-2(c).

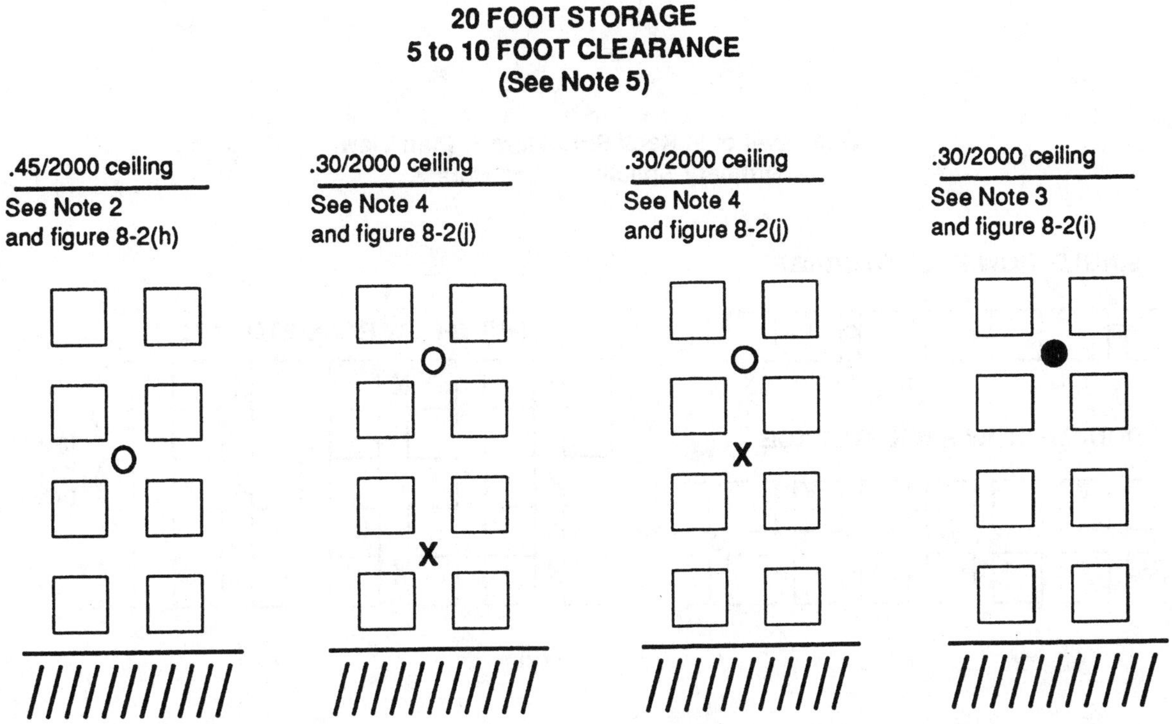

20 FOOT STORAGE
5 to 10 FOOT CLEARANCE
(See Note 5)

.45/2000 ceiling
See Note 2
and figure 8-2(h)

.30/2000 ceiling
See Note 4
and figure 8-2(j)

.30/2000 ceiling
See Note 4
and figure 8-2(j)

.30/2000 ceiling
See Note 3
and figure 8-2(i)

Figure 8-2(d).

25 FOOT STORAGE
< 5 FOOT CLEARANCE
(See Note 5)

.45/2000 ceiling

See Note 3
and figure 8-2(h)

.30/2000 ceiling

See Note 4
and figure 8-2(i)

0

X

Figure 8-2(e).

25 FOOT STORAGE
5 to 10 FOOT CLEARANCE
(See Note 5)

.30/2000 ceiling

See Note 4
and figure 8-2(i)

0

X

Figure 8-2(f).

One Level of In Rack Sprinklers — Plan View
Ordinary Spacing — See Note 2

SINGLE ROW RACK STORAGE

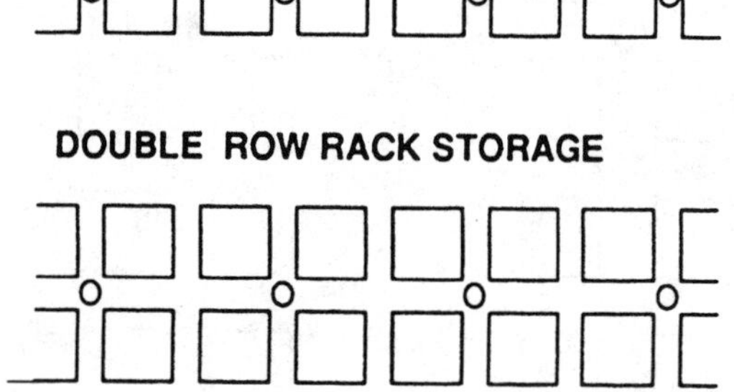

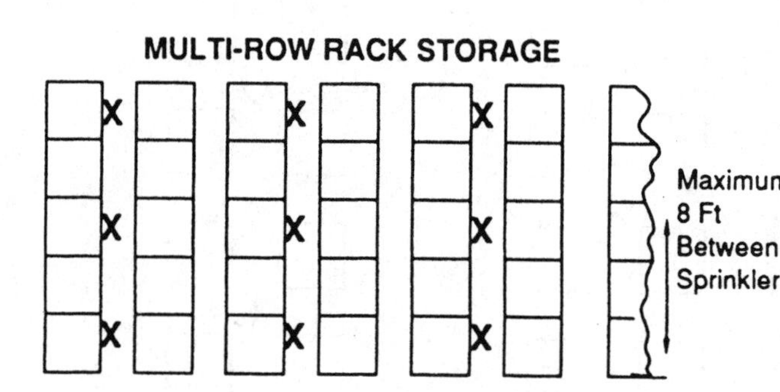

Figure 8-2(g).

One Level of In Rack Sprinklers—Plan View
Close Spacing—See Note 3

SINGLE ROW RACK STORAGE

MULTI-ROW RACK STORAGE

DOUBLE ROW RACK STORAGE

Maximum 8 Ft Between Sprinklers

Figure 8-2(h).

Two Levels of In Rack Sprinklers – Plan View
Ordinary Spacing – See Note 4

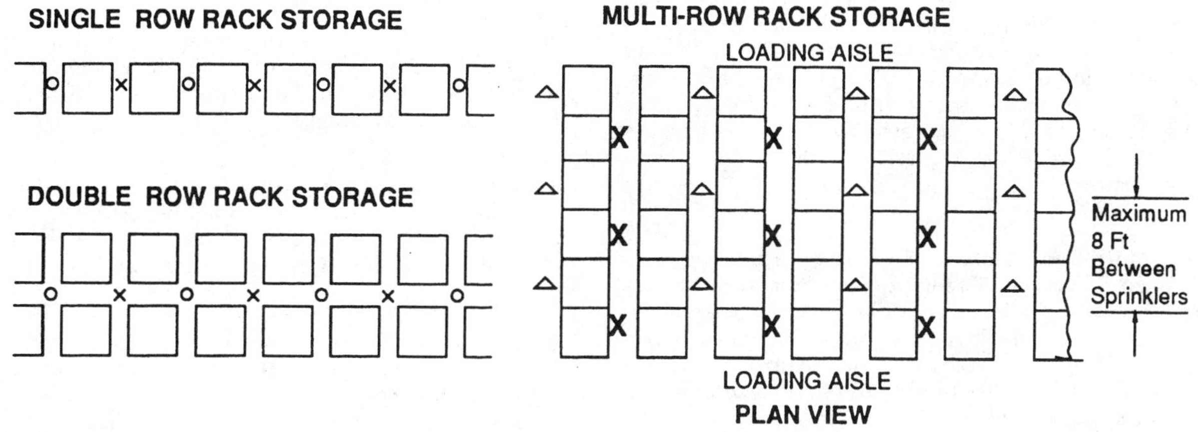

Figure 8-2(i).

Notes to Figures 8-2(a) — 8-2(i):

1. Each square in the figures represents a storage cube measuring 4 to 5 ft (1.25 to 1.56 m) on a side.
2. Single level of in-rack sprinklers ($^1/_2$ or $^{17}/_{32}$ in. operating at 15 psi minimum) installed on 8- to 10-ft (2.5- to 3.12-m) spacings located, as indicated, in the transverse flue spaces.
3. Single level of in-rack sprinklers ($^{17}/_{32}$ in. operating at 15 psi minimum or $^1/_2$ in. operating at 30 psi minimum) installed on 4- to 5-ft (1.25- to 1.56-m) spacings located, as indicated, in the longitudinal flue space at the intersection of every transverse flue space.
4. Two levels of in-rack sprinklered ($^1/_2$ or $^{17}/_{32}$ in. operating at 15 psi minimum) installed on 8- to 10-ft (2.5- to 3.12-m) spacings located as indicated and staggered in the transverse flue spaces.
5. Ceiling only protection is not acceptable for this storage configuration.

8-2.1.1 Single and Double Row Racks — 15-ft (4.6-m) Storage with Less than 5-ft (1.25-m) Clearance. The protection strategy utilizing ceiling sprinklers only as shown in Figure 8-2(a) shall be acceptable only for single and double row rack storage with 8-ft (2.4-m) aisles. For $3^1/_2$-ft (1-m) aisles, a density of 0.60 gpm/sq ft and an area of application of 1500 sq ft (139.5 m^2) shall be used. For aisle widths between $3^1/_2$ ft (1 m) and 8 ft (2.4 m), a direct linear interpolation shall be permitted between densities and areas of application.

8-2.1.2 Single and Double Row Racks — 15-ft (4.6-m) Storage with 10-ft (3-m) Clearance. Twenty-ft (6-m) Storage with Less than 5-ft (1.25-m) Clearance. The protection strategies utilizing ceiling sprinklers only as shown in Figures 8-2(b) and 8-2(c) shall be acceptable only for single and double row rack storage with 8-ft (2.4-m) aisles. In-rack sprinkler protection shall be required for aisles less than 8 ft (2.4 m) in width.

When utilizing the ceiling sprinklers only strategies as shown in Figures 8-2(b) and 8-2(c), column steel shall be protected in accordance with paragraph 3-2.3(a) or (b). Roof structural steel shall be protected in such a manner as to provide a minimum of 15 min fire resistance.

8-2.1.3 Multi-Row Racks — 15 ft (4.6 m) Storage with Less than 5-ft (1.25-m) Clearance. The protection strategy utilizing ceiling sprinklers only as shown in Figure 8-2(a) shall not be acceptable for multi-row rack storage. The density to be used shall be 0.60 gpm/sq ft over 2000 sq ft (186 m^2). The indicated combination of ceiling and in-rack sprinklers in Figure 8-2(a) shall be an acceptable alternative.

8-2.1.4 Multi-Row Racks — 15-ft (4.6-m) Storage with 10-ft (3-m) Clearance. Twenty-ft (6-m) Storage with Less than 5-ft (1.25-m) Clearance. The protection strategies utilizing ceiling sprinklers only as shown in Figures 8-2(b) and 8-2(c) shall not be acceptable for multi-row rack storage. Only the indicated combinations of ceiling and in-rack sprinklers shall be used.

8-2.2 In-Rack Sprinklers. In-rack sprinklers shall be installed in accordance with Figures 8-2(a) through 8-2(i).

8-3 Single and Double Row Racks — Storage over 25 Ft (7.7 m) in Height.

8-3.1 Ceiling Sprinkler Water Demand. For Group A plastic commodities in cartons, encapsulated or nonencapsulated in single and double row racks, ceiling sprinkler water demand in terms of density (gpm/ft^2) and area of operation (ft^2) shall be selected from Table 8-3.1.

Table 8-3.1 Single and Double Row Racks. Height of Storage over 25 Ft.

Storage Height Above Top Level In-Rack Sprinklers	Ceiling Sprinklers Density (gpm/ft^2)/Area of Application (ft^2)
5 ft or less	0.30/2000
Over 5 ft up to 10 ft	0.45/2000

NOTE: Provide in-rack sprinkler protection as per Figures 8-3.2.1(a) and (b) and Figures 8-3.2.3(a) through (c).

For SI Units: 1 ft = 0.3048 m
1 gpm = 3.785 L/min
1 gpm/ft^2 = 40.74 (L/min)/m^2

8-3.2 In-Rack Sprinkler Location.

8-3.2.1 In double row racks without solid shelves and with a maximum of 10 ft (3.05 m) between the top of storage and ceiling, in-rack sprinklers shall be installed as indicated in Figures 8-3.2.1(a) and (b). The highest level of in-rack sprinklers shall be not more than 10 ft (3.05 m) below the top of storage.

8-3.2.2 In-rack sprinklers for storage higher than 25 ft (7.62 m) in double row racks shall be spaced horizontally and located in the horizontal space nearest the vertical intervals indicated in Figures 8-3.2.1(a) and (b).

8-3.2.3 In single row racks without solid shelves with height of storage over 25 ft (7.62 m) and a maximum of 10 ft (3.05 m) between the top of storage and ceiling, sprinklers shall be installed as indicated in Figures 8-3.2.3(a) through (c).

8-3.3 In-Rack Sprinkler Size. Sprinklers in racks shall be $^1/_2$-in. (12.7-mm) or $^{17}/_{32}$-in. (13.5-mm) orifice size, pendent or upright.

8-3.4 In-Rack Sprinkler Discharge Pressure. Sprinklers in racks shall discharge at not less than 30 psi (2.07 bars).

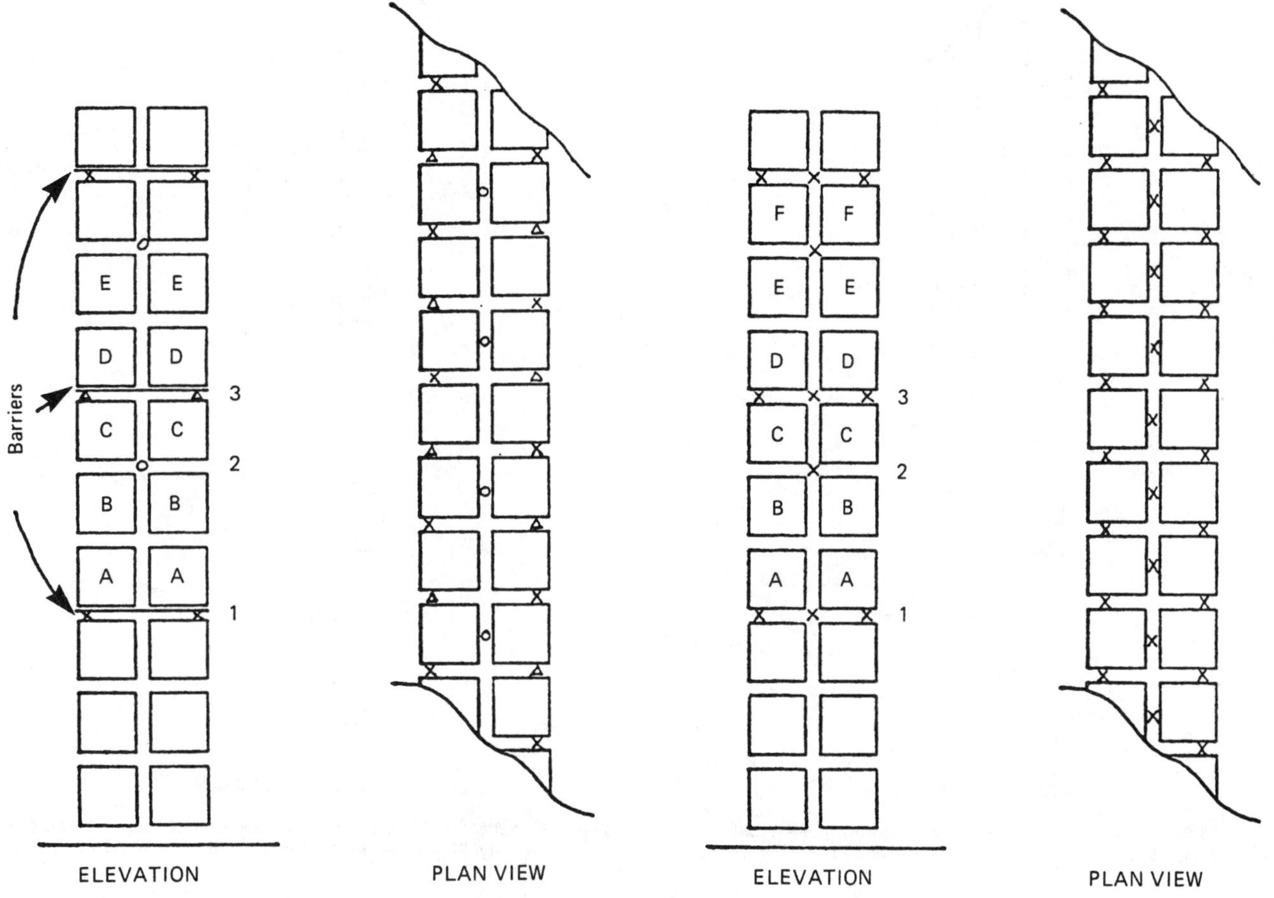

Figure 8-3.2.1(a) In-Rack Sprinkler Arrangement, Group A Plastic Commodity, Height of Storage over 25 Ft.

NOTES:

1. Sprinklers and barrier labeled 1 required when loads labeled A or B represent top of storage.
2. Sprinklers labeled 1 and 2 and barrier labeled 1 required when loads labeled C represent top of storage.
3. Sprinklers and barriers labeled 1 and 3 required when loads labeled D or E represent top of storage.
4. For storage higher than represented by loads labeled E, the cycle defined by Notes 2 and 3 is repeated.
5. Symbols Δ or X indicate face sprinklers on vertical or horizontal stagger.
6. Symbol 0 indicates longitudinal flue space sprinklers.
7. Each square in the figure represents a storage cube measuring 4 to 5 ft (1.25 to 1.56 m) on a side.

Figure 8-3.2.1(b) In-Rack Sprinkler Arrangement, Group A Plastic Commodity, Height of Storage over 25 Ft.

NOTES:

1. Sprinklers labeled 1 required when loads labeled A or B represent top of storage.
2. Sprinklers labeled 1 and 2 required when loads C represent top of storage.
3. Sprinklers labeled 1 and 3 required when loads D or E represent top of storage.
4. For storage higher than loads F, the cycle defined by Notes 2 and 3 is repeated.
5. Symbol X indicates face and in-rack sprinklers.
6. Each square in the figure represents a storage cube measuring 4 to 5 ft (1.25 to 1.56 m) on a side.

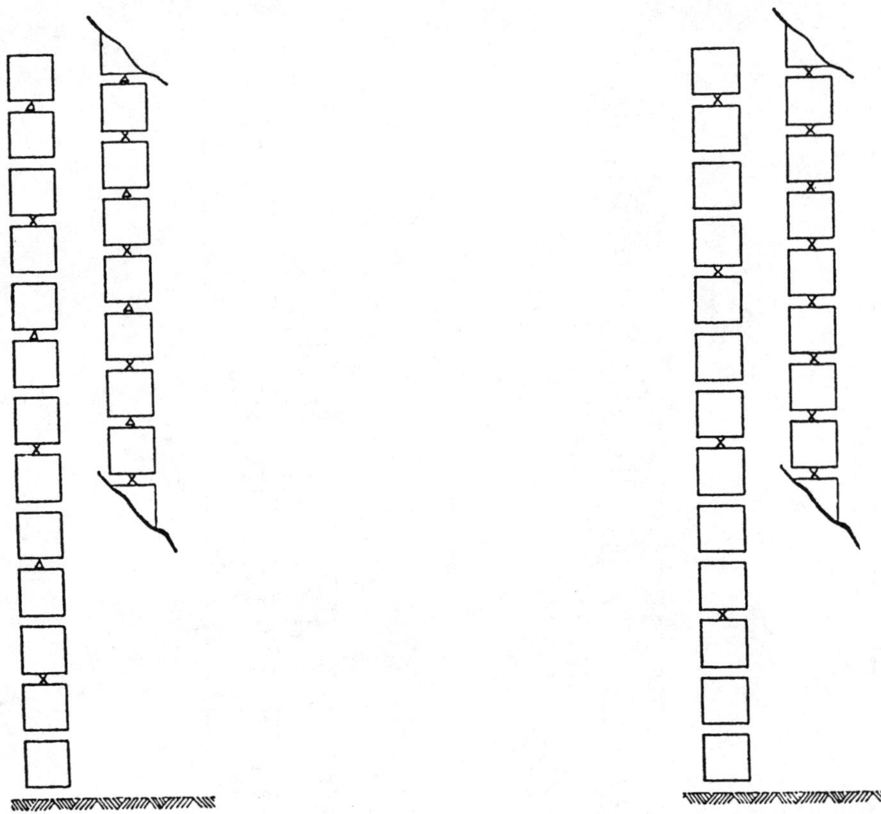

Figure 8-3.2.3(a) In-Rack Sprinkler Arrangement, Group A Plastic Commodity, Single Row Racks, Height of Storage over 25 Ft.

NOTE:
1. Each square in the figure represents a storage cube measuring 4 to 5 ft (1.25 to 1.56 m) on a side.

Figure 8-3.2.3(b) In-Rack Sprinkler Arrangement, Group A Plastic Commodity, Single Row Racks, Height of Storage over 25 Ft.

NOTE:
1. Each square in the figure represents a storage cube measuring 4 to 5 ft (1.25 to 1.56 m) on a side.

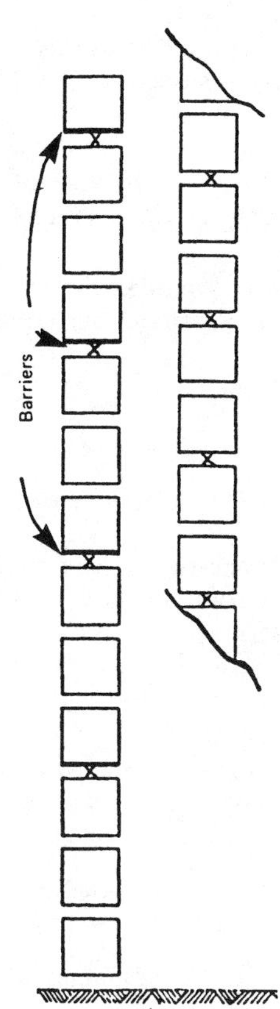

Figure 8-3.2.3(c) In-Rack Sprinkler Arrangement, Group A Plastic Commodity, Single Row Racks, Height of Storage over 25 Ft.

NOTE:
1. Each square in the figure represents a storage cube measuring 4 to 5 ft (1.25 to 1.56 m) on a side.

Chapter 9 Large-Drop Sprinklers

9-1 General.

9-1.1 Large-drop sprinklers are suitable for use with the hazards listed in Table 9-1.

Table 9-1 Pressure and Number of Design Sprinklers For Various Hazards.

Minimum Operating Pressure (Note 1)	**Number Design Sprinklers @ 25 psi**	**@ 50 psi**	**@ 75 psi**	**Sprinkler Temperature Rating**
Hazard (Note 2)				
Double Row Rack Storage with Minimum 5.5-ft aisle width (Note 4) having:				
Class I and II Commodities up to 25 ft with maximum 5-ft clearance to ceiling	20	Note 3	Note 3	High
Class I, II, and III Commodities up to 20 ft with maximum 10-ft clearance to ceiling	15	Note 3	Note 3	High
Class IV Commodities up to 20 ft with maximum 10-ft clearance to ceiling	Does Not Apply	20	15	High
Non-expanded Group A plastics in corrugated cartons up to 20 ft with maximum 10-ft clearance to ceiling	Does Not Apply	30	20	High
Non-expanded Group A plastics in corrugated cartons up to 20 ft with maximum 10-ft clearance to ceiling	Does Not Apply	20	Note 3	Ordinary
Non-expanded Group A plastics in corrugated cartons up to 20 ft with maximum 5-ft clearance to ceiling	Does Not Apply	15	Note 3	High

NOTES:
1. Open Wood Joist Construction. Testing with open wood joist construction showed that each joist channel shall be fully firestopped to its full depth at intervals not exceeding 20 ft. In unfirestopped open wood joist construction, or if firestops are installed at intervals exceeding 20 ft, the minimum operating pressures shall be increased by 40 percent.
2. Building steel required no special protection for the occupancies listed. Protection requirements are based on rack storage with no solid shelves nor slave pallets.
3. The required number of design sprinklers shall not be reduced from that required for the lower pressure.
4. In addition to the transverse flue spaces required by NFPA 231C, minimum 6-in. longitudinal flue spaces shall be maintained.

For SI Units:
1 ft = 0.3048 m
1 in. = 25.4 mm
1 psi = 0.0689 bars = 6.895 kPa

9-1.2 All requirements contained in NFPA 13, *Installation of Sprinkler Systems*, shall apply.

Chapter 10 Early Suppression Fast Response (ESFR) Sprinklers

10-1 General.

10-1.1* ESFR sprinklers having a nominal K factor of 14 shall be permitted for the protection of cartoned plastics (Group A, B, or C) and Class I through IV commodities in single row, double row, or multi-row racks up to a height of 25 ft (7.7 m).

Exception: ESFR protection as now defined does not apply to:

1. *exposed plastics or expanded polystyrene plastics in cartons.*
2. *rack storage involving solid shelves.*
3. *rack storage involving combustible open top cartons or containers.*

10-1.2* ESFR sprinklers shall be permitted for use in buildings having a maximum ceiling height of 30 ft (9.2 m) and one of the following types of roof construction:

(a) smooth ceiling

(b) bar joist

(c) beam and girder

(d) panel.

10-1.3 Roof slope shall not exceed $^1/_4$ in./ft (19.6 mm/m).

10-2 Sprinkler System Design.

10-2.1 ESFR sprinkler systems shall be designed to provide a minimum operating pressure of 50 psi (3.4 bars) to the twelve most hydraulically remote sprinklers, based on flowing four sprinklers in each of three branch lines.

10-2.2 Only wet pipe systems are acceptable for use with ESFR sprinklers.

10-2.3 All requirements contained in NFPA 13, *Standard for the Installation of Sprinkler Systems*, particularly Chapter 8, shall apply unless modified within this standard.

10-2.4 ESFR sprinklers shall be ordinary temperature rated sprinklers.

Exception No. 1: Those located in proximity to heat sources.

Exception No. 2: Those located under skylights.

10-3 Water Demand.

10-3.1 A minimum of 250 gpm (16 L/s) shall be added to the sprinkler demand for combined large and small hose streams.

10-3.2 Water supply duration shall be at least 1 hr.

Chapter 11 Equipment

11-1 Mechanical Handling Equipment.

11-1.1 Industrial Trucks.

11-1.1.1 Power-operated industrial trucks shall be of the type designated in NFPA 505, *Firesafety Standard for Powered Industrial Trucks Including Type Designations, Areas of Use, Maintenance, and Operation*, and their maintenance and operation shall be in accordance with Chapters 2 and 3.

11-1.1.2† Industrial trucks using LP-Gas or liquid fuel shall be refueled outside of the storage building at a location designated for that purpose.

Chapter 12 Building Maintenance and Operation

12-1* Building Operations Other than Storage. Welding, soldering, brazing, and cutting shall be permitted to be performed on rack or building components that cannot be removed, provided no storage is located below and within 25 ft (7.62 m) of the working area, and flameproof tarpaulins enclose this section. During any of these operations the sprinkler system shall be in service. Two and one-half-gal (9.45-L) water-type extinguishers and charged inside hose lines shall be located in the working area. A fire watch shall be maintained during these operations and for at least 30 additional min.

12-2* Waste Disposal. Approved-type containers for rubbish and other trash materials shall be provided.

12-3 Smoking. Smoking shall be strictly prohibited, except in locations prominently designated as smoking areas, and "No Smoking" signs shall be posted in prohibited areas.

12-4* Maintenance. Fire walls, fire doors, and floors shall be maintained in good repair at all times.

12-5* Plant Emergency Organization. A fire watch shall be maintained when the sprinkler system is not in service.

12-6* General Fire Protection.

Chapter 13 Referenced Publications

13-1 The following documents or portions thereof are referenced within this standard and shall be considered part of the requirements of this document. The edition indicated for each reference is the current edition as of the date of the NFPA issuance of this document.

13-1.1 NFPA Publications. National Fire Protection Association, 1 Batterymarch Park, P.O. Box 9101, Quincy, MA 02269-9101.

NFPA 11A, *Standard for Medium- and High-Expansion Foam Systems*, 1988 edition

NFPA 13, *Standard for the Installation of Sprinkler Systems*, 1989 edition

NFPA 30, *Flammable and Combustible Liquids Code*, 1990 edition

NFPA 40, *Standard for the Storage and Handling of Cellulose Nitrate Motion Picture Film*, 1988 edition

NFPA 58, *Standard for the Storage and Handling of Liquefied Petroleum Gases*, 1988 edition

NFPA 81, *Standard for Fur Storage, Fumigation and Cleaning*, 1986 edition

NFPA 91, *Standard for the Installation of Blower and Exhaust Systems for Dust, Stock, and Vapor Removal or Conveying*, 1990 edition

NFPA 220, *Standard on Types of Building Construction*, 1985 edition

NFPA 231, *Standard for General Storage*, 1990 edition

NFPA 231D, *Standard for Storage of Rubber Tires*, 1989 edition

NFPA 231F, *Standard for the Storage of Roll Paper*, 1987 edition

NFPA 232, *Standard for the Protection of Records*, 1991 edition

NFPA 490, *Code for the Storage of Ammonium Nitrate*, 1986 edition

NFPA 505, *Firesafety Standard for Powered Industrial Trucks Including Type Designations, Areas of Use, Maintenance, and Operation*, 1987 edition

Appendix A

This Appendix is not a part of the requirements of this NFPA document, but is included for information purposes only.

A-4-1 Rack storage as referred to in this standard contemplates commodity in a rack structure, usually steel. Many variations of dimensions are found. Racks may be single row, double row, or multiple row, with or without solid shelves. The standard commodity used in most of the tests was 42 in. (1.07 m) on a side. The types of racks covered in this standard are:

Double Row Racks. Pallets rest on two beams parallel to the aisle. Any number of pallets can be supported by one pair of beams [*see Figures A-4-1(a), (b), (c), and (d)*].

Automatic Storage-Type Rack. The pallet is supported by two rails running perpendicular to the aisle [*see Figure A-4-1(e)*].

Multiple Row Racks are More than Two Pallets Deep, Measured Aisle to Aisle. This includes drive-in racks, drive-through racks, flow-through racks, portable racks arranged in the same manner, and conventional or automatic racks with aisles less than 42 in. (1.07 m) [*see Figures A-4-1(f) through (i)*].

Movable Racks. Movable racks are racks on fixed rails or guides. They can be moved back and forth only in a horizontal two-dimensional plane. A moving aisle is created as abutting racks are either loaded or unloaded, then moved across the aisle to abut other racks. [*See Figure A-4-1(k).*]

Solid Shelving. Conventional pallet rack with plywood shelves on the shelf beams [*see Figures A-4-1(c) and (d)*]. This is a special case (*see Chapter 5*).

Cantilever Rack. The load is supported on arms that extend horizontally from columns. The load may rest on the arms or on shelves supported by the arms [*see Figure A-4-1(j)*].

Load depth in conventional or automatic racks is considered a nominal 48 in. (1.22 m) [*see Figure A-4-1(b)*].

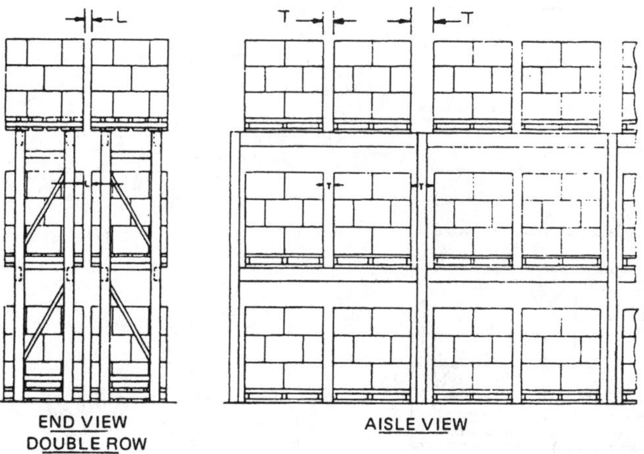

Legend

L — Longitudinal Flue Space

T — Transverse Flue Space

Figure A-4-1(a) Conventional Pallet Rack.

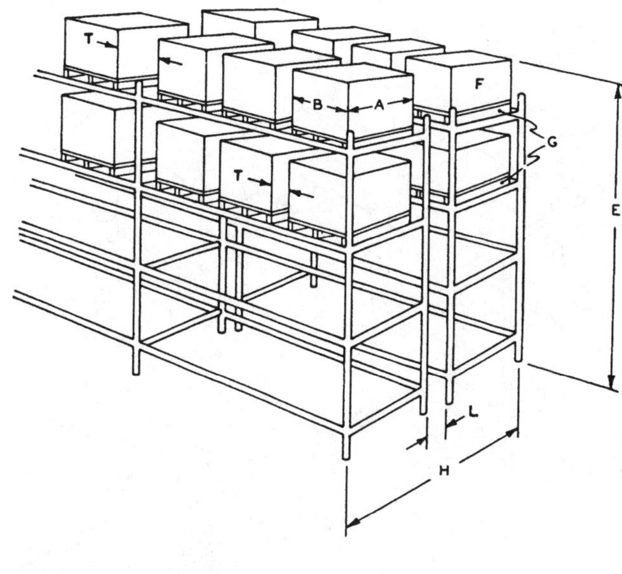

Legend

A — Load Depth
B — Load Width
T — Transverse Flue Space
L — Longitudinal Flue Space
E — Storage Height
F — Commodity
G — Pallet
H — Rack Depth

Figure A-4-1(b) Double Row Racks Without Solid or Slatted Shelves.

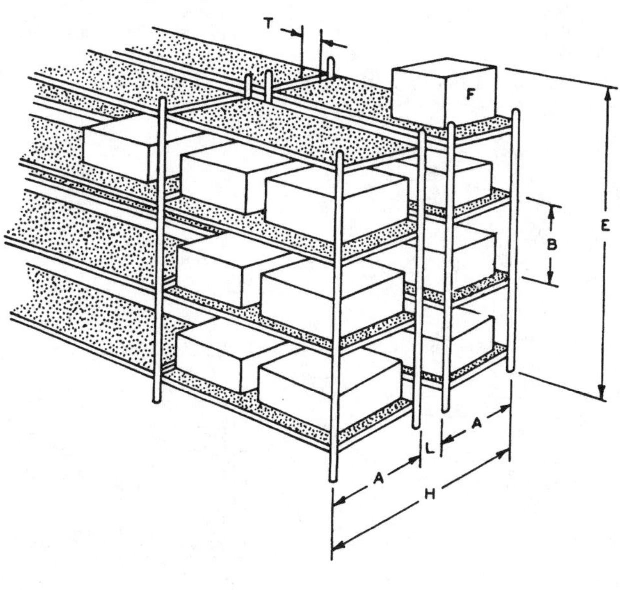

Legend

A — Shelf Depth
B — Shelf Height
T — Transverse Flue Space
L — Longitudinal Flue Space
E — Storage Height
F — Commodity
H — Rack Depth

Figure A-4-1(c) Double Row Racks With Solid Shelves.

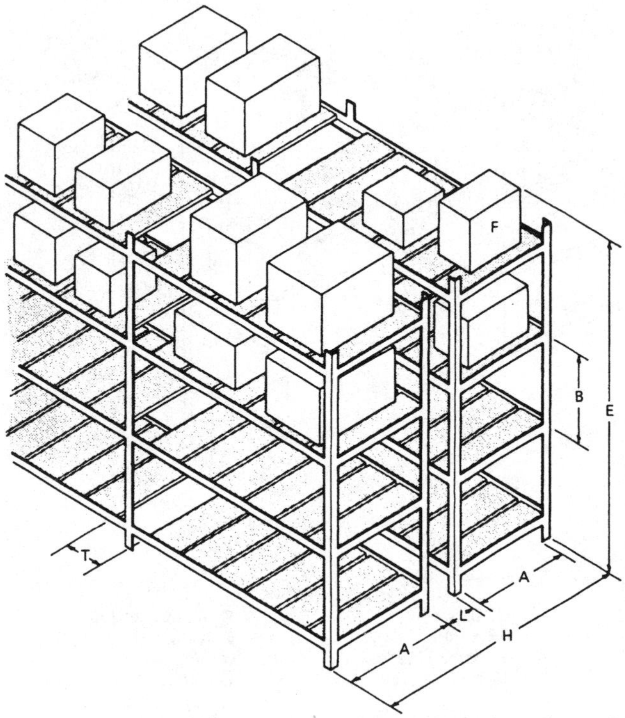

Legend

A — Shelf Depth
B — Shelf Height
H — Rack Depth
L — Longitudinal Flue Space
E — Storage Height
F — Commodity
T — Transverse Flue Space

Figure A-4-1(d) Double Row Racks With Slatted Shelves.

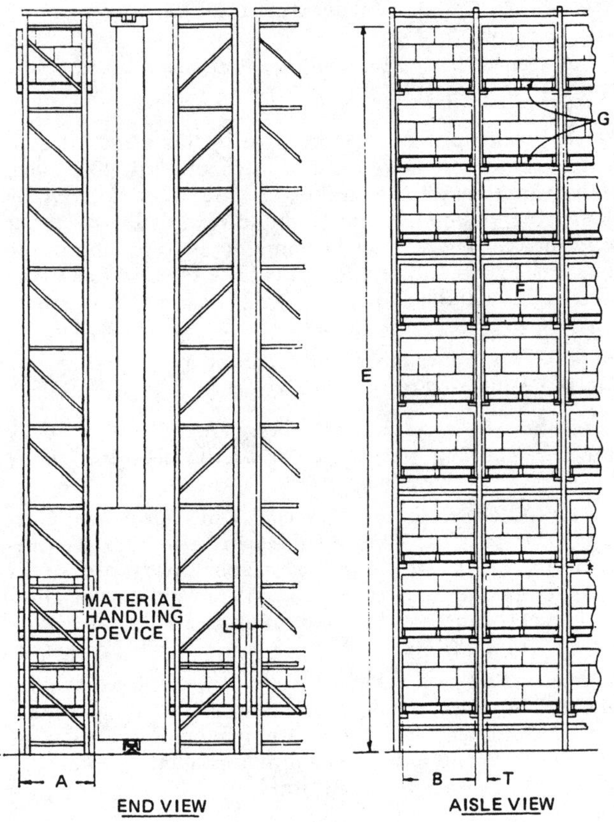

END VIEW

AISLE VIEW

Legend

A — Load Depth
B — Load Width
T — Transverse Flue Space
L — Longitudinal Flue Space
E — Storage Height
F — Commodity
G — Pallet

Figure A-4-1(e) Automatic Storage-Type Rack.

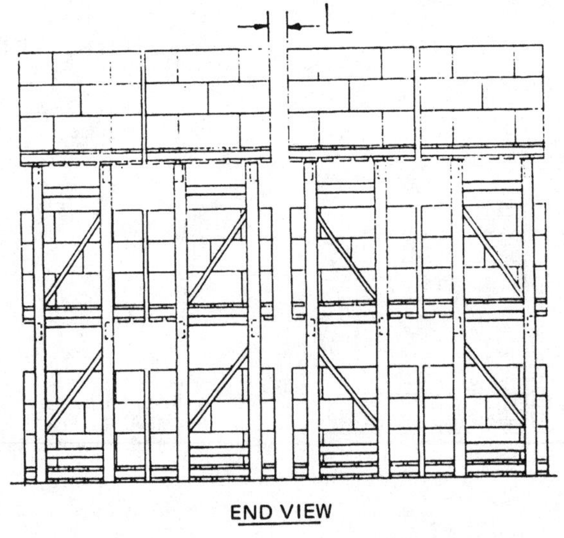

L — Longitudinal Flue Space

Figure A-4-1(f) Multi-Row Rack to be Served by a Reach Truck.

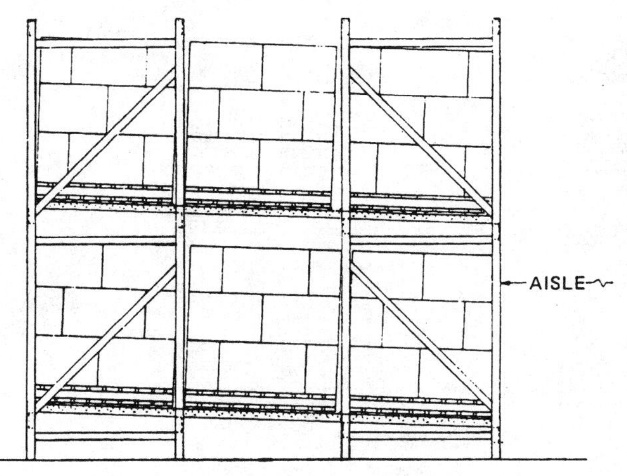

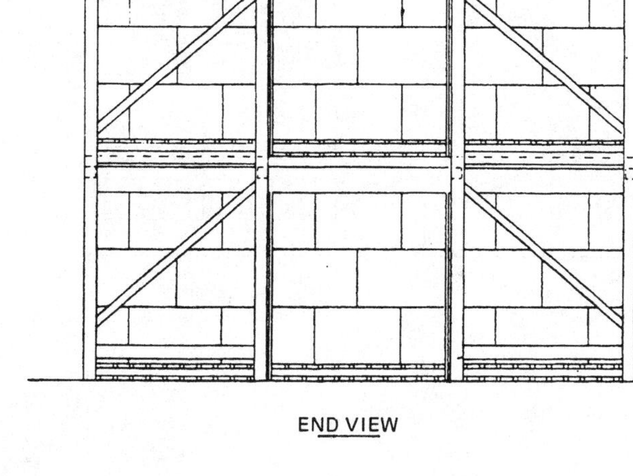

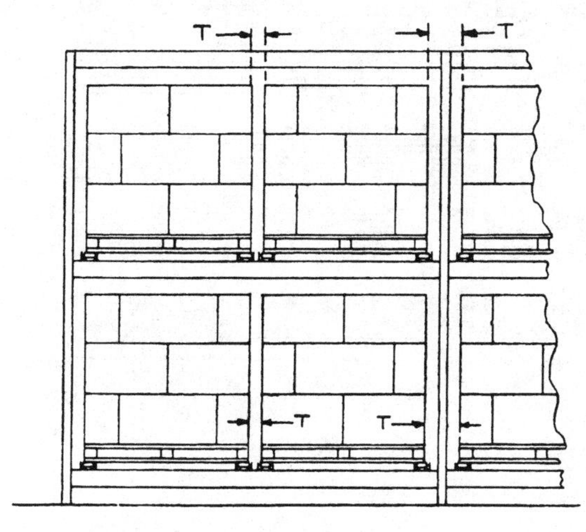

T — Transverse Flue Space

Figure A-4-1(g) Flow-Through Pallet Rack.

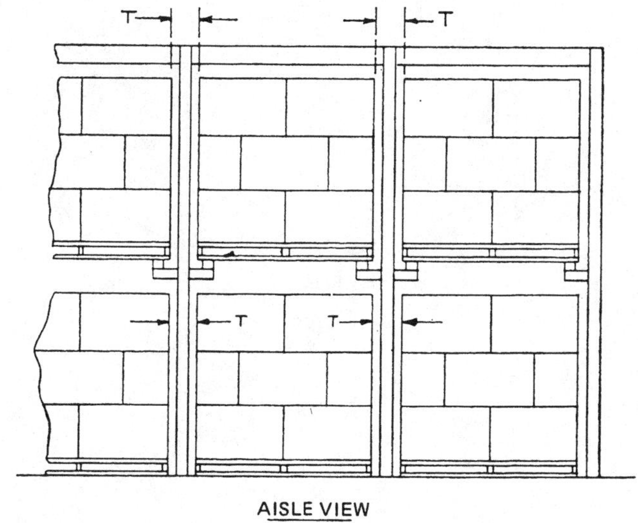

T — Transverse Flue Space

Figure A-4-1(h) Drive-In Rack — Two or More Pallets Deep.

Fork truck drives into the rack to deposit and withdraw loads in the depth of the rack.

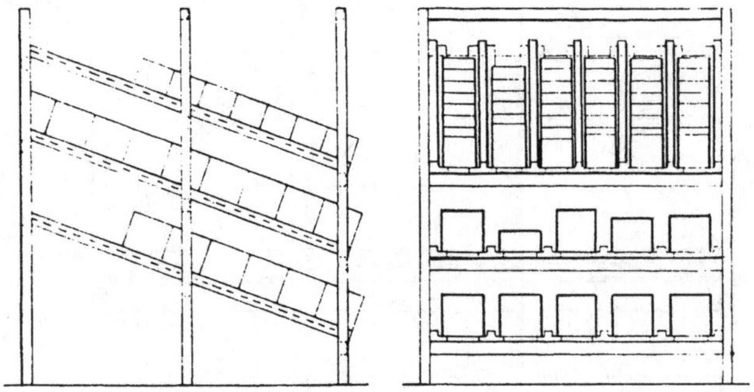

END VIEW
AISLE VIEW

Flow-Through Rack

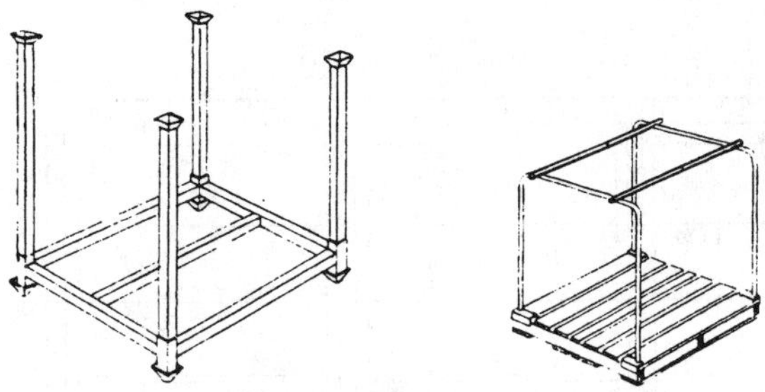

Portable Racks

Figure A-4-1(i).

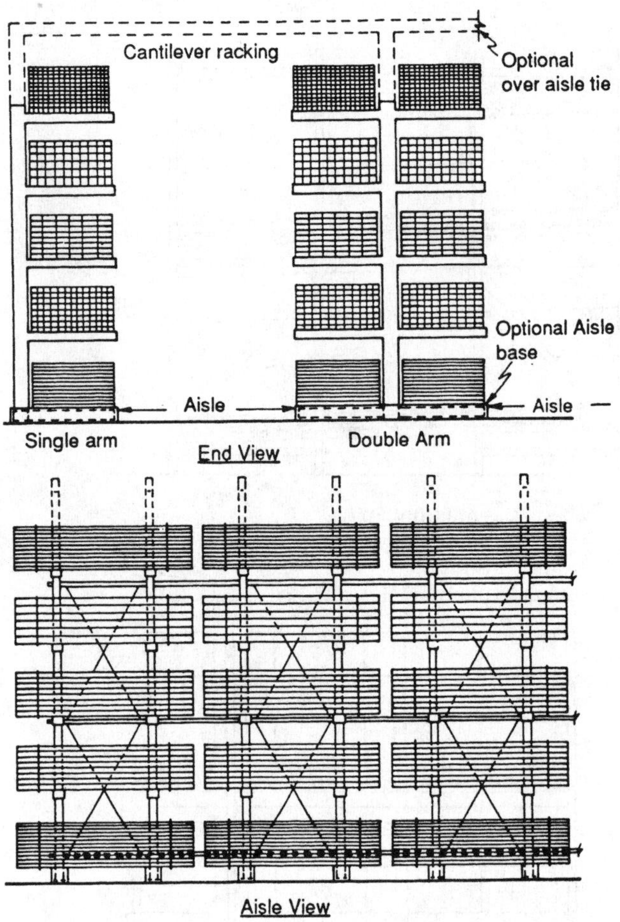

Cantilever racking
Optional over aisle tie
Optional Aisle base
Aisle
Aisle
Single arm
Double Arm
End View
Aisle View

Figure A-4-1(j) Cantilever Rack.

L
T
T
Moveable Pallet Rack Shown
Direction of Movement
Carriage Wheel
Carriage Wheel
Track in Floor
END VIEW DOUBLE ROW
AISLE VIEW

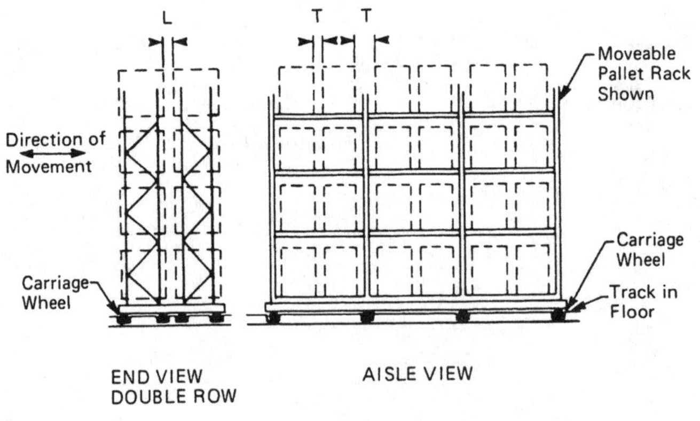

T — Transverse Flue Space
L — Longitudinal Flue Space

Figure A-4-1(k) Movable Rack.

A-4-2 Fixed rack structures should be designed to facilitate removal or repair of damaged sections without resorting to flame cutting or welding in the storage area. Where sprinklers are to be installed in racks, rack design should anticipate the additional clearances required to facilitate installation of sprinklers. The rack structure should be anchored to prevent damage to sprinkler lines and supply piping in racks.

Rack structures should be designed for seismic conditions in areas where seismic resistance of building structure is required.

A-4-3.1 Nominal 6-in. (152.4-mm) transverse flues should be provided in multiple row racks.

A-4-4 Storage in aisles may render protection ineffective and should be discouraged.

A-4-5 The fire protection system design should contemplate the maximum height of storage. For new sprinkler installations, maximum height of storage is the usable height at which commodities can be stored above the floor when the minimum required unobstructed space below sprinklers is maintained. For the evaluation of existing situations, maximum height of storage is the maximum existing if space between sprinklers and storage is equal or greater than required.

A-4-6.1 A horizontal clearance of at least 1 ft (0.30 m) should be maintained between storage and major unprotected roof structural members when storage is stored above the bottom of such members.

A-4-6.2 Incandescent light fixtures should have shades or guards to prevent ignition of commodity from hot bulbs where possibility of contact with storage exists.

A-4-7 Idle combustible pallets should not be stored in racks.

A-5-2.1 Ceiling Sprinklers. Wet systems are recommended for rack storage occupancies.

Dry systems are acceptable only where it is impractical to provide heat.

Preaction systems should be considered for rack storage occupancies that are unheated, particularly where in-rack sprinklers are installed or for those occupancies that are highly susceptible to water damage.

A-5-2.2 Where 286°F (141°C) sprinklers are installed at the ceiling, 286°F (141°C) sprinklers should also extend beyond storage in accordance with the following table:

Design Area for 286°F (141°C) Sprinklers		Distance Beyond Perimeter of High-Hazard Occupancy for High-Temp. Sprinklers	
(ft^2)	(m^2)	(ft)	(m)
2000	185.8	30	9.14
3000	278.7	40	12.2
4000	371.6	45	13.72
5000	464.5	50	15.24
6000	557.4	55	16.76

A-5-5 In-rack sprinklers and ceiling sprinklers selected for protection should be controlled by at least two separate indicating valves and drains.

A-5-5.1 In higher rack arrangements, consideration should be given to providing more than one in-rack control valve in order to limit the extent of any single impairment.

A-5-7 Approved supervisory alarm service should be provided for all fire detection and extinguishing systems.

Central station, auxiliary, remote station, or proprietary sprinkler waterflow alarm should be provided except that local waterflow alarm is acceptable where approved guard service is provided (*see NFPA 71, Standard for the Installation, Maintenance, and Use of Signaling Systems for Central Station Service, and NFPA 72, Standard for the Installation, Maintenance, and Use of Protective Signaling Systems*).

A-5-11.1 Detection systems, concentrate pumps, generators, and other system components essential to the operation of the system should have an approved standby power source.

A-5-13.1 In NFPA 13, *Standard for the Installation of Sprinkler Systems*, paragraph A-4-4.10 states: "Slatting of decks or walkways or the use of open grating as a substitute for automatic sprinkler thereunder is not acceptable."

Also when shelving of any type is employed, it is for the basic purpose of providing an intermediate support between the structural members of the rack. As a result, it becomes almost impossible to define and maintain transverse flue spaces across the rack as required in 4-3.1 and illustrated in Figure 4-3.1.

A-6-4.1 Where possible, it is preferable to locate in-rack sprinkler deflectors at least 6 in. (152.4 mm) above pallet loads.

A-6-4.2 Where possible, it is preferable to locate in-rack sprinklers away from rack uprights.

A-6-5.1 Spacing of sprinklers on branch lines in racks in the various tests indicates maximum spacing as indicated is proper.

A-6-8.1 Bulkheads are not a substitute for sprinklers in racks. Their installation does not justify reduction in sprinkler densities or design operating areas as called for in the design curves.

A-6-9.1 When high expansion foam is being contemplated as the protection media, consideration should be given to possible damage to the commodity from soaking and corrosion. Consideration should be given to the problems associated with removal of foam after discharge.

A-6-11.1 Where dry pipe systems are used, the areas of operation indicated in the design curves should be increased by 30 percent. Densities should be selected so that areas of operation, after the 30 percent increase, do not exceed 6,000 sq ft (557.4 m^2).

A-6-13.3 In-rack sprinklers at one level only for storage up to and including 25 ft (7.62 m) high in multiple row racks should be located at the tier level nearest one-half to two-thirds of the storage height.

A-7-10.3 In single-row racks with more than 10 ft (3.05 m) between top of storage and ceiling, a horizontal barrier should be installed above storage with one line of sprinklers under the barrier.

A-7-11 Double row racks — height of storage over 25 ft (7.62 m) — more than 10 ft (3.05 m) between maximum height of storage and ceiling.

When the ceiling is more than 10 ft (3.05 m) above maximum height of storage, a horizontal barrier should be installed above storage with one line of sprinklers under the barrier for Class I, II, and III commodities and two lines of sprinklers under the barrier for Class IV commodities. In-rack sprinkler arrays should be installed as indicated in Table 7-10.1 and Figures 7-10.1(a) through (j).

Barriers should be of sufficient strength to avoid sagging that interferes with loading and unloading operations.

Horizontal barriers need not be provided above a Class I or Class II commodity with in-rack sprinkler arrays according to Figure 7-10.1(a) and Figure 7-10.1(b), provided one line of in-rack sprinklers is installed above the top tier of storage.

A-7-12.1 Water demand for height of storage over 25 ft (7.62 m) on racks without solid shelves separated by aisles at least 4 ft (1.22 m) wide and with more than 10 ft (3.05 m) between top of storage and sprinklers should be based on sprinklers in 2,000 sq ft (185.8 m^2) operating area for double row racks and 3,000 sq ft (278.7 m^2) operating area for multiple row racks discharging a minimum of 0.18 gpm per sq ft [(7.33 L/min)/m^2] for Class I commodities, 0.21 gpm per sq ft [(8.56 L/min)/m^2] for Class II and III commodities, and 0.25 gpm per sq ft [(10.19 L/min)/m^2] for Class IV commodities, for 165°F (74°C) sprinklers; or a minimum of 0.25 gpm per sq ft [(10.19 L/min)/m^2] for Class I commodities, 0.28 gpm per sq ft [(11.41 L/min)/m^2] for Class II and III commodities, and 0.32 gpm per sq ft [(13.04 L/min)/m^2] for Class IV commodities, for 286°F (141°C) sprinklers. *(See A-7-11 and A-7-13.)*

Where such storage is encapsulated, ceiling sprinkler density should be 25 percent greater than for nonencapsulated.

A-7-13 In multiple row racks with more than 10 ft (3.05 m) between maximum height of storage and ceiling, a horizontal barrier should be installed above storage with a level of sprinklers, spaced as stipulated for in-rack sprinklers, installed directly beneath the barrier. In-rack sprinklers should be installed as indicated in Figures 7-13(a), (b), and (c).

A-8 All rack fire tests of plastics were run with an approximate 10-ft (3-m) maximum clearance between the top of storage and ceiling sprinklers. Within 30-ft (9.1-m) high buildings, greater clearances above storage configurations should be compensated for by the addition of more in-rack sprinklers and/or the provision of greater areas of application.

A-10-1.1 ESFR sprinklers were designed to respond quickly to growing fires and deliver heavy discharge to "suppress" fires rather than "control" them. ESFR sprinklers cannot be relied upon to provide suppression if they are used outside these design parameters.

A-10-2.1 Design parameters were determined from a series of full-scale fire tests conducted as a joint effort between Factory Mutual and the National Fire Protection Research Foundation. (Copies of the tests report are available from the National Fire Protection Research Foundation).

A-12-1 The use of welding, cutting, soldering, or brazing torches in the storage areas introduces a severe fire hazard. The use of mechanical fastenings and mechanical saws or cutting wheels is recommended. When welding or cutting operations are absolutely necessary, the precautions contained in NFPA 51B, *Standard for Fire Prevention in Use of Cutting and Welding Processes*, should be followed.

Locomotives should not be allowed to enter the storage area.

A-12-2 Containers should be emptied and contents removed from the premises at frequent intervals *(see NFPA 82, Standard on Incinerators, Waste, and Linen Handling Systems and Equipment)*.

A-12-4 Periodic inspections of all fire protection equipment should be made in conjunction with regular inspections of the premises. Unsatisfactory conditions should be immediately reported and necessary corrective measures taken promptly.

The sprinkler system and the water supplies should be checked and maintained in accordance with NFPA 13A, *Recommended Practice for the Inspection, Testing and Maintenance of Sprinkler Systems*.

A-12-5 Plant Emergency Organization. Arrangements should be made, in case of fire or other emergency, to permit rapid entry into the premises of the municipal fire department, police department, or other personnel as may be summoned to deal with any emergency. A well-trained plant emergency organization should be provided to control emergency conditions that may arise.

The plant emergency organization should be instructed and trained in the following procedures:

(a) Maintaining the security of the premises

(b) Means of summoning outside aid immediately in an emergency

(c) Use of hand extinguishers and hose lines on small fires and mop-up operations

(d) Operation of sprinkler system and water supply equipment

(e) Use of material handling equipment while sprinklers are still operating to effect final extinguishment

(f) Supervision of sprinkler valves after system is turned off so that system can be reactivated if rekindling occurs.

Attention should be given to advance planning and training with respect to fire department response, access, and fire fighting.

A-12-6 General Fire Protection.

All fire fighting and safety personnel should realize the great danger of shutting off sprinklers once opened by heat from fire. Shutting off sprinklers to locate fire could cause a disaster. Ventilation, use of smoke masks, smoke removal equipment, and removal of material are safer ways.

Sprinkler water may be safely shut off only after the fire is extinguished or completely under control of hose streams. Even then, rekindling is a possibility. To be ready for prompt valve reopening if fire rekindles, a person stationed at the valve, a fire watch, and dependable communications between them are needed until automatic sprinkler protection is restored.

Pre-Fire Emergency Planning. It is important that such planning be done by management and fire protection personnel, and the action to be taken discussed and correlated with the local fire department personnel.

The critical time of any fire is in the incipient stage, and the action taken by fire protection personnel upon notification of fire may permit containing the fire in early stages.

Pre-emergency planning should contemplate the following:

(a) Availability of hand fire fighting equipment for the height and type of commodity involved.

(b) Availability of fire fighting equipment and personnel properly trained for type of storage arrangement involved.

(c) Assurance that all automatic fire protection equipment, such as sprinkler systems, water supplies, fire pumps, hand hose, etc., is in service at all times.

Fire Department Operations. Sprinkler protection installed as recommended in this standard is expected to protect the building occupancy without supplemental fire department activity. Fires that occur in rack storage occupancies, protected in accordance with this standard, should be controlled within the limits outlined in B-1-1. No significant building damage is expected. Fire department activity can, however, minimize the extent of loss. The first fire department pumper arriving at a rack storage-type fire should immediately connect to the sprinkler siamese fire department connection and start pumping operations.

In the test series up to 25 ft (7.62 m), the average time from ignition to smoke obscuration in the test building was about 13 min. The first sprinkler operating time in these same fires averaged about 3 min. Considering response time for the waterflow device to transmit a waterflow signal, approximately 9 min remains between time of receipt of a waterflow alarm signal at fire department headquarters and time of smoke obscuration within the building as an overall average.

In the over-25-ft (7.62-m) high test series, the visibility time was extended. If the fire department or plant protection department arrives at the building in time to have sufficient visibility to locate the fire, suppression activities with small hose lines should be started. (Self-contained breathing apparatus is desirable.) If, on the other hand, the fire is not readily visible, hose should be laid to exterior doors or exterior openings in the building and charged lines provided to these points ready for ultimate mop-up operations. Manual fire fighting operations in such a warehouse are not a substitute for sprinkler protection.

The sprinkler system must be kept in operation during manual fire fighting and mop-up operations.

During the testing program, the installed automatic extinguishing system was capable of controlling the fire and reducing all temperatures to ambient within 30 min of ignition. Ventilation operations and mop-up were not started until this time period had been reached. The use of smoke removal equipment is important.

Smoke removal capability should be provided. Examples of smoke removal equipment include:

(a) Mechanical air handling systems

(b) Powered exhaust fans

(c) Roof mounted gravity vents

(d) Perimeter gravity vents.

Whichever system is selected, it should be designed for manual actuation by the fire department, thus allowing them to coordinate the smoke removal (ventilation) with their mop-up operations.

Appendix B

This Appendix is not a part of the requirements of this NFPA document, but is included for information purposes only.

Appendix B explains test data and procedures that led to the promulgation of this standard. The paragraphs bear the same number as the text of this standard to which they apply.

B-1-1 Application and Scope.

This standard uses as a basis the large-scale fire test series conducted at the Factory Mutual Research Center, West Glocester, Rhode Island.

The test building is approximately 200 ft × 250 ft [50,000 sq ft (4.65 km^2) in area], of fire-resistive construction, and contains a volume of approximately 2.25 million cu ft (63 761.86 m^3), the equivalent of a 100,000 sq ft (9.29 km^2) building 22.5 ft (6.86 m) high. The test building has two primary heights beneath a single large ceiling. The east section is 30 ft (9.15 m) high, and the west section is 60 ft (18.29 m) high.

The 20-ft (6.10-m) test series was conducted in the 30-ft (9.15-m) section with clearances from top of storage to ceiling nominally 10 ft (3.05 m).

Doors at the lower and intermediate levels and ventilation louvers at tops of walls were kept closed during the majority of the fire tests. This minimized effect of exterior conditions.

The entire test series was fully instrumented with thermocouples in rack members, simulated building column, bar joist, and at the ceiling.

Racks were constructed of steel vertical and horizontal members designed for 4000 lb (1814 kg) loads. Vertical members were 8 ft (2.44 m) O.C. for conventional racks and 4 ft (1.22 m) O.C. for simulated automated racks. Racks were 3$^1/_2$ ft (1.07 m) wide with 6-in. (12.7-mm) longitudinal flue space for an overall width of 7$^1/_2$ ft (2.29 m). Simulated automated racks and slave pallets were used in the main central rack in the 4-ft (1.22-m) aisle test. Conventional racks and conventional pallets were used in the main central rack in the 8-ft (2.44-mm) aisle tests. The majority of the tests were conducted with 100 sq ft (9.29 m^2) sprinkler spacing.

The test configuration in the 15-ft (4.57-m), 20-ft (6.10-m), and 25-ft (7.62-m) high tests covered an 1800-sq ft (167.2-m^2) floor area, including aisles between racks. Tests, which were used in producing this standard, limited fire damage to this area. Maximum water damage area anticipated in the standard is 6000 sq ft (557.4 m^2), the upper limit of the design curves.

The test data shows that as density is increased both the extent of fire damage and sprinkler operation are reduced. The data also indicates that with sprinklers installed in the racks a reduction is gained in the area of fire damage and sprinkler operations, or water damage.

The following table illustrates these points. Information shown is taken from the 20-ft (6.10-m) high test series using the standard commodity.

Density gpm/sq ft		Fire Damage in Test Array %	sq ft	Sprinkler Operation (165°F) Area — sq ft
0.30	(Ceiling only)	22	395	4500-4800
0.375	(Ceiling only)	17	306	1800
0.45	(Ceiling only)	9	162	700
0.20	(Ceiling only)	28-36	504-648	13,100-14,000
0.20	(Sprinklers at ceiling and in racks)	8	144	4100
0.30	(Sprinklers at ceiling and in racks)	7	126	700

For SI Units: 1 ft = 0.3048 m; C = $^5/_9$ (F-32);
1 gpm/ft^2 = 40.746 (L/min)/m^2

These basic facts, the reduction in both fire damage and area of water application as sprinkler densities are increased or when sprinklers are installed in racks, should be considered carefully by those responsible for applying this standard to the rack storage situation.

In the 25-ft (7.62-m) high test, a density of 0.55 gpm per sq ft [(22.4 L/min)/m^2] produced 42 percent, or 756 sq ft (70.26 m), fire damage in the test array and a sprinkler wetted area of 1400 sq ft (130.1 m^2). Lesser densities would not be expected to achieve the same limited degree of control. Therefore, if smaller areas of fire damage are to be achieved, sprinklers in racks should be considered.

The over-25-ft (7.62-m) test series was conducted in the 60-ft (18.29-m) section of the test building with nominal clearances from top of storage to ceiling of either 30 ft (9.15 m) or 10 ft (3.05 m).

Doors at the lower and intermediate levels and ventilation louvers at the top of walls were kept closed during the fire tests. This minimized the effect of exterior wind conditions.

The purpose of the over-25-ft (7.62-m) series was to:

1. Determine the arrangement of in-rack sprinklers that can be repeated as pile height increases and that provide control of the fire.

2. Determine other protective arrangements, such as high expansion foam, that provide control of the fire.

Control was felt to be accomplished if the fire was unlikely to spread from the rack of origin to adjacent racks or spread beyond the length of the 25-ft (7.62-m) test rack. To aid in this judgment, control was considered achieved if the fire did not:

1. Jump the 4-ft (1.22-m) aisles to adjoining racks.

2. Reach the end face of the end stacks (north or south ends) of the main rack.

Control is defined as holding the fire in check through the extinguishing system until commodities initially involved are consumed, or fire is extinguished by the extinguishing system or manual aid.

The standard commodity as selected in the 20-ft (6.1-m) test series was used in the majority of over-25-ft (7.62-m) tests. Hallmark products and 3-M products described in the 20 ft (6.1 m) report were also used as representative of Class III and/or IV commodities in several tests. The result of privately sponsored tests on Hallmark products and plastic encapsulated standard commodity were also made available to the committee.

A 25-ft (7.62-m) long test array was used for the majority of over-25-ft (7.62-m) high test series. This decision was reached as it was felt that a fire in racks over 25-ft (7.62-m) high that extended to the full length of a 50-ft (15.24-m) long rack could not be considered controlled, particularly as storage heights increased.

One of the purposes of the tests was to determine arrangements of in-rack sprinklers that can be repeated as pile height increases and that provide control of the fire. The 30-ft (9.15-m) tests explored the effect of such arrays. Many of these tests, however, produced appreciable fire spread in storage in tiers above the top level of protection within the racks. (In some cases, a total burnout of the top tiers of both the main rack and the target rack occurred.) In the case of the 30-ft (9.15-m) Hallmark Test 134 on the 60-ft (18.29-m) site, the material in the top tiers of storage burned vigorously, and the fire jumped the aisle above the fourth tier. The fire then burned itself downward into the south end of the fourth tier. In the test on the floor, a nominal 30-ft (9.15-m) clearance occurred between top of storage and ceiling sprinklers, whereas on the platform this clearance was reduced to nominal 10 ft (3.05 m). In most cases the in-rack sprinklers were effective in controlling fire below the top level of protection within the racks. It has been assumed by the Test Planning Committee that, in the actual case with clearance of 10 ft (3.05 m) or less above storage, ceiling sprinklers would be expected to control damage above the top level of protection within the racks. Tests are planned to investigate lesser clearances.

Tests 114 and 128 explore the effect of changing the ignition point from the in-rack standard ignition point to a face ignition location. It should be noted, however, that both of these tests were conducted with 30-ft (9.15-m) clearance from ceiling sprinklers to top of storage and, as such, ceiling sprinklers had little effect on the fire in the top two tiers of storage. Fire spread in the three lower tiers is essentially the same. A similar change in the fire spread when the ignition point is changed was noted in Tests 126 and 127. Here again, 30-ft (9.15-m) clearance occurred between top of storage and ceiling sprinklers, and, as such, ceiling sprinklers had little effect on the face fire. Comparisons of Tests 129, 130, and 131 in the 50-ft (15.24-m) series indicate little effect of point of ignition in the particular configuration tested.

Test 125 compared with Test 133 indicates no significant difference in result between approved low profile sprinklers and standard sprinklers in the racks.

B-2-1 A review of full-scale fire tests run on the standard commodity (double tri-wall carton with metal liner); of Hallmark products and 3-M products (abrasives, pressure sensitive tapes of plastic fiber, and paper, etc.); and of the considerable number of commodity tests conducted indicates a guide for commodity classifications. This guide is not related to any other method of classification of materials; therefore, sound engineering judgment and analysis of the commodity and the packaging must be made when selecting a commodity classification.

B-3-2.1 None of the tests that were conducted with densities in accordance with the design curves produced critical temperatures in bar joists 12 ft 6 in. (3.81 m) from the ignition source. Therefore, with sprinkler systems designed in accordance with the curves, fireproofing of roof steel is not necessary.

B-3-2.2 Temperatures in the test column were maintained below 1000°F (538°C) in all tests where sprinklers in racks were used.

B-3-2.3 Temperatures in the test column were maintained below 1000°F (538°C) with densities of roof ceiling sprinklers only of 0.375 gpm per sq ft [(15.3 L/min)/m^2] with 8-ft (2.44-m) aisles and 0.45 gpm per sq ft [(18.34 L/min)/m^2] with 4-ft (1.22-m) aisles using the standard commodity.

B-3-3 Tests were conducted as a part of this program with eave line windows or louvers open to simulate smoke and heat venting. These tests opened 87.5 percent and 91 percent more sprinklers than did comparative tests without windows or louvers open. Venting tests that have been conducted in other programs were without the benefit of sprinkler protection, and, as such, are not considered in this report, which is dealing only with buildings protected by sprinklers. The design curves are based upon roof vents or draft curtains not being installed in the building. During mop-up operations, ventilating systems, where installed, should be capable of manual exhaust operations.

B-4-3.1 Test 80 was conducted to determine the effect of closing back-to-back longitudinal 6-in. (152.4-mm) flue space in conventional pallet racks. Test results indicated fewer sprinklers operating than with the flue space open, and, as such, no minimum back-to-back clearance is necessary if the transverse flue space is maintained open.

Tests 145 and 146 were conducted to investigate the influence of longitudinal and transverse flue dimensions in double row racks without solid shelves. Results were compared with Tests 65 and 66. Flue dimensions in Tests 65, 66, 145, and 146 were 6 in. (152.4 mm), 6 in. (152.4 mm), 3 in. (76.2 mm), and 12 in. (0.30 m) respectively. All other conditions were the same.

In Tests 65 and 66, 45 and 48 sprinklers operate compared with 59 and 58 for Tests 145 and 146. Fire damage in Tests 145 and 146 was somewhat less than in Tests 65 and 66; 2,100 cu ft (59.51 m^3) and 1,800 cu ft (51 m^3) versus 2,300 cu ft (65.13 m^3) and 2,300 cu ft (65.13 m^3) of combustible material consumed.

Test results indicate narrow flue spaces on the order of 3 in. (76.2 mm) will allow reasonable passage of sprinkler water down through the racks.

Tests 96 and 107, on multiple row racks, had 6-in. (152.4-mm) transverse flue spaces. Water demand recommended in the standard is limited to those cases with nominal 6-in. (152.4-mm) transverse flues, in vertical alignment.

B-4-5 Most tests in the 25-ft (7.62-m) and under series were conducted with clearance of 10-ft (3.05 m) from top of storage to sprinkler deflectors, and the basic design curves in Figures 6-11.1(a) through (g) reflect this condition.

Tests 140 and 141 were conducted with 3-ft (0.91-m) clearance between the top of storage and ceiling sprinkler deflectors. In Test 140 with 0.30 density, 36 sprinklers operated compared with 45 and 48 sprinklers in tests 65 and 66 with 10-ft (3.05-m) clearance. In Test 141, 89 sprinklers operated compared with 140 sprinklers in Test 70 with 10-ft (3.05-m) clearance. Fire spread in Tests 140 and 141 was somewhat less than in Tests 65, 66, and 70.

Test 143 was conducted with 18-in. (0.46-m) clearance between the top of storage and ceiling sprinkler deflectors, and with 0.30 density. Thirty-seven sprinklers operated compared with 36 sprinklers in Test 140 with 3-ft (0.91-m) clearance and 45 and 48 sprinklers in Tests 65 and 76 with 10-ft (3.05-m) clearance. Fire spread in Test 143 with 18-in. (0.46-m) clearance was somewhat less than in tests 65, 66, and 140 with 10-ft (3.05-m) and 3-ft (0.91-m) clearance.

Privately sponsored tests, using a 0.45 ceiling sprinkler density and an encapsulated commodity, indicated 40 sprinklers operating with 10-ft (3.05-m) clearance, 11 sprinklers operating with 3-ft (0.91-m) clearance, and 10 sprinklers operating with 18-in. (0.46-m) clearance. Fire spread was less in the test with 18-in. (0.46-m) clearance than 3-ft (0.91-m) clearance, and was also less with 3-ft (0.46-m) clearance than with 10-ft (3.05-m) clearance.

B-4-7 No tests were conducted with idle pallets in racks. Such storage conceivably would introduce fire severity in excess of that contemplated by protection criteria for an individual commodity classification.

B-5-3 The highest operating pressure at any sprinkler in the test program was 62.5 psi (430.93 kPa).

Tests in the 20-ft (6.10-m) high series were conducted using wood and metal bulkheads to determine whether bulkheads could be a substitute for either higher ceiling sprinkler densities or for intermediate sprinklers. Bulkheads of either type had no appreciable beneficial effect on the overall sprinkler performance in double row rack tests.

Tests 125 and 134 were conducted to compare the effect of a different commodity in the 30-ft (9.15-m) high test array. If the degree of damage above the top level of protection (fifth and sixth tiers) is ignored, the Class III commodity represented by Hallmark cards would appear to be protected to the same degree as Class II commodity.

Tests 132 and 135 were conducted to determine the effect of a different commodity in the 50-ft (15.24-m) test array. The degree of control achieved with the 3-M commodity in Test 135 closely approximates that achieved with standard commodity in Test 132. The results of the Hallmark Test 134 and the private Hallmark Test with geometry, in-rack sprinkler array, and in-rack sprinkler flow rate different from other tests, conducted as a separate program, suggests that in storage over 25 ft (7.62 m) high, Class III commodities may be protected in the same fashion as Class II commodities.

Tests 112 and 115 compare 10-ft (3.05-m) clearance above storage to sprinklers with 30-ft (9.15-m) clearance above storage.

B-5-7 Time of operation of the first sprinkler varied from 52 sec to 3 min 55 sec with most tests under 3 min, except in Test 64 (commodity Class III) where the first sprinkler operated in 7 min 44 sec. Fire detection more sensitive than waterflow is, therefore, considered necessary only in exceptional cases.

B-5-8 In most tests conducted, it was necessary to use small hose for mop-up operations. Small hoses were not used in the high expansion foam test.

Test 97 was conducted to evaluate the effect of dry pipe sprinkler operation. Test results were approximately the same as base test with wet pipe system. A study of NFPA records, however, indicates an increase in area of operation of 30 percent to be in order for dry pipe systems as compared with wet pipe systems.

B-5-10 In all valid tests, with double row racks, sprinkler water supplies were shut off at approximately 60 min. In only one test did the last sprinkler operate in excess of 30 min after ignition; the last sprinkler operated in excess of 25 min in three tests with the majority of tests involving the last sprinkler operating within 20 min.

B-5-13.2 Test 98 with solid shelves 24 ft (7.32 m) long and 7 ft 6 in. (2.29 m) deep at each level produced total destruction of the commodity in the main rack and jumped the aisle. Density was 0.3 gpm per sq ft [(12.22 L/min)/m^2] from ceiling sprinklers only. Test 108 with shelves 24 ft (7.32 m) long and 3 ft 6 in. (1.07 m) deep and with 6-in. (152.4-mm) longitudinal flue space and one level of sprinklers in the rack resulted in damage to most of the commodity in the main rack, but did not jump the aisle. Density from ceiling sprinklers was 0.375 gpm per sq ft [(15.28 L/min)/m^2], and rack sprinklers discharged at 15 psi (103.41 kPa).

These tests did not yield sufficient information to develop a comprehensive protection standard for solid shelf racks. Items such as increased ceiling density, use of bulkheads, other configurations of sprinklers in racks, and limitation of shelf length and width require consideration.

Where such rack installations exist or are contemplated, the damage potential should be considered, and sound engineering judgment should be used in designing the protection system.

Test 98, with solid shelving obstructing both the longitudinal and transverse flue space, produced unsatisfactory results and indicates a need for sprinklers at each level in such a rack structure.

Test 147 was conducted with ceiling sprinklers only. Density was 0.45 gpm per sq ft [(18.34 L/min)/m^2] with a sprinkler spacing of 100 sq ft (9.29 m^2). A total of 47 sprinklers opened, and 83 percent of the commodity was consumed. The fire jumped both aisles and spread to both ends of the main and target racks. The test was considered unsuccessful.

Test 148 was conducted with ceiling sprinklers and in-rack sprinklers. In-rack sprinklers were provided at each level (top of first, second, and third tiers) and were located in the longitudinal flue. They were directly above each other and 24 ft (7.32 m) on center or 22 ft (6.71 m) on each side of the ignition flue. Ceiling sprinkler discharge density was 0.375 gpm per sq ft [(15.3 L/min)/m^2]. In-rack sprinkler discharge pressure was 30 psi (206.8 kPa). A total of 46 ceiling sprinklers and 3 in-rack sprinklers opened, and 34 percent of the commodity was consumed. The fire consumed most of the material between the in-rack sprinklers and jumped both aisles.

B-5-14 Fire tests with open-top containers in the upper tier of storage and a portion of the third tier of storage produced an increase in sprinkler operation from 36 to 41 sprinklers and a more pronounced aisle jump and increase in fire spread in the main array. The smooth underside of the containers closely approximates fire behavior of slave pallets.

Installation of in-rack sprinklers or an increase in ceiling sprinkler density should be considered.

B-6-3 Tests 71, 73, 81, 83, 91, 92, 95, and 100 in the 20-ft (6.10-m) high array involving single level of in-rack sprinklers were conducted without heat or water shields. Results were satisfactory.

Test 115 was conducted with two levels of sprinklers in racks with shields. Test 116, identical to 115 but without water shields, produced a lack of control. Visual observation of lower level in-rack sprinklers that did not operate although they were in the fire area indicated a need for water shields.

Tests 115 and 116 were conducted to investigate the necessity for water shields where multiple levels of in-rack sprinklers are installed. Where water shields were not installed in Test 116, the fire jumped the aisle, and approximately 76 boxes were damaged. In Test 115 with water shields, the fire did not jump the aisle, and only 32 boxes were damaged. Water shields are, therefore, suggested wherever multiple levels of in-rack sprinklers are installed. (With the exception of installations with horizontal barriers or shelves that serve as water shields.)

B-6-4.1 In one 20-ft (6.1-m) high test, sprinklers were buried in the flue space 1 ft (0.30 m) above the bottom of the pallet load; results were satisfactory. Coverage of aisles by in-rack sprinklers is, therefore, not necessary, and distribution across tops of pallet loads at any level is not necessary for the occupancy classes tested.

B-6-5.2 In all tests with in-rack sprinklers, obstructions measuring 3 in. (76.2 mm) wide by 3 ft (0.30 m) long were introduced on each side of the sprinkler approximately 3 in. (76.2 mm) from the sprinkler to simulate rack structure member obstruction. This obstruction had no effect on sprinkler performance in the 20-ft (6.10-m) high tests.

Tests 103, 104, 105, and 109 in the 30-ft (9.15-m) high test with in-rack sprinklers obstructed by rack uprights produced unsatisfactory results. Tests 113, 114, 115, 117, 118, and 120 in the 30-ft (9.15-m) high test series with in-rack sprinklers located a minimum of 2 ft (0.61 m) from rack uprights produced improved results.

B-6-6 Operating pressures were 15 psi (103.4 kPa) on all tests of sprinklers in racks with storage 20 ft (6.10 m) high and 30 psi (206.8 kPa) with storage 30 ft (9.15 m) and 50 ft (15.24 m) high.

Tests 112 and 124 were conducted to compare the effect of increasing sprinkler discharge pressure at in-rack sprinklers from 30 psi (206.8 kPa) to 75 psi (517.1 kPa). With the higher discharge pressure the fire did not jump the aisle, and damage below the top level of protection within the racks was somewhat better controlled by the higher discharge pressure of the in-rack sprinklers. A pressure of 15 psi (103.4 kPa) was maintained on in-rack sprinklers in the first 30-ft (9.15-m) high Tests 103 and 104. Pressure on in-rack sprinklers in subsequent tests was 30 psi (206.8 kPa) except in Test 124 where it was 75 psi (517.1 kPa).

B-6-7 In all except one case, using the standard commodity, with one line of sprinklers installed in racks, only two sprinklers opened. In the one exception, two sprinklers opened in the main rack, and two sprinklers opened in the target rack.

B-6-8.1 Tests 65 and 66 compared with Test 69, and Test 93 compared with Test 94, indicated a reduction in areas of application of 44.5 and 45.5 percent, respectively, with 286°F (141°C) sprinklers as compared with 165°F (74°C) sprinklers. Other extensive Factory Mutual tests produced an average reduction of 40 percent. Design curves are based on this area reduction. In constructing the design curves, the 286°F (141°C) curves above 3600 sq ft (334.6 m^2) of application therefore represent 40 percent reductions in area of application of the 165°F (74°C) curves in the 6,000 sq ft (557.6 m^2) to 10,000 sq ft (929.41 m^2) range.

Test 84 indicated the number of 212°F (100°C) sprinklers operating is essentially the same as 165°F (74°C) sprinklers.

B-6-8.8 Tests 77 and 95 were conducted to investigate protection required on encapsulated commodity. The standard commodity [38 in. (0.97 m) × 38 in. (0.97 m) × 36 in. (0.91 m) high sheet metal container inside a 42 in. (1.07 m) × 42 in. (1.07 m) × 42 in. (1.07 m) double tri-walled carton] was covered with a sheet of 4-6 mil thick polyethylene film stapled in place at the bottom. Test 77 at 0.30 density with ceiling sprinklers only went beyond parameters for validity. Subsequent privately sponsored tests indicated control at 0.45 density. Test 95 indicated sprinklers at ceiling and in racks adequately control this hazard. These test results were compared with Tests 65 and 66 and Test 82 with comparable test configurations but without the plastic film covering.

A privately sponsored test was made with ceiling sprinklers only. At a density of 0.45 gpm per sq ft [(18.30 L/min)/m^2] 40 sprinklers operated. Fire spread was slightly greater than in Test 65 with 0.3 gpm per sq ft [(12.22 L/min)/m^2] discharging from 45 sprinklers. When distance from top of storage to ceiling was reduced from 10 ft (3.05 m) to 3 ft (0.91 m) with 0.45 gpm per sq ft [(18.33 L/min)/m^2] density, 11 sprinklers operated. Fire spread was less than in Test 65 or the previous privately sponsored test.

In order to evaluate the effect on plastic wrapping or encapsulation of pallet loads, Tests 77 and 95 were conducted as a part of the 20-ft (6.10-m) test series within the rack storage testing program, and Tests 1 and 2 were conducted as a part of privately sponsored Society of the Plastic Industries, Inc. tests. Both SPI Tests 1 and 2 are considered valid and indicate that Class I and II commodity may be protected by ceiling sprinklers only, using densities as indicated in design curves. These two tests also compare results of 3-ft (0.91-m) clearance from top of storage to sprinkler head deflectors with 10-ft (3.05-m) clearance from top of storage to sprinkler head deflectors. A significant reduction in the number of sprinklers opening is indicated with the 3-ft (0.91-m) deflector clearance to top of storage.

Subsequently, Tests 140 and 141 were made with the standard commodity. Distance from top of storage to sprinkler deflector was reduced to 3 ft (0.91 m). With 0.30 gpm per sq ft [(12.22 L/min)/m^2] density, 36 sprinklers operated; and with 0.20 gpm per sq ft [(8.15 L/min)/m^2] density, 89 sprinklers operated. Fire spread was somewhat less than in Tests 65 and 70 with a 10-ft (3.05-m) space between top of storage and ceiling.

B-6-11.2 Tests were not conducted with aisles wider than 8 ft (2.44 m) or less than 4 ft (1.22 m). It is, therefore, not possible to determine whether lower ceiling densities might be in order for aisle widths greater than 8 ft (2.44 m) or higher densities for aisle widths less than 4 ft (1.22 m).

B-6-13.1 Test 107, a multiple row rack test conducted with pallet loads butted against each other, was 12 rows long. Each row was four boxes deep. With 0.45 density from ceiling sprinklers only, fire spread to a depth of three rows on both sides of ignition point. Fire damage, number of sprinklers open, and time rack steel temperature above 1,000°F (538°C) were considerably greater than in comparable double row rack Test 68. Temperatures at ceiling did not reach dangerous limits. Fire intensity at the ends of rows was sufficiently intense to conclude racks with deeper rows would need additional protection.

B-7-12.1 The use of 165°F (74°C) sprinklers at ceiling for storage higher than 25 ft (7.62 m) results from fire test data. A test with 286°F (141°C) sprinklers and 0.45 density resulted in fire damage in the two top tiers just within acceptable limits with three ceiling sprinklers operating. A test with 0.45 density and 165°F (74°C) sprinklers gave a dramatic reduction in fire damage with four ceiling sprinklers operating.

The four 165°F (74°C) ceiling sprinklers operated before the first of the three 286°F (141°C) ceiling sprinklers. In both tests, two in-rack sprinklers at two levels operated at approximately the same time. The 286°F (141°C) sprinklers were at all times fighting a larger fire with less water than the 165°F (74°C) ceiling sprinklers.

Tests 115 and 119 compare ceiling sprinkler density of 0.30 gpm/ft^2 [(12.22 L/min)/m^2] with 0.45 gpm/ft^2 [(18.3 L/min)/m^2]. Damage patterns coupled with the number of boxes damaged in the main rack suggest that the increase in density produces improved control, particularly in the area above the top tier of in-rack sprinklers.

Tests 119 and 122 compare 286°F (141°C) with 165°F (74°C) ceiling sprinkler temperature rating. A review of the number of boxes damaged and the fire spread patterns indicates that the use of 165°F (74°C) ceiling sprinklers on a rack configuration that incorporates in-rack sprinklers dramatically reduces the amount of fire spread. Considering that in-rack sprinklers in the over-25-ft (7.62-m) series operated prior to ceiling sprinklers, it would seem that the installation of in-rack sprinklers converts what would normally be rapidly developing fire from the standpoint of ceiling sprinklers to a slower developing fire with lesser degree of heat release.

In the 20-ft (6.10-m) high test series, ceiling sprinklers operated before in-rack sprinklers. In the 30-ft (9.15-m) high series, ceiling sprinklers operated after in-rack sprinklers. The 50-ft (15.24-m) high test did not operate ceiling sprinklers. They would, however, be needed if fire occurred in upper levels.

These results indicate the effect of in-rack sprinklers on storages higher than 25 ft (7.62 m). From the ceiling operation standpoint, expected high-heat-release-rate fire was converted to a fire with a much lower heat release rate.

Since the fires developed slowly and opened sprinklers at two levels in the racks, only a few ceiling sprinklers were needed to establish control. Thus, sprinkler operating area is not varied with height for storage over 25-ft (7.62-m) high or for changes in sprinkler temperature rating and density.

All tests with sprinklers in racks were conducted using nominal 1/2-in. (12.7-mm) orifice size sprinklers of ordinary temperature.

B-8-1 In the RSP Rack Storage test series as well as the Stored Plastics Program Palletized test series, compartmented 16-oz (0.47-L) polystyrene jars were found to produce significantly higher protection requirements than the same commodity in a nested configuration. Polystyrene glasses and expanded polystyrene plates were comparable to the nested jars.

Different storage configurations within cartons or different products of the same basic plastic may therefore produce lesser protection requirements.

In Test RSP-7, nominal 15 ft (4.57 m) high with compartmented jars, a 0.60 gpm/ft^2 [(24.4 L/min)/m^2] density, 8-ft (2.44-m) aisles and 10-ft (3.05-m) ceiling clearance, 29 sprinklers opened. In tests RSP-4 with polystryrene glasses, RSP-5 with expanded polystyrene plates, and RSP-16 with nested polystyrene jars all stored at nominal 15-ft (4.57-m) height, 10-ft (3.05-m) ceiling clearance, 8-ft (2.44-m) aisles, and 0.60 gpm/ft^2 [(24.4 L/min)/m^2] density, only 4 sprinklers opened.

Test RSP-11 with expanded polystyrene plates, however, with 6-ft (1.83-m) aisles, increased the number of operating sprinklers to 29. Test RSP-10 with expanded polystyrene plates, nominally 15 ft (4.57 m) high with 10-ft (3.05-m) clearance and 8-ft (2.44-m) aisles, but protected by only 0.45 gpm/ft^2 [(18.3 L/min)/m^2] density, opened 46 sprinklers and burned 100 percent of the plastic commodity.

At a nominal 20-ft (6.10-m) storage height with 8-ft (2.44-m) aisles and 3-ft (0.91-m) ceiling clearance, 0.60 gpm/ft^2 [(24.4 L/min)/m^2] density opened 4 sprinklers with polystyrene glasses in RSP-2 and 11 sprinklers with expanded polystyrene plates in RSP-6. In Test RSP-8, however, with the ceiling clearance increased to 10 ft (3.05 m) and other variables held constant, 51 sprinklers opened, and 100 percent of the plastic commodity burned.

Test RSP-3 with polystyrene glasses at a nominal height of 25 ft (7.62 m) with 3-ft (0.91-m) ceiling clearance, 8-ft (2.44-m) aisles and 0.60 gpm/ft^2 [(24.4 L/min)/m^2] ceiling sprinkler density in combination with one level of in-rack sprinklers, resulted in 4 ceiling sprinklers and 2 in-rack sprinklers operating. RSP-9 with the same configuration, but with polystyrene plates, opened 12 ceiling and 3 in-rack sprinklers.

No tests were conducted with compartmented polystyrene jars at storage heights in excess of a nominal 15 ft (4.51 m) as a part of this program.

B-8-1.4 All tests in the RSP series were conducted utilizing 165°F (73.9°C) sprinklers. However, after close review of all test data, the 231C Committee believes that using intermediate or high temperature rated sprinklers will not cause the demand areas to be any larger than those designated in Chapter 8; therefore, their use should be allowed.

B-10-1.1.2 Test 85 was conducted to evaluate results of a liquid spill fire. Test results indicate it is not practical from an economic standpoint to install sprinkler systems with densities capable of controlling such a fire, and, therefore, industrial trucks should be fueled outside of buildings only.

Appendix C Referenced Publications

C-1 The following documents or portions thereof are referenced within this standard for informational purposes only and thus should not be considered part of the requirements of this document. The edition indicated for each reference is the current edition as of the date of the NFPA issuance of this document.

C-1.1 NFPA Publications. National Fire Protection Association, 1 Batterymarch Park, P.O. Box 9101, Quincy, MA 02269-9101.

NFPA 13, *Standard for the Installation of Sprinkler Systems*, 1989 edition

NFPA 13A, *Recommended Practice for the Inspection, Testing and Maintenance of Sprinkler Systems*, 1987 edition

NFPA 40E, *Code for the Storage of Pyroxylin Plastic*, 1986 edition

NFPA 51B, *Standard for Fire Prevention in Use of Cutting and Welding Processes*, 1989 edition

NFPA 71, *Standard for the Installation, Maintenance, and Use of Signaling Systems for Central Station Service*, 1989 edition

NFPA 72, *Standard for the Installation, Maintenance, and Use of Protective Signaling Systems*, 1990 edition

NFPA 81, *Standard for Fur Storage, Fumigation and Cleaning*, 1986 edition

NFPA 82, *Standard on Incinerators, Waste, and Linen Handling Systems and Equipment*, 1990 edition

NFPA 231E, *Recommended Practice for the Storage of Baled Cotton*, 1989 edition

Index

-T-

-V-

-W-

UNIFORM FIRE CODE STANDARD 81-3
MECHANICAL SMOKE-REMOVAL SYSTEMS

See Section 8102.7.1, *Uniform Fire Code*

SECTION 81.301 — SCOPE

Mechanical smoke-removal systems designed to remove smoke from high-piled storage areas after a fire is extinguished and assist the fire department during suppression operations shall be in accordance with this standard. When mechanical smoke-removal systems are provided, curtain boards shall be provided as required by UFC Section 8102.7.1.

SECTION 81.302 — SYSTEM CAPACITY

The volume of mechanical ventilation required shall be 300 cubic feet per minute per square foot (1524 L per second per square meter) of roof vent area required by UFC Table 81-B.

SECTION 81.303 — SUPPLY AIR

Supply air for exhaust fans shall be provided at or near the floor level and shall be sized to provide a minimum of 50 percent of required exhaust. Openings for supply air shall be uniformly distributed around the periphery of the area served.

SECTION 81.304 — FANS

Fans shall be in accordance with the following:

1. The individual capacity of a fan shall not exceed 30,000 cubic feet per minute (14 158.4 L/s);

2. One or more exhaust fans shall be provided in each curtained area, and when more than one exhaust fan is provided in a curtained area, the fans shall be uniformly spaced within the curtained area. The distance between fans within a curtained area shall not exceed 100 feet (30 480.0 mm);

3. Wiring and smoke-removal fan units shall be thermally protected in a manner that will provide continued operation for not less than 15 minutes while exposed to a temperature of 1,000°F (537.8°C); and

EXCEPTION: Wiring and electrical equipment installed on the exterior of the building.

4. Controls for mechanical smoke-removal systems shall be as follows:

4.1 On combination comfort air-handling and smoke-removal systems, and on independent comfort air-handling systems, fans shall be controlled to shut down in accordance with the automatic shutoff requirements of the Mechanical Code or by activation of automatic extinguishing or detection systems;

4.2 Electrical service to the smoke-removal systems shall be connected on the line side of the main electrical disconnect; and

4.3 The smoke-removal system shall be provided with a fire department control panel located in an approved location and clearly identified. The control panel room shall be protected by not less than a one-hour occupancy separation in accordance with the Building Code. The room shall be accessible from the exterior of the building. Automatic sprinkler protection shall be provided in the control room.

UNIFORM FIRE CODE STANDARD 81-4
HIGH-PILED STORAGE OF COMBUSTIBLE RECORDS IN BUILDINGS

See Sections 8101.1, 8104.2.3.1, 8104.2.3.2 and 8106.1, *Uniform Fire Code*

NOTE: This is a new standard.

The National Fire Protection Association Standard for Rack Storage of Materials, NFPA 231C—1995, is hereby adopted by reference as UFC Standard 81-4.

Supplemental standards referenced by NFPA 231C—1995 shall only be considered as guideline standards subject to approval by the chief.

For storage height of 12 feet (3658 mm) or less, see NFPA 13, *Standard for the Installation of Sprinkler Systems.*

NFPA 231C—1995 is available from the National Fire Protection Association, 1 Batterymarch Park, Box 9101, Quincy, Massachusetts 02269-9101.

SECTION 81.401 — AMENDMENTS

1. Sec. 1-1 is revised as follows:

1-1 Application and Scope. This standard applies to storage of combustible paper records stored in racks over 12 feet (3658 mm) in height.

Storage of plastic products, plastic records or plastic containers are outside of the scope of this standard. See UFC Standard 81-2.

For storage on shelving 30 inches (762 mm) or less, see UFC Standard 81-1.

Storage of hazardous materials and flammable liquids is outside the scope of this standard. See the *Uniform Fire Code.*

2. Sec. 1-2 is revised by changing definitions as follows:

The definition of "approved" shall be as set forth in *Uniform Fire Code*, Volume 1.

Delete the definitions of "authority having jurisdiction," "bulkhead," "early suppression fast response sprinklers (ESFR)," "labeled," "listed," "solid shelving" and "transverse flue space" and substitute as follows:

AUTHORITY HAVING JURISDICTION is the official responsible for the administration and enforcement of this standard.

BULKHEAD is a barrier installed vertically across the storage rack that extends from the floor to the top of storage for the depth of the rack.

EARLY SUPPRESSION FAST-RESPONSE (ESFR) SPRINKLER is a listed thermosensitive device designed to react at a predetermined temperature by automatically releasing a stream of water and distributing it in a specified pattern and quantity over a designated area so as to provide early suppression of a fire when installed on the appropriate sprinkler piping.

LABELED shall be as set forth in the *Uniform Fire Code.*

LISTED shall be as set forth in the *Uniform Fire Code.*

SOLID SHELVING, see *Uniform Fire Code*, Article 81.

TRANSVERSE FLUE SPACE, see *Uniform Fire Code*, Article 81.

Add the following definition:

CATWALK is a walkway used to access equipment or record storage racks and/or shelving. Catwalks are supported by the equipment, rack or shelving served. Catwalks are independent of the building structure and are a component of the storage system.

3. Sec. 2-1.1 is revised as follows:

2-1.1 Commodity Classification. Paper records shall be classified as Class III commodities.

4. Sec. 3-1 is deleted.

5. Sec. 3-2.1 is deleted.

6. Sec. 3-2.2 is deleted.

7. Sec. 3-2.3 is revised by adding a paragraph to the end of the section as follows:

Regardless of the requirements of this section, fire protection for the structure shall comply with the requirements set forth in the Building Code.

8. Sec. 3-2.3 (b) is revised by adding a paragraph to the end of the section as follows:

Each sprinkler protecting a column shall be capable of discharging 30 gpm (113.6 L/min.). The demand for the column sprinklers in the hydraulic design area shall be added to the sprinkler system demand. The spray shall be directed toward the column such that as much of the column surface is wetted as possible.

9. Sec. 3-3 is deleted.

10. Chapter 4 is revised by adding a section as follows:

4-1 Bulkhead. Racks greater than 60 feet (18 288 mm) in length shall be separated by a bulkhead or by an aisle [minimum 30-inch (762 mm) wide] separation. Bulkheads shall extend through the storage rack from aisle face to aisle face and from the floor to the top of storage. When the rack length exceeds 60 feet (18 288 mm) the bulkhead shall be located at the approximate midpoint of the rack. The maximum distance between bulkheads and aisles shall be 60 feet (18 288 mm). Bulkheads shall be constructed of $^1/_2$-inch (12.7 mm) gypsum board, $^1/_2$-inch thick (12.7 mm) plywood, or other approved material.

11. Chapter 4 is revised by adding a section as follows:

4-2 Catwalk. Catwalks 42 inches (1067 mm) or less in width that are used for access to upper level storage systems shall be supported from a rack or shelving system and shall be of noncombustible bar grate construction. Bar grate openings shall be a minimum of $^1/_2$ inch (12.7 mm).

> **EXCEPTION:** Catwalks greater than 42 inches (1067 mm) in width may be of solid construction.

12. Chapter 4 is revised by adding a section as follows:

4-8 Aisle Widths. Aisles shall be provided as set forth in UFC Article 81. When aisles are less than 42 inches (1067 mm) in width, the storage system shall be classified as multirow racking. For protection requirements, see Chapter 5.

13. Sec. 4-7 is deleted and substitute as follows:

4-7 Storage of Idle Combustibles. Bulk storage of idle combustible pallets shall be in accordance with UFC Standard 81-1.

14. Sec. 4-3 is deleted and substitute as follows:

4-3 Flue Spaces. For records storage systems classified as multiple-row racks in accordance with this standard, the service aisles between the racks or shelving shall be considered the flue spaces.

15. Sec. 4-4 is deleted and substitute as follows:

4-4 Storage Arrangements. Paper records are allowed to be stored in cardboard cartons or as open files directly on the rack or shelf.

Plastic encapsulation of records is beyond the scope of this standard. See UFC Standard 81-2.

When records storage configuration consists of racks or shelving in single or double rows with a total width of 72 inches (1829 mm) or less and aisles with a clear width of 42 inches (1067 mm) or more, and no longitudinal flue, the storage shall be considered single-row racks.

When records storage configuration consists of racks or shelving in single or double rows with a total width greater than 72 inches (1829 mm) and less than 12 feet (3658 mm), measured from aisle to aisle, and aisles with a clear width of 42 inches (1067 mm) or more, the storage shall be considered double-row racks.

When records storage configuration consists of racks or shelving in single or double rows with a total width greater than 12 feet (3658 mm), measured from aisle to aisle, or with aisles less than 42 inches (1067 mm) in clear width regardless of the storage rack or shelving width, the storage shall be considered multirow racks.

16. Sec. 4-6 is deleted and substitute as follows:

4-6 Solid Shelving. Racks or shelf storage of paper records in cardboard cartons on wood or metal shelving shall be treated as racks without solid shelves.

17. Chapter 5 is revised by adding a section as follows:

5-1.3 This chapter shall apply when required by Table 81-A.

18. Sec. 5-2.1 is revised by substituting the phrase "the Building Code. See UBC Standard 9-1" for the phrase "NFPA 13, *Standard for the Installation of Sprinkler Systems.*"

19. Sec. 5-8 is revised by deleting the first sentence and substituting as follows:

When required by UFC Table 81-A, small hose valve stations shall be provided and shall be spaced such that they are accessible to reach all portions of the high-piled storage area, on all levels, based on the length of hose, hose stream, and travel paths.

20. Sec. 6-1 is revised by substituting the phrase "the Building Code. See UBC Standard 9-1" for the phrase "NFPA 13, *Standard for the Installation of Sprinkler Systems.*"

21. Sec. 6-9.2 is deleted and substitute as follows:

For storage over 20 feet (6096 mm), up to and including 25 feet (7620 mm), protected with ceiling sprinklers only, densities given in design curves shall be adjusted according to Figure 6-9.2. For storage less than 20 feet (6096 mm), with in-rack sprinklers, Figure 6-9.2 is applicable.

22. Sec. 6-12 is revised by deleting the last sentence of the paragraph.

23. Tables 6-12, 6-14 and 6-14.1 are revised by deleting "Yes" in the column titled "Apply Figure 6-9.2" under the "Without In-Rack Sprinklers" category and substituting "No."

24. Sec. 6-14 is revised by adding a section as follows:

6-14.4 In records storage systems with a catwalk, when sprinklers are required, in-rack sprinklers shall be located in the center of the aisle, below each level of catwalk.

25. Sec. 6-15.1 is revised to delete the last sentence of the paragraph.

26. Sec. 7-1 is revised by substituting the phrase "the Building Code. See UBC Standard 9-1" for the phrase "NFPA 13, *Standard for the Installation of Sprinkler Systems.*"

27. Sec. 7-2 is revised by adding a section as follows:

7-2.1 Maximum spacing of in-rack sprinklers shall not be more than 10 feet (3048 mm) along the branch line. The maximum area protected by an in-rack sprinkler shall not exceed 100 square feet (9.3 m^2). Sprinklers shall be staggered vertically and horizontally when more than one level is installed.

28. Sec. 7-5 is revised by adding a section as follows:

7-5.1 In multirow racks with catwalk systems, in-rack sprinklers are allowed to be located below the catwalk, in the center of the aisle. Sprinklers installed in the center of the aisles, below the catwalks, are considered in-rack flue sprinklers.

29. Table 7-10.1 is revised by adding the following footnote which is referenced in the second column, main heading titled "In-rack sprinklers—approximate vertical spacing at tier nearest the vertical distance and maximum horizontal spacing."

[9]Sprinkler spacing shall not exceed 100 square feet (9.3 m^2) spacing.

30. Sec. 7-14 is deleted and substitute as follows:

7-14 In-rack Sprinkler Spacing. Maximum spacing of in-rack sprinklers in multiple-row racks with storage higher than 25 feet (7620 mm) shall not be more than 10 feet (3048 mm) along the branch line. The maximum area protected by an in-rack sprinkler shall not exceed 100 square feet (9.3 m^2). Sprinklers shall be staggered vertically and horizontally when more than one level is installed. See Figures 7-13 (a), (b) and (c).

31. Chapter 8 is deleted.

32. Sec. 9-1.8 is revised by substituting the phase "the Building Code. See UBC Standard 9-1" for the phrase "NFPA 13, *Standard for the Installation of Sprinkler Systems.*"

33. Sec. 10-2.4 is revised by substituting the phase "the Building Code. See UBC Standard 9-1" for the phrase "NFPA 13, *Standard for the Installation of Sprinkler Systems.*"

34. Chapters 11, 12 and 13 are deleted.

UNIFORM FIRE CODE STANDARD 82-1
LIQUEFIED PETROLEUM GAS STORAGE AND USE

See Sections 5201.3.2, 5203.5.1, 8201, 8203, 8204, 8206, 8208, 8211, 8212.11.3 and 8214.3, *Uniform Fire Code*

This standard, with certain exceptions, is based on the National Fire Protection Association Standard for the Storage and Handling of Liquefied Petroleum Gases, NFPA 58—1989.[1]

Part I of this standard contains the exceptions to NFPA 58—1989.[1]

Part II of this standard contains NFPA 58—1989[1] reproduced in its entirety with permission of the publisher.

▬▬▬ vertically in the margin of Part II indicates there is a revision to the provisions within Part I.

Supplemental standards referenced by NFPA 58—1989[1] shall only be considered as guidelines subject to approval by the chief.

[1]The current edition is NFPA 58—1995.

Part I

SECTION 82.101 — AMENDMENTS

The Standard for the Storage and Handling of Liquefied Petroleum Gases, NFPA 58—1989, applies to the design, construction, location and installation of liquefied petroleum gas systems at consumer sites, except as otherwise provided in *Uniform Fire Code,* Volume 1 and Mechanical Code and except as follows:

1. Sec. 1-2.1.2 is revised by changing the second sentence as follows:

When the possibility of ammonia contamination exists (such as may be the result from the dual use of transportation or storage equipment), the LP-gas shall be tested in accordance with approved methods.

2. Sec. 1-2.3.1 (b) is revised as follows:

(b) Marine and pipeline terminals, natural gas processing plants, refineries or tank farms ("tank farm" storage at industrial locations is covered by this standard).

3. Sec. 1-2.3.1 (c) is deleted.

4. Sec. 1-2.3.1 (e) is revised as follows:

(e) LP-gas used with oxygen shall comply with *Uniform Fire Code* Article 49.

5. Sec. 1-2.3.1 (f) is revised as follows:

(f) Those portions of nonindustrial appliance and piping installations covered by the Mechanical and Plumbing Codes. For the purpose of application of this standard, the Mechanical and Plumbing Codes are applicable to piping beyond the first stage of pressure regulation.

6. Sec. 1-2.3.1 (h) is deleted.

7. Sec. 1-2.4 is deleted.

8. Sec. 1-3.1.1 is revised as follows:

1-3.1.1 Systems, or components assembled to make up systems, shall be approved as specified in Table 1-3. This provision shall be considered to have been met by one of the following methods:

1. Listing by a nationally recognized testing laboratory.
2. Approval by the chief.

9. Sec. 1-3.1.2 is revised as follows:

1-3.1.2 Approval applies to the complete system, or to the individual components of which it is composed, as specified in Table 1-3.

10. Sec. 1-5 is deleted.

11. Sec. 1-7 is revised by changing and adding definitions as follows:

AUTHORITY HAVING JURISDICTION is the official responsible for the administration and enforcement of this code.

NATIONAL ELECTRICAL CODE (NEC), NFPA 70 (as used in this standard), is the Electrical Code as defined in *Uniform Fire Code,* Volume 1.

SPECIAL PROTECTION is a means of limiting the temperature of an LP-gas container for purposes of minimizing the possibility of failure of the container as the result of fire exposure.

When required by this standard, special protection is allowed to consist of any of the following: applied insulated coatings, mounding, burial, water spray fixed systems or fixed monitor nozzles meeting the criteria specified in this standard (see 3-10.3), or by other means approved for this purpose.

The definitions of "AGA," "ANSI," "API," "approved," "ASME," "ASTM," "compressed gas," "labeled," "listed," "NFPA" and "UL" shall be as set forth in *Uniform Fire Code,* Volume 1.

12. Sec. 2-2.1.3 is revised as follows:

2-2.1.3 Containers shall be designed, fabricated, tested and marked (or stamped) in accordance with the Regulations of the U.S. Department of Transportation (DOT) or shall be in accordance with approved nationally recognized standards. See *Uniform Fire Code* Article 90, Standard a.5.1.

13. Sec. 2-2.2.3 (c) is revised as follows:

(c) Wind loading on containers shall be based on wind pressures on the projected area as required by the Building Code.

14. Sec. 2-2.2.3 (d) is revised as follows:

(d) Seismic loading on containers shall be as required by the Building Code.

15. Sec. 2-3.2.3 is revised as follows:

2-3.2.3 American Society of Mechanical Engineers containers for LP-gas shall be equipped with listed direct spring-loaded relief valves or equivalent.

Remainder of paragraph, exception and Table 2-3.2.3 are deleted.

16. Sec. 2-4.1.2 is revised as follows:

2-4.1.2 Piping, pipe and tubing fittings and valves used to supply utilization equipment shall be in accordance with the Mechanical Code or Plumbing Code for LP-gas service.

17. Sec. 2-4.1.3 is revised as follows:

2-4.1.3 Pipe and tubing shall comply with 2-4.2.1 and 2-4.3.1 or shall be of material which has been investigated and tested to determine that it is safe and suitable for the proposed service and is recommended for that service by the manufacturer and shall be acceptable to the chief.

18. Sec. 2-4.2.1 is revised as follows:

2-4.2.1 Pipe shall be wrought iron or steel (black or galvanized), brass, copper or polyethylene (see Section 3-7.6) and shall be in accordance with the Mechanical or Plumbing code for LP-gas service.

Also:
Delete Items (a) through (g).

19. Sec. 2-4.3.1 is revised as follows:

2-4.3.1 Tubing shall be steel, brass, copper or polyethylene (see Section 3-2.7.6) and shall be in accordance with the Mechanical or Plumbing code.

Also:
Delete Items (a) through (d).

20. Sec. 2-4.4.1 (c) 1 is revised as follows:

(1) Polyethylene fittings shall be designed in accordance with nationally recognized standards.

21. Sec. 2-4.6.2 is revised as follows:

2-4.6.2 Hose, hose connections, flex connectors and quick connectors shall be listed by a nationally recognized testing laboratory or may be approved.

22. Sec. 2-5.4.2 (a) is revised as follows:

(a) Indirect vaporizers with an inside diameter of more than 6 inches (152.4 mm) shall be constructed in accordance with the applicable provisions of nationally recognized standards for a design pressure of 250 psig (1723.7 kPa) and shall be permanently and legibly marked with:

Items (1) through (4) remain as printed.

23. Sec. 2-5.4.3 (a) is revised as follows:

(a) Design and construction of direct-fired vaporizers shall be in accordance with the applicable provisions of nationally recognized standards for the working conditions to which the vaporizer will be subjected and it shall be permanently marked with:

Items (1) through (6) remain as printed.

24. Sec. 2-5.4.3 (f) is revised by deleting "(or its ASME Code equivalent—see Note 1 of Table 2-2.2.2)."

25. Sec. 2-5.4.4 (a) is revised as follows:

(a) The vaporizing chamber, tubing, pipe coils or other heat exchange surface containing the LP-gas to be vaporized shall be constructed in accordance with the applicable provisions of nationally recognized standards for a minimum design pressure of 250 psig (1723.7 kPa) and shall be permanently and legibly marked with:

Items (1) through (4) remain as printed.

26. Sec. 2-5.4.6 (f) is revised by deleting "(for its ASME Code equivalent—see Note 1 of Table 2-2.2.2)."

27. Sec. 2-5.4.7 (f) is revised by deleting the third sentence.

28. Sec. 2-6 title is revised as follows:

2-6 Appliances in Buildings.

29. Sec. 2-6.1.1 is revised as follows:

2-6.1.1 LP-gas appliances in buildings shall be in accordance with the Mechanical and Plumbing codes.

30. Sec. 2-6.2 is deleted.

31. Sec. 3-1.1.4 is revised as follows:

3-1.1.4 LP-gas systems shall be installed in accordance with approved nationally recognized standards and the Mechanical and Plumbing codes.

Also:
Delete Items (a) through (j).

32. Sec. 3-2.2.6 (c) is revised by deleting the last sentence.

33. Sec. 3-2.2.6 (e) is revised by changing the last sentence as follows:

Horizontal separation is not required between aboveground LP-gas containers and underground tanks containing flammable or combustible liquids installed in accordance with the *Uniform Fire Code,* Article 79.

34. Sec. 3-2.2.6 (f) is revised as follows:

(f) The minimum separation between LP-gas containers and oxygen or gaseous hydrogen containers shall be in accordance with Table 3-2.2.6 (f) except that lesser distances are allowed where protective structures interrupt the line of sight between uninsulated portions of the oxygen or hydrogen containers and the LP-gas containers. The location and arrangement of such structures shall minimize the problems cited in the note to 3-2.2.8. The minimum separation between LP-gas containers and liquefied hydrogen containers shall be in accordance with Article 75 of the *Uniform Fire Code.*

35. Sec. 3-2.2.6 (h) is revised as follows:

(h) When LP-gas containers are to be stored or used in the same area with other compressed gases, the containers shall be marked to identify their contents in accordance with nationally recognized standards.

36. Sec. 3-2.6.1 (d) (1) b is revised by deleting the last sentence in the exception.

37. Sec. 3-2.7.6 is revised to require the minimum burial depth of 18 inches (457.2 mm) in lieu of 12 inches (304.8 mm).

38. Sec. 3-2.9.1 is revised as follows:

3-2.9.1 After assembly, piping systems, including hose, shall be tested and proven free of leaks at not less than the normal operating pressure. Piping within the scope of the Mechanical and Plumbing codes shall be pressure tested in accordance with the provisions of those codes. Tests shall not be made with a flame.

39. Sec. 3-4.2.3 (b) is revised by changing the first sentence as follows:

Hose, hose connections and flexible connectors shall be designed for a working pressure of not less than 350 psig (2413.2 kPa), shall comply with Section 2-4.6 and shall be installed in accordance with the Mechanical and Plumbing codes.

40. Sec. 3-4.3.8 is deleted.

41. Sec. 3-4.8.3 (a) is deleted.

42. Sec. 3-4.8.4 is added as follows:

3-4.8.4 Listed and approved LP-gas commercial food service appliances shall be permitted to be used inside restaurants and in attended commercial food catering operations provided that no commercial food service appliances shall have more than two 10-ounce (0.296 L) nonrefillable butane gas containers complying with nationally recognized standards and having a maximum water capacity of 1.08 pounds (0.49 kg) per container connected directly to the appliance at any time and containers shall not be manifolded. See Article 90, Standard u.1.8. The appliance's fuel container(s) shall be an integral part of the listed, approved, commercial food service device and shall be connected without the use of a rubber hose. Butane containers shall be listed. Storage of containers shall be in accordance with Section 5-3.1.

43. Sec. 3-4.9.1 is revised as follows:

3-4.9.1 Containers are allowed to be installed on noncombustible roofs of buildings constructed as required for an occupancy separation having a fire-resistive rating of not less than the following:

Groups B, F, M and S Occupancies	Two Hours
All other occupancies	Four Hours

EXCEPTION: When the quantity of gas does not exceed 60 gallons (227.1 L), a noncombustible roof without a fire-resistive rating is allowed.

44. Sec. 3-4.10.2 (d) is revised as follows:

(d) Hose shall not be used to carry liquid between the container and the building, or at any point in the liquid line except as the appliance connector complying with the Mechanical Code or Plumbing code.

45. Sec. 3-5 is deleted.

46. Sec. 3-6.2.2 (a) is revised as follows:

(a) Containers shall be designed, fabricated, tested and marked (or stamped) in accordance with the Regulations of the U.S. Department of Transportation (DOT) or shall be in accordance with approved nationally recognized standards. See *Uniform Fire Code* Article 90, Standard a.5.1.

Delete Items (1) and (2) and redesignate the remaining items.

47. Sec. 3-6.2.2 (a) (6) is revised as follows:

(6) ASME containers covered in this section shall be constructed for a minimum 250 psig (1723.7 kPa) design pressure except that containers installed in enclosed spaces on vehicles and engine fuel containers for industrial trucks and buses shall be constructed for at least a 312.5 psig (2154.6 kPa) design.

48. Sec. 3-6.2.5 (a) (1) is revised as follows:

(1) Pipe shall be wrought iron or steel (black or galvanized), brass or copper and shall comply with nationally recognized standards.

Delete Items (a) through (f).

49. Sec. 3-6.2.5 (b) is revised as follows:

(b) Tubing shall be steel, brass or copper and shall comply with nationally recognized standards.

Delete Items (b) (1) (a) through (d).

50. Sec. 3-6.3.1 is revised as follows:

3-6.3.1 This section applies to LP-gas installation or industrial trucks (including forklift trucks) both to propel them and to provide energy for their materials handling attachments.

51. Sec. 3-6.3.6 is revised as follows:

3-6.3.6 Industrial trucks (including forklift trucks) powered by LP-gas engine fuel systems shall comply with the following:

Items (a) through (b) remain as printed.

52. Sec. 3-6.5.1 is revised as follows:

3-6.5.1 Stationary engines and gas turbines installed in buildings including portable engines used in lieu of or to supplement stationary engines shall be approved and comply with the applicable provisions of Chapters 1 and 2 and Section 3-2 of this standard.

53. Sec. 3-9.5.2 is revised by substituting the phrase "UFC Standard 10-1" for the phrase "NFPA 10."

54. Sec. 3-10.3.4 is revised as follows:

3-10.3.4 If water spray fixed systems are used, they shall be in accordance with UFC Standard 79-2. Such systems shall be automatically actuated by fire-responsive devices and also have capability for manual actuation.

55. Sec. 3-10.3.5 is revised as follows:

3-10.3.5 If monitor nozzles are used, they shall be located and arranged so that all container surfaces likely to be exposed to fire shall be wetted. Such systems shall otherwise be in accordance with UFC Standard 79-2 and shall be automatically actuated by fire-responsive devices and also have capability for manual actuation.

56. Chapter 5 is revised by adding Section 5-3.3.4 as follows:

5-3.3.4 Buildings containing more than 60 gallons (227.1 L) of LP-gas shall be in accordance with the Building Code for hazardous occupancies, Group H, Division 2.

57. Chapter 7 is revised by adding Section 7-1.1.3 as follows:

7-1.1.3 Buildings used for storage or handling LP-gas in excess of 60 gallons (227.1 L) shall be in accordance with the Building Code for a Group H, Division 2 Occupancy. Such buildings shall also be in accordance with the requirements of this chapter.

58. Sec. 7-2.3 is revised by adding Section 7-2.3.2 to read as follows:

7-2.3.2 Occupancy separations shall be in accordance with the Building Code. Occupancy separations shall be designed to withstand a static pressure of at least 100 psf (4788.0 Pa).

59. Sec. 7-3 is deleted.

60. Sec. 8-1.1 is revised as follows:

8-1.1 Refrigerated containers shall be built in accordance with approved nationally recognized standards for the conditions of maximum allowable working pressure, design temperature and hydrostatic testing. See *Uniform Fire Code* Article 90.

61. Sec. 8-1.1.1 is revised as follows:

8-1.1.1 When the American Society of Mechanical Engineers Unfired Pressure Vessel Code Section VIII is used for containers having pressure of 15 psig (103.4 kPa) or more, joint efficiencies in Table UW 12, Column C, shall not be used.

62. Sec. 8-1.1.2 is revised as follows:

8-1.1.2 See *Uniform Fire Code* Article 90, Standard a.3.4, including Appendix R, for container construction having pressures less than 15 psig (103.4 kPa). For austenitic steels or nonferrous materials in such construction, see Appendix Q.

63. Chapter 9 is deleted.

Part II

Contents

NFPA 58

Standard for the Storage and Handling of

Liquefied Petroleum Gases

1989 Edition

Metric equivalents in this standard are approximate and shall not be used to lessen any provision.

NOTICE: An asterisk (*) following the number or letter designating a paragraph indicates explanatory material on that paragraph in Appendix A.

Information on referenced publications can be found in Chapter 9 and Appendix J.

Chapter 1 General Provisions

1-1 Introduction.

1-1.1 General Properties of LP-Gas.

1-1.1.1 LP-Gases, as defined in this standard (*see 1-2.1*), are gases at normal room temperatures and atmospheric pressure. They liquefy under moderate pressure, readily vaporizing upon release of this pressure. It is this property which permits transporting and storing them in concentrated liquid form, while normally using them in vapor form. The potential fire hazard of LP-Gas vapor is comparable to that of natural or manufactured gas, except that LP-Gas vapors are heavier than air. The ranges of flammability are considerably narrower and lower than those of natural or manufactured gas. For example, the lower flammable limits of the more commonly used LP-Gases are: propane, 2.15 percent; butane, 1.55 percent. These figures represent volumetric percentages of gas in gas-air mixtures.

1-1.1.2 The boiling point of pure normal butane is 31°F (-0.6°C); of pure propane, -44°F (-42°C). Both products are liquids at atmospheric pressure at temperatures lower than their boiling points. Vaporization is rapid at temperatures above the boiling point, thus liquid propane normally does not present a flammable liquid hazard. For additional information on these and other properties of the principal LP-Gases, see Appendix B.

1-1.2 Federal Regulations.

1-1.2.1 Regulations of the U.S. Department of Transportation (DOT) are referenced throughout this standard. Prior to April 1, 1967, these regulations were promulgated by the Interstate Commerce Commission (ICC).

1-2 Scope.

1-2.1 Liquefied Petroleum Gas.

1-2.1.1 As used in this standard, the terms "liquefied petroleum gas(es)," "LP-Gas" and "LPG" are synonymous and shall mean and include any material having a vapor pressure not exceeding that allowed for commercial propane composed predominantly of the following hydrocarbons, either by themselves or as mixtures: propane, propylene, butane (normal butane or isobutane), and butylene (including isomers).

1-2.1.2 LP-Gas stored or used in systems within the scope of this standard shall not contain ammonia. When such a possibility exists (such as may result from the dual use of transportation or storage equipment), the LP-Gas shall be tested as follows:

(a) Allow a moderate vapor stream of the product to be tested to escape from the container. A rotary, slip tube, or fixed level gauge is a convenient vapor source.

(b) Wet a piece of red litmus paper by pouring distilled water over it while holding it with clean tweezers.

(c) Hold the wetted litmus paper in the vapor stream from the container for 30 seconds.

(d) The appearance of any blue color on the litmus paper indicates that ammonia is present in the product.

NOTE 1: Since the red litmus paper will turn blue when exposed to any basic (alkaline) solution, care in making the test and interpreting the results is required. Tap water, saliva, perspiration or hands that have been in contact with water having a pH greater than 7, or with any alkaline solution, will give erroneous results.

NOTE 2: For additional information on the natùre of this problem and conducting the test, see *Recommendations for Prevention of Ammonia Contamination of LP-Gas*, published by the National Propane Gas Association.

1-2.2 Application of Standard.

1-2.2.1 This standard applies to the highway transportation of LP-Gas and to the design, construction, installation, and operation of all LP-Gas systems, including marine and pipeline terminals, except those designated by 1-2.3.

1-2.3 Nonapplication of Standard.

1-2.3.1 This standard does not apply to:

(a) Frozen ground containers used for the storage of LP-Gas.

(b) Natural gas processing plants, refineries and petrochemical plants except at the discretion of the owner/operator or the authority having jurisdiction, this standard may be utilized with respect to the storage and transfer portion of such installations.

(c) LP-Gas (including refrigerated storage) at utility gas plants. NFPA 59, *Standard for the Storage and Handling of Liquefied Petroleum Gases at Utility Gas Plants*, shall apply.

(d) Chemical plants where specific approval of construction and installation plans, based on substantially similar requirements, is obtained from the authority having jurisdiction.

(e) LP-Gas used with oxygen. NFPA 51, *Standard for the Design and Installation of Oxygen-Fuel Gas Systems for Welding, Cutting, and Allied Processes*, and ANSI Z49.1, *Safety in Welding and Cutting*, shall apply.

(f) Those portions of LP-Gas systems covered by NFPA 54 (ANSI Z223.1), *National Fuel Gas Code.*

NOTE: Several types of LP-Gas systems are not covered by the *National Fuel Gas Code* as noted in 1.1.1(b) therein. These include, but are not restricted to, most portable applications; many farm installations; vaporization, mixing, and gas manufacturing; temporary systems, e.g., in construction; and systems on vehicles. For those systems within its scope, the *National Fuel Gas Code* is applicable to those portions of a system downstream of the outlet of the first stage of pressure regulation.

(g) Transportation by air (including use in hot air balloons), rail, or water under the jurisdiction of the U.S. Department of Transportation.

(h) Marine fire protection. NFPA 302, *Fire Protection Standard for Pleasure and Commercial Motor Craft*, shall apply.

1-2.4 Retroactivity.

1-2.4.1 Unless otherwise stated, the provisions of this standard shall not be applied retroactively.

(a) Existing plants, appliances, equipment, buildings, structures, and installations for the storage, handling, or use of LP-Gas in compliance with the provisions of this standard in effect at the time of manufacture or installation may be continued in use provided that such continued use does not constitute a distinct hazard to life or adjoining property.

(b) The stocks of equipment and appliances on hand in such locations as manufacturer's storage, distribution warehouses, and dealer's storage and showrooms in compliance with the provisions of this standard in effect at the time of manufacture may be placed in use (provided such use does not constitute a distinct hazard to life or adjoining property), but all new equipment and appliances manufactured after the effective date of this standard shall comply with its provisions.

1-3 Acceptance of Equipment and Systems.

1-3.1 Method of Acceptance.

1-3.1.1 Systems, or components assembled to make up systems, shall be approved (*see Section 1-7, Approved*) as specified in Table 1-3.

1-3.1.2 Acceptance applies to the complete system, or to the individual components of which it is comprised, as specified in Table 1-3.

1-4 LP-Gas Odorization.

1-4.1 LP-Gas to be Odorized.

1-4.1.1* All LP-Gases shall be odorized prior to delivery to a distributing plant by the addition of a warning agent of such character that they are detectable, by a distinct odor, down to a concentration in air of not over one-fifth the lower limit of flammability.

Exception: Odorization, however, is not required if harmful in the use of further processing of the LP-Gas, or if such odorization will serve no useful purpose as a warning agent in such further use or processing.

1-4.1.2 If odorization is required, the presence of such odorant shall be determined by sniff testing or other means and the results documented:

(a) Whenever LP-Gas is delivered to a distributing plant, and

(b) When shipments of LP-Gas bypass the distributing plant.

1-5 Notification of Installations.

1-5.1 Fixed Installations.

1-5.1.1 Plans for fixed (stationary) installations utilizing storage containers of over 2,000 gal (7.6 m^3) individual water capacity, or with aggregate water capacity exceeding 4,000 gal (15.1 m^3), shall be submitted to the authority having jurisdiction before the installation is started. [*See also 3-4.9.1(e).*]

Table 1-3

Containers Used	Capacity in Water Gal (m^3)	Approval Applies to:
DOT Cylinders	Up to 120 (0.454) (1,000 lb, 454 kg)	1. Container Valves and Connectors 2. Manifold Valve Assemblies 3. Regulators and Pressure Relief Devices
ASME Tanks	2,000 (7.6 m^3) or less	1. Container System*, including Regulator, or 2. Container Assembly* and Regulator separately
ASME Tanks	Over 2,000 (7.6 m^3)	1. Container Valves 2. Container Excess Flow Valves, Back Flow Check Valves, or alternate means of providing this protection such as remotely controlled Manual or Automatic Internal Valves 3. Container Gauging Devices · 4. Regulators and Container Pressure Relief Devices

*Where necessary to alter or repair such systems or assemblies in the field in order to provide for different operating pressures, change from vapor to liquid withdrawal, or the like, such changes may be made by the use of approved components.

1-5.2 Temporary Installations.

1-5.2.1 The authority having jurisdiction shall be notified of temporary (not to exceed six months) installations of the sizes covered in 1-5.1.1 before the installation is started.

1-6 Personnel.

1-6.1 Qualification of Personnel.

1-6.1.1 In the interests of safety, all persons employed in handling LP-Gases shall be trained in proper handling and operating procedures.

1-7 Definitions, Glossary of Terms and Abbreviations.

AGA. American Gas Association.

ANSI. American National Standards Institute.

API. American Petroleum Institute.

API-ASME Container (or Tank). A container constructed in accordance with the pressure vessel code jointly developed by the American Petroleum Institute and the American Society of Mechanical Engineers (*see Appendix D*).

Approved. Acceptable to the "authority having jurisdiction."

NOTE: The National Fire Protection Association does not approve, inspect or certify any installations, procedures, equipment, or materials nor does it approve or evaluate testing laboratories. In determining the acceptability of installations or procedures, equipment or materials, the authority having jurisdiction may base acceptance on compliance with NFPA or other appropriate standards. In the absence of such standards, said authority may require evidence of proper installation, procedure or use. The authority having jurisdiction may also refer to the listings or labeling practices of an organization concerned with product evaluations which is in a position to determine compliance with appropriate standards for the current production of listed items.

ASME. American Society of Mechanical Engineers.

ASME Code. The *Boiler and Pressure Vessel Code* (Section VIII, "Rules for the Construction of Unfired Pressure Vessels") of the American Society of Mechanical Engineers. Only Division I of Section VIII of the ASME Code is applicable in this standard except UG-125 through UG-136 shall not apply.

ASME Container (or Tank). A container constructed in accordance with the ASME Code. (*See Appendix D.*)

ASTM. American Society for Testing and Materials.

Authority Having Jurisdiction. The "authority having jurisdiction" is the organization, office or individual responsible for "approving" equipment, an installation or a procedure.

NOTE: The phrase "authority having jurisdiction" is used in NFPA documents in a broad manner since jurisdictions and "approval" agencies vary as do their responsibilities. Where public safety is primary, the "authority having jurisdiction" may be a federal, state, local or other regional department or individual such as a fire chief, fire marshal, chief of a fire prevention bureau, labor department, health department, building official, electrical inspector, or others having statutory authority. For insurance purposes, an insurance inspection department, rating bureau, or other insurance company representative may be the "authority having jurisdiction." In many circumstances the property owner or his designated agent assumes the role of the "authority having jurisdiction"; at government installations, the commanding officer or departmental official may be the "authority having jurisdiction."

Bureau of Explosives (B of E). An agency of the Association of American Railroads.

Cargo Tank. (Primarily a DOT designation.) A container used to transport LP-Gas over the highway as liquid cargo, either mounted on a conventional truck chassis or as an integral part of a transporting vehicle in which the container constitutes in whole, or in part, the stress member used as a frame. Essentially a permanent part of the transporting vehicle.

CGA. Compressed Gas Association, Inc..

Charging. See Filling.

Compressed Gas. Any material or mixture having in the container an absolute pressure exceeding 40 psia (276 kPa absolute) at 70°F (21.1°C), or regardless of the pressure at 70°F (21.1°C), having an absolute pressure exceeding 104 psia (717 kPa absolute) at 130°F (54.4°C).

Container. Any vessel, including cylinders, tanks, portable tanks and cargo tanks, used for the transporting or storing of LP-Gases.

Container Appurtenances. Items connected to container openings needed to make a container a gastight entity. These include, but are not limited to, pressure relief devices; shutoff, backflow check, excess flow check and internal valves; liquid level gauges; pressure gauges; and plugs.

Container Assembly. An assembly consisting essentially of the container and fittings for all container openings. These include shutoff valves, excess flow valves, liquid level gauging devices, pressure relief devices and protective housings.

Cylinder. A portable container constructed to DOT (formerly ICC) cylinder specifications or, in some cases, constructed in accordance with the ASME Code of a similar size and for similar service. The maximum size permitted under DOT specifications is 1,000 lb (454 kg) water capacity.

Direct Gas-Fired Tank Heater. A gas-fired device which applies hot gas from the heater combustion chamber directly to a portion of the container surface in contact with LP-Gas liquid.

Dispensing Device (or Dispenser). A device normally used to transfer and measure LP-Gas for engine fuel into a fuel container, serving the same purpose for an LP-Gas service station as that served by a gasoline dispenser in a gasoline service station.

Distributing Plant. A facility, the primary purpose of which is the distribution of gas, and which receives LP-Gas in tank car, truck transport or truck lots, distributing this gas to the end user by portable container (package) delivery, by tank truck or through gas piping. Such plants have bulk storage [2,000 gal (7.6 m^3) water capacity or more] and usually have container filling and truck loading facilities on the premises. So-called "bulk plants" are considered as being in this category. Normally no persons other than the plant management or plant employees have access to these facilities.

Distributing Point. A facility, other than a distributing plant or industrial plant, which normally receives gas by tank truck, and which fills small containers or the engine fuel tanks of motor vehicles on the premises. Any such facility having LP-Gas storage of 100 gal (0.4 m^3) or more water capacity, and to which persons other than the owner of the facility or his employees have access, is considered to be a distributing point. An LP-Gas service station is one type of distributing point.

DOT. U.S. Department of Transportation.

DOT Cylinder. See Cylinder.

Emergency Shutoff Valve. A shutoff valve incorporating thermal and manual means of closing and providing for remote means of closing.

Excess-Flow Valve (also called Excess-Flow Check Valve). A device designed to close when the liquid or vapor passing through it exceeds a prescribed flow rate as determined by pressure drop.

Fill, Filling. Transferring liquid LP-Gas into a container.

Filling by Volume. See Volumetric Filling.

Filling by Weight. See Weight Filling.

Fixed Liquid Level Gauge. A type of liquid level gauge using a relatively small positive shutoff valve and designed to indicate when the liquid level in a container being filled reaches the point at which this gauge or its connecting tube communicates with the interior of the container.

Fixed Maximum Liquid Level Gauge. A fixed liquid level gauge which indicates the liquid level at which the container is filled to its maximum permitted filling density.

Flexible Connector. A short [not exceeding 36 in. (1 m) overall length] component of a piping system fabricated of flexible material (such as hose) and equipped with suitable connections on both ends. LP-Gas resistant rubber and fabric (or metal), or a combination of them, or all metal may be used. Flexible connectors are used where there is the need for, or the possibility of, greater relative movement between the points connected than is acceptable for rigid pipe.

Float Gauge. A gauge constructed with a float inside the container resting on the liquid surface which transmits its position through suitable leverage to a pointer and dial outside the container indicating the liquid level. Normally the motion is transmitted magnetically through a nonmagnetic plate so that no LP-Gas is released to the atmosphere.

Gallon. U.S. Standard. 1 U.S. gal = 0.833 Imperial gal = 231 cu in. = 3.785 liters.

Gas. Liquefied Petroleum Gas in either the liquid or vapor state. The more specific terms "liquid LP-Gas" or "vapor LP-Gas" are normally used for clarity.

Gas-Air Mixer. A device, or system of piping and controls, which mixes LP-Gas vapor with air to produce a mixed gas of a lower heating value than the LP-Gas. The mixture thus created is normally used in industrial or commercial facilities as a substitute for some other fuel gas. The mixture may replace another fuel gas completely, or may be mixed to produce similar characteristics and mixed with the basic fuel gas. Any gas-air mixer which is designed to produce a mixture containing more than 85 percent air is not subject to the provisions of this standard.

ICC. U.S. Interstate Commerce Commission.

ICC Cylinder. See Cylinder.

Ignition Source. See Sources of Ignition.

Industrial Plant. An industrial facility which utilizes gas incident to plant operations, with LP-Gas storage of 2,000 gal (7.6 m^3) water capacity or more, and which receives gas in tank car, truck transport, or truck lots. Normally LP-Gas is used through piping systems in the plant, but may also be used to fill small containers, such as for engine fuel on industrial (i.e., forklift) trucks. Since only plant employees have access to these filling facilities, they are not considered to be distributing points.

Internal Valve. A primary shutoff valve for containers which has adequate means of actuation and which is constructed in such a manner that its seat is inside the container and that damage to parts exterior to the container or mating flange will not prevent effective seating of the valve.

Labeled. Equipment or materials to which has been attached a label, symbol or other identifying mark of an organization acceptable to the "authority having jurisdiction" and concerned with product evaluation, that maintains periodic inspection of production of labeled equipment or materials and by whose labeling the manufacturer indicates compliance with appropriate standards or performance in a specified manner.

Liquefied Petroleum Gas (LP-Gas or LPG). Any material having a vapor pressure not exceeding that allowed for commercial propane composed predominantly of the following hydrocarbons, either by themselves or as mixtures: propane, propylene, butane (normal butane or isobutane) and butylenes.

Listed. Equipment or materials included in a list published by an organization acceptable to the "authority having jurisdiction" and concerned with product evaluation, that maintains periodic inspection of production of listed equipment or materials and whose listing states either that the equipment or material meets appropriate standards or has been tested and found suitable for use in a specified manner.

NOTE: The means for identifying listed equipment may vary for each organization concerned with product evaluation, some of which do not recognize equipment as listed unless it is also labeled. The "authority having jurisdiction" should utilize the system employed by the listing organization to identify a listed product.

Load, Loading. See Filling.

LPG. See Liquefied Petroleum Gas.

LP-Gas. See Liquefied Petroleum Gas.

LP-Gas Service Station. See Distributing Point. A facility open to the public which consists of LP-Gas storage containers, piping and pertinent equipment, including pumps and dispensing devices, and any buildings, and in which LP-Gas is stored and dispensed into engine fuel containers of highway vehicles.

LP-Gas System. An assembly consisting of one or more containers with a means for conveying LP-Gas from the container(s) to dispensing or consuming devices (either continuously or intermittently) and which incorporates components intended to achieve control of quantity, flow, pressure, or state (either liquid or vapor).

Magnetic Gauge. See Float Gauge.

Movable Fuel Storage Tenders or Farm Carts. Containers not in excess of 1,200 gal (4.5 m^3) water capacity, equipped with wheels to be towed from one location to another. They are basically non-highway vehicles, but may occasionally be moved over public roads or highways for short distances to be used as a fuel supply for farm tractors, construction machinery, and similar equipment.

Multipurpose Passenger Vehicle. A motor vehicle with motive power, except a trailer, designed to carry 10 persons or fewer which is constructed on a truck chassis or with special features for occasional off-road operations.

NFPA. National Fire Protection Association.

NPGA. National Propane Gas Association.

Permanent Installation. See Stationary Installation.

Piping, Piping Systems. Pipe, tubing, hose, and flexible rubber or metallic hose connectors made up with valves and fittings into complete systems for conveying LP-Gas in either the liquid or vapor state at various pressures from one point to another.

Point of Transfer. The location where connections and disconnections are made or where LP-Gas is vented to the atmosphere in the course of transfer operations.

Portable Container. A container designed to be readily moved, as distinguished from containers designed for stationary installations. Portable containers designed for transportation filled to their maximum filling density include "cylinders," "cargo tanks" and "portable tanks," all three of which are separately defined. Containers designed to be readily moved from one usage location to another, but substantially empty of product, are "portable storage containers" and are separately defined.

Portable Storage Container. A container similar to, but distinct from, those designed and constructed for stationary installation, designed so that it can be readily moved over the highways, substantially empty of liquid, from one usage location to another. Such containers either have legs or other supports attached, or are mounted on running gear (such as trailer or semitrailer chassis) with suitable supports, which may be of the fold-down type, permitting them to be placed or parked in a stable position on a reasonably firm and level surface. For large volume, limited duration product usage (such as at construction sites and normally for 12 months or less) portable storage containers function in lieu of permanently installed stationary containers.

Portable Tank (also called Skid Tank). A container of more than 1,000 lb (454 kg) water capacity used to transport LP-Gas handled as a "package," that is, filled to its maximum permitted filling density. Such containers are mounted on skids or runners and have all container appurtenances protected in such a manner that they can be safely handled as a "package."

Pressure Relief Device. A device designed to open to prevent a rise of internal fluid pressure in excess of a specified value due to emergency or abnormal conditions. (*See ANSI B95.1, Standard Terminology for Pressure Relief Devices.*)

Pressure Relief Valve. A type of Pressure Relief Device designed to both open and close to maintain internal fluid pressure.

Pressure Relief Valves are further characterized as follows:

External Pressure Relief Valve*. A relief valve in which the entire relief valve is outside the container connection except the threaded portion which is screwed into the container connection, and all of the parts are exposed to the atmosphere.

Flush Type Full Internal Pressure Relief Valve*. A full internal relief valve in which the wrenching section is also within the container connection, except for pipe thread tolerances on make up.

Full Internal Pressure Relief Valve*. A relief valve in which all working parts are recessed within the container connections, and the spring and guiding mechanism are not exposed to the atmosphere.

Internal Spring Type Pressure Relief Valve*. A relief valve in which only the spring and stem are within the container connection and the spring and stem are not exposed to the atmosphere. The exposed parts of the relief valve have a low profile.

Sump Type Full Internal Pressure Relief Valve*. A relief valve in which all working parts are recessed within the container connection, but the spring and guiding mechanism are exposed to the atmosphere.

PSI, PSIG, and PSIA. Pounds per square inch, pounds per square inch gauge, and pounds per square inch absolute, respectively.

Quick Connectors. Devices used for quick connections of the acme thread or lever-cam types. This does not include devices used for cylinder-filling connections.

Rotary Gauge. A variable liquid level gauge consisting of a small positive shutoff valve located at the outer end of a tube, the bent inner end of which communicates with the container interior. The tube is installed in a fitting designed so that the tube can be rotated with a pointer on the outside to indicate the relative position of the bent inlet end. The length of the tube and the configuration to which it is bent is suitable for the range of liquid levels to be gauged. By a suitable outside scale, the level in the container at which the inner end begins to receive liquid can be determined by the pointer position on the scale at which a liquid-vapor mixture is observed to be discharged from the valve.

Skid Tank. See Portable Tank.

Slip Tube Gauge. A variable liquid level gauge in which a relatively small positive shutoff valve is located at the outside end of a straight tube, normally installed vertically, and communicates with the container interior. The installation fitting for the tube is designed so that the tube can be slipped in and out of the container and the liquid level at the inner end determined by observing when the shutoff valve vents a liquid-vapor mixture.

Sources of Ignition. Devices or equipment which, because of their modes of use or operation, are capable of providing sufficient thermal energy to ignite flammable LP-Gas vapor-air mixtures when introduced into such a mixture or when such a mixture comes into contact with them, and which will permit propagation of flame away from them.

Special Protection. A means of limiting the temperature of an LP-Gas container for purposes of minimizing the possibility of failure of the container as the result of fire exposure.

When required in this standard, special protection consists of any of the following: applied insulating coatings, mounding, burial, water spray fixed systems or fixed monitor nozzles, meeting the criteria specified in this standard (*see 3-10.3*), or by any means listed (*see definition of Listed*) for this purpose.

Stationary Installation (also called "Fixed" or "Permanent" Installation). An installation of LP-Gas containers, piping and equipment for use indefinitely at a particular location; an installation not normally expected to change in status, condition or place.

UL. Underwriters Laboratories Inc.

Universal Cylinder. A DOT cylinder specification container, constructed and fitted with appurtenances in such a manner that it may be connected for service with its longitudinal axis in either the vertical or the horizontal position, and so that its fixed maximum liquid level gauge, pressure relief device(s) and withdrawal appurtenance will function properly in either position.

Vaporizer. A device other than a container which receives LP-Gas in liquid form and adds sufficient heat to convert the liquid to a gaseous state.

Vaporizer, Direct-Fired. A vaporizer in which heat furnished by a flame is directly applied to some form of heat exchange surface in contact with the liquid LP-Gas to be vaporized. This classification includes submerged-combustion vaporizers.

Vaporizer, Electric. A unit using electricity as a source of heat.

1. *Direct immersion electric vaporizer.* A vaporizer wherein an electric element is immersed directly in the LP-Gas liquid and vapor.

2. *Indirect electric vaporizer.* An immersion type wherein the electric element heats an interface solution in which the LP-Gas heat exchanger is immersed or heats an intermediate heat sink.

Vaporizer, Indirect (also called Indirect-Fired). A vaporizer in which heat furnished by steam, hot water, the ground, surrounding air or other heating medium is applied to a vaporizing chamber or to tubing, pipe coils, or other heat exchange surface containing the liquid LP-Gas to be vaporized; the heating of the medium used being at a point remote from the vaporizer.

Vaporizer, Waterbath (also called Immersion Type). A vaporizer in which a vaporizing chamber, tubing, pipe coils, or other heat exchange surface containing liquid LP-Gas to be vaporized is immersed in a temperature controlled bath of water, water-glycol combination, or other noncombustible heat transfer medium, which is heated by an immersion heater not in contact with the LP-Gas heat exchange surface.

Vaporizing-Burner (also called Vaporizer-Burner and Self-Vaporizing Liquid Burner). A burner containing an integral vaporizer which receives LP-Gas in liquid form and which uses part of the heat generated by the burner to vaporize the liquid in the burner so that it is burned as a vapor.

Variable Liquid Level Gauge. A device to indicate the liquid level in a container throughout a range of levels. See Float, Rotary, and Slip Tube Gauge.

Volumetric Filling. Filling a container by determination of the volume of LP-Gas in the container. Unless a container is filled by a fixed maximum liquid level gauge, correction of the volume for liquid temperature is necessary.

Volumetric Loading. See Volumetric Filling.

Water Capacity. The amount of water, in either lb or gal, at 60°F (15.6°C) required to fill a container liquid full of water.

Weight Filling. Filling containers by weighing the LP-Gas in the container. No temperature determination or correction is required as a unit of weight is a constant quantity regardless of temperature.

Chapter 2 LP-Gas Equipment and Appliances

2-1 Scope.

2-1.1 Application.

2-1.1.1 This chapter includes the basic provisions for individual components, or for such components shop-fabricated into subassemblies, container assemblies, or complete container systems.

2-1.1.2 The field assembly of components, subassemblies, container assemblies or complete container systems into complete LP-Gas systems is covered by Chapter 3. (*See Definition of LP-Gas System.*)

2-2 Containers.

2-2.1 General.

2-2.1.1 This section includes design, fabrication, and marking provisions for containers, and features normally associated with container fabrication, such as container openings, appurtenances required for these openings to make the containers gastight entities, physical damage protecting devices, and container supports attached to, or furnished with the container by the manufacturer.

2-2.1.2 Nonrefrigerated containers shall comply with 2-2.1.3 or shall be designed, fabricated, tested, and marked using criteria which incorporate an investigation to determine that it is safe and suitable for the proposed service, is recommended for that service by the manufacturer, and is acceptable to the authority having jurisdiction. Refrigerated containers shall comply with Chapter 8.

2-2.1.3* Containers shall be designed, fabricated, tested, and marked (or stamped) in accordance with the Regulations of the U.S. Department of Transportation (DOT), the "Rules for the Construction of Unfired Pressure Vessels," Section VIII, Division 1, ASME *Boiler and Pressure Vessel Code*, or the API-ASME *Code for Unfired Pressure Vessels for Petroleum Liquids and Gases* applicable at the date of manufacture; and as follows:

(a) Adherence to applicable ASME Code Case Interpretations and Addenda shall be considered as compliance with the ASME Code.

(b) Containers fabricated to earlier editions of regulations, rules or codes listed in 2-2.1.3 and the ICC *Rules for Construction of Unfired Pressure Vessels*, prior to April 1, 1967, may continue in use in accordance with 1-2.4.1. (*See Appendices C and D.*)

2-2.1.4 Containers complying with 2-2.1.3 may be reused, reinstalled, or continued in use as follows:

(a) The owner of a container shall be responsible for its suitability for continued service. DOT cylinders shall not be refilled, continued in service or transported unless they are properly qualified or requalified for LP-Gas service in accordance with DOT regulations.

(b) Containers which have been involved in a fire and showing no distortion shall be requalified for continued service before being used or reinstalled as follows:

(1) DOT containers shall be requalified by a manufacturer of the type of cylinder to be requalified or by a repair facility approved by DOT.

Exception: DOT 4E specification (aluminum) cylinders shall be permanently removed from service.

(2) ASME or API-ASME containers shall be retested, using the hydrostatic test procedure applicable at the time of original fabrication.

2-2.1.5 Containers showing serious denting, bulging, gouging, or excessive corrosion shall be removed from service.

2-2.1.6 Repair or alteration of containers shall comply with the Regulations, Rules or Code under which the container was fabricated. Other welding is permitted only on saddle plates, lugs, or brackets attached to the container by the container manufacturer.

2-2.1.7 Containers for general use shall not have individual water capacities greater than 120,000 gal (454 m^3). Containers in service stations shall not have individual water capacities greater than 30,000 gal (114 m^3).

2-2.1.8 Heating or cooling coils shall not be installed inside storage containers.

2-2.2 Container Design or Service Pressure.

2-2.2.1 The minimum design, or service, pressure of DOT specification containers shall be in accordance with the appropriate DOT regulations.

2-2.2.2 The minimum design pressure for ASME containers shall be in accordance with Table 2-2.2.2.

Table 2-2.2.2

For Gases with Vapor Pressure in psig (MPa gauge) at 100°F (37.8°C) not to Exceed	Minimum Design Pressure in psig (MPa gauge) ASME Code, Section VIII, Division 1, 1986 Edition (Note 1)
80 (0.6)	100 (0.7) (Note 2)
100 (0.7)	125 (0.9)
125 (0.9)	156 (1.1)
150 (1.0)	187 (1.3)
175 (1.2)	219 (1.5)
215 (1.5)	250 (1.7)
215 (1.5)	312.5 (2.2) (Note 3)

Note 1: See Appendix D for information on earlier ASME or API-ASME Code.

Note 2: New containers for 100 psig (0.7 MPa gauge) design pressure (or equivalent under earlier codes) not authorized after December 31, 1947.

Note 3: See 3-6.2.2 for certain service conditions which require a higher pressure relief valve start-to-leak setting.

2-2.2.3 In addition to the applicable provisions for horizontal ASME storage containers, vertical ASME storage containers over 125 gal (0.5 m^3) water capacity shall comply with 2-2.2.3(a) through (e).

(a) Containers shall be designed to be self-supporting without the use of guy wires and shall satisfy proper design criteria taking into account wind, seismic (earthquake) forces, and hydrostatic test loads.

(b) Design pressure (*see Table 2-2.2.2*) shall be interpreted as the pressure at the top head with allowance made for increased pressure on lower shell sections and bottom head due to the static pressure of the product.

(c) Wind loading on containers shall be based on wind pressures on the projected area at various height zones aboveground in accordance with *Design Loads for Buildings and Other Structures*, ANSI A58.1. Wind speeds shall be based on a Mean Occurrence Interval of 100 years.

(d) Seismic loading on containers shall be based on forces recommended in the ICBO *Uniform Building Code*. In those areas identified as zones 3 and 4 on the Seismic Risk Map of the United States, Figures 1, 2 and 3 of Chapter 23 of the UBC, a seismic analysis of the proposed installation shall be made which meets the approval of the authority having jurisdiction.

(e) Shop-fabricated containers shall be fabricated with lifting lugs or some other suitable means to facilitate erection in the field.

2-2.3 Container Openings.

2-2.3.1 Containers shall be equipped with openings suitable for the service in which the container is to be used. Such openings may be either in the container proper or in the manhole cover, or part in one and part in the other.

2-2.3.2 Containers of more than 30 gal (0.1 m^3) and less than 2,000 gal (7.6 m^3) water capacity, designed to be filled volumetrically, and manufactured after December 1, 1963, shall be equipped for filling into the vapor space.

2-2.3.3 Containers of 125 gal (0.5 m^3) or more water capacity manufactured after July 1, 1961, shall be provided with a connection for liquid evacuation, not smaller than ¾ in. National Pipe Thread. A plugged opening will not comply with this provision.

2-2.3.4 Containers of more than 2,000 gal (7.6 m^3) water capacity and all containers installed in LP-Gas service stations shall be provided with an opening for a pressure gauge (*see 2-3.5.2*).

2-2.3.5 Connections for pressure relief valves shall be located and installed in such a way as to have direct communication with the vapor space, whether the container is in storage or in use.

(a) If located in a well inside the container with piping to the vapor space, the design of the well and piping shall permit sufficient pressure relief valve relieving capacity.

(b) If located in a protecting enclosure, design shall be such as to permit this enclosure to be protected against corrosion and to permit inspection.

(c) If located in any position other than uppermost point of the container, it shall be internally piped to the uppermost point practical in the vapor space of the container.

2-2.3.6 Containers to be filled on a volumetric basis manufactured after December 31, 1965, shall be fabricated so that they can be equipped with a fixed liquid level gauge(s) capable of indicating the maximum permitted filling level(s) in accordance with 4-5.2.3.

2-2.4 Portable Container Appurtenance Physical Damage Protection.

2-2.4.1 Portable containers of 1,000 lb (454 kg) [nominal 120 gal (0.5 m^3)] water capacity or less shall incorporate protection against physical damage to container appurtenances and immediate connections to these while in transit, storage, while being moved into position for use, and when in use except in residential and commercial installations, by:

(a) Recessing connections into the container so that valves will not be struck if the container is dropped on a flat surface, or,

(b) A ventilated cap or collar designed to permit adequate pressure relief valve discharge and capable of withstanding a blow from any direction equivalent to that of a 30 lb (14 kg) weight dropped 4 ft (1.2 m). Construction shall be such that the force of the blow will not be transmitted to the valve. Collars shall be designed so that they do not interfere with the free operation of the cylinder valve.

2-2.4.2 Portable containers of more than 1,000 lb (454 kg) [nominal 120 gal (0.5 m^3)] water capacity, including skid tanks or for use as cargo containers, shall incorporate protection against physical damage to container appurtenances by recessing, protective housings, or by location on the vehicle. Such protection shall comply with the provisions under which the tanks are fabricated, and shall be designed to withstand static loadings in any direction equal to twice the weight of the container and attachments when filled with LP-Gas, using a safety factor of not less than four, based on the ultimate strength of the material to be used. (*See Chapters 3 and 6 for additional provisions applying to the LP-Gas system used.*)

2-2.5 Containers with Attached Supports.

2-2.5.1 Horizontal containers of more than 2,000 gal (7.6 m^3) water capacity designed for permanent installation in stationary service may be provided with steel saddles designed to permit mounting the containers on flat topped concrete foundations. The total height of the outside bottom of the container shell above the top of the concrete foundation shall not exceed 6 in. (152 mm).

2-2.5.2 Horizontal containers of 2,000 gal (7.6 m^3) water capacity or less, designed for permanent installation in stationary service, may be equipped with nonfireproofed structural steel supports and designed to permit mounting on firm foundations in accordance with 2-2.5.2 (a) or (b).

(a) For installation on concrete foundations raised above the ground level by more than 12 in. (305 mm), the structural steel supports shall be designed so that the bottoms of the horizontal members are not less than 2 in. (51 mm), nor more than 12 in. (305 mm) below the outside bottom of the container shell.

(b) For installation on paved surfaces or concrete pads within 4 in. (102 mm) of ground level, the structural steel supports may be designed so that the bottoms of the structural members are not more than 24 in. (610 mm) below the outside bottom of the container shell. [*See 3-2.3.2(a)(3) for installation provisions for such containers which are customarily used as components of prefabricated container-pump assemblies.*]

2-2.5.3 Vertical ASME containers over 125 gal (0.5 m^3) water capacity designed for permanent installation in stationary service shall be designed with steel supports designed to permit mounting the container on, and fastening it to, concrete foundations or supports. Such steel supports shall be designed to make the container self-supporting without guy wires and shall satisfy proper design criteria, taking into account wind, seismic (earthquake) forces, and hydrostatic test load criteria established in 2-2.2.3.

(a) The steel supports shall be protected against fire exposure with a material having a fire resistance rating of at least two hours. Continuous steel skirts having only one opening 18 in. (457 mm) or less in diameter need such fire protection applied only to the outside of the skirt.

2-2.5.4 Containers to be used as portable storage containers (*see definition*) for temporary stationary service (normally less than 12 months at any given location) and to be moved only when substantially empty of liquid shall comply with 2-2.5.4(a) and (b).

(a) If mounted on legs or supports, such supports shall be of steel, and shall either be welded to the container by the manufacturer at the time of fabrication or shall be attached to lugs which have been so welded to the container. The legs or supports or the lugs for the attachment of these legs or supports shall be secured to the container in accordance with the code or rule under which the container is designed and built, with a minimum factor of safety of four, to withstand loading in any direction equal to twice the weight of the empty container and attachments.

(b) If the container is mounted on a trailer or semitrailer running gear so that the unit can be moved by a conventional over-the-road tractor, attachment to the vehicle, or attachments to the container to make it a vehicle, shall comply with the appropriate DOT requirements for cargo tank service; except that stress calculations shall be based on twice the weight of the empty container. The unit shall also comply with applicable State and DOT motor carrier regulations and shall be approved by the authority having jurisdiction.

2-2.5.5 Portable tanks (*see definition*) shall comply with DOT portable tank container specifications as to container design and construction, securing of skids or lugs for the attachment of skids and protection of fittings. In addition, the bottom of the skids shall be not less than 2 in. (51 mm) or more than 12 in. (305 mm) below the outside bottom of the container shell.

2-2.6 Container Markings.

2-2.6.1 Containers shall be marked as provided in the Regulations, Rules or Code under which they are fabricated and in accordance with 2-2.6.2 through 2-2.6.5 as applicable.

2-2.6.2 When LP-Gas and one or more other compressed gases are to be stored or used in the same area, the containers shall be be marked "Flammable" and either "LP-Gas," "LPG," "Propane" or "Butane." Compliance with marking requirements of Title 49 of the *Code of Federal Regulations* shall meet this provision.

2-2.6.3 When being transported, portable DOT containers shall be marked and labeled in accordance with Title 49 of the *Code of Federal Regulations.*

2-2.6.4 Portable DOT containers designed to be filled by weight, including those optionally filled volumetrically but which may require check weighing, shall be marked with:

(a) The water capacity of the container in lb.

(b) The tare weight of the container in lb, fitted for service. The tare weight is the container weight plus the weight of all permanently attached valves and other fittings, but does not include the weight of protecting devices removed in order to load the container.

2-2.6.5 ASME containers shall be marked in accordance with 2-2.6.5(a) through (l). The marking specified shall be on a stainless steel metal nameplate attached to the container, so located as to remain visible after the container is installed. The nameplate shall be attached in such a way to minimize corrosion of the nameplate or its fastening means and not contribute to corrosion of the container.

(a) Service for which the container is designed; i.e. underground, aboveground, or both.

(b) Name and address of container supplier or trade name of container.

(c) Water capacity of container in lb or U.S. Gallons.

(d) Design pressure in psig.

(e) The wording "This container shall not contain a product having a vapor pressure in excess of ____ psig at 100°F." (*See Table 2-2.2.2.*)

(f) Tare weight of container fitted for service for containers to be filled by weight.

(g) Outside surface area in sq ft.

(h) Year of manufacture.

(i) Shell thickness ____ head thickness.

(j) OL ____ OD ____ HD ____.

(k) Manufacturer's Serial Number.

(l) ASME Code Symbol.

2-3 Container Appurtenances.

2-3.1 General.

2-3.1.1 This section includes fabrication and performance provisions for container appurtenances, such as pressure relief devices, container shutoff valves, backflow check valves, internal valves, excess-flow check valves, plugs, liquid level gauges and pressure gauges connected directly into the container openings described in 2-2.3. Shop installation of such appurtenances in containers listed as container assemblies or container systems in accordance with 1-3.1.1 is a responsibility of the fabricator under the listing. Field installation of such appurtenances is covered in Chapter 3.

2-3.1.2 Container appurtenances shall be fabricated of materials suitable for LP-Gas service and resistant to the action of LP-Gas under service conditions. The following shall also apply:

(a) Pressure containing metal parts of appurtenances, such as those listed in 2-3.1.1, except fusible elements, shall have a minimum melting point of 1500°F (816°C) such as steel, ductile (nodular) iron, malleable iron, or brass. Ductile iron shall meet the requirements of ASTM A 395 or equivalent and malleable iron the requirements of ASTM A 47 or equivalent. Approved or listed liquid level gauges used in containers of 3500 gal (13.2 m^3) water capacity or less are exempted from this provision.

(b) Cast iron shall not be used.

(c) Non-metallic materials shall not be used for parts such as bonnets or bodies.

2-3.1.3 Container appurtenances shall have a rated working pressure of at least 250 psig (1.7 MPa gauge).

2-3.1.4 Gaskets used to retain LP-Gas in containers shall be resistant to the action of LP-Gas. They shall be made of metal or other suitable material confined in metal having a melting point over 1500°F (816°C) or shall be protected against fire exposure, except that aluminum O-rings and spiral wound metal gaskets are acceptable and gaskets for use with approved or listed liquid level gauges for installation on a container of 3500 gal (13.2 m^3) water capacity or less are exempted from this provision. When a flange is opened, the gasket shall be replaced.

2-3.2 Pressure Relief Devices. (*See 2-4.7 for hydrostatic relief valves.*)

2-3.2.1 Containers shall be equipped with one or more pressure relief devices which, except as otherwise provided for in 2-3.2.2, shall be designed to relieve vapor.

2-3.2.2 DOT containers shall be equipped with pressure relief valves or fusible plug devices as required by DOT Regulations. (*See Appendix E for additional information.*)

2-3.2.3 ASME containers for LP-Gas shall be equipped with direct spring-loaded pressure relief valves conforming with applicable requirements of the *Standard on Safety Relief Valves for Anhydrous Ammonia and LP-Gas*, UL 132; or other equivalent pressure relief valve standards. The start-to-leak setting of such pressure relief valves, with relation to the design pressure of the container, shall be in accordance with Table 2-3.2.3.

Exception: On containers of 40,000 gal (151 m³) water capacity or more, a pilot operated pressure relief valve in which the relief device is combined with and is controlled by a self-actuated, direct, spring-loaded pilot valve may be used provided it complies with Table 2-3.2.3, is approved (see definition), is inspected and maintained by persons with appropriate training and experience, and is tested for proper operation at intervals not exceeding 5 years.

Table 2-3.2.3

Containers	Minimum	Maximum
All ASME Codes prior to the 1949 Edition, and the 1949 Edition, paragraphs U-68 and U-69	110%	125%*
ASME Code, 1949 Edition, Paragraphs U-200 and U-201, and all ASME Codes later than 1949	100%	100%*

*Manufacturers of pressure relief valves are allowed a plus tolerance not exceeding 10 percent of the set pressure marked on the valve.

2-3.2.4 Pressure relief valves for ASME containers shall also comply with 2-3.2.4(a) through (e).

(a) Pressure relief valves shall be of sufficient individual or aggregate capacity as to provide the relieving capacity in accordance with Appendix E for the container on which they are installed, and to relieve at not less than the rate indicated before the pressure is in excess of 120 percent of the maximum (not including the 10 percent referred to in the footnote of Table 2-3.2.3) permitted start-to-leak pressure setting of the device. This provision is applicable to all containers (including containers installed partially aboveground) except containers installed wholly underground in accordance with E-2.3.1.

(b) Each pressure relief valve shall be plainly and permanently marked with: (1) the pressure in psig at which the valve is set to start-to-leak; (2) rated relieving capacity in cu ft per minute of air at 60°F (16°C) and 14.7 psia (0.1 MPa absolute); and (3) the manufacturer's name and catalog number. Example: A pressure relief valve is marked 250-4050 AIR. This indicates that the valve is set to start-to-leak at 250 psig (1.7 MPa gauge); and that its rated relieving capacity is 4050 cfm (1.9 m³/s) of air.

(c) Shutoff valves shall not be located between a pressure relief device and the container, unless the arrangement is such that the relief device relieving capacity flow specified in 2-3.2.4(a) will be achieved through additional pressure relief devices which remain operative.

(d) Pressure relief valves shall be so designed that the possibility of tampering will be minimized. Externally set or adjusted valves shall be provided with an approved means of sealing the adjustment.

(e) Fusible plug devices, with a yield point of 208°F (98°C) minimum and 220°F (104°C) maximum, with a total discharge area not exceeding 0.25 sq in. (1.6 cm²), and which communicate directly with the vapor space of the container, may be used in addition to the spring-loaded pressure relief valves (as specified in Table 2-3.2.3) for aboveground containers of 1,200 gal (4.5 m³) water capacity or less.

2-3.2.5 All containers used in industrial truck (including forklift truck cylinders) service shall have the container pressure relief valve replaced by a new or unused valve within 12 years of the date of manufacture of the container and each 10 years thereafter.

2-3.3 Connections for Flow Control (Filling, Withdrawal, Equalizing).

2-3.3.1 Shutoff valves, excess-flow check valves, backflow check valves and quick closing internal valves, used individually or in suitable combinations, at container filling, withdrawal, and equalizing connections, shall comply with 2-3.1.2 and 2-3.1.3.

2-3.3.2 Filling, withdrawal and equalizing connections shall be equipped with the appurtenances for the appropriate type and capacity of container and the service in which they are to be used in accordance with Table 2-3.3.2. Cylinder valve outlet connections on all DOT cylinders except those used for engine fuel, from which vapor can be withdrawn, shall not be interchangeable with those used for liquid withdrawal.

(a) If the loading or transfer point is not on the container, it shall be equipped as specified for filling connections on the container.

2-3.3.3 The appurtenances specified in Table 2-3.3.2 shall comply with 2-3.3.3(a) through (d).

(a) Manual shutoff valves shall be designed to provide positive closure under service conditions.

(b) Excess-flow check valves shall be designed to close automatically at the rated flows of vapor or liquid specified by the manufacturer. Excess flow valves shall be designed with a bypass, not to exceed a No. 60 drill size opening, to allow equalization of pressure.

(c) Backflow check valves, which may be of spring-loaded or weight-loaded type with in-line or swing operation, shall close when flow is either stopped or reversed. Both valves of double backflow check valves shall comply with this provision.

(d) Internal valves (*see definition*), either manually or automatically operated and designed to remain closed except during operating periods, shall be considered positive shutoff valves. [*See 6-3.2.1(a) for special requirements for such valves used on cargo units.*]

2-3.3.4 The appurtenances specified in Table 2-3.3.2 may be installed as individual components or as combinations completely assembled by the appurtenance manufacturer.

2-3.4 Liquid Level Gauging Devices.

2-3.4.1 Liquid level gauging devices shall be provided on

Table 2-3.3.2 Filling Withdrawal and Equalizing Connections

Type of Use		General Uses												Used as Fuel on Vehicles			Portable Tanks		
Type of Container		DOT Cylinder Specifications									ASME			DOT or ASME			ASME		
Water Capacity of Containers	Pounds (kg)	1 (0.5) to 1,000 (454)			50 (23) to 1,000 (454)			2.5 (1) to 245 (110)			—			Any			Any		
	Gallons (m³)	—			—			—			Up to 120,000 (454 m³)			Any			Any		
Conditions under which Container is Used		Replacement or Exchange Outdoors			Filled at Point of Use Outdoors			When Used Inside Buildings			Filled at Point of Use Outdoors			Replacement or Fixed			Trans-portation of LP-Gas		
Connection Use (Note 1): "F"—Filling, "W"—Withdrawal, "E"—Equalizing		F	W	E	F	W	E	F	W	E	F	W	E	F	W	E	F	W	E
Appurtenances to be provided (Note 2):																			
1. Positive (Manual) Shutoff Valve		✓ 3*	✓ 3*	✓	5*	5*						✓ 6*							
2. Positive (Manual) Shutoff & Internal Excess Flow Check Valve				✓	✓	✓	✓	✓	✓	✓	✓	✓	✓	✓ 8*	✓	✓	✓	✓	✓
3. Positive (Manual) Shutoff & External Excess Flow Check Valve (Note 4)					✓	✓	✓	✓	✓	✓	✓	✓	✓				✓	✓	✓
4. Single Back Flow Check Valve					✓														
5. Positive (Manual) Shutoff & Internal Back Flow Check Valve											✓			✓			✓		
6. Excess Flow Check Valve & Back Flow Check Valve				✓	✓		✓				✓		✓			✓	✓		✓
7. Double Back Flow Check Valve					✓						✓			✓			✓		
8. Quick Closing Internal Valve											✓	✓	✓				✓	✓	✓
Column Number		1			2			3			4			5			6		

*Note Number.

Notes to Table 2-3.3.2

Note 1: Containers are not required to be equipped with all three connections, but if used, appurtenances shall be those shown. Suitably fitted multipurpose valves may be used.

Note 2: If more than one appurtenance, or combination of appurtenances, is shown for any connection use, any one of the appurtenances or combinations shown will comply. (*See also DOT regulations for cargo and portable containers.*)

Note 3: Single manual shutoff valve normally used for both filling and withdrawal.

Note 4: External excess-flow check valves shall be installed in such a way that any undue strain beyond them will not cause breakage between the container and the excess-flow check valves.

Note 5: Containers of less than 50 lb (23 kg) water capacity need only be equipped with a positive shutoff valve for filling at the point of use.

Note 6: An excess-flow check valve is not required in the withdrawal connection provided the following are all complied with:

(a) Container water capacity does not exceed 2,000 gal (7.6 m³)

(b) Withdrawal outlet is equipped with a manually operable (having a handwheel or the equivalent) shutoff valve, which is:

(1) threaded directly into the container outlet, or

(2) an integral part of a substantial fitting which is threaded directly into or on the container outlet, or

(3) threaded directly into a substantial fitting which is threaded directly into or on the container outlet.

(c) The controlling orifice between the container contents and the shutoff valve outlet does not exceed 5/16 in. (8 mm) in diameter for vapor withdrawal or 1/8 in. (3 mm) for liquid withdrawal.

(d) An approved pressure-reducing regulator is directly attached to the outlet of the shutoff valve and is rigidly supported, or is adequately supported and properly protected on or at the container, and is connected to the shutoff valve by means of a suitable flexible connection.

Note 7: See 6-3.2.1(a) for special requirements for containers constructed to DOT cargo tank specifications.

Note 8: Authorized for exchangeable (removable) containers only.

all containers filled by volume. Fixed level gauges or variable gauges of the slip tube, rotary tube or float types (or combinations of such gauges) may be used to comply with this provision.

2-3.4.2 Every container constructed after December 31, 1965, designed to be filled on a volumetric basis, shall be equipped with a fixed liquid level gauge(s) to indicate the maximum filling level(s) for the service(s) in which the container is to be used (*see 4-5.3.3*). This may be accomplished either by using a dip tube of appropriate length, or by the position of the gauging device in the container. The following shall apply:

(a) ASME containers manufactured after December 31, 1969, shall have permanently attached to the container adjacent to the fixed liquid level gauge, or on the container nameplate, markings showing the percentage full that is indicated by that gauge.

(b) Containers constructed to DOT cylinder specifications shall have stamped on the container the letters "DT" followed by the vertical distance (to the nearest tenth inch) from the top of the boss or coupling into which the gauge, or the container valve of which it is a part, is made up, to the end of the dip tube. [*See 2-3.4.2(c)(2) for DOT containers designed for loading in either the vertical or horizontal position.*]

(c) Each container manufactured after December 31, 1972, equipped with a fixed liquid level gauge for which the tube is not welded in place shall be permanently marked adjacent to such gauge or on container nameplate as follows:

(1) Containers designed to be filled in one position shall be marked with the letters "DT" followed by the vertical distance (to the nearest tenth inch) measured from the top center of the container boss or coupling into which the gauge is installed to the maximum permitted filling level.

(2) Portable universal type containers that may be filled in either vertical or horizontal position shall be marked as follows:

a. *For Vertical Filling:* With the letters "VDT" followed by the vertical distance (to the nearest tenth inch), measured from the top center of the container boss or coupling into which the gauge is installed to the maximum permitted filling level.

b. *For Horizontal Filling:* With the letters "HDT" followed by the vertical distance (to the nearest tenth inch), measured from the top centerline of the container boss or coupling opening into which the gauge is installed to the inside top of the container when in the horizontal position.

(d) Cargo tanks having several fixed level gauges positioned at different levels shall have stamped adjacent to each gauge the loading percentage (to the nearest 2/10 percent) of the container content which that particular gauge indicates.

2-3.4.3 The intent of 2-3.4.2 may be achieved by other methods acceptable to the authority having jurisdiction.

2-3.4.4 Variable liquid level gauges shall comply with 2-3.4.4(a) through (e).

(a) Variable liquid level gauges shall be so marked that the maximum liquid level, in in. or percent of capacity of the container in which they are to be installed, is readily determinable. These markings shall indicate the maximum liquid level for propane, for 50/50 butane-propane mixtures, and for butane at liquid temperatures from 20°F (−6.7°C) to 130°F (54.4°C) and in increments not greater than 20 Fahrenheit degrees.

(b) The markings indicating the various liquid levels from empty to full shall either be directly on the system nameplate or on the gauging device or on both.

(c) Dials of magnetic float or rotary gauges shall show whether they are for cylindrical or spherical containers, and whether for aboveground or underground service.

(d) The dials of gauges for use only on aboveground containers of over 1,200 gal (4.5 m^3) water capacity shall be so marked.

(e) Variable liquid level gauges shall comply with the accuracy provisions of 4-5.3.3(b) if they are used for filling containers.

2-3.4.5 Gauging devices requiring bleeding of product to the atmosphere, such as fixed liquid level, rotary tube, and slip tube gauges, shall be designed so that the bleed valve maximum opening to the atmosphere is not larger than a No. 54 drill size, unless equipped with excess-flow check valves.

2-3.5 Pressure Gauges.

2-3.5.1 Pressure gauges shall comply with 2-3.1.2 and 2-3.1.3.

2-3.5.2 Pressure gauges shall be attached directly to the container opening or to a valve or fitting which is directly attached to the container opening. If the effective opening into the container will permit a flow greater than that of a No. 54 drill size, an excess-flow check valve shall be provided.

2-3.6 Other Container Connections.

2-3.6.1 Container openings, other than those equipped as provided in 2-3.2, 2-3.3, 2-3.4, and 2-3.5, shall be equipped with one of the following:

(a) A positive shutoff valve in combination with either an excess-flow check valve or a backflow check valve, plugged.

(b) An internal valve, plugged.

(c) A backflow check valve, plugged.

(d) An internal excess-flow check valve, normally closed and plugged, with provision to allow for external actuation.

(e) A plug, blind flange, or plugged companion flange.

2-4 Piping (Including Hose), Fittings, and Valves.

2-4.1 General.

2-4.1.1 This section includes basic design provisions and material specifications for pipe, tubing, pipe and tubing fittings, valves (including hydrostatic relief valves), hose, hose connections and flexible connectors used to connect container appurtenances with the balance of the LP-Gas system in accordance with the installation provisions of Chapter 3.

2-4.1.2 Piping, pipe and tubing fittings and valves used to supply utilization equipment within the scope of NFPA 54, *National Fuel Gas Code*, shall comply with that Code.

2-4.1.3 Pipe and tubing shall comply with 2-4.2.1 and 2-4.3.1 or shall be of material which has been investigated and tested to determine that it is safe and suitable for the proposed service and is recommended for that service by the manufacturer, and be acceptable to the authority having jurisdiction.

2-4.2 Pipe.

2-4.2.1 Pipe shall be wrought iron or steel (black or galvanized), brass, copper, or polyethylene (*see 3-2.7.6*) and shall comply with 2-4.2.1(a) through (g).

(a) Wrought iron pipe; ANSI B36.10, *Welded and Seamless Wrought Steel Pipe.*

(b) Steel Pipe; *Specification for Pipe, Steel, Black and Hot-Dipped, Zinc-Coated Welded and Seamless* (ANSI/ASTM A 53).

(c) Steel pipe; *Specification for Seamless Carbon Steel Pipe for High Temperature Service* (ANSI/ASTM A 106).

(d) Steel pipe; *Specification for Pipe, Steel, Black and Hot-Dipped Zinc-Coated (Galvanized) Welded and Seamless, for Ordinary Uses* (ANSI/ASTM A 120).

(e) Brass Pipe; *Specification for Seamless Red Brass Pipe, Standard Sizes* (ANSI/ASTM B 43).

(f) Copper Pipe; *Specification for Seamless Copper Pipe, Standard Sizes* (ANSI/ASTM B 42).

(g) Polyethylene Pipe; *Specification for Thermoplastic Gas Pressure Pipe, Tubing and Fittings* (ANSI/ASTM D 2513) and be listed or approved.

2-4.3 Tubing.

2-4.3.1 Tubing shall be steel, brass, copper, or polyethylene (*see 3-2.7.6*) and shall comply with 2-4.3.1(a) through (d):

(a) Steel tubing; *Specification for Electric-Resistance-Welded Coiled Steel Tubing for Gas Fuel Oil Lines* (ANSI/ASTM A 539).

(b) Brass tubing [*see 3-2.6.1(d)(3)*]; *Specification for Seamless Brass Tube* (ANSI/ASTM B 135).

(c) Copper tubing [*see 3-2.6.1(d)(3)*]:

(1) Type K or L, *Specification for Seamless Copper Water Tube* (ANSI/ASTM B 88).

(2) *Specification for Seamless Copper Tube for Air Conditioning and Refrigeration Field Service* (ANSI/ASTM B 280).

(d) Polyethylene tubing; *Specification for Thermoplastic Gas Pressure Pipe, Tubing and Fittings* (ASTM D 2513) and be listed or approved.

2-4.4 Pipe and Tubing Fittings.

2-4.4.1 Fittings shall be steel, brass, copper, malleable iron, ductile (nodular) iron or polyethylene, and shall comply with 2-4.4.1(a) through (c). Cast iron pipe fittings (ells, tees, crosses, couplings, unions, flanges, or plugs) shall not be used.

(a) Pipe joints in wrought iron, steel, brass or copper pipe may be screwed, welded or brazed.

(1) Fittings used at pressures higher than container pressure, such as on the discharge of liquid transfer pumps, shall be suitable for a working pressure of at least 350 psig (2.4 MPa gauge).

(2) Except as provided in 2-4.4.1(a)(1), fittings used with liquid LP-Gas, or with vapor LP-Gas at operating pressures over 125 psig (0.9 MPa gauge), shall be suitable for a working pressure of 250 psig (1.7 MPa gauge).

(3) Fittings for use with vapor LP-Gas at pressures not exceeding 125 psig (0.9 MPa gauge) shall be suitable for a working pressure of 125 psig (0.9 MPa gauge).

(4) Brazing filler material shall have a melting point exceeding 1,000°F (538°C).

(b) Tubing joints in steel, brass, or copper tubing shall be flared, brazed, or made up with approved gas tubing fittings.

(1) Fittings used at pressures higher than container pressure, such as on the discharge of liquid transfer pumps, shall be suitable for a working pressure of at least 350 psig (2.4 MPa gauge).

(2) Except as provided in 2-4.4.1(b)(1), fittings used with liquid LP-Gas, or with vapor LP-Gas at operating pressures over 125 psig (0.9 MPa gauge), shall be suitable for a working pressure of 250 psig (1.7 MPa gauge).

(3) Fittings for use with vapor LP-Gas at pressures not exceeding 125 psig (0.9 MPa gauge) shall be suitable for a working pressure of 125 psig (0.9 MPa gauge).

(4) Brazing filler material shall have a melting point exceeding 1,000°F (538°C).

(c) Joints in polyethylene pipe and tubing shall be made by heat fusion in accordance with the manufacturer's instructions.

(1) Polyethylene fittings shall conform to ANSI/ASTM D 2683, *Specification for Socket-Type Polyethylene (PE) Fittings for Outside Diameter—Controlled Polyethylene Pipe*, or ASTM D 3261, *Specification for Butt Heat Fusion Polyethylene (PE) Plastic Fittings for Polyethylene (PE) Plastic Pipe and Tubing*, and be listed or approved.

2-4.5 Valves, Other than Container Valves.

2-4.5.1 Pressure containing metal parts of valves (except appliance valves), including manual positive shutoff valves, excess-flow check valves, backflow check valves, emergency shutoff valves (*see 2-4.5.4*), and remotely controlled valves (either manually or automatically operated), used in piping systems shall be of steel, ductile (nodular) iron, malleable iron, or brass. Ductile iron shall meet the requirements of ANSI/ASTM A 395 or equivalent and malleable iron shall meet the requirements of ANSI/ASTM A 47 or equivalent. All materials used, including valve seat discs, packing, seals, and diaphragms shall be resistant to the action of LP-Gas under service conditions.

2-4.5.2 Valves shall be suitable for the appropriate working pressure, as follows:

(a) Valves used at pressures higher than container pressure, such as on the discharge of liquid transfer pumps, shall be suitable for a working pressure of at least 350 psig (2.4 MPa gauge). [400 psig (2.8 MPa gauge) WOG valves comply with this provision.]

(b) Valves to be used with liquid LP-Gas, or with vapor LP-Gas at pressures in excess of 125 psig (0.9 MPa gauge), but not to exceed 250 psig (1.7 MPa gauge), shall be suitable for a working pressure of at least 250 psig (1.7 MPa gauge).

Exception: Valves used at higher pressure as specified in 2-4.5.2(a).

(c) Valves (except appliance valves) to be used with vapor LP-Gas at pressures not to exceed 125 psig (0.9 MPa gauge) shall be suitable for a working pressure of at least 125 psig (0.9 MPa gauge).

2-4.5.3 Manual shutoff valves, emergency shutoff valves (*see 2-4.5.4*), excess-flow check valves, and backflow check valves used in piping systems shall comply with the provisions for container valves. [*See 2-3.3.3(a), (b) and (c).*]

2-4.5.4 Emergency shutoff valves shall be approved and incorporate all of the following means of closing (*see 3-2.7.9 and 3-3.3.4*):

(a) Automatic shutoff through thermal (fire) actuation. When fusible elements are used they shall have a melting point not exceeding 250°F (121°C).

(b) Manual shutoff from a remote location.

(c) Manual shutoff at the installed location.

2-4.6 Hose, Quick Connectors, Hose Connections, and Flexible Connectors.

2-4.6.1 Hose, hose connections, and flexible connectors (*see definition*) shall be fabricated of materials resistant to the action of LP-Gas both as liquid and vapor. If wire braid is used for reinforcement it shall be of corrosion resistant material such as stainless steel.

2-4.6.2 Hose and quick connectors shall be approved (*see Section 1-7, Approved*).

2-4.6.3 Hose, hose connections, and flexible connectors used for conveying LP-Gas liquid or vapor at pressures in excess of 5 psig (34.5 kPa gauge), and as provided in Section 3-4 regardless of the pressure, shall comply with 2-4.6.3(a) and (b):

(a) Hose shall be designed for a working pressure of 350 psi (240 MPa) with a safety factor of 5 to 1 and be continuously marked "LP-GAS," "PROPANE," "350 PSI WORKING PRESSURE," and the manufacturer's name or trademark.

(b) Hose assemblies, after the application of connections, shall have a design capability of withstanding a pressure of not less than 700 psig (4.8 MPa gauge). If a test is made, such assemblies shall not be leak tested at pressures higher than the working pressure [350 psig (2.4 MPa gauge) minimum] of the hose.

2-4.6.4 Hoses or flexible connectors used to supply LP-Gas to utilization equipment or appliances shall be installed in accordance with the provisions of 3-2.7.8 and 3-2.7.10.

2-4.7 Hydrostatic Relief Valves.

2-4.7.1 Hydrostatic relief valves designed to relieve the hydrostatic pressure which might develop in sections of liquid piping between closed shutoff valves shall have pressure settings not less than 400 psig (2.8 MPa gauge) or more than 500 psig (3.5 MPa gauge) unless installed in systems designed to operate above 350 psig (2.4 MPa gauge). Hydrostatic relief valves for use in systems designed to operate above 350 psig (2.4 MPa gauge) shall have settings not less than 110 percent or more than 125 percent of the system design pressure.

2-5 Equipment.

2-5.1 General.

2-5.1.1 This section includes fabrication and performance provisions for the pressure containing metal parts of LP-Gas equipment such as pumps, compressors, vaporizers, strainers, meters, sight flow glasses and regulators. Containers are not subject to the provisions of this section.

2-5.1.2 Equipment shall be suitable for the appropriate working pressure as follows:

(a) Equipment to be used at pressures higher than container pressure, such as on the discharge of a liquid pump, shall be suitable for a working pressure of at least 350 psig (2.4 MPa gauge). If pressures above 350 psig (2.4 MPa gauge) are necessary, the pump and all equipment under pressure from the pump shall be suitable for the pump discharge pressure.

(b) Equipment to be used with liquid LP-Gas, or vapor LP-Gas at pressures over 125 psig (0.9 MPa gauge) but not to exceed 250 psig (1.7 MPa gauge), shall be suitable for a working pressure of at least 250 psig (1.7 MPa gauge).

(c) Equipment to be used with vapor LP-Gas at pressures over 20 psig (138 kPa gauge), but not to exceed 125 psig (0.9 MPa gauge), shall be suitable for a working pressure of at least 125 psig (0.9 MPa gauge).

(d) Equipment to be used with vapor LP-Gas at pressures not to exceed 20 psig (138 kPa gauge) shall be suitable for a working pressure adequate for the service in which it is to be used.

2-5.1.3 Equipment shall be fabricated of materials suitable for LP-Gas service and resistant to the action of LP-Gas under service conditions. The following shall also apply:

(a) Pressure containing metal parts shall be of steel, ductile (nodular) iron (ASTM A 395-77 or A 536-77 Grade 60-40-18 or 65-45-12), malleable iron (ASTM A 47-77), higher strength gray iron (ASTM A 48-76, Class 40B), brass, or the equivalent.

(b) Cast iron shall not be used for strainers or flow indicators which shall comply with provisions for materials for construction of valves (*see 2-4.5.1*).

(c) Aluminum may be used for approved meters.

(d) Aluminum or zinc may be used for approved regulators. Zinc used for regulators shall comply with ASTM B 86-76.

(e) Non-metallic materials shall not be used for upper and lower casings of regulators.

2-5.2 Pumps.

2-5.2.1 Pumps shall be designed for LP-Gas service and may be of rotary, centrifugal, turbine or reciprocating type.

2-5.2.2 The maximum discharge pressure of a liquid pump under normal operating conditions shall be limited to 350 psig (2.4 MPa gauge).

2-5.3 Compressors.

2-5.3.1 Compressors shall be designed for LP-Gas service and may be of the rotary or reciprocating type and shall be equipped with suitable glands or seals to minimize any release of LP-Gas.

2-5.3.2 Means shall be provided to limit the suction pressure to the maximum for which the compressor is designed.

2-5.3.3 Means shall be provided to prevent the entrance of LP-Gas liquid into the compressor suction, either integral with the compressor, or installed externally in the suction piping [*see 3-2.10.2(b)*]. Portable compressors used with temporary connections are excluded from this requirement.

2-5.3.4 Engines used to drive portable compressors shall be equipped with exhaust system spark arrestors and shielded ignition systems.

2-5.4 Vaporizers, Tank Heaters, Vaporizing-Burners, and Gas-Air Mixers.

2-5.4.1 Vaporizers may be of the indirect type (utilizing steam, hot water, or other heating medium), or direct fired.

This subsection does not apply to engine fuel vaporizers or to integral vaporizer-burners such as those used with weed burners or tar kettles.

2-5.4.2 Indirect vaporizers shall comply with 2-5.4.2(a) through (e):

(a) Indirect vaporizers with an inside diameter of more than 6 in. (152 mm) shall be constructed in accordance with the applicable provision of the ASME Code for a design pressure of 250 psig (1.7 MPa gauge) and shall be permanently and legibly marked with:

(1) The marking required by the code.

(2) The allowable working pressure and temperature for which designed.

(3) The sum of the outside surface area and the inside heat exchange surface area in sq ft.

(4) The name or symbol of the manufacturer.

(b) Indirect vaporizers having an inside diameter of 6 in. (152 mm) or less are exempt from the ASME Code and need not be marked. They shall be constructed for a minimum 250 psig (1.7 MPa gauge) design pressure.

(c) Indirect vaporizers shall be provided with a suitable automatic means to prevent liquid passing through the vaporizer to the vapor discharge piping. This means may be integral with the vaporizer, or otherwise provided in the external piping (*see 3-7.2.6*).

(d) Indirect vaporizers, including atmospheric-type vaporizers using heat from the surrounding air or the ground, and of more than one quart (0.9 L) capacity, shall be equipped, at or near the discharge, with a spring-loaded pressure relief valve providing a relieving capacity in accordance with 2-5.4.5. Fusible plug devices shall not be used.

(e) Indirect atmospheric-type vaporizers of less than one quart (0.9 L) capacity need not be equipped with pressure relief valves, but shall be installed in accordance with 3-7.2.9.

2-5.4.3 Direct-fired vaporizers shall comply with 2-5.4.3(a) through (f).

(a) Design and construction shall be in accordance with the applicable requirements of the ASME Code for the working conditions to which the vaporizer will be subjected, and it shall be permanently and legibly marked with:

(1) The markings required by the code.

(2) The outside surface area in sq ft.

(3) The area of the heat exchange surface in sq ft.

(4) The maximum vaporizing capacity in gal per hour.

(5) The rated heat input in Btuh.

(6) The name or symbol of the manufacturer.

(b) Direct-fired vaporizers shall be equipped, at or near the discharge, with a spring-loaded pressure relief valve providing a relieving capacity in accordance with 2-5.4.5. The relief valve shall be located so as not to be subject to temperatures in excess of 140°F (60°C). Fusible plug devices shall not be used.

(c) Direct-fired vaporizers shall be provided with suitable automatic means to prevent liquid passing from the vaporizer to its vapor discharge piping.

(d) A means for manually turning off the gas to the main burner and pilot shall be provided.

(e) Direct-fired vaporizers shall be equipped with an automatic safety device to shut off the flow of gas to the main burner if the pilot light is extinguished. If the pilot flow exceeds 2,000 Btuh (2 MJ/h), the safety device shall shut off the flow of gas to the pilot also.

(f) Direct-fired vaporizers shall be equipped with a limit control to prevent the heater from raising the product pressure above the design pressure of the vaporizer equipment, and to prevent raising the pressure within the storage container above the pressure shown in the first column of Table 2-2.2.2 corresponding with the design pressure of the container (or its ASME Code equivalent—*see Note 1 of Table 2-2.2.2*).

2-5.4.4 Waterbath vaporizers shall comply with 2-5.4.4(a) through (j).

(a) The vaporizing chamber, tubing, pipe coils, or other heat exchange surface containing the LP-Gas to be vaporized, hereinafter referred to as "heat exchanger," shall be constructed in accordance with the applicable provisions of the ASME Code for a minimum design pressure of 250 psig (1.7 MPa gauge) and shall be permanently and legibly marked with:

(1) The marking required by the code.

(2) The allowable working pressure and temperature for which designed.

(3) The sum of the outside surface and the inside heat exchange surface area in sq ft.

(4) The name or symbol of the manufacturer.

(b) Heat exchangers for waterbath vaporizers having an inside diameter of 6 in. (152 mm) or less are exempt from the ASME Code and need not be marked. They shall be constructed for a 250 psig (1.7 MPa gauge) minimum design pressure.

(c) Heat exchangers for waterbath vaporizers shall be provided with a suitable automatic control to prevent liquid passing through the heat exchanger to the vapor discharge piping. This control shall be integral with the vaporizer.

(d) Heat exchangers for waterbath vaporizers shall be equipped at or near the discharge with a spring loaded pressure relief valve providing a relieving capacity in accordance with 2-5.4.5. Fusible plug devices shall not be used.

(e) Waterbath sections of waterbath vaporizers shall be

designed to eliminate a pressure buildup above the design pressure.

(f) The immersion heater which provides heat to the waterbath shall be installed so as not to contact the heat exchanger and may be electric or gas-fired.

(g) A control to limit the temperature of the waterbath shall be provided.

(h) Gas-fired immersion heaters shall be equipped with an automatic safety device to shut off the flow of gas to the main burner and pilot in the event of flame failure.

(i) Gas-fired immersion heaters with an input of 400,000 Btu (422 mJ/h) per hour or more shall be equipped with an electronic flame safeguard and programming to provide for pre-purge prior to ignition, proof of pilot before main burner valve opens, and full shutdown of main gas and pilot upon flame failure.

(j) A means shall be provided to shut off the source of heat in case the level of the heat transfer medium falls below the top of the heat exchanger.

2-5.4.5 The minimum rate of discharge in cubic-feet-of-air-per-minute for pressure relief valves for LP-Gas vaporizers, either of the indirect type or direct fired, shall be determined as follows:

(a) The surface area of that part of the vaporizer shell directly in contact with LP-Gas shall be added to the heat exchange surface area directly in contact with LP-Gas to obtain the total surface area in sq ft.

(b) Refer to Table E-2.2.2 to obtain the rate of discharge in cu ft of air per minute (Flow Rate CFM Air) for the total surface area in sq ft for the vaporizer computed in accordance with 2-5.4.5(a).

2-5.4.6 Direct gas-fired tank heaters shall be designed exclusively for outdoor aboveground use and so that there is no direct flame impingement upon the container. The provisions of 2-5.4.6(a) through (f) shall also apply.

(a) Tank heaters shall be approved and be permanently and legibly marked with:

(1) The rated input to the burner in Btuh.

(2) The maximum vaporizing capacity in gal per hour.

(3) The name or symbol of the manufacturer.

(b) The heater shall be designed so that it can be readily removed for inspection of the entire container.

(c) The fuel gas supply connection to the tank heater shall originate in the vapor space of the container being heated and shall be provided with a manually operated shutoff valve at the heater.

(d) The heater control system shall be equipped with an automatic safety shutoff valve of the manual-reset type arranged to shut off the flow of gas to both the main and pilot burners if the pilot flame is extinguished.

(e) When installed on a container exceeding 1,000 gal (3.8 m^3) water capacity, the heater control system shall include a valve to automatically shut off the flow of gas to both the main and pilot burners if the container becomes empty of liquid.

(f) Direct gas-fired tank heaters shall be equipped with a limit control to prevent the heater from raising the pressure in the storage container to more than 75 percent of the pressure shown in the first column of Table 2-2.2.2 corresponding with the design pressure of the container (or its ASME Code equivalent—*see Note 1 of Table 2-2.2.2*).

2-5.4.7 Vaporizing-burners shall be constructed with a minimum design pressure of 250 psig (1.7 MPa gauge) with a factor of safety of 5, and shall comply with 2-5.4.7(a) through (h):

(a) The vaporizing-burner, or the appliance in which it is installed, shall be permanently and legibly marked with:

(1) The maximum burner input in Btuh.

(2) The name or symbol of the manufacturer.

(b) Vaporizing coils or jackets shall be made of ferrous metals or high temperature alloys.

(c) The vaporizing section shall be protected by a hydrostatic relief valve, located where it will not be subjected to temperatures in excess of 140°F (60°C), and with a pressure setting such as to protect the components involved but not lower than 250 psig (1.7 MPa gauge). The relief valve discharge shall be directed upward and away from the component parts of the vaporizing burner. Fusible plug devices shall not be used.

(d) A means shall be provided for manually turning off the gas to the main burner and the pilot.

(e) Vaporizing-burners shall be provided with an automatic safety device to shut off the flow of gas to the main burner and pilot in the event the pilot is extinguished.

(f) Dehydrators and dryers utilizing vaporizing-burners shall be equipped with automatic devices both upstream and downstream of the vaporizing section. These devices shall be installed and connected to shut off in the event of excessive temperature, flame failure, and if applicable, insufficient air flow. See NFPA 61B, *Standard for the Prevention of Fires and Explosions in Grain Elevators and Facilities Handling Bulk Raw Agricultural Commodities*, for ignition and combustion controls applicable to vaporizing-burners associated with grain dryers.

(g) Pressure regulating and control equipment shall be so located or so protected as not to be subject to temperatures above 140°F (60°C), unless it is designed and recommended for use by the manufacturer for a higher temperature.

(h) Pressure regulating and control equipment located downstream of the vaporizing section shall be designed to withstand the maximum discharge temperature of the hot vapor.

2-5.4.8 Gas-air mixers shall comply with 2-5.4.8(a) through (e).

(a) Gas-air mixers shall be designed for the air, vapor and mixture pressures to which they are subjected. Piping materials shall comply with applicable portions of this standard.

(b) Gas-air mixers shall be designed so as to prevent the formation of a combustible mixture. Gas-air mixers which are capable of producing combustible mixtures shall be equipped with safety interlocks on both the LP-Gas and air supply lines to shut down the system if combustible limits are approached.

(c) In addition to the interlocks provided for in 2-5.4.8(b), a method shall be provided to prevent air from accidentally entering gas distribution lines without LP-Gas being present. Check valves shall be installed in the air and LP-Gas supply lines close to the mixer to minimize the possibility of backflow of gas into the air supply lines or of air into the LP-Gas system. Gas mixing control valves in the LP-Gas and air supply lines which are arranged to fail closed when actuated by safety interlock trip devices shall be considered as acceptable shutdown devices.

(d) Where it is possible for condensation to take place between the vaporizer and the gas-air mixer, an interlock shall be provided to prevent LP-Gas liquid from entering the gas-air mixer.

(e) Gas-air mixers which utilize the kinetic energy of the LP-Gas vapor to entrain air from the atmosphere, and are so designed that maximum air entrained is less than 85 percent of the mixture, need not include the interlocks specified in 2-5.4.8(b), (c) and (d), but shall be equipped with a check valve at the air intake to prevent the escape of gas to atmosphere when shut down. Gas-air mixers of this type receiving air from a blower, compressor or any source of air other than directly from the atmosphere, shall include a method of preventing air without LP-Gas, or mixtures of air and LP-Gas within the flammable range, from entering the gas distribution system accidentally.

2-5.5 Strainers.

2-5.5.1 Strainers shall be designed to minimize the possibility of particulate materials clogging lines and damaging pumps, compressors, meters, or regulators. The strainer element shall be accessible for cleaning.

2-5.6 Meters.

2-5.6.1 Vapor meters of the tin or brass case type of soldered construction shall not be used at pressures in excess of 1 psig (7 kPa gauge).

2-5.6.2 Vapor meters of the die cast or iron case type may be used at any pressure equal to or less than the working pressure for which they are designed and marked.

2-5.7 Dispensing Devices.

2-5.7.1 Components of dispensing devices, such as meters, vapor separators, valves and fittings within the dispenser, shall comply with 2-5.1.2(b) and 2-5.1.3.

2-5.7.2 Pumps of dispensers used to transfer LP-Gas shall comply with 2-5.1.2(b), 2-5.1.3 and with 2-5.2. Such pumps shall be equipped to permit control of the flow and to minimize the possibility of leakage or accidental discharge. Means shall be provided on the outside of the dispenser to readily shut off the power in the event of fire or accident. This means may be integral with the dispenser or provided externally when the dispenser is installed (*see 3-2.10.6*).

2-5.7.3 Dispensing hose shall comply with 2-4.6.1 through 2-4.6.3. An excess-flow check valve or an automatic shutoff valve complying with 2-3.3.3(a), (b), and (c) and 2-4.5.3, or 2-3.3.3(d) and 2-4.5.4, shall be installed in or on the dispenser at the point at which the dispenser hose is connected to the liquid piping. A differential back pressure valve shall be considered as meeting these provisions.

2-5.8 Regulators.

2-5.8.1 Final stage regulators (excluding appliance regulators) shall be equipped with one of the following [*see 3-2.5.2(b) for required protection from the elements which may be integral with the regulator*]:

(a) A pressure relief valve on the low pressure side having a start-to-leak pressure setting within limits specified in Table 2-5.8.1.

(b) A shutoff device that shuts the gas off at the regulator inlet when the downstream pressure reaches the overpressure limits specified in Table 2-5.8.1. Such a device shall not open to permit flow of gas until it has been manually reset.

2-5.9 Sight Flow Glasses.

2-5.9.1 Flow indicators, either of the simple observation type or combined with a backflow check valve, may be used in applications in which the observation of liquid flow through the piping is desirable or necessary.

2-6 Appliances.

2-6.1 General.

2-6.1.1 This section includes basic construction and performance provisions for LP-Gas consuming appliances.

2-6.2 Approved Appliances.

2-6.2.1 New residential, commercial, and industrial LP-Gas consuming appliances, except for those covered in 2-6.2.2 and 2-6.3.1, shall be approved.

2-6.2.2 For an appliance, class of appliance, or appliance accessory for which no applicable standard has been developed, approval of the authority having jurisdiction may be required before installation is made.

Table 2-5.8.1

Regulator Delivery Pressure in psig (kPa gauge)	Relief Valve Start-to-Leak Pressure Setting, % of Regulator Delivery Pressure	
	Minimum	Maximum
1 (7) or less	170%	300%
Above 1 (7), not over 3 (21)	140%	250%
Above 3 (21)	125%	250%

2-6.3 Provisions for Appliances.

2-6.3.1 Any appliance, originally manufactured for operation with a gaseous fuel other than LP-Gas, and in good condition, may be used with LP-Gas provided it is properly converted, adapted, and tested for performance with LP-Gas before being placed into use.

2-6.3.2 Unattended heaters used inside buildings for animal or poultry production or care shall be equipped with approved automatic devices to shut off the flow of gas to the main burners, and pilots if used, in the event of flame extinguishment or combustion failure. (*See 3-5.1.3 for exception to this provision when such heaters are used in buildings without enclosing walls.*)

2-6.3.3 Appliances using vaporizing-burners shall comply with 2-5.4.7.

2-6.3.4 Appliances used in mobile homes and recreational vehicles shall be approved for such service.

2-6.3.5 LP-Gas appliances used on commercial vehicles (*see Section 3-9*) shall be approved for the service (*see 2-6.2*) and shall comply with 2-6.3.5(a) through (c).

(a) Gas-fired heating appliances and water heaters shall

be equipped with automatic devices designed to shut off the flow of gas to the main burner and the pilot in the event the pilot flame is extinguished.

(b) Catalytic heating appliances shall be equipped with an approved automatic device to shut off the flow of gas in the event of combustion failure.

(c) Gas-fired heating appliances and water heaters to be used in vehicles intended for human occupancy shall make provisions for complete separation of the combustion system and the living space. If this separation is not integral with the appliance, it shall be provided otherwise by the method of installation (*see 3-9.4.2*).

Chapter 3 Installation of LP-Gas Systems

3-1 Scope.

3-1.1 Application.

3-1.1.1 This chapter applies to the field installation of LP-Gas systems utilizing components, subassemblies, container assemblies and container systems fabricated in accordance with Chapter 2.

3-1.1.2 Section 3-2 includes general provisions applicable to most stationary systems. Sections 3-3 to 3-9 extend and modify Section 3-2 for systems installed for specific purposes.

3-1.1.3 Installation of systems used in the highway transportation of LP-Gas is covered in Chapter 6.

3-1.1.4 LP-Gas systems shall be installed in accordance with this standard and other national standards or regulations which may apply. These include:

(a) NFPA 54, *National Fuel Gas Code* (ANSI Z223.1).

(b) NFPA 37, *Standard for the Installation and Use of Stationary Combustion Engines and Gas Turbines.*

(c) NFPA 501A, *Standard for Firesafety Criteria for Mobile Home Installations, Sites, and Communities.*

(d) NFPA 501C, *Standard on Firesafety Criteria for Recreational Vehicles.*

(e) NFPA 96, *Standard for the Installation of Equipment for the Removal of Smoke and Grease-Laden Vapors from Commercial Cooking Equipment.*

(f) NFPA 86, *Standard for Ovens and Furnaces.*

(g) NFPA 82, *Standard on Incinerators, Waste and Linen Handling Systems and Equipment.*

(h) NFPA 302, *Fire Protection Standard for Pleasure and Commercial Motor Craft.*

(i) NFPA 61B, *Standard for the Prevention of Fires and Explosions in Grain Elevators and Facilities Handling Bulk Raw Agricultural Commodities.*

(j) U.S. DOT Regulations, 49 CFR 191 and 192, for LP-Gas pipeline systems subject to DOT.

3-2 General Provisions.

3-2.1 Application.

3-2.1.1 This section includes location and installation criteria for containers; the installation of container appurtenances and regulators; piping service limitations; the installation of piping (including flexible connectors and hose); hydrostatic relief valves and equipment (other than vaporizers, *see Section 3-7*); and the testing of piping systems.

3-2.1.2 The provisions of this section are subject to modification for systems used for certain specific purposes (*see 3-1.1.2*).

3-2.1.3 For container appurtenances and gaskets installed on containers in excess of 3,500 gal (13 m^3) w.c., see 2-3.1.2(a) and 2-3.1.4.

3-2.2 Location of Containers.

3-2.2.1 LP-Gas containers shall be located outside of buildings except as follows:

(a) Portable containers as specifically provided for in Section 3-4.

(b) Containers of less than 125 gal (0.5 m^3) water capacity for the purposes of being filled in buildings or structures complying with Chapter 7.

(c) Containers on LP-Gas vehicles complying with, and parked or garaged in accordance with, Chapter 6.

(d) Containers used with LP-Gas stationary or portable engine fuel systems complying with Section 3-6.

(e) Containers used with LP-Gas fueled industrial trucks complying with 3-6.3.6.

(f) Containers on LP-Gas fueled vehicles garaged in accordance with 3-6.7.

(g) Portable containers awaiting use or resale when stored in accordance with Chapter 5.

3-2.2.2 Containers installed outside of buildings, whether of the portable type replaced on a cylinder exchange basis, or permanently installed and refilled at the installation, shall be located with respect to the nearest container, important building, group of buildings, or line of adjoining property which may be built upon, in accordance with Table 3-2.2.2, 3-2.2.3 and 3-2.2.5.

3-2.2.3 Where storage containers having an aggregate water capacity of more than 4,000 gal (15 m^3) are located in heavily populated or congested areas, the siting provisions of 3-2.2.2 and Table 3-2.2.2 may be modified as indicated by the firesafety analysis described in 3-10.2.3.

3-2.2.4 Aboveground multi-container installations comprised of containers having an individual water capacity of 12,000 gal (45 m^3) or more installed for use in a single location shall be limited to the number of containers in one group and with each group separated from the next group in accordance with the degree of fire protection provided in accordance with Table 3-2.2.4.

3-2.2.5 In the case of buildings of other than wood-frame construction devoted exclusively to gas manufacturing and distribution operations, including LP-Gas service stations, the distances in Table 3-2.2.2 may be reduced provided that in no case shall containers having a water capacity exceeding 500 gal (1.9 m^3) be located closer than 10 ft (3 m) to such gas manufacturing and distributing buildings.

3-2.2.6 The following provisions shall also apply:

(a) Containers shall not be stacked one above the other.

(b) Loose or piled combustible material and weeds and

Table 3-2.2.2

Water Capacity Per Container Gallons (m^3)	Minimum Distances		
	Mounded or Underground Containers [Note (d)]	Aboveground Containers [Note (f)]	Between Containers [Note (e)]
Less than 125 (0.5) [Note (a)]	10 ft (3 m)	None [Note (b)]	None
125 to 250 (0.5 to 1.0)	10 ft (3 m)	10 ft (3 m)	None
251 to 500 (1.0 + to 1.9)	10 ft (3 m)	10 ft (3 m)	3 ft (1 m)
501 to 2,000 (1.9 + to 7.6)	10 ft (3 m)	25 ft (7.6 m) [Note (c)]	3 ft (1 m)
2,001 to 30,000 (7.6 + to 114)	50 ft (15 m)	50 ft (15 m)	5 ft (1.5 m)
30,001 to 70,000 (114 + to 265)	50 ft (15 m)	75 ft (23 m)	(¼ of sum of diameters of adjacent containers)
70,001 to 90,000 (265 + to 341)	50 ft (15 m)	100 ft (30 m)	
90,001 to 120,000 (341 + to 454)	50 ft (15 m)	125 ft (38 m)	
120,001 to 200,000 (454 to 757)		200 ft (61 m)	
200,001 to 1,000,000 (757 to 3 785)		300 ft (91 m)	
Over 1,000,000 (3 785)		400 ft (122 m)	

Notes to Table 3-2.2.2

Note (a): At a consumer site, if the aggregate water capacity of a multi-container installation comprised of individual containers having a water capacity of less than 125 gal (0.5 m^3) is 501 gal (1.9 + m^3) or more, the minimum distance shall comply with the appropriate portion of this table, applying the aggregate capacity rather than the capacity per container. If more than one such installation is made, each installation shall be separated from any other installation by at least 25 ft (7.6 m). Do not apply the MINIMUM DISTANCES BETWEEN CONTAINERS to such installations.

Note (b): The following shall apply to aboveground containers installed alongside of buildings:

(1) DOT specification containers shall be located and installed so that the discharge from the container pressure relief device is at least 3 ft (1 m) horizontally away from any building opening below the level of such discharge, and shall not be beneath any building unless this space is well ventilated to the outside and is not enclosed for more than 50 percent of its perimeter. The discharge from container pressure relief devices shall be located not less than 5 ft (1.5 m) in any direction away from any exterior source of ignition, openings into direct-vent (sealed combustion system) appliances, or mechanical ventilation air intakes.

(2) ASME containers of less than 125 gal (0.5 m^3) water capacity shall be located and installed so that the discharge from pressure relief devices shall not terminate in or beneath any building and shall be located at least 5 ft (1.5 m) horizontally away from any building opening below the level of such discharge, and not less than 5 ft (1.5 m) in any direction away from any exterior source of ignition, openings into direct-vent (sealed combustion system) appliances, or mechanical ventilation air intakes.

(3) The filling connection and the vent from liquid level gauges on either DOT or ASME containers filled at the point of installation shall be not less than 10 ft (3 m) in any direction away from any exterior source of ignition, openings into direct-vent (sealed combustion system) appliances, or mechanical ventilation air intakes.

Note (c): This distance may be reduced to not less than 10 ft (3 m) for a single container of 1,200 gal (4.5 m^3) water capacity or less provided such container is at least 25 ft (7.6 m) from any other LP-Gas container of more than 125 gal (0.5 m^3) water capacity.

Note (d): Minimum distances for underground containers shall be measured from the pressure relief device and filling or liquid level gauge vent connection at the container, except that no part of an underground container shall be less than 10 ft (3 m) from a building or line of adjoining property which may be built upon.

Note (e): When underground multi-container installations are made of individual containers having a water capacity of 125 gal (0.5 m^3) or more, such containers shall be installed so as to permit access at their ends or sides to facilitate working with cranes or hoists.

Note (f): In applying the distance between buildings and ASME containers of 125 gal (0.5 m^3) or more water capacity, a minimum of 50 percent of this horizontal distance shall also apply to all portions of the building which project more than 5 ft (1.5 m) from the building wall and which are higher than the relief valve discharge outlet. This horizontal distance shall be measured from a point determined by projecting the outside edge of such overhanging structure vertically downward to grade or other level upon which the container is installed. Under no conditions shall distances to the building wall be less than those specified in Table 3-2.2.2.

Exception to Note (f): Not applicable to installations in which overhanging structure is 50 ft (15 m) or more above the relief valve discharge outlet.

Table 3-2.2.4

Fire Protection Provided by	Maximum Number of Containers in One Group	Minimum Separation Between Groups—feet
Hose streams only— see 3-10.2.3	6	50 (15 m)
Fixed monitor nozzles per 3-10.3.5*	6	25 (7.6 m)
Fixed water spray per 3-10.3.4*	9	25 (7.6 m)
Insulation per 3-10.3.1	9	25 (7.6 m)

*In the design of fixed water spray and fixed monitor nozzle systems, the area of container surface to be protected may reflect portion of containers not likely to be subject to fire exposure as determined by good fire protection engineering practices.

long dry grass shall not be permitted within 10 ft (3 m) of any container.

(c) Suitable means shall be used to prevent the accumulation or flow of liquids having flash points below 200°F (93.4°C) under adjacent LP-Gas containers such as by dikes, diversion curbs or grading. Determination of flash points shall be in accordance with NFPA 321, *Standard on Basic Classification of Flammable and Combustible Liquids.*

(d) When tanks containing flammable or combustible liquids (*see NFPA 321 for definitions of these liquids*) are within a diked area, LP-Gas containers shall be outside the diked area and at least 10 ft (3 m) away from the centerline of the wall of the diked area.

(e) The minimum horizontal separation between aboveground LP-Gas containers and aboveground tanks containing liquids having flash points below 200°F (93.4°C) shall be 20 ft (6 m). This provision shall not apply when LP-Gas containers of 125 gal (0.5 m^3) or less water capacity are installed adjacent to fuel oil supply tanks of 660 gal (2.5 m^3) or less capacity. No horizontal separation is required between aboveground LP-Gas containers and underground tanks containing flammable or combustible liquids installed in accordance with NFPA 30, *Flammable and Combustible Liquids Code.* See 3-2.2.6(c) for flash point determinations.

(f) The minimum separation between LP-Gas containers and oxygen or gaseous hydrogen containers shall be in accordance with Table 3-2.2.6(f) except that lesser distances are permitted where protective structures having a minimum fire resistance rating of two hours interrupt the line of sight between uninsulated portions of the oxygen or hydrogen containers and the LP-Gas containers. The location and arrangement of such structures shall minimize the problems cited in the Note to 3-2.2.8. Also, see NFPA 50 and 51 for oxygen systems and NFPA 50A on gaseous hydrogen systems. The minimum separation between LP-Gas containers and liquefied hydrogen containers shall be in accordance with NFPA 50B.

(g) Where necessary to prevent flotation due to possible high flood waters around aboveground containers, or high water table for those underground, containers shall be securely anchored.

(h) When LP-Gas containers are to be stored or used in the same area with other compressed gases, the containers shall be marked to identify their content in accordance with ANSI Standard 748.1, *Method of Marking Portable Compressed Gas Containers to Identify the Material Contained* (CGA C-4).

(i) No part of an aboveground LP-Gas container shall be located in the area 6 ft (1.8 m) horizontally from a vertical plane beneath overhead electric power lines that are over 600 volts, nominal.

3-2.2.7 Because of the anticipated "flash" of nonrefrigerated LP-Gas when released to the atmosphere dikes normally serve no useful purpose for nonrefrigerated installations.

3-2.2.8 Structures such as fire walls, fences, earth or concrete barriers and other similar structures shall be avoided around or over installed nonrefrigerated containers.

Exception No. 1: Such structures partially enclosing containers are permissible if designed in accordance with a sound fire protection analysis.

Exception No. 2: Structures used to prevent flammable or combustible liquid accumulation or flow are permissible in accordance with 3-2.2.6(c).

Exception No. 3: Structures between LP-Gas containers and gaseous hydrogen containers are permissible in accordance with 3-2.2.6(f).

Exception No. 4: Fences are permissible in accordance with 3-3.6.1.

NOTE: The presence of such structures can create significant hazards, e.g., pocketing of escaping gas, interference with application of cooling water by fire departments, redirection of flames against containers, and impeding egress of personnel in an emergency.

3-2.3 Installation of Containers.

3-2.3.1 Containers shall be installed in accordance with 3-2.3.1(a) through (f):

(a) DOT cylinder specification containers shall be installed only aboveground, and shall be set upon a firm foundation, or otherwise firmly secured. Flexibility shall be provided in the connecting piping. (*See 3-2.7.5 and 3-2.7.8.*)

(b) All containers shall be positioned so that the pressure relief valve is in direct communication with the vapor space of the container.

(c) Where physical damage to LP-Gas containers, or systems of which they are a part, from vehicles is a possibility, precautions against such damage shall be taken.

(d) The installation position of ASME containers shall make all container appurtenances accessible for their normally intended use.

(e) Field welding on containers shall be limited to attachments to nonpressure parts, such as saddle plates, wear plates or brackets applied by the container manufacturer. Welding to container proper shall comply with 2-2.1.6.

(f)* Aboveground containers shall be kept properly painted.

3-2.3.2 Horizontal ASME containers designed for permanent installation in stationary service aboveground shall be placed on substantial masonry or noncombustible structural supports on concrete or firm masonry foundations, and supported as follows:

(a) Horizontal containers shall be mounted on saddles in such a manner as to permit expansion and contraction, and not to cause an excessive concentration of stresses. Structural steel supports may be used as follows, or if in compliance with 3-2.3.2(b).

Exception No. 1: Temporary use as provided in 3-2.3.2(a)(2)b.

Exception No. 2: Isolated locations as provided in 3-2.3.2(b).

(1) Containers of more than 2,000 gal (7.6 m^3) water capacity shall be provided with concrete or masonry foundations formed to fit the container contour, or if furnished with saddles in compliance with 2-2.5.1, may be placed on flat-topped foundations.

(2) Containers of 2,000 gal (7.6 m^3) water capacity or less may be installed on concrete or masonry foundations formed to fit the container contour, or if equipped with attached supports complying with 2-2.5.2(a), may be installed as follows:

a. If the bottoms of the horizontal members of the container saddles, runners or skids are to be more than 12 in. (305 mm) above grade, fire-resistive foundations shall be provided. A container shall not be mounted with the outside bottom of the container shell more than 5 ft (1.5 m) above the surface of the ground.

b. For temporary use at a given location, not to exceed 6 months, fire-resistive foundations or saddles are not required provided the outside bottom of the container shell is not more than 5 ft (1.5 m) above the ground and that flexibility in the connecting piping is provided. (*See 2-4.6.3.*)

(3) Containers or container-pump assemblies mounted

Table 3-2.2.6(f)

LP-Gas Containers Having An	Separation From Oxygen Containers Having An			Separation From Gaseous Hydrogen Containers Having An		
Aggregate water capacity of	Aggregate capacity of 400 CF (11 m³)* or less	Aggregate capacity of more than 400 CF (11 m³)* to 20,000 CF (566 m³),* including unconnected reserves.	Aggregate capacity of more than 20,000 CF (566 m³),* including unconnected reserves.	Aggregate capacity of less than 400 CF (11 m³)*	Aggregate capacity of 400 CF (11 m³)* to 3000 CF (85 m³)*	Aggregate capacity of more than 3000 CF (85 m³)*
1200 Gal (4.5 m³) or less	None	20 ft (6 m)	25 ft (7.6 m)			
Over 1200 Gal (4.5 m³)	None	20 ft (6 m)	50 ft (15 m)			
500 Gal (1.9 m³) or less				None	10 ft (3 m)	25 ft (7.6 m)
Over 500 Gal (1.9 m³)				None	25 ft (7.6 m)	50 ft (15 m)

*Cubic feet measured at 70°F and atmospheric pressure.

on a common base complying with 2-2.5.2(b) may be placed on paved surfaces or on concrete pads at ground level within 4 in. (102 mm) of ground level.

(b) With the approval of the authority having jurisdiction, single containers complying with 2-2.5.1 or 2-2.5.2 may be installed in isolated locations, with nonfireproofed steel supports resting on concrete pads or footings, provided the outside bottom of the container shell is not more than 5 ft (1.5 m) above the ground level.

(c) Suitable means of preventing corrosion shall be provided on that part of the container in contact with the saddles or foundations or on that part of the container in contact with masonry.

3-2.3.3 Vertical ASME containers over 125 gal (0.5 m³) water capacity designed for permanent installation in stationary service aboveground shall be installed on reinforced concrete or steel structural supports on reinforced concrete foundations which are designed to meet the loading provisions established in 2-2.2.3.

(a) Steel supports shall be protected against fire exposure with a material having a fire resistance rating of at least two hours. Continuous steel skirts having only one opening 18 in. (457 mm) or less in diameter need such fire protection applied only to the outside of the skirts.

3-2.3.4 Single containers constructed as portable storage containers (*see definition*) for temporary stationary service in accordance with 2-2.5.4(a) shall be placed on concrete pads, paved surfaces or firm earth for such temporary service (normally not more than 12 months at a given location) and the following shall apply:

(a) The surface on which they are placed shall be substantially level and, if not paved, shall be cleared (and kept cleared) of dry grass and weeds, and other combustible material within 10 ft (3 m) of the container.

(b) Flexibility shall be provided in the connecting piping.

(c) If such containers are to be set with the bottoms of the skids or runners above the ground, nonfireproofed structural supports may be used for isolated locations with the approval of the authority having jurisdiction, and provided the height of the outside bottom of the container shell above the ground does not exceed 5 ft (1.5 m). Otherwise, fire-resistive supports shall be provided.

3-2.3.5 If the container is mounted on, or is part of, a vehicle as provided in 2-2.5.4(b), the unit shall be parked in compliance with the provisions of 3-2.2.2 as to the location of a container of that capacity for normal stationary service, and in accordance with the following:

(a) The surface shall be substantially level and if not paved shall be suitable for heavy vehicular use, and shall be cleared (and kept cleared) of dry grass and weeds, and other combustible material within 10 ft (3 m) of the container.

(b) Flexibility shall be provided in the connecting piping.

3-2.3.6 Portable containers of 2,000 gal (7.6 m³) water capacity or less complying with 2-2.5.5 may be installed for stationary service as provided in 3-2.3.2(a)(2) for stationary containers.

3-2.3.7 Mounded containers shall be installed as follows:

(a) Mounding material shall be earth or sand and shall provide minimum thickness of cover for the container of at least 1 ft (305 mm).

(b) Unless inherently resistant to erosion, a suitable protective cover shall be provided.

3-2.3.8 ASME container assemblies listed for underground installation, including interchangeable aboveground-underground container assemblies may be installed underground as follows:

(a) The container shell shall be placed at least 6 in. (153 mm) below grade unless the container might be subject to abrasive action or physical damage from vehicular traffic within a parking lot area, driveway, or similar area. In this case, a noninterchangeable underground container shall be used and the container shell placed at least 18 in. (457 mm) below grade [*see 3-2.3.8(c)*] or equivalent protection shall be otherwise provided, such as the use of a concrete slab, to prevent imposing the weight of a vehicle directly on the container shell. Protection of the fitting housing, housing cover, tank connections, and piping shall be provided to protect against vehicular damage.

(b) Where containers are installed underground within 10 ft (3 m) where vehicular traffic may be reasonably expected, such as driveways and streets or within a utility easement subject to vehicular traffic, protection of the fitting housing, housing cover, tank connections, and piping shall be provided to protect against vehicular damage.

(c) Approved interchangeable aboveground-underground container assemblies installed underground shall not be placed with the container shell more than 12 in. (305 mm) below grade.

(d) Any party involved in construction and/or excavation in the vicinity of a buried container shall be responsible for determining the location of and providing protection for the container and piping against physical damage from vehicular traffic.

(e) The portion of the container to which the fitting cover or other connections are attached need not be covered. The discharge of the regulator vent shall be above the highest probable water level.

(f) Containers shall be protected against corrosion for the soil conditions at the container site by a method in accordance with good engineering practice. Precaution shall be taken to prevent damage to the coating during handling. Any damage to the coating shall be repaired before backfilling.

(g) Containers shall be set substantially level on a firm foundation (firm earth may be used) and surrounded by earth or sand firmly tamped in place. Backfill shall be free of rocks or similar abrasives.

(h) When a container is to be abandoned underground, the following procedure shall be followed:

(1) Remove as much liquid LP-Gas as possible through the container liquid withdrawal connection.

(2) Remove as much of the remaining LP-Gas vapor as possible by venting it through a vapor connection; either burning this vapor, or venting it to the open air at a safe location. The vapor shall not be vented at such a rapid rate as to exceed the vaporization rate of any residual liquid LP-Gas left after the liquid removal procedure of 3-2.3.8(h)(1).

NOTE: If vapor is vented too rapidly the pressure drop due to the refrigeration of the liquid may lead to the erroneous conclusion that no liquid remains in the container.

(3) When only vapor LP-Gas at atmospheric pressure remains in the container, it shall be filled with water, sand or foamed plastic, or purged with an inert gas. The displaced vapor may be burned or vented to the open air at a safe location.

3-2.3.9 Partially underground, unmounded ASME containers shall be installed as follows:

(a) The portion of the container below the surface, and for a vertical distance of at least 3 in. (75 mm) above the surface, shall be protected to resist corrosion as required for underground containers. [*See 3-2.3.8(f).*]

(b) Containers shall be set substantially level on a firm foundation, with backfilling to be as required for underground containers. [*See 3-2.3.8(g).*]

(c) Spacing provisions shall be as specified for aboveground containers in 3-2.2.2 and Table 3-2.2.2.

(d) The container shall be located so as not to be subject to vehicular damage, or shall be adequately protected against such damage.

3-2.4 Installation of Container Appurtenances.

3-2.4.1 Pressure relief devices shall be installed on containers in accordance with 3-2.4.2 through 3-2.4.5 and positioned so that the relief device is in direct communication with the vapor space of the container.

3-2.4.2 Pressure relief devices on portable DOT cylinder specification containers, or their equivalent of ASME construction, of 1,000 lb (454 kg) [120 gal (0.5 m^3)] water capacity or less, shall be installed to minimize the possibility of relief device(s) discharge(s) impingement on the container.

3-2.4.3 Pressure relief devices on ASME containers of 125 gal (0.5 m^3) water capacity or more permanently installed in stationary service, portable storage containers (*see definition*), portable containers (tanks) of nominal 120 gal (0.5 m^3) water capacity or more, or cargo tanks shall be installed so that any gas released is vented away from the container upward and unobstructed to the open air. The following provisions shall also apply:

(a) Means shall be provided, such as rain caps, to minimize the possibility of the entrance of water or other extraneous matter (which might render the relief device inoperative or restrict its capacity) into the relief device or any discharge piping. If necessary, provision shall be made for drainage. The rain cap or other protector shall be designed to remain in place except when the relief device operates and shall permit the relief device to operate at sufficient relieving capacity.

(b) On each aboveground container of more than 2,000 gal (7.6 m^3) water capacity, the relief device discharge shall be vertically upward and unobstructed to the open air at a point at least 7 ft (2 m) above the top of the container. The following also shall apply:

(1) Relief device discharge piping shall comply with 3-2.4.3(f).

(2) In providing for drainage in accordance with 3-2.4.3(a), the design of relief device discharge(s) and attached piping shall:

a. Be such as to protect the container against flame impingement which might result from ignited product escaping from the drain opening.

b. Be directed so that a container(s), piping or equipment which might be installed adjacent to container on which the relief device is installed is not subjected to flame impingement.

(c) On underground containers of 2,000 gal (7.6 m^3) or less water capacity, except those installed in LP-Gas service stations covered in 3-2.4.3(e), the relief device may discharge into the manhole or housing, provided such manhole or housing is equipped with ventilated louvers, or their equivalent, of adequate area as specified in 3-2.4.6(d).

(d) On underground containers of more than 2,000 gal (7.6 m^3) water capacity, except those installed in LP-Gas service stations, the discharge from relief devices shall be piped vertically and directly upward to a point at least 7 ft (2 m) above the ground. Relief device discharge piping shall comply with 3-2.4.3(f).

(e) On underground containers in LP-Gas service stations, the relief device discharge shall be piped vertically and directly upward to a point at least 10 ft (3 m) above the ground. Discharge piping shall comply with 3-2.4.3(f) and shall be adequately supported and protected against physical damage.

(f) The discharge terminals from relief devices shall be located so as to provide protection against physical damage. Discharge piping used shall be adequate in size to permit sufficient relief device relieving capacity. Such piping shall be metallic and have a melting point over 1500°F (816°C). Discharge piping shall be designed so that excessive force applied to the discharge piping will result in breakage on the discharge side of the valve rather than on the inlet side without imparing the function of the valve. Return bends and restrictive pipe or tubing fittings shall not be used.

(g) Shutoff valves shall not be installed between relief devices and the container, or between the relief devices and the discharge piping, except for specially designed relief device-shutoff valve combinations covered by 2-3.2.4(c), or where two or more separate relief devices are installed, each with its individual shutoff valve, and the shutoff valve stems are mechanically interconnected in a manner which will allow the rated relieving capacity required for the container from the relief device or devices which remain in communication with the container.

3-2.4.4 Pressure relief devices on portable storage containers (constructed and installed in accordance with 2-2.5.4 and 3-2.3.4 respectively) used temporarily in stationary type service shall be installed in accordance with the applicable provisions of 3-2.4.3.

3-2.4.5 Additional provisions (over and above the applicable provision in 3-2.4.2 and 3-2.4.3) apply to the installation of pressure relief devices in containers used in connection with vehicles as follows:

(a) For containers installed on vehicles in accordance with Sections 3-6 and 3-9.

(b) For cargo containers (tanks) installed on cargo vehicles in accordance with Section 6-3, see 6-3.2.1(a).

3-2.4.6 Container appurtenances other than pressure relief devices shall be installed and protected as follows:

(a) All container openings except those used for pressure relief devices (*see 2-3.2*), liquid level gauging devices (*see 2-3.4*), pressure gauges (*see 2-3.5*), those equipped with double check valves as allowed in Table 2-3.3.2, and plugged openings shall be equipped with internal valves [*see 2-3.3.3(d)*] or with positive shutoff valves and either excess-flow or backflow check valves (*also see 2-3.3 for specific application*) as follows:

(1) Except for DOT cylinders, excess-flow or backflow check valves shall be located between the LP-Gas in the container and the shutoff valves, either inside the container, or at a point immediately outside where the line enters or leaves the container. If outside, installation shall be made so that any undue strain beyond the excess-flow or backflow check valve will not cause breakage between the container and such valve. All connections, including couplings, nozzles, flanges, standpipes and manways, which are listed on the ASME Manufacturers' Data Report for the container, are considered part of the container. On DOT cylinders, the excess-flow valve where required may be located at the outlet of the cylinder shutoff valve.

(2) Shutoff valves shall be located as close to the container as practicable. The valves shall be readily accessible for operation and maintenance under normal and emergency conditions, either because of location or by means of permanently installed special provisions. Valves installed in an unobstructed location not more than 6 ft (1.8 m) above ground level shall be considered accessible. Special provisions include, but are not limited to, stairs, ladders, platforms, remote operators or extension handles.

(3) The connections, or line, leading to or from any individual opening shall have greater capacity than the rated flow of the excess-flow valve protecting the opening.

(b) Valves, regulators, gauges and other container appurtenances shall be protected against physical damage.

(c) Valves in the assembly of portable multicontainer systems shall be arranged so that replacement of containers can be made without shutting off the flow of gas in the system. This provision shall not be construed as requiring an automatic changeover device.

(d) Connections to containers installed underground shall be located within a substantial dome, housing or manhole and with access thereto protected by a substantial cover. Underground systems shall be installed so that all terminals for connecting hose and any opening through which there can be a flow from pressure relief devices or pressure regulator vents are located above the normal maximum water table. Terminals for connecting hoses, openings for flow from pressure relief devices, and the interior of domes, housing and manholes shall be kept clean of debris. Such manholes or housings shall be provided with ventilated louvers or their equivalent. The area of such openings shall equal or exceed the combined discharge areas of the pressure relief devices and other vent lines which discharge into the manhole or housing.

(e) Container inlet and outlet connections, except pressure relief devices, liquid level gauging devices and pressure gauges, on containers of 2,000 gal (7.6 m^3) water capacity or more, or on containers of any capacity used in LP-Gas service stations, shall be labeled to designate whether they communicate with the vapor or liquid space. Labels may be on valves. (*See Sections 3-6 and 3-9 for requirements for labeling smaller containers used for vehicular installations.*)

(f) Every storage container of more than 2,000 gal (7.6 m^3) water capacity shall be provided with a suitable pressure gauge (*see 2-3.5*).

3-2.5 Regulator Installation.

3-2.5.1 Regulators used to control distribution or utilization pressure shall be as close to the container or vaporizer outlets as is practicable. First stage regulating equipment shall be outside of buildings except as used with containers and liquid piping systems covered by 3-2.2.1(a), (b), (d), (e) and (f), and 3-2.6.1(d).

3-2.5.2 Regulators shall be securely attached to container valves, containers, supporting standards or building walls.

(a) First stage regulators shall be either directly connected to the container shutoff valve or outlet of vaporizer where used, unless attached thereto with flexibility provided in the connecting piping or the interconnecting piping of manifolded containers or vaporizers.

(b) All regulators for outdoor installations, except regulators used for portable industrial applications, shall be designed, installed, or protected so their operation will not be affected by the elements (freezing rain, sleet, snow, ice, mud, or debris). This protection may be integral with the regulator.

3-2.5.3 On regulating equipment installed outside of buildings, the discharge from a pressure relief device shall be located not less than 3 ft (1 m) horizontally away from any building opening below the level of such discharge, and not beneath any building unless this space is well ventilated to the outside and is not enclosed for more than 50 percent of its perimeter.

3-2.5.4 On regulators installed inside buildings, the discharge from the pressure relief device and from above the regulator and relief device diaphragms shall be vented to the outside air with the discharge outlet located not less than 3 ft (1 m) horizontally away from any building opening below the level of such discharge. This provision shall not apply to appliance regulators otherwise protected (*see NFPA 54*), or to regulators used in connection with containers in buildings as provided for in 3-2.2.1(a), (b), (d), (e) and (f).

3-2.6 Piping System Service Limitations.

3-2.6.1 This subsection describes the physical state (vapor or liquid) and pressure at which LP-Gas may be transmitted through piping systems under various circumstances:

(a) LP-Gas liquid or vapor may be piped at all normal operating pressures outside of buildings.

(b) Polyethylene piping systems shall be limited to vapor service not exceeding 30 psig (208 kPa gauge).

(c) LP-Gas vapor at pressures not exceeding 20 psig (138 kPa gauge) may be piped into any building.

(d) LP-Gas vapor at pressures exceeding 20 psig (138 kPa gauge) or LP-Gas liquid shall not be piped into any building except those meeting the following descriptions:

(1) Buildings, or separate areas of buildings, constructed in accordance with Chapter 7, and used exclusively to:

a. House equipment for vaporization, pressure reduction, gas mixing, gas manufacturing or distribution.

b. House internal combustion engines, industrial processes, research and experimental laboratories, or equipment or processing having a similar hazard.

Exception: Complete compliance with Chapter 7 for buildings, or separate areas of buildings, housing industrial processes and other occupancies cited in 3-2.6.1(d)(1)b may not be necessary depending upon the prevailing conditions. Construction of buildings or separate areas of buildings housing certain internal combustion engines is covered in NFPA 37.

(2) Buildings or structures under construction or undergoing major renovation, provided the temporary piping meets the provisions of 3-4.2 and 3-4.10.2.

(3) In buildings or structures other than those covered by 3-2.6.1(d)(1) and (2) in which liquid feed systems are used, liquid piping may enter the building or structure to connect to a vaporizer provided heavy walled seamless brass or copper tubing not exceeding $^{3}/_{32}$ in. (2.4 mm) internal diameter and with a wall thickness not less than $^{3}/_{64}$ in. (1.2 mm) is used.

3-2.7 Installation of Pipe, Tubing, Pipe and Tubing Fittings, Valves, and Hose.

3-2.7.1 LP-Gas normally is transferred into containers as a liquid, but may also be conveyed as a liquid or vapor under container or lower regulated pressure. Metallic piping except safety relief discharge piping (*see 3-2.4.3*) shall comply with the following:

(a) Piping used at pressures higher than container pressure, such as on the discharge side of liquid transfer pumps, shall be suitable for a working pressure of at least 350 psig (2.4 MPa gauge).

(b) Vapor LP-Gas piping with operating pressures in excess of 125 psig (0.9 MPa gauge), and liquid piping not covered by 3-2.7.1(a), shall be suitable for a working pressure of at least 250 psig (1.7 MPa gauge).

(c) Vapor LP-Gas piping, subject to pressures of not more than 125 psig (0.9 MPa gauge), shall be suitable for a working pressure of at least 125 psig (0.9 MPa gauge).

3-2.7.2 Metallic pipe joints may be threaded, flanged, welded or brazed using pipe and fittings complying with 2-4.2 and 2-4.4 as follows:

(a) When joints are threaded or threaded and back welded:

(1) For LP-Gas vapor at pressures in excess of 125 psig (0.9 MPa gauge), or for LP-Gas liquid, the pipe and nipples shall be Schedule 80 or

(2) For LP-Gas vapor at pressures of 125 psig (0.9 MPa gauge) or less, the pipe and nipples shall be Schedule 40 or heavier.

(b) When joints are welded or brazed:

(1) The pipe shall be Schedule 40 or heavier.

(2) The fittings or flanges shall be suitable for the service in which they are to be used.

(3) Brazed joints shall be made with a brazing material having a melting point exceeding 1,000°F (538°C).

(c) Gaskets used to retain LP-Gas in flanged connections in piping shall be resistant to the action of LP-Gas. They shall be made of metal or other suitable material confined in metal having a melting point over 1,500°F (816°C) or shall be protected against fire exposure, except that aluminum O-rings and spiral wound metal gaskets are acceptable. When a flange is opened, the gasket shall be replaced.

3-2.7.3 Metallic tubing joints may be flared, or brazed using tubing and fittings, and brazing material complying with 2-4.3 and 2-4.4.

3-2.7.4 Piping in systems shall be run as directly as is practicable from one point to another, and with as few restrictions, such as ells and bends, as conditions will permit, giving consideration to provisions of 3-2.7.5.

(a) Where condensation of vapor may occur, metallic and nonmetallic piping shall be pitched back to the container or suitable means provided for revaporizing the condensate.

3-2.7.5 Provision shall be made in piping including interconnecting of permanently installed containers, to compensate for expansion, contraction, jarring and vibration, and for settling. Where necessary, flexible connectors complying with 2-4.6 may be used (*see 3-2.7.8*). The use of nonmetallic pipe, tubing or hose for permanently interconnecting such containers is prohibited.

3-2.7.6 Metallic piping outside buildings may be underground or aboveground or both. Aboveground piping shall be well supported and protected against physical damage. Where underground piping is beneath driveways, roads or streets, possible damage by vehicles shall be taken into account. Nonmetallic piping, including the nonmetallic portions of transition fittings, shall be installed outside, a minimum of 12 in. (305 mm) underground and in accordance with the piping manufacturer's instructions.

3-2.7.7 Underground metallic piping shall be protected against corrosion as warranted by soil conditions. Corrosion protection shall comply with the following:

(a) Underground piping shall be protected as needed with a suitable coating to retard the effects of the corrosion conditions existing in the local soil. Coated pipe shall extend at least 6 in. (152 mm) aboveground on all risers.

(b) When dissimilar metals are joined underground, an insulating fitting shall be installed to electrically isolate them from each other.

(c) If cathodic protection is used, insulating fittings shall be installed to electrically isolate the cathodically protected underground system from all aboveground piping and systems.

(d) LP-Gas piping shall not be used as a grounding electrode.

3-2.7.8 Flexible components used in piping systems shall comply with 2-4.6 for the service in which they are to be used, shall be installed in accordance with the manufacturer's instructions, and shall also comply with the following:

(a) Flexible connectors in lengths up to 36 in. (1 m) (*see 2-4.6.3 and 2-4.6.4*) may be used for liquid or vapor piping, on portable or stationary tanks, to compensate for expansion, contraction, jarring, vibration and settling. This is not to be construed to mean that flexible connectors shall be used if provisions were incorporated in the design to compensate for these effects.

(b) Hoses may be installed if flexibility is required for liquid or vapor transfer. The use of wet hose (*see 4-2.3.4 for explanation of term "wet hose"*) is recommended for liquid.

3-2.7.9 On new installations, and by December 31, 1980, on existing installations, (1) stationary single container systems of over 4,000 gal (15.1 m^3) water capacity, or (2) stationary multiple container systems with an aggregate water capacity of more than 4,000 gal (15.1 m^3) utilizing a common or manifolded liquid transfer line, shall comply with 3-2.7.9(a) and (b).

(a) When a hose or swivel type piping 1 ½ in. (38 mm) or larger is used for liquid transfer or a 1 ¼ in. (32 mm) or larger vapor hose or swivel type piping is used in this service (excluding flexible connectors in such liquid and vapor piping), an emergency shutoff valve complying with 2-4.5.4 shall be installed in the fixed piping of the transfer system within 20 ft (6 m) of lineal pipe from the nearest end of the hose or swivel type piping to which the hose or swivel type piping is connected. The preceding sizes are nominal. Where the flow is only in one direction, a backflow check valve may be used in lieu of an emergency shutoff valve if installed in the fixed piping downstream of the hose or swivel type piping, provided the backflow check valve has a metal-to-metal seat or a primary resilient seat with a secondary metal seat not hinged with combustible material. When either a liquid or vapor line has two or more hoses or swivel type piping of the sizes designated, either an emergency shutoff valve or a backflow check valve shall be installed in each leg of the piping.

(1) Emergency shutoff valves shall be installed so that the temperature sensitive element in the valve, or a supplemental temperature sensitive element [250°F (121°C) maximum] connected to actuate the valve, is not more than 5 ft (1.5 m) from the nearest end of the hose or swivel type piping connected to the line in which the valve is installed.

(b) The emergency shutoff valve(s) or backflow check valve(s) specified in 3-2.7.9(a) shall be installed in the plant piping so that any break resulting from a pull will occur on the hose or swivel type piping side of the connection while retaining intact the valves and piping on the plant side of the connection. This may be accomplished by use of concrete bulkheads or equivalent anchorage or by the use of a weakness or shear fitting. Such anchorage is not required for tank car unloading.

3-2.7.10 Hose may be used on the low pressure side of regulators to connect to other than domestic and commercial appliances as follows:

(a) The appliance connected shall be of a portable type.

(b) For use inside buildings, the hose shall be of a minimum length, not exceeding 6 ft (1.8 m) [except as provided for in 3-4.2.3(b)], and shall not extend from one room to another, nor pass though any partitions, walls, ceilings or floors (except as provided for in 3-4.3.7). It shall not be concealed from view or used in concealed locations. For use outside buildings, hose length may exceed 6 ft (1.8 m), but shall be kept as short as practicable.

(c) Hose shall be securely connected to the appliance. The use of rubber slip ends is not permissible.

(d) A shutoff valve shall be provided in the piping immediately upstream of the inlet connection of the hose. When more than one such appliance shutoff is located near another, precautions shall be taken to prevent operation of the wrong valve.

(e) Hose used for connecting appliances to wall or other outlets shall be protected against physical damage.

3-2.8 Hydrostatic Relief Valve Installation.

3-2.8.1 A hydrostatic relief valve complying with 2-4.7.1 or a device providing pressure relieving protection shall be installed in each section of piping (including hose) in which liquid LP-Gas can be isolated between shutoff valves so as to relieve the pressure which could develop from the trapped liquid to a safe atmosphere or product-retaining section.

3-2.9 Testing Piping Systems.

3-2.9.1 After assembly, piping systems (including hose) shall be tested and proven free of leaks at not less than the normal operating pressure. Piping within the scope of NFPA 54, *National Fuel Gas Code*, [*see 1-2.3.1(f)*], shall be pressure tested in accordance with that Code. Tests shall not be made with a flame.

3-2.10 Equipment Installation.

3-2.10.1 Pumps shall be installed as recommended by the manufacturer and in accordance with 3-2.10.1(a) through (c).

(a) Installation shall be made so that the pump casing shall not be subjected to excessive strains transmitted to it by the suction and discharge piping. This shall be accomplished by piping design, the use of flexible connectors or expansion loops, or by other effective methods, in accordance with good engineering practice.

(b) Positive displacement pumps shall be installed in accordance with 2-5.2.2.

(1) The bypass valve or recirculating device to limit the normal operating discharge pressure to not more than 350 psig (2.4 MPa gauge) shall discharge either into a storage container (preferably the supply container from which the product is being pumped) or into the pump suction.

(2) If this primary device is equipped with a shutoff valve, an adequate secondary device designed to operate at not more than 400 psig (2.8 MPa gauge) shall, if not integral with the pump, be incorporated in the pump piping. This secondary device shall be designed or installed so that it cannot be rendered inoperative, and shall discharge either into the supply container or into the pump suction.

(c) A pump operating control or disconnect switch shall be located near the pump. Remote control points shall be provided as necessary for other plant operations such as container filling, loading or unloading of cargo vehicles and tank cars, or operation of motor fuel dispensers.

3-2.10.2 Compressors shall be installed as recommended by the manufacturer and in accordance with 3-2.10.2 (a) and (b).

(a) Installation shall be made so that the compressor housing shall not be subjected to excessive strains transmitted to it by the suction and discharge piping. Flexible connectors may be used where necessary to accomplish this.

(b) If the compressor is not equipped with an integral means to prevent the LP-Gas liquid entering the suction (*see 2-5.3.3*), a suitable liquid trap shall be installed in the suction piping as close to the compressor as practicable. Portable compressors used with temporary connections are excluded from this requirement.

(c) Engines used to drive portable compressors shall be equipped with exhaust system spark arrestors and shielded ignition systems.

3-2.10.3 The installation of vaporizers of the types covered by 2-5.4 is covered in Section 3-7 and of engine fuel vaporizers in Section 3-6. Integral vaporizing-burners, such as are used for weed burners or tar kettles, are considered to be part of these units (or "appliances"). For appliance installation standards, see Section 3-5.

3-2.10.4 Strainers shall be installed so that the strainer element can be serviced.

3-2.10.5 Liquid or vapor meters shall be installed as recommended by the manufacturer, and in compliance with the applicable provisions of 3-2.10.5(a) and (b).

(a) Liquid meters shall be securely mounted and shall be installed so that the meter housing is not subjected to excessive strains from the connecting piping. If not provided in the piping design, flexible connectors may be used where necessay to accomplish this.

(b) Vapor meters shall be securely mounted and installed so as to minimize the possibility of physical damage.

3-2.10.6 LP-Gas engine fuel dispensing devices installed in service stations shall be installed as recommended by the manufacturer and in accordance with 3-2.10.6(a) through (h).

(a) Installation shall not be within a building, but may be under weather shelter or canopy, provided this area is adequately ventilated and is not enclosed for more than 50 percent of its perimeter.

(b) Dispensing devices shall be located as follows:

(1) Not less than 10 ft (3 m) from aboveground storage containers of more than 2,000 gal (7.6 m^3) water capacity.

(2) Not less than 20 ft (6 m) from any building [not including canopies covered in 3-2.10.6(a)], basement, cellar, pit or line of adjoining property which may be built upon.

(3) Not less than 10 ft (3 m) from sidewalks, streets or thoroughfares.

(c) Dispensing devices shall either be installed on a concrete foundation or be part of a complete storage and dispensing unit mounted on a common base [to be mounted as provided in 3-2.3.1(b) and (d)]. In either case, they shall be adequately protected against physical damage.

(d) Control for the pump used to transfer LP-Gas through the dispensing device into motor vehicle tanks shall be provided at the device in order to minimize the possibility of leakage or accidental discharge. The following also shall apply:

(1) Means shall be provided at some point outside the dispensing device, such as a remote switch [*see 3-2.10.1(c)*], to shut off the power in the event of fire or accident.

(2) A manual shutoff valve and an excess-flow check valve of suitable capacity shall be located in the liquid line between the pump and dispenser inlet only when the dispensing device is installed at a remote location and not part of a complete storage and dispensing unit mounted on a common base.

(e) Provision shall be made for venting the LP-Gas contained in the dispenser to a safe location.

(f) The dispensing hose shall comply with 2-4.6. An excess-flow check valve, or an automatic shutoff valve [*see 2-3.3.3(d) and 2-4.5.4*] shall be installed at the terminus of the liquid piping at the point of attachment of the dispensing hose. A differential back pressure valve shall be considered as meeting this provision.

(g) Piping leading to, and within the dispenser, and the dispensing hose shall be provided with hydrostatic relief valves as specified in 3-2.8.1 (*see also 2-4.7.1*).

(h) No drains or blowoffs from the dispensing device shall be directed toward, or be in close proximity to sewer systems.

3-3 Distributing and Industrial LP-Gas Systems.

3-3.1 Application.

3-3.1.1 This section includes provisions for LP-Gas systems installed at distributing plants, industrial plants and distributing points (*see definitions*). These provisions extend and modify the provisions of Section 3-2 for these applications.

3-3.2 General.

3-3.2.1 The location and installation of storage containers and the installation of container appurtenances, piping, and equipment shall comply with Section 3-2.

3-3.3 Installation of Liquid Transfer Facilities.

3-3.3.1 Points of transfer (*see definition*) or the nearest part of a structure housing transfer operations shall be located in accordance with 4-3.2 and 4-3.3.

3-3.3.2 Separate buildings, and attachments to or rooms within other buildings, housing points of transfer or transfer pumps and compressors, constructed or converted to such use after December 31, 1972, shall comply with Chapter 7.

3-3.3.3 The track of the railroad siding or the roadway surface at the transfer points shall be relatively level. Adequate clearances from buildings, structures, or stationary containers shall be provided for the siding or roadway approaches to the unloading or loading points. Substantial bumpers shall be provided at the ends of sidings, and as necessary to protect storage containers and points of transfer.

3-3.3.4 Safeguards shall be provided to prevent the uncontrolled discharge of LP-Gas in the event of failure in the hose or swivel type piping. The provisions of 3-2.7.9 shall apply. For all other LP-Gas systems, the following shall apply:

(a) The connection, or connecting piping, larger than ½ in. (13 mm) internal diameter into which the liquid or vapor is being transferred shall be equipped with:

(1) A backflow check valve, or

(2) An emergency shutoff valve complying with 2-4.5.4, or

(3) An excess-flow valve properly sized in accordance with 3-2.4.6(a)(3).

(b) The connection, or connecting piping, larger than ½ in. (13 mm) internal diameter from which the liquid or vapor is being withdrawn shall be equipped with:

(1) An emergency shutoff valve complying with 2-4.5.4, or

(2) An excess-flow valve properly sized in accordance with 3-2.4.6(a)(3).

3-3.3.5 See 4-2.3.6 for railroad tank car transfer operations.

3-3.3.6 If gas is to be discharged from containers inside a building, the installation provisions of 4-4.2.1 shall apply.

3-3.4 Installation of Gas Distribution Facilities.

3-3.4.1 This subsection applies to the installation of facilities used for gas manufacturing, gas storage, gas-air mixing and vaporization, and compressors not associated with liquid transfer.

3-3.4.2 Separate buildings and attachments to or rooms within other buildings housing gas distribution facilities, constructed or converted to such use after December 31, 1972, shall comply with Chapter 7.

Exception No. 1: Facilities for vaporizing LP-Gas and gas-air mixing shall be designed, located and installed in accordance with Section 3-7.

Exception No. 2: Facilities for storing LP-Gas in portable containers at industrial plants and distributing points shall comply with Chapter 5.

3-3.4.3 Buildings housing vapor compressors shall be located in accordance with 4-3.3.2 considering the building as one housing a point of transfer.

3-3.4.4 The use of pits to house gas distribution facilities shall be avoided unless automatic flammable vapor detecting systems are installed in the pit. Drains or blowoff lines shall not be directed into or in proximity of sewer systems.

3-3.4.5 If gas is to be discharged from containers inside a building, the installation provisions of 4-4.2.1 shall apply.

3-3.5 Installation of Electrical Equipment.

3-3.5.1 Installation of electrical equipment shall comply with Section 3-8.

3-3.6 Protection Against Tampering for Section 3-3 Systems.

3-3.6.1 To minimize the possibilities for trespassing and tampering, the area which includes container appurtenances, pumping equipment, loading and unloading facilities and container filling facilities shall be protected by one of the following methods:

(a) Enclosure with at least a 6-ft (1.8-m) high industrial-type fence, unless otherwise adequately protected. There shall be at least two means of emergency access from the fenced or other enclosure. Clearance shall be provided to permit maintenance to be performed and a clearance of at least 3 ft (1 m) shall be provided to allow emergency access to the required means of egress. If guard service is provided, it shall be extended to the LP-Gas installation. Guard personnel shall be properly trained. (*See 1-6.1.1.*)

Exception: If a fenced or otherwise enclosed area is not over 100 sq ft (9 m²) in area, the point of transfer is within 3 ft (1 m) of a gate and containers being filled are not located within the enclosure, a second gate need not be provided.

(b) As an alternate to fencing the operating area, suitable devices which can be locked in place shall be provided. Such devices, when in place, shall effectively prevent unauthorized operation of any of the container appurtenances, system valves or equipment.

3-3.7 Lighting.

3-3.7.1 If operations are normally conducted during other than daylight hours, adequate lighting shall be provided to illuminate storage containers, containers being loaded, control valves and other equipment.

3-3.8 Ignition Source Control.

3-3.8.1 Ignition source control shall comply with Section 3-8.

3-4 LP-Gas Systems in Buildings or on Building Roofs or Exterior Balconies.

3-4.1 Application.

3-4.1.1 This section includes installation and operating provisions for LP-Gas systems containing liquid LP-Gas located inside of, or on the roofs or exterior balconies of, buildings or structures. Systems covered include those utilizing portable containers inside of or on the roofs or exterior balconies of buildings, and those in which the liquid is piped from outside containers into buildings or onto the roof. These systems are permitted only under the conditions specified in 3-4.1.1(a) through (d) and in accordance with 3-4.1 and 3-4.2. Containers in use shall mean connected for use.

(a) The portable use of containers indoors shall be only for the purposes specified in 3-4.3 through 3-4.8. Such use shall be limited to those conditions where operational requirements make portable use of containers necessary and location outside is impractical.

(b) Installations using portable containers on roofs shall be as specified in 3-4.9.1. Such use shall be limited to those conditions where operational requirements make portable use of containers necessary and location not on roofs of buildings or structures is impractical.

(c) Installations using portable containers on exterior balconies shall be as specified in 3-4.9.2.

(d) Liquid LP-Gas shall be piped into buildings or structures only for the purposes specified in 3-2.6.1(d).

3-4.1.2 Storage of containers awaiting use shall be in accordance with Chapter 5.

3-4.1.3 Transportation of containers within a building shall be in accordance with 3-4.2.7.

3-4.1.4 These provisions are in addition to those specified in Section 3-2.

3-4.1.5 Liquid transfer systems are covered in Chapter 4.

3-4.1.6 Engine fuel systems used inside buildings are covered in Section 3-6.

3-4.1.7 LP-Gas transport or cargo vehicles stored, serviced or repaired in buildings are covered in Chapter 6.

3-4.2 General Provisions for Containers, Equipment, Piping, and Appliances.

3-4.2.1 Containers shall comply with DOT cylinder specifications (*see 2-2.1.3 and 2-2.2.1*), shall not exceed 245 lb (111 kg) water capacity [nominal 100 lb (45 kg) LP-Gas capacity] each, shall comply with other applicable provisions of Section 2-2 and be equipped as provided in Section 2-3 (*see 2-3.3 and Table 2-3.3.2*). They shall also comply with the following:

(a) Containers shall be marked as provided in 2-2.6.

(b) Containers with water capacities greater than 2 ½ lb (1 kg) [nominal 1 lb (0.45 kg) LP-Gas capacity] shall be equipped with shutoff and excess-flow valves as provided in 2-3.3.2 (Column 3, Table 2-3.3.2). The installation of excess-flow valves shall take into account the type of valve protection provided for the container in accordance with 2-2.4.1.

(c) Valves on containers shall be protected in accordance with 2-2.4.1.

(d) Containers having water capacities greater than 2 ½ lb (1 kg) [nominal 1 lb (0.45 kg) LP-Gas capacity] connected for use shall stand on a firm and substantially level surface. If necessary, they shall be secured in an upright position.

(e) Containers and the valve protecting devices used with them shall be oriented so as to minimize the possibility of impingement of the pressure relief device discharge on the container and adjacent containers.

3-4.2.2 Regulators, if used, shall be suitable for use with LP-Gas. Manifolds and fittings connecting containers to pressure regulator inlets shall be designed for at least 250 psig (1.7 MPa gauge) service pressure.

3-4.2.3 Piping, including pipe, tubing, fittings, valves, and hose, shall comply with Section 2-4, except that a minimum working pressure of 250 psig (1.7 MPa gauge) shall apply to all components. The following also shall apply:

(a) Piping shall be installed in accordance with the provisions of 3-2.7 for liquid piping or for vapor piping for pressures above 125 psig (0.9 MPa gauge). [*See 3-2.7.1(b).*]

(b) Hose, hose connections, and flexible connectors used shall be designed for a working pressure of at least 350 psig (2.4 MPa gauge), shall comply with 2-4.6, and be installed in accordance with 3-2.7.10. Hose length may exceed that specified by 3-2.7.10(b), but shall be as short as practicable, although long enough to permit compliance with the spacing requirements (*see 3-4.3.3 and 3-4.3.4*) without kinking or straining hose or causing it to be close enough to a burner to be damaged by heat. See 3-4.9 for permanent roof installations.

3-4.2.4 Containers, regulating equipment, manifolds, pipe, tubing, and hose shall be located so as to minimize exposure to abnormally high temperatures (such as might result from exposure to convection and radiation from heating equipment or installation in confined spaces), physical damage or tampering by unauthorized persons.

3-4.2.5 Heat producing equipment shall be located and used so as to minimize the possibility of the ignition of combustibles.

3-4.2.6 When containers are located on a floor, roof, or balcony, provisions shall be made to minimize the possibility of containers falling over the edge.

(a) Filling containers on roofs or balconies is prohibited. See 4-3.1.1(b).

3-4.2.7 Transportation (movements) of containers within a building shall comply with 3-4.2.7(a) through (d).

(a) Movement of containers having water capacities greater than 2 ½ lb (1 kg) [nominal 1 lb (0.45 kg) LP-Gas capacity] within a building shall be restricted to movement directly associated with the uses covered by Sections 3-4.3 through 3-4.9 and be conducted in accordance with these provisions and 3-4.2.7(b) through (d).

(b) Valve outlets on containers having water capacities greater than 2 ½ lb (1 kg) [nominal 1 lb (0.45 kg) LP-Gas capacity] shall be tightly plugged and the provisions of 2-2.4.1 shall be complied with.

(c) Only emergency stairways not generally used by the public shall be used and reasonable precautions shall be taken to prevent the container from falling down the stairs.

(d) Freight or passenger elevators may be used when occupied only by those engaged in moving the container.

3-4.2.8 Portable heaters, including salamanders, shall be equipped with an approved automatic device to shut off the flow of gas to the main burner, and pilot if used, in the event of flame extinguishment or combustion failure. Such portable heaters shall be self-supporting unless designed for container mounting (*see 3-4.3.4*). Container valves, connectors, regulators, manifolds, piping, or tubing shall not be used as structural supports. The following shall also apply:

(a) Portable heaters manufactured on or after May 17, 1967, having an input of more than 50,000 Btuh (53 MJ/h), and those manufactured prior to May 17, 1967, with inputs of more than 100,000 Btuh (105 MJ/h), shall be equipped with either:

(1) A pilot which must be lighted and proved before the main burner can be turned on, or

(2) An approved electric ignition system.

(b) The provisions of 3-4.2.8 are not applicable to the following:

(1) Tar kettle burners, hand torches or melting pots.

(2) Portable heaters with less than 7,500 Btuh (8 MJ/h) input if used with containers having a maximum water capacity of 2 ½ lb (1 kg).

3-4.3 Buildings Under Construction or Undergoing Major Renovation.

3-4.3.1 Containers may be used and transported in buildings or structures under construction or undergoing major renovation when such buildings are not occupied by the public or, if partially occupied by the public, containers may be used and transported in the unoccupied portions with the prior approval of the authority having jurisdiction. Such use shall be in accordance with 3-4.3.1 through 3-4.3.8.

3-4.3.2 Containers, equipment, piping, and appliances shall comply with 3-4.2.

3-4.3.3 For temporary heating, such as curing concrete, drying plaster, and similar applications, heaters (other than integral heater-container units covered in 3-4.3.4) shall be located at least 6 ft (1.8 m) from any LP-Gas container.

3-4.3.4 Integral heater-container units specifically designed for the attachment of the heater to the container, or to a supporting standard attached to the container, may be used, provided they are designed and installed so as to prevent direct or radiant heat application to the container. Blower and radiant type units shall not be directed toward any LP-Gas container within 20 ft (6 m).

3-4.3.5 If two or more heater-container units of either the integral or nonintegral type are located in an unpartitioned area on the same floor, the container(s) of each such unit shall be separated from the container(s) of any other such unit by at least 20 ft (6 m).

3-4.3.6 If heaters are connected to containers manifolded together for use in an unpartitioned area on the same floor, the total water capacity of containers manifolded together serving any one heater shall not be greater than 735 lb (333 kg) [nominal 300 lb (136 kg) LP-Gas capacity], and if there is more than one such manifold it shall be separated from any other by at least 20 ft (6 m).

3-4.3.7 On floors on which no heaters are connected for use, containers may be manifolded together for connection to a heater or heaters on another floor, provided:

(a) The total water capacity of the containers connected to any one manifold is not greater than 2,450 lb (1111 kg) [nominal 1,000 lb (454 kg) LP-Gas capacity], and

(b) Manifolds of more than 735 lb (333 kg) water capacity [nominal 300 lb (136 kg) LP-Gas capacity], if located in the same unpartitioned area, shall be separated from each other by at least 50 ft (15 m).

3-4.3.8 The provisions of 3-4.3.5, 3-4.3.6, and 3-4.3.7 may be altered by the authority having jurisdiction if compliance is impractical.

3-4.4 Buildings Undergoing Minor Renovation when Frequented by the Public.

3-4.4.1 Containers may be used and transported for repair or minor renovation in buildings frequented by the public as follows:

(a) During the hours of the day the public normally is in the building the following shall apply:

(1) The maximum water capacity of individual containers shall be 50 lb (23 kg) [nominal 20 lb (9 kg) LP-Gas capacity] and the number of containers in the building shall not exceed the number of workers assigned to using the LP-Gas.

(2) Containers having a water capacity greater than 2 ½ lb (1 kg) [nominal 1 lb (0.45 kg) LP-Gas capacity] shall not be left unattended.

(b) During the hours of the day when the building is not open to the public, containers may be used and transported in the building for repair or minor renovation in accordance with 3-4.2 and 3-4.3, provided, however, that containers with a greater water capacity than 2 ½ lb (1 kg) [nominal 1 lb (0.45 kg) LP-Gas capacity] shall not be left unattended.

3-4.5 Buildings Housing Industrial Occupancies.

3-4.5.1 Containers may be used in buildings housing industrial occupancies for processing, research, or experimental purposes as follows:

(a) Containers, equipment, and piping used shall comply with 3-4.2.

(b) If containers are manifolded together, the total water capacity of the connected containers shall be not more than 735 lb (333 kg) [nominal 300 lb (136 kg) LP-Gas capacity]. If there is more than one such manifold in a room, it shall be separated from any other by at least 20 ft (6 m).

(c) The amount of LP-Gas in containers for research and experimental use in the building shall be limited to the smallest practical quantity.

3-4.5.2 Containers may be used to supply fuel for temporary heating in buildings housing industrial occupancies with essentially noncombustible contents, if portable equipment for space heating is essential and a permanent heating installation is not practicable, provided containers and heaters comply with and are used in accordance with 3-4.3.

3-4.6 Buildings Housing Educational and Institutional Occupancies.

3-4.6.1 Containers may be used in buildings housing educational and institutional laboratory occupancies for research and experimental purposes, but not in classrooms, as follows:

(a) The maximum water capacity of individual containers used shall be:

(1) 50 lb (23 kg) [nominal 20 lb (9 kg) LP-Gas capacity] if used in educational occupancies.

(2) 12 lb (5.4 kg) [nominal 5 lb (2 kg) LP-Gas capacity] if used in institutional occupancies.

(b) If more than one such container is located in the same room, the containers shall be separated by at least 20 ft (6 m).

(c) Containers not connected for use shall be stored in accordance with Chapter 5, except that they shall not be stored in a laboratory room.

3-4.7 Temporary Heating in Buildings in Emergencies.

3-4.7.1 Containers may be used in buildings for temporary emergency heating purposes if necessary to prevent damage to the buildings or contents, and if the permanent heating system is temporarily out of service, provided the containers and heaters comply with and are used and transported in accordance with 3-4.2 and 3-4.3, and the temporary heating equipment is not left unattended.

3-4.8 Use in Buildings for Demonstrations or Training, or in Small Containers.

3-4.8.1 Containers having a maximum water capacity of 12 lb (5.4 kg) [nominal 5 lb (2 kg) LP-Gas capacity] may be used temporarily inside buildings for public exhibitions or demonstrations, including use in classroom demonstrations. If more than one such container is located in the same room, the containers shall be separated by at least 20 ft (6 m).

3-4.8.2 Containers may be used temporarily in buildings for training purposes related to the installation and use of LP-Gas systems, provided:

(a) The maximum water capacity of individual containers shall be 245 lb (111 kg) [nominal 100 lb (45 kg) LP-Gas capacity], but not more than 20 lb (9 kg) of LP-Gas may be placed in a single container.

(b) If more than one such container is located in the same room, the containers shall be separated by at least 20 ft (6 m).

(c) The training location shall be acceptable to the authority having jurisdiction.

(d) Containers shall be promptly removed from the building when the training class has terminated.

3-4.8.3* Except as stipulated in 3-4.8.3(a) containers having a maximum water capacity of 2 ½ lb (1 kg) [nominal 1 lb (0.45 kg) LP-Gas capacity] may be used in buildings as part of approved self-contained torch assemblies or similar appliances.

(a) Containers of any capacity used to supply appliances for residential or commercial food service shall not be used in buildings except as provided in 3-4.8.1.

3-4.9 Portable Containers on Roofs or Exterior Balconies.

3-4.9.1 Containers may be permanently installed on roofs of buildings of fire-resistive construction, or noncombustible construction having essentially noncombustible contents, or of other construction or contents which are protected with automatic sprinklers (*see NFPA 220, Standard on Types of Building Construction*) in accordance with 3-4.2 and the following:

(a) The total water capacity of containers connected to any one manifold shall not be greater than 980 lb (445 kg) [nominal 400 lb (181 kg) LP-Gas capacity]. If more than one manifold is located on the roof, it shall be separated from any other by at least 50 ft (15 m).

(b) Containers shall be located in areas where there is free air circulation, at least 10 ft (3 m) from building openings (such as windows and doors) and at least 20 ft (6 m) from air intakes of air conditioning and ventilating systems.

(c) Containers shall not be located on roofs which are entirely enclosed by parapets more than 18 in. (457 mm) high unless either (1) the parapets are breached with low-level ventilation openings no more than 20 ft (6 m) apart, or (2) all openings communicating with the interior of the building are at or above the top of the parapets.

(d) Piping shall be in accordance with 3-4.2.3, provided, however, that hose shall not be used for connecting to containers.

(e) The fire department shall be advised of each such installation.

3-4.9.2 Containers having water capacities greater than 2 ½ lb (1 kg) [nominal 1 lb (0.5 kg) LP-Gas capacity] shall not be located on balconies above the first floor attached to a multiple family dwelling of three or more living units located one above the other.

Exception: Not applicable when such balconies are served by outside stairways and when only such stairways are used to transport the container.

3-4.10 Liquid Piped into Buildings or Structures.

3-4.10.1 Liquid LP-Gas piped into buildings in accordance with 3-2.6.1(d)(1) shall comply with 3-2.7.

3-4.10.2 Liquid LP-Gas piped into buildings in accordance with 3-2.6.1(d)(2) from containers located and installed outside the building or structure in accordance with 3-2.2 and 3-2.3 shall comply with the following:

(a) Liquid piping shall not exceed ¾ in. I.P.S. and shall comply with 3-2.6 and 3-2.7. If approved by the authority having jurisdiction, copper tubing complying with 2-4.3.1(c)(1) and with a maximum outside diameter of ¾ in. may be used. Liquid piping in buildings shall be kept to a minimum, and shall be protected against construction hazards by:

(1) Securely fastening it to walls or other surfaces to provide adequate protection against breakage.

(2) Locating it so as to avoid exposure to high ambient temperatures.

(b) A readily accessible shutoff valve shall be located at each intermediate branch line where it leaves the main line. A second shutoff valve shall be located at the appliance end of the branch and upstream of any flexible appliance connector.

(c) Excess-flow valves complying with 2-3.3.3(b) and 2-4.5.3 shall be installed in the container outlet supply line, downstream of each shutoff valve, and at any point in the piping system where the pipe size is reduced. They shall be sized for the reduced size piping.

(d) Hose shall not be used to carry liquid between the container and the building, or at any point in the liquid line except as the appliance connector. Such connectors shall be as short as practicable and shall comply with 2-4.6, 3-2.7.8, and 3-2.7.10.

(e) Hydrostatic relief valves shall be installed in accordance with 3-2.8.

(f) Provision shall be made so that the release of fuel when any section of piping or appliances are disconnected shall be minimized by use of one of the following methods:

(1) An approved automatic quick-closing coupling which shuts off the gas on both sides when uncoupled.

(2) Closing the shutoff valve closest to the point to be disconnected and allowing the appliance or appliances on that line to operate until the fuel in the line is consumed.

3-5 Installation of Appliances.

3-5.1 Application.

3-5.1.1 This section includes installation provisions for LP-Gas appliances fabricated in accordance with Section 2-6.

3-5.1.2 Installation of appliances on commercial vehicles is covered in Section 3-9.

3-5.1.3 With the approval of the authority having jurisdiction, unattended heaters used for the purpose of animal or poultry production inside structures without enclosing walls need not be equipped with an automatic device designed to shut off the flow of gas to main burners and pilot, if used, in the event of flame extinguishment or combustion failure.

3-5.2 Reference Standards.

3-5.2.1 LP-Gas appliances shall be installed in accordance with this standard and other national standards which may apply. These include:

(a) NFPA 37, *Standard for the Installation and Use of Stationary Combustion Engines and Gas Turbines.*

(b) NFPA 54, *National Fuel Gas Code* (ANSI Z223.1).

(c) NFPA 61B, *Standard for the Prevention of Fires and Explosions in Grain Elevators and Facilities Handling Bulk Raw Agricultural Commodities.*

(d) NFPA 82, *Standard on Incinerators, Waste and Linen Handling Systems and Equipment.*

(e) NFPA 86, *Standard for Ovens and Furnaces.*

(f) NFPA 96, *Standard for the Installation of Equipment for the Removal of Smoke and Grease-Laden Vapors from Commercial Cooking Equipment.*

(g) NFPA 302, *Fire Protection Standard for Pleasure and Commercial Motor Craft.*

(h) NFPA 501A, *Standard for Firesafety Criteria for Mobile Home Installations, Sites, and Communities.*

(i) NFPA 501C, *Standard on Firesafety Criteria for Recreational Vehicles* (ANSI A119.2).

3-6 Engine Fuel Systems.

3-6.1 Application.

3-6.1.1 This section applies to fuel systems using LP-Gas as a fuel for internal combustion engines. Included are provisions for containers, container appurtenances, carburetion equipment, piping, hose and fittings, and provisions for their installation. This section covers engine fuel systems for engines installed on vehicles for any purpose, as well as fuel systems for stationary and portable engines. It also includes provisions for garaging of vehicles upon which such systems are installed.

See Section 3-9 for systems on vehicles for purposes other than for engine fuel.

3-6.1.2 Containers supplying fuel to stationary engines, or to portable engines used in lieu of stationary engines, shall be installed in accordance with Section 3-2 (*see Section 3-4 for portable engines used in buildings, roofs, or exterior balconies under certain conditions*).

3-6.1.3 Containers supplying fuel to engines on vehicles, regardless of whether the engine is used to propel the vehicle or is mounted on it for other purposes, shall be constructed and installed in accordance with this section.

3-6.1.4 In the interest of safety, each person engaged in installing, repairing, filling, or otherwise servicing an LP-Gas engine fuel system shall be properly trained in the necessary procedures.

3-6.2 General Purpose Vehicle Engines Fueled by LP-Gas.

3-6.2.1 This section covers the installation of fuel systems supplying engines used to propel vehicles such as passenger cars, taxicabs, multipurpose passenger vehicles, buses, recreational vehicles, vans, trucks (including tractors, tractor semi-trailer units, and truck trains), and farm tractors.

3-6.2.2 Containers.

(a)* Containers designed, fabricated, tested, and marked (or stamped) in accordance with the regulations of the U.S. Department of Transportation (DOT); or the "Rules for Construction of Unfired Pressure Vessels," Section VIII, Division I, ASME *Boiler and Pressure Vessel Code*, applicable at the date of manufacture shall be used as follows:

(1) Adherence to applicable ASME Code Case Interpretations and Addenda shall be considered as compliance with the ASME Code.

(2) Containers fabricated to earlier editions of regulations, rules or codes may be continued in use in accordance with 1-2.4.1. (*See Appendices C and D.*)

(3) Containers which have been involved in a fire and showing no distortion shall be requalified for continued service in accordance with the Code under which they were constructed before being reused.

(4) DOT containers shall be designed and constructed for at least 240 psig (1.6 MPa gauge) service pressure.

(5) DOT specification containers shall be requalified in accordance with DOT regulations. The owner of the container shall be responsible for such requalification. (*See Appendix C.*)

(6) ASME containers covered in this section shall be constructed for a minimum 250 psig (1.7 MPa gauge) design pressure except that containers installed in enclosed spaces

on vehicles and all engine fuel containers for industrial trucks, buses (including school buses), and multipurpose passenger vehicles shall be constructed for at least a 312.5 psig (2.1 MPa gauge) design pressure.

(7) Repair or alterations of containers shall comply with the Regulations, Rules or Code under which the container was fabricated. Field welding on containers shall be limited to attachments to nonpressure parts, such as saddle pads, wear plates, lugs, or brackets applied by the container manufacturer.

(8) Containers showing serious denting, bulging, gouging, or excessive corrosion shall be removed from service.

(b) Containers shall comply with 3-6.2.2(a) or shall be designed, fabricated, tested, and marked using criteria which incorporate an investigation to determine that they are safe and suitable for the proposed service, are recommended for that service by the manufacturer, and are acceptable to the authority having jurisdiction.

(c) ASME containers shall be marked in accordance with 3-6.2.2(c)(1) through (12). The markings specified shall be on a stainless steel metal nameplate attached to the container so located as to remain visible after the container is installed. The nameplate shall be attached in such a way to minimize corrosion of the nameplate or its fastening means and not contribute to corrosion of the container.

(1) Service for which the container is designed; i.e., aboveground.

(2) Name and address of container manufacturer or trade name of container.

(3) Water capacity of container in lb or U.S. Gallons.

(4) Design pressure in psig.

(5) The wording "This container shall not contain a product having a vapor pressure in excess of 215 psig at 100°F (37.8°C)."

(6) Tare weight of container fitted for service for containers to be filled by weight.

(7) Outside surface area in sq ft.

(8) Year of manufacture.

(9) Shell thickness _____ head thickness _____.

(10) OL _____ OD _____ HD _____.

(11) Manufacturer's Serial Number.

(12) ASME Code Symbol.

(d) LP-Gas fuel containers used on passenger carrying vehicles shall not exceed 200 gal (0.8 m^3) aggregate water capacity.

(e) Individual LP-Gas containers used on other than passenger carrying vehicles normally operating on the highway shall not exceed 300 gal (1 m^3) water capacity.

(f) Containers covered in this section shall be equipped for filling into the vapor space.

Exception: Containers having a water capacity of 30 gal (0.1 m^3) or less may be filled into the liquid space.

(1) The connections for pressure relief valves shall be located and installed in such a way as to have direct communication with the vapor space of the container and shall not reduce the relieving capacity of the relief device.

(2) If the connection is located in any position other than the uppermost point of the container, it shall be internally piped to the uppermost point practical in the vapor space of the container.

(g) The container openings, except those for pressure relief valves and gauging devices, shall be labeled to designate whether they communicate with the vapor or liquid space. Labels may be on valves.

3-6.2.3 Container Appurtenances.

(a) Container appurtenances (such as valves and fittings) shall comply with Section 2-3 and 3-6.2.3(a). Container appurtenances subject to working pressures in excess of 125 psig (0.9 MPa gauge) but not to exceed 250 psig (1.7 MPa gauge) shall be suitable for a working pressure of at least 250 psig (1.7 MPa gauge).

(1) Manual shutoff valves shall be designed to provide positive closure under service conditions and be equipped with an internal excess-flow check valve designed to close automatically at the rated flows of vapor or liquid specified by the manufacturers.

(2) Double backflow check valves shall be of the spring loaded type and shall close when flow is either stopped or reversed. This valve shall be installed in the fill opening of the container for either remote or direct filling.

(3) Containers shall be fabricated so they can be equipped with a fixed liquid level gauge capable of indicating the maximum permitted filling level in accordance with 4-5.2.3. Fixed liquid level gauges in the container shall be designed so the bleeder valve maximum opening to the atmosphere is not larger than a No. 54 drill size. If the bleeder valve is installed at a remote location away from the container, the container fixed liquid level gauge opening and the remote bleeder valve shall be orificed to a No. 54 drill size.

(4) ASME containers shall be equipped with internal type spring loaded pressure relief valves conforming with applicable requirements of UL 132, *Safety Relief Valves for Anhydrous Ammonia and LP-Gas*, or other equivalent pressure relief valve standards. The start-to-leak setting of such pressure relief valve, with relation to the design pressure of the container, shall be in accordance with Table 2-3.2.3. These relief valves shall be plainly and permanently marked with (1) the pressure in psig (MPa gauge) at which the valve is set to start to leak; (2) the rated relieving capacity in cu ft per minute of air at 60°F (15.6°C) and 14.7 psia (0.1 MPa absolute); and (3) the manufacturer's name and catalog number. Fusible plugs shall not be used.

(5) DOT containers shall be equipped with internal pressure relief valves in accordance with DOT regulations (*see Appendix E for additional information*). Fusible plugs shall not be used.

(6) A float gauge if used shall be designed and approved for use with LP-Gas.

(7) A solid steel plug shall be installed in unused openings.

(8) Containers fabricated after January 1, 1984, for use as engine fuel containers on vehicles shall be equipped or fitted with an automatic means to prevent filling in excess of the maximum permitted filling density.

a. An over-filling prevention device may be installed on the container or exterior of the compartment when remote filling is used, provided that a double back check valve is installed in the container fill valve opening.

3-6.2.4 Carburetion Equipment.

(a) Carburetion equipment shall comply with 3-6.2.4(b) through (e) or shall be designed, fabricated, tested, and marked using criteria which incorporate an investigation to determine that they are safe and suitable for the proposed service, are recommended for that service by the manufacturer, and are acceptable to the authority having jurisdiction. Carburetion equipment subject to working pressures in excess of 125 psig (0.9 MPa gauge) but not to exceed 250 psig (1.7 MPa gauge) shall be suitable for a working pressure of at least 250 psig (1.7 MPa gauge).

(b) *Vaporizer.*

(1) Vaporizers shall be fabricated of materials suitable for LP-Gas service and resistant to the action of LP-Gas under service conditions. Such vaporizers shall be designed and approved for engine fuel service and shall comply with the following:

a. The vaporizer proper, any part of it or any devices used with it which may be subjected to container pressure, shall have a design pressure of at least 250 psig (1.7 MPa gauge), where working pressures do not exceed 250 psig (1.7 MPa gauge), and shall be plainly and permanently marked at a readily visible point with a design pressure of the fuel containing portion in psig (MPa gauge).

(2) The vaporizer shall not be equipped with a fusible plug.

(3) Each vaporizer shall have a valve or suitable plug located at or near the lowest portion of the section occupied by the water or other heating liquid to permit substantially complete drainage. The engine cooling system drain or water hoses may serve this purpose, if effective.

(4) Engine exhaust gases may be used as a direct source of heat to vaporize the fuel if the materials of construction of those parts of the vaporizer in contact with the exhaust gases are resistant to corrosion from these gases and if the vaporizer system is designed to prevent pressure in excess of 200 psig (1.4 MPa gauge).

(5) Devices which supply heat directly to the fuel container shall be equipped with an automatic device to cut off the supply of heat before the pressure in the container reaches 200 psig (1.4 MPa gauge).

(c) *Regulator.* The regulator shall be approved and can either be part of the vaporizer unit or a separate unit.

(d) *Automatic Shutoff Valve.* An approved automatic shutoff valve shall be provided in the fuel system as close as practical to the inlet of the gas regulator. The valve shall prevent flow of fuel to the carburetor when the engine is not running even if the ignition switch is in the "on" position. Atmospheric type regulators (zero governors) shall not be considered as automatic shutoff valves for this purpose.

(e) *Fuel Filter.* Fuel filters if used shall be approved and can be either a separate unit or part of a combination unit.

3-6.2.5 Piping, Hose, and Fittings.

(a) Pipe.

(1) Pipe shall be wrought iron or steel (black or galvanized), brass, or copper and shall comply with the following:

a. Wrought iron pipe; ANSI B36.10, *Wrought-Steel and Wrought Steel Pipe.*

b. Steel pipe; ANSI B125.1, *Specification for Pipe, Steel, Black and Hot-Dipped, Zinc-Coated Welded and Seamless Steel Pipe* (ASTM A 53).

c. Steel pipe; ANSI B125.30, *Specification for Seamless Carbon Steel Pipe for High-Temperature Service* (ASTM A 106).

d. Steel pipe; ANSI B125.2, *Specification for Pipe, Steel, Black and Hot-Dipped Zinc-Coated (Galvanized) Welded and Seamless, for Ordinary Uses* (ASTM A 120).

e. Brass pipe; ANSI H27.1, *Specification for Seamless Red Brass Pipe,* Standard Sizes (ASTM B 43).

f. Copper pipe; ANSI H26.1, *Specification for Seamless Copper Pipe, Standard Sizes* (ASTM B 42).

(2) For LP-Gas vapor in excess of 125 psig (0.9 MPa gauge) or for LP-Gas liquid, the pipe shall be Schedule 80 or heavier. For LP-Gas vapor at pressures of 125 psig (0.9 MPa gauge) or less, the pipe shall be Schedule 40 or heavier.

(b) Tubing.

(1) Tubing shall be steel, brass or copper and shall comply with the following:

a. Steel tubing; ASTM A 539, *Specification for Electric-Resistance-Welded Coiled Steel Tubing for Gas Fuel Oil Lines,* with a minimum wall thickness of 0.049 in.

b. Copper tubing; Type K or L, ANSI H23.1, *Specification for Seamless Copper Water Tube* (ASTM B 88).

c. Copper tubing; ANSI H23.5, *Specification for Seamless Copper Tube for Air Conditioning and Refrigeration Field Service* (ASTM B 280).

d. Brass tubing; ANSI H36.1, *Specification for Seamless Brass Tube* (ASTM B 135).

(c) Pipe and Tube Fittings.

(1) Cast iron pipe fittings such as ells, tees, crosses, couplings, unions, flanges or plugs shall not be used. Fittings shall be steel, brass, copper, malleable iron or ductile iron and shall comply with the following:

a. Pipe joints in wrought iron, steel, brass, or copper pipe may be screwed, welded, or brazed. Tubing joints in steel, brass, or copper tubing shall be flared, brazed, or made up with approved gas tubing fittings.

(i) Fittings used with liquid LP-Gas, or with vapor LP-Gas at operating pressures over 125 psig (0.9 MPa gauge), where working pressures do not exceed 250 psig (1.7 MPa gauge), shall be suitable for a working pressure of at least 250 psig (1.7 MPa gauge).

(ii) Fittings for use with vapor LP-Gas at pressures in excess of 5 psig (34.5 kPa gauge) and not exceeding 125 psig (0.9 MPa gauge) shall be suitable for a working pressure of 125 psig (0.9 MPa gauge).

(iii) Brazing filler material shall have a melting point exceeding 1,000°F (538°C).

(d) Hose, Hose Connections, and Flexible Connectors.

(1) Hose, hose connections, and flexible connectors (*see definition*) used for conveying LP-Gas liquid or vapor at pressures in excess of 5 psig (34.5 kPa gauge) shall be fabricated of materials resistant to the action of LP-Gas both as liquid and vapor, and be of wire braid reinforced

construction. The wire braid shall be stainless steel. The hose shall comply with the following:

a. Hose shall be designed for a working pressure of 350 psi (240 MPa) with a safety factor of 5 to 1 and be continuously marked "LP-GAS," "PROPANE," "350 PSI WORKING PRESSURE" and the manufacturer's name or trademark. Each installed piece of hose shall contain at least one such marking.

b. Hose assemblies after the application of connections shall have a design capability of withstanding a pressure of not less than 700 psig (4.8 MPa gauge). If a test is made, such assemblies shall not be leak tested at pressures higher than the working pressure [350 psig (2.4 MPa gauge) minimum] of the hose.

(2) Hose used for vapor service at 5 psig (34.5 kPa gauge) or less shall be constructed of material resistant to the action of LP-Gas.

(3) Hose in excess of 5 psig (34.5 kPa gauge) service pressure and quick connectors shall have the approval for this application of any of the authorities listed in 1-3.1.1.

3-6.2.6 Installation of Containers and Container Appurtenances.

(a) Containers shall be located in a place and in a manner to minimize the possibility of damage to the container and its fittings. Containers located in the rear of the vehicles, when protected by substantial bumpers, shall be considered in conformance with this requirement. In case the fuel container must be installed near the engine or exhaust system, it shall be shielded against direct heating.

(b) Container markings shall be readable after a container is permanently installed on a vehicle. A portable lamp and mirror may be used when reading markings.

(c) Container valves, appurtenances, and connections shall be adequately protected to prevent damage due to accidental contacts with stationary objects or from stones, mud, or ice thrown up from the ground, and from damage due to overturn or similar vehicular accident. Location on the container where parts of the vehicle furnish the necessary protection or a fitting guard furnished by the manufacturer of the container may meet these requirements.

(d) Containers shall not be mounted directly on roofs or ahead of the front axle or beyond the rear bumper of the vehicles. So as to minimize the possibility of physical damage, no part of a container or its appurtenances shall protrude beyond the sides or top of the vehicle.

(e) Containers shall be installed with as much road clearance as practicable. This clearance shall be measured to the bottom of the container or the lowest fitting, support, or attachment on the container or its housing, if any, whichever is lowest, as follows [*see Figure 3-6.2.6(e)*]:

(1) Containers installed between axles shall comply with 3-6.2.6(e)(3) or be not lower than the lowest point forward of the container on:

a. the lowest structural component of the body;

b. the lowest structural component of the frame or subframe if any;

c. the lowest point on the engine;

d. the lowest point of the transmission (including the clutch housing or torque converter housing as applicable) [Part 1, Figure 3-6.2.6(e)].

(2) Containers installed behind the rear axle and extending below the frame shall comply with 3-6.2.6(e)(3) or be not lower than the lowest of the following points and surfaces.

a. Not lower than the lowest point of a structural component of the body, engine, transmission (including clutch housing or torque converter housing, as applicable), forward of the container. Also not lower than lines extending rearward from each wheel at the point where the wheels contact the ground directly below the center of the axle to the lowest and most rearward structural interference (i.e. bumper, frame, etc.). [Part 2, Figure 3-6.2.6(e).]

b. Where there are two or more rear axles the projections shall be made from the rearmost one of them.

(3) Where an LP-Gas container is substituted for the fuel container installed by the original manufacturer of the vehicle (whether or not that fuel container was for LP-Gas), the LP-Gas container shall either fit within the space in which the original fuel container was installed or comply with 3-6.2.6(e)(1) or (2).

(f) Fuel containers shall be securely mounted to prevent jarring loose and slipping or rotating, and the fastenings shall be designed and constructed to withstand without permanent visible deformation static loading in any direction equal to four times the weight of the container filled with fuel.

(g) Welding for the repair or alterations of containers shall comply with 3-6.2.2(a)(7).

(h) Main shutoff valves on a container for liquid and vapor shall be readily accessible without the use of tools, or other means shall be provided to shut off the container valves.

(i) Pressure relief valve installations shall comply with the following requirements:

(1) The relief valve discharge on fuel containers on vehicles other than passenger cars shall be directed upward within 15 degrees of vertical so that any gas released will not impinge upon containers or part of the vehicle, or on adjacent persons or vehicles or discharge inside of the passenger compartment. On passenger cars, the relief valve discharge on fuel containers shall be directed upward within 45 degrees of vertical so that gas may not be discharged inside of the passenger or luggage compartment and so that any gas released will not impinge upon a container, part of the vehicle or on an adjacent vehicle.

(2) Pressure relief valve discharge lines shall be metallic and have a melting point over 1500°F (816°C). Discharge lines and adaptors shall be sized, located and secured so as to minimize the possibility of physical damage and to permit required pressure relief valve discharge capacity. When the relief valve discharge must be piped away from the container, the relief valve shall be fitted with an approved break-away type adaptor or designed such that in the event of excessive stress the piping will break away without impairing the function of the relief valve. Flexible metal hose or tubing used shall be able to withstand the pressure from the relief vapor discharge when the relief valve is in full open position. A means shall be provided (such as loose fitting caps) to minimize the possibility of the entrance of water or dirt into either the relief valve or its discharge piping. The protecting means shall remain in place except when the relief valve operates. In this event, it shall permit the relief valve to operate at required capacity.

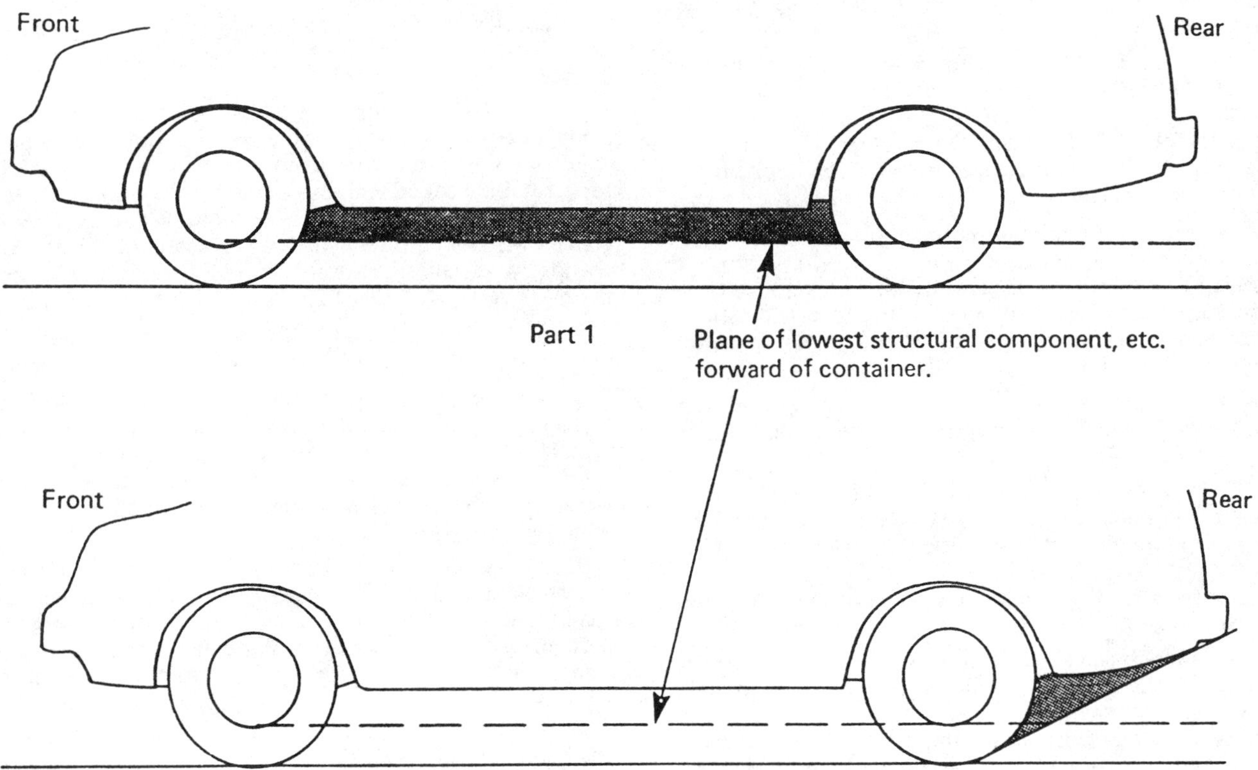

Figure 3-6.2.6(e) Container Installation Clearances.

(3) Relief valve adaptors installed directly in the relief valve to deflect the flow upward shall be metallic and have a melting point over 700°F (371°C).

3-6.2.7 Containers Mounted in the Interior of Vehicles.

(a) Containers mounted in the interior of vehicles shall be installed so that any LP-Gas released from container appurtenances due to operation, leakage or connection of the appurtenances will not be in an area communicating directly with the driver or passenger compartment or with any space containing radio transmitters or other spark producing equipment. This may be accomplished by 3-6.2.7(a)(1) or (2).

(1) Locating the container, including its appurtenances, in an enclosure which is securely mounted to the vehicle, is gastight with respect to driver or passenger compartments and to any space containing radio transmitters or other spark producing equipment, and which is vented outside the vehicle.

a. The luggage compartment (trunk) of a vehicle may constitute such an enclosure provided it meets all these requirements.

(2) Enclosing the container appurtenances and their connections in a structure which is securely mounted on the container, is gastight with respect to the driver or passenger compartments or with any space carrying radio transmitters or other spark producing equipment, and which is vented to outside the vehicle.

(b) Fuel containers shall be installed and fitted so that no gas from fueling and gauging operations can be released inside of the passenger or luggage compartments, by permanently installing the remote filling connections (double backflow check valve), see 3-6.2.3(a)(2), and fixed liquid level gauging device to the outside of the vehicle.

(c) Container pressure relief valve installation shall comply with 3-6.2.6(i).

(d) Enclosures, structures, seals and conduits used to vent enclosures shall be fabricated of durable materials and be designed to resist damage, blockage or dislodgement through movement of articles carried in the vehicle or by the closing of luggage compartment enclosures or vehicle doors, and shall require the use of tools for removal.

3-6.2.8 Pipe and Hose Installation.

(a) The piping system shall be designed, installed, supported, and secured in such a manner as to minimize the possibility of damage due to expansion, contraction, vibration, strains or wear, and to preclude any working loose while in transit.

(b) Piping (including hose) shall be installed in a protected location. If outside, piping shall be under the vehicle and below any insulation or false bottom. Fastening or other protection shall be installed to prevent damage due to vibration or abrasion. At each point where piping passes through sheet metal or a structural member, a rubber grommet or equivalent protection shall be installed to prevent chafing.

(c) Fuel line piping which must pass through the floor of a vehicle shall be installed to enter the vehicle through the floor directly beneath, or adjacent to, the container. If a branch line is required, the tee connection shall be in the main fuel line under the floor and outside the vehicle.

(d) When liquid service lines of two or more individual containers are connected together, a spring loaded backflow check valve or equivalent shall be installed in each of the liquid lines prior to the point where the liquid lines tee together to prevent the transfer of LP-Gas from one container to another.

(e) Exposed parts of the piping system shall either be of corrosion-resistant material or adequately protected against exterior corrosion.

(f) Piping systems, including hose, shall be tested and proven free of leaks at not less than normal operating pressure.

(g) There shall be no fuel connection between a tractor and trailer or other vehicle units.

(h) A hydrostatic relief valve shall be installed in each section of piping (including hose) in which liquid LP-Gas can be isolated between shutoff valves so as to relieve to a safe atmosphere the pressure which could develop from the trapped liquid. This hydrostatic relief valve shall have a pressure setting not less than 400 psig (2.8 MPa gauge) or more than 500 psig (3.5 MPa gauge).

3-6.2.9 Equipment Installation.

(a) Installation shall be made in accordance with the manufacturer's recommendations and, in the case of listed or approved equipment, it shall be installed in accordance with the listing or approval.

(b) Equipment installed on vehicles shall be considered a part of the LP-Gas system on the vehicle and shall be protected against vehicular damage in accordance with 3-6.2.6(a).

(c) The gas regulator and the approved automatic shutoff valve shall be installed as follows:

(1) Approved automatic pressure reducing equipment, properly secured, shall be installed between the fuel supply container and the carburetor to regulate the pressure of the fuel delivered to the carburetor.

(2) An approved automatic shutoff valve shall be provided in the fuel system in compliance with 3-6.2.4(d).

(d) Vaporizers shall be securely fastened in position.

3-6.2.10 Marking. Each over-the-road general purpose vehicle powered by LP-Gas shall be identified with a weather-resistant diamond shaped label located on an exterior vertical or near vertical surface on the lower right rear of the vehicle (on the trunk lid of a vehicle so equipped, but not on the bumper of any vehicle) inboard from any other markings. The label shall be approximately 4-3/4 in. (120 mm) long by 3-1/4 in. (83 mm) high. The marking shall consist of a border and the letters "PROPANE" [1 in. (25 mm) minimum height centered in the diamond] of silver or white reflective luminous material on a black background. (*See Figure 3-6.2.10.*)

Figure 3-6.2.10 Example of Vehicle Identification Marking.

3-6.3 Industrial (and Forklift) Trucks Powered by LP-Gas.

3-6.3.1 This subsection applies to LP-Gas installation on industrial trucks (including forklift trucks) both to propel them and to provide the energy for their materials handling attachments. LP-Gas fueled industrial trucks shall comply with NFPA 505, *Firesafety Standard for Powered Industrial Trucks.*

3-6.3.2 ASME and DOT fuel containers shall comply with 3-6.2.2 and 3-6.2.3(a)(1) through (7).

(a) Portable containers may be designed, constructed, and fitted for filling in either the vertical or horizontal position, or if of the portable universal type [*see 2-3.4.2(c)(2)*], in either position. The container shall be in the appropriate position when filled or, if of the portable universal type, may be loaded in either position, provided:

(1) The fixed level gauge indicates correctly the maximum permitted filling level in either position.

(2) The pressure relief valves are located in, or connected to, the vapor space in either position.

3-6.3.3 The container relief valve shall be vented upward within 45 degrees of vertical and otherwise comply with 3-6.2.6(i).

3-6.3.4 Gas regulating and vaporizing equipment shall comply with 3-6.2.4(b)(1) through (5) and 3-6.2.4(c), (d), and (e).

3-6.3.5 Piping and hose shall comply with 3-6.2.5(a) through (d) except that hose 60 in. (1.5 m) in length or less need not be of stainless steel wire braid construction.

3-6.3.6 Industrial trucks (including forklift trucks) powered by LP-Gas engine fuel systems shall comply as to operation with NFPA 505, *Firesafety Standard for Powered Industrial Trucks*, and with the following:

(a) Refueling of such trucks shall be accomplished as follows:

(1) Trucks with permanently mounted containers shall be refueled out-of-doors.

(2) Exchange of removable fuel containers preferably should be done out-of-doors, but may be done indoors. If done indoors, means shall be provided in the fuel piping system to minimize the release of fuel when containers are exchanged, using one of the following methods:

a. Use of an approved quick-closing coupling (a type closing in both directions when uncoupled) in the fuel line, or

b. Closing the shutoff valve at the fuel container, and allowing the engine to run until the fuel in the line is exhausted.

(b) LP-Gas fueled industrial trucks may be used in buildings or structures as follows:

(1) The number of fuel containers on such a truck shall not exceed two.

(2) With the approval of the authority having jurisdiction, industrial trucks may be used in buildings frequented by the public, including the times when such buildings are occupied by the public. The total water capacity of the fuel containers on an individual truck shall not exceed 105 lb (48 kg) [nominal 45 lb (20 kg) LP-Gas capacity].

(3) Trucks shall not be parked and left unattended in areas occupied by or frequented by the public except with the approval of the authority having jurisdiction. If so left, the fuel system shall be checked to be sure there are no leaks and that the container shutoff valve is closed.

(4) In no case shall industrial trucks be parked and left unattended in areas of excessive heat or near sources of ignition.

3-6.4 General Provisions for Vehicles Having Engines Mounted on Them (Including Floor Maintenance Machines).

3-6.4.1 This subsection includes provisions for the installation of equipment on vehicles to supply LP-Gas as a fuel for engines mounted on these vehicles. The term "vehicles" includes floor maintenance and any other readily portable mobile unit, whether the engine is used to propel it or is mounted on it for other purposes.

3-6.4.2 Gas vaporizing, regulating and carburetion equipment to provide LP-Gas as a fuel for engines shall be installed in accordance with 3-6.2.8 and 3-6.2.9.

(a) In the case of industrial trucks (including forklift trucks) and other engines on vehicles operating in buildings other than those used exclusively to house engines, an approved automatic shutoff valve shall be provided in the fuel system in compliance with 3-6.2.4(d).

(b) The source of air for combustion shall be completely isolated from the driver and passenger compartment, ventilating system or air conditioning system on the vehicle.

3-6.4.3 Piping and hose shall comply with 3-6.3.5.

3-6.4.4 Non-self-propelled floor maintenance machinery (floor polishers, scrubbers, buffers) and other similar portable equipment shall be listed and comply with 3-6.4.4(a) and (b).

(a) The provisions of 3-6.3.2 through 3-6.3.5 and 3-6.3.6(a) and (b) shall apply.

(b) The storage of LP-Gas containers mounted or used on such machinery or equipment shall comply with Chapter 5.

(1) A label shall be affixed to the machinery or equipment, with the label facing the operator, denoting that the container or portion of the machinery or equipment containing the LP-Gas container, must be stored in accordance with Chapter 5.

3-6.5 Engine Installation Other than on Vehicle.

3-6.5.1 Stationary engines and gas turbines installed in buildings, including portable engines used in lieu of, or to supplement, stationary engines, shall comply with NFPA 37, *Standard for the Installation and Use of Stationary Combustion Engines and Gas Turbines*, and the applicable provisions of Chapters 1 and 2 and Section 3-2 of this standard.

3-6.5.2 Portable engines, except as provided in 3-6.4.1, may be used in buildings only for emergencies and the following shall apply:

(a) The capacity of the LP-Gas containers used with such engines and the equipment used to provide fuel to them shall comply with the applicable provisions of Section 3-4.

(b) An approved automatic shutoff valve shall be provided in the fuel system in compliance with 3-6.2.4(d). Atmospheric type regulators (zero governors) used for portable engines of 12 horsepower or less with magneto ignition and used exclusively outdoors shall be considered as in compliance with 3-6.2.4(d).

(c) Provision shall be made to supply sufficient air for combustion and cooling. Exhaust gases shall be discharged to a point outside the building, or to an area in which they will not constitute a hazard.

3-6.5.3 Piping and hose shall comply with 3-6.2.5(a) through (d).

3-6.5.4 Gas regulating, vaporizing, and carburetion equipment shall comply with 3-6.2.4(b)(1) through (5), 3-6.2.4(c) and 3-6.2.4(e).

3-6.5.5 Installation of piping, carburetion, vaporizing, and regulating equipment for the engine fuel system shall comply with 3-6.2.8 and 3-6.2.9.

3-6.5.6 Engines installed or operated exclusively outdoors shall comply with 3-6.5.3, 3-6.5.4 and 3-6.5.5.

(a) Atmospheric type regulators (zero governor) shall be considered as automatic shutoff valves only in the case of completely outdoor operations, such as farm tractors, construction equipment or similar outdoor engine applications.

3-6.5.7 Engines used to drive portable compressors shall be equipped with exhaust system spark arrestors and shielded ignition systems.

3-6.6 Garaging of Vehicles.

3-6.6.1 Vehicles with LP-Gas engine fuel systems mounted

Table 4-5.2.3(c)
Maximum Permitted Liquid Volume
(Percent of Total Water Capacity)

All Underground Containers

Liquid Temperature °F (°C)	Specific Gravity												
	.496 to .503	.504 to .510	.511 to .519	.520 to .527	.528 to .536	.537 to .544	.545 to .552	.553 to .560	.561 to .568	.569 to .576	.577 to .584	.585 to .592	.593 to .600
−50 (−45.6)	77	78	79	80	80	81	82	83	83	84	85	85	86
−45 (−42.8)	77	78	79	80	81	82	82	83	84	84	85	86	87
−40 (−40)	78	79	80	81	81	82	83	83	84	85	86	86	87
−35 (−37.2)	78	79	80	81	82	82	83	84	85	85	86	87	87
−30 (−34.4)	79	80	81	81	82	83	84	84	85	86	86	87	88
−25 (−31.5)	79	80	81	82	83	83	84	85	85	86	87	87	88
−20 (−28.9)	80	81	82	82	83	84	84	85	86	86	87	88	88
−15 (−26.1)	80	81	82	83	84	84	85	86	86	87	87	88	89
−10 (−23.3)	81	82	83	83	84	85	85	86	87	87	88	88	89
− 5 (−20.6)	81	82	83	84	84	85	86	86	87	88	88	89	89
0 (−17.8)	82	83	84	84	85	85	86	87	87	88	89	89	90
5 (−15)	82	83	84	85	85	86	87	87	88	88	89	90	90
10 (−12.2)	83	84	85	85	86	86	87	88	88	89	90	90	91
15 (−9.4)	84	84	85	86	86	87	88	88	89	89	90	91	91
20 (−6.7)	84	85	86	86	87	88	88	89	89	90	90	91	91
25 (−3.9)	85	86	86	87	87	88	89	89	90	90	91	91	92
30 (−1.1)	85	86	87	87	88	89	89	90	90	91	91	92	92
35 (1.7)	86	87	87	88	88	89	90	90	91	91	92	92	93
40 (4.4)	87	87	88	88	89	90	90	91	91	92	92	93	93
45 (7.8)	87	88	89	89	90	90	91	91	92	92	93	93	94
*50 (10)	88	89	89	90	90	91	91	92	92	93	93	94	94
55 (12.8)	89	89	90	91	91	91	92	92	93	93	94	94	95
60 (15.6)	90	90	91	91	92	92	92	93	93	94	94	95	95
65 (18.3)	90	91	91	92	92	93	93	94	94	94	95	95	96
70 (21.1)	91	91	92	93	93	93	94	94	94	95	95	96	96
75 (23.9)	92	93	93	93	94	94	94	95	95	95	96	96	97
80 (26.7)	93	93	94	94	94	95	95	95	96	96	96	97	97
85 (29.4)	94	94	95	95	95	95	96	96	96	97	97	97	98
90 (32.2)	95	95	95	95	96	96	96	97	97	97	98	98	98
95 (35)	96	96	96	96	97	97	97	97	98	98	98	98	99
100 (37.8)	97	97	97	97	97	98	98	98	98	99	99	99	99
105 (40.4)	98	98	98	98	98	98	98	99	99	99	99	99	99

*See 4-5.3.3(a).

Chapter 5 Storage of Portable Containers Awaiting Use or Resale

5-1 Scope.

5-1.1 Application.

5-1.1.1 The provisions of this chapter are applicable to the storage of portable containers of 1,000 lb (454 kg) water capacity, or less, whether filled, partially filled or empty (if they have been in LP-Gas service) as follows:

(a) At consumer sites or distributing points, but not connected for use.

(b) In storage for resale by dealer or reseller.

5-1.1.2 The provisions of this chapter do not apply to:

(a) Containers stored at distributing plants.

5-2 General Provisions.

5-2.1 General Location of Containers.

5-2.1.1 Containers in storage shall be so located as to minimize exposure to excessive temperature rise, physical damage or tampering.

5-2.1.2 Containers in storage having individual water capacity greater than 2 ½ lb (1 kg) [nominal 1 lb (0.45 kg) LP-Gas capacity] shall be positioned such that the pressure relief valve is in direct communication with the vapor space of the container.

5-2.1.3 Containers stored in buildings in accordance with Section 5-3 shall not be located near exits, stairways, or in areas normally used, or intended to be used, for the safe egress of people.

5-2.1.4 Empty containers which have been in LP-Gas service shall preferably be stored in the open. If stored inside, they shall be considered as full containers for the purposes of determining the maximum quantities of LP-Gas permitted in 5-3.1.1, 5-3.2.1, and 5-3.3.1.

5-2.1.5 Containers not connected for use shall not be stored on roofs.

5-2.2 Protection of Valves on Containers in Storage.

5-2.2.1 Container valves shall be protected as required by 2-2.4.1. Screw-on type caps or collars shall be securely in place on all containers stored regardless of whether they are full, partially full or empty, and container outlet valves shall be closed and plugged or capped. The provisions of 4-2.2.2 shall apply.

5-3 Storage within Buildings.

5-3.1 Storage within Buildings Frequented by the Public.

5-3.1.1 DOT specification cylinders with a maximum water capacity of 2 ½ lb (1 kg), used with completely self-contained hand torches and similar applications, may be stored or displayed in a building frequented by the public. The quantity of LP-Gas shall not exceed 200 lb (91 kg) except as provided in 5-3.3.

5-3.2 Storage within Buildings Not Frequented by the Public (Such as Industrial Buildings).

5-3.2.1 The maximum quantity allowed in one storage location shall not exceed 735 lb (334 kg) water capacity [nominal 300 lb (136 kg) LP-Gas]. If additional storage locations are required on the same floor within the same building, they shall be separated by a minimum of 300 ft (91 m). Storage beyond these limitations shall comply with 5-3.3.

5-3.2.2 Containers carried as part of the service equipment on highway mobile vehicles are not to be considered in the total storage capacity in 5-3.2.1 provided such vehicles are stored in private garages and carry no more than 3 LP-Gas containers with a total aggregate capacity per vehicle not exceeding 100 lb (45 kg) of LP-Gas. Container valves shall be closed when not in use.

5-3.3 Storage within Special Buildings or Rooms.

5-3.3.1 The maximum quantity of LP-Gas which may be stored in special buildings or rooms shall be 10,000 lb (4 540 kg).

5-3.3.2 Special buildings or rooms for storing LP-Gas containers shall not be located adjoining the line of property occupied by schools, churches, hospitals, athletic fields, or other points of public gathering.

5-3.3.3 The construction of all such special buildings, and rooms within, or attached to, other buildings, shall comply with Chapter 7 and the following:

(a) Adequate vents, to the outside only, shall be provided at both top and bottom, located at least 5 ft (1.5 m) away from any building opening.

(b) The entire area shall be classified for purposes of ignition source control in accordance with Section 3-8.

5-3.4 Storage Within Residential Buildings.

5-3.4.1 Storage of containers within a residential building including the basement or any storage area in a common basement storage area in multiple family buildings and attached garages shall be limited to 2 containers each with a maximum water capacity of 2 ½ lb (1.1 kg) and not exceed 5 lbs (2.3 kg) total water capacity for smaller containers per each living space unit. Each container shall meet DOT specifications.

5-4 Storage Outside of Buildings.

5-4.1 Location of Storage Outside of Buildings.

5-4.1.1 Storage outside of buildings, for containers awaiting use or resale, shall be located in accordance with Table 5-4.1.1 with respect to:

Table 5-4.1.1

Quantity of LP-Gas Stored	Distance to: (a) and (b)	(c) and (d)
500 lb (227 kg) or less	0	0
501 (227+ kg) to 2,500 lb (1134 kg)	0	10 ft (3 m)
2,501 (1134+ kg) to 6,000 lb (2721 kg)	10 ft (3 m)	10 ft (3 m)
6,001 (2721+ kg) to 10,000 lb (4540 kg)	20 ft (6 m)	20 ft (6 m)
Over 10,000 lb (4540 kg)	25 ft (7.6 m)	25 ft (7.6 m)

(a) Nearest important building or group of buildings.

(b) Line of adjoining property which may be built upon.

(c) Busy thoroughfares or sidewalks.

(d) Line of adjoining property occupied by schools, churches, hospitals, athletic fields, or other points of public gathering.

5-4.2 Protection of Containers.

5-4.2.1 Containers shall be stored within a suitable enclosure or otherwise protected against tampering.

5-4.3 Alternate Location and Protection of Storage.

5-4.3.1 When the provisions of 5-4.1.1 and 5-4.2.1 are impractical at construction sites, or at buildings or structures undergoing major renovation or repairs, the storage of containers shall be acceptable to the authority having jurisdiction.

5-5 Fire Protection.

5-5.1 Fire Extinguisher Requirements.

5-5.1.1 Storage locations, other than supply depots at separate locations apart from those of the dealer, reseller, or user's establishments, shall be provided with at least one approved portable fire extinguisher having a minimum capacity of 20 lb dry chemical with a B:C rating. (*Also see NFPA 10, Standard for Portable Fire Extinguishers.*)

Chapter 6 Vehicular Transportation of LP-Gas

6-1 Scope.

6-1.1 Application.

6-1.1.1 This chapter includes provisions applying to containers, container appurtenances, piping, valves, equipment, and vehicles used in the transportation of LP-Gas, as follows:

(a) Transportation of portable containers.

Exception: The provisions of this chapter are not applicable to LP-Gas containers and related equipment incident to their use on vehicles as covered in Sections 3-6 and 3-9.

(b) Transportation in cargo vehicles, whether fabricated by mounting cargo tanks on conventional truck or trailer chassis, or constructed as integral cargo units in which the container constitutes in whole, or in part, the stress member of the vehicle frame. Transfer equipment and piping, and the protection of such equipment and the container appurtenances against overturn, collision, or other vehicular accidents are also included.

(c) Most truck transportation of LP-Gas is subject to regulation by the U.S. Department of Transportation. Many of the provisions of this chapter are identical or similar to DOT regulations and are intended to extend these provisions to areas not subject to DOT regulation. Vehicles and procedures under the jurisdiction of DOT shall comply with DOT regulations.

6-1.1.2 The provisions of this chapter are not applicable to the transportation of LP-Gas on vehicles incident to its use on these vehicles as covered in 3-6.5, 3-6.6, 3-6.7, and Section 3-9.

6-1.1.3 If LP-Gas is used for engine fuel, the supply piping and regulating, vaporizing, gas-air mixing and carburetion equipment, shall be designed, constructed, and installed in accordance with Section 3-6. Fuel systems (including fuel containers) shall be constructed and installed in accordance with Section 3-9. Fuel may be used from the cargo tank of tank trucks, but not from cargo tanks on trailers or semitrailers.

6-1.1.4 No artificial light other than electrical shall be used with the vehicles covered by this chapter. Wiring used shall have adequate mechanical strength and current-carrying capacity with suitable overcurrent protection (fuses or automatic circuit breakers) and shall be properly insulated and protected against physical damage.

6-2 Transportation in Portable Containers.

6-2.1 Application.

6-2.1.1 This section applies to the vehicular transportation of portable containers filled with LP-Gas delivered as "packages," including containers built to DOT cylinder specifications and of other portable containers (such as DOT portable tank containers and skid tanks). The design and construction of these containers is covered in Chapter 2.

6-2.2 Transportation of DOT Specification Cylinders or Portable ASME Containers.

6-2.2.1 Portable containers having an individual water capacity not exceeding 1,000 lb (454 kg) [nominal 420 lb (191 kg) LP-Gas capacity], when filled with LP-Gas, shall be transported in accordance with 6-2.2.2 through 6-2.2.9

6-2.2.2 Containers shall be constructed as provided in Section 2-2 and equipped in accordance with Section 2-3 for transportation as portable containers.

6-2.2.3 The quantity of LP-Gas in containers shall be in accordance with Chapter 4.

6-2.2.4 Valves of containers shall be protected in accordance with 2-2.4.1. Screw-on type protecting caps or collars shall be secured in place.

(a) The provisions of 4-2.2.2 shall apply.

6-2.2.5 The cargo space of the vehicle shall be isolated from the driver's compartment, the engine and its exhaust system, except as provided in 6-2.2.5(a). Open-bodied vehicles shall be considered as in compliance with this provision. Closed-bodied vehicles having separate cargo, driver's, and engine compartments shall be considered as in compliance with this provision.

(a) Closed-bodied vehicles such as passenger cars, vans, and station wagons shall not be used for transporting more than 215 lb (98 kg) water capacity [nominal 90 lb (41 kg) LP-Gas capacity] but not more than 108 lb (49 kg) water capacity [nominal 45 lb (20 kg) LP-Gas capacity] per container (*see 6-2.2.6 and 6-2.2.7*), unless the driver's and engine compartments are separated from the cargo space by a vapor-tight partition which contains no means of access to the cargo space.

6-2.2.6 Containers and their appurtenances shall be determined to be leak-free before being loaded into vehicles. Containers shall be loaded into vehicles with substantially flat floors or equipped with suitable racks for holding containers. Containers shall be securely fastened in position to minimize the possibility of movement, tipping over, or physical damage.

6-2.2.7 Containers having an individual water capacity exceeding 108 lb (49 kg) [nominal 45 lb (20 kg) LP-Gas capacity] transported in open vehicles shall be transported with the relief devices in direct communication with the vapor spaces. Containers having an individual water capacity exceeding 10 lb (4.5 kg) [nominal 4.2 lb (2 kg) LP-Gas capacity] transported in enclosed spaces of the vehicle shall be transported with the relief device in direct communication with the vapor spaces.

6-2.2.8 Containers having an individual water capacity not exceeding 108 lb (49 kg) [nominal 45 lb (20 kg) LP-Gas capacity] transported in open vehicles may be transported in other than the upright position. Containers having an individual water capacity not exceeding 10 lb (4.5 kg) [nominal 4.2 lb (2 kg) LP-Gas capacity] transported in enclosed spaces of the vehicle may be transported in other than the upright position.

6-2.2.9 Vehicles transporting more than 1,000 lb (454 kg) of LP-Gas, including the weight of the containers, shall be placarded as required by DOT regulations and/or state law.

6-2.3 Transportation of Portable Containers of More than 1,000 lb (454 kg) Water Capacity.

6-2.3.1 Portable containers having an individual water capacity exceeding 1000 lb (454 kg) [nominal 420 lb (191 kg) LP-Gas capacity] when filled with LP-Gas shall be transported in compliance with 6-2.3.2 through 6-2.3.9.

6-2.3.2 Containers shall be constructed in accordance with Section 2-2 and equipped in accordance with Section 2-3 for portable use, or shall comply with DOT portable tank container specifications for LP-Gas service.

6-2.3.3 The quantity of LP-Gas put into containers shall be in accordance with Chapter 4.

6-2.3.4 Valves and other container appurtenances shall be protected in accordance with 2-2.4.2.

6-2.3.5 Containers and their appurtenances shall be determined to be leak-free before being loaded into vehicles. Containers shall be loaded into vehicles with substantially flat floors or equipped with suitable racks for holding containers. Containers shall be securely fastened in position to minimize the possibility of movement, tipping over, or physical damage.

6-2.3.6 Containers and their appurtenances shall be determined to be leak-free before being loaded into vehicles. Containers shall be loaded onto a flat vehicle floor or platform, or onto a suitable vehicle frame. In either case, containers shall be securely blocked or held down to minimize movement, relative to each other or to the supporting structure, while in transit.

6-2.3.7 Containers shall be transported with relief devices in communication with the vapor space.

6-2.3.8 Vehicles carrying more than 1,000 lb (454 kg) of LP-Gas, including the weight of the containers, shall be placarded as required by DOT regulations and/or state law.

6-2.3.9 When portable containers complying with 6-2.3.1 through 6-2.3.8 are permanently or semipermanently mounted on vehicles to serve as cargo tanks, so that the assembled vehicular unit can be used for making liquid deliveries to other containers at points of use, the provisions of Section 6-3 shall apply.

6-2.4 Fire Extinguishers.

6-2.4.1 Each truck or trailer transporting portable containers as provided by 6-2.2 or 6-2.3 shall be equipped with at least one approved portable fire extinguisher having a minimum capacity of 20 lb dry chemical with a B:C rating. (*Also see NFPA 10, Standard for Portable Fire Extinguishers.*)

6-3 Transportation in Cargo Vehicles.

6-3.1 Application.

6-3.1.1 This section includes provisions for cargo vehicles used for the transportation of LP-Gas as liquid cargo, normally loaded into the cargo container at the distributing or manufacturing point, and transferred into other containers at the point of delivery. Transfer may be made by a pump or compressor mounted on the vehicle or by a transfer means at the delivery point.

6-3.1.2 All LP-Gas cargo vehicles, whether used in interstate or intrastate service, shall comply with the applicable portion of the US Department of Transportation Hazardous Materials Regulations (Title 49 Code of Federal Regulations Parts 171-179) and Parts 393, 396, and 397 of the DOT Federal Motor Carrier Safety Regulations and shall also comply with the added requirements of this standard.

6-3.2 Containers Mounted on, or a Part of, Cargo Vehicles.

6-3.2.1 Containers mounted on, or comprising in whole, or in part, the stress member used in lieu of a frame for cargo vehicles shall comply with DOT cargo tank specifications for LP-Gas service. Such containers shall also comply with Section 2-2, be equipped with appurtenances as provided in Section 2-3 for cargo service, and comply with 6-3.2.1(a):

(a) Liquid hose of 1 ½ in. (nominal size) and larger size and vapor hose of 1 ¼ in. (nominal size) and larger size shall be protected with an emergency shutoff valve complying with 2-4.5.4, except that:

(1) If an internal valve meets the functional provisions for an emergency shut-off valve in compliance with 2-4.5.4 and 3-2.7.9(a)(1), an emergency shutoff valve shall not be required in the cargo container piping.

(2) A backflow check valve may be used in the cargo container piping or container in lieu of an emergency shutoff valve if the flow is only into the cargo container.

6-3.3 Piping (Including Hose), Fittings, and Valves.

6-3.3.1 Pipe, tubing, pipe and tubing fittings, valves, hose and flexible connectors shall comply with Section 2-4, with the provisions of DOT cargo tank specifications for LP-Gas, and shall be suitable for the working pressure specified in 6-3.3.2. In addition, 6-3.3.1(a) through (e) shall apply:

(a) Pipe shall be wrought iron, steel, brass or copper in accordance with 2-4.2.1.

(b) Tubing shall be steel, brass or copper in accordance with 2-4.3.1(a), (b), or (c).

(c) Pipe and tubing fittings shall be steel, brass, copper, malleable iron or ductile (nodular) iron suitable for use with the pipe or tubing used as specified in 6-3.3.1(a) or (b).

(d) Pipe joints may be threaded, flanged, welded or brazed. Fittings when used shall comply with 6-3.3.1(c).

(1) When joints are threaded, or threaded and back welded, pipe and nipples shall be Schedule 80 or heavier. Copper or brass pipe and nipples shall be of equivalent strength.

(2) When joints are welded or brazed, the pipe and nipples shall be Schedule 40 or heavier. Fittings or flanges shall be suitable for the service. (*See 6-3.3.2.*)

(3) Brazed joints shall be made with a brazing material having a melting point exceeding 1,000°F (538°C).

(e) Tubing joints shall be brazed, using a brazing material having a melting point of at least 1,000°F (538°C).

6-3.3.2 Pipe, tubing, pipe and tubing fittings, valves, hose and flexible connectors, and complete cargo vehicle piping systems including connections to equipment (*see 6-3.4*), after assembly, shall comply with 2-5.1.2.

6-3.3.3 Valves, including shutoff valves, excess-flow valves, backflow check valves and remotely controlled valves, used in piping shall comply with the applicable provisions of DOT cargo tank specifications for LP-Gas service, and with 2-4.5, provided, however, that their minimum design pressure shall comply with 6-3.3.2.

6-3.3.4 Hose, hose connections, and flexible connectors shall comply with 2-4.6 and 6-3.3.1. Flexible connectors used in the piping system to compensate for stresses and vibration shall be limited to 3 ft (1 m) in overall length. Flexible connectors on existing LP-Gas cargo units replaced after December 1, 1967, shall comply with 2-4.6.

(a) Flexible connectors assembled from rubber hose and couplings installed after December 31, 1974, shall be permanently marked to indicate the date of assembly of the flexible connector and the flexible portion of the connector shall be replaced within six years of the indicated date of assembly of the connector.

(b) The rubber hose portion of flexible connectors shall be replaced whenever a cargo unit is remounted on a different chassis, or whenever the cargo unit is repiped, if such repiping encompasses that portion of piping in which the connector is located, unless the remounting and/or repiping is performed within one year of the date of assembly of the connector.

6-3.3.5 All threaded primary valves and fittings used in liquid filling or vapor equalization directly on the cargo container of transportation equipment shall be of steel, malleable or ductile iron construction. All existing equipment shall be so equipped not later than the scheduled requalification date of the container.

6-3.4 Equipment.

6-3.4.1 LP-Gas equipment, such as pumps, compressors, meters, dispensers, regulators, and strainers, shall comply with Section 2-5 as to design and construction and shall be installed in accordance with the applicable provisions of 3-2.10. Equipment on vehicles shall be securely mounted in place and connected into the piping system in accordance with the manufacturer's instructions, taking into account the greater (than for stationary service) jarring and vibration problems incident to vehicular use.

6-3.4.2 Pumps or compressors used for LP-Gas transfer may be mounted on tank trucks, trailers, semitrailers, or tractors, and may be driven by the truck or tractor motor power takeoff, by a separate internal combustion engine, or by hand, mechanical, hydraulic, or electrical means. If an electric drive is used, obtaining energy from the electrical installation at the delivery point, the installation on the vehicle (and at the delivery point) shall comply with 3-8.2.

6-3.4.3 The installation of compressors shall comply with the applicable provisions of 3-2.10.1 and 6-3.4.1.

6-3.4.4 The installation of liquid meters shall be in accordance with 3-2.10.5(a). If venting of LP-Gas to the air is necessary, provision shall be made to vent it at a safe location.

6-3.4.5 When wet hose is carried connected to the truck liquid pump discharge piping, an automatic device, such as a differential regulator, shall be installed between the pump discharge and the hose connection to prevent liquid discharge when the pump is not operating. When a meter or dispenser is used, this device shall be installed between the meter outlet and the hose connection. An excess-flow valve may also be used but shall not be the exclusive means of complying with this provision.

6-3.5 Protection of Container Appurtenances, Piping System and Equipment.

6-3.5.1 Container appurtenances, piping, and equipment comprising the complete LP-Gas system on the cargo vehicle shall be securely mounted in position (*see 6-3.2.1 for container mounting*), shall be protected against damage to the extent it is practical, and in accordance with DOT regulations.

6-3.6 Painting and Marking Liquid Cargo Vehicles.

6-3.6.1 Painting of cargo vehicles shall comply with Code of Federal Regulations, Title 49, Part 195. Placarding and marking shall comply with CFR 49.

6-3.7 Fire Extinguishers.

6-3.7.1 Each tank truck or tractor shall be provided with at least one approved portable fire extinguisher having a minimum capacity of 20 lb dry chemical with a B:C rating. (*Also see NFPA 10, Standard for Portable Fire Extinguishers.*)

6-3.8 Chock Blocks for Liquid Cargo Vehicles.

6-3.8.1 Each tank truck and trailer shall carry chock blocks which shall be used to prevent rolling of the vehicle whenever it is being loaded or unloaded, or is parked.

6-3.9 Exhaust Systems.

6-3.9.1 The truck engine exhaust system shall comply with Federal Motor Carrier Safety Regulations.

6-3.10 Smoking Prohibition.

6-3.10.1 No person may smoke or carry lighted smoking material on or within 25 ft (7.6 m) of a vehicle required to be placarded per DOT regulations containing LP-Gas liquid or vapor. This shall also apply at points of liquid transfer and while delivering or connecting to containers.

6-4 Trailers, Semitrailers, Movable Fuel Storage Tenders, or Farm Carts.

6-4.1 Application.

6-4.1.1 This section applies to all cargo vehicles, other than trucks, which may be parked at locations away from distributing points.

6-4.2 Trailers or Semitrailers Comprising Parts of Section 6-3 Vehicles.

6-4.2.1 When parked, cargo tank trailers or semitrailers covered by Section 6-3 shall be positioned so that the pressure relief valves shall communicate with the vapor space of the container.

6-4.3 Trailers, Including Movable Storage Tenders or Farm Carts.

6-4.3.1 Trailers, including fuel storage tenders or farm carts, shall comply with 6-4.3.2 through 6-4.3.6. If normally used over public ways they shall comply with applicable state regulations.

6-4.3.2 Cargo containers mounted on such vehicles shall be constructed in accordance with Section 2-2, and equipped with appurtenances as provided in Section 2-3. Container mounting shall be adequate for the service involved.

6-4.3.3 Threaded piping shall not be less than Schedule 80 and fittings shall be designed for not less than 250 psig (1.7 MPa gauge).

6-4.3.4 Piping, hoses and equipment, including valves, fittings, pressure relief valves and container accessories, shall be adequately protected against collision or upset.

6-4.3.5 Parked vehicles shall be so positioned that container safety relief valves communicate with the vapor space.

6-4.3.6 Such cargo units shall not be filled on a public way.

6-5 Transportation of Stationary Containers to and from Point of Installation.

6-5.1 Application.

6-5.1.1 This section applies to the transportation of containers designed for stationary service at the point of use and secured to the vehicle only for transportation. Such containers may be transported partially filled with LP-Gas.

6-5.2 Transportation of Containers.

6-5.2.1 Except as provided in 6-5.2.1(a), containers of 125 gal (0.5 m^3) or more water capacity shall contain no more than 5 percent of their water capacity in liquid form during transportation.

(a) Containers containing more LP-Gas than 5 percent of their water capacity may be transported subject to such limitations as may be specified by the authority having jurisdiction.

6-5.2.2 Containers shall be safely secured to minimize movement relative to each other or to the carrying vehicle while in transit, giving consideration to the sudden stops, starts and changes of direction normal to vehicular operation.

6-5.2.3 Valves, regulators and other container appurtenances shall be adequately protected against physical damage during transportation.

6-5.2.4 Pressure relief valves shall be in direct communication with the vapor space of the container.

6-5.2.5 Lifting lugs in good repair on containers filled to no more than five percent of their water capacity may be used for lifting and lowering.

(a) Additional means for securing and supporting the container shall be provided for transporting or when lifting or lowering with more than 5 percent of its water capacity [see 6-5.2.1(a)].

6-6 Parking and Garaging Vehicles Used to Carry LP-Gas Cargo.

6-6.1 Application.

6-6.1.1 This section applies to the parking (except parking associated with a liquid transfer operation) and garaging of vehicles used for the transportation of LP-Gas. Such vehicles include those used to carry portable containers (*see Section 6-2*) and those used to carry LP-Gas in cargo tanks (cargo vehicles, see Section 6-3).

6-6.2 Parking.

6-6.2.1 Vehicles carrying or containing LP-Gas parked out-of-doors shall comply with the following:

(a) Vehicles, except in an emergency and except as provided in 6-6.2.1(b), shall not be left unattended on any street, highway, avenue or alley, provided that this shall not prevent a driver from the necessary absence from the vehicle in connection with his normal duties, nor shall it prevent stops for meals or rest stops during the day or at night.

(b) Vehicles shall not be parked in congested areas. Such vehicles may be parked off the street in uncongested areas if at least 50 ft (15 m) from any building used for assembly, institutional or multiple residential occupancy. This shall not prohibit the parking of vehicles carrying portable containers or cargo vehicles of 3500 gal (13 m^3) water capacity or less on streets adjacent to the driver's residence in uncongested residential areas, provided such points of parking are at least 50 ft (15 m) from a building used for assembly, institutional, or multiple residential occupancy.

6-6.2.2 Vehicles parked indoors shall comply with the following:

(a) Cargo vehicles parked in any public garage or building shall have LP-Gas liquid removed from the cargo container, piping, pump, meter, hoses and related equipment and the pressure in the delivery hose and related equipment reduced to approximately atmospheric, and all valves closed before being moved inside. Delivery hose or valve outlets shall be plugged or capped before the vehicle is moved inside.

(b) Vehicles used to carry portable containers shall not be moved into any public garage or building for parking until all portable containers have been removed from the vehicle.

(c) Vehicles carrying or containing LP-Gas are permitted to be parked in buildings complying with Chapter 7 and located on premises owned or under the control of the operator of such vehicles, provided:

(1) The public is excluded from such buildings.

(2) There is adequate floor level ventilation in all parts of the building where these vehicles are parked.

(3) Leaks in the vehicle LP-Gas systems are repaired before the vehicle is moved inside.

(4) Primary shutoff valves on cargo tanks and other LP-Gas containers on the vehicle (except propulsion engine fuel containers) are closed and delivery hose outlets plugged or capped to contain system pressure before the vehicle is moved inside. Primary shutoff valves on LP-Gas propulsion engine fuel containers shall be closed when the vehicle is parked.

(5) No LP-Gas container is located near a source of heat or within the direct path of hot air being blown from a blower-type heater.

(6) LP-Gas containers are gauged or weighed to determine that they are not filled beyond the maximum filling density according to 4-5.1.

6-6.2.3 Vehicles are permitted to be serviced or repaired indoors as follows:

(a) When it is necessary to take a vehicle into any building located on premises owned and/or operated by the operator of such vehicle for service on engine or chassis, the provisions of 6-6.2.2(a) or (c) shall be followed.

(b) When it is necessary to take a vehicle carrying or containing LP-Gas into any public garage or repair facility for service on the engine or chassis, the provisions of 6-6.2.2(a) or (b) shall be followed, unless the driver or qualified representative of an LP-Gas operator is in attendance at all times when the vehicle is inside. In that case, the following provisions shall be followed under the supervision of such qualified persons:

(1) Leaks in the vehicle LP-Gas systems shall be repaired before the vehicle is moved inside.

(2) Primary shutoff valves on cargo tanks, portable containers and other LP-Gas containers installed on the vehicle (except propulsion engine fuel containers) are closed. LP-Gas liquid shall be removed from the piping, pump, meter, delivery hose, and related equipment and the pressure therein reduced to approximately atmospheric before the vehicle is moved inside. Delivery hose or valve outlets shall be plugged or capped before the vehicle is moved inside.

(3) No container shall be located near a source of heat or within the direct path of hot air blown from a blower or from a blower-type heater.

(4) LP-Gas containers shall be gauged or weighed to determine that they are not filled beyond the maximum filling capacity according to 4-5.1.

(c) If repair work or servicing is to be performed on a cargo tank system, all LP-Gas shall be removed from the cargo tank and piping and the system thoroughly purged before the vehicle is moved inside.

Chapter 7 Buildings or Structures Housing LP-Gas Distribution Facilities

7-1 Scope.

7-1.1 Application.

7-1.1.1 This chapter includes the construction, ventilation and heating of structures housing certain types of LP-Gas systems as referenced in this standard. Such structures may be separate buildings used exclusively for the purpose (or for other purposes having similar hazards), or they may be rooms attached to, or located within, buildings used for other purposes.

7-1.1.2 The provisions of this chapter apply only to buildings constructed or converted after December 31, 1972, except for those previously constructed under the provisions of 5-3.3. Also, see 1-2.4.1.

7-2 Separate Structures or Buildings.

7-2.1 Construction of Structures or Buildings.

7-2.1.1 Separate buildings or structures shall be one story in height and shall have walls, floors, ceilings, and roofs constructed of noncombustible materials. Exterior walls, ceilings, and roofs shall be constructed as follows:

(a) Of lightweight material designed for explosion venting, or

(b) If of heavy construction, such as solid brick masonry, concrete block or reinforced concrete construction, explosion venting windows or panels in walls or roofs shall be provided having an explosion venting area of at least 1 sq ft (0.1 m^2) for each 50 cu ft (1.4 m^3) of the enclosed volume.

7-2.1.2 The floor of such structures shall not be below ground level. Any space beneath the floor shall preferably be of solid fill. If not so filled, the perimeter of the space shall be left entirely unenclosed.

7-2.2 Structure or Building Ventilation.

7-2.2.1 The structure shall be ventilated utilizing air inlets and outlets arranged to provide air movement across the floor as uniformly as practical and in accordance with 7-2.2.1(a) or (b). The bottom of such openings shall not be more than 6 in. (152 mm) above the floor.

(a) When mechanical ventilation is used, air circulation shall be at least at the rate of one cu ft per minute per sq ft (0.4 $m^3/s/m^2$) of floor area. Outlets shall discharge at least five ft (1.5 m) away from any opening into the structure or any other structure.

(b) When natural ventilation is used, each exterior wall [up to 20 ft (6.1 m) in length] shall be provided with at least one opening, with an additional opening for each 20 ft (6.1 m) of length or fraction thereof. Each opening shall have a minimum size of 50 sq in. (12 900 mm²) and the total of all openings shall be at least 1 sq in. (645 mm²) per ft² (0.1 m²) of floor area.

7-2.3 Structure or Building Heating.

7-2.3.1 Heating shall be by steam or hot water radiation or other heating transfer medium with the heat source located outside of the building or structure (*see Section 3-8, Ignition Source Control*), or by electrical appliances installed in the building, if they are listed for Class I, Group D, Division 2 locations, in accordance with NFPA 70, *National Electrical Code* (*see Table 3-8.2.2*).

7-3 Attached Structures or Rooms within Structures.

7-3.1 Construction of Attached Structures.

7-3.1.1 Attached structures shall comply with 7-2.1 (attachment shall be limited to 50 percent of the perimeter of the space enclosed; otherwise such space shall be considered as a room within a structure—*see 7-3.2*), and with the following:

(a) Common walls at points at which structures are to be attached shall:

(1) Have, as erected, a fire resistance rating of at least one hour, as determined by NFPA 251, *Standard Methods of Fire Tests of Building Construction and Materials.*

(2) Have no openings. Common walls for attached structures used only for storage of LP-Gas are permitted to have doorways which shall be equipped with 1 ½ hour (B) fire doors. See NFPA 80, *Standard for Fire Doors and Windows.*

(3) Be designed to withstand a static pressure of at least 100 lb (0.7 MPa) per sq ft (0.1 m²).

(b) The provisions of 7-3.1.1(a) may be waived if the building to which the structure is attached is occupied by operations or processes having a similar hazard.

(c) Ventilation and heating shall comply with 7-2.2.1 and 7-2.3.1.

7-3.2 Construction of Rooms within Structures.

7-3.2.1 Rooms within structures shall be located in the first story and shall have at least one exterior wall with sufficient exposed area to permit explosion venting as provided in 7-3.2.1(a). The building in which the room is located shall not have a basement or unventilated crawl space and the room shall comply with the following:

(a) Walls, floors, ceilings, or roofs of such rooms shall be contructed of noncombustible materials. Exterior walls and ceilings shall either be of lightweight material designed for explosion venting, or, if of heavy construction (such as solid brick masonry, concrete block, or reinforced concrete construction), shall be provided with explosion venting windows or panels in the walls or roofs having an explosion venting area of at least 1 sq ft (0.1 m²) for each 50 cu ft (1.4 m³) of the enclosed volume.

(b) Walls and ceilings common to the room and to the building within which it is located shall:

(1) Have, as erected, a fire resistance rating of at least one hour as determined by NFPA 251, *Standard Methods of Fire Tests of Building Construction and Materials.*

(2) Not have openings. Common walls for rooms used only for storage of LP-Gas are permitted to have doorways which shall be equipped with 1 ½-hour (B) fire doors. See NFPA 80, *Standard for Fire Doors and Windows.*

(3) Be designed to withstand a static pressure of at least 100 lb (0.7 MPa) per sq ft (0.1 m²).

(c) The provisions of 7-3.2.1(b) may be waived if the building within which the room is located is occupied by operations or processes having a similar hazard.

(d) Ventilation and heating shall comply with 7-2.2.1 and 7-2.3.1.

Chapter 8 Refrigerated Storage

8-1 Refrigerated Containers.

8-1.1 Refrigerated containers shall be built in accordance with applicable provisions of one of the following codes as appropriate for conditions of maximum allowable working pressure, design temperature, and hydrostatic testing:

8-1.1.1 For pressures of 15 psig (103 kPa gauge) or more, use the ASME Code, Section VIII, except that construction using joint efficiencies in Table UW 12, Column C, Division 1 is not permitted. Material shall be selected from those recognized by ASME which meet the requirements of Appendix R of ANSI/API 620.

8-1.1.2 For pressures below 15 psig (103 kPa gauge) use ANSI/API 620, *Recommended Rules for the Design and Construction of Large, Welded, Low Pressure Storage Tanks,* including Appendix R.

8-1.2 Wind loading on containers shall be in accordance with paragraph 2-2.2.3(c).

8-1.3 Seismic loading on containers shall be in accordance with paragraph 2-2.2.3(d).

8-1.4 Field-erected containers for refrigerated storage shall be designed as an integral part of the storage system including tank insulation, compressors, condensors, controls, and piping. Proper allowance shall be made for the service temperature limits of the particular process and the products to be stored when determining material specifications and the design pressure. Welded construction shall be used.

8-1.5 When austenitic steels or nonferrous materials are used, ANSI/API 620, Appendix Q shall be used as a guide in the selection of materials for use at the design temperature.

8-1.6 Prior to initial operation, containers shall be inspected to the extent necessary to assure compliance with the engineering design and material, fabrication, assembly, and test provisions of this standard. The operator shall be responsible for this inspection.

8-1.7 The operator may delegate performance of any part of the inspection to inspectors who may be employees of his own organization, an engineering or scientific organization, or of a recognized insurance or inspection company. Inspectors shall be qualified in accordance with the code or standard applicable to the container and as specified in this standard.

8-1.8 The operator shall specify the maximum allowable working pressure, which includes a suitable margin above the operating pressure, and the maximum allowable vacuum.

8-1.9 All piping that is a part of an LPG container shall be in accordance with ANSI B31.3. This container piping shall include all piping internal to the container, within the insulation spaces, and external piping attached or connected to the container up to the first circumferential external joint of the piping. Inert gas purge systems wholly within the insulation spaces are exempt from this provision.

8-1.10 LPG containers shall be installed on suitable foundations designed by a qualified engineer and constructed in accordance with recognized structural engineering practices. Prior to the start of design and construction of the foundation, a sub-surface investigation shall be conducted by a qualified soils engineer to determine the stratigraphy and physical properties of the soils underlying the site.

NOTE: See ASCE 56, *Sub-Surface Investigation for Design and Construction of Foundation for Buildings,* and Appendix C, API Standard 620, for further information.

8-1.11 The bottom of the outer tank shall be above the ground water table or otherwise protected from contact with ground water at all times, and the material in contact with the bottom of the outer tank shall be selected to minimize corrosion.

8-1.12 When the bottom of an outer tank is in contact with the soil, a heating system shall be provided to prevent the 32° F (0°C) isotherm from penetrating the soil. The heating system shall be designed so as to permit functional and performance monitoring, which shall be done, at a minimum, on a weekly basis. Where there is a discontinuity in the foundation, such as for bottom piping, careful attention and separate treatment shall be given to the heating system in this zone. Heating systems shall be installed so that any heating elements or temperature sensor used for control can be replaced. Provisions shall be incorporated to protect against the detrimental effects of moisture accumulation in the conduit which could result in galvanic corrosion or other forms of deterioration within the conduit or heating element.

8-1.13 If the foundation is installed to provide adequate air circulation in lieu of a heating system, then the bottom of the outer tank shall be of a material suitable for temperatures to which it will be exposed.

8-2 Marking on Refrigerated Containers.

8-2.1 Each refrigerated container shall be identified by the attachment of a nameplate on the outer covering in an accessible place marked as specified in the following:

(a) Manufacturers name and date built.

(b) Liquid volume of the container in gal (US Standard) or barrels.

(c) Maximum allowable working pressure in lbs per sq in.

(d) Minimum temperature in degrees Fahrenheit for which the container was designed.

(e) Maximum allowable water level to which the container may be filled for test purposes.

(f) Density of the product to be stored in lbs per cu ft for which the container was designed.

(g) Maximum level to which the container is permitted to be filled with the liquefied petroleum gas for which it was designed.

8-3 Refrigerated Container Impoundment.

8-3.1 Refrigerated containers shall be located within an impoundment area that complies with 8-3.2 through 8-3.8.

8-3.2 The following provisions shall be made to minimize the possibility of accidental discharge of LPG from containers from endangering adjoining property or important process equipment and structures, or reaching waterways.

8-3.3 Enclosed drainage channels for LP-Gas are prohibited.

Exception: Container downcomers used to rapidly conduct spilled LP-Gas away from critical areas may be enclosed provided that an adequate drainage rate is achieved.

8-3.4 Dikes, impounding walls, and drainage systems for LP-Gas and flammable refrigerant containment shall be of compacted earth, concrete, metal, and/or other suitable materials. They may be independent of the container or they may be mounted, integral to, or constructed against the container. They, and any penetrations thereof, shall be designed to withstand the full hydrostatic head of impounded LP-Gas or flammable refrigerant, the effect of rapid cooling to the temperature of the liquid to be confined, any anticipated fire exposure, and natural forces such as earthquake, wind, and rain.

8-3.5 Dikes, impounding walls, and drainage channels for flammable liquid containment shall conform to NFPA 30, *Flammable and Combustible Liquids Code.*

8-3.6 To assure that any accidentally discharged liquid stays within an area enclosed by a dike or impounding wall and yet to provide a reasonably wide margin for area configuration design, the dike or impounding wall, height and distance shall be determined in accordance with Figure 8-3.6

8-3.7 Provision shall be made to clear rain or other water from the impounding area. Automatically controlled sump pumps are permitted if equipped with an automatic cutoff device which shall prevent their operation when exposed to LP-Gas temperatures. Piping, valves, and fittings whose failure could permit liquid to escape from the impounding area shall be suitable for continuous exposure to LP-Gas temperatures. If gravity drainage is employed for water removal, provision shall be made to prevent the escape of LP-Gas by way of the drainage system.

8-3.8 Insulation systems used for impounding surfaces shall be, in the installed condition, noncombustible and suitable for the intended service considering the anticipated thermal and mechanical stresses and loadings. If flotation is a problem, mitigation measures shall be provided. Such insulation systems shall be inspected as appropriate for their intended service.

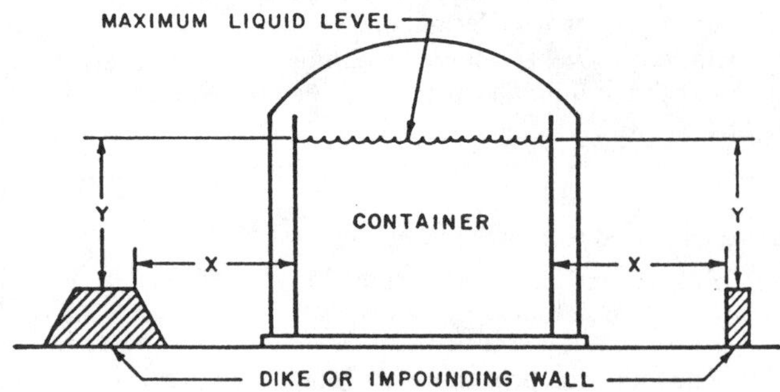

Figure 8-3.6 Dike or Impounding Wall Proximity to Containers.

Notes to Figure 8-3.6:

Dimension "X" must equal or exceed the sum of dimension "Y" plus the equivalent head in LP-Gas of the pressure in the vapor space above the liquid.

Exception: When the height of the dike or impounding wall is equal to, or greater than the maximum liquid level, "X" may have any value.

Dimension "X" is the distance from the inner wall of the container to the closest face of the dike or impounding wall.

Dimension "Y" is the distance from the maximum liquid level in the container to the top of the dike or impounding wall.

8-4 Refrigerated Aboveground Containers.

8-4.1 Containers shall be located outside of buildings.

8-4.2 A container or containers with aggregate water capacity in excess of 120,000 gal (454 m³) shall be located 100 ft (31 m) or more from buildings associated with the LP-Gas plant which are occupied for generation, compression, or purification of manufactured gas, from natural gas stationary refrigerated containers, or from natural gas compressor buildings or from outdoor installations essential to the maintenance of operation in such buildings. Such a container or containers shall be 100 ft (31 m) or more from aboveground storage of flammable liquids and from any buildings of such construction or occupancy which constitute a material hazard of exposure to the containers in the event of fire or explosion in said buildings. If the container or containers are located closer to any such buildings or installations, then the latter shall be protected by walls adjacent to such storage containers or by other appropriate means against the entry of escaped liquefied petroleum gas, or of drainage from the storage container area and its loading points—all in such a manner as may be required and approved by the authority having jurisdiction.

8-4.3 Refrigerated liquefied petroleum gas containers shall not be located within dikes enclosing flammable liquid tanks or within dikes enclosing nonrefrigerated liquefied petroleum gas containers.

8-4.4 Refrigerated containers shall not be installed one above the other.

8-4.5 The ground within 25 ft (8 m) of any aboveground refrigerated container and all ground within a diked area shall be kept clear of readily ignitible material such as weeds and long dry grass.

Chapter 9 Referenced Publications

9-1 The following documents or portions thereof are referenced within this standard and shall be considered part of the requirements of this document. The edition indicated for each reference is the current edition as of the date of the NFPA issuance of this document.

9-1.1 NFPA Publications. National Fire Protection Association, Batterymarch Park, Quincy, MA 02269.

NFPA 10-1988, *Standard for Portable Fire Extinguishers*

NFPA 15-1985, *Standard for Water Spray Fixed Systems for Fire Protection*

NFPA 30-1987, *Flammable and Combustible Liquids Code*

NFPA 37-1984, *Standard for the Installation and Use of Stationary Combustion Engines and Gas Turbines*

NFPA 50-1985, *Standard for Bulk Oxygen Systems at Consumer Sites*

NFPA 50A-1989, *Standard for Gaseous Hydrogen Systems at Consumer Sites*

NFPA 50B-1989, *Standard for Liquefied Hydrogen Systems at Consumer Sites*

NFPA 51-1987, *Standard for the Design and Installation of Oxygen-Fuel Gas Systems for Welding, Cutting, and Allied Processes*

NFPA 54 (ANSI Z223.1)-1988, *National Fuel Gas Code*

NFPA 59-1989, *Standard for the Storage and Handling of Liquefied Petroleum Gases at Utility Gas Plants*

NFPA 61B-1989, *Standard for the Prevention of Fires and Explosions in Grain Elevators and Facilities Handling Bulk Raw Agricultural Commodities*

NFPA 70-1987, *National Electrical Code*

NFPA 80-1986, *Standard for Fire Doors and Windows*

NFPA 82-1983, *Standard on Incinerators, Waste and Linen Handling Systems and Equipment*

NFPA 86-1985, *Standard for Ovens and Furnaces*

NFPA 96-1987, *Standard for the Installation of Equipment for the Removal of Smoke and Grease-Laden Vapors from Commercial Cooking Equipment*

NFPA 220-1985, *Standard on Types of Building Construction*

NFPA 251-1985, *Standard Methods of Fire Tests of Building Construction and Materials*

NFPA 302-1989, *Fire Protection Standard for Pleasure and Commercial Motor Craft*

NFPA 321-1987, *Standard on Basic Classification of Flammable and Combustible Liquids*

NFPA 501A-1987, *Standard for Firesafety Criteria for Manufactured Home Installations, Sites, and Communities*

NFPA 501C-1986, *Standard on Firesafety Criteria for Recreational Vehicles*

NFPA 505-1987, *Firesafety Standard for Powered Industrial Trucks Including Type Designations, Areas of Use, Maintenance, and Operation*

9-1.2 ANSI Publications. American National Standards Institute, 1430 Broadway, New York, NY 10018.

ANSI A58.1-1972, *Design Loads for Buildings and Other Structures*

ANSI B36.10-1979, *Welded and Seamless Wrought Steel Pipe*

ANSI B95.1-1977, *Standard Terminology for Pressure Relief Devices*

9-1.3 API Publications. American Petroleum Institute, 2101 L ST., NW, Washington, DC 20037.

API-ASME *Code for Unfired Pressure Vessels for Petroleum Liquids and Gases*, Pre - July 1, 1961.

ANSI/API 620, *Recommended Rules for Design and Construction of Large, Welded, Low-Pressure Storage Tanks*, 1982.

9-1.4 ASME Publications. American Society for Mechanical Engineers, 345 East 47th St., New York, NY 10017.

"Rules for the Construction of Unfired Pressure Vessels," Section VIII, Division 1, *ASME Boiler and Pressure Vessel Code*, 1986, and all addenda and errata thru 1988.

ANSI/ASME B31.3-1988, Chemical Plant and Refinery Piping.

9-1.5 ASTM Publications. American Society for Testing and Materials, 1916 Race St., Philadelphia, PA 19103.

ASTM A 47-1984, *Standard Specification for Ferritic Malleable Iron Castings*

ASTM A 48-1983, *Standard Specification for Gray Iron Castings*

ASTM A 53-1987, *Standard Specification for Pipe, Steel, Black and Hot-Dipped, Zinc-Coated Welded and Seamless*

ASTM A 106-1987, *Standard Specification for Seamless Carbon Steel Pipe for High-Temperature Service*

ASTM A 120-1984, *Standard Specification for Pipe, Steel, Black and Hot-Dipped Zinc Coated (Galvanized) Welded and Seamless, for Ordinary Uses*

ASTM A 395-1980, *Standard Specification for Ferritic Ductile Iron Pressure—Retaining Castings for Use at Elevated Temperatures*

ASTM A 536-1984, *Standard Specification for Ductile Iron Castings*

ASTM A 539-1985, *Standard Specification for Electric-Resistance-Welded Coiled Steel Tubing for Gas Fuel Oil Lines*

ASTM B 42-1988, *Standard Specification for Seamless Copper Pipe, Standard Sizes*

ASTM B 43-1988, *Standard Specification for Seamless Red Brass Pipe, Standard Sizes*

ASTM B 86-1988, *Standard Specification for Zinc-Alloy Die Casting*

ASTM B 88-1988, *Standard Specification for Seamless Copper Water Tube*

ASTM B 135-1986, *Standard Specification for Seamless Brass Tube*

ASTM B 280-1988, *Standard Specification for Seamless Copper Tube for Air Conditioning and Refrigeration Field Service*

ASTM D 2513-1987, *Standard Specification for Thermoplastic Gas Pressure Pipe, Tubing and Fittings*

ASTM D 2683-1987, *Standard Specification for Socket-Type Polyethylene (PE) Fittings for Outside Diameter —Controlled Polyethylene Pipe*

ASTM D 3261-1987, *Standard Specification for Butt Heat Fusion Polyethylene (PE) Plastic Fittings for Polyethylene (PE) Plastic Pipe and Tubing*

9-1.6 AWS Publication. American Welding Society, 2501 NW 7th St., Miami, FL 33125.

ANSI Z49.1-1988, *Safety in Welding and Cutting.*

9-1.7 CGA Publications. Compressed Gas Association, Inc., 1235 Jefferson Davis Highway, Arlington, VA 22202.

ANSI/CGA C-4-1978, *Method of Marking Portable Compressed Gas Containers to Identify the Material Contained*

Pressure-Relief Device Standards,

S-1.1-1979, *Cylinders for Compressed Gases* (Errata, 1982)

S-1.2-1980, *Cargo and Portable Tanks for Compressed Gases*

S-1.3-1980, *Compressed Gas Storage Containers*

9-1.8 Federal Regulations. U.S. Government Printing Office, Washington, DC.

Code of Federal Regulations, Title 49, Parts 171-192 and Parts 393 and 397. (Also available from the Association of American Railroads, American Railroads Bldg., 1920 L St. NW, Washington, DC 20036 and American Trucking Assns., Inc., 2201 Mill Rd., Alexandria, VA 22314.)

9-1.9 ICBO Publication. International Conference of Building Officials, 5360 S. Workman Mill Rd., Whittier, CA 90601.

Uniform Building Code, 1988.

9-1.10 UL Publication. Underwriters Laboratories, Inc., 333 Pfingsten Rd., Northbrook, IL 60062.

UL 132-1984, *Safety Relief Valves for Anhydrous Ammonia and LP-Gas.*

Appendix A

This Appendix is not a part of the requirements of this NFPA document, but is included for information purposes only.

A-1-4.1.1 It is recognized that no odorant will be completely effective as a warning agent in every circumstance.

It is recommended that odorants be qualified as to compliance with 1-4.1.1 by tests or experience. Where qualifying is by tests, such tests should be certified by an approved laboratory not associated with the odorant manufacturer. Experience has shown that ethyl mercaptan in the ratio of 1.0 lb (0.45 kg) per 10,000 gal (37.9 m^3) of liquid LP-Gas has been recognized as an effective odorant. Other odorants and quantities meeting the provisions of 1-4.1.1

may be used. Research* on odorants has shown that thiophane (tetrahydrothiophene) in a ratio of at least 6.4 lb (2.9 kg) per 10,000 gal (37.9 m^3) of liquid LP-Gas may satisfy the requirements of 1-4.1.1.

*"A New Look at Odorization Levels for Propane Gas," BERC/RI-77/1, United States Energy Research & Development Administration, Technical Information Center, September, 1977.

A-1-7 External Pressure Relief Valve. Describes the type relief valves used on older domestic tanks, relief valve manifolds and piping protection.

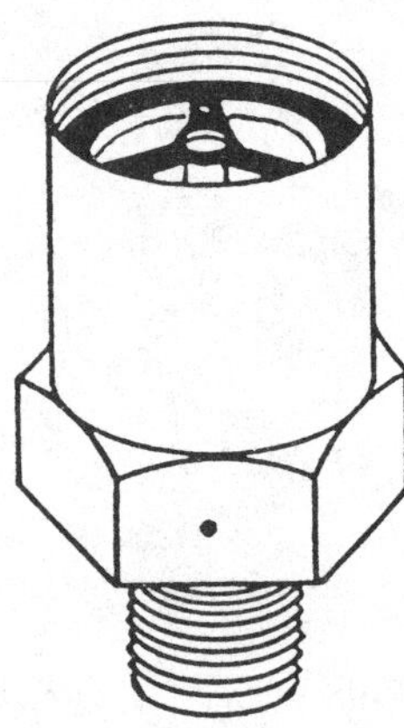

External Relief Valve.

Flush Type Full Internal Pressure Relief Valve. Describes the type relief valve being required on cargo vehicles in most states.

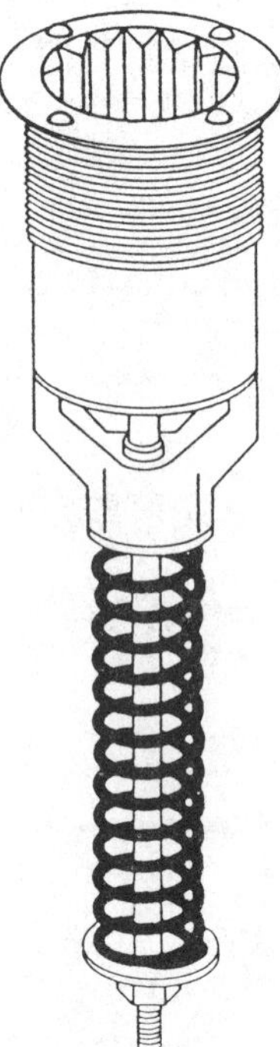

Flush Type Full Internal Relief Valve.

Full Internal Pressure Relief Valve. Describes the type relief valve being changed to for engine fuel use.

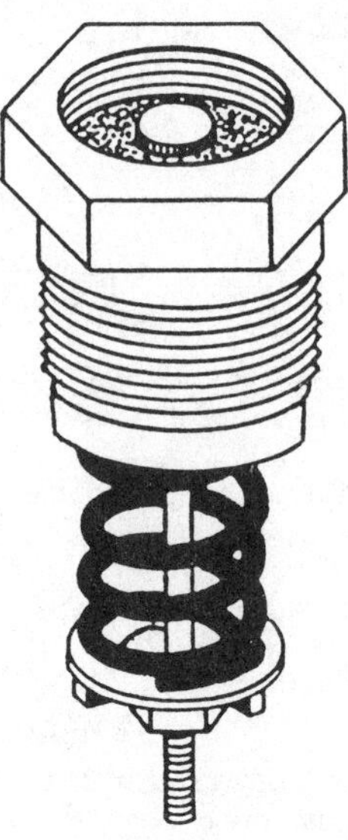

Full Internal Relief Valve.

Internal Spring Type Pressure Relief Valve. Describes the type relief valves used on modern domestic tanks, looks similar to Full Internal Relief Valve, but has seat and poppet above the tank connection.

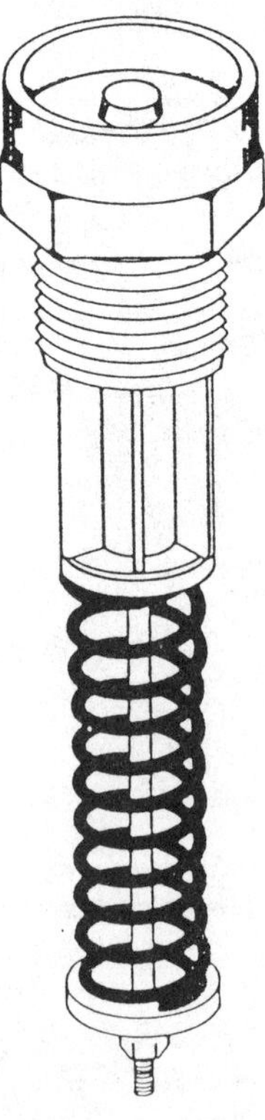

Internal Spring Type Relief Valve.

Sump Type Full Internal Pressure Relief Valve. Describes the type relief valve used on older engine fuel tanks.

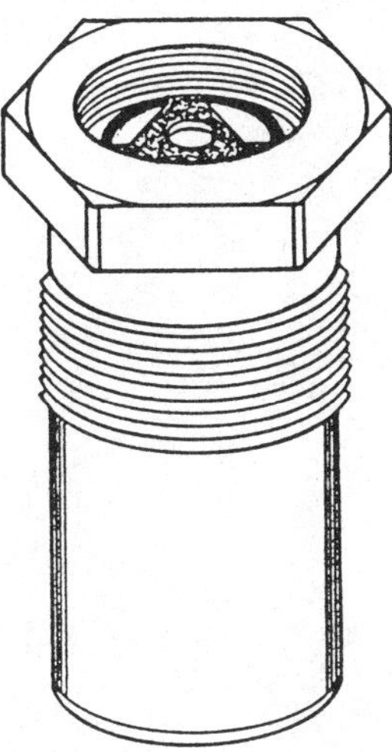

Sump Type Full Internal Relief Valve.

A-2-2.1.3 Prior to April 1, 1967, these regulations were promulgated by the Interstate Commerce Commission. In Canada, the regulations of the Canadian Transport Commission apply.

Construction of containers to the API-ASME Code has not been authorized after July 1, 1961.

A-3-2.3.1(f) Aboveground Storage Tank Paint Color. Generally a light reflecting color paint is preferred unless the system is installed in an extremely cold climate.

A-3-4.8.3 The weight will be affected by the specific gravity of the liquefied petroleum (LP) gas. Weights varying from 16.0 (454g) to 16.8 oz (476g) are recognized as being within the range of what is nominal.

A-3-6.2.2(a) Prior to April 1, 1967, these regulations were promulgated by the Interstate Commerce Commission. In Canada, the regulations of the Canadian Transport Commission apply. Available from the Canadian Transport Commission, Union Station, Ottawa, Canada.

A-3-10.2.2 The National Fire Protection Association, American Petroleum Institute and National Propane Gas Association publish material, including visual aids, useful in such planning.

A-3-10.3.1 For LP-Gas fixed storage facilities of 60,000 gal (227 m^3) water capacity or less, a competent firesafety analysis (*see 3-10.2.3 and 3-10.2.5*) could indicate that applied insulating coatings are quite often the most practical solution for special protection.

It is recommended that insulation systems be evaluated on the basis of experience or listings by an approved testing laboratory.

Appendix B Properties of LP-Gases

This Appendix is not a part of the requirements of this NFPA document, but is included for information purposes only.

B-1 Approximate Properties of LP-Gases.

B-1.1 Source of Property Values.

B-1.1.1 The property values for the LP-Gases are based on average industry values and include values for LP-Gases coming from natural gas liquids plants as well as those coming from petroleum refineries. Thus, any particular commerical propane or butane might have properties varying slightly from the values shown. Similarly, any propane-butane mixture might have properties varying from those obtained by computation from these average values (*see B-1.2.1 for computation method used*). Since these are average values, the interrelationships between them (i.e., lb per gal, specific gravity, etc.) will not cross-check perfectly in all cases.

B-1.1.2 Such variations are not sufficient to prevent the use of these average values for most engineering and design purposes. They stem from minor variations in composition. The commerical grades are not pure (CP-Chemically Pure) propane or butane, or mixtures of the two, but may also contain small and varying percentages of ethane, ethylene, propylene, isobutane, or butylene which can cause slight variations in property values. There are limits to the accuracy of even the most advanced testing methods used to determine the percentages of these minor components in any LP-Gas.

B-1.2 Approximate Properties of LP-Gases.

B-1.2.1 The principal properties of commercial propane and commercial butane are shown in Table B-1.2.1. Reasonably accurate property values for propane-butane mixtures may be obtained by computation, applying the percentages by weight of each in the mixture to the values for the property it is desired to obtain. Slightly more accurate results for vapor pressure are obtained by using the percentages by volume. Very accurate results can be obtained using data and methods explained in petroleum and chemical engineering data books.

B-1.3 Specifications of LP-Gases. Specifications of LP-Gases covered by this standard are listed in Gas Processors Association, *Liquefied Petroleum Gas Specifications for Test Methods Standard 2140* and/or *Specification for Liquefied Petroleum (LP) Gases*, ASTM D 1835.

Appendix C Design, Construction, and Requalification of DOT (ICC) Cylinder Specification Containers

This Appendix is not a part of the requirements of this NFPA document, but is included for information purposes only.

C-1 Scope.

C-1.1 Application.

Table B-1.2.1 (English) Approximate Properties of LP-Gases

	Commercial Propane	Commercial Butane
Vapor Pressure in psig at:		
70°F	127	17
100°F	196	37
105°F	210	41
130°F	287	69
Specific Gravity of Liquid at 60°F	0.504	0.582
Initial Boiling Point at 14.7 psia, °F	−44	15
Weight per Gallon of Liquid at 60°F, lb	4.20	4.81
Specific Heat of Liquid, Btu/lb at 60°F	0.630	0.549
Cu. ft of Vapor per Gallon at 60°F	36.38	31.26
Cu. ft of Vapor per Pound at 60°F	8.66	6.51
Specific Gravity of Vapor (Air = 1) at 60°F	1.50	2.01
Ignition Temperature in Air, °F	920–1120	900–1000
Maximum Flame Temperature in Air, °F	3,595	3,615
Limits of Flammability in Air, Percent of Vapor in Air-Gas Mixture:		
(a) Lower	2.15	1.55
(b) Upper	9.60	8.60
Latent Heat of Vaporization at Boiling Point:		
(a) Btu per Pound	184	167
(b) Btu per Gallon	773	808
Total Heating Values after Vaporization:		
(a) Btu per Cubic Foot	2,488	3,280
(b) Btu per Pound	21,548	21,221
(c) Btu per Gallon	91,502	102,032

Table B-1.2.1 (Metric) Approximate Properties of LP-Gases

	Commercial Propane	Commercial Butane
Vapor Pressure in kPa gauge at:		
20°C	895	103
40°C	1 482	285
45°C	1 672	345
55°C	1 980	462
Specific Gravity	0.504	0.582
Initial Boiling Point at atm, Pressure, °C	−42	−9
Weight per Cubic Metre of Liquid at 15.56°C, kg	504	582
Specific Heat of Liquid, Kilojoule per Kilogram, at 15.56°C	1.464	1.276
Cubic Metre of Vapor per Litre of Liquid at 15.56°C	0.271	0.235
Cubic Metre of Vapor per Kilogram of Liquid at 15.56°C	0.539	0.410
Specific Gravity of Vapor (Air = 1) at 15.56°C	1.50	2.01
Ignition Temperature in Air, °C	493–549	482–538
Maximum Flame Temperature in Air, °C	1 980	2 008
Limits of Flammability in Air, % of Vapor in Air-Gas Mixture:		
(a) Lower	2.15	1.55
(b) Upper	9.60	8.60
Latent Heat of Vaporization at Boiling Point:		
(a) Kilojoule per kilogram	428	388
(b) Kilojoule per litre	216	226
Total Heating Value after Vaporization:		
(a) Kilojoule per Cubic Metre	92 430	121 280
(b) Kilojoule per Kilogram	49 920	49 140
(c) Kilojoule per Litre	25 140	28 100

C-1.1.1 This appendix provides general information on DOT cylinder specification containers referred to in this standard. For complete information consult the applicable specification (*see C-2.1.1*). The water capacity of such cylinders may not be more than 1,000 lb (454 kg).

C-1.1.2 This appendix is not applicable to DOT tank car portable tank container or cargo tank specifications. Portable and cargo tanks are basically ASME containers and are covered in Appendix D.

C-1.1.3 Prior to April 1, 1967, these specifications were promulgated by the Interstate Commerce Commission (ICC). On this date, certain functions of the ICC, including the promulgation of specifications and regulations dealing with LP-Gas cylinders, were transferred to the Department of Transportation (DOT). Throughout this appendix both ICC and DOT are used; ICC applying to dates prior to April 1, 1967, and DOT to subsequent dates.

C-2 LP-Gas Cylinder Specifications.

C-2.1 Publishing of DOT Cylinder Specifications.

C-2.1.1 DOT cylinder specifications are published under Title 49, *Code of Federal Regulations*, Parts 171-190, available from U.S. Government Printing Office, Washington, D.C. The information in this publication is also issued as a Tariff at approximately three-year intervals by the Bureau of Explosives, American Railroads Building, 1920 L Street, NW, Washington, DC 20036.

C-2.2 DOT Specification Nomenclature.

C-2.2.1 The specificaion designation consists of a one-digit number, sometimes followed by one or more capital letters, then by a dash and a three-digit number. The one-digit number alone, or in combination with one or more capital letters, designates the specification number. The three-digit number following the dash shows the service pressure for which the container is designed. Thus, "4B-240" indicates a cylinder built to Specification 4B for a 240 psig service pressure. (*See C-2.2.3.*)

C-2.2.2 The specification gives the details of cylinder construction, such as material used, method of fabrication, tests required and inspection method, and prescribes the service pressure, or range of service pressures for which that specification may be used.

C-2.2.3 The term "service pressure" is analagous to, and serves the same purpose as, the ASME "design pressure." However, it is not identical, representing instead the highest pressure to which the container will normally be subjected in transit or in use but not necessarily the maximum pressure to which it may be subjected under emergency conditions in transportation. The service pressure stipulated for the LP-Gases is based on the vapor pressures exerted by the product in the container at two different temperatures, the higher pressure of the two becoming the service pressure, as follows:

(a) The pressure in the container at 70°F must be less than the service pressure for which the container is marked, and

(b) The pressure in the container at 130°F must not exceed 5/4 times the pressure for which the container is marked.

EXAMPLE: Commercial propane has a vapor pressure at 70°F of 132 psig. However, its vapor pressure at 130°F is 300 psig, so service pressure (5/4 times which must not exceed 300 psig) is 300 divided by 5/4, or 240 psig. Thus commercial propane requires at least 240 psig service pressure cylinder.

C-2.3 DOT Cylinder Specifications Used for LP-Gas.

C-2.3.1 A number of different specifications were approved by ICC, and since 1967 by DOT, for use with LP-Gases. Some of these are no longer published or used for new construction. However, containers built under these old specifications, if properly maintained and requalified, are still acceptable for LP-Gas transportation.

C-2.3.2 DOT specifications cover primarily safety in transportation. However, in order for the product to be used, it is necessary for it to come to rest at the point of use and serve as LP-Gas storage during the period of use. Containers adequate for transportation are also deemed to be adequate for use as provided in NFPA 58. As small size ASME containers were not available at the time tank truck delivery was started, ICC (now DOT) cylinders have been equipped for tank truck deliveries and permanently installed.

C-2.3.3 The DOT cylinder specifications most widely used for the LP-Gases are shown in Table C-2.3.3. The differing materials of construction, method of fabrication and the date of the specification reflect the progress made in knowledge of the products to be contained and improvement in metallurgy and methods of fabrication.

C-3 Requalification, Retesting and Repair of DOT Cylinder Specification Containers.

C-3.1 Application.

C-3.1.1 This section outlines the requalification, retesting and repair requirements for DOT cylinder specification containers but should be used only as a guide. For official information, the applicable DOT regulations should be consulted.

Table C-2.3.3

Specification No. & Marking	Material of Construction	Method of Fabrication
26–150*	Steel	Welded and Brazed
3B–300	Steel	Seamless
4–300	Steel	Welded
4B–300	Steel	2 piece Welded & Brazed
4B–240	Steel	2 piece Welded & Brazed
4BA–240	Alloy Steel	2 piece Welded & Brazed
4E–240	Aluminum	Welded and Brazed
4BW–240	Steel	3 piece Welded

* The term "service pressure" had a different connotation at the time the specification was adopted.

C-3.2 Requalification (Including Retesting) of DOT Cylinders.

C-3.2.1 DOT cylinders may not be refilled, continued in service or transported unless they are properly qualified or requalified for LP-Gas service in accordance with DOT regulations.

C-3.2.2 A careful examination must be made of every container each time it is to be filled and it must be rejected if there is evidence of exposure to fire, bad gouges or dents, seriously corroded areas, leaks or other conditions indicating possible weaknesses which might render it unfit for service. The following disposition is to be made of rejected cylinders:

(a) Containers subjected to fire must be requalified, reconditioned or repaired in accordance with C-3.3.1, or permanently removed from service except that DOT 4E (aluminum) cylinders must be permanently removed from service.

(b) Containers showing serious physical damage, leaks or with a reduction in the marked tare weight of 5 percent or more must be retested in accordance with C-3.2.4(a) or (b) and, if necessary, repaired in accordance with C-3.3.1.

C-3.2.3 All containers, including those apparently undamaged, must be periodically requalified for continued service. The first requalification for a new cylinder is required within 12 years after the date of manufacture. Subsequent requalifications are required within the periods specified under the requalification method used.

C-3.2.4 DOT regulations permit three alternative methods of requalification for most commonly used LP-Gas specification containers (*see DOT regulations for permissible requalification methods for specific cylinder specifications*). Two use hydrostatic testing, and the third uses a carefully made and duly recorded visual examination by a competent person. In the case of the two hydrostatic test methods, only test results are recorded but a careful visual examination of each container is also required. DOT regulations cite in detail the data to be recorded for the hydrostatic test methods, the observations to be made during the recorded visual examination method, and the marking of containers to indicate the requalification date and the method used. The three methods are outlined as follows:

(a) The water jacket type hydrostatic test may be used to requalify containers for 12 years before the next requalification is due. A pressure of twice the marked service pressure is applied, using a water jacket (or the equivalent) so that the total expansion of the container during the application of the test pressure can be observed and recorded for comparison with the permanent expansion of the container after depressurization. The following disposition is made of containers tested in this manner:

(1) Containers which pass the retest, and the visual examination required with it (*see C-3.2.4*), are marked with the date and year of the test (Example: "6-70," indicating requalification by the water jacket test method in June 1970) and may be placed back in service.

(2) Containers which leak, or for which the permanent expansion exceeds 10 percent of the total expansion (12 percent for Specification 4E aluminum cylinders) must be rejected. If rejected for leakage, containers may be repaired in accordance with C-3.3.1.

(b) The simple hydrostatic test may be used to requalify containers for seven years before the next requalification is due. A pressure of twice the marked service pressure is applied but no provision is made for measuring total and permanent expansion during the test outlined in C-3.2.4(a) above. The container is carefully observed while under the test pressure for leaks, undue swelling or bulging indicating weaknesses. The following disposition is made of containers tested in this matter:

(1) Containers which pass the test, and the visual examination required with it (*see C-3-2.4*), are marked with the date and year of the retest followed by an "S" (Example: "8-71S," indicating requalification by the simple hydrostatic test method in August 1971), and may be placed back in service.

(2) Containers developing leaks or showing undue swelling or bulging must be rejected. If rejected for leaks, containers may be repaired in accordance with C-3.3.1.

(c) The recorded visual examination may be used to requalify containers for five years before the next qualification is due provided the container has been used exclusively for LP-Gas commerically free from corroding components. Inspection is to be made by a competent person, using as a guide Compressed Gas Association *Standard for Visual Inspection of Steel Compressed Gas Cylinders* (CGA Pamphlet C-6), and recording the inspection results as required by DOT regulations. [Note: reference to NLPGA Safety Bulletin, *Recommended Procedures for Visual Inspection and Requalification of DOT (ICC) Cylinders in LP-Gas Service*, is also recommended.] The following disposition is to be made of containers inspected in this manner:

(1) Containers which pass the visual examination are marked with the date and year of the examination followed by an "E" (Example: "7-70E," indicating requalification by the recorded visual examination method in July 1970), and may be placed back in service.

(2) Containers which leak, show serious denting or gouging, or excessive corrosion must either be scrapped or repaired in accordance with C-3.3.1.

C-3.3 Repair of DOT Cylinder Specification Containers.

C-3.3.1 Repair of DOT cylinders must be performed by a manufacturer of the type of cylinder to be repaired or by a repair facility authorized by DOT.

Repairs normally made are for fire damage, leaks, denting, gouges and for broken or detached valve protecting collars or foot rings.

Appendix D Design of ASME and API-ASME Containers

This Appendix is not a part of the requirements of this NFPA document, but is included for information purposes only.

D-1 General.

D-1.1 Application.

D-1.1.1 This appendix provides general information on containers designed and constructed in accordance with ASME or API-ASME Codes, usually referred to as ASME containers. For complete information on either ASME or API-ASME containers the applicable code should be consulted. Construction of containers to the API-ASME Code has not been authorized since July 1, 1961.

D-1.1.2 DOT (ICC) specification portable tank containers and cargo tanks are basically either ASME or API-ASME containers. In writing these specifications, which should be consulted for complete information, additions were made to these pressure vessel codes to cover the following:

(a) Protection of container valves and appurtenances against physical damage in transportation.

(b) Holddown devices for securing cargo containers to conventional vehicles.

(c) Attachments to relatively large [6,000 gal (22.7 m^3) or more water capacity] cargo containers in which the container serves as a stress member in lieu of a frame.

D-1.2 Development of ASME and API-ASME Codes.

D-1.2.1 ASME type containers of approximately 12,000 gal (45.4 m^3) water capacity or more were initially used for bulk storage in processing, distribution and industrial plants. As the industry expanded and residential and commercial usage increased, the need for small ASME containers with capacities greater than the upper limit for DOT cylinders grew. This ultimately resulted in the development of cargo containers for tank trucks and the wide use of ASME containers ranging in size from less than 25 gal (0.1 m^3) to 120,000 gal (454 m^3) water capacity.

D-1.2.2 The American Society of Mechanical Engineers (ASME) in 1911 set up the Boiler and Pressure Vessel Committee to formulate "standard rules for the construction of steam boilers and other pressure vessels." The ASME *Boiler and Pressure Vessel Code*, first published in 1925, has been revised and republished in 22 separate editions including the 1980 edition. During this period there have been changes in the code as materials of construction improved and more was known about them, and as fabrication methods changed and inspection procedures were refined.

D-1.2.3 One major change involved the so-called "factor of safety" (the ratio of the ultimate strength of the metal to the design stress used). Prior to 1946, a 5:1 safety factor was used. Fabrication changed from the riveting widely used when the code was first written (some forge welding was used), to fusion welding. This latter method was incorporated into the code as welding techniques were perfected, and now predominates.

D-1.2.4 The safety factor change in the ASME Code was based on the technical progress made since 1925 and on experience with the use of the API-ASME Code. This offshoot of the ASME Code, initiated in 1931, was formulated and published by the American Petroleum Institute (API) in cooperation with the ASME. It justified the 4:1 safety factor on the basis of certain quality and inspection controls not at that time incorporated in the ASME Code editions.

D-1.2.5 ASME Code Case Interpretations and Addenda are published between Code editions and normally become part of the Code in the new edition. Adherence to these is considered compliance with the Code. [*See 2-2.1.3(a).*]

D-2 Design of Containers for LP-Gas.

D-2.1 ASME Container Design.

D-2.1.1 When ASME containers were first used to store LP-Gas, the properties of the CP grades of the principal constituents were available, but the average properties for the commercial grades of propane and butane were not. Also there was no experience as to what temperatures and pressures to expect for product stored in areas with high atmospheric temperatures. A 200 psi (1.4 MPa) design pressure was deemed appropriate for propane [the CP grade of which has a vapor pressure of 176 psi (1.2 MPa) at 100°F (38°C) and 80 psi (0.6 MPa) for butane (CP grade has vapor pressure of 37 psi (0.6 MPa) at 100°F (38°C).] These containers were built with a 5:1 safety factor (*see D-1.2.3*).

D-2.1.2 Pressure vessel codes, following boiler pressure relief valve practice, require that the pressure relief valve start-to-leak setting be the design pressure of the container. In specifying pressure relief valve capacity, however, they stipulate that this relieving capacity be adequate to prevent the internal pressure from rising above 120 percent of the design pressure under fire exposure conditions.

D-2.1.3 Containers built in accordance with D-2.1.1 were entirely adequate for the commercial grades of the LP-Gases [the vapor pressure of propane at 100°F (38°C) is 205 psi (1.43 MPa); the vapor pressure of butane at 100°F (38°C) is 37 psi (0.26 MPa)]. However, as they were equipped with pressure relief valves set to start-to-leak at the design pressure of the container, these relief valves occasionally opened on an unusually warm day. Since any unnecessary release of a flammable gas is potentially dangerous, and giving weight to recommendations of fire prevention and insurance groups as well as to the favorable experience with API-ASME containers (*see D-2.2.1*), relief valve settings above the design pressure [up to 250 psi (1.7 MPa) for propane and 100 psi (0.7 MPa) for butane] were widely used.

D-2.1.4 In determining safe filling densities for compressed liquefied gases, DOT (ICC) uses the criterion that the container shall not become liquid full at the highest temperature the liquid may be expected to reach due to the normal atmospheric conditions to which the container may be exposed. For containers of more than 1,200 gal (4.5 m^3) water capacity, the liquid temperature selected is 115°F (46°C). The vapor pressure of the gas to be contained at 115°F (46°C) is specified by DOT as the minimum design pressure for the container. The vapor pressure of CP propane at 115°F (46°C) is 211 psig (1.4 MPa gauge), and of commercial propane, 243 psig (1.5 MPa gauge). The vapor pressure of both normal butane and commercial butane at 115°F (46°C) is 51 psig (0.4 MPa gauge).

D-2.1.5 The ASME *Boiler and Pressure Vessel Code* editions generally applicable to LP-Gas containers, and the design pressures, safety factors and exceptions to these editions for LP-Gas use, are shown in Table D-2.1.5. These reflect the use of the information in D-2.1.1 through D-2.1.4.

D-2.2 API-ASME Container Design.

D-2.2.1 The API-ASME Code was first published in 1931 (*see D-2.1.4*). Based on petroleum industry experience using certain material quality and inspection controls not at that time incorporated in the ASME Code, the 4:1 safety factor

Table D-2.1.5

Year ASME Code Edition Published	Design Pressure, psi (Pascals) Butane	Propane	Safety Factor
1931 through 46[2]	100[1] (0.7)	200 (1.4)	5:1
1949 Par. U-68 & U-69[2]	100 (0.7)	200 (1.4)	5:1
1949 Par. U-200 & U-201[2]	125 (0.9)	250 (1.7)	4:1
1952 through 80	125 (0.9)	250[3] (1.7)	4:1

[1]Until December 31, 1947, containers designed for 80 psi (0.6 MPa) under prior (5:1 safety factor) codes were authorized for butane. Since that time, either 100 psi (0.7 MPa) (under prior codes) or 125 psi (0.9 MPa) (under present codes) is required.

[2]Containers constructed in accordance with 1949 and prior editions of the ASME Code were not required to be in compliance with paragraphs U-2 to U-10 inclusive, or with paragraph U-19. Construction in accordance with paragraph U-70 of these editions was not authorized.

[3]Higher design pressure [312.5 psi (2.2 MPa)] is required for small ASME containers used for vehicular installations (such as forklift trucks used in buildings or those installed in enclosed spaces) because they may be exposed to higher temperatures and consequently develop higher internal pressure.

Table D-2.3.1 Vapor Pressure, Design Pressures and Container Type

As Shown in Table 2-2.2.2: Maximum Vapor Press. at 100°F (37.8°C)	Design Press. Present ASME Code[1]	Design Press. Earlier Codes: API-ASME	ASME[2]	Container Type
80 (.6)	100 (.7)	100 (.7)	80 (.6)	80 (.6)
100 (.7)	125 (.9)	125 (.9)	100 (.7)	100 (.7)
125 (.9)	156 (1.1)	156 (1.1)	125 (.9)	125 (.9)
150 (1.0)	187 (1.3)	187 (1.3)	150 (1.0)	150 (1.0)
175 (1.2)	219 (1.5)	219 (1.5)	175 (1.2)	175 (1.2)
215 (1.5)	250 (1.7)	250 (1.7)	200 (1.4)	200 (1.4)
215 (1.5)	312.5 (2.2)	312.5 (2.2)	—	250 (1.7)

[1]ASME Code edition for 1949, Par. U-200 and U-201 and all later editions (*See D-2.1.5*).

[2]All ASME Codes up to the 1946 edition and paragraphs U-68 and U-69 of the 1949 edition (*See D-2.1.5*).

was first used. Many LP-Gas containers were built under this code with design pressures of 125 psi (0.9 MPa) [100 psi (0.7 MPa) until December 31, 1947] for butane and 250 psi (1.7 MPa) for propane. Containers constructed in accordance with the API-ASME Code were not required to comply with Section 1, or the appendix to Section 1. Paragraphs W-601 through W-606 of the 1943 and earlier editions were not applicable to LP-Gas containers.

D-2.2.2 The ASME Code, by changing from the 5:1 to the 4:1 safety factor through consideration of the factors described in D-2.1.1 through D-2.1.4, became nearly identical in effect to the API-ASME Code by the 1950's. Thus, the API-ASME Code was phased out and construction was not authorized after July 1, 1961.

D-2.3 Design Criteria for LP-Gas Containers.

D-2.3.1 To prevent confusion in earlier editions of NFPA 58, the nomenclature "container type" was used to designate the design pressure of the container to be used for various types of LP-Gases. With the adoption of the 4:1 safety factor in the ASME Code and the phasing out of the API-ASME Code, the need for "container type" ceased to exist. Table D-2.3.1 makes it possible to compare older containers which may have carried this designation with the new containers complying with 2-2.2.2 and Table 2-2.2.2 in this standard.

D-2.4 DOT (ICC) Specifications Utilizing ASME or API-ASME Containers.

D-2.4.1 DOT (ICC) Specifications for portable tank containers and cargo tanks require ASME or API-ASME construction for the container proper (*see D-1.1.2*). Several such specifications were written by the ICC prior to 1967 and DOT has continued this practice.

D-2.4.2 ICC Specifications written prior to 1946, and to some extent through 1952, used ASME containers with a 200 psig (1.4 MPa gauge) design pressure for propane and 80 psig (0.6 MPa gauge) for butane [100 psig (0.7 MPa gauge) after 1947] with a 5:1 safety factor. During this period and until 1961, ICC Specifications also permitted API-ASME containers with a 250 psig (1.7 MPa gauge) design pressure for propane and 100 psig (0.7 MPa gauge) for butane [125 psig (0.9 MPa gauge) after 1947].

D-2.4.3 To prevent any unnecessary release of flammable vapor during transportation (*see D-2.1.3*), the use of safety relief valve settings 25 percent above the design pressure was common for ASME 5:1 safety factor containers. To eliminate confusion, and in line with the good experience with API-ASME containers, the ICC permitted the rerating of these particular ASME containers used under its specifications to 125 percent of the originally marked design pressure.

D-2.4.4 DOT (ICC) Specifications applicable to portable tank containers and cargo tanks currently in use are listed in Table D-2.4.4. New construction is not permitted under the older specifications. However, these older containers may continue to be used provided they have been maintained in accordance with DOT (ICC) regulations.

Table D-2.4.4

Spec. Number	ASME Construction: Design Pressure, psig Propane	Butane	Safety Factor	API-ASME Construction: Design Pressure, psig Propane	Butane	Safety Factor
ICC-50[1]	200[3]	100[3]	5:1	250	125	4:1
ICC-51[1]	250	125	4:1	250	125	4:1
MC-320[2, 4]	200[3]	100[3]	5:1	250	125	4:1
MC-330[2]	250	125	4:1	250	125	4:1
MC-331[2]	250	125	4:1	250	125	4:1

[1]Portable Tank Container.
[2]Cargo Tank.
[3]Permitted to be rerated to 125 percent of original ASME Design Pressure.
[4]Require DOT Exemption.

For SI Units
100 psig = 0.7 MPa gauge; 125 psig = 0.9 MPa gauge; 200 psig = 1.4 MPa gauge; 250 psig = 1.7 MPa gauge

D-3 Underground ASME or API-ASME Containers.

D-3.1 Use of Containers Underground.

D-3.1.1 ASME or API-ASME containers are used for underground or partially underground installation in accordance with 3-2.3.8 or 3-2.3.9. The temperature of the soil is normally low so that the average liquid temperature and vapor pressure of product stored in underground containers will be lower than in aboveground containers. This lower operating pressure provides a substantial corrosion allowance for underground containers.

D-3.1.2 Containers listed to be used interchangeably for either installation aboveground or underground must comply as to pressure relief valve rated relieving capacity and filling density with aboveground provisions when installed aboveground [*see 2-3.2.4(a)*]. When installed underground the pressure relief valve rated relieving capacity and filling density may be in accordance with underground provisions (*see E-2.3.1*), provided all other underground installation provisions are met. Partially underground containers are considered as aboveground insofar as loading density and pressure relief valve rated relieving capacity are concerned.

Appendix E Pressure Relief Devices

This Appendix is not a part of the requirements of this NFPA document, but is included for information purposes only.

(This Appendix contains non-NFPA mandated provisions.)

E-1 Pressure Relief Devices for DOT (ICC) Cylinders.

E-1.1 Source of Provisions for Relief Devices.

E-1.1.1 The requirements for relief devices on DOT cylinders are established by the Bureau of Explosives with DOT approval. Complete technical information as to these requirements will be found in the Compressed Gas Association (CGA) Pamphlet S-1.1, Pressure-Relief Device Standards, Part 1—*Cylinders for Compressed Gases.*

E-1.2 Essential Requirements of LP-Gas Cylinder Relief Devices.

E-1.2.1 CGA Pamphlet S-1.1 provides that LP-Gas cylinders shall be equipped with fusible plugs, spring-loaded pressure relief valves, or a combination of the two. Fusible plugs are not permitted on cylinders used in certain vehicular installations [*see 3-6.2.3(a)(4)*]. The provisions of E-1.2.2 through E-1.2.4 outline the generally accepted industry practice in the use of fusible plugs and safety pressure devices on LP-Gas cylinders.

E-1.2.2 If fusible plugs constitute the only relief devices the plugs used shall comply with the flow capacity requirements of CGA S-1.1 with a nominal melting or yield point of 165°F (74°C) [not less than 157°F (69°C) nor more than 170°F (77°C)]. For cylinders over 30 in. (0.8 m) long (exclusive of neck), a plug is required in each end of the cylinder.

E-1.2.3 If a spring-loaded pressure relief valve(s) constitutes the only relief device, the valves used shall comply with the flow capacity requirements of CGA S-1.1, with the set pressure not less than 75 percent nor more than 100 percent of the minimum required test pressure of the cylinder. For example, the test pressure for a 240 psig (1.6 MPa gauge) service pressure is 480 psig (3.2 MPa gauge); 75 percent of this is 360 psig (2.5 MPa gauge). In practice, such valves are set at 375 psig (2.6 MPa gauge).

E-1.2.4 If fusible plugs and spring-loaded pressure relief valves are used in combination, this combined use shall be in accordance with CGA S-1.1, or in substance as follows:

(a) If 100 percent of the relief device capacity is provided by the pressure relief valve, the supplementary fuse plug may be of any convenient size provided the total plug area does not exceed 0.25 sq in. (1.6 cm^2), and may have a melting point of more than 170°F (77°C) [usually a nominal yield point of 212°F (100°C), with the upper limit not to exceed 220°F (104°C)]. Combination devices are required at one end of a cylinder only, or may be separated and installed at opposite ends.

(b) If at least 70 percent of the relief device capacity is provided by the pressure relief valve, the balance of the capacity requirement shall be supplied by a 165°F (74°C) nominal yield point fusible plug in accordance with E-1.2.2. Combined devices are required at one end of a cylinder only or may be separated and installed at opposite ends.

E-2 Pressure Relief Devices for ASME Containers.

E-2.1 Source of Provisions for Relief Devices.

E-2.1.1 Capacity requirements for relief devices are in accordance with the applicable provisions of Compressed Gas Association (CGA) Pamphlet S-1.2, Pressure-Relief Device Standards, Part 2—*Cargo and Portable Tanks for Compressed Gases*; or with CGA Pamphlet S-1.3, Safety Relief-Device Standards, Part 3—*Compressed Gas Storage Containers.*

E-2.2 Spring-Loaded Pressure Relief Valves for Aboveground and Cargo Containers.

E-2.2.1 The minimum rate of discharge for spring-loaded pressure relief valves is based on the outside surface of the containers on which the valves are installed. Paragraph 2-2.6.5(g) provides that new containers shall be marked with the surface area in sq ft. The surface area of containers not so marked (or not legibly marked) may be computed by use of the applicable formula:

(a) Cylindrical container with hemispherical heads:

Surface area = overall length × outside diameter × 3.1416.

(b) Cylindrical container with other than hemispherical heads:

Surface area = (overall length + 0.3 outside diameter) × outside diameter × 3.1416.

NOTE: This formula is not precise, but will give results with limits of practical accuracy in sizing relief valves.

(c) Spherical containers:

Surface area = outside diameter squared × 3.1416.

E-2.2.2 The minimum required relieving capacity in cu ft per minute of air at 120 percent of the maximum permitted start-to-leak pressure (or Flow Rate CFM Air), under standard conditions of 60°F (16°C) and atmospheric pressure [14.7 psia (0.1 MPa absolute)], shall be as shown in Table E-2.2.2 for the surface area in sq ft of the container on which the pressure relief valve is to be installed. The flow rate may be interpolated for intermediate values of surface area. For containers with a total outside surface area exceeding 2,000 sq ft, the required flow rate shall be calculated, using the formula: Flow Rate CFM Air = $53.632 \times A^{0.82}$ where A = total outside surface area of container in sq ft.

Table E-2.2.2

Surface Area Sq. Ft.	Flow Rate CFM Air	Surface Area Sq. Ft.	Flow Rate CFM Air	Surface Area Sq. Ft.	Flow Rate CFM Air
20 or less	626	170	3620	600	10170
25	751	175	3700	650	10860
30	872	180	3790	700	11550
35	990	185	3880	750	12220
40	1100	190	3960	800	12880
45	1220	195	4050	850	13540
50	1330	200	4130	900	14190
55	1430	210	4300	950	14830
60	1540	220	4470	1000	15470
65	1640	230	4630	1050	16100
70	1750	240	4800	1100	16720
75	1850	250	4960	1150	17350
80	1950	260	5130	1200	17960
85	2050	270	5290	1250	18570
90	2150	280	5450	1300	19180
95	2240	290	5610	1350	19780
100	2340	300	5760	1400	20380
105	2440	310	5920	1450	20980
110	2530	320	6080	1500	21570
115	2630	330	6230	1550	22160
120	2720	340	6390	1600	22740
125	2810	350	6540	1650	23320
130	2900	360	6690	1700	23900
135	2990	370	6840	1750	24470
140	3080	380	7000	1800	25050
145	3170	390	7150	1850	25620
150	3260	400	7300	1900	26180
155	3350	450	8040	1950	26750
160	3440	500	8760	2000	27310
165	3530	550	9470		

E-2.3 Spring-Loaded Pressure Relief Valves for Underground or Mounded Containers.

E-2.3.1 In the case of containers installed underground or mounded, the pressure relief valve relieving capacities may be as small as 30 percent of those specified in Table D-2.2.2 provided the container is empty of liquid when installed, that no liquid is placed in it until it is completely covered with earth, and that it is not uncovered for removal until all liquid has been removed.

E-2.3.2 Containers partially underground must have pressure relief valve relieving capacitites in accordance with 2-3.2.4.

E-2.4 Provisions for Fusible Plugs.

E-2.4.1 Fusible plugs, supplementing spring-loaded pressure relief valves, and complying with 2-3.2.4(e), are permitted only with aboveground stationary containers of 1,200 gal (4.5 m^3) or less water capacity. They shall not be used on larger containers nor on portable or cargo containers of ASME construction. The total fusible plug discharge area is limited to 0.25 sq in. (1.6 cm^2) per container.

E-2.5 Pressure Relief Valve Testing.

E-2.5.1 Frequent testing of pressure relief valves on LP-Gas containers is not considered necessary for the following reasons:

(a) The LP-Gases are so-called "sweet gases" having no corrosive or other deleterious effect on the metal of the containers or relief valves.

(b) The relief valves are constructed of corrosion-resistant materials, and are installed so as to be protected against the weather. The variations of temperature and pressure due to atmospheric conditions are not sufficient to cause any permanent set in the valve springs.

(c) The required odorization of the LP-Gases makes escape almost instantly evident.

(d) Experience over the years with the storage of LP-Gases has shown a good safety record on the functioning of pressure relief valves.

E-2.5.2 Since no mechanical device can be expected to remain in operative condition indefinitely, it is suggested that the pressure relief valves on containers of more than 2,000 gal (7.6 m^3) water capacity be tested at approximately 10-year intervals. Some types of valves may be tested by the use of an external lifting device having an indicator to show the pressure equivalent at which the valve may be expected to open. Others must be removed from the container for testing, requiring that the container first be emptied.

Appendix F Liquid Volume Tables, Computations, and Graphs

This Appendix is not a part of the requirements of this NFPA document, but is included for information purposes only.

F-1 Scope.

F-1.1 Application.

F-1.1.1 This appendix explains the basis for Table 4-5.2.1, includes the LP-Gas liquid volume temperature correction table, Table F-3.1.3, and describes its use. It also explains the methods of making liquid volume computations to determine the maximum permissible LP-Gas content of containers in accordance with Tables 4-5.2.3(a), (b), and (c).

F-2 Basis for Determination of LP-Gas Container Capacity.

F-2.1 The basis for determination of the maximum permitted filling densities shown in Table 4-5.2.1 is the maximum safe quantity which will assure that the container will not become liquid full when the liquid is at the highest anticipated temperature.

(a) For portable containers built to DOT specifications and other aboveground containers with water capacities of 1,200 gal (4.5 m^3) or less, this temperature is assumed to be 130°F (54°C).

(b) For other aboveground uninsulated containers with

water capacities in excess of 1,200 gal (4.5 m^3), including those built to DOT portable or cargo tank specifications, this temperature is assumed to be 115°F (46°C).

(c) For all containers installed underground, this temperature is assumed to be 105°F (41°C).

F-3 Liquid Volume Correction Table.

F-3.1 Correction of Observed Volume to Standard Temperature Condition (60°F and Equilibrium Pressure).

F-3.1.1 The volume of a given quantity of LP-Gas liquid in a container is directly related to its temperature, expanding as temperature increases and contracting as temperature decreases. Standard conditions, often used for weights and measures purposes and, in some cases, to comply with safety regulations, specify correction of the observed volume to what it would be at 60°F (16°C).

F-3.1.2 To correct the observed volume to 60°F (16°C), the specific gravity of LP-Gas at 60°F in relation to water at 60°F (16°C) (usually referred to as "60°F/60°F"), and its average temperature must be known. The specific gravity normally appears on the shipping papers. The average liquid temperature may be obtained as follows:

(a) Insert a thermometer in a thermometer well in the container into which the liquid has been transferred and read the temperature after the completion of the transfer [*see F-3.1.2(c) as to proper use of a thermometer*].

(b) If the container is not equipped with a well, but is essentially empty of liquid prior to loading, the temperature of the liquid in the container from which liquid is being withdrawn may be used. Otherwise, a thermometer may be inserted in a thermometer well or other temperature sensing device installed in the loading line at a point close to the container being loaded, reading temperatures at intervals during transfer and averaging. [*See F-3.1.2(c)*].

(c) A suitable liquid should be used in thermometer wells to obtain an efficient heat transfer from the LP-Gas liquid in the container to the thermometer bulb. The liquid used should be noncorrosive and should not freeze at the temperatures to which it will be subjected. Water should not be used.

F-3.1.3 The volume observed or measured is corrected to 60°F (16°C) by use of Table F-3.1.3. The column headings, across the top of the tabulation, list the range of specific gravities for the LP-Gases complying with 1-2.1.1. Specific gravities are shown from 0.500 to 0.590 by 0.010 increments, except that special columns are inserted for chemically pure propane, isobutane and normal butane. To obtain a correction factor, follow down the column for the specific gravity of the particular LP-Gas to the factor corresponding with the liquid temperature. Interpolation between the specific gravities and temperatures shown may be used if necessary.

F-3.2 Use of Liquid Volume Correction Factors, Table F-3.1.3.

F-3.2.1 To correct the observed volume in gal for any LP-Gas (the specific gravity and temperature of which is known) to gal at 60°F (16°C), Table F-3.1.3 is used as follows:

(a) Obtain the correction factor for the specific gravity and temperature as described in F-3.1.3.

(b) *Multiply* the gal observed by this correction factor to obtain the gal at 60°F (16°C).

EXAMPLE: A container has in it 4,055 gal of LP-Gas with a specific gravity of 0.560 at a liquid temperature of 75°F. The correction factors in the 0.560 column are 0.980 at 76°F and 0.983 at 74°F, or, interpolating, 0.9815 for 75°F. The volume of liquid at 60°F is 4,055 × 0.9815, or 3980 gal.

F-3.2.2 To determine the volume in gal of a particular LP-Gas at temperature "t" to correspond with a given number of gal at 60°F (16°C), Table F-3.1.3 is used as follows:

(a) Obtain the correction factor for the LP-Gas, using the column for its specific gravity and reading the factor for temperature "t."

(b) *Divide* the number of gal at 60°F (16°C) by this correction factor to obtain the volume at temperature "t."

EXAMPLE: It is desired to pump 800 gal at 60°F into a container. The LP-Gas has a specific gravity of 0.510 and the liquid temperature is 44°F. The correction factor in the 0.510 column for 44°F is 1.025. Volume to be pumped at 44°F is 800 ÷ 1.025 = 780 gal.

F-4 Maximum Liquid Volume Computations.

F-4.1 Maximum Liquid LP-Gas Content of a Container at Any Given Temperature.

F-4.1.1 The maximum liquid LP-Gas content of any container depends upon the size of the container, whether it is installed aboveground or underground, the maximum permitted filling density and the temperature of the liquid [*see Tables 4-5.2.3(a), (b), and (c).*]

F-4.1.2 The maximum volume "V_t" (in percent of container capacity) of an LP-Gas at temperature "t," having a specific gravity "G" and a filling density of "L," is computed by use of the formula:

$$V_t = \frac{L}{G} \div F, \text{ or } V_t = \frac{L}{G \times F} \text{ where:}$$

V_t = percent of container capacity which may be filled with liquid

L = filling density

G = specific gravity of particular LP-Gas

F = correction factor to correct volume at temperature "t" to 60°F (16°C).

EXAMPLE 1: The maximum liquid content, in percent of container capacity, for an aboveground 500 gal water capacity container of an LP-Gas having a specific gravity of 0.550 and at a liquid temperature of 45°F is computed as follows:

From Table 4-5.2.1, L = 0.47, and from Table F-3.1.3, °F = 1.019.

$$\text{Thus } V_{45} = \frac{0.47}{0.550 \times 1.019} = 0.838 \text{ (83\%), or 415 gallons.}$$

EXAMPLE 2: The maximum liquid content, in percent of container capacity, for an aboveground 30,000 gal water capacity container of LP-Gas having a specific gravity of 0.508 and at a liquid temperature of 80°F is computed as follows:

Table F-3.1.3 Liquid Volume Correction Factors.

Observed Temperature Degrees Fahrenheit	SPECIFIC GRAVITIES AT 60° F./60° F.												
	0.500	Propane 0.5079	0.510	0.520	0.530	0.540	0.550	0.560	iso-Butane 0.5631	0.570	0.580	n-Butane 0.5844	0.590
	VOLUME CORRECTION FACTORS												
–50	1.160	1.155	1.153	1.146	1.140	1.133	1.127	1.122	1.120	1.116	1.111	1.108	1.106
–45	1.153	1.148	1.146	1.140	1.134	1.128	1.122	1.117	1.115	1.111	1.106	1.103	1.101
–40	1.147	1.142	1.140	1.134	1.128	1.122	1.117	1.111	1.110	1.106	1.101	1.099	1.097
–35	1.140	1.135	1.134	1.128	1.122	1.116	1.112	1.106	1.105	1.101	1.096	1.094	1.092
–30	1.134	1.129	1.128	1.122	1.116	1.111	1.106	1.101	1.100	1.096	1.092	1.090	1.088
–25	1.127	1.122	1.121	1.115	1.110	1.105	1.100	1.095	1.094	1.091	1.087	1.085	1.083
–20	1.120	1.115	1.114	1.109	1.104	1.099	1.095	1.090	1.089	1.086	1.082	1.080	1.079
–15	1.112	1.109	1.107	1.102	1.097	1.093	1.089	1.084	1.083	1.080	1.077	1.075	1.074
–10	1.105	1.102	1.100	1.095	1.091	1.087	1.083	1.079	1.078	1.075	1.072	1.071	1.069
– 5	1.098	1.094	1.094	1.089	1.085	1.081	1.077	1.074	1.073	1.070	1.067	1.066	1.065
0	1.092	1.088	1.088	1.084	1.080	1.076	1.073	1.069	1.068	1.066	1.063	1.062	1.061
2	1.089	1.086	1.085	1.081	1.077	1.074	1.070	1.067	1.066	1.064	1.061	1.060	1.059
4	1.086	1.083	1.082	1.079	1.075	1.071	1.068	1.065	1.064	1.062	1.059	1.058	1.057
6	1.084	1.080	1.080	1.076	1.072	1.069	1.065	1.062	1.061	1.059	1.057	1.055	1.054
8	1.081	1.078	1.077	1.074	1.070	1.066	1.063	1.060	1.059	1.057	1.055	1.053	1.052
10	1.078	1.075	1.074	1.071	1.067	1.064	1.061	1.058	1.057	1.055	1.053	1.051	1.050
12	1.075	1.072	1.071	1.068	1.064	1.061	1.059	1.056	1.055	1.053	1.051	1.049	1.048
14	1.072	1.070	1.069	1.066	1.062	1.059	1.056	1.053	1.053	1.051	1.049	1.047	1.046
16	1.070	1.067	1.066	1.063	1.060	1.056	1.054	1.051	1.050	1.048	1.046	1.045	1.044
18	1.067	1.065	1.064	1.061	1.057	1.054	1.051	1.049	1.048	1.046	1.044	1.043	1.042
20	1.064	1.062	1.061	1.058	1.054	1.051	1.049	1.046	1.046	1.044	1.042	1.041	1.040
22	1.061	1.059	1.058	1.055	1.052	1.049	1.046	1.044	1.044	1.042	1.040	1.039	1.038
24	1.058	1.056	1.055	1.052	1.049	1.046	1.044	1.042	1.042	1.040	1.038	1.037	1.036
26	1.055	1.053	1.052	1.049	1.047	1.044	1.042	1.039	1.039	1.037	1.036	1.036	1.034
28	1.052	1.050	1.049	1.047	1.044	1.041	1.039	1.037	1.037	1.035	1.034	1.034	1.032
30	1.049	1.047	1.046	1.044	1.041	1.039	1.037	1.035	1.035	1.033	1.032	1.032	1.030
32	1.046	1.044	1.043	1.041	1.038	1.036	1.035	1.033	1.033	1.031	1.030	1.030	1.028
34	1.043	1.041	1.040	1.038	1.036	1.034	1.032	1.031	1.030	1.029	1.028	1.028	1.026
36	1.039	1.038	1.037	1.035	1.033	1.031	1.030	1.028	1.028	1.027	1.025	1.025	1.024
38	1.036	1.035	1.034	1.032	1.031	1.029	1.027	1.026	1.025	1.025	1.023	1.023	1.022
40	1.033	1.032	1.031	1.029	1.028	1.026	1.025	1.024	1.023	1.023	1.021	1.021	1.020
42	1.030	1.029	1.028	1.027	1.025	1.024	1.023	1.022	1.021	1.021	1.019	1.019	1.018
44	1.027	1.026	1.025	1.023	1.022	1.021	1.020	1.019	1.019	1.018	1.017	1.017	1.016
46	1.023	1.022	1.022	1.021	1.020	1.018	1.018	1.017	1.016	1.016	1.015	1.015	1.014
48	1.020	1.019	1.019	1.018	1.017	1.016	1.015	1.014	1.014	1.013	1.013	1.013	1.012
50	1.017	1.016	1.016	1.015	1.014	1.013	1.013	1.012	1.012	1.011	1.011	1.011	1.010
52	1.014	1.013	1.012	1.012	1.011	1.010	1.010	1.009	1.009	1.009	1.009	1.009	1.008
54	1.010	1.010	1.009	1.009	1.008	1.008	1.007	1.007	1.007	1.007	1.006	1.006	1.006
56	1.007	1.007	1.006	1.006	1.005	1.005	1.005	1.005	1.005	1.005	1.004	1.004	1.004
58	1.003	1.003	1.003	1.003	1.003	1.003	1.002	1.002	1.002	1.002	1.002	1.002	1.002
60	1.000	1.000	1.000	1.000	1.000	1.000	1.000	1.000	1.000	1.000	1.000	1.000	1.000
62	0.997	0.997	0.997	0.997	0.997	0.997	0.997	0.998	0.998	0.998	0.998	0.998	0.998
64	0.993	0.993	0.994	0.994	0.994	0.994	0.995	0.995	0.995	0.995	0.996	0.996	0.996
66	0.990	0.990	0.990	0.990	0.991	0.992	0.992	0.993	0.993	0.993	0.993	0.993	0.993
68	0.986	0.986	0.987	0.987	0.988	0.989	0.990	0.990	0.990	0.990	0.991	0.991	0.991
70	0.983	0.983	0.984	0.984	0.985	0.986	0.987	0.988	0.988	0.988	0.989	0.989	0.989
72	0.979	0.980	0.981	0.981	0.982	0.983	0.984	0.985	0.986	0.986	0.987	0.987	0.987
74	0.976	0.976	0.977	0.978	0.980	0.980	0.982	0.983	0.983	0.984	0.985	0.985	0.985
76	0.972	0.973	0.974	0.975	0.977	0.978	0.979	0.980	0.981	0.981	0.982	0.982	0.983
78	0.969	0.970	0.970	0.972	0.974	0.975	0.977	0.978	0.978	0.979	0.980	0.980	0.981
80	0.965	0.967	0.967	0.969	0.971	0.972	0.974	0.975	0.976	0.977	0.978	0.978	0.979
82	0.961	0.963	0.963	0.966	0.968	0.969	0.971	0.972	0.973	0.974	0.976	0.976	0.977
84	0.957	0.959	0.960	0.962	0.965	0.966	0.968	0.970	0.971	0.972	0.974	0.974	0.975
86	0.954	0.956	0.956	0.959	0.961	0.964	0.966	0.967	0.968	0.969	0.971	0.971	0.972
88	0.950	0.952	0.953	0.955	0.958	0.961	0.963	0.965	0.966	0.967	0.969	0.969	0.970
90	0.946	0.949	0.949	0.952	0.955	0.958	0.960	0.962	0.963	0.964	0.967	0.967	0.968
92	0.942	0.945	0.946	0.949	0.952	0.955	0.957	0.959	0.960	0.962	0.964	0.965	0.966
94	0.938	0.941	0.942	0.946	0.949	0.952	0.954	0.957	0.958	0.959	0.962	0.962	0.964
96	0.935	0.938	0.939	0.942	0.946	0.949	0.952	0.954	0.955	0.957	0.959	0.960	0.961
98	0.931	0.934	0.935	0.939	0.943	0.946	0.949	0.952	0.953	0.954	0.957	0.957	0.959
100	0.927	0.930	0.932	0.936	0.940	0.943	0.946	0.949	0.950	0.952	0.954	0.955	0.957
105	0.917	0.920	0.923	0.927	0.931	0.935	0.939	0.943	0.943	0.946	0.949	0.949	0.951
110	0.907	0.911	0.913	0.918	0.923	0.927	0.932	0.936	0.937	0.939	0.943	0.944	0.946
115	0.897	0.902	0.904	0.909	0.915	0.920	0.925	0.930	0.930	0.933	0.937	0.938	0.940
120	0.887	0.892	0.894	0.900	0.907	0.912	0.918	0.923	0.924	0.927	0.931	0.932	0.934
125	0.876	0.881	0.884	0.890	0.898	0.903	0.909	0.916	0.916	0.920	0.925	0.927	0.928
130	0.865	0.871	0.873	0.880	0.888	0.895	0.901	0.908	0.909	0.913	0.918	0.921	0.923
135	0.854	0.861	0.863	0.871	0.879	0.887	0.894	0.901	0.902	0.907	0.912	0.914	0.916
140	0.842	0.850	0.852	0.861	0.870	0.879	0.886	0.893	0.895	0.900	0.905	0.907	0.910

From Table 4-5.2.1, L = 0.45, and from Table F-3.1.3, °F = 0.967.

$$\text{Thus } V_{80} = \frac{0.45}{0.508 \times 0.967} = 0.915\ (91\%), \text{ or } 27{,}300 \text{ gallons.}$$

F-4.2 Alternate Method of Filling Containers.

F-4.2.1 Containers equipped only with fixed maximum level gauges or only with variable liquid level gauges, when temperature determinations are not practical, may be filled with either gauge provided the fixed maximum liquid level gauge is installed, or the variable gauge is set, to indicate the volume equal to the maximum permitted filling density as provided in 4-5.3.3(a). This level is computed on the basis that the liquid temperature will be 40°F (4°C) for aboveground containers, or 50°F (10°C) for underground containers.

F-4.2.2 The percentage of container capacity which may be filled with liquid is computed by use of the formula shown in F-4.1.2, substituting the appropriate values as follows:

$$V_t = \frac{L}{G \times F}, \text{ where:}$$

t = the liquid temperature. Assumed to be 40°F (4°C) for aboveground containers or 50°F (10°C) for underground containers.

L = the loading density obtained from Table 4-5.2.1 for:

(a) the specific gravity of the LP-Gas to be contained.

(b) the method of installation, aboveground or underground, and if aboveground, then:

(1) for containers of 1,200 gal (4.5 m^3) water capacity or less.

(2) for containers of more than 1,200 gal (4.5 m^3) water capacity.

G = the specific gravity of the LP-Gas to be contained.

F = the correction factor. Obtained from Table F-3.1.3, using G and 40°F (4°C) for aboveground containers or 50°F (10°C) for underground containers.

EXAMPLE: The maximum volume of LP-Gas with a specific gravity of 0.550 which may be in a 1,000 gal water capacity aboveground container which is filled by use of a fixed maximum liquid level gauge is computed as follows:

t is 40°F for an aboveground container.

L for 0.550 specific gravity, and an aboveground container of less than 1,200 gal water capacity, from Table 4-5.2.1, is 47 percent.

G is 0.550.

F for 0.550 specific gravity at 40°F from Table F-3.1.3 is 1.025.

$$\text{Thus } V_{40} = \frac{.47}{0.550 \times 1.025} = 0.834\ (83\%), \text{ or } 830 \text{ gallons.}$$

F-4.2.3 Percentage values, such as in the example in F-4.2.2, are rounded off to the next lower full percentage point, or to 83 percent in this example.

F-4.3 Location of Fixed Maximum Liquid Level Gauges in Containers.

F-4.3.1 Due to the diversity of fixed liquid gauges, and the many sizes (from DOT cylinders to 120,000 gal (454 m^3) ASME vessels) and types (vertical, horizontal, cylindrical and spherical) of containers in which gauges are installed, it is not possible to tabulate the liquid levels such gauges should indicate for the maximum permitted filling densities [*see Table 4-5.2.1 and 4-5.3.3(a)*].

F-4.3.2 The percentage of container capacity which these gauges should indicate is computed by use of the formula in F-4.1.2. The liquid level this gauge should indicate is obtained by applying this percentage to the water capacity of the container in gal [water at 60°F (16°C)], then using the strapping table for the container (obtained from its manufacturer) to determine the liquid level for this gallonage. If such a table is not available, this liquid level is computed from the internal dimensions of the container, using data from engineering handbooks.

F-4.3.3 The formula of F-4.1.2 is used to determine the maximum LP-Gas liquid content of a container to comply with Table 4-5.2.1 and 4-5.3.3(a), as follows:

$$\text{Volumetric percentage, or } V_t = \frac{L}{G \times F}, \text{ and}$$

Volume in Gallons = V_t × Container Gallons Water Capacity, or

Vol. in Gal. at t =

$$\frac{\text{L (Table 4-5.2.1)} \times \text{Container Gallons Water Capacity}}{\text{G (Spec. Grav.)} \times \text{F (For G and at temperature t)}}$$

EXAMPLE 1: Assume a 100 gal water capacity container for underground storage of propane with a specific gravity of 0.510. From Table 4-5.2.1, L = 46 percent; from 4-5.3.3(a), t = 50°F; and from Table F-3.1.3, °F for 0.510 specific gravity and a temperature of 50°F is 1.016; or

$$\text{Vol. in Gal. at 50°F} = \frac{.46 \times 100}{0.510 \times 1.016} = 88.7 \text{ gallons.}$$

EXAMPLE 2: Assume an 18,000 gal water capacity container for aboveground storage of a mixture with a specific gravity of 0.550. From Table 4-5.2.1, L = 50 percent; from 4-5.3.3(a), t = 40°F; and from Table F-3.1.3, °F for 0.550 specific gravity and 40°F temperature is 1.025; or

$$\text{Vol. in Gal. at 40°F} = \frac{.50 \times 18{,}000}{0.550 \times 1.025} = 15{,}950 \text{ gallons.}$$

Appendix G Wall Thickness of Copper Tubing

This Appendix is not a part of the requirements of this NFPA document, but is included for information purposes only.

Table G-1 Wall Thickness of Copper Tubing
(Specification for Copper Water Tube, ASTM B 88)

Standard Size Inches	Nominal OD Inches	Nominal Wall Thickness Inches	
		Type K	Type L
¼	0.375	0.035	0.030
⅜	0.500	0.049	0.035
½	0.625	0.049	0.040
⅝	0.750	0.049	0.042
¾	0.875	0.065	0.045

Table G-2 Wall Thickness of Copper Tubing
(Specification for Seamless Copper Tube for Air Conditioning and Refrigeration Field Service, ASTM B 280)

Standard Size Inches	Outside Diam. Inches	Wall Thickness Inches
¼	0.250	0.030
5/16	0.312	0.032
⅜	0.375	0.032
½	0.500	0.032
⅝	0.625	0.035
¾	0.750	0.042
⅞	0.875	0.045

Appendix H Procedure for Torch Fire and Hose Stream Testing of Thermal Insulating Systems for LP-Gas Containers

This Appendix is not a part of the requirements of this NFPA document, but is included for information purposes only.

A. Performance Standard. Thermal protection insulating systems, proposed for use on LP-Gas containers as a means of "Special Protection" under paragraph 3-10.3.1, are required to undergo thermal performance testing as a precondition for acceptance. The intent of this testing procedure is to identify insulation systems which retard or prevent the release of the container's contents in a fire environment of a 50 minute duration; and which will resist a concurrent hose stream of a 10 minute duration.

B. Reference Test Standards. The testing procedure described herein was taken with some modification from segments of the two following test standards:

1. *Code of Federal Regulations* - Title 49, Part 179.105-4, "Thermal Protection."

2. National Fire Code - NFPA 252, *Standard Methods of Fire Tests of Door Assemblies*, Chapter 4, Part 4-3 "Hose Stream Test."

C. Thermal Insulation Test.

1. A torch fire environment shall be created in the following manner:

(i) The source of the simulated torch shall be a hydrocarbon fuel. The flame temperature from the simulated torch shall be 2,200°F ± 100°F (1200°C ± 56°C) throughout the duration of the test. Torch velocities shall be 40 miles per hour ± 10 miles per hour (64 km/h ± 16 km/h) throughout the duration of the test.

(ii) An uninsulated square steel plate with thermal properties equivalent to ASME pressure vessel steel shall be used. The plate dimensions shall be not less than 4 feet by 4 feet (1.2 m × 1.2 m) by nominal ⅝ in. (16 mm) thick. The plate shall be instrumented with not less than 9 thermocouples to record the thermal response of the plate. The thermocouples shall be attached to the surface not exposed to the simulated torch, and shall be divided into 9 equal squares with a thermocouple placed in the center of each square.

(iii) The steel-plate holder shall be constructed in such a manner that the only heat transfer to the back side of the plate is by heat conduction through the plate and not by other heat paths. The apex of the flame shall be directed at the center of the plate.

(iv) Before exposure to the torch fire, none of the temperature recording devices shall indicate a plate temperature in excess of 100°F (38°C) or less than 32°F (0°C).

(v) A minimum of two thermocouples shall indicate 800°F (427°C) in a time of 4.0 ± 0.5 minutes of torch fire exposure.

2. A thermal insulation system shall be tested in the torch fire environment described in paragraph (1) of this section in the following manner:

(i) The thermal insulation system shall cover one side of a steel plate identical to that used under paragraph C.1.(ii) of this section.

(ii) The back of the steel plate shall be instrumented with not less than 9 thermocouples placed as described in paragraph C.1.(ii) of this section to record the thermal response of the steel.

(iii) Before exposure to the torch fire, none of the thermocouples on the thermal insulation system steel plate configuration shall indicate a plate temperature in excess of 100°F (38°C) or less than 32°F (0°C).

(iv) The entire outside surface of the thermal insulation system shall be exposed to the torch fire environment.

(v) A torch fire test shall be run for a minimum of 50 minutes. The thermal insulation system shall retard the heat flow to the steel plates so that none of the thermocouples on the uninsulated side of the steel plate indicates a plate temperature in excess of 800°F (427°C).

D. Hose Stream Resistance Test.

1. After 20 minutes exposure to the torch test, the test sample shall be hit with a hose stream concurrently with the torch for a period of 10 minutes. The hose stream test shall be conducted in the following manner:

(i) The stream shall be directed first at the middle and then at all parts of the exposed surface, making changes in direction slowly.

(ii) The hose stream shall be delivered through a 2 ½ inch (64 mm) hose discharging through a National Standard Playpipe of corresponding size equipped with 1 ⅛ in. (29 mm) discharge tip of the standard-taper smooth-bore pattern without shoulder at the orifice. The water pressure at the base of the nozzle and for the duration of the test shall be 30 psi (207 kPa). (Estimated delivery rate is 205 gallons (776 l/min) per minute.)

(iii) The tip of the nozzle shall be located 20 ft (6 m) from and on a line normal to the center of the test specimen. If impossible to be so located, the nozzle may be on a line deviating not to exceed 30 degrees from the line normal to the center of the test specimen. When so located the distance from the center shall be less than 20 ft (6 m) by an amount equal to 1 ft (0.3 m) for each 10 degrees of deviation from the normal.

(iv) Subsequent to the application of the hose stream, the torching shall continue until any thermocouple on the uninsulated side of the steel plate indicates a plate temperature in excess of 800°F (427°C).

(v) The thermal insulation system shall be judged to be resistant to the action of the hose stream if the time from initiation of torching for any thermocouple on the uninsulated side of the steel plate to reach in excess of 800°F (427°C) is 50 minutes or greater.

(vi) One (1) successful combination torch fire and hose stream test shall be required for certification.

Appendix I Container Spacing

This Appendix is not a part of the requirements of this NFPA document, but is included for information purposes only.

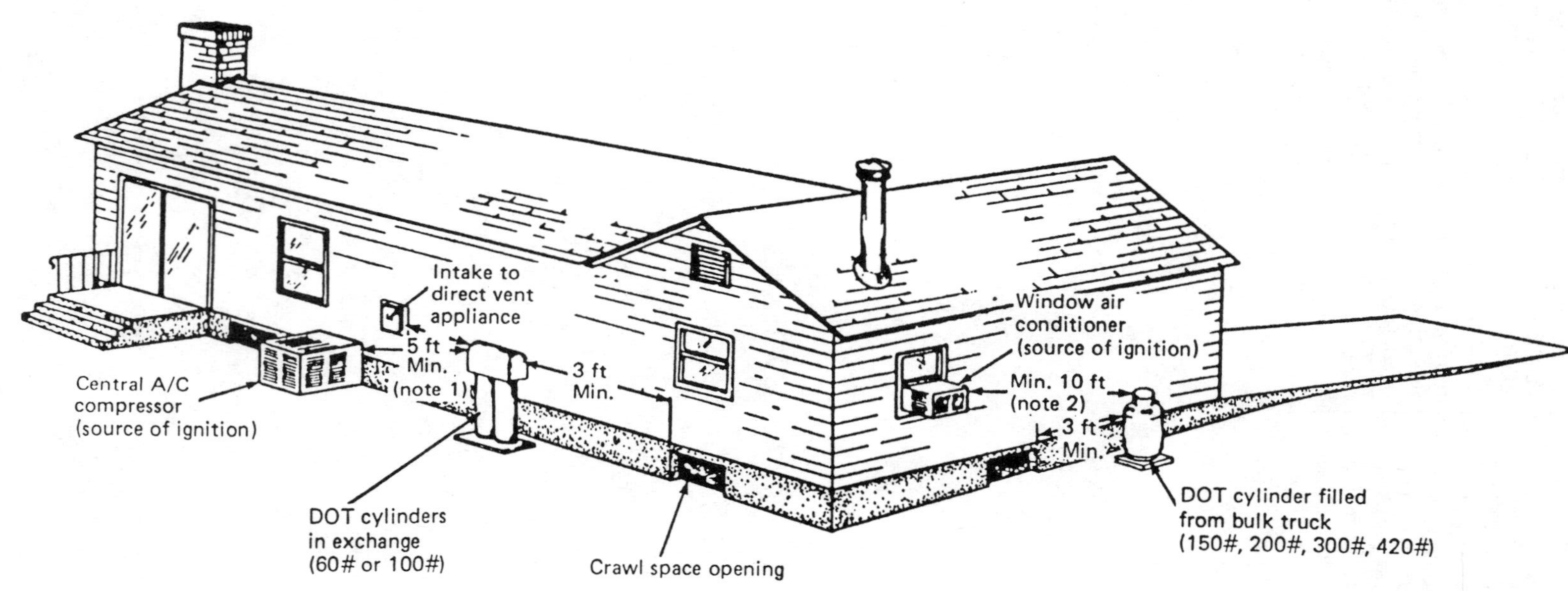

NOTE 1: 5 ft minimum between relief valve discharge and external source of ignition (air conditioner), direct vent, or mechanical ventilation system (attic fan).

NOTE 2: If the DOT cylinder is filled on-site from a bulk truck, the filling connection and vent valve must be at least 10 ft from any external source of ignition, direct vent, or mechanical ventilation system.

(For SI Units: 1 ft = 0.3048 m)

Figure I-1 DOT Cylinders.

(This figure for illustrative purposes only; text shall govern.)

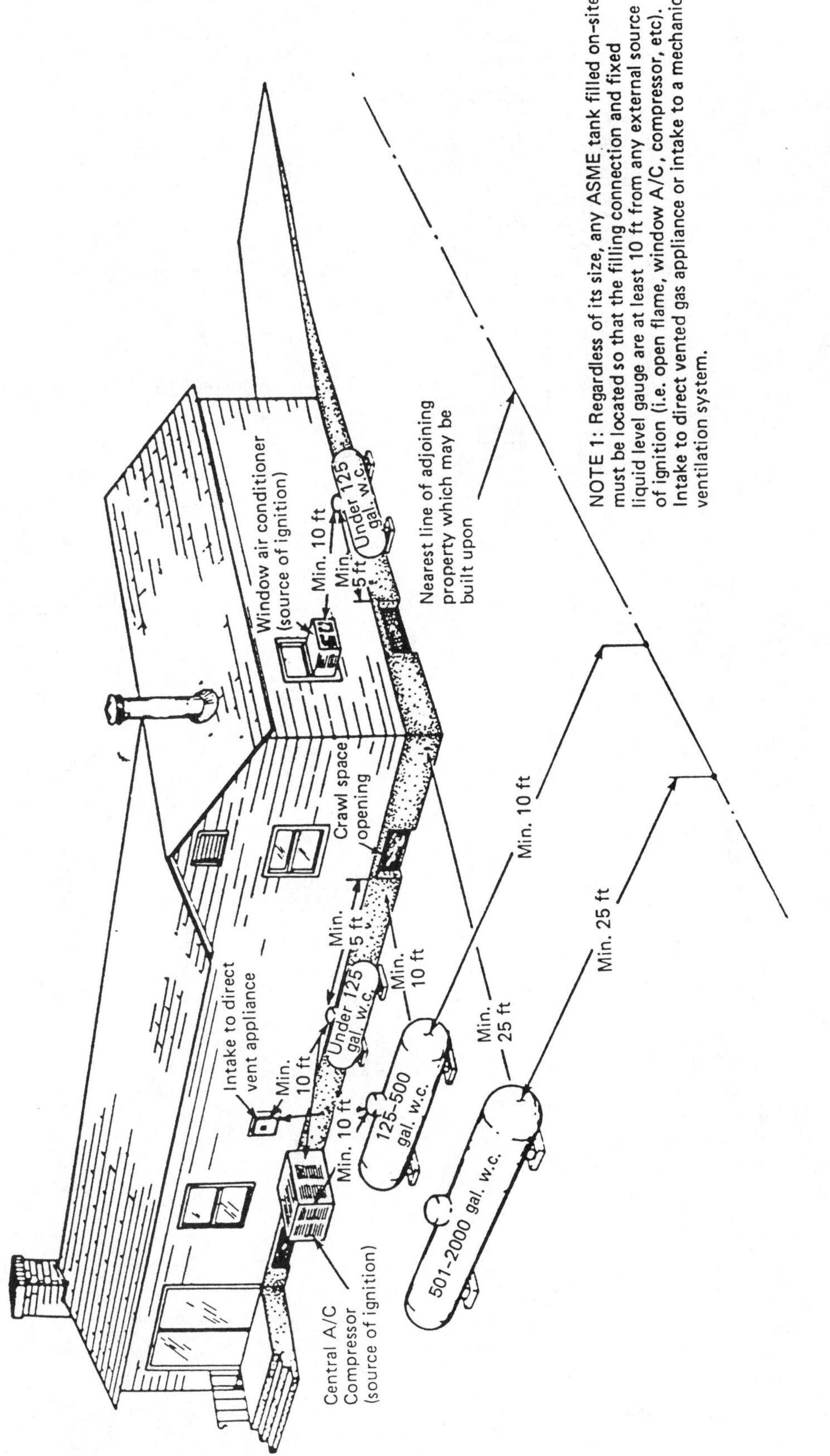

(For SI Units: 1 ft = 0.3048 m)

Figure I-2 Aboveground ASME Containers.

(This figure for illustrative purposes only; text shall govern.)

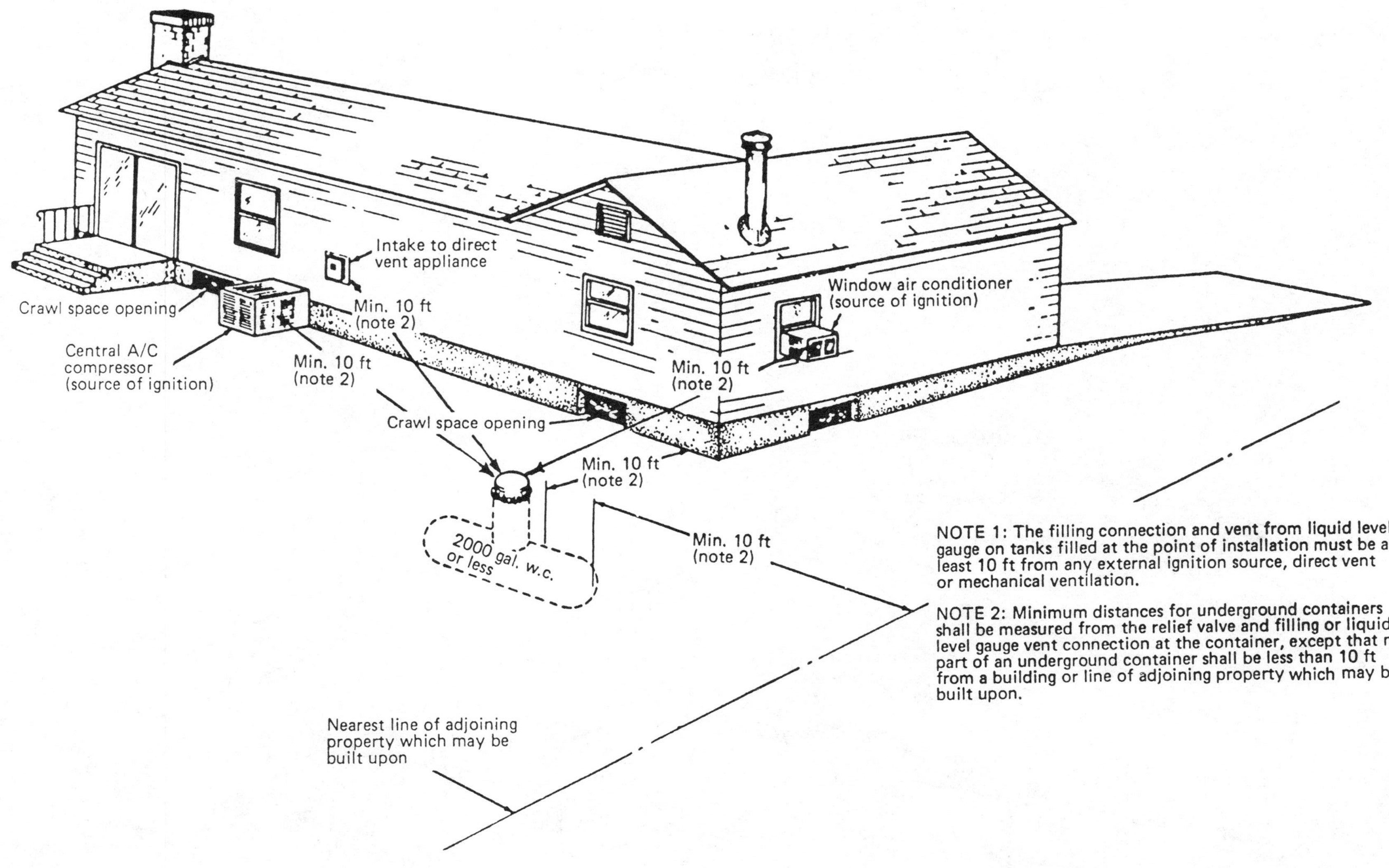
Intake to direct
vent appliance
Window air conditioner
(source of ignition)
Crawl space opening
Central A/C
compressor
(source of ignition)
Min. 10 ft
(note 2)
Min. 10 ft
(note 2)
Min. 10 ft
(note 2)
Crawl space opening
Min. 10 ft
(note 2)
2000 gal. w.c.
or less
Min. 10 ft
(note 2)
Nearest line of adjoining
property which may be
built upon
NOTE 1: The filling connection and vent from liquid level gauge on tanks filled at the point of installation must be at least 10 ft from any external ignition source, direct vent or mechanical ventilation.
NOTE 2: Minimum distances for underground containers shall be measured from the relief valve and filling or liquid level gauge vent connection at the container, except that no part of an underground container shall be less than 10 ft from a building or line of adjoining property which may be built upon.

(For SI Units: 1 ft = 0.3048 m)

Figure I-3 Underground ASME Containers.

(This figure for illustrative purposes only; text shall govern.)

Appendix J Referenced Publications

J-1 The following documents or portions thereof are referenced within this standard for informational purposes only and thus are not considered part of the requirements of this document. The edition indicated for each reference is the current edition as of the date of the NFPA issuance of this document.

J-1.1 NFPA Publications. National Fire Protection Association, Batterymarch Park, Quincy, MA 02269.

NFPA 77-1988, *Recommended Practice on Static Electricity*

NFPA 78-1986, *Lightning Protection Code*

J-1.2 ASCE Publication. American Society of Civil Engineers, United Engineering Center, 345 East 47th St., New York, NY 10017.

ASCE *Manual and Report on Engineering Practice No. 56.*

J-1.3 ASTM Publication. American Society for Testing and Materials, 1916 Race St., Philadelphia, PA 19103.

ASTM D 1835-1982, *Specification for Liquefied Petroleum (LP) Gases.*

J-1.4 CGA Publication. Compressed Gas Association, Inc., 1235 Jefferson Davis Highway, Arlington, VA 22202.

CGA Pamphlet C-6-1984, *Standards for Visual Inspection of Steel Compressed Gas Cylinders.*

J-1.5 Federal Publications. National Technical Information Service, U.S. Dept. of Commerce, Springfield, VA 22161.

BERC/RI-77/1, September 1977, *New Look at Odorization Levels for Propane Gas,* United States Energy Research and Development Administration, Technical Information Center.

Code of Federal Regulations, Title 49, Part 195, Transportation of Hazardous Liquids by Pipeline.

J-1.6 GPA Publication. Gas Processors Association, 1812 First National Bank Bldg., Tulsa, OK 74103.

Liquefied Petroleum Gas Specifications for Test Methods Standard 2140.

J-1.7 NPGA Publications. National Propane Gas Association, 1301 W. 22nd St., Oak Brook, IL 60521.

NPGA 122-1970, *Recommendations for Prevention of Ammonia Contamination of LP-Gas.*

NPGA Safety Bulletin 118-1979, *Recommended Procedures for Visual Inspection and Requalification of DOT (ICC) Cylinders in LP-Gas Service.*

INDEX

—A—

—Q—

—R—

—S—

—T—

UNIFORM FIRE CODE STANDARD 88-1
CLASSIFICATION OF AEROSOL PRODUCTS

See Section 8801.1, *Uniform Fire Code*

SECTION 88.101 — SCOPE

Aerosol products shall be classified into three levels, identified as Level 1, Level 2 and Level 3 in accordance with this standard.

SECTION 88.102 — LIMITED APPLICATION DEFINITIONS

For the purpose of this standard, "chemical heat of combustion" is defined as follows:

CHEMICAL HEAT OF COMBUSTION is the amount of energy associated with the chemical reactions that generate carbon monoxide and carbon dioxide, and consume oxygen.

SECTION 88.103 — CLASSIFICATION

88.103.1 General. The fire hazard of an aerosol product is a function of the chemical heat of combustion. The chemical heat of combustion, ΔH_c, in kilojoules per gram (kJ/g), is a product of the theoretical heat of combustion and combustion efficiency. For an aerosol product that consists of a number of components, the chemical heat of combustion is the sum of the weight fraction of each component multiplied by the heat of combustion for each individual component.

$$\Delta H_c \text{ (Product)} = \Sigma\ [I\% \times \Delta H_c\ (I)]$$

WHERE:

$I\%$ = weight fraction of component I in the product.

ΔH_c = chemical heat of combustion, kJ/g.

$\Delta H_c(I)$ = chemical heat of combustion of component I, kJ/g.

When the chemical heat of combustion is not provided, the theoretical heat of combustion shall be used to classify the aerosol. When neither a chemical nor theoretical heat of combustion is provided, the value of 44.0 kJ/g shall be used for the purpose of aerosol classification.

88.103.2 Classification Method. Aerosol products shall be classified in accordance with Table 88-1-A.

TABLE 88-1-A—CLASSIFICATION OF AEROSOLS[1]

CHEMICAL HEAT OF COMBUSTION		AEROSOL CLASSIFICATION LEVEL
Greater than:	And Less than or Equal to:	
0	8,600 Btu/lb. (20 kJ/g)	1
8,600 Btu/lb. (20 kJ/g)	13,000 Btu/lb. (30 kJ/g)	2
13,000 Btu/lb. (30 kJ/g)	—	3

88.103.3 Selected Chemical Heats of Combustion. See Table 88-1-B for the chemical heats of combustion of selected chemicals.

TABLE 88-1-B—SELECTED CHEMICAL HEATS OF COMBUSTION

CHEMICAL NAME	CAS NUMBER	CHEMICAL HEAT OF COMBUSTION (ΔH_c) (kJ/g)
Acetone	67-64-1	27.7
Acrylic Resin	68122-72-5	[1]
Alkyd Resin	68122-72-5	[1]
Aluminum	7429-90-5	[1]
Asphalt	8052-42-4	22.7
Barium Sulfate	7727-43-7	0.0
Benzidine (yellow)	92-87-5	[1]
Butane	106-97-8	43.3
2-Butoxyethanol	111-76-2	29.6
Butyl Benzyl Phthalate	85-68-7	31.5
Calcium Carbonate	1317-65-3	0.0
Carbon Black	1333-86-4	[1]
Carbon Dioxide	124-38-9	0.0
1-Chloro-1,1-Difluoroethane (HCFC 142b)	75-68-3	3.3
Chromium Hydroxide	1308-14-1	0.0
Corn Oil	8001-30-7	35.3
Diacetone Alcohol	123-42-2	35.1
1,1-Dichloro-1-Fluoroethane	1717-00-6	2.9
Diethylene Glycol Methyl Ether	112-34-5	33.0
1,1-Difluoroethane (HFC 152a)	75-37-6	6.3
1,2-Dimethyoxyethane	110-71-4	25.9
Dimethyl Ether	115-10-6	26.5
Dipropylene Glycol Methyl Ether	34590-94-8	32.2
Ethanol	64-17-5	24.7
Ethanol (95.6% azetrope)	64-17-5	23.6
2-Ethoxyethanol	110-80-5	25.9

(Continued)

TABLE 88-1-B—SELECTED CHEMICAL HEATS OF COMBUSTION—(Continued)

CHEMICAL NAME	CAS NUMBER	CHEMICAL HEAT OF COMBUSTION (ΔH_c) (kJ/g)
2-Ethoxyethyl Acetate	111-15-9	30.9
Ethyl 3-Ethoxypropionate	763-69-9	32.0
Ethylbenzene	100-41-4	29.0
Ethylene Glycol	107-21-1	16.4
Ethylene Glycol Diacetate	111-55-7	32.0
Graphite	7782-42-5	[1]
Hexylene Glycol	107-41-5	28.5
Iron Oxide	1309-37-1	0.0
Isobutyl Alcohol	78-83-1	29.8
Isopropyl Acetate	108-21-4	25.5
Isopropyl Alcohol	67-63-0	27.4
Isopropyl Myristate	110-27-0	36.2
Isopropyl Palmitate	142-91-6	37.2
Kaolin Clay (Aluminum Silicate Hydroxide)	1332-58-7	0.0
Kerosene	8008-20-6	41.4
d-Limonene	5989-27-5	39.8
Magnesium Silicate (Talc)	14807-96-6	0.0
Methanol	67-56-1	19.0
1-Methoxy-2-Propanol Acetate	108-65-6	30.9
Methyl Ethyl Ketone	78-93-3	30.6
Methyl Isopropyl Ketone	563-80-4	31.1
Methyl n-Amyl Ketone	110-43-0	35.0
Methylene Chloride	75-09-2	2.1
2-Methylpropane (Isobutane)	75-28-5	42.8
Mica (Mica Silicate)	12001-26-2	0.0
Mineral Oil	8012-95-1	31.5
Mineral Spirits (Petroleum Distillate)	64742-47-8	41.2
Mineral Spirits (Petroleum Distillate)	64742-88-7	41.2
N, N-Diethyl-m-Toluamide (DEET)	134-62-3	28.2
n-Butyl Acetate	123-86-4	27.6
n-Heptane	142-82-5	41.0
n-Hexane	110-54-3	41.1
n-Octyl Bicycloheptane Dicarboximide	113-48-4	30.0
Naptha, High Flash	8052-41-3	41.2
Naptha, Petroleum Distillate	8030-30-6	41.2
Naptha, VM&P (Petroleum Distillate)	64742-95-6	41.2
Naptha, VM&P (Petroleum Distillate)	64742-48-9	41.2
Naptha, VM&P (Petroleum Distillate)	64742-94-5	41.2
Nitrogen	7727-37-9	0.0
Paraffin (Wax)	8002-74-2	[1]
Pentane	109-66-0	41.9
Perchloroethylene (Tetrachloroethylene)	127-18-4	[1]
Petroleum Distillate	64741-65-7	41.2
Phthalocyanine Blue	147-14-8	[1]
Phthalocyanine Green	1328-53-6	[1]
Piperonyl Butoxide	51-03-6	32.0
Polyoxyethlene Sorbitan Oleate	9005-65-6	[1]
Polyoxyethlene (20) Sorbitan Monolaurate	9005-64-5	[1]
Propane	74-98-6	44.0
Propylene Glycol	57-55-6	20.5
sec-Butyl Alcohol	78-92-2	39.9
Silica, Amorphous Hydrated	7631-86-9	0.0
Silica, Crystalline	No CAS Number	0.0
Silicone Oil	63148-58-3	[1]
Silicone Oil	63148-62-9	[1]

(Continued)

TABLE 88-1-B—SELECTED CHEMICAL HEATS OF COMBUSTION—(Continued)

CHEMICAL NAME	CAS NUMBER	CHEMICAL HEAT OF COMBUSTION (ΔH_c) (kJ/g)
Sorbitan Monolaurate	1338-39-2	37.9
Sorbitan Monopalmitate	26266-57-9	37.9
Styrene Butadiene Rubber	25038-32-8	[1]
Tin Oxide (Stannic Oxide)	18282-10-5	0.0
Titanium Dioxide	13463-67-7	0.0
Toluene	108-88-3	28.4
Triacetin	102-76-1	35.4
1, 1, 1-Trichloroethane	71-55-6	[1]
Trichlorethylene	79-01-6	[1]
1, 2, 4-Trimethylbenzene (Pseudocumene)	96-63-6	27.5
Water	7732-18-5	0.0
Xylene	1330-20-7	27.4
Zinc Oxide	1314-13-2	0.0

[1]Materials that either have a flashpoint greater than 500°F (260°C), when tested in accordance with nationally recognized standards (see Standard a.4.3) or are combustible solids. Such materials contribute very little to the overall fire hazard of aerosol products in an actual fire, due to incomplete combustion or inconsistent burning behavior (i.e., the majority of the released material does not burn). Such materials do not contribute to the overall determination of the product's level classification and are assigned a chemical heat of combustion (ΔH_c) of 0 kJ/g.

88.103.4 Change of Classification Level. The classification level of an aerosol is allowed to be reduced or increased based upon evidence supporting a different classification. Such classification shall be based on data obtained from a full-scale fire test using a 12-pallet test array, an aerosol flammability test, engineering calculations based on large-scale fire tests, or other scientific information or data.

UNIFORM FIRE CODE STANDARD A-III-C-1

INSPECTION, TESTING AND MAINTENANCE OF WATER-BASED FIRE-PROTECTION SYSTEMS

See Appendix III-C, *Uniform Fire Code*

NOTE: This is a new standard.

The National Fire Protection Association Standard for Inspection, Testing and Maintenance of Water-based Fire-protection Systems, NFPA 25—1992, is hereby adopted by reference as UFC Appendix Standard A-III-C-1.

The provisions of this standard shall apply to the inspection, testing and maintenance of water-based fire-protection systems except when a provision of *Uniform Fire Code,* Volume 1 or an amendment specified in Section 10.201 is applicable, in which case *Uniform Fire Code,* Volume 1 provisions or the amendment shall take precedence.

Supplemental standards referenced by NFPA 25—1992 shall only be considered as guidelines subject to approval by the chief.

NFPA 25—1992 is available from the National Fire Protection Association, 1 Batterymarch Park, Box 9101, Quincy, Massachusetts 02269-9101.

SECTION A-III-C-1 — AMENDMENTS

The Standard for Inspection Testing and Maintenance of Water-based Fire-protection Systems, NFPA 25—1992, applies to the inspection, testing and maintenance of water-based fire-protection systems, except as follows:

1. Sec. 1-1 is deleted and substitute as follows:

1-1 Scope. The provisions of this standard apply to the inspection, testing and maintenance of water-based fire-protection systems except when a provision in the *Uniform Fire Code* is applicable, in which case the *Uniform Fire Code* provisions take precedence.

2. Sec. 1-2 is deleted.

3. Sec. 1-4 is deleted and substitute as follows:

1-4 Responsibility of the Owner or Occupant. The responsibility for properly maintaining a water-based fire-protection system shall be the obligation of the owner, operator, occupant or other person responsible for the condition of the property. By means of periodic inspections, tests and maintenance, the equipment shall be shown to be in good operating condition or any defects or impairments shall be revealed.

4. Sec. 1-5 is revised by changing the definition of "authority having jurisdiction" as follows:

AUTHORITY HAVING JURISDICTION is the official responsible for the administration and enforcement of this standard.

The definitions of "approved" and "listed" shall be as set forth in the *Uniform Fire Code,* Volume 1.

5. Table 2-1 is revised by changing all frequencies of inspection requirements shown as less than one year to "quarterly."

6. Sec. 2-2.4.1 is revised by changing "monthly" to "quarterly."

7. Sec. 2-2.4.2 is revised by changing "weekly" to "quarterly" in the section and "monthly" to "quarterly" in the exception.

8. Sec. 2-2.6 is revised by changing "monthly" to "quarterly."

9. Table 3-1 is revised by changing all frequencies of inspection requirements shown as less than one year to "quarterly."

10. Sec. 3-2.1 is revised by changing "monthly" to "quarterly."

11. Sec. 3-2.2 is revised by changing "weekly" to "quarterly" and "monthly" to "quarterly."

12. Table 4-1 is revised by changing all frequencies of inspection requirements shown as less than one year to "quarterly."

13. Sec. 4-3.2.7 is revised by changing "monthly" to "quarterly."

14. Table 5-1 is revised by changing all frequencies of inspection requirements shown as less than one year to "quarterly."

15. Sec. 5-2.2 is revised by changing "weekly" to "quarterly."

16. Table 5-2.2 is revised by changing "weekly" to "quarterly in the title."

17. Table 5-3.2.4 is revised by changing "weekly" to "quarterly in the title."

18. Table 5-5.1 is revised by changing all frequencies of inspection requirements shown as less than one year to "at least quarterly."

19. Sec. 6-2.1 is revised by changing "monthly" to "quarterly."

20. Sec. 6-2.2 is revised by changing "monthly" to "quarterly."

21. Sec. 6-2.3 is revised by changing "monthly" to "quarterly."

22. Table 6-1 is revised by changing all frequencies of inspection requirements shown as less than one year to "quarterly."

23. Sec. 7-4.1.2 is revised by changing "weekly" to "quarterly."

24. Table 7-4 is revised by changing all frequencies of inspection requirements shown as less than one year to "quarterly."

25. Sec. 8-3.6.1 is revised by changing "weekly" to "quarterly" and "monthly" to "quarterly."

26. Table 8-3 is revised by changing all frequencies of inspection requirements shown as less than one year to "quarterly."

27. Table 9-1 is revised by changing all frequencies of inspection requirements shown as less than one year to "quarterly."

28. Sec. 9-3.3.1 is revised by changing "weekly" to "quarterly" in the main paragraph and "monthly" to "quarterly" in Exception No. 1.

29. Sec. 9-4.1.1 is revised by changing "monthly" to "quarterly."

30. Sec. 9-4.3.1.1 is revised by changing "weekly" to "quarterly" in the main paragraph and "monthly" to "quarterly" in Exception Nos. 1 and 2.

31. Sec. 9-4.4.1.1 is revised as follows:

9-4.4.1.1 Valve enclosure heating equipment shall be inspected at least quarterly during cold weather for its ability to maintain a minimum temperature of at least 40°F (4°C).

EXCEPTION: Valve enclosures equipped with low temperature alarms shall be inspected quarterly.

32. Sec. 9-4.4.1.2 is revised by changing "weekly" to "quarterly" in the main paragraph and "monthly" to "quarterly" in the exception.

33. Sec. 9-4.4.1.3 is revised by changing "weekly" to "quarterly."

34. Sec. 9-5.1.1 is revised by changing "monthly" to "quarterly."

35. Sec. 9-5.2.1 is revised by changing "weekly" to "quarterly."

36. Sec. 9-5.3.1 is revised by changing "monthly" to "quarterly."

37. Sec. 9-5.4.1 is revised by changing "weekly" to "quarterly."

38. Sec. 9-5.4.2 is revised by changing "weekly" to "quarterly."

39. Sec. 9-6.1.1 is revised by changing "weekly" to "quarterly."

40. Sec. 9-6.1.2 is revised by changing "monthly" to "quarterly" in the exception.

41. Chapter 11 is deleted.